ANNUAL REVIEW OF BIOCHEMISTRY

ADVISORY COMMITTEE

J. M. LUCK
C. L. ALSBERG
D. R. HOAGLAND
C. L. A. SCHMIDT

ANNUAL REVIEW OF BIOCHEMISTRY

EDITED BY

JAMES MURRAY LUCK
Stanford University

VOLUME I

1932

STANFORD UNIVERSITY PRESS
STANFORD UNIVERSITY, CALIFORNIA

STANFORD UNIVERSITY PRESS
STANFORD UNIVERSITY, CALIFORNIA

———

THE BAKER & TAYLOR COMPANY
55 FIFTH AVENUE, NEW YORK

MARTINUS NIJHOFF
9 LANGE VOORHOUT, THE HAGUE

THE MARUZEN COMPANY
TOKYO, OSAKA, KYOTO, SENDAI

———

PRINTED AND BOUND IN THE UNITED STATES
OF AMERICA BY STANFORD UNIVERSITY PRESS

First printing, May 1932
Second printing, August 1932

Third printing, by photolith reproduction,
April, 1936

PREFACE

It is not without significance that the last few years have witnessed the inception of new journals, of interest to chemists, at no less a rate than one every two weeks. The periodical literature of other sciences has swollen likewise. New journals have been established and the existing ones expanded. Most of us find ourselves buried amidst piles of unread papers. To keep abreast of the literature in biochemistry has become a Herculean task. It is the exceptional individual who succeeds in reading an appreciable proportion of the papers outside the confines of his own restricted field of research.

The recognition of such a situation would seem to call for apologies and explanations from any who would venture to introduce still another publication. We hope, however, that the *Review* will be of material assistance; for it is in the belief that critical surveys of the literature will minimize the task of constantly referring to original works that the *Annual Review of Biochemistry* will present from year to year reviews of the current developments in from twenty-five to thirty of the major fields of interest. It is expected that these systematic surveys of the literature will supplement the valuable service already given by existing reviews in closely related fields.

Doubtless, all readers of the *Review* will appreciate the difficulties with which the reviewers have been confronted in the selection of papers for consideration. Although it has been intended that the reviews shall be as comprehensive as possible, severe restrictions have been imposed by the space available. It became necessary for the reviewers either to omit many papers from treatment or to prepare a mere compendium of the literature. Guided by the principle that critical analyses and résumés would be of greater value, attention has been centered, in most instances, upon selected aspects of the particular topic under review, and every effort has been made to discuss, as adequately as space permitted, the most significant contributions to the subject. In consequence, other fields of major interest, even though embraced by one or another of the topics contained in the volume, have been deliberately omitted for the present. It is fully expected that such omissions will be remedied by adequate consideration in future volumes, in which such topics may simply alternate from year to year with some of those now receiving treatment.

Despite every effort to keep the volume of moderate size, it has far outgrown our original expectations. This expansion has been due to the need of developing historical backgrounds in certain of the reviews and to unexpectedly numerous items requiring mention. Volume II, which will appear in the spring of 1933, will closely approach the standard size of 400 pages intended for the *Review*.

Acknowledgment must be made of the encouragement, advice, and material aid received from colleagues in this country and abroad. Whatever of merit may be attached to the *Review* is due, in large part, to the judgment and experience of the many from whom advice was solicited.

In response to a widely circulated request, many have been good enough to send reprints of recent publications to the reviewers. Some of these pertained to topics beyond the scope of the *Review,* but others were of the greatest convenience and aid. Where the journal of original publication was inaccessible, the use of reprints became especially urgent. The courteous co-operation of all who have joined in supplying reprints is most gratefully acknowledged.

We are especially indebted to Mr. Francis Garvan and the Chemical Foundation for a generous subsidy covering the first three years of the *Review,* and to Dr. Richard J. Block for additional financial aid. Without such support, the *Review* could not have been established.

To Stanford University our thanks are due for encouragement, cordial endorsement of the enterprise, and substantial assistance during months of organization. The Stanford University Press has given to the *Review* its enthusiastic support and has labored patiently and carefully over the editing, the composition, and the final preparation of the volume.

Every attempt has been made by all associated with the *Review* to produce an excellent and useful work. Nevertheless, the enterprise is young and its deficiencies are manifold. It will be a satisfaction to the reviewers, the advisory committee, and the Press if readers will suggest freely the ways in which improvement may be made.

J. M. L.
C. L. A.
D. R. H.
C. L. A. S.

STANFORD UNIVERSITY, CALIFORNIA
April 15, 1932

CONTENTS

PERMEABILITY*

By Rudolf Höber

University of Kiel, Germany

Permeability in so far as it concerns physiology is that property which permits water and substances dissolved in water to pass through the limiting surfaces of a cell or a tissue, as through an inert membrane separating two different aqueous solutions one from the other. The relative speeds of diffusion and osmosis permit deductions as to the composition as well as the physical properties of the membranes which play a rôle in the passage.

The differences in the permeability of cells and tissues have, up to the present time, led to two views concerning the nature of the membranes: (*a*) that they have the properties of a solvent, and (*b*) that they have those of a sieve for molecules. Many authors are inclined to combine both views, the solubility theory and the pore theory, in the sense that a complex structure of membranes would qualify to act as a solvent as well as a sieve. In accord with the general principle of Overton, under the term solubility lipoid solubility is understood.

The experiments on permeability published during 1931 have been often performed with the aim of advancing arguments for one or the other of these theories.

We will consider separately the new findings in cell and tissue permeability.

I. Cell Permeability

1. *Permeability to non-electrolytes.*—The main facts that are contributed by Overton and many others as a basis for the lipoid theory relate to the non-electrolytes. However, a series of new investigations, especially those of Collander and Bärlund on *Rhoeo*, of Mond and Hoffmann on erythrocytes, of S. Schönfelder on *Beggiatoa*, and others have brought about the result that a number of non-electrolytes with relatively small molecules permeate more rapidly than their lipoid solubility would indicate. This behavior is explained by the

* Received February 8, 1932. The author states that his paper covers 1931 only.

1

assumption that, in addition to passage through the lipoid of the plasma-membrane, diffusion through pores takes place.

A new contribution to this question was published by Dorothy Stewart (1). She observed the change in diameter of unfertilized eggs of the sea urchin *Arbacia,* which were carried over either into the pure solutions of non-electrolytes approximately isosmotic with sea-water or into sea-water in which the same substances in equimolecular amounts were dissolved. Nineteen different non-electrolytes of different lipoid solubility and of different molecular size were examined. The volume change with regard to the distinctly lipoid-soluble substances followed without exception the degree of lipoid solubility: acetins and chlorhydrin penetrated more rapidly than glycerol; butyramide penetrated more rapidly than propionamide and acetamide; the quickest were monovalent alcohols and urethane. The substances of low lipoid solubility grouped themselves, for the most part, in the order of their molecular size; for example, saccharose, dextrose, erythritol, and glycocoll failed to enter; glycerol and urea penetrated at a slow rate; ethylene glycol entered more rapidly, and acetamide even still more rapidly. Stewart concludes from this that especially ethylene glycol and glycerol fall out of their proper position in relation to their molecular volume, and suggests that a certain degree of lipoid solubility may be responsible for this. We shall see, from other investigations, that the same difficulty arises in explaining the behavior of these substances. Though not mentioned by Stewart, the impermeability for glycocoll represents a very distinct exception, for its calculated molecular volume lies between that of acetamide and that of glycerol; probably this abnormal behavior is associated with the ampholytic character of glycocoll.

For the further development of the permeability theory, the proof that cells of different organisms or of different organs show profound specific differences in permeability for the same substance is of great significance. Especially important in this regard are the studies of Jacobs (1) on osmotic hemolysis in approximately fifty species of vertebrates: (a) The time in seconds required for 75 per cent hemolysis to be attained, when the erythrocytes were exposed to pure water, was measured. Differences of from 1 to 71 seconds were found. From this it follows that the zoölogical relationship is often determinative for the time of hemolysis. Mammals and teleosts are characterized by low figures, elasmobranchs and amphibia by high values; reptiles give hemolytic times somewhat higher than mammals, and birds show a peculiar behavior inasmuch as the value for the chicken is high, while those of the pigeon and duck are low. (b) In another series of experiments the relative penetration power of the three substances, urea, ethylene glycol, and glycerol, was compared by evaluating the time of hemolysis in isosmotic solutions. There resulted again unmistakable differences from group to group of related animals. In mammals permeability to urea is much greater than to ethylene glycol; the reverse is true for elasmobranchs and teleosts. Reptiles resemble mammals; birds and amphibia approach the fishes. The comparison between urea and glycerol gave similar results. The penetrating faculty of urea exceeded by far that of glycerol in the case of mammalian cells, and to a somewhat smaller degree in reptiles and the frog, while the permeability of the two substances is about the same in fishes.

Urea, ethylene glycol, and glycerol have been selected as compounds insoluble or only slightly soluble in the lipoids but of small molecular size; so the question arises how to reconcile the experimental results with the predictions of the pore theory of permeability. The same problem is presented by another study of Jacobs (2, 3) which concerns especially the very pronounced differences in hemolytic power displayed toward the erythrocytes of different mammals by a series of alcohols of increasing molecular volume— ethylene glycol, glycerol, and erythritol. Besides other interesting facts it was found that the penetration of erythritol for the mouse is more rapid than for the rat; on the other hand, the penetration of glycerol is more rapid for the rat than for the mouse. Jacobs tries to give an explanation by the hypothesis, based upon the pore theory of permeability, that the erythrocyte of the mouse has a number of large pores and relatively few small ones, while that of the rat has fewer large pores but many more small ones.

In these investigations as well as in many previous ones, an explanation was sought for the differences in permeability in different animals and plants through the assumption that differences in pore diameter exist.

An investigation by Höber and Pupilli demonstrates also differences in the composition of the lipoid phase. These investigators compared the partition-equilibria of about twenty acid dyestuffs in suspensions of erythrocytes with the partition in mixtures of almond oil, oleic acid, and diamylamine, which, according to Nirenstein, compare very well with the cell-lipoids. Almost without exception only those dyes which were soluble in the oil-mixtures penetrated the erythrocytes. By varying the concentration it was shown that with regard to certain dyes (e.g., metanil-yellow) the partition-coefficient (erythrocytes to solution) increased with the concentration of the dye, while with others (e.g., orange R) it decreased; the partition-coefficients between oil-mixtures and the aqueous phase changed in the same direction. It is true that this rise and fall cannot be explained at present, but it follows that the lipoids are participating to a measurable degree in the amount of absorption. The most important result is the following: with six dyes it could be shown that the partition-coefficient (erythrocytes to solution) differs greatly in the horse, ox, and pig, being smallest in the horse and greatest in the pig. This may be due either to the fact that the volume of the lipoid phase varies in the three animals, or that the lipoids themselves are different, and that their relative capacity as a solvent varies from species to species. That the last is true follows from the fact that bromphenolblue is strongly absorbed by the erythrocytes of the pig, less by those of the ox, and practically not at all by those of the horse, even after a long time. Apparently the lipoids of the horse do not dissolve bromphenolblue. The behavior of tropaeolin 000 is similar. Evidence is thus furnished that variations in erythrocyte permeability, from species to species, can be explained as well by differences in lipoid solubility as by differences of pore diameter. The former hypothesis is here the more plausible, because differences in the composition of lipoids in erythrocytes have been well known for a long time through the analyses of Abderhalden and others.

Likewise, an investigation by Wilbrandt on the epidermal cells of various plants concerns the structure of the plasma membrane. Höfler and Stiegler had observed that cells of *Gentiana, Rhoeo,* and *Allium,* though they have the same permeability for potassium nitrate, show very different degrees of permeability for urea. Wilbrandt inquires, with regard to other non-electrolytes with physical properties similar to those of urea, whether or not their capacity to penetrate is different in the same way from cell species to cell species. He observed the rate of deplasmolysis of the epidermal cells of *Rhoeo, Begonia,* and *Basella* at different times in solutions of eight non-electrolytes and calculated the speed of permeation with special regard to the different ratios of surface to volume in the various cells. The results are shown in Table I.

These figures show that the relative penetration values of the eight substances vary from species to species. Neither the lipoid theory nor the pore theory can give a simple explanation for this behavior. On the other hand, evidence is furnished by the table that the amino groups are especially favorable for absorption in *Basella* cells, and the hydroxyl groups, on the contrary, are unfavorable for

TABLE I

RATIOS OF THE CONSTANTS OF PERMEATION

Substances	*Rhoeo* to *Basella*	*Rhoeo* to *Begonia*
Urea	1 : 80.0	1.0 : 1
Biuret	1 : 28.0	1.0 : 1
Methyl urea	1 : 10.0	2.0 : 1
Succinimide	1 : 2.8	1.2 : 1
Acetamide	1 : 1.6	2.1 : 1
Pinacon hydrate	1 : 2.8	2.6 : 1
Ethylene glycol	1 : 0.8	12.3 : 1
Glycerol	1 : 0.5	50.0 : 1

absorption in *Begonia* cells. Thus it may again be inferred that permeation depends upon the presence of different solvents in the plasma-membrane.

In a discussion concerning the fundamental basis of the pore theory Gicklhorn has advanced the opinion that it rests upon too uncertain ground as long as an exact measure of the relative sizes of the dissolved substances is lacking from nearly all of the experimental investigations. In each case the diffusion constants need to be measured as in the experimental work of Nistler and Süllmann, who show that the size of dyestuff solutes changes with the concentration and with the age of the solution; that with lactose the size of the diffusing particles increases markedly with rising concentration, and that with maltose it remains unchanged. It appears questionable, however, whether the measurement of diffusion constants has such an importance as Gicklhorn attributes to it, because it is to be assumed that an equilibrium exists between the molecules and the molecular aggregates, which, according to Gicklhorn, are present in the solutions.

2. *Permeability to ions.*—Since the investigations of Overton it is agreed that the alkaloid from solutions of alkaloid salts penetrates, not in the form of its ions, but as free base. Boresch believed he had found an exception to this rule in the leaves of *Fontinalis*. He stated that: (*a*) the toxicity of quinine hydrochloride is increased by the addition of 0.1 millimol of HCl, although by this addition the concentration of free base is decreased; and (*b*) the fat in the so-called *Fettknäuel* of the cells of *Fontinalis* is emulsified as easily by the alkaloidal salts as by the free base. Collander and Somer recently repeated the experiments of Boresch; they were unable to confirm the first assertion of this investigator, and explained the second result as uncertain, owing to improper fixation of the hydrogen ion concentration; they used, therefore, buffered solutions of pH 6 to 8, and found in five alkaloidal salts and in amylamine hydrochloride that the solution with the higher pH is always the more effective, and that the emulsifying effect in each case increases with the concentration of the free base in relation to the total alkaloid concentration.

A further investigation by Collander with Turpeinen and Fabritius concerns the speed of penetration of free NH_3 and of the free acids, acetic acid, butyric acid, and lactic acid, measured by the speed of deplasmolysis of the cells of *Rhoeo* in hypertonic solutions of ammonium salts. For these salts the concentration of free NH_3 and free acid can be calculated from the known values of the dissociation constants and from the pH. For various reasons it can be assumed that the cells are impermeable to the ions contained in the solutions. Thus, if the pH value of the outside solution is so increased, by means of a sufficient surplus of NH_3, that the concentration of free acetic acid in the cell sap may be disregarded, the speed of permeation of the acetic acid can be calculated according to the equation $m/t = PC$, where the amount m which penetrates during the time t is obtained from the decrease of plasmolysis, where C signifies the outside concentration of free acetic acid, and where P is the permeation constant. In this way (at pH 7.25) $P_{acet.\ ac.}$ has been found to equal 20 to 60, t being calculated in hours, C and m in mols. The measurement of P_{NH3} is based upon the following consideration: the permeation of ammonium acetate must be greatest at that pH, at which NH_3 and acetic acid penetrate in equivalent amounts; in this case

$$P_{NH_2} \cdot C_{NH_2} = P_{acet.\ ac.} \cdot C_{acet.\ ac.}$$

It follows that P_{NH_3} can be evaluated from the three other known factors. In the experiments the maximal speed of deplasmolysis was found to exist at pH 6.3 to 6.5. From this P_{NH_3} is determined to be 11 to 28 times greater than $P_{acet. ac.}$, i.e., 200 to 2,000. In a corresponding manner $P_{lact. ac.}$ has been found to equal 2, $P_{butyr. ac.}$ to equal 200. The differences in the three "P" values are related to the differences in the lipoid solubility of the three free acids, the high P_{NH_3} value to the small molecular volume.

Further investigations concerning the question of permeability for salts and their ions are published by Howard and Stewart. With regard to erythrocytes it is well known that the entrance of ammonium salts is made possible by the fact that the free NH_3 permeates and, owing to the selective anion permeability of the erythrocytes, the Cl^- in the solution outside (e.g., serum) exchanges with the OH^- inside. In a similar way, in the case of sea-urchin eggs the salts of the fatty acids are enabled to penetrate by the influence of a selective cation permeability. Howard demonstrated this in the following manner: If the eggs of *Arbacia* are centrifuged, the yolk granules of the interior are separated, and above the layer of granules a hyalin plasma segment is formed, the depth of which depends upon the time of centrifuging the eggs. The depth is measured after fixing the eggs with formalin; it is in inverse proportion to the viscosity, which itself is diminished by the acids which penetrate as the pH decreases. Howard found that mineral acids did not penetrate; phosphate buffer, up to pH 4.3, is without influence on the stratification. On the other hand, the fatty acids of from two to five carbon atoms caused liquefaction, which varied directly as the length of the carbon chain, even when the pH outside was higher than during the action of mineral acids. In addition, the sodium salts of the fatty acids caused liquefaction, and their action was augmented by the addition of an alkali salt with a common anion (e.g., sodium acetate + potassium acetate). If one increased the concentration of the free acid without changing the concentration of the salt, the liquefaction increased. Vice versa, if one increased the salt concentration without changing the acid concentration, the liquefaction decreased, though in the latter case the concentration of the free acid increased. It follows, therefore, that the salts also penetrate the living cell and depress the dissociation of the free acid within. According to Howard, this penetration perhaps takes place in the following manner: at first the free acid permeates, and then the hydrogen ion inside exchanges with the cation outside. In good agreement with this supposition is the observation that when the chlorides of Rb, K, or Na (0.05 molar) were added to the outer solution of fatty-acid salts (pH 5) the ion with the highest mobility, Rb, had the greatest buffering effect during a known time of exposure (2 to 9 minutes), that is, it brings about the smallest liquefaction. On the other hand, the Na ion with the lowest mobility produces the greatest liquefaction.

The paper of Stewart (2) is a supplement to that of Howard in so far as it deals with the investigation of the osmotic reaction and cytolysis of *Arbacia* eggs in the solutions of ammonium salts of organic and inorganic acids. In contrast with the erythrocytes, the eggs remained unchanged in the solutions of ammonium nitrate and chloride, owing to the deficient permeability of anions. On the other hand, they cytolyzed in $M/2$ solutions of the ammonium salts of the fatty acids of one to five carbon atoms; in valerate cytolysis was most rapid and in formate it was slowest, because valeric acid is the most lipoid-soluble while formic acid is not only of relatively low lipoid solubility but also of relatively high strength. The action of the fatty-acid salts decreased with increasing pH; e.g., ammonium acetate at pH 7.8 was almost without effect.

The anion permeability of erythrocytes with regard to bromine was investigated in two series of experiments by van Dyke and Hastings because of the following two reasons: (*a*) since pharmacological literature contains references to the ability of bromides to displace chlorides from the body and (*b*) for testing further the general applicability of the Donnan law. Two equal quantities of defibrinated dog blood were mixed with equimolar NaCl and NaBr solutions, and after the establishment of equilibrium the content of Cl and Br was determined by means of an electro-titrimetric method. It was observed that, the pH value being the same, the partition-coefficient inside to outside was equal in both tests as far as the total halogen was concerned; however, in test 2 the bromide concentration in the erythrocytes was about ten per cent higher than the chloride concentration; thus, Br displaced a portion of the Cl. The distribution was reversible. As in other cases it was also observed here that following a decrease of pH (by CO_2) and following reduction of the blood (by hydrogen) the partition-coefficient rose. The authors further investigated the distribution after oral administration of NaBr. The partition-coefficient of Cl is, under normal conditions, approximately 0.7; after the addition of NaBr a coefficient of 1 to 2 for Br was found, while the chloride ratios observed were commonly less than 0.7 and often in the neighborhood of 0.5. The authors believe that this provides a clue to a possible explanation for the apparently anomalous distributions. Electrometric methods of measuring the hydrogen ion concentration gave the ratio inside to outside as 0.5 at pH 7.4. This ratio is the only one thus far determined for ionic activity distributions. Thus if by analytical methods higher values are found, they may result because of special circumstances. Therefore, the assumption is made by the authors that even in normal blood a certain proportion of the chloride of cells is present in non-ionic form, but that the chloride can be displaced from this form by bromide. It remains to be asked why in numerous experiments *in vitro* bromide ratios greater than unity have never been found.

The distribution of ions inside and outside and changes in the ion-binding power of the erythrocytes appear to be also the cause of alterations in the osmotic resistance of the cells, as demonstrated by Jacobs and Parpart in experiments on the effect of the three factors, hydrogen ion concentration, temperature, and oxygen tension of the medium. The exact results are based upon the very sensitive method of osmotic hemolysis worked out by Jacobs (4), which enables one to distinguish the osmotic effects of solutions differing from one another by 0.0002 mol of salt. (a) The influence of pH of the medium: small amounts of defibrinated ox blood were mixed with a series of NaCl-NaHCO$_3$ solutions of different concentrations with different tensions of carbon dioxide. It was observed that the percentage of hemolysis increased to the same degree either by a pH decrease of 0.5 or by a concentration decrease of 0.01 mol. (b) The influence of temperature: lowering the temperature produced a higher degree of hemolysis. Change in temperature of 10° C. was balanced by one in concentration of 0.0035 to 0.0075 mol. (c) The influence of oxygen tension: the blood was added to a series of different NaCl phosphate-buffered solutions through which oxygen and hydrogen, respectively, were bubbled. The effect on the osmotic resistance was small. By complete reduction of the hemoglobin, hemolysis increased nearly to the same degree as by decrease in concentration of 0.0016 mol. From the observed effects the authors conclude that the changes in hemolysis are produced mainly by changes in the base-binding power of the hemoglobin, as evaluated chiefly by the investigations of E. J. Warburg and van Slyke. To show this, they applied the relevant equations of van Slyke, so modifying them that they were applicable to the simpler system of erythrocytes suspended in salt solution instead of in whole blood. Thus the observed behavior could be predicted by the equation:

$$\frac{W_1}{W_2} = \frac{2R + 1 + F_1}{2R + 1 + F_2} \cdot \frac{C_2}{C_1},$$

where W_1 and W_2 are the amounts of water contained in an erythrocyte under two given conditions, F_1 and F_2 are the amounts of base bound by one equivalent of hemoglobin under the same conditions, C_1 and C_2 the concentrations of salt in the external solutions, and R is the ratio of base to hemoglobin within the cell. Therefore, if equal percentages of hemolysis indicate the entrance into the cells of equal quantities of water (i.e., if W_1 under these conditions be equal to W_2),

$$\frac{2R + 1 + F_1}{2R + 1 + F_2} \cdot \frac{C_2}{C_1} = 1$$

This has been found to agree in fairly satisfactory measure with the actual experimental results.

3. *Permeability to water.*—In several papers there are communicated newer measurements of the rate of penetration of water in order to obtain an exact numerical value of the amount of water which penetrates in unit time with unit difference in osmotic pressure across unit surface of the plasma membrane and to establish in this way a physical constant characterizing the permeability to water. But the existence of secondary factors has presented considerable difficulty in the realization of this plan, e.g., viscosity, surface tension, and elasticity of the plasma, in plant cells, permeability of the cellulose membrane and adherence of the plasma to it. Huber and Höfler (1, 2) have tried to calculate a constant of permeability of plant cells to water by measuring the velocity, with which the volume of the protoplast is diminished by plasmolysis in hypertonic solutions according to the equation:

$$\frac{dg}{dt} = -k \left(C - \frac{O}{g} \right),$$

where g is the rate of plasmolysis, i.e., the volume of the protoplast in relation to the initial volume (equaling 1), t the time, C the concentration of the plasmolyzing solution, and O the initial osmotic value of the cell sap. Thus by integration we obtain:

$$k = \frac{1}{C\,(t_2 - t_1)} \left(g_1 - g_2 + G\ln \frac{g_1 - G}{g_2 - G} \right),$$

where G is the rate of plasmolysis in osmotic equilibrium and k the change in the degree of plasmolysis, i.e., the decrease of volume in 1 minute effected by a difference in osmotic pressure of 1 mol. The application of the equation assumes that plant cells so behave that the penetration of water through the protoplasm is the limiting factor and that secondary factors as named before can be practically neglected. This appears to be the case, e.g., in *Majanthemum* cells, which are plasmolyzed with equal velocity by saccharose, glycerol, urea, and potassium nitrate, or in *Salvinia* cells, where the protoplast at the beginning of plasmolysis divides into portions of different size and the osmotic equilibrium of the smaller portions, because of the relatively larger surface, is established more rapidly than that of the greater ones, or in *Allium,* where the naked protoplasts of cells, opened by cutting the cellulose membrane, deplasmolyze no more rapidly than the protoplasts in uninjured cells.

The k values obtained by the experiments vary from 0.2 to 10. Relating k to the unit surface, there results, e.g., with *Salvinia,* a speed of permeability equaling 33 µ for 1 hour and 1 atmosphere. The resistance of the plasma is of course very high, owing to the very small size of the pores. Assuming that the formula of Poiseuille may be applied here—which seems to be not quite correct—the calculation gives a pore size of about 1 mµ; the value proves to be within the range of molecular diameters. The calculated speed of permeability for water surpasses by far that of dissolved substances; for *Majanthemum,* e.g., the value exceeds 10,000 times that of saccharose, 600 times that of potassium nitrate.

By an equation conforming to that of Huber and Höfler, Lucké, Hartline, and McCutcheon (1) have evaluated the permeability to water with regard to *Arbacia* eggs, the volume of which changed in sea-water dilutions ranging from 80 to 20 per cent. The constant of penetration, i.e., the velocity of water intake per hour at 1 atmosphere pressure, as computed from the volume changes in the first 10 minutes of swelling, was nearly 3 µ, or about ten times slower than for *Salvinia* in the experiments of Huber and Höfler, just mentioned; in earlier experiments Jacobs had found with erythrocytes of man the value 180 μ. The permeability of the *Arbacia* eggs during exosmosis (after being allowed to swell) is remarkably greater than during endosmosis; this is inverse to the behavior of plant cells, where, according to Huber and Höfler, the speed of deplasmolysis surpasses that of plasmolysis. In both cases the higher value may be the sign of incipient injury to the protoplast.

A second paper of McCutcheon, Lucké, and Hartline (2) deals with the *Arbacia* eggs as osmometers as in the well-known earlier papers of Hamburger, Ege, and others with erythrocytes. The eggs were distributed into sea-water of different concentrations and the volume measured at equilibrium. The observed changes were in satisfactory agreement with the equation: $P(V - b) = k$, where P is the osmotic pressure of the dissolved substances in the egg, V the volume of the egg, b the volume occupied by osmotically inactive material inside the egg, and k a constant according to the law of Boyle–van't Hoff. It has been found that b equals 7 to 14 per cent. In comparison with this value Ege found the "non-dissolving space" in rabbit erythrocytes equal to about 40 per cent, Wieringa in certain yeasts about 64 per cent. The experimental results would agree also with the supposition of leakage of salts or other substances from the swelling cells, instead of the assumption that an appreciable amount of osmotically inactive material exists in the eggs. However, the swelling effect is completely reversible and eggs, first swollen in sea-water diluted to 60 per cent and then returned to ordinary sea-water, may be fertilized like normal cells.

One of the simplest methods of analyzing the osmotic properties of cells is the measurement of the osmotic resistance by observing the cytolysis in solutions hypotonic in different degree. New investigations of this sort by Jacobs with erythrocytes of different animals in relation to zoölogical classification have already been referred to. Höfler (3) studied the osmotic resistance in marine algae of the order *Florideae*. In fresh water or in diluted sea-water these algae usually change in color from clear red to opaque orange, because the phycoerythrin normally localized in the chromatophores enters the cell sap, forming there a fluorescent dye. This takes place by bursting of the plasma wall, usually without injury of the cellulose membrane. The osmotic resistance varies over a broad range; most of the algae were killed by hypotonicity in a few minutes; only *Antithamnion* was found to resist fresh water more than two and a half hours. The plasmolytic concentration decreased during this time from 1.9 sea-water to 1.4, apparently by exosmosis of salts. Strong solutions, such as concentrated sea-water, are generally not less injurious, but the damaging effect is not due to hypertonicity; hypertonic solutions kill the cells only if they plasmolyze. Only a few species, e.g., of the genera *Ceramium* and *Cladophora,* appear to resist plasmolytic concentrations.

4. *The colloidal structure of the plasma membrane.*—Changing the ion content of the surrounding medium is often accompanied by alterations of the normal cell permeability; especially, disturbing the physiological relation between univalent and divalent cations is often followed by anomalous entrance or exit of substances through the superficial layer of the protoplast. Many reasons support the well-known opinion of J. Loeb, that these influences are due to changes in the colloidal state of the plasma membrane.

Gellhorn (1, 2) tried to demonstrate this influence of ions on permeability by some vital staining experiments. Eggs of the sea-urchin *Strongylocentrotus* are stained to a fairly small degree by the acid dyestuffs erythrosine, eosine, and fluorescine in isotonic solutions of sodium, potassium, and lithium chloride buffered with glycocoll-HCl to pH 6.4. The staining effect is gradually hindered and finally completely prevented by the addition of increasing amounts of $CaCl_2$. Other divalent cations, such as Mg, Sr, or Ba, have not the inhibiting influence of Ca; on the contrary, the pure solutions increase the staining, and accordingly it is possible to balance Mg and Ca with one another so that no staining occurs. Sr and Ba also show a small antagonistic effect toward Mg. In a similar way the alkaline dyestuffs methyleneblue and methylviolet behave in solutions buffered with glycocoll-NaOH to pH 7.4. In order to determine whether the solutions promoting the penetration of the dyestuffs themselves produced a significant disturbance, the eggs were put into the solutions free from dyestuff and after a sufficient interval re-transferred into sea-water; unfertilized eggs were now fertilized, and those already fertilized continued in normal development. Furthermore, in order to determine whether some mixtures of cations produce complete impermeability for the dyestuffs, fertilized eggs were permitted to remain for thirty or more minutes in these mixtures in presence of erythrosine and in light; carried over again to sea-water the eggs developed normally. It followed that the well-known photosensibility of protoplasm toward the fluorescent dyestuffs was totally prevented.

In a second series of experiments unfertilized eggs of *Strongylocentrotus* were first treated with unbalanced solutions free from dye but able to delay or to augment the staining; afterward they were exposed to a standard solution containing the dyestuff (neutral red or Nile blue). The result was nearly the same as observed before with eggs treated at the same time with dye and unbalanced salt solution. It appears clear that the different staining effects were produced by the preceding alterations of the cell surface.

5. *Physiological and experimental changes in permeability.*— Weber (1) has observed that from a thread of *Spirogyra* put into 8 to 10 per cent of urea only some of the cells were plasmolyzed, others were not. The reason is not to be attributed to differences of osmotic pressure, because in 15 per cent of saccharose the cells were all plasmolyzed at the same rate, but to differences in permeability relating to the urea as a substance of small molecular size. The cells, which were penetrated easily by urea, were soon killed; the others remained plasmolyzed for a long time. The differences in permeability are due to the age of the cells; those with lower permeability are the younger, i.e., the shorter cells with notably thinner cross-walls; likewise daughter-cells, still connected one to another by a plasma bridge, were not plasmolyzed.

According to Weber the guard cells (*Schliesszellen*) of the stomata of *Ranunculus* show corresponding behavior; cells with normal function are readily permeable to urea; on the other hand, cells from young leaves the development of which is not yet complete, or cells from old yellow leaves, are plasmolyzed by hypertonic solutions of urea.

Mestscherskaja made investigations on the permeability of the growing oöcytes in the ovaries of insects. The surface is semipermeable; dissolved substances as foodstuffs are conveyed to them only by the aid of specialized cells. Generally the ovary consists of a chain of oöcytes connected with each other by mid-canals (*Zwischenkammern*) or nourishing chambers (*Nährkammern*), formed by a number of small and plain cells.

The ovary tubes of *Blatta* are preserved best in Ringer solution of 0.7 per cent NaCl; in 1 per cent or more the growing oöcytes are plasmolyzed, i.e., they become detached and shrink from the enveloping epithelium of the follicle; on the other hand, the youngest oöcytes in the *Endkammer* of the ovary as well as the cells of the *Zwischenkammer* do not change their volume. It follows that the growing oöcyte generally is impermeable to salt. Only at the junction with the *Zwischenkammer* is it enabled to absorb substances:

a) Dyestuffs (especially neutral red) stain the cells of the *Zwischenkammer* easily; if the oöcytes are plasmolyzed before, their staining takes place only when the junction between oöcyte and *Zwischenkammer* has not been interrupted by the plasmolysis; deplasmolysis allows the staining only if the connection is re-established.

b) Hydrogen peroxide is able to penetrate only the cells of the *Zwischenkammer* and the youngest oöcytes; this is recognized by the formation of oxygen bubbles at these places; only growing oöcytes with injured surface allow the peroxide to pass.

c) Hydrochloric acid and ammonia change the color of the granules stained by neutral red only in the *Zwischenkammer,* not in the oöcyte.

d) Hemoglobin is taken in first by the cells of the *Zwischenkammer,* later by the oöcytes, where the hemoglobin is split off. Narcotics and potassium cyanide prevent the intake of hemoglobin.

The permeability of the oöcytes of *Dytiscus* is differentiated in a way similar to that of *Blatta*. In this material there can be observed a plasmatic current transporting neutral red or foodstuffs from the *Zwischenkammer* into the protoplasm of the neighboring oöcyte. Other insects in place of several *Zwischenkammern* are endowed with one *Endkammer* serving for the food supply. The *Endkammer* is joined with the whole series of oöcytes by strings of protoplasm; its cells are not plasmolyzed in hypertonic salt solution; they rapidly take up dyestuffs and hydrogen peroxide.

Gellhorn (3) observed that the fatigue of the frog sartorius induced by rhythmical electrical stimulation is delayed when a part of the NaCl in Ringer solution is replaced by $CaCl_2$, although the excess of $CaCl_2$ is notably less favorable for the unstimulated muscle in comparison with its behavior in normal Ringer. The effect of Ca is specific; it can be substituted neither by Ba nor by Mg. Sr, Ba, and Mg delay the fatigue, however, when added to normal Ringer solution. Beside the influence of an excess of Ca on fatigue, Gellhorn observed increase of muscle tonus during stimulation; the resting muscle, on the contrary, under the same conditions gives decrease in tonus or increase only if the Ca excess is very high. Gellhorn believes he has demonstrated by these experiments that the optimum composition of the physiological salt mixtures is not a definite one but is dependent upon the degree of permeability which changes from unstimulated to stimulated tissue.

Several years ago Höber and Banus observed that *Spirogyra* cells can be stimulated electrically so that they become permeable to acid dyestuffs which are not otherwise able to penetrate. The effect is reversible. Usually by the electric current some cells are killed, and the dye stains the dead protoplasts; others conserve their normal impermeability and only into few cells does the dye penetrate the plasma in such a way that after an interval of rest the cells are restored and, when retransferred into pure water, retain the dye in their cell-sap vacuole. These experiments have been repeated by Gicklhorn and Dejdar on leaves of *Scilla* and on epidermis of *Allium* and on *Spirogyra,* but, in the author's opinion, without success. They believe that the experiments of Höber and Banus have no physiological significance, because the stains (acid fuchsine and rubine) enter only into damaged or dying cells, judging from their observation, that in stained cells the turgor has remarkably decreased and, following this, the chloroplasts are dislocated. However, against this argument it must be remembered that it is impossible to abolish impermeability without releasing the turgor; whenever the permeability so increases as a result of electrical stimulation that dyestuffs permeate, which otherwise would not do so, permeability to small-sized molecules, e.g., to inorganic ions, necessarily has been brought about before.

Lepeschkin has published new experiments regarding the influence of light upon cell-permeability. He investigated the speed of penetration of methylene blue into the leaves of *Elodea* with a colorimetric method especially worked out for *Elodea*. The permeability increases in the light and decreases in the dark. It may be objected: (1) that the difference in coloring may be produced by a change in the adsorption of the dye in light—but dead cells adsorb dyes with equal velocity in the light and in the dark; or (2) the affinity of the cell sap may be increased by the illumination—but also the amount of dye absorbed by the cell is the same in light and dark. By shading a part of the leaf by means of a strip of tin-foil it can be demonstrated that the increase of permeability does not spread to neighboring cells. The greater the change of the illumination—in positive and negative direction—the greater is the change of permeability; this can be explained by the supposition that there exist in the cells substances essential for permeability, destroyed by light and restored in the dark; therefore, the more products of the decomposition the protoplasm contains, the more rapidly the restoration proceeds, and conversely. The rays most active are those with a wave-length of 320 to 420 mμ.

Wildervanck investigated periodic changes in the osmotic properties of *Nitella* by direct determination of the vapor pressure with Barger's method. The changes, in some way, may be dependent upon light and temperature, but primarily they are "autonomous." Cultivation in 0.1 to 0.2 molar saccharose or glucose raised the osmotic values without extinguishing the autonomous factors. By microanalysis it has been shown that the osmotic increase in 0.2 molar cane sugar is 87 per cent due to anatonosis, and 13 per cent to penetration of the sugar.

II. Permeability of Tissues

As in the first part of this review with cells, so in this part the tissues will be regarded as though they were inert membranes separating different solutions from one another.

Bethe has already demonstrated in an earlier paper that, in contradiction to Frédéricq and Bottazzi, there exists an exchange of ions through the surface of animals living in water. New experiments performed by Berger and Bethe on marine animals (Echinoderms, Crustaceans) and on *Astacus,* as an example of a fresh-water animal, demonstrate the entrance of sodium iodide (0.025 to 0.0125 mol) from the surrounding medium; at equilibrium the concentration of iodine in the blood was found to amount to 60 to 90 per cent of the outside concentration. In the sea urchin the path of absorption is through the ambulacral feet, in crustaceans through the gills; but, beside this, iodine is taken up by the cephalothorax of the crabs, probably through the thin areas in which are inserted the tangoreceptors. The authors suppose that iodine is exchanged with chlorine. The exit of the iodine proceeds more slowly than the entrance; apparently the iodine is partially removed by the green gland of the crustaceans and by the intestine of the sea urchin.

By Schlieper and Duval it has been pointed out that in fresh-water and brackish-water crustaceans, transferred to sea-water, the osmotic pressure of the blood becomes gradually adjusted to that of the surrounding medium. In view of these observations Berger recently has analyzed the blood of *Astacus* and of *Eriocheir,* with the result that the percentage of the blood in K, Na, and Ca increases without any remarkable diminution of the body weight and falls again, after the animals are returned to their normal surroundings. Long-continued life in fresh water is connected with diminution of the salt content in the blood, but the decrease is very slow in relation to the concentration fall; the presence of ions diffused out of the body has been demonstrated analytically. The author supposes that the permeability of the body surface is high for the ions only if there is realized a high concentration fall between inside and outside, but that it is in some way diminished when the concentration inside and outside nearly correspond to the normal condition.

Three papers by E. F. Adolph (1, 2, 3) deal with experiments concerning the water balance of the frog as dependent on various factors, such as permeability of the skin, osmotic ånd swelling processes, narcosis, destruction of the central nervous system, stopping of the circulation, and special metabolic conditions of the different tissues.

Schlossmann (1) has investigated the permeability of the placenta. In dogs and cats a short time before parturition the pregnant uterus was opened under sodium chloride solution at 37° C., and samples of blood were taken from the *arteria umbilicalis* and the *vena umbilicalis* of the embryo, while swimming in the salt solution, and from the *vena jugularis* of the mother still in connection with the embryo. By this procedure it was demonstrated that glucose diffuses easily in both directions between mother and embryo until equilibrium is attained. In a second series of experiments Schlossmann (2), by the same method, has answered the question whether or not the placenta is permeable to insulin. It is well known that Carlson previously advanced the opinion that after pancreatectomy a pregnant dog is protected against diabetes by the insulin of the embryo. Schlossmann believes that the placenta is impermeable to this hormone. Injection of large amounts of insulin into the embryo is followed only by a small and slowly rising decrease of blood sugar in the mother; the glucose content does not fall below about 80 per cent, and it does not matter whether the injection is into the *arteria umbilicalis* or into the peritoneal cavity of the embryo. After the glucose in the blood of the embryo has decreased considerably, owing to the injection of insulin, the sugar percentage of the blood in the *vena umbilicalis* returning from the placenta is much higher than in the *arteria umbilicalis;* it is evident that the mother supplies the embryo with sugar.

LITERATURE CITED

ADOLPH, E. F. (1), *Am. J. Physiol.*, **96**, 569 (1931)
ADOLPH, E. F. (2), *Am. J. Physiol.*, **96**, 587 (1931)
ADOLPH, E. F. (3), *Am. J. Physiol.*, **96**, 598 (1931)
BERGER, E., AND BETHE, A., *Arch. ges. Physiol.*, **228**, 769 (1931)
BERGER, E., *Arch. ges. Physiol.*, **228**, 790 (1931)
BETHE, A., AND BERGER, E., *Arch. ges. Physiol.*, **228**, 769 (1931)
BORESCH, K., *Biochem. Z.*, **101**, 110 (1919)
COLLANDER, R., AND SOMER, K., *Protoplasma*, **14**, 1 (1931)
COLLANDER, R., TURPEINEN, O., AND FABRITIUS, E., *Protoplasma*, **13**, 348 (1931)
GELLHORN, E. (1), *Protoplasma*, **12**, 66 (1931)
GELLHORN, E. (2), *Protoplasma*, **14**, 28 (1931)
GELLHORN, E. (3), *Biol. Bull. Marine Biol. Lab.*, **60**, 382 (1931)
GICKLHORN, J., *Protoplasma*, **13**, 567 (1931)
GICKLHORN, J., AND DEJDAR, E., *Protoplasma*, **13**, 592 (1931)
HASTINGS, A. B., AND VAN DYKE, H. B. (1), *J. Biol. Chem.*, **92**, 13 (1931)
HASTINGS, A. B., AND VAN DYKE, H. B. (2), *J. Biol. Chem.*, **92**, 27 (1931)
HÖBER, R., AND PUPILLI, G., *Arch. ges. Physiol.*, **226**, 585 (1931)
HÖFLER, K. (1), *Protoplasma*, **12**, 564 (1931)
HÖFLER, K. (2), *Oesterr. botan. Z.*, **80**, 51 (1931)
HÖFLER, K., AND HUBER, B., *Jahrb. wiss. Botanik*, **73**, 300 (1930)
HOWARD, E., *Biol. Bull. Marine Biol. Lab.*, **60**, 132 (1931)
HUBER, B., *Naturwissenschaften*, **19**, 649 (1931)
HUBER, B., AND HÖFLER, K., *Jahrb. wiss. Botanik*, **73**, 300 (1930)
JACOBS, M. H. (1), *Am. Phil. Soc.*, **70**, 363 (1931)
JACOBS, M. H. (2), *Am. Phil. Soc.*, **70**, 167 (1931)
JACOBS, M. H. (3), *Ergebnisse Biol.*, **17**, 1 (1931)
JACOBS, M. H. (4), *Biol. Bull. Marine Biol. Lab.*, **58**, 104 (1930)
JACOBS, M. H., AND PARPART, A., *Biol. Bull. Marine Biol. Lab.*, **60**, 95 (1931)
LEPESCHKIN, W. W., *Am. J. Botany*, **17**, 953 (1931)
LUCKÉ, B., HARTLINE, H. K., AND MCCUTCHEON, M. (1), *J. Gen. Physiol.*, **14**, 405 (1931)
LUCKÉ, B., HARTLINE, H. K., AND MCCUTCHEON, M. (2), *J. Gen. Physiol.*, **14**, 393 (1931)
MCCUTCHEON, M., LUCKÉ, B., AND HARTLINE, H. K. (1), *J. Gen. Physiol.*, **14**, 405 (1931)
MCCUTCHEON, M., LUCKÉ, B., AND HARTLINE, H. K. (2), *J. Gen. Physiol.*, **14**, 393 (1931)
MESTSCHERSKAJA, K., *Z. Zellforsch. mikroskop. Anat.*, **13**, 109 (1931)
NISTLER, A., *Kolloidchem. Beihefte*, **31**, 1 (1930)
PARPART, A., AND JACOBS, M. H., *Biol. Bull. Marine Biol. Lab.*, **60**, 95 (1931)
SCHLOSSMANN, H. (1), *Z. ges. exptl. Med.*, **72**, 401 (1930)
SCHLOSSMANN, H. (2), *Arch. exptl. Path. Pharmakol.*, **159**, 213 (1931)
STEWART, D. (1), *Biol. Bull. Marine Biol. Lab.*, **60**, 152 (1931)
STEWART, D. (2), *Biol. Bull. Marine Biol. Lab.*, **60**, 171 (1931)
SÜLLMANN, H., *Protoplasma*, **13**, 546 (1931)

van Dyke, H. B., and Hastings, A. B. (1), *J. Biol. Chem.*, **92**, 13 (1931)
van Dyke, H. B., and Hastings, A. B. (2), *J. Biol. Chem.*, **92**, 27 (1931)
Weber, F. (1), *Protoplasma*, **12**, 129 (1931)
Weber, F. (2), *Protoplasma*, **14**, 75 (1931)
Wilbrandt, W., *Arch. ges. Physiol.*, **229**, 86 (1931)
Wildervanck, L. S., *Proc. Acad. Sci. Amsterdam*, **34**, 297 (1931)

Physiologisches Institut der Universität
Hegewischstr. 5, Kiel, Germany

THE RÔLE OF WATER IN THE STRUCTURE AND PROPERTIES OF PROTOPLASM*

By Ross Aiken Gortner

Division of Agricultural Biochemistry
University of Minnesota

"The vortex of vital activities is with respect to water more than analogous to the whirlpool. Without water both the body and the pool would be but paleontological specimens, showing only (in Huxley's phrase) where activity had been" [Adolph (1)]. It is accordingly fitting that a chapter of this book should be devoted to the rôle of water in the reactions of the living organism.

During recent years the attention of the biologist, the physiologist, and the biochemist has been directed more and more toward the solution of those problems which involve a knowledge of the state of water in living structures, and more and more it is becoming evident that the water in living tissues and even in inanimate colloidal systems does not exist wholly as "free" water such as characterizes water in bulk, but that a greater or a smaller fraction of the water in such systems is intimately "bound" to the organic structures and becomes an essential part of the "disperse phase" as contrasted with the "free" water of the "dispersions medium." This view has been summarized by Gortner (2) in a general paper on the "State of Water in Colloidal and Living Systems";[1] by Adolph (1) in a paper on "Living Water"; by Wöhlbier (3) in a discussion of "The Importance of Water in Animal Growth"; by Marinesco (4) on "The Physical State of Water Bound by Organic Colloids and by the Tissues"; and by Shull (5) in a consideration of the "Absorption of Water by Plants and the Forces Involved."

Contrasted with these views are the views of Hill (6, 7) and Grollman (8), where the conclusion is reached that the water in biological tissues and fluids is largely "free." Inasmuch as these papers contain much new data, a discussion of them will be deferred until later.

---

* Received January 12, 1932.

[1] Presented before a symposium of the Faraday Society in September 1930. This paper is of especial value owing to the 18 pages of "general discussion" contributed by various workers who were present at the symposium.

21

STUDIES ON THE NATURE OF BOUND WATER AND METHODS
WHEREBY BOUND WATER CAN BE ESTIMATED

Balcar, Sansum, and Woodyatt (9) were apparently the first persons to suggest a bound ⇌ free water equilibrium as being of importance in physiological processes, but they were unable to devise a technic which would differentiate these forms of water. Unaware of their suggestion, Newton and Gortner (10) in 1922 suggested that "bound water" was not free to act as a solvent, and they accordingly proposed that the bound water be determined by cryoscopic technic in the presence of a (theoretical) molar solution of sucrose. Any excess depression of the freezing-point would be due to the bound water which was present in the system. This method has been tested and confirmed by Kruyt and Winkler (11), who found that starch binds about 80 per cent of its weight of water and that the "bound" water effect disappears when a sufficient amount of a dehydrating agent (tannin) is added to the system. Kruyt and Winkler note that the viscosity effects are very much greater than would correspond to the binding of the water as measured by the cryoscopic method and conclude that the cryoscopic method measures only the closely adhering primary oriented water shells, whereas the more diffuse water shells contribute to the viscosity of the system.

Grollman (8) has rightly criticized the formula proposed by Newton and Gortner in so far as it applies to biological fluids, inasmuch as no provision was made in the original formula for the concentration of solutes in the biological fluid due to the separation of pure water in the form of ice. Grollman suggests that the correction may be of sufficient magnitude to account for all of the apparent "bound" water which has been estimated by the cryoscopic method. It should be pointed out that the original formula is satisfactory in systems where no molecularly dispersed solutes are present [gum arabic, Newton and Gortner (10); gelatin, agar, blood fibrin, dextrin, etc., Newton and Martin (12); starch and tannin, Kruyt and Winkler (11)], and where "bound" water is shown to be present, and also that in many samples of plant saps studied by Newton (13), and Newton and Martin (12), the "bound" water values are of sufficient magnitude to be only slightly affected by the application of the correction suggested by Grollman.

Rubner (14) in 1922 suggested that "bound" water be defined as that portion of the water which did not freeze when the system was held at —20°C., and by measuring the latent heat of fusion of ice, knowing the total water content of the system, the bound water could be readily determined. This method has proved a very fruitful technic as evidenced by the papers of Thoenes (15) and Robinson (16, 17, 18, 19). Robinson (20) has lately published explicit directions for carrying out such studies. The applications by Robinson and Parsons (20a) of this technic to problems of surgical shock are noted in a later section.

Jones and Gortner (21) have studied the problem of bound water using dilatometric technic. This method has a distinct advantage over the Rubner method in that it enables one to follow changes in bound water in the same sample of material over a wide range of temperature changes. It was assumed by Jones and Gortner that "free" water would be converted into ice by the lowering of the temperature and that the amount of ice which was formed could be quantitatively determined by the expansion of the system. The study included gelatin gels and the thick portion of egg white as examples of elastic gel systems, and systems of silica gel-H_2O and Fe_2O_3-H_2O as examples of non-elastic gel systems. The studies were carried out in the temperature range from 0°C. to —75°C., and it was found in all systems which were studied that there were very appreciable quantities of water which were not frozen even at temperatures as low as —75°C. The most surprising feature of their findings, however, was that the amount of bound water in each system was essentially a constant which did not change with temperature lowering, at least in the range —6° to —50°C. Thus in the case of gelatin all of the water which would freeze was frozen when the temperature was lowered to —6° C. and *no additional water froze even when the temperature was lowered to —50°C.* The freezing process for gelatin was found to be completely reversible, the temperature-lowering and temperature-raising cycles falling on the same curve. Water-binding in the system, gelatin-water, appears to be an adsorption reaction. A logarithmic relationship was found to exist between the concentration of the gelatin gel and the grams of water which were "bound" per gram of dry gelatin. In these studies 0.70 gm. of water per gm. of dry gelatin was "bound" in a 32 per cent gel, and 4.675 gm. of water per gm. of dry gelatin were "bound" in a 2 per cent gel. Figure 1 shows this relationship as found by the dilatometric studies of Jones and Gortner, and Figure 2 shows the same from the data of Newton and Martin (12) obtained by cryoscopic

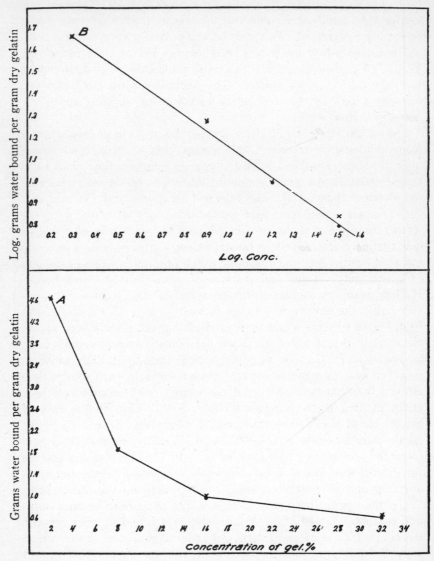

Fig. 1.—Curves of bound water in gelatin gels and sols of various concentrations from dilatometric data of Jones and Gortner (21)

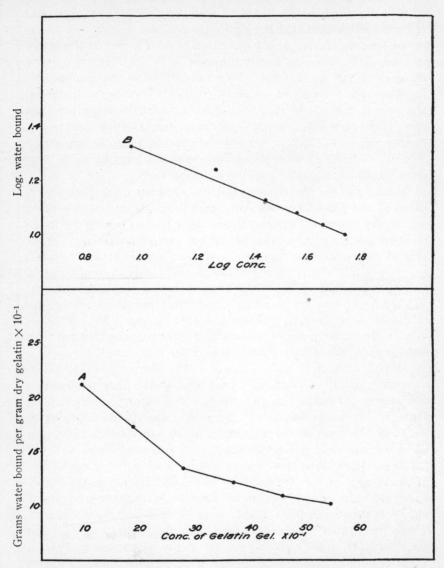

Fig. 2.—Curves of bound water in gelatin gels and sols of various concentrations from cryoscopic data of Newton and Martin (12)

technic. It would be expected that, even if a relatively large amount of bound water existed at the higher temperature (—6°C.), a lowering of the temperature would transform at least a part of this water into ice. This, however, does not appear to be the case. A possible explanation may be that two factors are affecting the equilibrium; (a) the vapor pressure of ice *decreasing* with lowering temperature, and (b) an adsorption pressure *increasing* with lowering temperature. If the increased adsorption tendency should be sufficient to just balance the lowered vapor pressure of the ice, then the amount of "bound" (adsorbed) water should be a constant irrespective of temperature, which coincides with the observed facts.

Freezing of the non-elastic gel of Fe_2O_3 caused a complete flocculation of the colloid but did not greatly alter the amount of water which was bound by the Fe_2O_3 micelles. In gels having an initial moisture content of approximately 85 per cent, approximately 20 per cent of the water was found to be in the "bound" state at —6°C., and 14 per cent still remained in the "bound" state at equilibrium at —47°C. Kinoshita (22) has also studied the freezing of gelatin gels and concludes that in the more concentrated gels there are present relatively large amounts of bound water. Moran (23), however, using dilatometric technics, reports that muscle tissue contains very little, if any, "bound" water (less than 2 per cent at —20°).

Hill (6, 8), Hill and Kupalov (24), Margaria (25), Grollman (8), and Briggs (26, 27) have studied the state of water in colloid gels, tissues, or biological fluids, using vapor-pressure technic. Hill (6, 7) defines the "free" water fraction as that "weight of water in one gram of tissue or fluid which can dissolve substances added to it with a normal depression of the vapor pressure" and concludes from his studies that in blood, in centrifuged corpuscles, in casein sols, in concentrated egg white, and in muscle the "free" water is almost exactly equal to the total water and that very little if any (less than 2 per cent) of the water in these systems is "bound." These conclusions are in agreement with the findings of Hill and Kupalov (24) on the osmotic pressure of the frog's resting muscles. Their studies on the osmotic pressure of fatigued muscle indicate that some unknown substance is liberated during muscle activity, since the osmotic pressure of fatigued muscle exceeds the calculated value, providing the lactic acid and creatine liberated by muscle activity are dissolved in the water present. Grollman (8) studied the depression of the vapor pressure of water in aqueous solutions of

NaCl, KCl, CaCl$_2$, urea, sucrose, lactic and succinic acids, creatine, and mixtures of those substances with each other and with sols of gelatin and gum acacia. He concludes that organic substances, such as urea and sucrose, showed anomalous effects and were unsuited for studies of water-binding. The vapor-pressure studies of solutions containing mixtures of gelatin or gum acacia with NaCl or KCl indicated that the "hydration" of gelatin is relatively small (1 to 3 gm. of water per gm. of colloid) at pH 7.0, and no appreciable hydration of gum acacia was apparent. He also was unable to demonstrate any change in the state of hydration of gelatin when it passed from a gel to a sol or in blood when the clot formed, and concluded that the view that hydrophilic colloids are strongly hydrated was not substantiated, suggesting that the water is simply held in its usual state in the gel fibrillae.

Briggs (26) in a critical study of the vapor-pressure method for measuring water relationships in colloids points out that one is really measuring the *activity coefficient* of the water in the system and accordingly the free energy content of the water. He points out that the energy change upon the dilution of an ideal dilute solution consists in a kinetic-energy exchange between the molecules of the added solvent and the molecules of the solvent already present in the solution, whereas for ideal concentrated solutions the energy change in the solvent is accompanied by the evolution or absorption of heat by the system. Briggs finds that aqueous colloid systems of agar, fibrin, casein, and cellulose behave as ideal concentrated solutions, at least in the more concentrated systems. He measured the amount of water which was "bound" by casein at pH 4.7, by sodium caseinate at pH 6.9 and pH 10.1, and by calcium caseinate at pH 6.4, at relative vapor pressures varying from 0.180 to 0.996, and found values which indicated that isoelectric casein would bind approximately 0.50 gram of water per gram of dry casein when immersed in pure water (of activity $= 1$). The water-binding capacity of the alkali caseinates "is the sum of the water-binding capacities of the positive ions and of the negative micelle, this latter being the same as for the isoelectric micelle." His studies indicated that the sodium caseinates were completely ionized, whereas the calcium caseinate was only about 20 per cent ionized.

In a second paper Briggs (27) considers the problem of the nature of the bound water in colloidal systems. He points out that the relative vapor-pressure–water-content curve for crystalloidal systems approximates closely the theoretical for dilute solutions, but that with colloids no approximation to the laws of dilute solutions is observed. He notes that the forces acting on the water are not the same in the two cases; that in crystalloidal solutions the forces are kinetic, whereas in colloidal systems the forces are the gravitational forces of the partial valences on the surface of the micellae, and furthermore that the relative vapor-pressure–water-content curve cannot be predicted from the laws of dilute solutions nor from any other data except those which are obtained for the particular colloidal system in question.

Briggs points out that bound water as measured by Hill's (6, 7) vapor-pressure technic or the Newton and Gortner cryoscopic method will be lower than the amount which is actually associated with the colloid, owing to the fact that the measurements were made in systems where the activity of the "free" water had already been markedly reduced by the presence of solutes, and notes that the ratio of the water associated with the colloid will vary with the activity of the water in the system. Briggs finds, using gum acacia–sucrose–water systems and the cryoscopic technic, that gum acacia binds 1.004 grams of water per gram of colloid at a water activity of 0.9866 and that this value falls to 0.538 gram of water per gram of colloid at a water activity of 0.9322; similarly, the values for gum acacia–ethyl alcohol–water systems indicate 1.428 grams of water bound per gram of gum acacia at a water activity of 0.9914, decreasing to 0.697 gram at a water activity of 0.9562. Briggs extended the bound water—water activity curves to lower water activity values by the use of vapor-pressure studies and found that the values so obtained formed a continuous curve with those calculated from the cryoscopic data.

In further experiments Briggs compares his cryoscopic and vapor-pressure data with data obtained by Rubner's method and finds that Rubner's method gives much higher results for bound water and furthermore that the "bound" water increased as the total water in the system was increased. This is in accordance with the findings of Jones and Gortner (21) and is perhaps not surprising when we consider that relative vapor-pressure measures the "freest" part of the free water, i.e., the surface film. If the system were in true equilibrium, there should, of course, be an exact equivalence between the activity coefficient of the "free" water and the activity coefficient of the "bound" water. However, colloid systems are probably not in such an equilibrium, the forces of syneresis and hysteresis are active, and it seems probable to the reviewer that these forces account for the differences˙ which Briggs finds to exist between the vapor-pressure and the Rubner technics.

DuNoüy (28) suggests that the water is not simply adsorbed on the surface of the protein molecules but actually penetrates into the interior of a huge molecular structure, thus changing the relative position of the chemical groups and accounting for the change in optical behavior. This may continue until the volume of the molecules occupies the entire volume of the system with no free solvent being present, resulting in the formation of a very dense gel.

Krevisky (29) considers that free water is osmotically transferable, whereas bound water is not, and by comparing the centrifuged volume of red blood cells in contact with solutions of NaCl of varying (hypertonic) concentrations he concludes that from 30 to 35 per cent of the volume of the cell consists of free water and that the water in the remaining 30 to 37 per cent of the cell volume is bound water. He notes that his values agree with those of Gough (30). However, Schiødt (31) does not accept these values and notes that they were obtained in highly hypertonic solutions. Schiødt states that when one uses hypotonic, isotonic, or only slightly hypertonic solutions and inserts the volume values for the corpuscles in the van't Hoff–Boyle–Mariotte formula, a free water value of 65 per cent is obtained.

Collins (32) has suggested a new type of cryoscopic technic which may be of value in the study of bound water. He notes that in the usual cryoscopic technic a correction is made for the separation of ice and accordingly the concentration of the solution due to undercooling, and notes that when the solid content is high, there will be a greater concentration of the solutes than when the solid content is low, owing to the fact that all of the concentration takes place in the "free" portion of the water. He accordingly suggests the formula

$$\varDelta = \varDelta' - \left[\frac{su\,\varDelta'}{80\,w}\right]$$

Where $\varDelta =$ the corrected (true) freezing-point

$\varDelta' =$ the observed freezing-point

$u =$ degrees undercooling

$s =$ specific heat of the system

$w =$ the weight of the water acting as a solvent plus the solutes dissolved in it

By making a series of readings at varying undercoolings it was possible to extrapolate $\varDelta'$ to the true $\varDelta$ where no undercooling existed and also to determine the amount of the water in the system which did not act as a solvent. His data show that only about 34 per cent of the volume of beef-blood corpuscles is water which acts as a solvent, the difference between this value and the 60 per cent of water in the corpuscles (26 per cent) being considered as "bound." It is of interest to note that these values closely approximate those obtained by Krevisky.

That water is strongly compressed on the surface of colloid gels has been emphasized again by Ewing and Spurway (33), who find that water adsorbed on silica gel has a greater density than has water in bulk.

WATER AND WINTER HARDINESS AND DROUGHT RESISTANCE

Newton and Martin (12) have contributed an extensive series of physico-chemical studies on the problem of drought resistance. Their paper includes a discussion of plant structures which are concerned in the absorption and transportation of water, a study of bound water (using the cryoscopic method) as a measure of hydrophilic colloid content, a study of the application of the cryoscopic method to plant-tissue fluids including the dialysis of the fluids so as to secure colloidal sols free from the solutes which are normally present, and a study of the relationships which exist between drought resistance and the bound water of the tissue fluids. Their paper contains so much experimental data that it is impossible to present an adequate review within the limits of this chapter. Suffice it to remark that in colloidal systems which contain minimal quantities of molecularly dispersed solutes, such as sols of gelatin, agar, blood fibrin, gum acacia, dextrin, and egg white, they found appreciable quantities of bound water and in practically every instance found the bound water per gram of dry colloid to increase with decreasing colloid content (cf. Fig. 2). They believe that bound-water content is frequently related to the state of dispersion of the colloid, increasing with increased dispersion and decreasing during coagulation. In their studies of the plant saps, using both cultivated crops and native vegetation where adequate botanical information as to the ability to resist drought is available, they found that "both grasses and wheats could be classified very satisfactorily with respect to drought resistance on the basis of the bound-water content of the fresh juice. . . . . It seems probable that bound-water content is a more stable and characteristic property than osmotic pressure. It is suggested that a high colloidal content must reduce the rate of abstraction of water from plant cells and may also confer on a plant the property of wilt endurance. *Populus certinensis,* which holds its leaves longer in the fall and is highly frost-resistant, has a higher content of bound water, colloids, and probably also of sugars, than *P. petrovski,* of which the leaves fall earlier and are non-resistant to frost."

In their studies Newton and Martin arrange nine wheat varieties and thirteen species of native grasses in tables *in the order of their known ability to resist drought,* and when the averages of the bound-water, values for the seasons 1925 and 1926 are placed opposite each species there is an absolutely regular descending order of bound-water values from the most drought-resistant to the least drought-resistant species. Such biological evidence as this, coupled with similar biological evidence on winter hardiness in both plants and animals which is in the earlier literature, indicates that the cryoscopic technic is measuring some factor of real biological importance and throws the burden of proof upon those who insist that bound water either does not exist or is of negligible importance.

The problem of cold resistance in insects has been studied by Sacharov (34), who finds that those insects which are resistant to cold contain a minimal quantity of free water and that during the preparation for hibernation there is a great increase in bound water. This is in agreement with the earlier observations of Robinson (16, 17, 18, 19). Miss Payne (35) reports that repeated freezing and thawing cause no visible microscopic changes in the cell walls of cat brains, various species of insect larvae, and the eggs and adults of certain other invertebrates. She concludes that probably the effect of repeated freezing and thawing is to bring about changes in the structure of the protoplasm.

WATER AND THE NERVOUS SYSTEM

McQuarrie (36) has made the important discovery that at least certain types of epilepsy appear to be due to disturbed water relationships and that when water is withheld from the patient the patient becomes free from seizures and may remain entirely free from seizures providing that the water intake is reduced to a minimum. A sudden increase in the water intake or the parenteral administration of a solution of the pituitary or the anti-diuretic hormone of the hypophysis produces a positive water balance in such "dehydrated" patients and a corresponding recurrence of the seizures. If, however, sufficient urea is added to the ingested water, the seizures do not develop. In later papers Manchester, Husted, and McQuarrie (37), and McQuarrie and Peeler (38) studied, respectively, the influence of hydration of the body on the insensible loss in weight in children, and the effect of pituitary diuresis and forced water-drinking on epileptic children; and they find that with children in a normal state of hydration there is a close parallelism between the "perspiratio insensibilis" and the energy metabolism but that with children in a fairly marked stage of dehydration the total insensible water loss is very greatly reduced without a corresponding reduction in the metabolic rate. With superhydration, such as follows excessive water-drinking or administration of pituitrin or pitressin, the total insensible water loss is greatly augmented, again without a corresponding change in metabolic rate. With sustained pituitary diuresis and water-drinking the seizures in epileptic children can be markedly increased, a typical *grand mal* seizure being induced within 12 to 48 hours by giving water at the rate of 2 to 5 cc. per kg. of body weight per hour, at the same time retaining the water in the body by the administration of pituitary extracts. Non-epileptic children do not acquire seizures under such technic. The effect of the water does not appear to be due to intercellular brain edema, since the spinal-fluid pressure appears to be within the normal range.

In a later paper McQuarrie, Manchester, and Husted (39) studied the effect of diuresis, catharsis, luminal therapy, and water storage on the water and mineral balance of epileptic children, and they report that a positive water balance was regularly followed by convulsive seizures except during luminal therapy. If diuresis or catharsis prevents water retention, a high level of water exchange does not necessarily favor the occurrence of convulsions. During periods of diuresis when no seizures occurred, Na⁺ and Cl⁻ were the predominating ions in the urine, but during rehydration there was a marked negative potassium balance and a striking increase in the K^+/Na^+ ratio; apparently there was a marked "leakage" of potassium from the cells, this "leakage" being most marked during pituitary antidiuresis, which the authors note "may indicate an innate weakness in the retaining membranes, presumably of the cells of the central nervous system. It is possible that abnormal amounts of water and even Na^+ found entry to the cells at the same time. The data recorded are tentatively interpreted as favoring the view that an inherent defect in the mechanism for regulating permeability of the brain-cell membranes is characteristic of the epileptic state. The specific action of phenylethylbarbituric acid (luminal) would appear, from the limited data presented, to be that of maintaining the normal relationships of the electrolytes and water on the two sides of the cell membrane."

It appears possible that there may be a relationship between these observations of McQuarrie and those of Bancroft and Rutzler (40, 41) on the effect of narcotics, alkaloids, and various inorganic salts on nervous tissues. Bancroft and Rutzler have presented a theory that the various types of insanity are due either to an increased dispersion or an increased coagulation of the brain colloids. McQuarrie's results indicate that water relationships may be even more important, although, of course, an increased dispersion may be interpreted as resulting in an increased hydration, and coagulation as resulting from a loss of water, perhaps by syneresis.

That there may be a shift in brain-water relationships is indicated by Barbour (42), who reports that during anaesthesia there is a change in the ratio of medulla H_2O / cerebrum H_2O, the cerebrum losing water and the medulla gaining water. In normal rats the ratio was found to be 0.922 ± 0.003, in etherized rats 0.936, in rats anaesthetized with amytal 0.931, and in rats anaesthetized with morphine 0.939 ± 0.007. "The water shift described appears (to be) directly associated with the process of *narcosis,* not with preliminary stimulation of any sort."

Lucké (43) notes that narcotics (the urethanes) show some tendency to reduce the permeability of cells for water, but notes that their effect is less than that of bivalent cations. May (44) finds that in the initial stages of nerve degeneration the water content of the nerve may greatly increase, later falling to normal, and that a similar marked increase of water content occurs when the cerebral hemisphere degenerates following trauma (45). Perhaps this may be explained by the observation of Johannes (46) that there appears to be a relationship between water exchange and the vegetative innervation of the body.

GLANDULAR SECRETION AND WATER RELATIONS

Molitor (47) has discussed in a general address the recent advances in the study of the influence of hormones on the water exchange of the organism.

The pituitary.—Heller (48) notes that the hormone of the posterior lobe of the pituitary when injected into frogs causes a marked increase in water content which may increase the weight as much as 29 per cent. Roboz (49) suggests that the hydremia which "hypophysin" causes in rabbits, and which prevents diuresis when Ringer's solution is injected, is due to a direct action of the hormone on the kidney, the hydremia being due to a damming back of the water and the mobilization of this water by the tissues. This view that extract of the posterior lobe has its primary effect on renal activity accords with the observations of McIntyre and van Dyke (50) and with that of Poulsson (51), who concludes that the effect is upon the proximal renal tubules with an increased water resorption from the glomerular filtrate. As contrasted with this view of an almost exclusive kidney effect, Kiss (52) notes that when "pituitrin" is injected subcutaneously there is an increased hydration of the connective tissue, and he suggests that the connective-tissue elements have an increased avidity for water. Steggerda (53) reports that, while "pitressin" causes an increase of 14 to 15 per cent in the weight of an intact frog due to water absorption, there is no increase in the weight of an isolated frog's muscle immersed in an isotonic solution containing the hormone. He accordingly suggests that the antidiuretic action of the hormone is not responsible for the increase in weight of the intact frog but rather that there is an increase in skin permeability which is responsible for the water absorption following an injection of the hormone. In mammals (dogs and rabbits) Barbour, Ellerbrook, and Howard (54) find that "pitressin probably disappears from the blood within 45 minutes after subcutaneous injection in rabbits. . . . . The brain edema previously demonstrated seems to result from the blood hydration which in turn is associated with anuria, and as previous experiments have shown, with loss of water from the skin."

The thyroid.—Kusakari and Takeda (55) report that in hyper-thyroidism the body as a whole loses water. The loss is greatest from the skin. In hypothyroidism there is a marked retention of water and again the skin predominates in the effect.

The pancreas.—Wiechmann and Liang (56), Althausen and Mancke (57), Sorge (58), and Goldberger and Goldberger (59) all report an antidiuretic effect following the injection of insulin.

WATER INTOXICATION AND WATER DIURESIS

Harding and Harris (60) report that in order to produce convulsive spasms in dogs the retention of water must exceed 60 cc. per kg. of body weight and that, while the administration of 10 per cent NaCl solution will cause recovery, the administration of hypertonic urea solutions is relatively ineffective. These authors express doubt that the convulsions of epilepsy and eclampsia are due to water intoxication even though they may be accompanied by a positive water balance.

Rioch (61), Bayliss and Fee (62), and Govaerts and Cambier (63) have studied water diuresis with particular reference to the effect of the absorption of large quantities of water on changes in the composition of the blood. Rioch concludes that the water diuresis is probably the resultant of the dilution of the blood electrolytes. Bayliss and Fee state that there is a greater fall in the concentration of the plasma colloids than of the plasma electrolytes, the fall in concentration of the plasma colloids being approximately the theoretical amount on the assumption that the extra ingested water was uniformly distributed throughout the tissues. On the other hand, Govaerts and Cambier find that the dilution of the arterial blood during water diuresis is very slight (less than 2 per cent).

DESICCATION AND WATER RELATIONSHIPS

McIntosh, Kajdi, and Meeker (64) studied blood volume and serum electrolyte concentration in 11 infants suffering from diarrhea dehydration and found that the blood volume may decrease as much as 20 per cent, the decrease being almost entirely from the plasma fraction. Dehydration was accompanied by a decrease in total fixed bases and of Cl^- and HCO_3^- in the serum, but the consequent acidosis could not be correlated with blood changes, nor could these be correlated with the severity of the toxic symptoms.

Drake, McKhann, and Gamble (65) studied the effect of intestinal obstruction on body water and chloride content of the rat. They found that obstruction of the lower intestine caused little if any water changes, whereas obstruction of the upper intestine caused a dehydration amounting to 12.6 per cent of the total body water during the first 12 hours. The water loss arose from two sources: (a) fasting, with accompanying water deprivation, during which period respiration of water and the chemical combination of water in the hydrolytic processes of metabolism continues, and (b) loss of water into the stomach in the form of gastric secretions. The first process is accompanied by a decrease in body solids and does not disturb the water content of the body tissues. The second process accounts for the dehydration of the tissues, the water being derived mainly from the skin and the blood. Such water as is lost from the tissues appears to be lost from the interstitial fluids and not from tissue cells. Coincident with a total body water loss of 12.6 per cent there was a loss of 28.3 per cent of the total body chlorides, the chlorides being secreted into the stomach. Nearly half of the chloride loss came from the skin.

Caldwell (66) studied the influence of dehydration on the blood concentration, thermoregulation, respiratory exchange, and metabolic water production in the cat, the dehydration being induced by keeping cats in a dry atmosphere for from 6 to 16 days without the complications of acute starvation. Loss in body weight was as great as 26.8 per cent, the blood concentration increasing an average of 45 per cent with a maximal increase of 75 per cent above normal. Thermoregulation and the production of metabolic water were not affected. The respiratory exchange increased but the respiratory quotient remained unchanged.

Heller (67) reports from a study of water loss during the dehydration of frogs that during the loss of the first 10 per cent of the total body water there is a differential loss from the various tissues, the gastrocnemius losing 11.1 per cent and the liver 15 per cent. As the desiccation proceeds to a loss of 25 per cent of the body water there is no further loss of water from the liver, whereas the gastrocnemius loses water to the extent of 17.8 per cent. When such desiccated frogs are replaced in water, an increase in weight takes place which exceeds the original weight by 6.9 per cent (gastrocnemius = +2.3 per cent).

Schulz (68) reports that the meal worm, *Tenebrio molitor,* is extraordinarily resistant to desiccation forces, the larvae remaining alive for months in vacuum-dried bran in a dry air current, and undergoing metamorphosis under such conditions. He finds that metabolic water condenses on the bran surrounding the larvae and on the surface of the larvae, and in addition there is the production of a wax-like coating which, with the normal covering of chitin, tends toward the maintenance of their water content.

THE INFLUENCE OF CHEMICALS AND DRUGS ON WATER RELATIONSHIPS

Vitamins.—Newcomb (69) reports that pigeons dying of beriberi (*Beriberi columbarium*) have larger hearts than is normal but that there is no marked increase in the water content of these larger hearts; accordingly the increase in the size of the heart cannot be explained by water retention. Pigeons suffering from polyneuritis (*Polyneuritis columbarium*) and starvation show a diminution in the size of the heart and an increased water content of the heart muscle.

Hayasaka (70) reports that patients suffering from beriberi show a smaller effect of blood concentration through muscular exercise than do normal persons or those who have recovered from the disease. This is probably due to an increased permeability of the capillaries for protein and is especially noted in those suffering from the beriberi edema. Water passes into the edemous areas during muscular exercise but is transferred again to the blood during rest periods. In guinea-pig scurvy Randoin and Michaux (71) find that both the kidney and the liver show some increase in Cl⁻ and water content.

Alkaloids.—Barbour and co-workers (72, 73) have studied the effect of cocaine on the water relationships in cocaine fever induced in rabbits. They find that following pyretic doses of cocaine there is a definite loss of water from the blood with a corresponding gain in water by the liver, which gain in water corresponds to an increased heat production by the liver. The increased solid content of the blood reduces the rate of peripheral circulation, and the inability to increase heat elimination by vaporization accounts for the onset of the fever. The brain, the muscles, and the kidneys of the febrile animals showed no significant change in water content. There was possibly a slight dehydration of the skin. "The retention of water by the liver in the first stages of fever seems to play a leading rôle in the interference with heat elimination which causes the febrile temperatures."

Cholesterol and lecithin.—The effect of cholesterol and lecithin on water and acid-base economy in rabbits has been studied by Dahmlos and Sole (74) and by Degkwitz (75) with essentially identical findings in both cases. Cholesterol injected into rabbits caused a transfer of Cl⁻ and water from the tissues into the blood and urine, resulting in a pronounced hydremia and a very high Cl⁻ value for both blood and urine. Lecithin, on the other hand, causes a retention of water by the tissues, a concentration of the blood, and a minimal content of Cl⁻ in both blood and urine. Paradoxically these conditions are reversed under prolonged cholesterol or lecithin feeding. In such cases cholesterol favors a retention of water and Cl⁻ by the tissues and decreased urinary excretion, whereas the lecithin-fed animals showed an increase in urinary water and Cl⁻ elimination. It is suggested that this antagonistic behavior of cholesterol and lecithin is due to their effect on cell permeability and may be associated with their behavior toward emulsion formation, cholesterol favoring a water-in-oil system, lecithin favoring an oil-in-water type.

Carbohydrates.—Both McClendon (76) and Baisch (77) note that excessive carbohydrate intake results in a retention of water in the body. McClendon records an increase in blood volume and Baisch an increase in tissue water which is unrelated to salt content. Baisch suggests that carbohydrates may show a specific tendency to increase water binding. However, Kallinikova (78) states that hyperglucemia and hydremia in children are not related. Bridge and Bridges (79) have experimentally shown that there is no relationship between the glycogen content and the water content of the liver and state that the idea that 3 grams of water are stored in the body for every gram of glycogen is erroneous. They believe that shifts in body water are much more likely to result from fat metabolism than from carbohydrate metabolism.

Sodium chloride.—The intravenous injection of isotonic solutions of sodium chloride [Simone (80)] or as sea-water [Rabbeno (81)] causes diuresis and the elimination of more water and Cl⁻ than was injected. The lethal dose of sea-water for rabbits was 144 cc. per kg. of body weight.

Blood anti-coagulants.—Guillaumin (82) reports that anti-coagulants such as sodium fluoride, sodium oxalate, and sodium citrate cause the migration of water from the corpuscles to the plasma to such an extent that the corpuscle volume may be decreased by as much as 20 per cent. There are also marked induced changes in the ratios of the inorganic constituents as between corpuscles and plasma, and the author suggests that in studies of the equilibrium of inorganic constituents in the blood such anti-coagulants be not used. Hirudin is recommended.

Magnesium sulfate.—The long-continued subcutaneous injection of magnesium sulfate into dogs causes an increase in plasma albumin and globulin but no change in the water content of the blood [Lang and Rigo (83)].

Arsphenamine.—According to Collier (84) the curative action of arsphenamine is increased by the simultaneous administration of water or saline solution. Withholding water causes a decrease in the action of the drug.

Diet.—Grzycki (85) notes that the various elements of the diet affect the excretion of water in different manners. Thus water is readily eliminated on an exclusive diet of carbohydrates, whereas a protein or fat diet causes a retention of water in the body and a diminution in the solid residue of the blood.

Plant physiology.—The effect of various mineral salts added to the soil on transpiration and water requirement of the cotton plant has been studied by Meyer (86), who finds in general a decrease in transpiration rate and a decrease in the water requirement. The effect of the added chemicals [$NaCl$, KCl, $NaNO_3$, KNO_3, $CaCl_2$, $Ca(NO_3)_2$] appeared to be predominantly osmotic rather than specifically ionic. A progressive increase in the concentration of $NaCl$ or $CaCl_2$ in the soil resulted in a progressively decreased water requirement and in a progressively increased final water content of the aërial parts of the plant.

WATER RELATIONSHIPS IN PHYSIOLOGICAL PROCESSES

The Rubner (14) method for measuring bound water, as modified by Robinson (20), has been applied by Robinson and Parsons (20a) to the problem of water changes in blood and muscle following hemorrhage, histamine injection, and traumatic shock. Dogs were used as the experimental animals. Traumatic shock was induced by beating the left hind leg of the anaesthetized (barbital) animal with a padded hammer. Arterial blood was drawn from the left femoral

TABLE I

Tissue	Condition	Total Water		Free Water		Bound Water	
		Percentage Present	Gm. per Gm. Dry Wt.	Percentage of Total	Gm. per Gm. Dry Wt.	Percentage of Total	Gm. per Gm. Dry Wt.
Venous blood*	Normal	79.4	3.86	74.4	2.87	25.6	0.99
	After hemorrhage	81.6	4.44	79.5	3.53	20.5	0.91
Muscle	Normal	75.0	3.00	79.0	2.37	21.0	0.63
	After hemorrhage	63.2	1.77	89.5	1.54	10.5	0.18
Arterial blood	Normal	77.2	3.38	85.5	2.89	14.5	0.49
	After histamine	75.1	3.01	85.4	2.57	14.6	0.44
Venous blood	Normal	76.8	3.32	85.9	2.85	14.1	0.47
	After histamine	75.1	3.01	83.7	2.52	16.3	0.49
Arterial blood	Normal	80.2	4.05	75.6	3.06	24.4	0.99
	After trauma	82.7	4.77	73.2	3.49	26.8	1.28
Venous blood	Normal	80.1	4.04	73.0	2.95	27.0	1.09
	After trauma	81.9	4.53	72.1	3.26	27.9	1.26
Muscle	Normal	71.0	2.45	64.5	1.58	35.5	0.87
	After trauma	67.4	2.07	60.9	1.26	39.1	0.81

* The figures for arterial blood are not included because of obvious error in the original tabulation. There was a gain in total water in the arterial blood.

artery, except for the traumatized animals, when it was drawn from the carotid artery; venous blood was taken from the right femoral vein, and muscle tissue was taken from the right fore leg. They report rapid exchange of water from the blood to the tissues and vice versa. The barbital anaesthesia was shown to be essentially without effect in inducing changes in the normal water relationships. A study of bound water in blood plasma and blood corpuscles indicated that in plasma 17.6 per cent of the water was bound (total water content $= 91.6$ per cent) and in the corpuscles 28.9 per cent was bound (total water 66.3 per cent).

Under the influence of hemorrhage, "there was a compensation transfer of water chiefly in the 'free' state from the muscles to the blood. In 'histamine shock' the fall of blood pressure is associated with, and perhaps is partly the result of, a transfer of water from the blood to the muscles. In 'shock' produced by severe traumatism of a leg, the evidence indicates that with minor trauma there is in some cases a loss of fluid from the blood to the muscles associated with a fall in blood pressure, and that with major trauma the picture is that of hemorrhage, in that there is a dilution of the blood remaining in the general circulation with water withdrawn from the muscle."

Table I, taken from the data of Robinson and Parsons (20a), shows maximum changes which they observed in water relations in experiments on blood and muscle of dogs, following hemorrhage, injection of histamine, and trauma to the leg. It will be noted that they report very appreciable amounts of "bound" water, i.e., water not frozen at $-20°C.$, to be present in blood and muscle tissues.

Water exchange.—Newburgh, Johnston, and Falcon-Lesses (87) have determined the total water exchange of humans including that evaporated by the skin and lungs and that formed by the oxidation of food and body tissue.

Underhill and co-workers (88, 89, 90, 91, 92) have studied the general problem of water exchange in the animal organism (rabbits) through dehydration induced by superficial burns, by the repeated injection of pilocarpine, by the withholding of food and water, by bleeding, or by giving phlorhizin or hypertonic solutions. Capillary permeability (outward) is increased in a heat burn, and since resorption of the edema fluid is extremely slow, it is postulated that there may be a decreased capillary permeability in the opposite direction. With a burn involving 17 per cent of the total body surface the edema fluid may amount to 70 per cent of the initial blood volume.

The edema fluid of a superficial burn is drawn largely from the blood, the composition of the tissues being very slightly altered. The composition of the edema fluid approximates that of the blood serum of the burned animal. Under water-starvation conditions, augmented by bleeding or the addition of phlorhizin, the blood becomes greatly concentrated, the skin may lose as much as 20 per cent of its water, and some water may be lost from the muscles, but the liver (and probably the kidney) never loses water, and any marked loss from the tissues results in death. Pilocarpine causes pulmonary edema, blood concentration, and an increase in the water content of most of the animal organs. It is evident from these studies that water exchange is largely through the blood and that the blood can gain or lose water within rather wide limits without profoundly affecting the water content of the tissue parts of the body and that if the water relationships of the tissues are appreciably altered, death will ensue.

Kayser (93), and Mayer and Nichita (94) have studied the ratio between the water evaporated and oxygen consumed and report that it is a constant at constant temperature. Mayor and Nichita state that the ratio H_2O/O_2 is 1.02 at 18° and is constant for all mammals, including man. Adjustment to external temperature (within the limits where the animal can maintain its body temperature) is compensated for by a change in metabolic rate.

Nakamura (95) reports that, following an operative reduction of kidney surface, rabbits show a better excretion of water and NaCl than do normal animals. The partial nephrectomy results in a hydremia and a rise in blood chlorides, indicating a shift of fluids from the tissues to the blood.

Adolph and Lepore (96) find that the arterial blood pressure is the chief factor regulating the water content of the tissues. When the blood pressure is lowered there is an exchange of water from the tissues to the blood, which is reversed when the arterial pressure is increased. There is usually a lag of 7 to 10 minutes in the reaction with maximum effects occurring within 15 minutes. Drinker and Field (97), in a study of the relationship between the protein content of lymph and the relation of the lymph to the tissue fluid, conclude that the blood capillaries normally "leak" protein, which does not re-enter the blood stream except by way of the lymph. The tissue fluid contains protein in the same proportion as the lymph, and in the tissues the protein-containing fluid has two functions: (a) the holding of extravascular water and (b) the promotion of the growth of the tissues. The permeability of the capillaries is greater in young than in old animals, and accordingly the old animals are unable to hold water in the tissue spaces, because the permeability of the capillaries for protein has been lost and there is nothing extravascular to retain the water when the capillary blood pressure falls.

Machebœuf (98) concludes that the phosphoamino lipoids play an important rôle in maintaining the water exchange between the blood and the fluids on the outer side of the capillaries, and that this action of the lipoids is due to the formation and the differential ionization of the various lipo-proteins.

Meyerhof (99) has studied the effect of fatigue and *rigor mortis* on the osmotic pressure of muscle, and Cassinis and Bracaloni (100) have studied the osmotic changes in blood during fatigue and at rest. Prolonged fatigue increases the osmotic pressure of muscle 30 per cent above that which can be calculated from the concentration of the known products of hydrolysis. In fatigue the water content of the blood is increased, probably owing to a transfer of water from the tissues. Margaria (25) reports an interesting sex difference in the vapor-pressure of human blood, the values expressed in gm. NaCl in 100 cc. water being for men 0.9447 ± 0.00495, and for women 0.9269 ± 0.0059. The difference was found to be accounted for in the content of bicarbonate and urea.

The water exchange of the developing trout embryo has been studied by Scheminzky (101), who finds that the growth rate is more or less paralleled by the change in water absorption. Water absorption in the early stages appears to be almost wholly through the yolk sac and not directly from the environment to the embryo.

Permeability.—The literature on permeability has been reviewed by Höber in a separate chapter. There are, however, a few references which should be mentioned in this connection, viz., those by Brooks (102) on "The accumulation of ions in living cells," by McCutcheon, Lucké, and Hartline (103) on the "Osmotic properties of living cells," and by Wieringa (104) on the measurement of permeability.

Wieringa, studying yeast cells, concludes that the total water (75 per cent) of the cell can be divided into three fractions: (*a*) the imbibition water of the cell membrane (13 per cent); (*b*) the free solution water of the cell (13.6 per cent); and (*c*) the water of imbibition which is held by the protoplasmic colloids (48.4 per cent). The water exchange of the cells under various environmental forces and the shift in the three classes of water were studied. The change in permeability as influenced by ions followed the usual lyotropic series.

The skin and water exchange.—Adolph (105, 106) has studied water exchange in the normal frog, in the flayed frog, and in the pithed intact frog. He finds that the flayed and pithed frogs behave like true osmometers where the movements of water from the medium to the organism or vice versa are proportional to the concentration of the medium, whereas this is not the case with the normal frog where the skin exerts a specific effect. Frog skin shows a differential directional osmosis[2] which is reversed as one passes the isoelectric point. The circulation of the blood is not necessary for the exchange of fluid to take place through the skin at a normal rate.

WATER RELATIONSHIPS IN PATHOLOGICAL CONDITIONS

Lucké and McCutcheon (108), from a study of the effect of injury on the unfertilized egg of *Arbacia punctulata*, find that injury increases cell permeability to water and that the increase in permeability parallels the degree of injury.

Miss Fishberg (109) has attempted to find a physico-chemical basis for the abnormalities which certain pathological sera show with respect to viscosity. She attributes the relatively slight changes in viscosity in nephrosis, in spite of the high dilution, to a special molecular state of the serum proteins. The high viscosity in cyanosis is brought about by the transfer of water from the serum into the corpuscles. The low viscosity characteristic of kidney damage is possibly due to an increased cholesterol content, which would favor a water-in-oil type of emulsion. Urea lowers the viscosity in uremia, and the bile acids raise the viscosity in obstructive jaundice.

Adlersberg and Perutz (110) have made an experimental study of resorption of intracutaneously injected fluids in order to apply the results to the interpretation of the wheal test. The effects of a number of drugs on the rate of resorption are noted. Amyl nitrite, theo-

---

[2] A similar differential permeability is noted by Brauner (107) for the testa of *Aesculus hippocastanum*, which is about 60 per cent more permeable to water from the outside than in the opposite direction. This is accounted for as being due to the electrical forces of the streaming potential through a 2-layered membrane, the layers having different degrees of permeability, and the streaming potential accelerating or retarding water movement, depending upon the orientation of the membrane.

phylline, and pituitrin administered systematically all accelerate resorption, although when pituitrin is administered at the same time as either of the others there is a mutual cancellation of the action. Narcotics affecting the cerebral cortex or brain stem do not alter the rate of resorption in contrast to those affecting the central nervous system. In fever, diabetes, and Basedow's disease there is increased resorption.

Edemas.—Labbé (111) has discussed the various factors concerned in the formation of edemas and concludes that osmotic, mineral, acid-base, protein, and lipoid factors are all involved as well as the circulation, the nerves, and certain of the endocrine glands.

Ort and Markowitz (112, 113), and Ort, Power, and Markowitz (114) have studied the edema produced by perfusing the beating isolated hearts of rabbits and dogs. They note that perfused hearts under all conditions gain in weight and that even when the perfusing liquid has twice the normal osmotic concentration of blood, or when it contains hydrophilic colloids (gum acacia 6 to 9 per cent), the heart still absorbs approximately as much water as it would from a standard Ringer-Locke solution at the same pH. The pH of the perfusing liquid was found to have a marked effect on water absorption, least rapid absorption of water occurring in solutions as alkaline as pH 9.5. In the absence of erythrocytes the heart tissue becomes permeable even to colloids such as gum acacia, which is found in considerable amounts in the tissue of hearts perfused with blood plasma to which gum acacia has been added. If, however, considerable quantities of functional erythrocytes are present in the perfusing fluid, practically no gum acacia penetrates into the heart tissue, and edema is at a minimum.

Kylin (115) has studied the osmotic pressure of the colloids in normal and edematous persons and finds that, whereas in the normal individual the colloid osmotic pressure of the arterial blood is 30 to 40 mm. H_2O higher than that of the venous blood, during the development of edema the conditions are reversed and the colloid osmotic pressure of the venous blood exceeds that of the arterial blood.

Hydremia.—Hydremia in children is paralleled by a fall in plasma proteins and plasma viscosity, according to Jochims (116), which he takes to indicate that the excess water in the plasma is free and not bound by the plasma colloids.

Fever.—Sunderman and Austin (117) have studied the water balance in patients with lobar pneumonia, and the evidence is that there is a negative water balance prior to the crisis except in those patients who received large doses of sodium chloride. The water content of the body tissues increases for several days prior to the crisis. The thirst exhibited by the patients is interpreted as evidence of a demand of certain body tissues for water.

Anemia.—Kofanov (118) notes that patients with pernicious anemia show a decreased solid content of the blood and, according to the severity of the disease, a greater or a lesser retention of water in the tissues.

GEL STRUCTURE AND THE HYDRATION AND DEHYDRATION OF GELS

The structure of gelatin gels has been investigated by Sheppard and Houck (119, 120), and Sheppard and McNally (121). Sheppard and Houck, using viscometric technic, were unable to find a true "transition temperature" (i.e., a temperature where the viscosity is independent of time) for the sol ⇌ gel transformation. If gelatin sols were kept above a certain temperature zone, viscosity progressively fell with time, indicating hydrolysis; if kept below that temperature zone, the viscosity increased with time. In the intermediate zone there was first a rise followed by a fall in viscosity, which probably represented gelation effects followed by hydrolysis. According to these authors, collagen consists of a mass of more or less crystal-like fibers, and "these crystallites are composed of primary valence chains of anhydro-amino acids, the protein macromolecules. Gelatin is formed by peptization of these fibers when not only the crystallites but the primary valence chains become disoriented and separated. These chains then bind water by dipole orientation.. On this view the molecules of gelatin and collagen are similar except for differences in orientation and association. The mutual attraction and water-binding capacity are reduced as hydrolysis progressively shortens the chain." This view is expanded by Sheppard and McNally, who note that it is in agreement with X-ray data and suggest that the process of gelation may be at least a partial reorientation of the micelles. This reorientation effect becomes greatly increased by stretching or drying gelatin gels.

Pleass (122) has studied the effects of temperature and pH on the formation of gelatin gels and notes that heat is evolved during gelation and absorbed during sol formation. She interprets her data as indicating that lowering the temperature changes the system from "a solution of gelatin in water to one of water in gelatin with the formation of a framework of hydrated gelatin and the evolution of heat. Turbidity is regarded as an indication of heterogeneity, one phase being hydrated gelatin and the other a dilute solution of water in gelatin. The presence of acid or alkali causes a reduction in the hydration of the gelatin aggregates accompanied by an increase in the free water and a decrease in the strength of the gel."

The swelling and hydration of gels.—Kruyt (123) proposes the theory that the hydration of hydrophilic colloids is due to shells of water molecules oriented around the micelle, the degree of orientation diminishing as the distance from the particle increases. He recognizes two types of water envelopes, a compact one composed of fully oriented molecules which remains intact even at the isoelectric point and in the presence of dehydrating agents such as a moderate concentration of alcohol, and a diffuse water atmosphere where relatively little orientation is present and from which the water may be readily removed.

Lloyd (124, 125), Pleass (126), Northrop and Kunitz (127), Bigwood and Majmin (128), Adair and Callow (129), and Neville and Theis (130) have all dealt with the problem of the swelling of gelatin under various conditions. Lloyd finds that the swelling of gelatin in salt solution and in alkalies is independent of the volume of the solution in which the gelatin is immersed, and she regards a gelatin gel as composed of a network of fibrils arranged haphazardly throughout the gel with a liquid interstitial phase, and considers that any force which will distort this mass of fibrils will cause a volume change in the gel. She suggests that whereas the swelling in acids is largely osmotic, due to salt formation, the swelling in alkalies is in part osmotic and in part due to the hydration of the fibrils, in the latter respect being similar to the swelling which is induced at the isoelectric point by salts.

Swelling of isoelectric gelatin in salt solutions is independent of the volume of the salt solution and is directly proportional to the logarithm of the salt concentration, following the formula

$$s = a \log C$$

where $s =$ swelling

$a =$ a constant depending on the nature of the salt and independent of temperature in so far as the coherent framework of the gel has not begun to rupture.

Lloyd notes that the swelling of gelatin in pure water is not by osmosis but by imbibition, and that the water of imbibition is combined in some manner with the gelatin, resulting in a decrease in the free energy of the system.

Northrop and Kunitz consider that all swelling is due to osmotic forces and that gelatin gels are 2-phase, 3-component systems, a solid phase of "insoluble" gelatin and a liquid phase of an aqueous solution of the "insoluble" fraction and the "soluble" fraction of gelatin. Each micelle would thus consist of a network of "insoluble" gelatin confining an interior "solution" of "soluble" gelatin. The paper includes extensive experimental data in support of these hypotheses. Bigwood and Majmin propose a similar hypothesis.

Friedman and Kraemer (131) and Friedman (132) have studied the size of the pores in gelatin and agar gels by diffusion coefficient technic, on the assumption that the gel structure is a random three-dimensional aggregation of fibrils.

They find values of pore radii of 4.7–5.5 mμ in a 5 per cent gelatin gel, 1.4–1.7 mμ for a 10 per cent gel, and 0.5–1.0 mμ for a 15 per cent gel. The size of the pore radii is inversely related to the temperature at which the system gelated.

Pore radii for a 2 per cent agar gel range between 2.9 and 5.65 mμ and for a 5 per cent agar gel between 0.74 and 1.43 mμ. The rate of diffusion through the gel decreases linearly with increase in concentration of the gel.

Neville and Theis believe that there is a distinction between swelling and hydration, and that hydration is not due to osmosis or to a Donnan equilibrium, but rather to an adsorption or binding of water by residual valencies. Hydration results in a volume decrease of the system and is favored by a lowering of the temperature, as one would anticipate from an adsorption reaction.

Weber (133) has discussed the hydration of protein from the standpoint of the "twin ion" theory of Bjerrum and concludes that at the isoelectric point proteins exist as completely or nearly completely charged twin ions, the basic groups of one micelle being attracted by the acid groups of another micelle, thus accounting for maximum association of the protein and maximum flocculation and rigidity of the gel. Weber believes that hydration is not a consequence of protein ionization. This agrees with the observations of Jones and Gortner (21), who did not find any appreciable effect of pH on the water which was "bound" by gelatin, indicating that water binding resides in the presence of "polar" (in the sense of Harkins) groups in the molecule.

SYNERESIS

Hydration and syneresis in "geraninic" acid gels, $C_{24}H_{17}N_3O_4S_2$, have been studied by Lipatov and Korobova (134), who conclude that the electrical charge is the only true factor of stability in lyophilic systems. They find that the velocity of syneresis is a function of the distance between the particles and depends upon the intensity of attractional forces. The velocity of syneresis follows the law of a first-order reaction.

The finding of Ferguson and Applebey (135) from a study of syneresis in silica gels is essentially similar, i.e., that the velocity of syneresis is favored by the tendency of SiO_2 micelles to further consolidate through the forces of unsatisfied residual valencies and hindered by the tendency of the gel structure to resist deformation.

The clotting and syneresis of blood were studied by Prakash and Dhar (136), who find that electrolytes affect blood clotting in the same manner as they affect the formation and the syneresis of other organic and inorganic gels. The anti-coagulating action of fluorides, citrates, and oxalates is stated to be due, not to a removal of Ca^{++} but rather to the effect of the anion on the colloidal system, and, in support of this view, the authors were able to suppress clotting, or syneresis from the clot, by appropriate concentrations of $CaCl_2$.

That the water of guttation from the leaf tips of *Colocasia antiquorum* is not a true "liquid of syneresis" is indicated by the observations of Dixon and Dixon (137) that the exuded water is devoid of solutes, the solutes probably having been screened out by semipermeable membranes.

HYSTERESIS

Banerji and Ghosh (138) have studied hysteresis in the sol-gel transformation of aqueous systems of gelatin and the sodium salts of various fatty acids and note that the time-solidification and time-liquefaction curves tend to coincide as time is increased. Hysteresis in such systems is ascribed to a low orientation velocity of the micelles.

Visco (139) observes that hysteresis is also evident in conductivity measurements of various colloidal sols, the conductivity being higher when the sol was cooled to a given temperature than was the case when the temperature was raised to the same point. The conductivity effects were paralleled by viscosity effects and are explained on the basis of viscosity effects as influencing the mobility of the ions.

PROTOPLASM

Seifriz (140) has presented a general review of "the plasticity of protoplasm" in which he discusses the various technics whereby the consistency may be measured, and he arrives at the conclusion that protoplasm is both plastic and elastic and that protoplasm may vary in consistency from a thin fluid ($\eta = 0.2$) to a dense gel. Using micro-dissection technic, Seifriz and Plowe (141) measured the extensibility of the protoplasm of the epidermal cells of the onion (*Allium cepa*) previously treated with $0.01\ M$ solutions of various nitrates. They report a lyotropic series of cations as affecting the elastic limit, $Ca^{++} > Sr^{++}$ favoring elongation, Mg^{++} essentially without effect, and $Na^+ > Li^+ > K^+$ decreasing elongation. "The extensibility of protoplasm is only slightly influenced by viscosity and surface tension; it is essentially a matter of structure."

LITERATURE CITED

1. ADOLPH, E. F., *Quart. Rev. Biol.*, **5**, 51 (1930)
2. GORTNER, R. A., *Trans. Faraday Soc.*, **26**, 678 (1930). (Note especially the discussion, pp. 686–704)
3. WÖHLBIER, W., *Tierernähr.*, **2**, 530 (1931)
4. MARINESCO, N., *Compt. rend. soc. biol.*, **103**, 872 (1930)
5. SHULL, C. A., *J. Am. Soc. Agron.*, **22**, 459 (1930)
6. HILL, A. V., *Proc. Roy. Soc.* (*London*), *B*, **106**, 477 (1930)
7. HILL, A. V., *Adventures in Biophysics* (University of Pennsylvania Press, 1931)
8. GROLLMAN, A., *J. Gen. Physiol.*, **14**, 661 (1931)
9. BALCAR, J. O., SANSUM, W. D., AND WOODYATT, R. T., *Arch. Intern. Med.*, **24**, 116 (1919)
10. NEWTON, R., AND GORTNER, R. A., *Botan. Gaz.*, **74**, 442 (1922)
11. KRUYT, H. R., AND WINKLER, K. C., *Z. anorg. allgem. Chem.*, **188**, 200 (1930)
12. NEWTON, R., AND MARTIN, W. M., *Can. J. Research*, **3**, 336 (1930)
13. NEWTON, R., *J. Agr. Sci.*, **12**, 1 (1922) ; **14**, 178 (1924)
14. RUBNER, M., *Abhandl. preuss. Akad. Wiss. phys.-math. Klasse*, pp. 3–70 (1922)
15. THOENES, F., *Biochem. Z.*, **157**, 174 (1925)

16. ROBINSON, W., *J. Econ. Entomol.*, **20**, 80 (1927)
17. ROBINSON, W., *Ann. Entomol. Soc. Am.*, **21**, 407 (1928)
18. ROBINSON, W., *J. Econ. Entomol.*, **21**, 897 (1928)
19. ROBINSON, W., *Colloid Symposium Monograph*, **5**, 199 (1928)
20. ROBINSON, W., *J. Biol. Chem.*, **92**, 699 (1931)
20a. ROBINSON, W., AND PARSONS, ELOISE, *Arch. Path.*, **12**, 869 (1931)
21. JONES, I. D., AND GORTNER, R. A., *J. Phys. Chem.*, **36**, 387 (1932)
22. KINOSHITA, K., *Bull. Chem. Soc. Japan*, **5**, 261 (1930)
23. MORAN, T., *Proc. Roy. Soc. (London)*, B, **107**, 182 (1930)
24. HILL, A. V., AND KUPALOV, P. S., *Proc. Roy. Soc. (London)*, B, **106**, 445 (1930)
25. MARGARIA, R., *J. Physiol.*, **70**, 417 (1930)
26. BRIGGS, D. R., *J. Phys. Chem.*, **35**, 2914 (1931)
27. BRIGGS, D. R., *J. Phys. Chem.*, **36**, 367 (1932)
28. DUNOÜY, P. L., *Science*, **72**, 224 (1930)
29. KREVISKY, C., *Biochem. J.*, **24**, 815 (1930)
30. GOUGH, A., *Biochem. J.*, **18**, 202 (1924)
31. SCHIØDT, E., *Biochem. J.*, **25**, 8 (1931)
32. COLLINS, D. A., *Proc. Soc. Exptl. Biol. Med.*, **28**, 896 (1931)
33. EWING, D. T., AND SPURWAY, C. H., *J. Am. Chem. Soc.*, **52**, 4635 (1931)
34. SACHAROV, N. L., *Ecology*, **11**, 505 (1930)
35. PAYNE, NELLIE M., *Ecology*, **11**, 500 (1930)
36. McQUARRIE, I., *Am. J. Diseases Children*, **38**, 451 (1929)
37. MANCHESTER, R. C., HUSTED, CLARA, AND McQUARRIE, I., *J. Nutrition*, **4**, 39 (1931)
38. McQUARRIE, I., AND PEELER, D. B., *J. Clin. Investigation*, **10**, 915 (1931)
39. McQUARRIE, I., MANCHESTER, R. C., AND HUSTED, CLARA, *Symposium on Epilepsy* (monograph, in press). (Assoc. for Research in Nervous and Mental Diseases, 1932)
40. BANCROFT, W. D., AND RUTZLER, J. E., JR., *Proc. Nat. Acad. Sci.*, **17**, 105 (1931)
41. BANCROFT, W. D., AND RUTZLER, J. E., JR., *J. Phys. Chem.*, **35**, 1185, 3036, 3452 (1931)
42. BARBOUR, H. G., *Science*, **73**, 346 (1931)
43. LUCKÉ, B., *Biol. Bull. Marine Biol. Lab.*, **60**, 72 (1931)
44. MAY, R. M., *Compt. rend.*, **190**, 1150 (1930); *Bull. soc. chim. biol.*, **12**, 934 (1930)
45. MAY, R. M., *Bull. soc. chim. biol.*, **11**, 312 (1929)
46. JOHANNES, T., *Arch. ges. Physiol.*, **224**, 760 (1930)
47. MOLITOR, H., *Wiener med. Wochschr.*, **80**, 430, 466 (1930)
48. HELLER, J., *Arch. exptl. Path. Pharmakol.*, **157**, 298, 323 (1930)
49. ROBOZ, P., *Klin. Wochschr.*, **10**, 456 (1931)
50. McINTYRE, A. R., AND VAN DYKE, H. B., *J. Pharmacol.*, **42**, 155 (1931)
51. POULSSON, L. T., *Klin. Wochschr.*, **9**, 1245 (1930)
52. KISS, A., *Klin. Wochschr.*, **10**, 162 (1931)
53. STEGGERDA, F. R., *Am. J. Physiol.*, **98**, 255 (1931)
54. BARBOUR, H. G., ELLERBROOK, G. E., AND HOWARD, M. W., *Proc. Soc. Exptl. Biol. Med.*, **28**, 551 (1931)

55. KUSAKARI, H., AND TAKEDA, K., *Tôhoku J. Exptl. Med.*, **16**, 329 (1930)
56. WIECHMANN, E., AND LIANG, S., *Deut. Arch. klin. Med.*, **163**, 282 (1929)
57. ALTHAUSEN, T. L., AND MANCKE, R., *Deut. Arch. klin. Med.*, **170**, 294 (1931)
58. SORGE, G., *Boll. soc. ital. biol. sper.*, **5**, 762 (1930)
59. GOLDBERGER, B., AND GOLDBERGER, J., *Klin. Wochschr.*, **9**, 1249 (1930)
60. HARDING, V. J., AND HARRIS, L. J., *Trans. Roy. Soc. Can.*, V, **24**, 101 (1930)
61. RIOCH, D. McK., *J. Physiol.*, **70**, 45 (1930)
62. BAYLISS, L. E., AND FEE, A. R., *J. Physiol.*, **70**, 60 (1930)
63. GOVAERTS, P., AND CAMBIER, P., *Compt. rend. soc. biol.*, **103**, 940 (1930)
64. McINTOSH, R., KAJDI, L., AND MEEKER, DOROTHY, *J. Clin. Investigation*, **9**, 333 (1930)
65. DRAKE, T. G. H., McKHANN, C. F., AND GAMBLE, J. L., *J. Exptl. Med.*, **51**, 867 (1930)
66. CALDWELL, G. T., *Physiol. Zoöl.*, **4**, 324 (1931)
67. HELLER, J., *Arch. exptl. Path. Pharmakol.*, **157**, 286 (1930)
68. SCHULZ, F. N., *Biochem. Z.*, **227**, 340 (1930)
69. NEWCOMB, C., *Indian J. Med. Research*, **17**, 721 (1930)
70. HAYASAKA, E., *Tôhoku J. Exptl. Med.*, **14**, 72 (1930)
71. RANDOIN, L., AND MICHAUX, A., *Compt. rend.*, **192**, 108 (1931)
72. BARBOUR, H. G., AND MARSHALL, H. T., *J. Pharmacol.*, **43**, 147 (1931)
73. MARSHALL, H. T., AYDELOTTE, B. F., AND BARBOUR, H. G., *Am. J. Physiol.*, **98**, 615 (1931)
74. DAHMLOS, J., AND SOLE, A., *Biochem. Z.*, **227**, 401 (1930)
75. DEGKWITZ, R., *Klin. Wochschr.*, **9**, 2336 (1930)
76. McCLENDON, J. F., *Am. J. Physiol.*, **98**, 216 (1931)
77. BAISCH, A., *Jahrb. Kinderheilk.*, **124**, 323 (1929)
78. KALLINIKOVA, M. N., *Russ. Physiol. J.*, **13**, 193 (1930)
79. BRIDGE, E. M., AND BRIDGES, E. M., *J. Biol. Chem.*, **93**, 181 (1931)
80. SIMONE, I., *Biochim. terap. sper.*, **17**, 469 (1930)
81. RABBENO, A., *Arch. ital. biol.*, **83**, 73 (1930)
82. GUILLAUMIN, C. O., *Bull. soc. chim. biol.*, **12**, 491 (1930)
83. LANG, S., AND RIGO, L., *Z. ges. exptl. Med.*, **71**, 741 (1930)
84. COLLIER, W. A., *Z. Hyg. Infektionskrankh.*, **112**, 426 (1931)
85. GRZYCKI, S., *Compt. rend. soc. biol.*, **104**, 1096 (1930)
86. MEYER, B. S., *Am. J. Botany*, **18**, 79 (1931)
87. NEWBURGH, L. H., JOHNSTON, M. W., AND FALCON-LESSES, M., *J. Clin. Investigation*, **8**, 161 (1930)
88. UNDERHILL, F. P., KAPSINOW, R., AND FISK, M. E., *Am. J. Physiol.*, **95**, 302, 315 (1930)
89. UNDERHILL, F. P., FISK, M. E., AND KAPSINOW, R., *Am. J. Physiol.*, **95**, 325 (1930)
90. UNDERHILL, F. P., AND FISK, M. E., *Am. J. Physiol.*, **95**, 330 (1930)
91. UNDERHILL, F. P., FISK, M. E., AND KAPSINOW, R., *Am. J. Physiol.*, **95**, 334, 339 (1930)
92. UNDERHILL, F. P., AND FISK, M. E., *Am. J. Physiol.*, **95**, 348, 364 (1930)
93. KAYSER, C., *Ann. physiol. physicochim. biol.*, **6**, 721 (1930)

94. MAYER, A., AND NICHITA, G., *Compt. rend.*, **189**, 869 (1929)
95. NAKAMURA, T., *Z. ges. exptl. Med.*, **74**, 32 (1930)
96. ADOLPH, E. F., AND LEPORE, M. J., *Am. J. Physiol.*, **97**, 501 (1931)
97. DRINKER, C. K., AND FIELD, MADELEINE E., *Am. J. Physiol.*, **97**, 32 (1931)
98. MACHEBŒUF, A., *Compt. rend.*, **192**, 1413 (1931)
99. MEYERHOF, O., *Biochem. Z.*, **226**, 1 (1930)
100. CASSINIS, U., AND BRACALONI, L., *Arch. fisiol.*, **28**, 128 (1930); *Atti. accad. Lincei,* **11**, 515 (1930)
101. SCHEMINZKY, F., *Arch. ges. Physiol.*, **223**, 645 (1930)
102. BROOKS, S. C., *Protoplasma*, **8**, 389 (1929–30)
103. McCUTCHEON, M., LUCKÉ, B., AND HARTLINE, H. K., *J. Gen. Physiol.*, **14**, 393 (1931)
104. WIERINGA, K. T., *Protoplasma,* **8**, 522 (1929–30)
105. ADOLPH, E. F., *Am. J. Physiol.*, **96**, 569 (1931)
106. ADOLPH, E. F., *Am. J. Physiol.*, **96**, 587 (1931)
107. BRAUNER, L., *Ber. deut. botan. Ges.*, **48**, 109 (1930)
108. LUCKÉ, B., AND McCUTCHEON, M., *Arch. Path.*, **10**, 662 (1930)
109. FISHBERG, ELLA H., *J. Biol. Chem.*, **85**, 465 (1930)
110. ADLERSBERG, D., AND PERUTZ, A., *Arch. exptl. Path. Pharmakol.*, **151**, 106, 129, 257 (1930); *Klin. Wochschr.*, **9**, 1165 (1930)
111. LABBÉ, M., *Ann. med.*, **28**, 105 (1930); *Semana méd.* (*Buenos Aires*), **37**, 1259 (1930)
112. ORT, J. M., AND MARKOWITZ, J., *Am. J. Physiol.*, **94**, 60 (1930)
113. ORT, J. M., AND MARKOWITZ, J., *Am. J. Physiol.*, **96**, 541 (1931)
114. ORT, J. M., POWER, M. H., AND MARKOWITZ, J., *Am. J. Physiol.*, **98**, 163 (1931)
115. KYLIN, E., *Z. ges. exptl. Med.*, **77**, 289 (1931)
116. JOCHIMS, J., *Klin. Wochschr.*, **9**, 2115 (1930)
117. SUNDERMAN, F. W., AND AUSTIN, J. H., *Am. J. Med. Sci.*, **179**, 167 (1930)
118. KOFANOV, J., *Wien. Arch. inn. Med.*, **19**, 303 (1929)
119. SHEPPARD, S. E., AND HOUCK, R. C., *J. Phys. Chem.*, **34**, 273 (1930)
120. SHEPPARD, S. E., AND HOUCK, R. C., *J. Phys. Chem.*, **34**, 2187 (1930)
121. SHEPPARD, S. E., AND McNALLY, J. G., *Colloid Symposium Monograph,* **7**, 17 (1930)
122. PLEASS, WINNIFRED B., *Proc. Roy. Soc.* (*London*), *A,* **126**, 406 (1930)
123. KRUYT, H. R., *Chem. Weekblad,* **27**, 160 (1930)
124. LLOYD, DOROTHY J., *Kolloid Z.*, **54**, 46 (1931)
125. LLOYD, DOROTHY J., *Biochem. J.*, **24**, 1460 (1930)
126. PLEASS, WINNIFRED B., *Biochem. J.*, **24**, 1472 (1930)
127. NORTHROP, J. H., AND KUNITZ, M., *J. Phys. Chem.*, **35**, 162 (1931)
128. BIGWOOD, E. J., AND MAJMIN, R., *Compt. rend. soc. biol.*, **104**, 815 (1930)
129. ADAIR, G. S., AND CALLOW, E. H., *J. Gen. Physiol.*, **13**, 819 (1930)
130. NEVILLE, H. A., AND THEIS, E. R., *Colloid Symposium Monograph,* **7**, 41 (1930)
131. FRIEDMAN, L., AND KRAEMER, E. O., *J. Am. Chem. Soc.*, **52**, 1295 (1930)
132. FRIEDMAN, L., *J. Am. Chem. Soc.*, **52**, 1305, 1311 (1930)
133. WEBER, H. H., *Biochem. Z.*, **218**, 1 (1930)

134. LIPATOV, S. M., AND KOROBOVA, L. N., *Z. anorg. allgem. Chem.,* **194,** 369, 377 (1930)
135. FERGUSON, J., AND APPLEBEY, M. P., *Trans. Faraday Soc.,* **26,** 642 (1930)
136. PRAKASH, S., AND DHAR, N. R., *J. Phys. Chem.,* **35,** 629 (1931)
137. DIXON, H. H., AND DIXON, G. J., *Sci. Proc. Roy. Dublin Soc.,* **20,** 7 (1930)
138. BANERJI, S. N., AND GHOSH, S., *Z. anorg. allgem. Chem.,* **194,** 305 (1930)
139. VISCO, S., *Atti. accad. Lincei,* **11,** 583 (1930)
140. SEIFRIZ, W., *J. Rheology,* **1,** 261 (1930)
141. SEIFRIZ, W., AND PLOWE, JANET, *J. Rheology,* **2,** 263 (1931)

UNIVERSITY OF MINNESOTA
  ST. PAUL, MINNESOTA

BIOLOGICAL OXIDATIONS AND REDUCTIONS*

By René Wurmser

Directeur du Laboratoire de Biophysique
L'École des Hautes Études, Paris

The considerable amount of research in the domain of oxidations and reductions must be grouped, even if arbitrarily, into distinct chapters. A purely chemical study of oxidations and reductions (which includes the study of the stages of degradation and synthesis of various substances found in living organisms, i.e., intermediary metabolism) is made in special chapters reserved for this or that group of substances. In this review, another aspect of the question is considered, namely, the thermodynamic and kinetic conditions which make these reactions possible.

DETERMINATION OF THE FREE ENERGY OF REACTIONS

Biochemistry tends to become as quantitative as the rest of chemistry. Many problems of intermediary metabolism, the chemistry of muscular contraction, specific dynamic action, and the growth of organisms can be clarified or even solved by a knowledge of the free energy of the reactions which occur during these processes. These determinations can be made either by direct methods, when it is possible to obtain equilibrium, or else may be computed from purely thermic data, by applying Nernst's theorem. G. N. Lewis and his collaborators have done much work in this direction—work which is today of significance in biochemistry.

In this type of research, mention should be made of a careful work by Borsook and Schott (1). It has been shown by Wishart, Quastel and Whetham, Thunberg, and Lehman that the oxidation of succinic acid to fumaric acid in the presence of a dehydrase and a . hydrogen acceptor (methylene blue), presents the character of a reversible system. Borsook and Schott also determine the oxidation-reduction potential of mixtures of succinate and fumarate in the presence of methylene blue and dehydrases derived from different muscles.

* Received January 13, 1932.

The reaction that takes place is as follows:

$$\text{Succinate}^= \rightleftarrows \text{fumarate}^= + 2H^+ + 2e$$

At 25° C., the normal potential of this system, referred to a hydrogen electrode at the same pH, is $E = 0.437$ volt, which corresponds to a variation in the free energy of $\Delta F = 20,460$ calories, the activity of each constituent of this reaction being unity. This value corresponds exactly to the one that may be deduced from thermic data.

In this reaction the ratio of free energy to heat of reaction, $\Delta F/\Delta H$, is equal to 0.68; this is an example where the difference between the free energy and the heat of reaction is very great. This very probably ought to be found in all formations of double linkages.

It is evident that numerous reactions, in particular those which correspond to syntheses, are possible only if they are coupled with reactions corresponding to a diminution in free energy. The determination of stoichiometric formulae which represent these various coupled reactions is in general very difficult, and the knowledge of the free energies of the supposed reactions would be a valuable guide. The simplest case is apparently that in which the synthesis which corresponds to an increase in free energy is a reduction compensated by an oxidation. These oxido-reductions will be considered below. When the synthesis is the inverse of hydrolysis, as in the recovery phase of muscular contraction, the mechanism is certainly very complicated. It is known that during the contraction phase there occurs a scission of the phosphagen or creatine-phosphoric acid. This phosphagen must be reconstituted. At the same time there occurs a scission of glycogen into lactic acid.

It is shown by the recent researches of Meyerhof and Lohmann (2) on the extract from muscles of cold-blooded animals, that during the esterification of the phosphate which precedes the scission of glucose into lactic acid the adenyl-pyrophosphate, which is the coenzyme of this transformation, undergoes scission. The resynthesis of phosphagen in anaerobiosis is rendered possible by the energy of scission of this adenyl-pyrophosphoric acid, while the energy of formation of the lactic acid serves to reconstitute the decomposed pyrophosphate. Under conditions of aerobiosis the chain of energy-transfer, which makes possible the resynthesis of glycogen from the lactic acid, and in part of the phosphagen, is still longer, and is yet incompletely known [see the recent review of Meyerhof (3)].

CATALYSIS OF OXIDATIONS AND REDUCTIONS

Importance of the catályser containing iron in cellular oxidations. —In the past twenty years considerable research has been devoted to examining whether in the course of biological oxidations the mechanism of catalysis operates on the hydrogen of oxidisable bodies or the oxygen which combines with them. The present tendency is to admit that these two types of catalysis, which are not exclusive, coexist. The recent opinion of Warburg on this subject should be cited; Warburg is known as the protagonist of the rôle of iron as oxygen activator. Whereas at the beginning of his work Warburg thought it to be inorganic iron, he now considers chiefly certain compounds of iron—the hematin compounds.

Warburg and Christian (4) pointed out that if the oxygen in respiring cells is transported by hematin compounds and if one does not succeed *in vitro* in oxidising the glucose in the presence of such compounds, the reason is that in the cell the glucose is probably activated. The protoplasm must activate its hydrogen, as Wieland says. Furthermore, in certain cases the respiration may occur without iron as oxygen carrier.

The question to be broached is the rôle which this catalysis by iron plays in cellular oxidations. Even *in vitro* it is necessary not to confuse absolute unautoxidisability and the acceleration of the oxidation by the iron. Gerwe (5) in the case of cysteine and Hill (6) in the case of dialuric acid show that these substances are autoxidisable in the absence of iron, but that the iron catalyses their oxidation and that KCN inhibits only that part of the oxidation which is catalysed by the iron.

In vivo, a number of authors have drawn attention to the fact that methylene blue augments the metabolism of living cells. In the case of erythrocytes, Warburg, Kubowitz, and Christian (7) have shown that the dye reacts with hemoglobin to give methemoglobin. It is the latter that plays the rôle of a transporter; but this is not always the case, and for adequate concentrations, it is the methylene blue itself, i.e., a non-iron system, which catalyses the respiration.

Amongst the non-iron systems, found in cells, which could catalyse respiration, mention should be made of saline extracts of various organs, which have been studied by Michaelis and Salomon (8) and by Zeile and v. Euler (9).

Besides, in favor of the doctrine of non-iron systems intervening in cellular oxidations mention should also be made of the work of various authors that show the part of respiration which resists inhibition by cyanides [Banga, Schneider, and Szent-Györgyi (10) ; Shoup and Boykin (11)]. Indeed, this KCN test is perhaps open to question, if one no longer considers the inorganic iron, as in Warburg's original series, but the hematin compounds [see the work of Wright and Van Alstyne (12)].

To sum up, reserving opinion as to the value of the KCN test, these measurements show the existence in respiratory catalysis of two types of action: one, generally the more important, is due to the intervention of hematin compounds; the other is independent of these.

Indeed, in each of these two types of mobilisation, there seem to intervene numerous catalytic agents, the discovery of which has already been made possible by an increasingly minute analysis. Their interaction is as yet not well established.

Dehydrases.—The first of these agents which are to be discussed are the dehydrases, which are the enzymes responsible for the preliminary catalysis, acting on the hydrogen. The importance of these enzymes is intimately connected with Wieland's conception of oxidation. This doctrine is most clearly presented by Thunberg. This author in a recent work (13) recalls that, according to him, the catabolism of foodstuff takes place in a series of continuous dehydrogenations carried out by a series of dehydrogenases. In the presence of oxygen, the hydrogen split off by the dehydrogenases is transported to this oxygen with formation of water.

It was particularly important to find a dehydrase which acts on glucose. Harrison (14) has succeeded in extracting from liver and muscle an enzyme capable of oxidising hexosediphosphoric acid in the presence of methylene blue. Another enzyme which acts on glucose has been obtained by Harrison (15) from the liver of the ox, sheep, cat, and dog. The oxidation product is gluconic acid. According to Thunberg's conception, there should exist a gluconic acid dehydrase.

It is very likely that the preparations of Harrison's dehydrase contain cozymase. In fact, von Euler and Nilson (16) have established that dehydrase extracted from seeds of *Corchorus capsularis* and acting on hexosephosphate, is active only in the presence of this coenzyme.

Few new data have been brought to light on the mechanism of dehydrase action.

Thunberg (17) believes that the substrate in the dehydrogenation of hexosediphosphoric acid and adenosintriphosphoric acid is particularly oxidisable because · the hexosediphosphoric and adenosintriphosphoric ions have a high electric charge which facilitates the reaction between the dehydrase and the substrate.

In connection with these results must be mentioned those of Barmore and Luck (18), who in an oxidation without enzyme (the oxidation of glyceric aldehyde by methylene blue, 1-naphthol 2-sulfonate indophenol, and phenol-indophenol) have studied the effect of phosphates and have shown that the ion $PO_4^{\equiv}$ is the active catalytic species.

Finally, a work by Banga, Schneider, and Szent-Györgyi (19) shows quite clearly that arsenious acid has a toxic effect on dehydrogenating action, the mobilisation of the hydrogen and the total respiration being proportionally reduced.

This action of various toxic agents is one of the rare means at our disposal for studying the mechanism of the catalytic actions of cells. It is this method that was employed by Cook, Haldane, and Mapson (20). These authors have studied the inhibitory effect of 8-hydroxyquinolinesulfonic acid and 1-amino 8-naphthol 4-sulfonic acid and suggest that formic dehydrogenase contains copper. The oxidation of succinate to fumarate is stimulated by small amounts of cyanide which can probably be explained by its combination with small amounts of heavy metal which inhibit succinate dehydrogenase. At high concentrations of cyanide, inhibition occurs which may be due to the union with heavy metals forming part of the enzymes.

The question of the specificity of dehydrases is still a matter of controversy. For Warburg, when different enzymes occur in an extract of one kind of cell, they are not enzymes which were preformed in the living cell, but transformation products of a substance uniform in life. Quastel and Wheatley (21) think that this view cannot be correct; for not only the various hydrogenases of bacteria are selectively poisoned but in the intact cell the rate of oxidation of a mixture of the substances at their saturation concentrations is greater than the highest of the individual rates. The oxidation rate is the sum of the individual rates. There are then distinct centers of dehydrogenase systems in the cell which treating and extracting alter.

Oxygenase (Keilin's indophenoloxidase).—Cook, Haldane, and Mapson (20) propose giving the name oxygenase to the cell catalyser which activates the molecular oxygen. The term oxygenase is to be preferred to *"Atmungsferment"* because it is not a single catalyser which comes into play in respiration; in Keilin's conception the donator yields its hydrogen to cytochrome which acts as carrier and combines it with oxygen in the presence of indophenoloxidase. Oxygenase is the catalyser which permits this last reaction.

For example, Harrison (15) shows that glucose is not oxidised in the presence of oxygen and dehydrase but is oxidised when combined with Keilin's cytochrome-indophenoloxidase.

As in the case of dehydrogenases, there exists the question of specificity and of the unity of the catalyser. With this in view, Cook, Haldane, and Mapson (20) have studied the oxidation of succinate to fumarate, lactate to pyruvate, and formate to bicarbonate by toluene-treated *B. coli.* The activators of oxygen concerned in the three catalyses differ in their susceptibilities to various poisons and are regarded as differing as do different hemoglobins. Cook and Haldane in another work (22) find that the effects of CO and KCN on the oxidations differ greatly with the toluene-treated organism, thus confirming the view that at least three different oxygenases are present in the cell.

Peroxidase and catalase.—When the dehydrogenase and its substrate act directly on O_2, hydrogen peroxide is produced. Bertho and Glück (23), for example, have shown that at least 90 per cent of the oxygen consumed by *Bacillus acidophilus* is converted into H_2O_2. This peroxide can be activated by two different types of enzyme, catalase and peroxidase.

Concerning the nature of peroxidase and catalase, Kühn, Hand, and Florkin (24) have established by the spectrophotometric method that the active group of peroxidase is a ferroporphyrinic combination. By this same method Zeile and Hellstrom had shown that the active group in catalase is a ferroporphyrinic combination.

Finally, the absolute activity of peroxidase and of catalase [Zeile (25)] are very markedly of the same order of magnitude as the *"Atmungsferment"* (10^5 mol. per sec.).

Kühn, Hand, and Florkin (26) conclude that, in conformity with Warburg's definition, *"Atmungsferment* is the sum of the iron compounds acting as a catalyser in the cell"; peroxidase and catalase make up part of the *"Atmungsferment,"* just as oxygenase does.

Hydrogen carriers in the cell.—According to Keilin's now classic theory the cytochrome brings about the union of the hydrogen mobilised by the hydrogenases and the oxygenase. Nevertheless according to what has been seen above, not only is the respiration not totally dependent on the catalyser containing iron (of which cytochrome is the carrier element, oxygenase being the activator) but the cytochrome and other carriers do not always seem necessary to bring about this union. Cook, Haldane, and Mapson (20) in consequence of their experiments on the respiratory catalysis of *B. coli* think that the hydrogenase and oxygenase molecules are actually in contact. Haldane and his collaborators remark, however, that the results obtained must not be regarded as a picture of the mechanism of respiration in a typical cell, because *B. coli* is a facultative anaerobe, that its dehydrogenases are almost entirely confined to its surface and, finally, that Keilin has found in it only cytochrome *b* and protohematin, but no cytochrome *a* or *c*.

Besides cytochrome there may exist other hydrogen carriers between dehydrases and oxygenase, for instance, Szent-Györgyi's hexuronic acid. Certain natural pigments may perform the same function. Thus, Friedheim (27) has shown that the blue pigment of *B. pyocyaneus* can increase the respiration of living cells to a great degree, owing to the reversibility of its oxidation and reduction. This effect is dependent on the presence of another respiratory ferment, sensitive to KCN and CO, that is, oxygenase.

Glutathione, discovered and studied by Hopkins and his collaborators, is another hydrogen carrier, the earliest known, though its physiological function has, as yet, not been clearly established.

In their most recent work Hopkins and Elliott (28) have shown that there exist in some tissues (especially in well-fed animals) substances, as yet unknown, which reduce glutathione. This reduction disappears by heating at 50–52°C. Hopkins' efforts are now being directed toward the determination of these substances, the physiological significance of which promises to be important, although the oxidation of these substances constitutes (quantitatively) but a small part of respiration. Rapkine (29) suggests that these substances are the proteins which, owing to a denaturing enzyme, become capable (by liberation of –SH radicals) of reducing glutathione.

ORIENTATION OF REACTIONS

The rôle of hydrogen carriers discussed above is intimately bound up with another problem which may be termed the orientation of reactions, which is as follows.

Experience shows that the same kind of molecule is susceptible of transformation in totally different manners, not only according to the nature of the organism into which it is introduced, but even in the same organism, according to its localisation or certain external circumstances. For example, a molecule of glucose may be completely oxidised into CO_2 and water, or be transformed into lactic acid, or enter into combination with nitrogen, etc.

Finally, these various reactions may take place now in one direction, now in a direction quite opposite.

The first question is to know whether for a given molecule there exists a common point of departure, from which takes place such and such a deviation. For example, it is generally admitted in accord with Pfeffer that the two phenomena, the normal respiration and the intramolecular respiration, are always necessarily united, and that the glucides cannot be directly oxidised without preliminary anaerobic scission.

Among recent studies that of Lund (30), although done with another purpose, may be cited in support of this conception. He shows by a measure of difference of potential that after a skin has been exposed to low oxygen concentration and then suddenly transferred to high concentration, the potential difference varies in the predicted manner, if one admits a change in concentration of oxidisable substances caused by an oxygen deficit in living cells. This is what one should expect if the first act of respiration is a formation of bodies containing mobilisable hydrogen. The increase of respiration, after preliminary maintenance *in vacuo,* which has been observed by Lund and Shoup, and in numerous aërial plants by Chevillard, Mayer, and Plantefol (31), is temporary and, according to the latter authors, does not oxidise the totality of substances formed *in vacuo.*

Pfeffer's conception encounters a number of difficulties: (*a*) the discovery of enzymes which permit the fixation of oxygen by glucose but not the reduction of methylene blue, and by maltose without preliminary hydrolysis [Muller (32)]; (*b*) the fact that fermentation is stopped though respiration is maintained in the presence of monoiodoacetic acid [Lundsgaard (33)]; (*c*) the fact that the rate of intramolecular respiration was found too small to account for the normal respiration [Boysen Jensen (34)]; (*d*) finally, respiration at the expense of maltose by yeast not containing maltase [Trautwein and Weigand (35)].

However, these objections to the unitary theory are not definitive

Though Nilson, Zeile, and v. Euler (36) have confirmed the results of Lundsgaard, they have also shown with yeast that if the dose of monoiodoacetic acid is increased, respiration as well as fermentation is stopped. Furthermore, it seems evident from the results obtained by Krebs (37), and by Meyerhof and Boyland (38) that respiration can continue if lactic acid or pyruvic acid is furnished. Monoiodoacetic acid [see particularly Lohmann (39)] intervenes at various intermediary stages in the degradation chain of glucose (supposedly common both to fermentation and to respiration). It is the non-formation of these products that prevents respiration when the dose of monoiodoacetic acid is sufficient. If respiration subsists at feeble doses of monoiodoacetic acid, it is due to the fact that these products are formed. It is then possible to infer that the catalysers belonging to the last stages of fermentation are more sensitive to the poison than those which act on the last stages of respiration.

The second question which arises concerning the orientation of reactions is evidently the mechanism which permits the "switching" of a molecule toward other destinations.

In the case which we have just presented, that of alcoholic fermentation, as well as in the case of lactic or glycolic fermentation, it is known that the oxygen is the determining factor. According to Meyerhof there is, properly speaking, no deviation but a resynthesis of the products of fermentation, due to the fact that respiration is superimposed on fermentation. The relative velocities of respiration and fermentation are supposed to depend in great part on the different amounts of catalysers present.

New data have been brought to light on the differences between the catalysers concerned in these two processes. These data concern only coenzymes.

The question has been brought up as to whether the coenzyme of alcoholic fermentation is identical with that of lactic acid fermentation of muscle and with that of respiration. It is known that the systematic researches of v. Euler and Myrbäck (40) on the extract of heated yeast have attributed the action of the coferment to a nucleotide—a particular adenylic acid. Meyerhof, Lohmann, and Meyer (41) have since found that a constituent of the coenzyme of the lactic acid fermentation of muscle is destroyed by autolysis. Finally Lohmann (42) shows that the autolysable constituent is adenylpyrophosphoric acid and the non-autolysable, magnesium. It is thus more appropriate to speak of a coenzyme *system* rather than of a *coenzyme* (43). The adenylpyrophosphate + inorganic phosphate + Mg is the coferment system of lactic acid formation.

This system, although not without a certain relationship, differs from that which v. Euler and Myrbäck have isolated and which intervenes in alcoholic fermentation. It is not identical with the coferment of respiration nor with that which permits the action of methylglyoxalase.

Alongside of the velocity factor, which plays a rôle in the orientation of chemical transformations in cells, another factor to which Wurmser, on the one hand, and Knoop, on the other, have drawn attention is the possibility of equilibrium reactions, principally in the synthesis of amino acids. These syntheses result from oxidoreductions and constitute the simplest mode of energy coupling between a reaction which corresponds to a diminution in free energy and a reaction which occurs with increase in free energy.

As a result of the work of Clark and his collaborators, and of Needham and Needham, the microinjection into the cell of oxidation-reduction indicators has shown as conceivable the existence within living cells of a substance capable of being oxidised or reduced reversibly. In the cases where the oxido-reductions occur through the intermediary action of enzymes of simple specificity, the carriers in the cellular environment may enter into competition with the other acceptors. If then certain synthetic processes are in the neighborhood of their equilibria in the zone of potential corresponding to a reversible system, the state of reduction of the latter may determine the direction of the cellular reactions.

Furthermore, the oxido-reduction potential of the environment may govern the reactions which are not oxido-reductions by acting on the catalyser itself. It is perhaps in this way that the bodies containing cysteine intervene in certain hydrolytic reactions. To Grassman, Dyckerhof, and Schoenbeile's observations in this matter are now to be joined those of Salaskin and Solowjew (44), which show that cysteine activates arginase, and those of Pringsheim, Borchadt, and Huffer (45), which indicate that glutathione activates the saccharification of starch in the presence of pancreatic amylase.

It is therefore appropriate to look for the relations between oxidoreduction potentials and the functioning of organisms. Some relations had already been found between the oxido-reduction potential of the environments of cultures and the development of certain anaerobic microbes. [See among the most recent publications that of

Plotz and Geloso (46).] Kusnetzow (47) also establishes a relation between oxido-reduction potential of the exterior environment and the manner of fermentation by *Aspergillus niger*.

The facts above permit the opinion that the rôle of reducing systems existing in the cell is important. The work, considerable in amount, relative to oxido-reduction potentials may be grouped in two classes. One class concerns itself with the technique of potential measurements; it consists in the determination of new oxido-reduction indicators. This type of work, besides having technical interest, is nearly always of notable importance from the point of view of organic chemistry.

New research has been carried out on the oxido-reduction indicators: Cohen and Preisler (48), Michaelis (49, 50, 51), Friedheim and Michaelis (52), Elema and Sanders (53).

The second class is directed to determining the nature of oxido-reduction systems of cells.

With the purpose of identifying, if possible, the oxido-reduction system of the cell, Wurmser and Geloso have for several years made a study of the oxido-reduction properties of glucide solutions. In this way, Wurmser and Geloso (54) have shown by electrometric titration the existence of two oxido-reduction systems. The first attains rapid equilibrium, of which the normal potential, at pH 7 and 20°C. is + 0.030 volts ($rH_2 = 15$). This system reacts very rapidly and yields its hydrogen to various acceptors, amongst others to molecular oxygen, which must give it important biological properties. The second system has a normal potential of − 0.040 volts at pH 7 and at 20°C. ($rH_2 = 12.5$). These results show that one can expect to find in the cell oxido-reducing systems intervening in ordinary metabolism and having well-defined potentials.

There is no doubt that great progress was realised in the study of cell media by microinjection of oxido-reduction potential indicators. This technique has still great service to perform. It has enabled Rey (55) to show that the difference of oxido-reduction potential that Joyet-Lavergne has observed between male and female cells was due to an error in interpretation.

But the qualitative measurements have up to the present not permitted the affirmation that the cell contains an oxido-reduction system truly in equilibrium, existing in notable quantity, and responsible for the reduction of the dyes. It is conceivable that these dyes might fix the hydrogen issuing from certain donators due to the presence of enzymes, without this hydrogen having existed in mobile form in the cell before the introduction of an acceptor. It is to be remarked that all measurements effected up to the present furnish information only about potential, that is, the factor intensity of the work of reduction which a cell can furnish, and gives no information about its factor capacity, about the mass of mobile hydrogen.

It was for the purpose of undertaking this study that Wurmser and Rapkine (56) have established a method permitting the introduction of known and determined quantities of substance into a cell or an element of a cell that is to perform quantitative microinjection. The first results showed that the nucleus of the cell (cell of the salivary gland of *Chironomus* larvae) was about $\frac{1}{40}$ molecular in mobile H_2, and contained further reserves of hydrogen, rapidly mobilisable. The authors are, on this account, in favor of the belief in the existence of an oxido-reducing system of notable mass in the cell and feel confident that the knowledge of these systems would be of real interest for determination of the chemical reactions within the cell.

LITERATURE CITED

1. Borsook, H., and Schott, H. F., *J. Biol. Chem.*, **92**, 535 (1931)
2. Meyerhof, O., and Lohmann, K., *Naturwissenschaften*, **19**, 575 (1931)
3. Meyerhof, O., *Naturwissenschaften*, **19**, 923 (1931)
4. Warburg, O., and Christian, W., *Biochem. Z.*, **238**, 131 (1931)
5. Gerwe, E. G., *J. Biol. Chem.*, **92**, 525 (1931)
6. Hill, E. S., *J. Biol. Chem.*, **92**, 471 (1931)
7. Warburg, O., Kubowitz, F., and Christian, W., *Biochem. Z.*, **233**, 240 (1931)
8. Michaelis, L., and Salomon, K., *Proc. Soc. Exptl. Biol. Med.*, **28**, 966 (1931)
9. Zeile, K., and Euler, H. von, *Z. physiol. Chem.*, **195**, 35 (1931)
10. Banga, T., Schneider, L., and Szent-Györgyi, A., *Biochem. Z.*, **240**, 454 (1931)
11. Shoup, C. S., and Boykin, J. T., *J. Gen. Physiol.*, **15**, 107 (1931)
12. Wright, G. P., and Van Alstyne, M., *J. Biol. Chem.*, **93**, 71 (1931)
13. Thunberg, T., *Quart. Rev. Biol.*, **5**, 318 (1930)
14. Harrison, D. C., *Biochem. J.*, **25**, 1011 (1931)
15. Harrison, D. C., *Biochem. J.*, **25**, 1016 (1931)
16. Euler, H. von, and Nilson, Ragnar, *Z. physiol. Chem.*, **194**, 260 (1931)
17. Thunberg, T., *Lunds Universitets Arsskrift*, **27**, Nr. 10 (1931)
18. Barmore, M., and Luck, J. M., *J. Gen. Physiol.*, **15**, 97 (1931)
19. Banga, T., Schneider, L., and Szent-Györgyi, A., *Biochem. Z.*, **240**, 462 (1931)
20. Cook, R. P., Haldane, J. B. S., and Mapson, L. W., *Biochem. J.*, **25**, 534 (1931)
21. Quastel, J. H., and Wheatley, A. H. M., *Biochem. J.*, **25**, 629 (1931)
22. Cook, R. P., and Haldane, J. B. S., *Biochem. J.*, **25**, 880 (1931)
23. Bertho, A., and Glück, H., *Naturwissenschaften*, **19**, 88 (1931)
24. Kühn, R., Hand, D. B., and Florkin, M., *Z. physiol. Chem.*, **201**, 255 (1931)
25. Zeile, K., *Z. physiol. Chem.*, **195**, 39 (1931)
26. Kühn, R., Hand, D. B., and Florkin, M., *Naturwissenschaften*, **37**, 771 (1931)
27. Friedheim, E. A. H., *J. Exptl. Med.*, **54**, 207 (1931)
28. Hopkins, F. G., and Elliott, K. A. C., *Proc. Roy. Soc. (London), B*, **109**, 58 (1931)
29. Rapkine, L., *Ann. physiol. physicochim. biol.*, **7**, 382 (1931)
30. Lund, E. J., *Protoplasma*, **13**, 236 (1931)
31. Chevillard, L., Mayer, A., and Plantefol, L., *Ann. physiol. physico-chim. biol.*, **6**, 506 (1930)
32. Muller, D., *Biochem. Z.*, **232**, 433 (1931)
33. Lundsgaard, E., *Biochem. Z.*, **220**, 8 (1930)
34. Boysen Jensen, P., *Biochem. Z.*, **236**, 211 (1931)
35. Trautwein, K., and Weigand, K., *Biochem. Z.*, **240**, 423 (1931)
36. Nilson, R., Zeile, K., and Euler, H. von, *Z. physiol. Chem.*, **194**, 53 (1931)

37. KREBS, H. A., *Biochem. Z.*, **234**, 278 (1931)
38. MEYERHOF, O., AND BOYLAND, E., *Biochem. Z.*, **237**, 406 (1931)
39. LOHMAN, K., *Biochem. Z.*, **236**, 444 (1931)
40. EULER, H. VON, AND MYRBÄCK, K., *"Biokatalysatoren"* (1930)
41. MEYERHOF, O., LOHMAN, K., AND MEYER, K., *Biochem. Z.*, **237**, 437 (1931)
42. LOHMANN, K., *Naturwissenschaften*, **19**, 180 (1931)
43. LOHMANN, K., *Biochem. Z.*, **237**, 444 (1931)
44. SALASKIN, A., AND SOLOWJEW, L., *Z. physiol. Chem.*, **102**, 259 (1931)
45. PRINGSHEIM, H., BORCHADT, H., AND HUFFER, H., *Biochem. Z.*, **238**, 477 (1931)
46. PLOTZ, H., AND GELOSO, J., *Ann. inst. Pasteur*, **45**, 613 (1930)
47. KUSNETZOW, S. J., *Zentr. Bakt., Parasitenk. II Abt.*, **83**, 37 (1931)
48. COHEN, B., AND PREISLER, P. W., *U.S. Pub. Health Reports, Suppl. 92* (1931)
49. MICHAELIS, L., *J. Biol. Chem.*, **91**, 369 (1931)
50. MICHAELIS, L., *J. Biol. Chem.*, **92**, 211 (1931)
51. MICHAELIS, L., *J. Am. Chem. Soc.*, **53**, 2953 (1931)
52. FRIEDHEIM, E. A. H., AND MICHAELIS, L., *J. Biol. Chem.*, **91**, 355 (1931)
53. ELEMA, B., AND SANDERS, A. C., *Rec. trav. chim.*, **50**, 796, 807 (1931)
54. WURMSER, R., AND GELOSO, J., *J. chim. phys.*, **28**, 260 (1931)
55. REY, P., *Compt. rend. soc. biol.*, **107**, 611 (1931)
56. WURMSER, R., AND RAPKINE, L., *Compt. rend.*, **193**, 430 (1931)

INSTITUT DE BIOLOGIE PHYSICO-CHIMIQUE
PARIS, FRANCE

ENZYMES

By Ernst Waldschmidt-Leitz

Deutsche Technische Hochschule, Prague

The modern development of enzyme research is directed above all into two particular lines of inquiry, first, the question of the chemical nature of enzymes, and, secondly, the question of the character and cause of their peculiar mode of action—their specificity. These two questions seem intimately connected, for they have a common basis in view of the structure of enzymes first advanced by Willstätter (1), a view which has held good and has found wide acceptance [cf. Fodor and Frankenthal (2)]. According to this theory, enzymes are composed of one or more specific active groups, and of one more or less unspecific, and therefore changeable, colloidal bearer; the former is considered responsible for the specificity and the latter primarily for the catalytic activity and for the stability of the active groups. On the basis of experiments with amylases of leucocytes this doctrine has been deepened and further developed [Willstätter and Rohdewald (3)]. In these experiments it is applied to explain the existence in the same cell of soluble (lyo-amylases) and insoluble amylases (desmo-amylases). The colloidal bearer is to be distinguished from the high molecular concomitant materials which vary with the state of solution of the cell material and which are the "tugs" of the enzymes. It can be broken down more or less completely without having any essential effect on the enzymatic activity [thus, Waldschmidt-Leitz and Steigerwaldt (4); Stern (5)]; hence sharply differentiated compounds of the active groups with insoluble or with soluble high-molecular materials arise.

In the question of the mode of action of enzymes, familiar and well-established views have been further developed. Since Michaelis' doctrine of the intermediary formation of enzyme-substrate compounds in enzymatic catalyses [Michaelis and Menten (6)], a doctrine founded on kinetic measurements of saccharase, the interest of investigators has been directed toward the chemical nature of such intermediate compounds and to the cause of their formation. Here the assumption of the operation of specific chemical affinities between enzyme and substrate, as expressed for instance in Euler's so-called "Two-Affinity Theory" [thus, Euler and Josephson (7)] has held good. The explanation of the nature of such active groups has been furthered in recent years above all by experiments with peptide-splitting enzymes, which will be reported on later. Such dissociable enzyme-substrate compounds may have the character of stable chemical compounds or of addition compounds [Woolf (8)]. Their formation may be regulated by the co-operation of materials which are active on the surface, as well as by the pH; this idea is discussed in the tests on the spatial separation of amylase and starch within the cell by, for instance, phosphatides, soaps, or bile salts [Mühlbauer (9)].

While the process of enzymatic hydrolysis has found an explanation in the assumption of the formation of easily dissociable intermediary compounds of enzyme and substrate, Haber and Willstätter (10) interpret the mechanism of enzymatic oxidation and reduction processes in a wholly different sense. They consider as the first stage in these reactions a disproportion between enzyme and substrate, as a result of which the enzyme undergoes a monovalent reduction while the substrate undergoes a monovalent oxidation. On the unpaired radicals thus formed from paired substances a chain reaction is assumed to take place which gives a better explanation of the course of these biological processes than the theory that the oxidation and reduction processes are fundamentally paired because they are paired in their initiation and in their end. The separate stages in such a chain reaction for the simple example of the decomposition of hydrogen peroxide by catalase would be as follows:

$$a) \qquad Catalase + H_2O_2 = Desoxy\text{-}Catalase + O_2H$$
$$b) \qquad O_2H + H_2O_2 = O_2 + H_2O + OH$$
$$c) \qquad OH + H_2O_2 = H_2O + O_2H$$

The monodesoxy-enzyme thus formed from the enzyme is regenerated by oxidation; the specific-active groups of those enzymes of biological oxidation, which come into consideration here, are regarded as peculiarly active metal compounds (ferri-), which agrees with recent findings concerning their chemical nature, to be discussed later.

Esterases.—In the domain of ester-splitting enzymes the most important questions are those of the causes of their specificity, especially of their capacity for steric selectivity. The specificity of esterases and lipases, for instance, that of animal lipase with respect to simple esters, like natural fats, is mainly only relative; their activity is easily influenced by concomitant and by added materials in degrees that vary with varying substrates. This is even true for their configurative specificity. Bamann and Laeverenz (11) have shown that in splitting racemic esters of the mandelic acid group by liver esterase, a reversal of the optical selectivity can be obtained by adding strychnine; the rotatory direction of the more quickly saponified component of the racemate was found to be different with and without strychnine. Later researches have developed this observation. The change in steric specificity under the influence of the alkaloid has proved, within the limits tested, to be independent of the degree of purity of the enzyme from the accidental and separable concomitant materials of the enzyme preparations; there seems to be a reaction of the strychnine with the enzyme itself [Bamann and Laeverenz (12)] which has an unequal influence on the decomposition velocity of the esterase compounds with the dextrorotatory and the laevorotatory ester [Ammon and Fischgold (13)]. In the synthesis of the mandelic acid n-butyl ester, on the other hand, no configurative specificity has been observed [Rona, Ammon, and Awetissowa (14)].

Some recently described, more or less specific, phenomena of inhibition and activation in esterases have been examined from the standpoint of their relation to the reaction between enzyme and substrate or to the decomposition of the enzyme-substrate compound. The powerful inhibition of the liver esterase by lactones of γ-hydroxy butyric acid and of γ-hydroxy valeric acid, which has been described, seems to be an interference with the combination of enzyme and ester by these lactones which are not in themselves decomposable [Bamann and Schmeller (15)]; the mechanism of other recently discovered phenomena of inhibition and activation of the esterase like those caused by indicators such as bromothymol blue [Bamann and Schmeller (16)], or the inhibition by urethanes [Stedman and Stedman (17)], has not yet been clearly explained. Special interest is due to the observation that the action of liver esterase (from sheep) is inhibited by an excess of substrate [Murray (18)]; Haldane (19) explains this phenomenon by assuming that, besides the usual compound of 1 mol of enzyme and 1 mol of substrate (ester), which is easily decomposed on hydrolysis with liberation of the enzyme, there is also formed a complex of 1 mol of enzyme and 2 mols of substrate which is not hydrolysable; with increasing excess of substrate, therefore, more and more esterase should be withdrawn from the catalytic reaction.

Phosphatases and sulfatases.—The specificity of phosphatases has not yet been sufficiently examined, particularly the question whether phosphatases and esterases represent absolute specific catalysts in all cases where they have been differentiated. The cleavage of the different organic esters of phosphoric acid and also of the nucleotides is accomplished according to researches of Levene and Dillon (20) by one and the same enzyme of the intestinal mucous membrane, which is called intestinal nucleotidase; a special nucleinase, on the other hand, is held responsible for the liberation of mononucleotides from nucleic acids, during which process no phosphoric acid is split off. Hence it is probable that also intracellular phosphatases can effect the cleavage of all phosphoric acid esters which are transformed in natural metabolism. Besides the phosphatase responsible for the cleavage and synthesis of organic phosphoric acid esters we must differentiate a specific pyrophosphatase which brings about the degradation of pyrophosphate into orthophosphate [thus, Jacobsen (21)]; it is found, for example, in malt and yeast [Lüers, Zychlinski, and Bengtsson (22)]. It is worthy of note that a very active phosphatase is described as being present in tumor cells [Edlbacher and Kutscher (23)].

At any rate the sulfatase seems to be different from the phosphatase. For while samples from different organs generally show the same proportion between the actions of phosphatase and sulfatase, in autolysates only a dephosphatising enzyme is found; moreover, the sulfatase action, in contrast to the phosphatase action, proves to be incapable of activation by magnesium-ion [Hommerberg (24)]. According to Neuberg and Hofmann (25), one must distinguish from the ordinary sulfatase, which completes hydrolysis of phenol sulfuric-acid esters, a so-called chondro-sulfatase which is found in putrefactive bacteria, such as *B. pyocyaneus* and *B. proteus,* and which is able to split chondroitin sulfuric acid, but not phenol sulfuric acid. Chondroitin sulfuric acid is not attacked by ordinary sulfatase.

Proteinases.—The investigation of protein-splitting proteases, i.e., of proteinases, which are to be distinguished from the peptidases, has been furthered by attempts to obtain pepsin and pancreas trypsin in a pure state. Northrop (26) has reported on the preparation of crystallised pepsin also from inactive denatured pepsin preparations; by this method it has proved possible, by the use of acid, to re-activate and to obtain again crystalline pepsin, which had been previously inactivated and denatured by the action of alkali. Pepsin is described as a protein. A method for obtaining pancreas trypsin in crystalline preparations of protein nature has been worked out [Northrop and Kunitz (27)]. According to Levene and Helberger (28) the constitution of crystallised pepsin preparations is characterised by a particularly low content of basic units. It is doubtful whether these crystallised enzyme preparations represent simple substances; for crystallised pepsin has been successfully split by adsorption with alumina into fractions, one of which is characterised, particularly, by a liquefying action and the other by a more hydrolising action on gelatin [Holter (29)]; Northrop (30) has also indicated the presence of an enzyme constituent in crude pepsin preparations which liquefies gelatin. The conception therefore that crystallised pepsin is pure, and that the enzyme is a protein, requires further proof, as it has been shown to be a compound body.

In the pancreas, and probably also in its secretions, besides the pancreas proteinase, trypsin, the conditions of whose stability Pace (31) has examined, a protaminase [Waldschmidt-Leitz, Ziegler, Schäffner, and Weil (32)] which may be classified under the .proteinases has also been found. This enzyme is very similar to the pancreas proteinase in the dependence of its action on pH, and in its behavior on adsorption; but, in contrast to the proteinase, its action is not inhibited by albumin. The action of the protaminase on protamines, for instance, is limited to splitting off basic amino acids, e.g., arginine; like the proteinase, it reacts with the carboxyl group of the substrate. The existence of a special "keratinase" in the digestive tract of animals, capable of splitting horn substance, was concluded from researches on clothes moths [Schulz (33)], and on birds of prey [Stankovic, Arnovljevic, and Matavulj (34)] but according to Mangold and Dubiski (35) this requires further proof. On the other hand, a collagen-splitting enzyme has been described as present in the larvae of *Lucilia sericata* [Hobson (36)].

Evidence has already been given of the presence in small quantities in the secretion of the parotid gland of a proteinase similar to trypsin, with an alkaline reaction-optimum [Willstätter, Bamann, and Rohdewald (37)], and this has been confirmed by Voss (38); contrary to earlier results, the enzyme seems to exist in solution in the parotid and is not bound to remnants of cells. Saliva from the sublingual and the submaxillary glands, on the other hand, does not show tryptic action; only the parotid gland seems similar to the pancreas. The description of a proteinase of tryptic character, but not activable by enterokinase, present in leucocytes along with a kathepsin [Willstätter, Bamann, and Rohdewald (39)] has also been confirmed [Husfeldt (40) ; Stern (41)] ; the enzyme seems to be present chiefly in cells with polymorphic nuclei.

In investigating animal and plant intracellular proteinases, belonging to the kathepsin type, special attention has been paid to the question of their activation. The doctrine that these enzymes are specifically activated, not only by hydrocyanic acid and hydrogen sulphide [Willstätter and Grassmann (42) ; Waldschmidt-Leitz, Schäffner, Bek, and Blum (43)] but also by organic sulfhydryl compounds—cysteine or SH-glutathione [Grassmann, Schoenebeck, and Eibeler (44)]—has been extended by the identification of the natural kathepsin activator with SH-glutathione and its isolation in crystalline form and in quantitative yield from liver [Waldschmidt-Leitz and Purr (45)]. The concept that an increased content of SH-glutathione, an increased katheptic activity, is characteristic for the tissues of malignant tumors [Waldschmidt-Leitz and Schäffner (46)] has not yet been confirmed; these do not seem to occupy any particular position with regard to proteolytic activity [Krebs (47) ; Kleinmann and Werr (48) ; Rona and Kleinmann (49)]. The reason for the activation of kathepsin by hydrosulphide compounds, which, according to Krebs (50), is to be sought in the liberation of an inhibition of the proteolysis by heavy metal ions by means of complex formation, does not seem to have found a final explanation; it has been shown that the action of heavy metals on the proteolysis varies, being partly activating, and partly inhibiting [Michaelis and Stern (51) ; Stern (52)] ; moreover the action of many metal salts is found to be independent of the state of combination of the metal and of the degree of its oxidation.

Hopkins and Kelly (53) have also described a proteinase of the kathepsin type in extracts of green malt.

Peptidases.—In recent researches on peptidases which are divided into two groups, viz., the dipeptidases and the polypeptidases, problems of their specificity have received most attention. The question of the existence of several dipeptidases has been frequently examined. According to Linderström-Lang (54) at least two dipeptidases are to be distinguished in the mucous membrane of the intestine; two have also been found by Sato (55) in malt, one of which is specific for the hydrolysis of leucyl-peptides, and capable of splitting higher leucyl-peptides, therefore not being regarded as a true dipeptidase.

Grassmann and Klenk (56) found that the fundamental experiments proving, for instance, that alanyl-glycine and leucyl-glycine are decomposed differently by different enzyme solutions were conditioned only by concomitant materials, which influence in different degrees the affinity toward different substrates of the dipeptidase, which is considered as homogeneous. The question of the simultaneous occurrence of several specific dipeptidases has not yet found a final solution.

Linderström-Lang and Holter (57) have described a micro-method for measuring enzymatic splitting of peptides, which may be applied to the determination of the quantity of enzyme in a single cell, or at least in very few cells.

Experiments by Balls and Köhler (58) are concerned with the mechanism of the enzymatic splitting of dipeptides. While the enzyme couples up with the free amino group of the dipeptides, there must be a second linkage between enzyme and dipeptide in order to induce hydrolytic cleavage, and in this linkage the imino group of the peptide linkage seems to play a part as the so-called "second linking-point." A certain acid character of the imino group seems to determine the onset of this reaction, this being concluded from the specificity with regard to different "aniline-peptides" (that is, glycyl-anilines substituted in the aromatic nucleus), and also from inhibition experiments. The reaction with the imino group as second linking-point seems to be a function common to all peptidases, also to poly-peptidases, while the separate peptidases can be distinguished according to the nature of the first point of linkage in the substrate; this is either the amino group (aminopeptidases) or the carboxyl group (carboxypeptidases). Further, in extracts of intestinal mucous membrane, a peptidase of peculiar character is described, which requires for its union with the substrate neither free carboxyl nor amino groups; it can, for instance, decompose chloracetyl o-nitraniline [Balls and Köhler (59)]; the experimenters have succeeded in separating it from the accompanying peptidases. Perhaps the cleavage of certain halogen acyl amino acids such as chloracetyl-alanine can be ascribed to the presence of such an enzyme [Abderhalden and Ehrenwall (60)], these having been found resistant to all peptidases hitherto known.

It is worthy of note that peptides of lysine in which the ε-amino group participates in the peptide linkage are not split by peptidases [Abderhalden and Schweitzer (61)]; proteins, therefore, do not apparently contain such linkages. On the other hand, the observations on the ease of cleavage of prolyl peptides containing the imino group of the proline at the end of the chain, ascribed to the existence of a special "prolin-peptidase" (present, for instance, in the mucous membrane of the intestine and in yeast) [Grassmann, Dyckerhoff, and Schoenebeck (62)], have been confirmed by Abderhalden and Zumstein (63) as well as by Fodor, Frankel, and Kuk (64).

Among the polypeptidases we must distinguish the amino- and the carboxy-polypeptidase; they are generally found together in crude enzyme solutions of animal or plant cells and can be separated by adsorption [thus, Waldschmidt-Leitz (65)]. On the basis of the observation that solutions of polypeptidases from yeast, which are freed from dipeptidase, could, after the addition of ultra-filtrates also free from dipeptidase, once more split dipeptides, Fodor and Frankenthal (66) ascribed the specificity for poly- and dipeptides merely to the presence of particular bearers and not to the existence of specific enzymes; the results hitherto obtained, however, are scarcely sufficient to establish securely such a far-reaching theory. Abderhalden and Ehrenwall (67) have also reported on their experiments which show that enzyme solutions free from dipeptidase, when kept for some time, regain their ability to split dipeptides. It appears that this phenomenon is due to the removal, possibly by enzymatic breakdown, of concomitant materials which inhibit the dipeptidase activity.

The amino-polypeptidase of the animal digestive tract, which Balls and Köhler (68) have purified very thoroughly, seems to contain phosphoric acid as an integral constituent essential for enzymatic action; in the dialysis of highly purified enzyme solutions, a decrease of activity and, concurrently, a splitting-off of phosphate ions can be observed.

Their observations on the splitting of halogen acyl amino acids lead Abderhalden and Schwab (69) to postulate the presence in the pancreas of a special "acylase" which exists along with the carboxy-polypeptidase and hydrolyses peptides of a special constitution, such as peptides with a terminal tyrosine group, e.g., leucyl-glycyl-tyrosine; there are found in different enzyme solutions, to different extents and quite independently, both of these kinds of enzymatic activity toward polypeptides and halogen acyl amino acids, hitherto both ascribed to the carboxy-polypeptidase.

According to Waldschmidt-Leitz and Balls (70), different causes for the steric selectivity of peptidases must be taken into consideration, according as the selectivity is concerned with the amino acid participating in the first linking-point of the enzyme or with that carrying the NH group of the cleavable peptide linkage (second linking-point). In the first case, steric adaptability of the enzyme in Emil Fischer's sense, in the latter, a different electrochemical nature of the imino groups in the two antipodes, seems to be responsible for the selectivity. For the phenomenon of steric adaptability we may quote the "unnatural" model of the specificity of carboxy-polypeptidase for the three isomeric chloracetyl-aminobenzoic acids of which only the *m*-compound has shown itself to be cleavable.

Aminoacylases

a) *Histozyme.*—The specificity limit between peptidases, above all carboxy-peptidases, on the one side, and the histozyme on the other, has not yet been sufficiently defined. Experiments thereon should be of interest as determining the specific cleavability of halogen acyl amino acids. The histozyme, for which as a rule benzoylated amino acids serve as substrates, brings about the cleavage of other acylated amino acids, for instance, of bile acids naturally occurring in combination with glycocoll [Grassmann and Basu (71)]; but it has not yet been decided whether or not the histozyme, like the carboxy-peptidases, reacts on the carboxyl group of the substrate.

b) *Arginase.*—For the arginase of the liver, Edlbacher and Burchard (72) have established the fact that the enzyme is able to attack arginine only when its carboxyl group is free; therefore arginylarginine, obtained from clupein, is only split halfway. In order to reach this conclusion it was first necessary to separate the dipeptidase from the arginase in the liver extracts.

In confirmation of observations on the activation of liver arginase by hydrogen sulphide and cysteine [Salaskin and Solowjew (73)] Waldschmidt-Leitz, Schäffner, and Kocholaty (74) have shown that arginase, like kathepsin, requires for its action the presence of hydrosulphide compounds. After separating the natural activator of the arginase, the SH-glutathione, from the enzyme, the latter is found to be absolutely inactive, but activatable by cysteine, SH-glutathione or H_2S, though not by cystine.

c) *Histidase.*—The existence of histidase found in the liver by Edlbacher (75) the action of which consists in opening the imidazole ring in histidine, thereby liberating ammonia [Edlbacher and Kraus (76)], has been confirmed by Mislowitzer and Kauffmann (77), also by Abderhalden and Buadze (78); but to what extent the formation of the products which appear when the histidine is split, viz., ammonia (2 mols), glutaminic acid (1 mol), and formic acid (1 mol), is due to the effects of the histidase has not yet been explained.

d) *Urease.*—Attempts to obtain highly purified crystalline urease [Sumner (79)] have opened up the question of the absolute degree of purity of these preparations and of the chemical nature of urease itself. Differing from previous results with impure urease preparations [Zakowski (80)], Waldschmidt-Leitz and Steigerwaldt (81) have been able to establish the fact that the protein of crystallised urease can be broken down by pancreas trypsin without any loss of ureatic activity; the identification of the urease with this protein cannot therefore be maintained any longer. According to Tauber and Kleiner (82), who confirm the constancy of ureatic activity toward trypsin, crystallised urease is said to possess anti-tryptic properties, to inhibit trypsin; when subcutaneously injected into the organism, it proves toxic as a result of the formation of large quantities of ammonia [Tauber and Kleiner (83)]. The enzymatic decomposition of urea into ammonia and carbonic acid goes by way of ammonium carbamate, not by way of cyanic acid [Sumner, Hand, and Holloway (84)].

CARBOHYDRASES

a) *Polyases.*—In malt, according to the researches of Ohlsson (85), there are to be distinguished a starch-liquefying enzyme and one which converts starch into sugar, i.e., a dextrinogen- and a saccharogen-amylase. Kuhn's (86) distinction between the α- and β-amylases is parallel but not yet definitely comparable. Since then, the separation of the amylatic components in malt-extracts has been accomplished by the help of adsorbents [thus, Waldschmidt-Leitz and Purr (87)], as has the separation of amylase from maltase. According to Borchardt and Pringsheim (88) the saccharogen-amylase is a β-amylase; α- and β-amylases are present in different proportions in malt, potatoes, and *Aspergillus oryzae*. The "liquefying" and "saccharifying" components of amylase are supposed to be distinguishable kinetically in the degradation of starch [Artom and Orestano (89);

Narayanamurti (90)]; Fletcher and Westwood (91) have described new methods for their determination.

According to Willstätter and Rohdewald (3), there are present together in the white blood corpuscles several (probably five) different amylases which can be classified as lyo- and desmo-amylases according to their solubility, and according as their action depends on the presence of phosphate ions. In these leucocyte enzymes a parallelism to the division into α- and β-amylases has not yet been discovered.

In the question of the formation of amylase, e.g., during the germination of seeds, as well as in the question of the proportion at any given time between the "liquefying" and "saccharifying" powers, the co-action of specific natural activators of starch degradation has to be taken into account. Waldschmidt-Leitz and Purr (87) have described such an activator, the "amylokinase," which is formed during the germination of barley, and they have also separated it from amylase. In addition, we also know the complement of the so-called "limit-degradation" of starch, found earlier in yeast by Pringsheim and Fuchs (92); its existence has recently been questioned by Weidenhagen and Wolf (93) [thus, Pringsheim, Borchardt, and Hupfer (94)]. The activation of amylase by organic substances of known structure, such as haematin [Cosack (95)] and glutathione [Pringsheim, Borchardt, and Hupfer (96)] has also been reported.

According to Samec and Waldschmidt-Leitz (97) the "iodine-blueing" (amylo-amylose) and the "iodine-reddening" (erythro-amylose) components of starch may be distinguished by a different enzymatic cleavability; the hydrolysis of the amylo-bodies by amylases of animal and of vegetable origin goes right to the stage of maltose, but for the saccharification of the erythro-bodies by pancreas amylase a limit to the degradation is found at about 70 per cent maltose; from this, the two components of starch are concluded to have a different structural constitution.

Ziese (98) recommends for the detection and determination of another polyase, the cellulase, from the gastric juice of *Helix pomatia,* or from malt, a water-soluble substrate, cellulose-glycolether; under the action of the enzyme, which seems to be characterised by a considerable heat-stability, this is saccharified with a rapid reduction of the viscosity.

b) Hexosidases.—In describing enzymes of this group, we may mention successful attempts to obtain purified preparations of the β-glucosidase of emulsin [Helferich and Schneidmüller (99)], which have led to a β-glucosidase value of 7.0; the stability of the enzyme is greatest by far in neutral solution.

According to experiments by Weidenhagen (100) on yeast maltase, it has to be assumed that the specificity of the hexosidases is determined only by the nature of the sugar residue in a saccharide which reacts with the enzyme and is split from it, and not by the neighboring sugar residues: maltase, as an α-glucosidase, should in all cases be able to hydrolyse cane sugar which contains α-glucose as a constituent. This view has been rendered very doubtful by observations by Karström (101) that *B. coli* can split and ferment maltose but not cane sugar. This very serious objection to the above-mentioned theory of the specificity of hexosidases has not yet been satisfactorily disposed of [Weidenhagen (102)], indeed, the observations on which it rests have been confirmed [Myrbäck (103); Virtanen (104)]. One cannot therefore generalise on results from yeast maltase without further proof.

Oparin and Kurssanow (105) have reported on the important observation of an enzymatic synthesis of cane sugar. Having found that the transformation of γ-fructose <2,5> present in cane sugar into β-fructose <2,6> which takes place after its hydrolysis, is retarded by phosphorylating the cane sugar, they succeeded by simultaneous action of saccharase and phosphatase on solutions of invert sugar in the presence of phosphate, in obtaining a synthetic sugar identical with cane sugar.

OXIDATIVE ENZYMES

a) Catalases.—Among the researches on the enzymes which participate in oxidation processes (the oxido-reducases proper being left out of account here), the most remarkable are those dealing with the chemical nature of the catalases. Zeile and Hellström (106) have shown that an iron-porphyrin complex is to be regarded as the active group of liver catalase; this was shown by photo-spectrometric measurements on highly purified enzyme preparations, for which, when further purified, the relation of catalytic activity to the content of porphyrin-bound iron (measured by the intensity of the absorption spectrum) was found to be constant. The catalase as an iron-porphyrin compound forms dissociable compounds with hydrocyanic acid and hydrogen sulphide; the dissociation constant of the hydrocyanic acid compound was estimated at $8 \cdot 10^{-7}$. These findings concerning the chemical nature of the catalytically active group were confirmed by experiments on pumpkin catalase [Zeile (107)], except that the dissociation constant of the catalase-HCN compound and the specific catalytic activity of the porphyrin-bound iron were found to deviate somewhat, numerically. In this connection, it is of interest to note that, according to Haurowitz (108) and contrary to earlier statements [Willstätter and Pollinger (109); Kuhn and Brann (110)], pure, repeatedly recrystallised oxyhaemoglobin also shows a slight catalatic activity of the order of magnitude of that of protohaemin; from another source, reports have been given of a proportional increase of the catalase and haemoglobin content of blood under the influence of rarefaction of the air [Radeff (111)].

b) Peroxidases.—Starting from the results mentioned above on catalases, Kuhn, Hand, and Florkin (112) have also described the active group of the peroxidase of horse radish as an iron-porphyrin compound. The quantitative photometric determination of the absorption spectrum of highly purified peroxidase preparations has given the result that, with an increasing degree of purity, the total iron content does indeed decrease [thus, Willstätter and Pollinger (113)], but the content of porphyrin-bound iron, on the other hand, increases in proportion to the activity of the peroxidase. From the porphyrin-iron content, we can calculate that the purest enzyme preparations hitherto accessible (with a purpurogallin number of 4,000 to 5,000) contain only about 0.1 per cent of pure peroxidase. The inhibition of peroxidase by carbon monoxide was less than that by hydrocyanic acid, and the carbon monoxide compound was not reactivable by irradiation.

We may mention as further studies concerning special oxidative enzymes observations on the nature of the tyrosinase from potatoes, according to which this enzyme must be regarded as homogeneous [Narayanamurti and Ramaswami (114)], as well as experiments on the luciferase from *Cypridina hilgendorfii,* a crustacean, in which the kinetics of the action of the enzyme on luciferin and its affinity to the substrate and to the oxidation product thereof are described in detail [Harvey and Snell (115)].

Fermentation enzymes.—In further confirmation of Neuberg's familiar and well-established view of the mechanism of fermentation processes, Neuberg and Kobel (116) have given new methods of collecting and isolating the intermediate products of alcoholic fermentation, methylglyoxal and pyruvic acid. One of these methods succeeds, for instance, by the action of plasmolytic agents (toluene or bromo-benzene) on the yeast, or by the use of higher substrate concentrations: here, when little yeast is used, an accumulation of methylglyoxal is particularly observed, and when much yeast is used, pyruvic acid accumulates predominantly. Methylglyoxal is also formed as an intermediary product in the degradation of carbohydrates by the enzymes of germinating seeds [Neuberg and Kobel (117)]. The experiments of Barthel, Euler, and Nilsson (118) are important for our view of the independence of the fermentation processes from the life of the cells; these show that water- and fat-free yeast, in which the capacity for reproduction has been completely suppressed, has almost the same fermentative power as it had before it was killed.

Very numerous are the researches on the nature and the number of natural activators participating in fermentation processes. According to the present state of our knowledge at least three different activators are concerned in the fermenting action of dry yeast, by the washing out of which, Harden, as is well known, proved the existence of a "co-zymase" [thus, Euler (119)]. The co-zymase has been examined in detail. Myrbäck and Euler (120) have extensively purified this activator by a series of operations; it is extracted from dry yeast by washing with water in neutral, or slightly acid reaction, and in fermentation it plays the part of a "co-mutase." On the basis of chemical analysis of the purest preparations (A Co = up to 160,000), which seem to be homogeneous, the activator is considered to be an adenylic acid, which view is supported by diffusion measurements giving a molecular weight of 355. The co-zymase differs from the ordinary yeast adenylic acid; it is much more akin to muscle adenylic acid, since like this, it can be easily transformed into inosinic acid by deamination. Yeast adenylic acid and also muscle adenylic acid cannot take the place of the co-zymase in glucose fermentation. This is also true for the adenosine-triphosphoric acid from muscle extract, identified by Lohmann with co-zymase (121) [Euler and Myrbäck (122)]. The activating action of this substance on fermentation by dry yeast is found to be of a different order of magnitude from that of co-zymase, and appears to be traceable rather to a contamination with co-zymase. The co-zymase is therefore related chemically to muscle adenylic acid, is probably isomeric, but not identical with it.

According to Lohmann (123) the presence of magnesium ion as

well as of co-zymase is necessary for fermentation by dry yeast. The conjoint action of the magnesium is responsible for the partial process of glucose-phosphorylation [Euler, Nilsson, and Auhagen (124)], since the activity of the phosphatase can, it is well known, be much increased by magnesium ion [Erdtman (125)].

In order to arrive at a certain uniformity in the nomenclature of the zymase activating systems and to avoid confusion, Neuberg and Euler (126) have suggested the following terms: holozymase = zymase + all activators; apozymase = holozymase, freed only from co-zymase, and still containing magnesium, that is holozymase less co-zymase; zymase = the pure enzymatic component, freed from all activators. Meanwhile, Auhagen (127) has isolated a further zymatic activator from dry yeast, which is present in extracts prepared by alkaline media and which seems to function as a specific activator of carboxylase action, that is, as co-carboxylase [Auhagen (128)]. Extending the suggestion given above as to nomenclature, the ferment system freed also from co-carboxylase may be termed aetio-zymase (perhaps = zymase).

Activators of alcoholic fermentation acting in press juice of yeast and in dry yeast are different from those in living yeast. Yeast contains materials which cannot indeed accelerate fermentation by dry yeast but which possess an activating effect on the fermenting capacity of fresh yeast, though without increasing the number of its cells. These so-called "Z-factors" which are also found in animal tissues and urine and in higher plants, have been examined in detail and fractionated by Euler and Philipson (129). Like the co-zymase, they seem to be of low molecular weight, but are more stable.

For comparison with the action of naturally occurring fermentation activators, Zuckerkandl and Messiner-Klebermass (130) have described the activating effect of amines like aniline, tyrosine or p-phenylene diamine on yeast poisoned by iodoacetic acid or sodium fluoride. It is assumed that, under the action of these amines, with intermediate formation of imines through splitting off of water, the hexose is split into two three-carbon-atom compounds; it may be compared with the action of the adenine residue in co-zymase.

Special researches are concerned with the question of the existence of a "carboligase." Dirscherl (131) has pointed out that the formation of acyloines when aldehydes are added to ferment mixtures, which has been ascribed to the action of carboligase, is due merely to the nascent acetaldehyde formed by the action of carboxylase. This view is supported by the observation that carboxylase and "carboligase" in the zymase system are, for instance, destroyed by heat to the same extent, and that acetoine can be obtained by purely chemical means by decarboxylating pyruvic acid with formic acid. We seem justified, however, in accepting the existence of a special carboligase, particularly on account of the optical activity of the acyloines isolated from ferment mixtures [Neuberg (132)].

LITERATURE CITED

1. WILLSTÄTTER, R., GRASER, J., AND KUHN, R., *Z. physiol. Chem.*, 123, 1 (1922); WILLSTÄTTER, R., *Ber.*, 55, 3601 (1922)
2. FODOR, A., AND FRANKENTHAL, L., *Biochem. Z.*, 228, 101 (1930)
3. WILLSTÄTTER, R., AND ROHDEWALD, M., *Z. physiol. Chem.*, 203, 189 (1931)
4. WALDSCHMIDT-LEITZ, E., AND STEIGERWALDT, F., *Z. physiol. Chem.*, 195, 260 (1931)
5. STERN, K. G., *Klin. Wochschr.*, 10, 1226 (1931)
6. MICHAELIS, L., AND MENTEN, M. L., *Biochem. Z.*, 49, 333 (1913)
7. EULER, H. VON, AND JOSEPHSON, K., *Z. physiol. Chem.*, 133, 279 (1923–24)
8. WOOLF, B., *Biochem. J.*, 25, 342 (1930–31)
9. MÜHLBAUER, M., *Fermentforschung*, 12, 273 (1931)
10. HABER, F., AND WILLSTÄTTER, R., *Ber.*, 64, 2844 (1931)
11. BAMANN, E., AND LAEVERENZ, P., *Ber.*, 63, 394 (1929–30)
12. BAMANN, E., AND LAEVERENZ, P., *Z. physiol. Chem.*, 193, 201 (1930–31)
13. AMMON, R., AND FISCHGOLD, H., *Biochem. Z.*, 234, 54 (1931)
14. RONA, P., AMMON, R., AND AWETISSOWA, A. N., *Biochem. Z.*, 231, 59 (1930–31)
15. BAMANN, E., AND SCHMELLER, M., *Z. physiol. Chem.*, 194, 14 (1930–31)
16. BAMANN, E., AND SCHMELLER, M., *Z. physiol. Chem.*, 194, 1 (1930–31)
17. STEDMAN, E., AND STEDMAN, E., *Biochem. J.*, 25, 1147 (1931)
18. MURRAY, D. R. P., *Biochem. J.*, 24, 1890 (1930)
19. HALDANE, J. B. S., *"Enzymes,"* Longmans Green, London (1930), p. 84
20. LEVENE, P. A., AND DILLON, R. T., *J. Biol. Chem.*, 88, 753 (1930–31)
21. JACOBSEN, E., *Biochem. Z.*, 242, 292 (1931)
22. LÜERS, H., ZYCHLINSKI, B. VON, AND BENGTSSON, K., *Wochenschr. Brau.*, Nr. 50 and 51 (1931)
23. EDLBACHER, S., AND KUTSCHER, W., *Z. physiol. Chem.*, 199, 200 (1931)
24. HOMMERBERG, C., *Z. physiol. Chem.*, 200, 69 (1931)
25. NEUBERG, C., AND HOFMANN, E., *Naturwissenschaften*, 19, 484 (1931); *Biochem. Z.*, 234, 345 (1931)
26. NORTHROP, J. H., *J. Gen. Physiol.*, 14, 713 (1931)

27. NORTHROP, J. H., AND KUNITZ, M., *Science, 73*, 262 (1931)
28. LEVENE, P. A., AND HELBERGER, J. H., *Science, 73*, 494 (1931)
29. HOLTER, H., *Z. physiol. Chem., 196*, 1 (1931)
30. NORTHROP, J. H., *J. Gen. Physiol., 15*, 29 (1931)
31. PACE, J., *Biochem. J., 25*, 422, 1485 (1931)
32. WALDSCHMIDT-LEITZ, E., ZIEGLER, F., SCHÄFFNER, A., AND WEIL, L., *Z. physiol. Chem., 197*, 219 (1931)
33. SCHULZ, F. N., *Biochem. Z., 156*, 124 (1925)
34. STANKOVIC, R., ARNOVLJEVIC, V., AND MATAVULJ, P., *Z. physiol. Chem.,* 181, 291 (1929)
35. MANGOLD, E., AND DUBISKI, J., *Wiss. Arch. Landw. Abt. B (Tierernähr- u. Tierzucht),* 4, 200 (1930)
36. HOBSON, R. P., *Biochem. J., 25*, 1458 (1931)
37. WILLSTÄTTER, R., BAMANN, E., AND ROHDEWALD, M., *Z. physiol. Chem.,* 186, 85 (1929)
38. VOSS, O., *Z. physiol. Chem., 197*, 42 (1931)
39. WILLSTÄTTER, R., BAMANN, E., AND ROHDEWALD, M., *Z. physiol. Chem.,* 180, 127 (1928–29); 185, 267 (1929); 188, 107 (1930)
40. HUSFELDT, E., *Z. physiol. Chem., 194*, 137 (1930–31)
41. STERN, K. G., *Z. physiol. Chem., 199*, 169 (1931)
42. WILLSTÄTTER, R., AND GRASSMANN, W., *Z. physiol. Chem., 138*, 184 (1924)
43. WALDSCHMIDT-LEITZ, E., SCHÄFFNER, A., BEK, J. J., AND BLUM, E., *Z. physiol. Chem., 188*, 17 (1929–30)
44. GRASSMANN, W., SCHOENEBECK, O. VON, AND EIBELER, H., *Z. physiol. Chem., 194*, 124 (1930–31)
45. WALDSCHMIDT-LEITZ, E., AND PURR, A., *Z. physiol. Chem., 198*, 260 (1931)
46. WALDSCHMIDT-LEITZ, E., AND SCHÄFFNER, A., *Naturwissenschaften, 18*, 280 (1930)
47. KREBS, H. A., *Biochem. Z., 238*, 174 (1931)
48. KLEINMANN, H., AND WERR, F., *Biochem. Z., 241*, 108, 140, 181 (1931)
49. RONA, P., AND KLEINMANN, H., *Biochem. Z., 241*, 283, 316 (1931)
50. KREBS, H. A., *Biochem. Z., 220*, 269 (1930); *Naturwissenschaften, 18*, 736 (1930)
51. MICHAELIS, L., AND STERN, K. G., *Biochem. Z., 240*, 192 (1931)
52. STERN, K. G., *Biochem. Z., 234*, 116 (1931)
53. HOPKINS, R. H., AND KELLY, H. E., *Biochem. J., 25*, 256 (1931)
54. LINDERSTRÖM-LANG, K., *Z. physiol. Chem., 188*, 48 (1930)
55. SATO, M., *Compt. rend. trav. lab. Carlsberg, 19*, Nr. 2, p. 1 (1931)
56. GRASSMANN, W., AND KLENK, L., *Z. physiol. Chem., 186*, 26 (1930)
57. LINDERSTRÖM-LANG, K., AND HOLTER, H., *Z. physiol. Chem., 201*, 9 (1931)
58. BALLS, A. K., AND KÖHLER, F., *Ber., 64*, 34, 294 (1930–31)
59. BALLS, A. K., AND KÖHLER, F., *Ber., 64*, 383 (1930–31)

60. ABDERHALDEN, E., AND EHRENWALL, E. VON, *Fermentforschung*, 12, 223 (1930) ; 12, 376 (1930–31)

61. ABDERHALDEN, E., AND SCHWEITZER, F., *Fermentforschung*, 12, 350 (1930–31)

62. GRASSMANN, W., DYCKERHOFF, H., AND SCHOENEBECK, O. VON, *Ber.*, 62, 1307 (1929)

63. ABDERHALDEN, E., AND ZUMSTEIN, O., *Fermentforschung*, 12, 341 (1930–31)

64. FODOR, A., FRANKEL, M., AND KUK, S., *Biochem. Z.*, 229, 28 (1930)

65. WALDSCHMIDT-LEITZ, E., *Z. angew. Chem.*, 44, 573 (1931) ; *Physiol. Rev.*, 11, 358 (1931)

66. FODOR, A., AND FRANKENTHAL, L., *Biochem. Z.*, 233, 283 (1931)

67. ABDERHALDEN, E., AND EHRENWALL, E. VON, *Fermentforschung*, 12, 411 (1930–31)

68. BALLS, A. K., AND KÖHLER, F., *Naturwissenschaften*, 19, 737 (1931)

69. ABDERHALDEN, E., AND SCHWAB, E., *Fermentforschung*, 12, 432 (1930–31)

70. WALDSCHMIDT-LEITZ, E., AND BALLS, A. K., *Ber.*, 64, 45 (1930–31)

71. GRASSMANN, W., AND BASU, K. P., *Z. physiol. Chem.*, 198, 247 (1931)

72. EDLBACHER, S., AND BURCHARD, H., *Z. physiol. Chem.*, 194, 69 (1930–31)

73. SALASKIN, S., AND SOLOWJEW, L., *Z. physiol. Chem.*, 200, 259 (1931)

74. WALDSCHMIDT-LEITZ, E., SCHÄFFNER, A., AND KOCHOLATY, W., *Naturwissenschaften*, 19, 964 (1931)

75. EDLBACHER, S., *Z. physiol. Chem.*, 157, 106 (1926)

76. EDLBACHER, S., AND KRAUS, J., *Z. physiol. Chem.*, 195, 267 (1931)

77. MISLOWITZER, E., AND KAUFFMANN, F., *Biochem. Z.*, 234, 101 (1931)

78. ABDERHALDEN, E., AND BUADZE, S., *Z. physiol. Chem.*, 200, 87 (1931)

79. SUMNER, J. B., *J. Biol. Chem.*, 69, 435; 70, 97 (1926) ; SUMNER, J. B., AND HAND, D. B., *Naturwissenschaften*, 16, 145 (1928)

80. ZAKOWSKI, J., *Biochem. Z.*, 229, 41 (1930)

81. WALDSCHMIDT-LEITZ, E., AND STEIGERWALDT, F., *Z. physiol. Chem.*, 195, 260 (1931)

82. TAUBER, H., AND KLEINER, I. S., *J. Gen. Physiol.*, 15, 155 (1931)

83. TAUBER, H., AND KLEINER, I. S., *J. Biol. Chem.*, 92, 177 (1931)

84. SUMNER, J. B., HAND, D. B., AND HOLLOWAY, R. G., *J. Biol. Chem.*, 91, 333 (1931)

85. OHLSSON, E., *Compt. rend. soc. biol.*, 87, 1183 (1922) ; *Compt. rend. trav. lab. Carlsberg*, 16, No. 7, p. 1 (1926) ; *Z. physiol. Chem.*, 189, 17 (1930)

86. KUHN, R., *Ann.*, 443, 1 (1925)

87. WALDSCHMIDT-LEITZ, E., AND PURR, A., *Z. physiol. Chem.*, 203, 117 (1931)

88. BORCHARDT, H., AND PRINGSHEIM, H., *Biochem. Z.*, 239, 193 (1931)

89. ARTOM, C., AND ORESTANO, G., *Bull. soc. chim.*, 13, 516 (1931)

90. NARAYANAMURTI, D., *J. Indian Inst. Sci.*, 13A, 63 (1930)

91. FLETCHER, L., AND WESTWOOD, J. B., *J. Inst. Brewing*, 36, 470 (1930) ; 37, 550 (1931)

92. PRINGSHEIM, H., AND FUCHS, W., *Ber.*, **56**, 1762 (1923)

93. WEIDENHAGEN, R., AND WOLF, A., *Z. Ver. deut. Zuckerind.*, **80**, 866 (1930)

94. PRINGSHEIM, H., BORCHARDT, H., AND HUPFER, H., *Z. Ver. deut. Zuckerind.*, **81**, 633 (1931)

95. COSACK, G., *Biochem. Z.*, **235**, 469 (1931)

96. PRINGSHEIM, H., BORCHARDT, H., AND HUPFER, H., *Biochem. Z.*, **238**, 476 (1931)

97. SAMEC, M., AND WALDSCHMIDT-LEITZ, E., *Z. physiol. Chem.*, **203**, 16 (1931)

98. ZIESE, W., *Z. physiol. Chem.*, **203**, 87 (1931)

99. HELFERICH, B., AND SCHNEIDMÜLLER, A., *Z. physiol. Chem.*, **198**, 100 (1931)

100. WEIDENHAGEN, R., *Z. Ver. deut. Zuckerind.*, **79**, 115 (1929); *Fermentforschung*, **11**, 155 (1930)

101. KARSTRÖM, H., *Biochem. Z.*, **231**, 399 (1930–31)

102. WEIDENHAGEN, R., *Biochem. Z.*, **233**, 318 (1931); *Z. physiol. Chem.*, **200**, 279 (1931)

103. MYRBÄCK, K., *Z. physiol. Chem.*, **198**, 196 (1931)

104. VIRTANEN, A. I., *Biochem. Z.*, **235**, 490 (1931)

105. OPARIN, A., AND KURSSANOW, A., *Biochem. Z.*, **239**, 1 (1931)

106. ZEILE, K., AND HELLSTRÖM, H., *Z. physiol. Chem.*, **192**, 171 (1930)

107. ZEILE, K., *Z. physiol. Chem.*, **195**, 39 (1930–31)

108. HAUROWITZ, F., *Z. physiol. Chem.*, **198**, 9 (1931)

109. WILLSTÄTTER, R., AND POLLINGER, A., *Z. physiol. Chem.*, **130**, 281 (1923)

110. KUHN, R., AND BRANN, L., *Ber.*, **59**, 2370 (1926)

111. RADEFF, T., *Biochem. Z.*, **220**, 445 (1930)

112. KUHN, R., HAND, D. B., AND FLORKIN, M., *Naturwissenschaften*, **19**, 771 (1931); *Z. physiol. Chem.*, **201**, 255 (1931)

113. WILLSTÄTTER, R., AND POLLINGER, A., *Ann.*, **430**, 269 (1922–23)

114. NARAYANAMURTI, D., AND RAMASWAMI, C. V., *Biochem. J.*, **25**, 749 (1931)

115. HARVEY, E. N., AND SNELL, P. A., *J. Gen. Physiol.*, **14**, 529 (1931)

116. NEUBERG, C., AND KOBEL, M., *Biochem. Z.*, **229**, 255 (1930)

117. NEUBERG, C., AND KOBEL, M., *Biochem. Z.*, **229**, 433 (1930)

118. BARTHEL, C., EULER, H. VON, AND NILSSON, R., *Z. physiol. Chem.*, **198**, 251 (1931)

119. EULER, H. VON, *Z. angew. Chem.*, **44**, 583 (1931)

120. MYRBÄCK, K., AND EULER, H. VON, *Z. physiol. Chem.*, **198**, 219, 236; **203**, 143 (1931)

121. LOHMANN, K., *Naturwissenschaften*, **17**, 624 (1929); *Biochem. Z.*, **241**, 67 (1931)

122. EULER, H. VON, AND MYRBÄCK, K., *Z. physiol. Chem.*, **199**, 189 (1931)

123. LOHMANN, K., *Naturwissenschaften*, **19**, 180 (1931)

124. EULER, H. VON, NILSSON, R., AND AUHAGEN, E., *Z. physiol. Chem.*, **200**, 1 (1931)

125. ERDTMAN, H., *Z. physiol. Chem.*, **172**, 182 (1927); **177**, 211, 238 (1928)
126. NEUBERG, C., AND EULER, H. VON, *Biochem. Z.*, **240**, 245 (1931)
127. AUHAGEN, E., *Naturwissenschaften*, **19**, 916 (1931)
128. AUHAGEN, E., *Z. physiol. Chem.*, **204**, 149 (1931–32)
129. EULER, H. VON, AND PHILIPSON, T., *Z. physiol. Chem.*, **195**, 81; **198**, 1 (1931)
130. ZUCKERKANDL, F., AND MESSINER-KLEBERMASS, L., *Biochem. Z.*, **239**, 172 (1931)
131. DIRSCHERL, W., *Z. physiol. Chem.*, **201**, 47, 78 (1931)
132. NEUBERG, C., *Biochem. Z.*, **225**, 238 (1930)

INSTITUT FÜR BIOCHEMIE
DEUTSCHE TECHNISCHE HOCHSCHULE
PRAG, 2; HORSKÁ, 3

THE CHEMISTRY OF THE ACYCLIC CONSTITUENTS OF NATURAL FATS AND OILS*

By R. J. ANDERSON

Department of Chemistry, Yale University

The chemistry of fats, fatty acids, and lipoids in general has received much attention during the past few years. The present interest in this field of investigation is due partly to the important relation of the ether-soluble constituents of plant and animal tissues to the fat-soluble vitamins and especially the relation of carotene to vitamin A which has recently been recognized.

Rapid progress has been made in the study of fatty acids. Improved methods have been developed, such as catalytic hydrogenation and distillation in very high vacuum, which have greatly aided in the separation and identification of pure individual fatty acids. Catalytic hydrogenation followed by esterification and fractionation of the esters in high vacuum has made it possible to determine the nature of certain unsaturated fatty acids which are present in the lipoids from brain, liver, and other tissues more completely than could be done by means of the older methods.

The application of catalytic hydrogenation to a mixture of fatty acids containing unsaturated and saturated liquid fatty acids, all of which give lead soaps which are soluble in ether, has made it possible to remove and to identify the reduced acid by repeating the lead soap-ether treatment and at the same time the liquid-saturated fatty acids can be recovered from the ether-soluble lead salts. The separation of such a mixture would be practically impossible by the methods which were formerly available. By the use of this procedure it has been possible to isolate a series of new liquid-saturated fatty acids of high molecular weight such as tuberculostearic acid and phthioic acid which have been found to occur in all of the lipoid fractions of the tubercle bacillus and in other acid-fast bacteria. By the same method it has also been possible to isolate other new liquid-saturated fatty acids from the liquid acid fraction of the fat from the cat kidney. It is not at all improbable that other liquid-saturated fatty acids will be discovered in other fats when this method of investigation is applied to the liquid acid fraction which is obtained from the ether-soluble lead soaps.

* Received January 12, 1932.

Rapid and important developments have also been made in the application of high-pressure hydrogenation at elevated temperatures for the production of higher alcohols and of hydrocarbons from esters of higher fatty acids. This phase, which is just now beginning, appears to offer many fascinating possibilities in the near future not only for research but for the commercial utilization of new products.

THE FATTY ACIDS OCCURRING IN PHOSPHATIDES

The nature of the fatty acids which occur in phosphatides isolated from various animal tissues as well as from plants and bacteria has been extensively investigated and much additional information has been obtained. The fatty acids of the cephalin and lecithin fractions from brain (1) and of the phosphatide from beef liver (2) have been examined by Klenk. The saturated fatty acids were found to consist principally of stearic acid, together with a small amount of palmitic acid. The unsaturated fatty acids were hydrogenated and the resulting reduced acids were esterified and the esters were fractionated by distillation. The only acids obtained were stearic acid and behenic acid, and they were present in the proportion of about 3 to 1. The fact that no arachidic acid could be isolated would indicate that arachidonic acid was absent. The degree of unsaturation of the C_{22} acid could not be determined accurately, but the evidence obtained indicates that at least 4 and possibly 5 double bonds were present.

In examining a larger quantity of the unsaturated fatty acids obtained from mixed ether-soluble phosphatides from brain, Klenk (3) has shown that an uninterrupted series of even-numbered acids from palmitic acid to behenic acid is present. In this case also the unsaturated fatty acids had been hydrogenated, esterified, and the esters had been separated by distillation *in vacuo*. The saturated fatty acids obtained from the mixture mentioned above consisted of palmitic and stearic acids.

Experiments reported by Brown (4) and by Brown and Ault (5) indicate that the brain tissue from beef and sheep contain one or more fatty acids which are more unsaturated and of higher molecular weight than arachidonic acid, and it is suggested that tetracosapentenoic acid, $C_{24}H_{38}O_2$, is present; but the highly unsaturated acid from the brain tissue of the hog corresponds more closely to arachidonic acid.

The unsaturated fatty acids in sheep liver have been investigated by Turner (6) who reports the presence of oleic, linoleic, and arachidonic acids. The same author in a study of the fatty acids of the cat kidney (7) finds that the saturated acids consist of a mixture of palmitic and stearic acids. The liquid acids obtained from the cat kidney are distinguished by having a very low iodine number. The liquid acids were hydrogenated and the reduced acid was removed by means of the lead soap–ether procedure and identified as stearic acid. From the ether-soluble lead soaps a liquid saturated fatty acid was isolated and converted into the methyl ester. The ester on distillation yielded two fractions. Fraction 1, which distilled at 105°–115° at 15–20 mm., gave on saponification a saturated acid which was a liquid at room temperature, and it corresponded in composition to the formula $C_{14}H_{28}O_2$. Fraction 2 apparently was a mixture which probably consisted of C_{14} and C_{16} acids.

The highly unsaturated fatty acids contained in human liver have been examined by Müller (8), and the results obtained indicate that arachidonic acid is present together with a C_{16} acid with 3 double bonds.

Extensive studies on the degree of unsaturation of the phosphatide fatty acids, as measured by the iodine number, have been reported by Terroine, Hatterer, and Roehrig (9). The investigation included phosphatides from warm-blooded and cold-blooded animals, certain higher plants, and microörganisms. It was found that the iodine number of the phosphatide fatty acids from any tissue of warm-blooded animals is nearly a constant value for different animals of the same species as well as for different species, while in the case of cold-blooded animals the iodine number showed wide variations. In the case of microörganisms the temperature at which the cultures were grown was found to influence the iodine number to some extent. Terroine and Hatterer (10) found no significant differences in the iodine number of the phosphatide fatty acids from muscle and liver tissue of pigeons and rabbits fed radically different diets. On the other hand, Sinclair (11) has reported distinct differences in the iodine number of the phosphatide fatty acids from various tissues of the cat and white rat, and this difference apparently depends upon the degree of unsaturation of the fat contained in the food.

The composition of sphingosine, the unsaturated nitrogenous base occurring in cerebrosides and sphingomyelin, for which the formula $C_{17}H_{35}O_2N$ had been established, has been reinvestigated by Klenk (12) and by Klenk and Diebold (13). The values found on analyses of triacetylsphingosine, dihydrosphingosine picrate, and dihydrosphingosine hydrobromide were in agreement with the formula $C_{18}H_{37}O_2N$. Further, myristic acid was formed when sphingosine sulfate was oxidized with chromic acid and also after ozonizing the triacetylsphingosine. Oxidation of dihydrosphingosine with chromic acid led to the formation of palmitic acid. In view of these results it is believed that the constitution of sphingosine is best expressed by the formula $CH_3(CH_2)_{12} \cdot CH:CH \cdot CH(OH) \cdot CH(OH) \cdot CH_2NH_2$. Incidentally it is pointed out that the dihydrosphingosine hydrobromide crystallizes more readily than other salts of this base.

In connection with studies on cerebrosides the partial synthesis of kerasin has been reported by Klenk and Härtle (14). Galactosidosphingosine was treated in pyridine with lignoceryl chloride. The reaction product after it had been purified resembled kerasin, and on hydrogenation it gave dihydrokerasin, which was found to be identical with tetrahydronervone.

A study of sphingomyelin prepared from human brain has been reported by Merz (15). The properties of the purified preparation were in agreement with those reported by Levene. In order to determine the nature of the fatty acid component, the purified sphingomyelin was separated into six fractions by treatment with acetone. These fractions were saponified and the fatty acids were isolated. It was found that all of the fractions contained stearic, lignoceric, and nervonic acids. It is concluded therefore that ordinary sphingomyelin is a mixture of three sphingomyelins which differ only in the nature of the fatty acid which is combined in the molecule.

Proximate analyses of the saturated and unsaturated fatty acids contained in egg lecithin have been reported by Sueyoshi and Furukbo (16). Similar studies on the composition of soy-bean lecithin have been published by Suzuki and Yokoyama (17) and by Yokoyama and Suzuki (18). A preparation of lysolecithin has been isolated from polished rice by Iwata (19), and the spontaneous formation of lysolecithin from lecithin suspended in physiological saline solution has been reported by Fiori (20).

Considerable new information concerning the fatty acids contained in bacterial phosphatides, especially in the phosphatides from the acid-fast group of bacteria, has been published during the past two years. In connection with a comprehensive co-operative investigation on tuberculosis which was initiated several years ago by the Research Committee of the National Tuberculosis Association, the opportunity was provided for preparing and studying large quantities of the lipoids of various standard strains of tubercle bacilli. Comparative studies have also been made with non-pathogenic acid-fast bacteria such as the timothy bacillus and the leprosy bacillus. All of the bacteria were grown on the Long synthetic medium under carefully standardized conditions.

The phosphatide fractions after separation from the other lipoids were studied by chemical and biological methods. The chemical investigations indicate in the first place that the tuberculophosphatides differ decidedly in composition from the usual plant and animal phosphatides, since they contain only about 2 per cent of phosphorus and from 0.2 to 1 per cent of nitrogen. The phosphorus is apparently present as glycerophosphoric acid, but the nature of the nitrogen component is unknown. Another point of difference in the composition of the bacterial phosphatides has been noted in that they contain a large percentage of a new type of polysaccharide (21) which on hydrolysis yields mainly mannose and inosite, but since several fatty acids are obtained on hydrolyzing the phosphatides it is believed that the polysaccharide component is also combined with fatty acids. Biologically the bacterial phosphatides possess peculiar interest because when injected subcutaneously they cause a decided proliferation of monocytes, epithelioid cells, and giant cells, which leads to a massive formation of tubercular tissue, as shown by the experiments of Sabin and Doan (22). The phosphatides also act as true antigens (23).

The fatty acids of the tuberculophosphatides were separated by the lead soap–ether procedure into solid and liquid fatty acids. The solid acid was always found to consist of practically pure palmitic acid. The liquid acids always had a very low iodine number, and this fact indicated that some liquid saturated fatty acid was present. The separation of a mixture consisting of liquid unsaturated and liquid saturated fatty acids presents considerable difficulties, but in this case the separation was accomplished by means of catalytic hydrogenation when the unsaturated acid was converted into stearic acid and the latter could then be removed by repeating the lead soap–ether treatment. The phosphatide from every acid-fast bacillus so far examined, including the human (24), avian (25), and bovine (26) types of tubercle bacilli and the timothy bacillus (27), contains a liquid saturated fatty acid, the amount varying from about 14 to 21 per cent. The liquid saturated fatty acid from the human tubercle bacillus is optically active, and investigations have shown that this acid is the biologically active constituent of the phosphatide, since the acid itself when injected into normal animals acts as a maturation factor for monocytes and epithelioid cells and causes the formation of tubercular tissue. For this reason the acid was named *phthioic acid* (28). The liquid fatty acids obtained from the phosphatide of the avian and bovine tubercle bacilli and of the timothy bacillus possess chemical and biological properties similar to those of phthioic acid, but they differ to the extent that they are optically inactive. The liquid saturated fatty acids from the tuberculophosphatides have high molecular weights, the values obtained on titration being over 300. These acids are probably mixtures of at least two higher fatty acids and, as will be mentioned in a subsequent paragraph, similar acids can be isolated from every lipoid fraction of the acid-fast bacilli. It has been possible from such sources to obtain sufficiently large quantities of the crude liquid acids to permit of the separation and partial purification of the individual acids.

Preliminary studies on other bacterial phosphatides isolated from the turtle and smegma bacilli (29) and the diphtheria bacillus (30) have been conducted by Chargaff. The nature of the lipoids synthesized by *B. coli* and the amount of phosphatide contained in the total ether-soluble lipoids have been studied by Eckstein and Soule (31). Incidentally it may be mentioned that these investigators failed to find any sterols in the *B. coli* fat, and a similar observation has been reported by von Behring (32) with regard to the fats extracted from *B. coli* and diphtheria bacillus.

THE CONSTITUENTS OF WAXES

The component waxes and glycerides of the commercially important head and blubber oils of the sperm whale have been analyzed by Hilditch and Lavern (33). The head oils contain mainly saturated alcohols, the chief constituent being cetyl alcohol, together with small amounts of other alcohols including from 27 to 30 per cent of oleyl alcohol. The blubber oils contain from 1 to 2 per cent of saturated glycerides and about 27 per cent of saturated wax esters, but the chief constituent is oleyl alcohol.

The higher fatty acids occurring in Japan wax have been studied by Flaschenträger and Halle (34).

Japan wax, which consists mainly of the glyceride of palmitic acid, also contains some higher fatty acids, among which the dicarboxylic acid, japanic acid, $C_{21}H_{40}O_4$ (m.p. 117–118°) is said to be present to the extent of 1 per cent. In the present investigation, although 100 kg. of the wax were used, japanic acid could not be identified definitely, but two other higher acids were isolated. A small amount, 0.06 per cent, of eicosane carboxylic acid, $C_{21}H_{42}O_2$ (m.p. 74°), methyl ester (m.p. 49.5°) was obtained, together with 0.3 per cent of heneicosane dicarboxylic acid, $C_{23}H_{44}O_4$ (m.p. 124°). The monomethyl ester melted at 87° and the dimethyl ester melted at 70.8°.

A wax isolated by Tange (35) from rice polishings was purified, analyzed, and identified as melissyl cerotate. On saponification the cleavage products were identified as melissyl alcohol and cerotic acid. A comparative study of several kinds of Japanese beeswaxes has been reported by Ikuta (36). The results indicate that the wax produced by native Japanese bees has a higher iodine number, a higher acetyl value, and a higher percentage of unsaponifiable matter than the wax produced by the European type of bees.

In a study of insect waxes Schulz and Becker (37) have described a wax obtained from *Pemphigus xylostei* which resembles cochineal wax. It melts at 108–109° and its composition corresponds to the formula $C_{68}H_{136}O_4$. On saponification it yields a diatomic alcohol, named *pemphigus alcohol,* $C_{34}H_{70}O_2$ (m.p. 100–105°), and an oxyacid, pemphygic acid, $C_{33}H_{66}OHCOOH$ (m.p. 101–102°). The composition of coccerin, the wax from the cochineal insect, has been determined by Becker (38). This wax yields on saponification 1 molecule each of cocceryl alcohol and cocceric acid. Cocceryl alcohol is a diatomic alcohol, $C_{32}H_{64}(OH)_2$ (m.p. 102°), and cocceric acid is a hydroxy acid $C_{32}H_{64}O_3$ (m.p. 94–95°).

Some progress has been made in the study of the wax fractions obtained from the human tubercle bacillus and some new and interesting constituents have been isolated. The tubercle bacillus produces a large amount of waxy material which can be extracted with chloroform, benzene, or toluene from the partly defatted bacteria. The crude wax obtained on the evaporation of the solvent forms a yellowish solid (m.p. 50–51°); it resembles beeswax in appearance but it is more brittle. The crude wax can be separated by precipitating its ethereal solution with acetone into 2 fractions which differ markedly in properties and in composition. The insoluble portion is a white amorphous powder which melts with decomposition at 200–205° and contains 0.41 per cent of phosphorus and 0.77 per cent of nitrogen. The soluble portion is obtained on evaporation of the solvents as a soft, salve-like mass which is free from phosphorus and nitrogen. Analyses of the solid purified wax (39) and of the soft wax (40) have been reported by Anderson.

The purified wax is very stable and can be hydrolyzed only by means of boiling alcoholic potassium hydroxide or by boiling with acid alcohol. The cleavage products which are obtained consist of (a) about 56 per cent of a very stable unsaponifiable wax, (b) a small amount of fatty acids, and (c) about 40 per cent of water-soluble constituents. The fatty acids were separated into solid and liquid acids. The solid fatty acids were found to consist of hexacosanic acid, $C_{26}H_{52}O_2$ (m.p. 83–84°), mol. wt. 396, and apparently a eutectic mixture of palmitic and stearic acids. The liquid acids after catalytic hydrogenation and separation of the reduced acid by means of the lead soap–ether treatment yielded stearic acid and a liquid saturated fatty acid of high molecular weight. The latter acid possessed chemical and biological properties similar to the crude phthioic acid isolated from the phosphatide (24), but it differed to the extent that it was levorotatory.

The unsaponifiable wax (41) was a snow-white amorphous powder which melted at 57–58°. It was an optically inactive saturated compound and gave no sterol color reactions. The substance possesses acidic properties, since it forms salts, and it probably contains two hydroxyl groups, since it forms two acetyl derivatives. The properties correspond to those of a hydroxy acid of high molecular weight. The composition, determined by analysis of the free substance, the acetyl derivatives, the potassium salt, and the silver salt, agrees with the formula $C_{94}H_{188}O_4$. When the substance is heated to about 300° under reduced pressure, it decomposes or cracks and a colorless crystalline fatty acid distills over, leaving a nearly colorless non-volatile residue which is unsaturated. The fatty acid obtained by distillation crystallizes in colorless plates and melts at 88–89°. It has been identified as n-hexacosanic acid, $C_{26}H_{52}O_2$ (42).

The unsaponifiable wax is the only compound isolated from the tubercle bacilli lipoids which is acid-fast; it must be similar to the alcohol described by Tamura (43) under the name of mycol, but it differs from the latter compound not only in properties but in composition. The biological reactions of the unsaponifiable wax differ from those of phthioic acid since it does not cause the formation of tubercular tissue but stimulates the development of connective tissue cells (44).

The water-soluble constituents obtained from the purified wax, when hydrolyzed with dilute acid, were found to consist of pentose and hexose sugars. From this mixture it was possible to isolate about 35 per cent of d-arabinose, 17 per cent of galactose, and 2 per cent of mannose, together with traces of inosite and glucosamine (45).

The composition of the soft wax (46) was found to correspond more nearly to that of a complex glyceride than to a wax. On saponification there were obtained about 5 per cent of water-soluble and 95 per cent of ether-soluble constituents. The water-soluble material gave a positive acrolein reaction and was probably therefore impure glycerol. The ether-soluble components consisted of about 13 per cent of a neutral unsaponifiable fraction, 13 per cent of unsaponifiable wax, and 69 per cent of fatty acids. The solid saturated acids were apparently a mixture of palmitic and stearic acids. The liquid acids, after catalytic hydrogenation, were separated into a solid reduced acid and a liquid saturated fatty acid. The latter was analogous to crude phthioic acid and was undoubtedly a mixture of higher acids. It was optically active, $[\alpha]_D^{23} = +4.85°$ (m.p. 22.5°), and the neutralization value corresponded to a molecular weight of 424. The reduced acid contained in addition to stearic acid a small amount of a higher acid. In the examination of mixed lipoids from human and bovine tubercle bacilli Anderson and Chargaff (47) were able to isolate a larger amount of a similar reduced acid and to identify it as a hexacosanic acid, $C_{26}H_{52}O_2$ (m.p. 82–82.5°). It appears therefore to be well established that the lipoids of tubercle bacilli contain in the unsaturated acid fraction a small quantity of an unsaturated hexacosanic acid.

GLYCERIDES AND THEIR CONSTITUENT FATTY ACIDS

The systematic investigations on the glyceride structure of various types of animal and vegetable fats which have been conducted by Hilditch and collaborators (48) have yielded much interesting and valuable information. By oxidation of fats in acetone solution with potassium permanganate the unsaturated acids are converted into acidic products, while the saturated glycerides are left unaltered and can be isolated and their fatty acids examined. The proportion of fully saturated glycerides present in fats is in many cases characteristic, and it has been found that animal fats generally contain more saturated glycerides than do the seed fats. In the fat from plant seeds there is a tendency for the unsaturated fatty acids to be uniformly distributed throughout the fat, while the fat from other portions of the plant such as the pericarp resembles in many cases animal fats in that it contains more saturated glycerides.

The composition of various fats of plant origin has been determined, such as illipé tallow (49), dika fat (50), oil of laurel (51), palm oil (52), stillingia tallow (53), various Indian seed oils (54), and laurel fats (55). The glyceride structures of butter fats (56) and of beef tallows (57) have also been studied.

A new triglyceride, palmitostearoazelain, has been obtained by Baugault and Schuster (58) when cocoa butter is oxidized by the method of Hilditch. The yield indicated that cocoa butter consists of about 33 per cent of palmitostearoölein. By partial saponification the azelaic acid is split off, yielding a diglyceride, palmitostearin (m.p. 34°), and the latter compound was identified as the α-palmito α-stearin (59).

Wallflower-seed oil is supposed to contain some 65 per cent of cheiranthic acid, $C_{18}H_{34}O_2$, an isomer of oleic acid, but Lewkowitsch (60) considered that the properties attributed to cheiranthic acid agreed better with those of erucic acid, $C_{22}H_{42}O_2$. The composition of the oil obtained by extracting the seeds of *Cheiranthus cheiri*, L., with petroleum ether has been investigated by van Loon (61), and it was found that the fatty acids obtained on saponification consisted of 4.9 per cent of saturated acids, 40.6 per cent of erucic acid, 4.9 per cent of oleic acid, 24.7 per cent of linoleic acid, and 19.4 per cent of linolenic acid. It would appear, therefore, as if the cheiranthic acid originally described by Matthes and Boltze (62) was an impure specimen of erucic acid.

Bacterial fats have not been extensively investigated and such analyses as have been published have usually been made on mixed lipoids. It has been difficult in the past to obtain sufficient quantities of bacterial fats to permit of the separation and identification of the individual fatty acids, but during the past few years investigational work on tuberculosis has made it possible to secure larger amounts of the fats from acid-fast bacteria.

In the preliminary separation of the mixed lipoids from the tubercle bacillus as described by Anderson (24) a fraction was obtained which was soluble in cold acetone. This acetone-soluble fat was assumed to consist of glycerides, but in the analysis of this fraction reported by Anderson and Chargaff (63) it was found that glycerol could not definitely be identified. The water-soluble constituents of the fat, which amounted to 6.61 per cent, gave the acrolein reaction; but in attempting to separate the glycerol by distillation under reduced pressure only a slight amount of distillate was obtained, while the greater portion of the material decomposed and carbonized at a temperature of 190–200°. It is probable, therefore, that the fatty acids were combined with some higher polyhydric alcohol in place of glycerol.

The acetone-soluble fat contained about 27 per cent of free fatty acids, calculated as palmitic acid and about 11 per cent of unsaponifiable matter. The iodine number was 52.6 and the Reichert-Meissl number was 3.96. The fat was saponified and the fatty acids were separated by means of the lead soap–ether procedure into solid and liquid acids. The solid fatty acids consisted principally of palmitic acid, together with a smaller amount of stearic acid and a very small quantity of hexacosanic acid. The liquid acid had an iodine number of 53.8, and after catalytic reduction the reduced acid was separated and identified as stearic acid. The amount of the latter indicated that the unsaturated acid must have been linoleic acid. The greater portion of the liquid acid was a mixture of liquid-saturated fatty acids, and the methyl ester of this fraction was separated by distillation in a high vacuum, when two principal fractions were obtained (64).

Fraction 1, which distilled at 140–145°, was the methyl ester of an acid isomeric with stearic acid. The free acid obtained after saponification formed a faintly yellowish oil at ordinary temperature, but it solidified on cooling and liquefied at 14–15°. Its composition was in close agreement with that of stearic acid, $C_{18}H_{36}O_2$, hence the acid was named tuberculostearic acid. The acid is optically inactive and when injected into normal animals it does not cause the formation of tubercular tissue.

Fraction 2 of the ester distilled at about 200° and it corresponded in composition to the methyl ester of a hexacosanic acid. The ester was a thick yellowish oil which solidified at 10°, and it was optically active, $[\alpha]_D^{20} = +8.79°$. The free acid prepared by saponifying the ester was a snow-white, soft solid (m.p. 28°), $[\alpha]_D^{22} = +7.98°$ and the composition was in agreement with the formula $C_{26}H_{52}O_2$. This compound, which was regarded as the purest specimen of phthioic acid obtained up to that time, possessed biological properties similar to those reported for the crude phthioic acid isolated from the tuberculophosphatide. It appears, therefore, according to the investigations of Sabin and collaborators (44), that the biologically active constituent of the lipoids of tubercle bacilli is associated with the optically active phthioic acid.

Larger quantities of tuberculostearic acid and of phthioic acid were later prepared by Anderson and Chargaff (65) from the mixed lipoids from human and bovine tubercle bacilli. Some evidence was also obtained that other acids, analogous to phthioic acid, were present in the liquid saturated acid fraction, but the amounts available were insufficient to permit of adequate purification.

The acetone-soluble fat isolated from the bovine tubercle bacillus (66) has been analyzed by Burt and Anderson (67). This fat also contained a large proportion of free fatty acids. Glycerol could not be identified, but apparently some other higher polyhydric alcohol was present.

The fatty acids obtained after saponification of the fat were separated by methods similar to those employed in the study of the acetone-soluble fat from the human tubercle bacillus. The methyl esters of the solid acids were fractionated by distillation in a high vacuum, and the only acids that could be isolated were palmitic acid and hexacosanic acid. The liquid acid fraction amounted to 54 per cent of the total fatty acids, and the iodine number was 65.6. The amount of stearic acid obtained after catalytic hydrogenation was equal to 12.5 per cent of the total fatty acids, and this fact indicates that the unsaturated acid must have consisted mainly of linolenic acid.

The liquid saturated fatty acids were esterified and the methyl ester was fractionated by distillation in a high vacuum. The first and largest fraction corresponded in properties and composition to tuberculostearic acid. A small amount of a higher-boiling ester was obtained which on saponification gave a higher liquid saturated fatty acid. This acid differed from phthioic in properties and in composition and was optically inactive, but the amount of the substance was too small to permit of adequate purification.

Incidentally it may be mentioned that the acetone-soluble fat, from both the human and the bovine bacilli, contained traces of a volatile acid which had an odor similar to that of butyric acid. Further, the unsaponifiable fractions were highly unsaturated oils which gave no typical sterol color reactions.

The results obtained in the analyses of the lipoid fractions from the acid-fast bacteria show that a series of new saturated fatty acids are elaborated by these organisms. The low melting-points of these acids and the optical activity of certain members of this series indicate that these acids must possess a peculiar constitution, and they must contain branched chains. The characteristic biological effect of the optically active phthioic acid in stimulating the formation of monocytes and epithelioid cells with the formation of tubercular tissue makes it probable that this acid plays an important part in the development of certain lesions which are typical of tuberculosis.

THE SEPARATION AND IDENTIFICATION OF CERTAIN HIGHER FATTY ACIDS

Frequent reference is found in the literature dealing with fats and fatty acids to the occurrence of lignoceric acid. Following the work by Brigl and Fuchs (68) some years ago on the lignoceric acid of beechwood tar, in which it was claimed that lignoceric acid was not homogeneous but could be separated into two fractions, one of which was identical with the synthetic n-tetracosanic acid, the lignoceric acid of peanut oil was reinvestigated by Levene, Taylor, and Haller (69). The purified lignoceric acid isolated by these investigators melted at 80–81° and the melting-point could not be changed by further crystallizations.

It is interesting in this connection to note two recent investigations dealing with the higher fatty acids of peanut oil. The first of these investigations was reported by Jantzen and Tiedcke (70). The esters of the higher fatty acids were carefully fractionated in a high vacuum and the following acids were isolated in an apparently high state of purity: arachidic acid, $C_{20}H_{40}O_2$ (m.p. 74.9–75.1°); behenic acid, $C_{22}H_{44}O_2$ (m.p. 79.9–80.1°); and n-tetracosanic acid, $C_{24}H_{48}O_2$ (m.p. 84.1–84.3°). No evidence was found of the presence of lignoceric acid or of any acid with a branched chain such as lignoceric acid is supposed to contain.

The second investigation was reported by Taylor (71). The purification of the higher acids from peanut oil was carried out by means of distillation of the ethyl ester followed by repeated crystallization of the free acid from ether. The acid obtained in this manner melted at 84–85° and it agreed in composition and molecular weight with the formula $C_{24}H_{48}O_2$. There was no depression of the melting-point when the acid was mixed with some of the synthetic n-tetracosanic acid prepared by Levene and Taylor (72).

It would appear, therefore, that lignoceric acid is a mixture of several higher acids which are separated with extreme difficulty by ordinary recrystallizations.

The occurrence of a tetracosanic acid, $C_{24}H_{48}O_2$ (m.p. 80–81°), in the soaps obtained from Swedish pine oil, "tallöl," has been reported by Sandquist, Gorton, and Bengtson (73), and a similar tetracosanic acid (m.p. 80–81°) can be isolated in a yield of 15 per cent from the seeds of *Adenanthera pavonina* as reported by Ayyar (74). The presence of cerotic acid among the fatty acids isolated from spinach leaves has been reported by Collison and Smedley-Maclean (75).

Methods for the separation of higher solid fatty acids have been proposed by Baughman and Jamieson (76) and by Grossfeld and Simmer (77), while the preparation and properties of the higher-saturated fatty acids which occur in nature have been discussed by Holde and Bleyberg (78). A study of the melting-points and crystal-spacings of carefully purified higher fatty acids has been reported by Francis, Piper, and Malkin (79).

THE UNSATURATED FATTY ACIDS

Highly purified oleic acid has been prepared from olive oil by Skelton (80). The crude oleic acid was first partly purified by means of the barium or the lithium salt, followed by esterification and fractionation in a vacuum. The purified oleic acid melted at 13–14°, iodine number 90.6, molecular weight 282.5, $n_D^{20} = 1.4610$.

A method for the preparation of crude erucic acid from rape-seed oil has been described by Noller and Talbot (81), while Rider (82) has published a method for the preparation and purification of ricinoleic acid and sodium ricinoleate from castor oil.

The hydroxyoleic acid which was isolated from ergot by Matthes and Schutz (83) has been studied by Matthes and Kürscher (84) and found to be identical with ricinoleic acid.

The optical rotation of ricinoleamide has been studied by André and Vernier (85). The amide was prepared by the gradual addition of gaseous ammonia to an alcoholic solution of castor oil. Successive fractions of the crystalline amide showed increasing optical activity, which would indicate that ordinary ricinoleic acid may be a mixture of the *dl* acid.

The highly unsaturated fatty acid occurring in the fat obtained from the seeds of *Couepia grandiflora* has been investigated by van Loon and Steger (86). The acid, which is easily oxidized by atmospheric oxygen, was crystallized from petroleum ether and melted at

74–75°. The composition of the acid corresponds to the formula $C_{18}H_{30}O_2$, and it is regarded as a new isomer of eleostearic acid containing a conjugated system of double bonds and has been called e-eleostearic acid.

THE FATTY ACIDS CONTAINED IN STARCH

The fatty acids which are liberated when wheat starch (87) and rice starch (88) are hydrolyzed have been investigated by Lehman. The starch itself when extracted with petroleum ether yields only negligible amounts of free fat. After hydrolysis with dilute hydrochloric acid it was found that wheat starch yielded about 0.95 per cent of fatty acids, consisting of palmitic acid 35 per cent, oleic acid 41 per cent, and linoleic acid 24 per cent. Rice starch yielded about 0.6 per cent of fatty acids consisting of palmitic, oleic, and linoleic acids, and they were present in practically the same proportions as in the wheat starch.

HIGHER ALIPHATIC ALCOHOLS

Only a few naturally occurring higher alcohols have been isolated. In an investigation of the lipoids of spinach, Collison and Smedley-Maclean (75) were able to identify ceryl alcohol, $C_{26}H_{54}O$ (m.p. 77–78°). The same alcohol has also been isolated by Rabate (89) from the cortex of *Amelanchier vulgaris,* Moench. Cetyl alcohol and certain of its derivatives have been studied by Delcourt (90) in the synthesis of the hydrocarbon $C_{32}H_{66}$ from cetyl iodide, while Sandonnini and Bezzi (91) have determined some of the decomposition products which are formed when the vapors of cetyl alcohol are passed through a tube containing various metallic oxides as catalysts, heated to 325–350°. An unsaturated alcohol, called kanyl alcohol, of the formula $C_{10}H_{18}O_2$, has been isolated by Tsujimoto (92) from the unsaponifiable fraction of the liver oil of "Tarabakani," *Paralithodes camtschatica* (Tilesius). It has been shown by Mlle François (93) that large quantities of octadecyl alcohol, $C_{18}H_{38}O$, can be produced by catalytic hydrogenation of oleyl alcohol, $C_{18}H_{36}O$, which constitutes some 25 per cent of the oil of spermaceti.

An interesting attempt has been made by Knight (94) to determine the constitution of batyl, chimyl, and selachyl alcohols. These compounds are glyceryl ethers possessing the following formulae: batyl alcohol, $C_{18}H_{37}OC_3H_5(OH)_2$; selachyl alcohol, $C_{18}H_{35}OC_3H_5(OH)_2$; and chimyl alcohol, $C_{16}H_{33}OC_3H_5(OH)_2$. As a result of the measurements of the surface films it appears highly probable that the three alcohols are α-glyceryl ethers.

Some exceedingly interesting and important experiments have been reported during the past year on the production of saturated higher alcohols as well as hydrocarbons by catalytic hydrogenation of fatty-acid esters. Adkins and Folkers (95) have shown that ethyl laurate, myristate, valerate, cinnamate, trimethyl acetate, and succinate can be hydrogenated over a "copper chromite" catalyst at 250° and about 220 atmospheres pressure, with the formation of the corresponding alcohols in yields as high as 80 to 98.5 per cent. In a paper by Schrauth, Schenck, and Stickdorn (96) it is reported that, using nickel or copper catalysts, saturated hydrocarbons are formed when the reduction is carried out at pressures of about 200 atmospheres and at temperatures from 350° to 400°, whereas saturated alcohols are formed when the temperature is kept at about 320°. Schmidt (97) has reported similar results and describes the hydrogenation of ethyl oleate to octadecyl alcohol and the formation of octadecyl alcohol together with octadecandiol in the reduction of castor oil.

The formation of small amounts of higher alcohols (98), hydrocarbons (99), and aldehydes (100) during ordinary hydrogenation of fish oils has been observed by Ueno and Yamasaki.

Hydrocarbons

From the unsaponifiable fraction of the fat extracted from spinach leaves, Collison and Smedley-Maclean (75) isolated a hydrocarbon which was identified as hentriacontane, $C_{31}H_{64}$ (m.p. 68–68.5°). The same investigators (75) isolated from the unsaponifiable matter from the fat of cabbage leaves the hydrocarbon, nonacosane, $C_{29}H_{60}$ and di n-tetradecyl ketone, thus confirming the earlier work of Channon and Chibnall (101). The unsaponifiable matter from the fat of cabbage leaves has also been examined by Ozaki (102), who reports the isolation of a hydrocarbon which is regarded as hentriacontane $C_{31}H_{64}$. An unsaturated hydrocarbon called oleastene has been obtained by Sani (103) from the fruit of olives. The formula $C_{21}H_{36}$ is assigned to this hydrocarbon and it is said to absorb a maximum of 33 per cent of ozone.

One of the most interesting recent achievements in synthetic chemistry is the synthesis of squalene by Karrer and Helfenstein (104). The unsaturated hydrocarbon squalene was first isolated by Tsujimoto (105), who showed that it was the principal constituent of the liver oils of elasmobranch fish. The same investigator also determined the composition of squalene and assigned to it the correct formula, $C_{30}H_{50}$. The hydrocarbon has been carefully studied during the past few years by Heilbron and his collaborators, and in 1929 the following structural formula was proposed by Heilbron, Owens, and Simpson (106):

```
CH₃       CH₃        CH₃        CH₃        CH₃        CH₃
 | H H H  | H H H   | H H H   | H H H   | H H H   | H
C:C·C·C·C:C·C·C·C:C·C·C·C·C:C·C·C·C·C:C·C·C·C·C:C·CH₃
 |   H H      H H        H H        H H        H H
CH₃
```

By reason of the probable structural relationship of squalene to lycopin and carotene it was believed by Karrer that the following symmetrical formulation would more accurately represent the structure of squalene:

```
CH₃       CH₃        CH₃          CH₃        CH₃        CH₃
 | H H H  | H H H   | H H H H    | H H H   | H H H   |
C:C·C·C·C:C·C·C·C·C:C·C·C·C·C:C·C·C·C·C:C·C·C·C·C:C
 |   H H      H H        H H         H H        H H      |
CH₃                                                    CH₃
```

That this formulation is the correct one was shown by the actual synthesis which was done by coupling farnesyl bromide or chloride by means of potassium or magnesium.

```
CH₃       CH₃        CH₃                       CH₃        CH₃        CH₃
 | H H H  | H H H   | H H                 H H | H H H   | H H H   |
C:C·C·C·C:C·C·C·C·C:C·C·Br +Br·C·C:C·C·C·C·C:C·C·C·C·C:C
 |   H H      H H       H             H      H H        H H      |
CH₃                                                            CH₃
```

                    │ Mg or K

```
CH₃       CH₃        CH₃          CH₃        CH₃        CH₃
 | H H H  | H H H   | H H H H    | H H H   | H H H   |
C:C·C·C·C:C·C·C·C·C:C·C·C·C·C:C·C·C·C·C:C·C·C·C·C:C
 |   H H      H H        H H         H H        H H      |
CH₃                                                    CH₃
```

The reaction product was extracted with ether, the ethereal solution was washed with water, dried, and the ether was evaporated. The residue was fractionated under reduced pressure, and the squalene fraction collected between 215° and 240°. The squalene was identified by means of the two characteristic crystalline hexahydro-chlorides, one of which melts at 108–110° and the other at 144–145°. The synthetic and natural products had the same melting-point, and a mixture of the two gave no depression. Crystallographic examination of the higher-melting hexahydrochloride of the synthetic and natural squalene showed identical properties.

LITERATURE CITED

1. KLENK, E., Z. physiol. Chem., 192, 217 (1930)
2. KLENK, E., AND V. SCHOENEBECK, O., Z. physiol. Chem., 194, 191 (1931)
3. KLENK, E., Z. physiol. Chem., 200, 51 (1931)
4. BROWN, J. B., J. Biol. Chem., 83, 783 (1929)
5. BROWN, J. B., AND AULT, W. C., J. Biol. Chem., 89, 167 (1930)
6. TURNER, K., Biochem. J., 24, 1327 (1930)
7. TURNER, K., Biochem. J., 25, 49 (1931)
8. MÜLLER, P., Arch. exptl. Path. Pharmakol., 147, 219, 235, 240 (1930)
9. TERROINE, E. F., HATTERER, C., AND ROEHRIG, P., Bull. soc. chim. biol., 12, 657, 682 (1930)
10. TERROINE, E. F., AND HATTERER, C., Bull. soc. chim. biol., 12, 674 (1930)
11. SINCLAIR, R. G., J. Biol. Chem., 86, 579; 88, 575 (1930); 92, 245 (1931)
12. KLENK, E., Z. physiol. Chem., 185, 169 (1929)
13. KLENK, E., AND DIEBOLD, W., Z. physiol. Chem., 198, 25 (1931)
14. KLENK, E., AND HÄRTLE, R., Z. physiol. Chem., 189, 243 (1930)
15. MERZ, W., Z. physiol. Chem., 193, 59 (1930)
16. SUEYOSHI, Y., AND FURUKBO, T., J. Biochem. (Japan), 13, 155, 177 (1931)
17. SUZUKI, B., AND YOKOYAMA, Y., Proc. Imp. Acad. (Tokyo), 6, 341 (1930)
18. YOKOYAMA, Y., AND SUZUKI, B., Proc. Imp. Acad. (Tokyo), 7, 12, 226 (1931)
19. IWATA, M., Proc. Imp. Acad. (Tokyo), 6, 212 (1930)
20. FIORI, A., Biochim. terap. sper., 17, 267 (1930); Chem. Abst., 24, 4527 (1930)
21. ANDERSON, R. J., J. Am. Chem. Soc., 52, 1607 (1930); ANDERSON, R. J., AND RENFREW, A. G., J. Am. Chem. Soc., 52, 1252 (1930); ANDER-SON, R. J., ROBERTS, E. G., AND RENFREW, A. G., Proc. Soc. Exptl. Biol. Med., 27, 387 (1930); ANDERSON, R. J., AND ROBERTS, E. G., J. Biol. Chem., 89, 611 (1930); ANDERSON, R. J., AND ROBERTS, E. G., J. Am. Chem. Soc., 52, 5023 (1930)
22. SABIN, F. R., AND DOAN, C. A., J. Exptl. Med., 46, 645 (1927)
23. PINNER, M., Am. Rev. Tuberculosis, 18, 497 (1928); DOAN, C. A., Proc. Soc. Exptl. Biol. Med., 26, 672 (1929)
24. ANDERSON, R. J., J. Biol. Chem., 84, 537 (1927)
25. ANDERSON, R. J., AND ROBERTS, E. G., J. Biol. Chem., 85, 519 (1930)
26. ANDERSON, R. J., AND ROBERTS, E. G., J. Biol. Chem., 89, 599 (1930)
27. PANGBORN, M. C., AND ANDERSON, R. J., J. Biol. Chem., 94, 465 (1931)
28. ANDERSON, R. J., J. Biol. Chem., 83, 169 (1929)

29. CHARGAFF, E., *Z. physiol. Chem.*, **201**, 198 (1931)
30. CHARGAFF, E., *Z. physiol. Chem.*, **201**, 191 (1931)
31. ECKSTEIN, H. C., AND SOULE, M. H., *J. Biol. Chem.*, **91**, 395 (1931)
32. BEHRING, H. VON, *Z. physiol. Chem.*, **192**, 112 (1930)
33. HILDITCH, T. P., AND LAVERN, J. A., *J. Soc. Chem. Ind.*, **48**, 359T, 365T (1929)
34. FLASCHENTRÄGER, B., AND HALLE, F., *Z. physiol. Chem.*, **190**, 120 (1930)
35. TANGE, U., *Sci. Papers Inst. Phys. Chem. Research (Tokyo)*, **14**, 275 (1930) ; *Chem. Abst.*, **25**, 912 (1931)
36. IKUTA, H., *Chem. Umschau Fette, Öle, Wachse Harze*, **38**, 7 (1931)
37. SCHULZ, F. N., AND BECKER, M., *Biochem. Z.*, **235**, 233 (1931)
38. BECKER, M., *Biochem. Z.*, **239**, 235 (1931)
39. ANDERSON, R. J., *J. Biol. Chem.*, **83**, 505 (1929)
40. ANDERSON, R. J., *J. Biol. Chem.*, **85**, 327 (1929)
41. ANDERSON, R. J., *J. Biol. Chem.*, **85**, 339 (1929)
42. ANDERSON, R. J., *J. Biol. Chem.*, **85**, 351 (1929)
43. TAMURA, S., *Z. physiol. Chem.*, **87**, 85 (1913)
44. SABIN, F. R., DOAN, C. A., AND FORKNER, C. E., *J. Exptl. Med.*, **52**, Supplement No. 3, 1–152 (1930)
45. ROBERTS, E. G., AND ANDERSON, R. J., *J. Biol. Chem.*, **90**, 33 (1931)
46. ANDERSON, R. J., *J. Biol. Chem.*, **85**, 327 (1929)
47. ANDERSON, R. J., AND CHARGAFF, E., *Z. physiol. Chem.*, **191**, 166 (1930)
48. COLLIN, G., AND HILDITCH, T. P., *Biochem. J.*, **23**, 1272 (1929) ; CHRISTIAN, B. C., AND HILDITCH, T. P., *Analyst*, **55**, 75 (1930); HILDITCH, T. P., *Allgem. Oel- u. Fett-Ztg.*, **27**, 93, 111 (1930)
49. HILDITCH, T. P., AND PRIESTMAN, J., *J. Soc. Chem. Ind.*, **49**, 197T (1930)
50. COLLIN, G., AND HILDITCH, T. P., *J. Soc. Chem. Ind.*, **49**, 138T (1930)
51. COLLIN, G., AND HILDITCH, T. P., *J. Soc. Chem. Ind.*, **49**, 141T (1930)
52. HILDITCH, T. P., AND JONES, E. E., *J. Soc. Chem. Ind.*, **49**, 363T (1930)
53. HILDITCH, T. P., AND PRIESTMAN, J., *J. Soc. Chem. Ind.*, **49**, 397T (1930)
54. DHINGRA, D. R., AND HILDITCH, T. P., *J. Soc. Chem. Ind.*, **50**, 9T (1931)
55. COLLIN, G., *Biochem. J.*, **25**, 95 (1931)
56. HILDITCH, T. P., AND SLEIGHTHOLME, J. J., *Biochem. J.*, **25**, 507 (1931)
57. BANKS, A., AND HILDITCH, T. P., *Biochem. J.*, **25**, 1168 (1931)
58. BAUGAULT, J., AND SCHUSTER, G., *Compt. rend.*, **192**, 953 (1931)
59. BAUGAULT, J., AND SCHUSTER, G., *Compt. rend.*, **192**, 1240 (1931)
60. LEWKOWITSCH, J., *"Chemical Technology and Analysis of Oils, Fats, and Waxes"* (London, 6th edition, 1921)
61. VAN LOON, J., *Rec. trav. chim.*, **49**, 745 (1930)
62. MATTHES, H., AND BOLTZE, W., *Arch. Pharm.*, **250**, 211 (1912)
63. ANDERSON, R. J., AND CHARGAFF, E., *J. Biol. Chem.*, **84**, 703 (1929)
64. ANDERSON, R. J., AND CHARGAFF, E., *J. Biol. Chem.*, **85**, 77 (1929)
65. ANDERSON, R. J., AND CHARGAFF, E., *Z. physiol. Chem.*, **191**, 157 (1930)
66. ANDERSON, R. J., AND ROBERTS, E. G., *J. Biol. Chem.*, **85**, 529 (1930)
67. BURT, M. L., AND ANDERSON, R. J., *J. Biol. Chem.*, **94**, 451 (1931)
68. BRIGL, P., AND FUCHS, E., *Z. physiol. Chem.*, **119**, 280 (1922)
69. LEVENE, P. A., TAYLOR, F. A., AND HALLER, H. L., *J. Biol. Chem.*, **61**, 157 (1924)

70. JANTZEN, E., AND TIEDCKE, C., *J. prakt. Chem.,* **127,** 277 (1930)
71. TAYLOR, F. A., *J. Biol. Chem.,* **91,** 541 (1931)
72. LEVENE, P. A., AND TAYLOR, F. A., *J. Biol. Chem.,* **59,** 905 (1924)
73. SANDQUIST, H., GORTON, J., AND BENGTSON, E., *Ber.,* **64B,** 2172 (1931)
74. AYYAR, P. R., *Proc. 15th Indian Sci. Cong.,* 1928, 161; *Chem. Abst.,* **25,** 2971 (1931)
75. COLLISON, D., AND SMEDLEY-MACLEAN, I., *Biochem. J.,* **25,** 606 (1931)
76. BAUGHMAN, W. F., AND JAMIESON, G. S., *Oil & Fat. Ind.,* **7,** 331 (1930)
77. GROSSFELD, J., AND SIMMER, A., *Z. Untersuch. Lebensm.,* **59,** 237 (1930)
78. HOLDE, D., AND BLEYBERG, W., *Z. angew. Chem.,* **43,** 897 (1930)
79. FRANCIS, F., PIPER, H., AND MALKIN, T., *Proc. Roy. Soc. (London),* **A, 128,** 214 (1930)
80. SKELTON, J. H., *J. Soc. Chem. Ind.,* **50,** 131T (1931)
81. NOLLER, C. R., AND TALBOT, R. H., *Organic Syntheses,* **10,** 44 (1930)
82. RIDER, T. H., *J. Am. Chem. Soc.,* **53,** 4130 (1931)
83. MATTHES, H., AND SCHUTZ, P., *Arch. Pharm.,* **265,** 541 (1926)
84. MATTHES, H., AND KÜRSCHER, O. H., *Arch. Pharm.,* **269,** 88, 101 (1931)
85. ANDRÉ, E., AND VERNIER, C., *Compt. rend.,* **193,** 178 (1931)
86. VAN LOON, J., AND STEGER, A., *Rec. trav. chim.,* **50,** 936 (1931)
87. LEHMAN, L., *J. Am. Chem. Soc.,* **52,** 803 (1930)
88. LEHMAN, L., *J. Am. Chem. Soc.,* **51,** 2185 (1929)
89. RABATE, J., *Bull. soc. chim. biol.,* **12,** 758 (1930)
90. DELCOURT, Y., *Bull. soc. chim. Belg.,* **40,** 284 (1931)
91. SANDONNINI, C., AND BEZZI, S., *Atti. accad. Lincei,* **12,** 154 (1930)
92. TSUJIMOTO, M., *J. Soc. Chem. Ind., Japan,* **32,** 362 (1930)
93. FRANÇOIS, M. T., *J. pharm. chim.* (8), **12,** 189 (1930)
94. KNIGHT, B. C. J. G., *Biochem. J.,* **24,** 257 (1930)
95. ADKINS, H., AND FOLKERS, K., *J. Am. Chem. Soc.,* **53,** 1095 (1931)
96. SCHRAUTH, W., SCHENCK, O., AND STICKDORN, K., *Ber.,* **64B,** 1314 (1931)
97. SCHMIDT, O., *Ber.,* **64B,** 2051 (1931)
98. UENO, S., AND YAMASAKI, R., *J. Soc. Chem. Ind., Japan,* **34,** Supplement, 35 (1931)
99. UENO, S., AND YAMASAKI, R., *J. Soc. Chem. Ind., Japan,* **33,** Supplement, 451 (1930)
100. UENO, S., AND YAMASAKI, R., *J. Soc. Chem. Ind., Japan,* **34,** Supplement, 151 (1931)
101. CHANNON, H. J., AND CHIBNALL, A. C., *Biochem. J.,* **23,** 168 (1929)
102. OZAKI, J., *J. Agr. Chem. Soc. Japan,* **6,** 773 (1930)
103. SANI, G., *Atti. accad. Lincei,* **12,** 238 (1930)
104. KARRER, P., AND HELFENSTEIN, A., *Helv. Chim. Acta,* **14,** 78 (1931)
105. TSUJIMOTO, M., *Ind. Eng. Chem.,* **8,** 889 (1916)
106. HEILBRON, I. M., OWENS, W. M., AND SIMPSON, I. A., *J. Chem. Soc.,* 1929, 873; HEILBRON, I. M., AND THOMPSON, A., *J. Chem. Soc.,* 1929, 883

YALE UNIVERSITY
NEW HAVEN, CONNECTICUT

THE CHEMISTRY OF THE STEROLS, BILE ACIDS, AND OTHER CYCLIC CONSTITUENTS OF NATURAL FATS AND OILS*

By A. WINDAUS

University of Göttingen

BILE ACIDS

I. CONSTITUTION OF CHOLIC ACID

H. Wieland in his Nobel dissertation on the chemistry of the bile acids (1) suggested for the constitution of cholic acid the following formula:

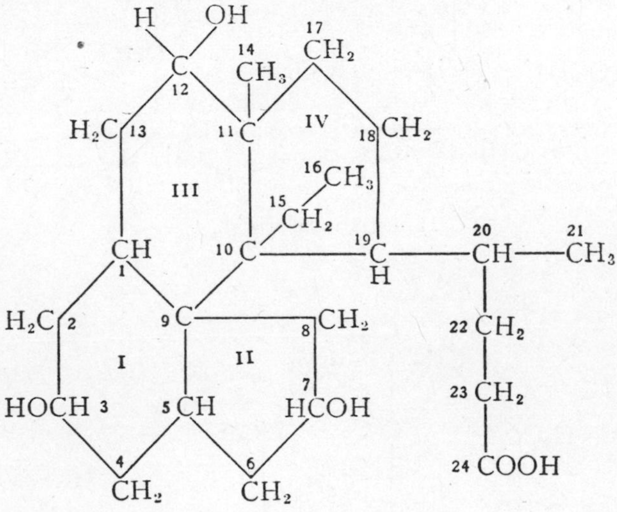

I. Cholic acid

In this structural formula the position of carbon atoms 15 and 16 attached to carbon atom 10 is not assured. Systematic analysis of the bile acids since 1929 shows that these two carbon atoms must be attached elsewhere in the molecule.

The following is a review of some of the previous work in this field. Deoxy-cholic acid (II), oxidized with potassium permanganate,

* Received January 26, 1932.

gives deoxy-bilianic acid (III), which in turn by a thermal reaction yields pyro-deoxy-bilianic acid (IV). These reactions according to the old formulae, are shown as follows:

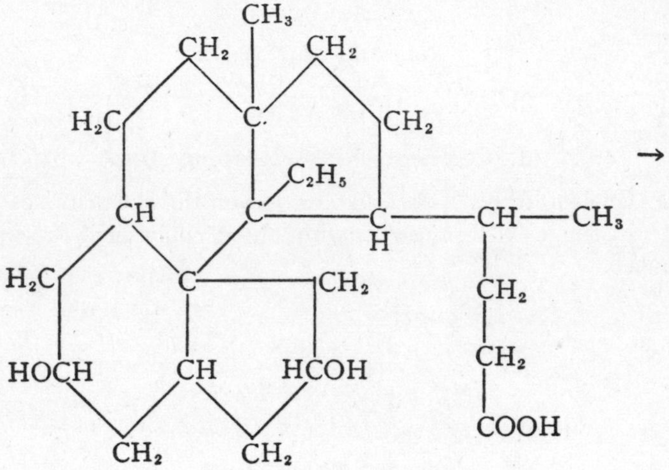

II. Deoxy-cholic acid

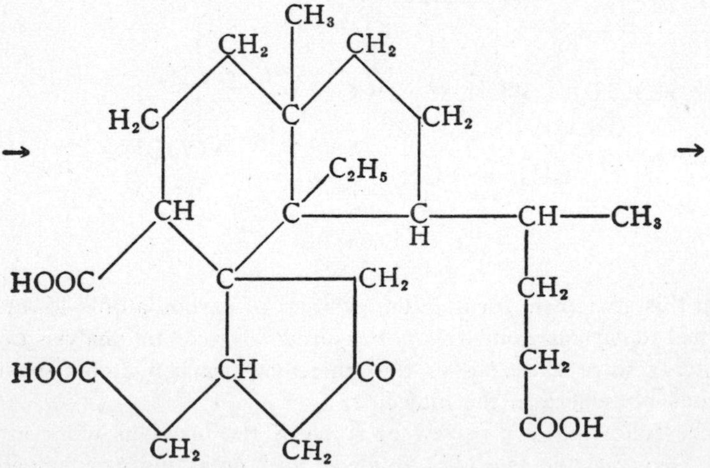

III. Deoxy-bilianic acid

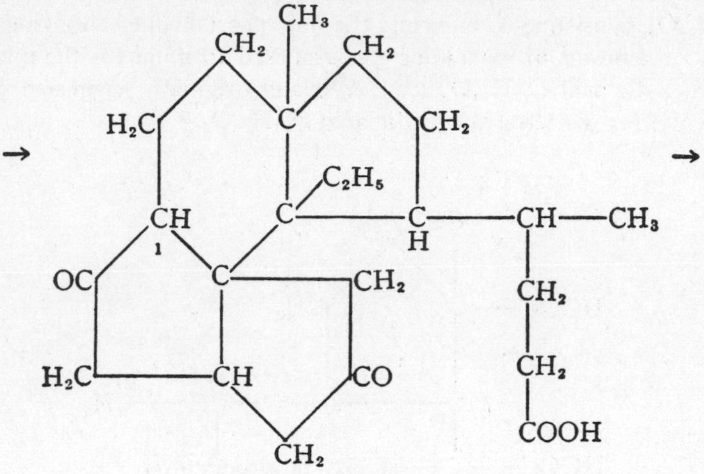

IV. Pyro-deoxy-bilianic acid

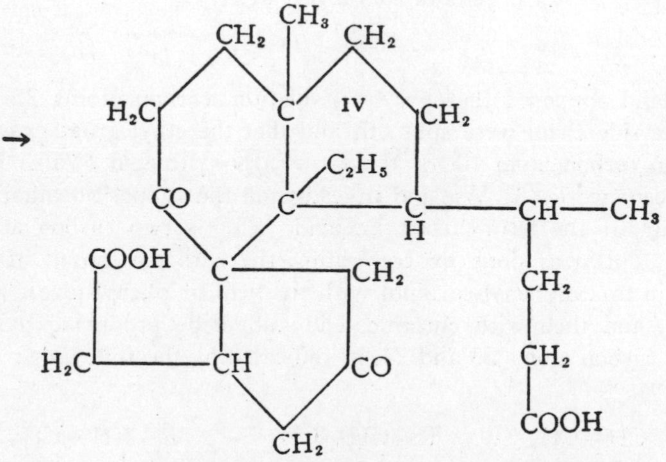

V. Diketo-dicarboxylic acid, $C_{23}H_{34}O_6$

The pyro-deoxy-bilianic acid, by means of potassium permanganate, is split between carbon atom 1 and the carbonyl group, yielding a diketo-dicarboxylic acid $C_{23}H_{34}O_6$ (V). This substance, on oxidation with nitric and sulfuric acid, gives a tetra-carboxylic acid $C_{16}H_{24}O_8$, consisting of one ring, the only possible one being ring IV, (2). As a means of explaining the proposed formula for the diketo-dicarboxylic acid $C_{23}H_{34}O_6$ (V), Wieland originally suggested Formula VI, for the tetra-carboxylic acid $C_{16}H_{24}O_8$.

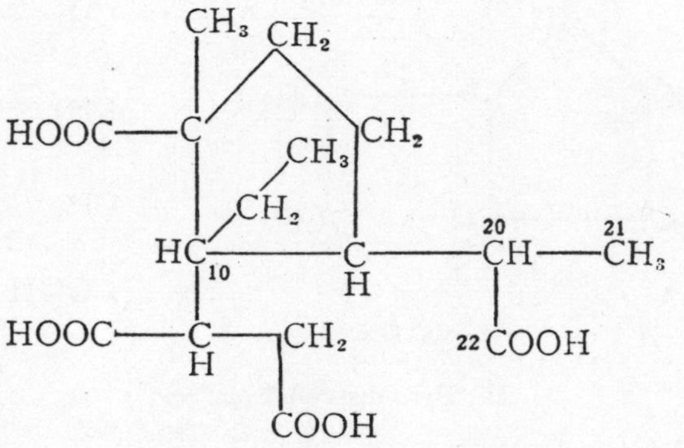

VI. Tetra-carboxylic acid, $C_{16}H_{24}O_8$

Wieland supposed that by the oxidation, carbon atoms 23 and 24 of the side chain were split off, and that the ethyl group was attached to carbon atom 10, of the tetra-carboxylic acid (VI). In a more recent work (3) Wieland investigated the supposition that the side chain of the tetra-carboxylic acid (VI) is two carbon atoms shorter. This was done by converting the carboxyl group of the side chain to a diphenyl-carbinol with the help of phenyl-magnesium bromide, and then with chromic acid anhydride producing a split between carbon atoms 23 and 24, as indicated by the following:

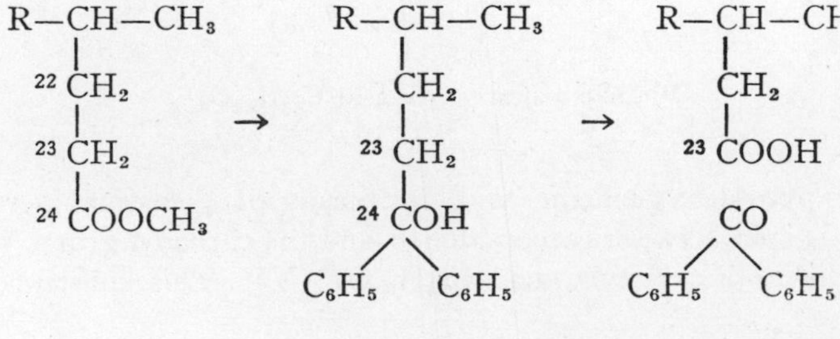

By a repetition of this method Wieland proved that the side chain

$$
\begin{array}{l}
-\text{CH}-\text{CH}_3 \\
\quad | \\
\text{CH}_2-\text{CH}_2-\text{COOH}
\end{array}
$$

remained unchanged in acid VI. Therefore the previous assumption of the oxidative cleavage of two carbon atoms was erroneous. Probably the tetra-carboxylic acid $C_{16}H_{24}O_8$ should be represented, not by Formula VI, but instead by Formula VII.

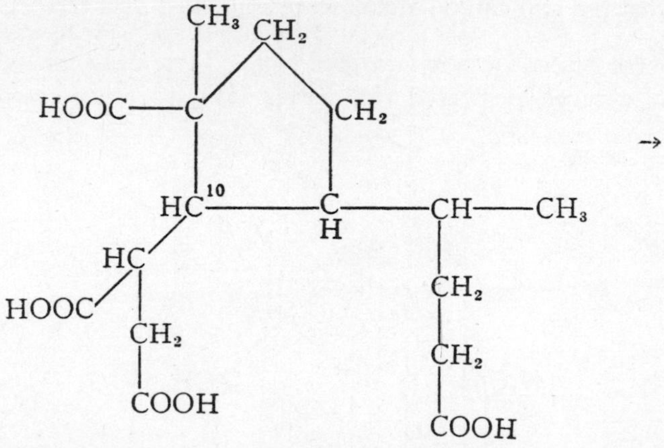

VII. Tetra-carboxylic acid, $C_{16}H_{24}O_8$

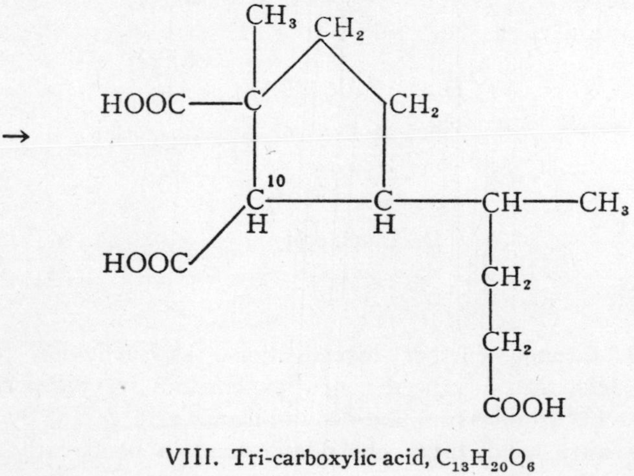

VIII. Tri-carboxylic acid, $C_{13}H_{20}O_6$

The tetra-carboxylic acid $C_{16}H_{24}O_8$ (VII), by means of further thermal and oxidative treatment, yields a tri-carboxylic acid, for which Wieland suggests Formula VIII. Therefore, in contradistinction to what was previously supposed, the acids VII and VIII have no ethyl group on carbon 10. Since it is highly improbable that, by the oxidation, the ethyl group was split off and replaced by hydrogen, it seems reasonable to assume that the position of the ethyl group (carbon atoms 15 and 16 of cholic acid I) is not on ring IV of cholic acid but elsewhere in the molecule. The possibility also occurred to Wieland that the two carbon atoms were combined as a $CH-CH_3$ group and were placed between carbon atoms 11 and 12, thereby giving rise to a seven-membered ring (ring III), as represented by Formula IX.

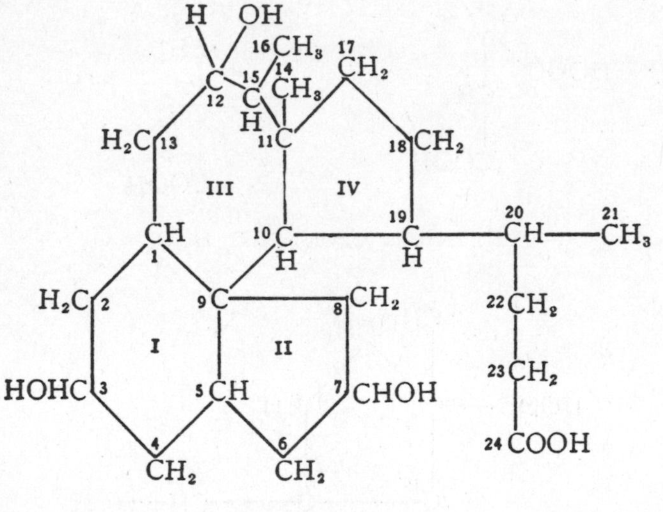

IX. Cholic acid

Wieland, through further investigations, especially on pyrocholoidanic acid, then advanced a new explanation for the position of carbon atoms 15 and 16. The deoxy-bilianic acid (III), by oxidation with nitric acid, gives choloidanic acid, a penta-carboxylic acid, represented by Formula X (assuming Formula I for cholic acid).

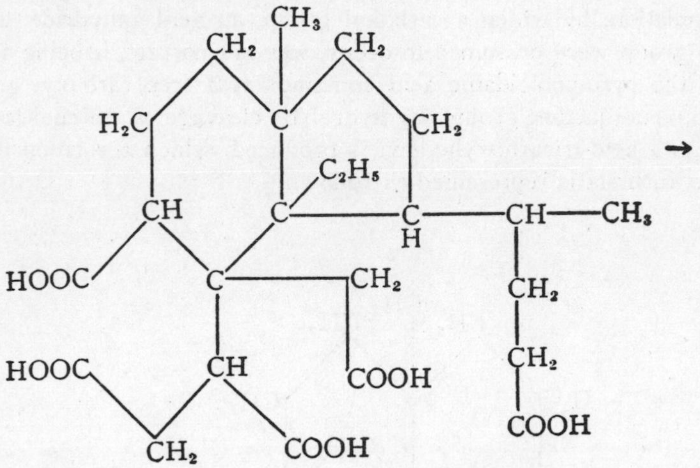

X. Choloidanic acid, $C_{24}H_{36}O_{10}$

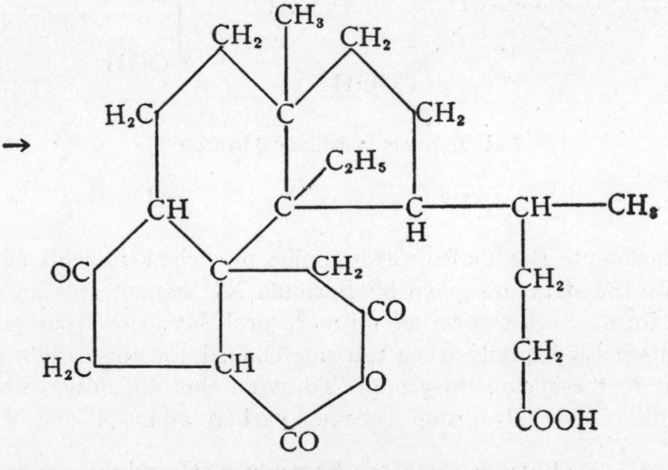

XI. Pyro-choloidanic acid

Choloidanic acid, on heating, loses one molecule of carbon dioxide and two molecules of water, yielding a pyro-choloidanic acid, $C_{23}H_{32}O_6$. This acid was previously formulated as an acid anhydride, as shown by Formula XI. Later research (4) showed that this formulation, by which a carboxyl group, an acid anhydride, and a keto group were presumed to occur, was not correct, it being found that the pyro-choloidanic acid contained two free carboxyl groups and an enol-lactone group. By hydrolytic cleavage of the enol-lactone group, a keto-tricarboxylic acid is produced, which according to the older formula is represented as follows:

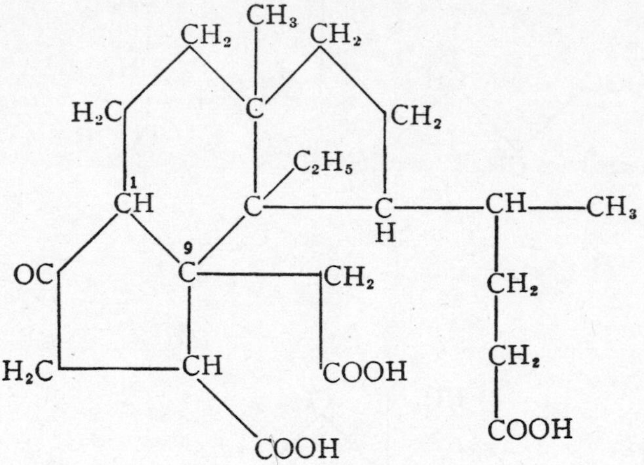

XII. Pyro-choloidanic acid hydrate

According to Bredt's Rule as it applies to cyclic keto-acids (5), an acid with the structure given by Formula XII cannot give an enol-lactone form. Such a form would more probably arise from gamma or delta keto-acids, only when the side chain is on the carbon atom adjacent to the cyclo-keto group. To avoid this difficulty, Wieland places the CH—CH₃ group between carbon atoms 1 and 9, the deoxy-cholic acid having therefore Formula XIII and the choloidanic acid, Formula XIV:

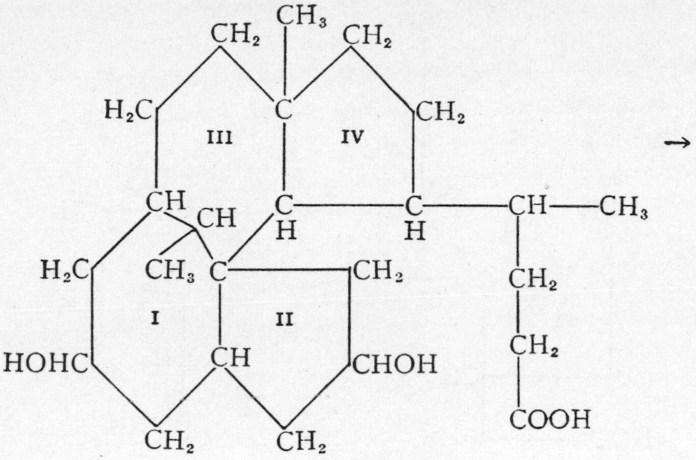

XIII. Deoxy-cholic acid

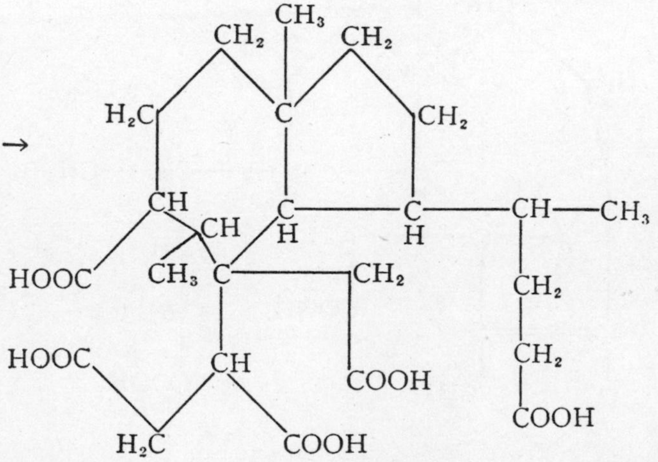

XIV. Choloidanic acid

The hydrate of the pyro-choloidanic acid then has Formula XV. The substituents are now arranged, making possible, according to Bredt's Rule, the formation of an enol-lactone di-carboxylic acid and can be formulated as in XVI.

As yet, it is difficult to arrive at any decision whether the

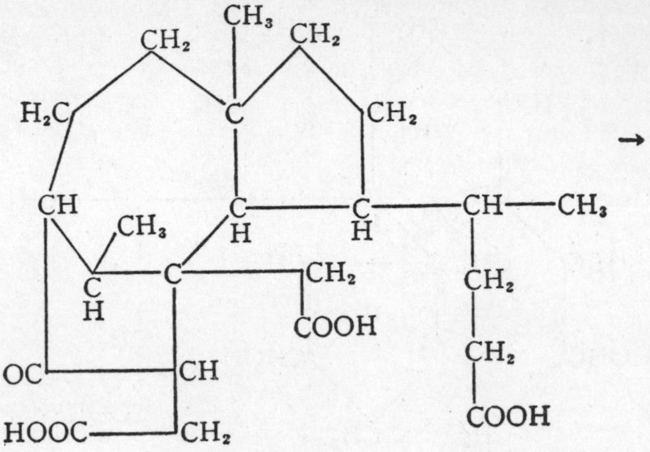

XV. Pyro-choloidanic acid hydrate

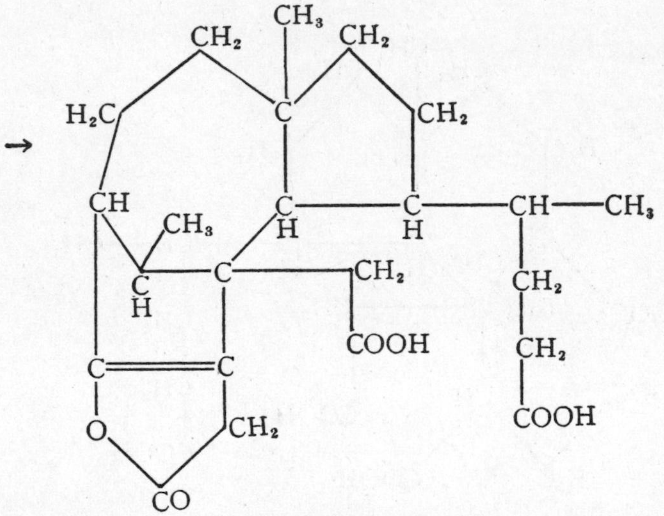

XVI. Pyro-choloidanic acid

CH—CH₃ group is correctly placed in rings I and III of deoxy-cholic acid (XIII) thereby resulting in a seven-membered ring, or whether a new position must be sought elsewhere in the molecule. Wieland believes, nevertheless, that this new formula offers a possible explanation for the peculiar behavior of apocholic acid. Apocholic acid,

$C_{24}H_{38}O_4$, is made, according to F. Bödecker (6), by eliminating from cholic acid just one molecule of water. Besides obtaining apocholic acid, the isomer dioxy-cholenic acid is produced. Whereas the dioxy-cholenic acid is easily hydrogenated to deoxy-cholic acid, the apocholic acid remains unaffected. Wieland (7) suggests as the formulae for dioxy-cholenic acid and apocholic acid, Formulae XVII and XVIII, respectively:

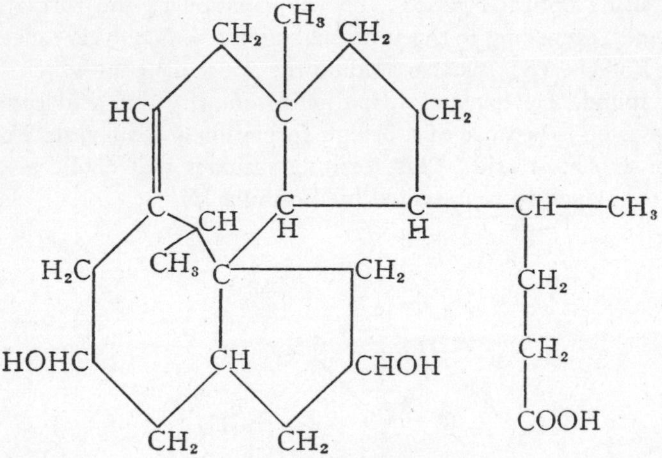

XVII. Dioxy-cholenic acid

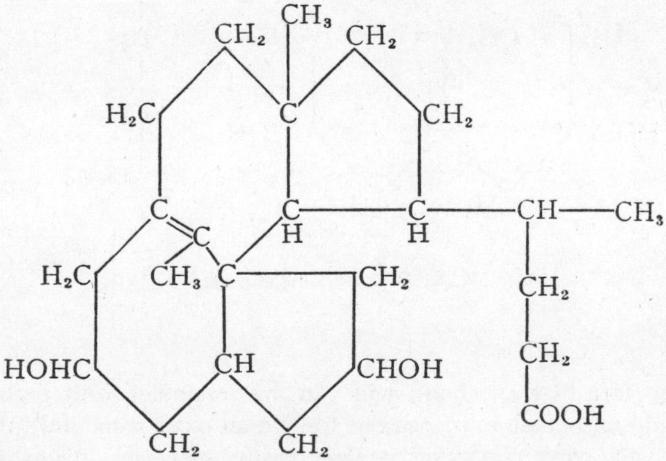

XVIII. Apocholic acid

Wieland is of the opinion that Formula XVIII explains the indifference of apocholic acid toward catalytic reduction. It is also worth while here to mention that, by treating apocholic acid with bromine or perbenzoic acid, it yields, by dehydrogenation, dioxy-choladienic acid, for which Wieland suggests Formula XIX. This last named acid, by catalytic reduction, takes up one mol of hydrogen, giving a new "apocholic acid," which differs from the original apocholic acid mainly in its optical rotation. The explanation of the formation of this isomer, according to the formula suggested, is not very clear.

W. Borsche (8) has also studied the apocholic acid which F. Bödecker found. He explains that the reason why this acid cannot be hydrogenated is because of a bridge formation and suggests Formula XX for apocholic acid. This formula assumes that cholic acid possesses the structure represented by Formula IX.

XIX. Dioxy-choladienic acid

The fact that apocholic acid can, by treatment with perbenzoic acid, add on one atom of oxygen to give an oxy-compound in which the oxygen-containing ring is very easily split (8), seems, in my opinion, to speak against the hypothesis that a bridge formation exists.

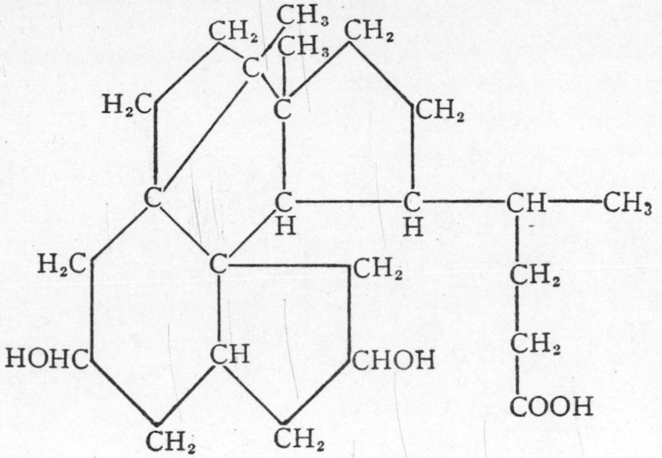

XX. Apocholic acid, according to Borsche

II. Constitution of Pseudo-choloidanic Acid

By oxidizing deoxy-bilianic acid with nitric acid, two substances are obtained, namely, choloidanic acid, $C_{24}H_{36}O_{10}$, and pseudo-choloidanic acid, $C_{24}H_{34}O_{10}$. Wieland believed that the formation of the pseudo-choloidanic acid from deoxy-bilianic acid occurred as follows: ring II remained intact, but in ring III a rupture took place between carbon atoms 11 and 12, as represented in Formula XXI, in which three carbon atoms are not drawn in (9).

This formula must be incorrect, because Wieland, in his most recent formula for bilianic acid, places a methyl group on carbon atom 11; therefore a rupture between carbon atoms 11 and 12, as postulated, is not possible. Detailed work on pseudo-choloidanic acid (10) shows that it contains no keto group but that the question resolves itself about a lactone-tetra-carboxylic acid. This opinion is supported, also, by a new work on deoxy-bilianic acid, in which a di-bromine derivative was obtained. The difference between the oxy-penta-carboxylic acid corresponding to the lactone-tetra-carboxylic acid (pseudo-choloidanic acid), and choloidanic acid is that a hydrogen atom on carbon atom 5 is changed into a tertiary hydroxyl. This hydroxyl, together with the carboxyl group attached to carbon atom 1,

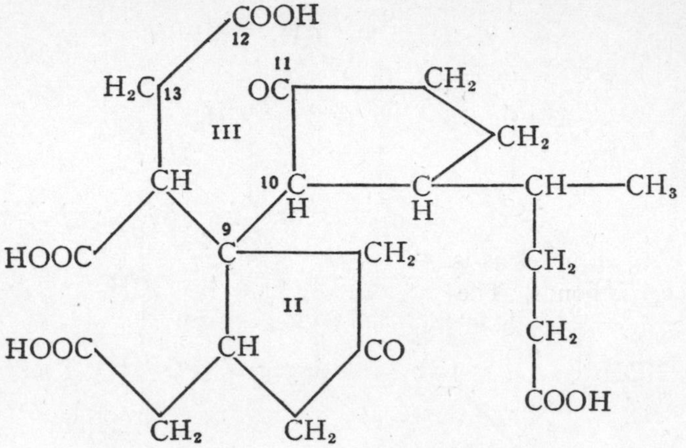

XXI. Original formula for pseudo-choloidanic acid

splits water off, with the resulting formation of lactone-tetra-car-boxylic acid.

Because of these new facts, the formulae for choloidanic acid, pseudo-choloidanic acid hydrate, and pseudo-choloidanic acid itself, are XXII, XXIII, and XXIV, respectively.

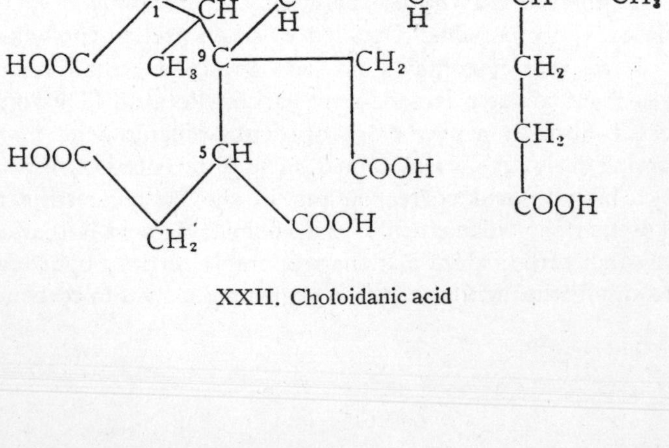

XXII. Choloidanic acid

XXIII. Pseudo-choloidanic acid hydrate

XXIV. Pseudo-choloidanic acid

By a thermal reaction, the pseudo-choloidanic acid loses water and carbon dioxide, yielding then a pyroacid, Formula XXV, which very readily takes up water, forming a lactonic acid, Formula XXVI.

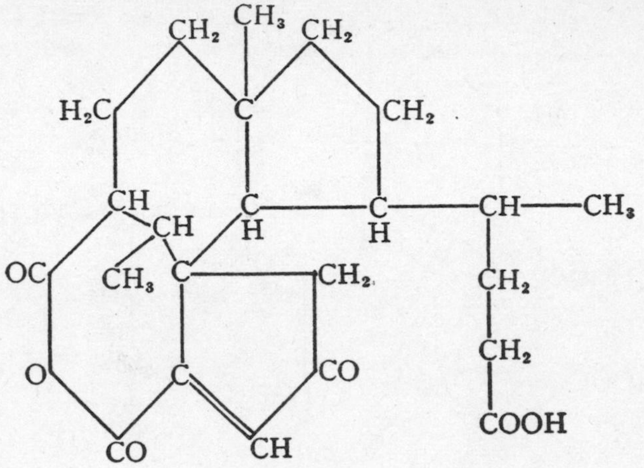

XXV. Pyro-pseudo-choloidanic acid, $C_{23}H_{30}O_6$

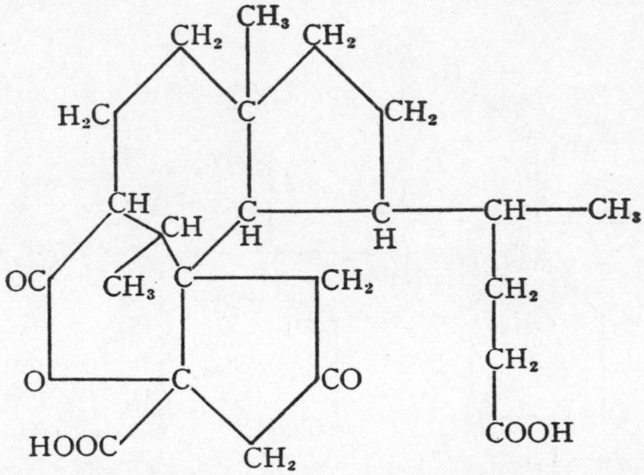

XXVI. Lactonic acid, $C_{23}H_{32}O_7$

III. A New Change from the Cholic Acid to the Lithocholic Acid Series

W. Borsche (11) recently devised a worth-while method of changing cholic acid to lithocholic acid. He does this by treating dehydro-cholic acid (XXVII) with phosphorus pentachloride. He obtained thereby the 3-dichlor 7,12-diketo cholanic acid (XXVIII), from which one molecule of hydrogen chloride was easily split off,

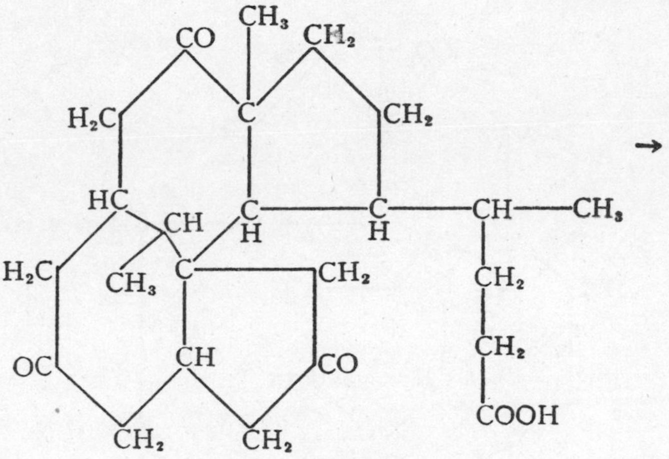

XXVII. Dehydro-cholic acid

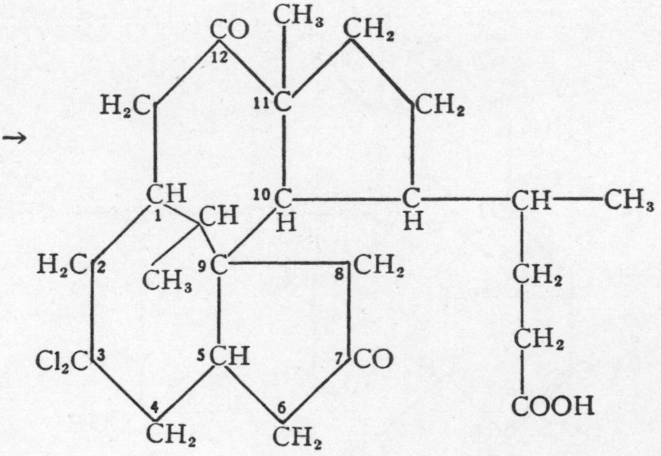

XXVIII. Dichlor-diketo-cholanic acid

giving a 3-chlor 7,12-diketo cholenic acid (XXIX). This acid was reduced, according to the method of Clemmensen, to 3-chlor-cholenic acid (XXX) and then saponified with aqueous sulfuric acid to dehydro-lithocholic acid (XXXI).

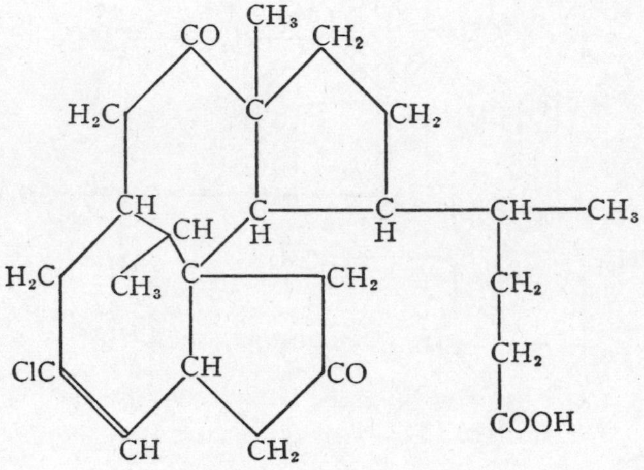

XXIX. 3-chlor 7,12-diketo cholenic acid

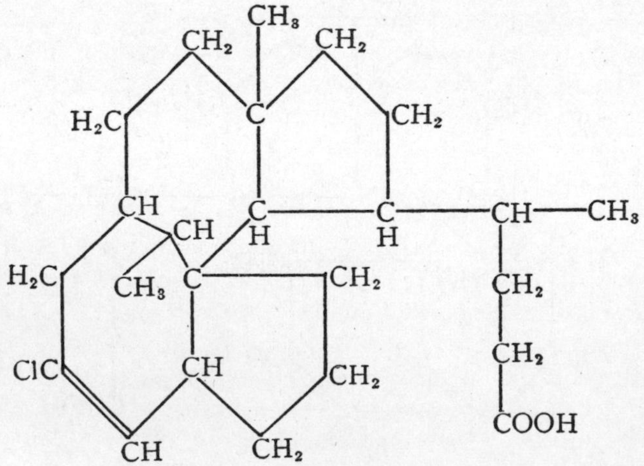

XXX. 3-chlor-cholenic acid

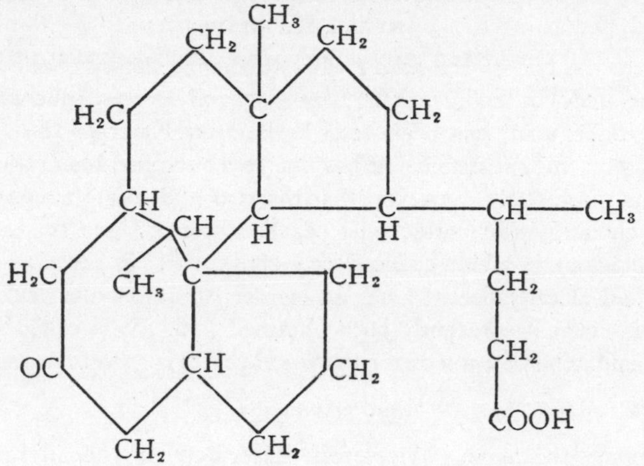

XXXI. Dehydro-lithocholic acid

IV. HALOGEN DERIVATIVES OF THE BILE ACIDS

Many halogen derivatives of the keto-acids of the bile acid series have been prepared by Wieland, Borsche, and associates (12) in the hope that new information could in this way be obtained. From dehydrocholic acid, dehydro-deoxy-cholic acid was prepared, and from deoxy-bilianic acid and other keto-acids, mono, di, and higher brominated derivatives were made, and many transformations produced. These experiments are as yet not so far advanced as to give much new information on the structure of the bile acids.

V. OXIMES IN THE BILE ACID SERIES

M. Schenck (13) recently has made some far-reaching studies of the oximes of the keto-bile acids. He found that, by treatment with nitric acid, oxime groups in ring III are easily oxidized to nitroso and nitro-derivatives, whereas oxime groups in ring II, on treatment with sulfuric acid, are easily converted into lactams. From these lactams, Schenck made the corresponding amino acids, which he also closely examined. This careful work as yet has brought forth no new deductions which might be used to clear up the formula of cholic acid.

VI. The Occurrence of Various Bile Acids in the Animal Kingdom

From the bile of the rabbit (14), ordinary deoxy-cholic acid has been isolated. In the bile of the bear a special deoxy-cholic acid, urso-deoxy-cholic acid, has been found. Koozoo Kaziro (15) has been working on this substance, but has not yet concluded his investigation; it seems most likely, however, that the two hydroxyl groups of urso-deoxy-cholic acid are attached to carbon atoms 3 and 6. In the bile of the chicken, in which cheno-deoxy-cholic acid (3, 12-dioxy-cholanic acid) had already been found, an isomer of lithocholic acid (3-oxy-cholanic acid) has recently been obtained (16); it is called iso-litho-cholic acid. The position of the hydroxyl group is as yet not established.

PHYTOSTEROLS

Among the new phytosterols described in the literature are a-typhasterol, from the pollen of *Typha orientalis,* and hygrosterol extracted from the roots of *Hygrophila spinosa.* The a-typhasterol (17) is levorotatory, melts at 133°–134°, and is quite similar to the sitosterols. Hygrosterol (18), on the other hand, belongs to the dextrorotatory phytosterols. It possesses a high melting-point (194°), and with digotinin gives an addition compound of difficult solubility.

The most important chemical investigation of the phytosterols has been made by Sandquist and his co-workers (19). They prepared acetates of cholesterol, sitosterol, dihydro-sitosterol, and stigmasterol and made extremely careful acetyl determinations. They then came to the conclusion that the formulae for these phytosterols, as generally accepted, are incorrect. Whereas for cholesterol acetate, using their method, they found the equivalent weight to be 427 (calculated 428), for sitosterol acetate, dihydro-sitosterol acetate, and stigmasterol acetate, an equivalent weight of 452 was found, which is about 25 higher than that of cholesterol acetate; therefore the sitosterols, it was calculated, have 29 carbon atoms, the same number as stigmasterol. This value may be contrasted with that of 27 carbon atoms, based upon the sitosterol molecular weight determinations of Burian (20). Sandquist suggests as the formula for sitosterol $C_{29}H_{50}O$, and for stigmasterol $C_{29}H_{48}O$, while Windaus and Hauth (21) gave for this alcohol the formula $C_{30}H_{50}O$.

It should also be mentioned that in wheat sprouts sitosterol-glucoside (phytosterolin) (22) has been found to occur, while sito-sterylpalmitate has been isolated (23) from barley fat.

MYCOSTEROLS

In yeast the sterol found in greatest quantity is ergosterol. Other sterols also are present, which have been investigated, primarily by Wieland. These sterols are very difficult to obtain in pure form, because of their tendency to form addition compounds and mixed crystals.

It seems that in yeast, next to ergosterol in amount, exists zymo-sterol, a substance discovered by Maclean (24) and investigated by both Wieland (25) and Reindel (26) (cf. also 27, 28). Zymosterol, according to Reindel, melts at 107°–110° and has a specific rotatory power of $[\alpha]_D = +49.2°$. The acetate, benzoate, the dihydro, and several other derivatives have been described. It seems probable that zymosterol has only two double bonds and possesses the formula $C_{27}H_{44}O$. Wieland and his co-workers have isolated from the mother liquor of technical preparations of ergosterol still other sterols. The separation was accomplished through fractional crystallization of the benzoyl-esters; it is not definitely established, however, that these sterols are actually different, distinct, chemical individuals. Faeco-sterol and ascosterol are probably simple unsaturated sterols, while zymosterol, episterol, anasterol, and kryptosterol are doubly unsat-urated. Both ergosterol and hyposterol contain three double bonds.

Detailed investigation has recently been made on the sterol content and the antirachitic activity of the mycelium of a number of molds (29). This work did not extend to the isolation in pure form of the sterols present. The sterol content was highest in *Aspergillus oryzae* (0.89 per cent), the sterol content being proportional to the fat content.

Bills (30) and his co-workers found that a neutral or weakly alkaline reaction in the medium and a liberal provision of oxygen were important factors in increasing the sterol content of the molds. [Cf. also Sumi (31) and Takata (32).]

Preparation of ergosterol in pure form.—Callow (33) has found that commercial ergosterol, obtained from yeast, always has some dihydro-ergosterol as a contamination product. He believes that neo-ergosterol described by Wieland really consists of mixed crystals of ergosterol and dihydro-ergosterol. To obtain absolutely pure ergo-sterol, Callow prepares the ergosterol benzoate and then recrystal-lizes it a number of times from ethyl acetate. The regenerated ergosterol melts at 160°–162° and has a specific rotatory power of $[\alpha]^{15°}_{5461} = +165°$. To prove the presence of dihydro-ergosterol in the crude ergosterol, Callow treats the benzoates with an insufficient quantity of bromine in carbon-tetrachloride. The ergosterol benzoate is attacked by the bromine before the dihydro-ergosterol benzoate, and is converted into readily soluble products. With alcohol the dihydro-ergosterol benzoate may be precipitated out and then saponified to give dihydro-ergosterol. It should be mentioned that Heyl and Swoap (34) had previously isolated dihydro-ergosterol from among the sterols found in ergot. Page and Menschick (35) have reported the presence of ergosterol in the human brain (0.05–0.01 per cent).

Color reactions.—Rosenheim (36), who in 1929 announced an important color reaction between ergosterol and chloral hydrate or trichloro-acetic acid, recently, with Callow (37), has found a color reaction between sterols and nitric acid. As reagent a solution of 25 grams of mercuric acetate in 100 cc. of nitric acid (1.42) is employed. Ergosterol produces in dilute solution a blue color, which gradually changes to reddish brown.

Isomerism of ergosterol.—The isomerization of ergosterol with mineral acids has received extensive study (38), yet only one publication (39) came out during the year under review. Unfortunately the facts are contradictory, although they agree that the reaction product has an absorption maximum at 248 mμ. By treating ergosterol acetate with hydrogen chloride, Windaus and his co-workers believe they have obtained three isomers, which they name ergosterol B_1, B_2, and B_3. These isomers differ from one another in melting-point and optical rotation, and with digitonin all give insoluble addition products. On catalytic hydrogenation they give ergostenol and ergostanol, and with sodium and ethyl alcohol are not hydrogenated. Treated with sodium methylate, a certain percentage goes into epi-derivatives, which differ from the initial substances only in the steric arrangement of the substituents on the secondary alcohol group. Of the three isomers only ergosterol B_3 forms an addition compound with maleic acid anhydride.

Below is a summary of the various methods by which isomers of ergosterol have been prepared. The literature on this subject can best be found by referring to a publication by Windaus (39).

First method: Isomerization by the use of strong acids.

Second method: Ergosterol is converted to dihydro-ergosterol by the addition of two atoms of hydrogen. Then with the aid of perbenzoic acid or mercuric acetate two atoms of hydrogen from elsewhere in the molecule are split off. Several isomers are formed, also ergosterol D. Ergosterol may also, by dehydrogenation, give dehydro-ergosterol which with sodium and ethyl alcohol is hydrogenated to ergosterol F. Heilbron (40) believes he has produced a new isomer of ergosterol, called ergosterol E, by treatment of dihydro-ergosterol with hydrogen chloride to give β-dihydro-ergosterol, followed by dehydrogenation of the latter to ergosterol E.

Third method: Ergosterol is dehydrogenated to dehydro-ergosterol. This alcohol, containing four double bonds by treatment with finely divided nickel, is isomerized to yield unsaturated ketones with three double bonds. These ketones are known as ergosta-trienon D and *u*-ergosta-trienol, which with sodium and ethyl alcohol can be hydrogenated to ergosterol D and *u*-ergosta trienol. The *u*-ergosta-trienol, in contrast to the previously mentioned isomers, gives with digitonin no difficultly soluble addition compound, and with hydrogen chloride undergoes molecular rearrangement.

Fourth method: By irradiation of ergosterol with ultra-violet light, in the absence of oxygen, isomerization takes place. Four crystal-line substances have been isolated, one of which is vitamin D (41, 42, 43, 44, 45, 46). At this place, nothing further will be said about vitamin D, which is discussed under its own heading (cf. page 394).

Fifth method: By treatment of certain isomers of ergosterol with sodium ethylate epi-derivatives, in varying yields, are formed. This method is not applicable to ergosterol itself, since at 200°, in the presence of sodium ethylate, it undergoes hydrogenation.

Sixth method: Water is split off from ergosterol and re-added to the hydrocarbon so produced (47).

The isomers prepared by the methods described above may be divided into three main groups. In the first division are those isomers which with digitonin form insoluble addition products. In the second group are those isomers which themselves do not precipitate with digitonin but which, when heated with sodium ethylate, are changed into precipitable isomers of the first type. To the third group belong those isomers which neither precipitate with digitonin nor become precipitable on heating with sodium ethylate.

The numerous experiments on the isomerization of ergosterol have as yet not led to any method whereby vitamin D can be obtained, other than by irradiation of ergosterol with ultra-violet light.

The isomerization of dihydro-ergosterol and tetrahydro-ergosterol (α-ergostenol) has also been attempted, but the results of these experiments are still inconclusive (48, 49).

The behavior of ergosterol and its derivatives toward maleic acid anhydride.—Diels and Alder found that maleic acid anhydride and similar substances combine with conjugated double bonds, therefore giving a very delicate reagent for the detection of such systems. Since several double bonds are present in the ergosterols, their behavior toward maleic acid anhydride has been investigated (50). Dehydro-ergosterol and ergosterol B_3 combine very easily with maleic acid anhydride, producing addition compounds which crystallize very well. Ergosterol will combine with maleic acid anhydride only at temperatures of 100° and over, again forming a crystalline addition compound. On distillation this compound is broken up into its original components, with relatively poor yield. From these experiments it was concluded that ergosterol, ergosterol B_3, and dehydro-ergosterol contain systems of conjugated double bonds. Ergosterols B_1 and B_2 and ergosterol D, which show spectra similar to that of ergosterol B_3, do not combine with maleic acid anhydride; yet it does not follow necessarily that these isomers contain no conjugated double bonds, because on viewing a model it can be seen that when a conjugated double bond is divided between two hydro-aromatic rings the chance that maleic acid anhydride will combine is small.

Suprasterol I and II and dihydro-ergosterol do not combine with maleic acid anhydride. It seems probable, from the consideration of still other properties, that these substances do not have conjugated double bonds.

ZOOSTEROLS

Cholesterol.—The occurrence of cholesterol in the rain-worm *Lumbricus* (51) and in the mussel *Anodonta cygnea* (52) has been reported. In buffalo butter another cholesterol has been isolated, which may be different from the one found in cow butter; but this seems improbable (53).

In the chemistry of cholesterol few papers have recently been published that still remain to be substantiated by other workers. These publications are on metacholesterol, which was prepared twelve years ago by T. Lifschütz (54) from cholesterol and was regarded by him as an isomer of that substance. Windaus and Lüders, on the contrary, have expressed the opinion that metacholesterol is nothing more than cholesterol containing impurity that is very difficult to remove (55). E. Montignie (56) and Remo de Fazi (57) in their investigations have encountered this problem, and believe metacholesterol to be a distinct chemical individual which changes, extremely readily, to cholesterol; this property reminds one of allo-cholesterol.

Of the new derivatives of cholesterol, one worth mentioning is thio-cholesterol (58), which melts at 191°.

For the determination of cholesterol only unimportant modifications of the usual colorimetric and gravimetric determinations have been made.

LITERATURE CITED

1. WIELAND, H., Z. angew. Chem., **42**, 421 (1929)
2. WIELAND, H., AND SCHLICHTING, O., Z. physiol. Chem., **134**, 276 (1924)
3. WIELAND, H., AND VOCKE, F., Z. physiol. Chem., **191**, 69 (1930)
4. WIELAND, H., ERTEL, L., AND SCHÖNBERGER, W., Z. physiol. Chem., **197**, 31 (1931)
5. WINDAUS, A., AND BOHNE, A., Ann., **442**, 7 (1925)
6. BÖDECKER, F., AND VOLK, H., Ber., **54**, 2489 (1921); **53**, 1852 (1920); **55**, 2302 (1922)
7. WIELAND, H., AND DEULOFEU, V., Z. physiol. Chem., **198**, 127 (1931)
8. BORSCHE, W., AND TODD, A. R., Z. physiol. Chem., **197**, 173 (1931)
9. WIELAND, H., SCHLICHTING, O., AND JACOBI, R., Z. physiol. Chem., **161**, 89 (1926)
10. WIELAND, H., ERTEL, L., AND DANE, E., Z. physiol. Chem., **194**, 107 (1931)
11. BORSCHE, W., AND MORRISON, A. L., Z. physiol. Chem., **198**, 165 (1931)
12. WIELAND, H., AND NOGUCHI, T., Z. physiol. Chem., **194**, 248 (1931); WIELAND, H., AND POSTERNAK, T., ibid., **197**, 17 (1931); BORSCHE, W., AND DIACONT, K., ibid., **198**, 115 (1931); NOGUCHI, T., ibid., **200**, 48 (1931)
13. SCHENCK, M., Z. physiol. Chem., **194**, 33; **196**, 276; **200**, 41; **203**, 76 (1931)
14. SEKITOO, T., Z. physiol. Chem., **199**, 225 (1931)
15. KOOZOO KAZIRO, Z. physiol. Chem., **197**, 206 (1931)
16. HOSIZIMA, T., TAKATA, H., URAKI, Z., AND SIBUYA, S., Chem. Zentr., I, 3130 (1931)
17. KIMURA, Y., Chem. Zentr., I, 110 (1931)
18. GHATAK, N. N., AND DUTT, S., Chem. Zentr., II, 725 (1931)
19. SANDQUIST, H., AND GORTON, J., Ber., **63**, 1935 (1930); SANDQUIST, H., AND BENGTSSON, E., ibid., **64**, 2167 (1931)
20. BURIAN, R., Monatsh., **18**, 551 (1897)
21. WINDAUS, A., and HAUTH, A., Ber., **39**, 4378 (1906)
22. NAKAMURA, N., AND ICHIBA, A., Chem. Zentr., I, 3015 (1931)
23. TÄUFEL, K., AND GAMPERL, G., Biochem. Z., **235**, 353 (1931)
24. SMEDLEY-MACLEAN, I., Biochem. J., **22**, 22 (1928)
25. WIELAND, H., AND ASANO, M., Ann., **473**, 300 (1929); WIELAND, H., AND GOUGH, G. A. C., ibid., **482**, 36 (1930); WIELAND, H., AND STANLEY, W. M., ibid., **489**, 31 (1931)
26. REINDEL, F., AND WEICKMANN, A., Ann., **475**, 86 (1929)

27. HEILBRON, I. M., AND SEXTON, W. A., *J. Chem. Soc.,* 2255 (1929)
28. PÉNAU, H., AND TANRET, G., *Compt. rend.,* **188,** 1317 (1929)
29. PRUESS, L. M., PETERSON, W. H., STEENBOCK, H., AND FRED, E. B., *J. Biol. Chem.,* **90,** 369 (1931)
30. PRICKETT, P. S., MASSENGALE, O. N., COX, W. M., JR., AND BILLS, C. E., *Proc. Soc. Exptl. Biol. Med.,* **27,** 701 (1930)
31. SUMI, M., *Chem. Zentr.,* **I,** 1773 (1931)
32. TAKATA, R., *Chem. Zentr.,* **II,** 2748 (1931)
33. CALLOW, R. K., *Biochem. J.,* **25,** 79, 87 (1931)
34. HEYL, F. W., AND SWOAP, O. F., *J. Am. Chem. Soc.,* **52,** 3688 (1930)
35. PAGE, H., AND MENSCHICK, W., *Biochem. Z.,* **231,** 446 (1931)
36. ROSENHEIM, O., *Biochem. J.,* **23,** 47 (1929)
37. ROSENHEIM, O., AND CALLOW, R. K., *Biochem. J.,* **25,** 74 (1931)
38. REINDE, F., AND RAUCH, H., *Ann.,* **452,** 134 (1927); HEILBRON, T. M., AND SPRING, F. S., *J. Chem. Soc.,* 2807 (1929); BILLS, E. C., AND COX, W. M., JR., *J. Biol. Chem.,* **84,** 455 (1929); BILLS, E. C., AND McDONALD, F. G., *ibid.,* **88,** 337 (1930); DE BOE, Z., *Bull. acad. roy. Med. Belg.,* 336 (1930)
39. WINDAUS, A., DITHMAR, K., MURKE, H., AND SUCKFÜLL, F., *Ann.,* **488,** 91 (1931)
40. HEILBRON, I. M., JOHNSTONE, F., AND SPRING, F. S., *J. Chem. Soc.,* 2248 (1929)
41. ANGUS, T. C., ASKEW, F. A., BOURDILLON, R. B., BRUCE, H. M., CALLOW, R. K., FISCHMANN, C., PHILPOT, T. ST. L., AND WEBSTER, T. A., *Proc. Roy. Soc. (London) B,* **108,** 340 (1931)
42. WINDAUS, A., *Proc. Roy. Soc. (London) B,* **108,** 568 (1931)
43. WINDAUS, A., LÜTTRINGHAUS, A., AND DEPPE, M., *Ann.,* **489,** 252 (1931)
44. WINDAUS, A., AND LÜTTRINGHAUS, A., *Z. physiol. Chem.,* **203,** 70 (1931)
45. ASKEW, F. A., BRUCE, H. M., CALLOW, R. K., PHILPOT, T. ST. L., AND WEBSTER, T. A., *Nature,* 758 (1931)
46. WINDAUS, A., GAEDE, J., KÖSER, J., AND STEIN, G., *Ann.,* **483,** 17 (1930)
47. STOLL, W., *Z. physiol. Chem.,* **202,** 232 (1931)
48. SPRING, F. S., *J. Chem. Soc.,* 2664 (1930)
49. HART, M. C., AND HEYL, F. W., *J. Am. Chem. Soc.,* **53,** 1413 (1931)
50. WINDAUS, A., AND LÜTTRINGHAUS, A., *Ber.,* **64,** 850 (1931)
51. WAELE, A. DE, *Chem. Zentr.,* **I,** 804 (1931)
52. WAELE, A. DE, *Chem. Zentr.,* **I,** 3479 (1931)
53. CONNO, E. DE, AND FINELLI, L., *Chem. Zentr.,* **I,** 1192 (1931)
54. LIFSCHÜTZ, T., *Z. physiol. Chem.,* **106,** 271 (1919)
55. WINDAUS, A., AND LÜDERS, H., *Z. physiol. Chem.,* **109,** 183 (1920); **115,** 257 (1921)
56. MONTIGNIE, E., *Bull. soc. chim.,* **47,** 1323 (1930)
57. FAZI, R. DE, *Gazz. chim. ital.,* **61,** 630 (1931)
58. MONTIGNIE, E., *Bull. soc. chim.,* **49,** 73 (1931)

ALLGEMEIN-CHEMISCHES INSTITUT DER UNIVERSITÄT
GÖTTINGEN, GERMANY

THE CHEMISTRY OF THE LIPINS[*]

By I. Smedley-MacLean

Lister Institute, London

The group of lipins[1] contains two main subdivisions:

(*a*) The phospholipins (phosphatides) comprising an unknown number of substances, grouped in three classes, the lecithins, the kephalins, and the sphingomyelins. It is now recognised that the lecithin, kephalin, and sphingomyelin prepared from plant and animal sources are not single substances but mixtures of individuals, conforming to the same type of structure but differing in the nature of the two fatty acid groups in the molecule. Another class of phospholipins of complicated structure have been isolated from the tubercle bacillus, but at present the constitution of these is unknown.

(*b*) The galactolipins (cerebrosides) comprising phrenosin (cerebrone), kerasin, nervone, and hydroxynervone. These are regarded as well-characterised substances of the same type of structure, differing only in the nature of the single fatty acid radical present. It is possible that small amounts of other yet unidentified galactolipins may be present in these as impurities.

THE PHOSPHOLIPINS

1. *The Lecithins*

Structure.—$CH_2OR \cdot CHOR' \cdot CH_2O \cdot PO \cdot OC_2H_4 \cdot N(CH_3)_3$.
$\underset{O}{\underline{\hspace{4cm}}}$

In the formula of lecithin there is place for only two fatty acid radicals, but the list of fatty acids previously obtained from lecithins includes palmitic, stearic, oleic, linolenic, and arachidonic acids. Sueyoshi (1) claims that the palmitic acid present in egg-yolk lecithin melts at 57° and differs from normal palmitic acid. Klenk and Schoenebeck (2) have now isolated from brain lecithin an unsaturated

---

[*] Received January 18, 1932.

[1] The term lipoid is retained in this *Review* to denote the ether-soluble constituents of a tissue, without regard to their nature.

acid containing 22 carbon atoms with 4 ethylenic linkages and have definitely established its composition by its complete reduction to behenic acid and by the preparation of an octobromide. The same acid was found in liver phospholipins and in egg lecithin. Klenk (3) investigated the acids of the mixed ether-soluble phospholipins of the brain and showed that an unsaturated acid containing 20 carbon atoms was present, confirming the previous finding of Levene and Rolf (4) ; this must have come from the lecithin, since it was not detected when the kephalin fraction alone was examined. The percentages of the total acids isolated from this mixture were as follows: stearic, 21.4; palmitic, 8; unsaturated acids containing (*a*) 18 C atoms, 39.6; (*b*) 20 C atoms, 8.7; (*c*) 22 C atoms, 19.8. This analysis showed that a considerable proportion of brain phospholipins must exist in which both the acid radicals are unsaturated.

The occurrence of natural lecithins containing only unsaturated acid radicals has been confirmed by Hateyama (5) who found the proportion of arachidonic acid in egg yolk so large that the existence of a lecithin containing two arachidonyl radicals was indicated.

No natural lecithin containing two saturated fatty acid radicals had previously been described, although Ritter (6) had prepared a saturated lecithin from egg yolk which had been completely hydrogenated. Merz (7) has now prepared lecithin from the lipin residue from brain after removing all material soluble in ether and in acetone. This product resembled the synthetic distearyl lecithin of Grün and Limpächer (8) in that it dissolved only in ether or in light petroleum with great difficulty. Eighty per cent of the total acids present consisted of stearic and palmitic acids, the remaining twenty per cent being oleic acid. The proportions of acids showed that a dipalmityl lecithin must have been present. If a saturated lecithin is present, therefore, in a tissue, it will remain mainly in the alcohol-soluble fraction and not pass into the ether extract.

In addition to adding one more to the list of fatty acids already isolated from lecithin, the work of the past two years has therefore established the existence of natural lecithins containing, respectively, two unsaturated or two saturated fatty acid radicals.

Iwata (9) claims to have isolated from polished rice a monopalmityl lecithin similar to the lysolecithin prepared by Delezenne and Fourneau (10) from the action of cobra venom on egg yolk.

Merz's ether-insoluble lecithin contained both the α and β forms of glycerophosphoric acid, the β form accounting for 58 per cent.

Suzukui and Yokoyama (11) have described the separation of the isomeric lecithins derived from an alcoholic extract of soya bean containing, respectively, α and β glycerophosphoric acids by using the difference in solubility in acetone of their double compounds with cadmium chloride.

Synthesis of lecithin in the body.—Rosenfeld (12) found from feeding experiments on hens that lecithin could be formed in the body if phosphorus and fatty acids were supplied. When glycine was added to a basal diet containing ether-extracted casein, starch, sugar, stearic acid, and salts, the quantity of lecithin formed in the body was much increased. Rosenfeld therefore regards glycine as a forerunner of lecithin.

2. The Kephalins

Structure.—$CH_2OR \cdot CHOR' \cdot CH_2O \cdot PO(OH) \cdot OC_2H_4NH_2$

In investigating the fatty acids of pure brain kephalin, great difficulty has been experienced in completely freeing the kephalin from small amounts of galactolipins and sphingomyelin, both of which yield fatty acids on hydrolysis. Klenk (13) has overcome this by saponifying the crude kephalin under such mild conditions that the accompanying substances were left unattacked. This was effected by adding to the ether solution one-quarter of the amount of potash necessary for complete saponification, dissolved in hot methyl alcohol. The precipitate which separated overnight contained the saturated acids, the unsaturated ones remaining in the ether solution and being subsequently extracted by acetone. Stearic was the only saturated acid present. On complete hydrogenation, the unsaturated acids yielded only stearic and behenic acids. Arachidonic acid had previously been found in brain kephalin by Levene and Rolf (14), but if present the amount can only be exceedingly small. Corresponding to the behenic acid, dicosan tetrenoic acid ($C_{22}H_{36}O_2$) was isolated from the mixture of unsaturated acids. The unsaturated acid, previously isolated from brain by Brown and Ault (15) and provisionally identified as tetracosan pentenoic acid, is probably identical with Klenk's dicosan tetrenoic acid. Since stearic, oleic, and dicosan tetrenoic acids certainly occur in brain kephalin, at least two kephalins must be present.

Separation of lecithin and kephalin and the preparation of pure kephalin.—All the earlier preparations of kephalin from brain in which the whole of the nitrogen was present in the amino form contained less than the 66 to 68 per cent of the carbon demanded by theory. Two explanations of this discrepancy have been put forward: (a) that some oxidation of the highly unsaturated acids always occurs; and (b) that the kephalin had not been completely freed from the degradation products, which are more easily split off than in the case of lecithin. The synthesis of distearyl kephalin by Grün and Limpächer (16) suggested useful improvements in the isolation of the natural product which have proved fruitful in the hands of Rudy and Page (17). The marked differences in the properties of synthetic lecithin and kephalin are probably related to the presence in lecithin of the strong base choline and its substitution in kephalin by the weak base amino ethyl alcohol. Kephalin is much more sensitive to the action of acids and alkalies than is lecithin and is more readily hydrolysed by alcoholic potash in the cold. Lecithin has an anhydride structure and in benzene or ether-alcohol solution is neutral to phenol phthalein, whereas kephalin acts as a monobasic acid with a definite neutralisation value. This neutral character of lecithin probably accounted for the failure by Fabisch (18) to find any buffering action. Rudy and Page found the determination of the neutralisation value in benzene-alcohol solution of great help in examining any mixture of phospholipins; the indication of the relative quantities of kephalin and lecithin thus obtained agreed very well with those obtained by estimating the proportion of the nitrogen present in the amino form. Since kephalin is soluble in the same solvents as lecithin but with more difficulty, the precipitation of kephalin by alcohol from an ethereal solution of mixed phospholipins must be incomplete; Rudy and Page investigated the petrol-alcohol mother liquors of brain phospholipins after removal of the alcohol-insoluble fractions. A concentrated solution in ether (or ethyl acetate) of the residual substance was fractionally precipitated with alcohol and a kephalin obtained containing 66.17 per cent of carbon and agreeing closely in composition with that of a pure linolenyl kephalin. Since the oxidation and decomposition products of kephalin are less soluble in alcohol than kephalin, the more soluble fractions furnish the best starting material for the preparation of kephalin. MacLean (19) had earlier pointed out that when a tissue was obtained in as fresh a condition as possible and quickly dried it might yield the whole of the phospholipin fraction in an alcohol-soluble condition but that after standing for some hours a considerable fraction which was regarded as the kephalin fraction became insoluble. The insolubility of kephalin in alcohol seems to be largely due to its association with degradation or oxidation products.

Other methods found effective for the separation of the lecithin-kephalin mixture were: (a) the addition of a methyl-alcoholic solution of baryta to a benzene-alcohol solution of the mixture. The kephalin, unlike the lecithin, was converted to a barium salt, which separated on the addition of alcohol and methyl alcohol [Rudy and Page (17)]. (b) The fraction precipitated by alcohol from concentrated ether solution was dissolved in ether, poured into hot methyl-alcohol solution, and filtered hot. On cooling, kephalin was deposited and further purified [Wadsworth, Maltaner, and Maltaner (20)].

The properties of lecithin and kephalin.—Remesow (21) has described methods for the preparation of sols of pure lecithin and cholesterol, the coagulation limit of the highest concentration of sol which he was able to reach being pH $= 5.6$ for lecithin and 6.2 for hydrolecithin. The lecithin sol was negatively charged and completely undialysable to water [Remesow (22)].

Recent studies on the colloidal properties of lecithin have been especially concerned with two questions, (a) the mutually antagonistic effect of solutions of lecithin and cholesterol; and (b) the effect of the addition of lecithin on the precipitation of serum proteins. Theorell and Widström (23) have confirmed the antagonistic action of lecithin and cholesterol on the haemolysis of red blood corpuscles. Spränger (24) studied the resistance to water, acids, and bases, respectively, of red blood corpuscles which had been previously treated with isotonic glucose solutions containing highly dispersed suspensions of lecithin or cholesterol in the concentrations in which they are present in blood serum. Whereas the untreated blood corpuscles of the sheep were haemolysed in a 0.62 per cent solution of NaCl, after treatment with lecithin they were hydrolysed by a 0.72 per cent solution; after treatment with cholesterol, a 0.50 per cent solution of NaCl produced haemolysis. The lecithin-treated red blood corpuscles were haemolysed by one-hundredth of the amount of ammonia necessary to haemolyse the controls. Degkwitz (25) found that if an isotonic solution of glucose containing lecithin was injected intravenously into rabbits the concentration of chloride in both urine and serum was diminished and a diminished volume of urine excreted. If cholesterol was substituted for lecithin, the opposite effect was produced. This result was also obtained by Dahmlos and Solé (26).

Dahmlos (27) found that when dogs were injected with solutions of lecithin or cholesterol these substances were picked out by the liver since no lipaemia followed their injection into the portal vein, whereas injected into the general circulation lipaemia followed.

Went and Farago (28) found that addition of aqueous emulsions of lecithin to a serum altered the proportion of protein precipitated in the fraction containing euglobulin and pseudoglobulin I and in that containing pseudoglobulin II and albumin. Merklen, le Breton, and Adnot (29) also found that the serum lipins exercised an inhibiting influence on the precipitation of the globulins. Theorell and Widström (23) added lecithin to serum, removed the excess by centrifuging and found that the additional lecithin was precipitated with the various fractions of protein salted out. When the proteins were fractionally precipitated by electrodialysis or salted out, the quotient $\frac{Cholesterol}{Lipoid\ P.}$ sank successively from fibrinogen through globulin to albumin. According to Macheboeuf (30) this association of lipin with protein plays an important part in regulating the passage of water to and from the tissues.

Wadsworth, Maltaner, and Maltaner (31) compared the actions of lecithin and kephalin in producing coagulation of the blood. An alkaline solution of heart lipins added together with a drop of calcium chloride solution to oxalated blood produced coagulation. A solution of lecithin was active only after it had undergone preliminary hydrolysis by heating for some minutes in alkaline solution. Kephalin solution was active; on adding to it a drop of calcium chloride solution, free acid was liberated and a precipitate of calcium salt formed which was inactive as a coagulant. The active substance was again obtained by shaking the calcium salt with acid. The precipitation of proteins in the presence of lipins was also studied and the conclusion reached that lipin and protein form an insoluble complex in the presence of free acid. The inactivity of lecithin before hydrolysis is explained by its internal anhydride structure and furnishes another instance of the difference of properties of lecithin and kephalin due to the presence of a free acid group in kephalin. The oxidation which kephalin undergoes in air was studied by Page and Bülow (32), who found that as the percentages of carbon, hydrogen, and nitrogen and the iodine value fell, the neutralisation value rose. These changes were catalysed by the presence of iron and prevented by keeping the kephalin under alcohol.

3. *The Sphingomyelins*

$$Structure.—CH_2OH \cdot CH \cdot CHNHR \cdot CH : CH(CH_2)_{12}CH_3$$
$$\underset{O}{\overset{|}{}}$$
$$\overset{|}{O} = P(OH) \cdot OC_2H_4N(CH_3)_3OH$$

In 1929 Klenk (33) established that the base sphingosine contained 18 and not 17 carbon atoms as had been hitherto accepted. Lapworth (34) had shown that the amino- and the two hydroxyl groups were attached to the three terminal carbon atoms; Klenk and Diebold (35) have now shown that the hydroxyl groups occupy the two terminal positions, the amino group being in the α-position to the ethylene linkage. Tri-acetyl sphingosine was ozonised, the product hydrolysed, and the resulting aldehydes oxidised. Myristic acid and dihydroxy aminobutyric acid were obtained, the latter giving on reduction with hydriodic acid α-aminobutyric acid.

Merz (36) showed that starting with a pure sphingomyelin fraction three fatty acids, stearic, lignoceric, and nervonic, could be isolated from it. Three sphingomyelins must therefore be present, each containing a different acid radical.

Phospholipins of Unknown Constitution Isolated from Tubercle Bacilli

Anderson and Roberts (37, 38, 39) have made a further study of the complicated phosphorus compounds isolated from tubercle bacilli. The amounts of these substances isolated from human, bovine, and avian strains formed, respectively, 27.5, 11.5, and 15.0 per cent of the total lipoids extracted from the dry bacilli. The cleavage products are similar in all three cases, though the proportions of water-soluble and ether-soluble constituents differ somewhat. The percentages of nitrogen (0.4) and of phosphorus (2.2) were the same in specimens derived from avian and human strains. The lipin from the bovine strain was hydrolysed with more difficulty and contained 1 per cent of nitrogen. From all three samples oleic, palmitic, and stearic acids were isolated. In the phospholipin from the human and avian strains, the saturated liquid and optically inactive phthioic acid $C_{26}H_{52}O_2$ isomeric with cerotic acid was present; from the bovine strain the liquid tuberculostearic acid $C_{18}H_{36}O_2$ isomeric with stearic acid was isolated. On hydrolysis, mannose [Anderson and Renfrew (40)] and inosite [Anderson (41); Anderson and Roberts (42, 43)] were found. The preparation from the human strain also yielded invert sugar. Phosphoric and glycerophosphoric acids were identified, but nothing is yet known as to the nature of the nitrogenous constituent. Pangborn and Anderson (44) showed that similar substances were present in the timothy bacillus.

Estimation of phospholipins.—Bang first used an oxidative process for estimating the amount of lipin, the carbon and hydrogen being completely oxidised to carbonic acid and water; this process was subsequently improved by Bloor (45). Boyd (46) found that Bloor's method was entirely satisfactory for the estimation of amounts of the order of 2 milligrams of phospholipins but could not be used with safety for less quantities. Osato and Heki (47) have recommended the preliminary freezing, moistening, and grinding of the tissue before extracting it with a mixture of alcohol and ether; Bloor's nephelometric method was then used to determine the phosphorus in the extract. Lintzel and Fomin (48) have described a method for the estimation of lecithin which relies on the separation of the choline by oxidation with permanganate. Any ammonia and methyl- or dimethyl-amines were converted into non-volatile compounds by treatment with formaldehyde and the trimethylamine then estimated. The same principle was used by Lintzel and Monasterio (49) as the basis of a micro-method for the determination of lecithin in blood plasma. This method has the advantage of estimating only the lecithin in any mixture of lecithin and kephalin. A comparison of the various micro methods for determining the iodine values of the lipins was made by Yasuda (50), who found the Rosenmund-Kuhnheim method most satisfactory.

THE GALACTOLIPINS (CEREBROSIDES)

Structure.—$CH_2OH \cdot CH \cdot CHNHR \cdot CH : CH \cdot (CH_2)_{12} \cdot CH_3$

$$\underset{\underset{\underset{|}{CH \cdot (CHOH)_3 \cdot CH \cdot CH_2OH}}{|}}{\overset{|}{O}}$$

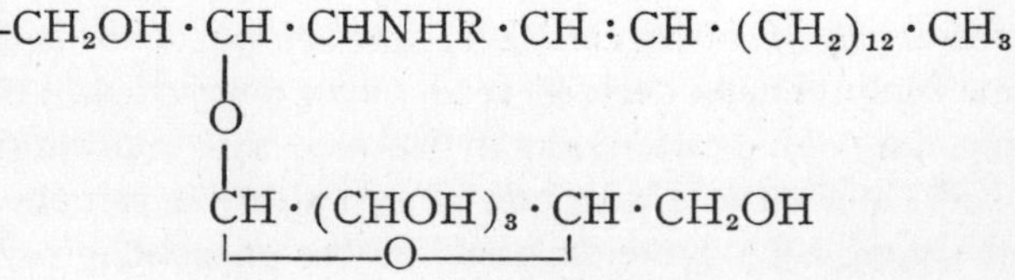

Klenk and Härle (51) have studied the fatty acids present in the ether-insoluble portion of the brain lipides, 90 per cent of which are present in amide combination, hydrolysable only with difficulty. Of the acids in this fraction 90 per cent contain 24 carbon atoms, the remaining 10 per cent containing 18 carbon atoms. Cerebronic, lignoceric, nervonic, and hydroxynervonic acids were all identified. All these acids contain chains of 24 carbon atoms such as would be formed by the condensation of four hexose molecules.

Hydrolysis with baryta of a mixture of cerebrosides consisting essentially of nervone and hydroxynervone yielded a galactosido-sphingosine identical with that obtained from kerasin. Klenk has made clear the close relationship existing between the four acids isolated from the cerebrosides, phrenosin, kerasin, nervone, and hydroxynervone, respectively.

Kerasin yields lignoceric acid,

$$CH_3 \cdot (CH_2)_7 \cdot CH_2 \cdot CH_2 \cdot (CH_2)_{12}CH_2COOH$$

Phrenosin yields α-hydroxylignoceric acid,

$$CH_3 \cdot (CH_2)_7 \cdot CH_2 \cdot CH_2 \cdot (CH_2)_{12} \cdot CHOH \cdot COOH$$

Nervone yields nervonic acid,

$$CH_3 \cdot (CH_2)_7 \cdot CH:CH \cdot (CH_2)_{12}CH_2COOH$$

Hydroxynervone yields α-hydroxynervonic acid,

$$CH_3 \cdot (CH_2)_7 \cdot CH:CH \cdot (CH_2)_{12}CHOH \cdot COOH$$

Confirmation of the constitution of kerasin was obtained by combining the galactosidosphingosine split off from a mixture of brain galactolipins with lignoceric acid, when a synthetic kerasin was obtained. This agreed closely in its properties with the kerasin obtained by Rosenheim (52) from brain. The kerasin derived from spleen has a slightly higher rotation and may contain a different acid radical.

Preparation of the galactolipin fraction from brain.—Rosenheim (53) after removing the cholesterol and phospholipin fractions by extracting with acetone and light petroleum, respectively, dissolved the galactolipins by means of pyridine. Page (54) has modified this method by replacing the solvent pyridine by the cheaper tetralin, which is also pleasanter to use in large quantity. From the tetralin solution the galactolipins are precipitated in the usual manner by means of acetone.

Properties of sphingomyelin, phrenosin, and kerasin.—The similarity in the properties of these three lipins all of which contain a single saturated fatty acid radical bound in amide-like combination with the base sphingosine, was brought out by Turner and Watson (55) in the measurements they have made of the areas occupied by films of these substances, one molecule thick, on water. In these three substances, two saturated paraffin chains containing, respectively, 15 and 23 carbon atoms are united by a chain with polar properties containing one nitrogen and four carbon atoms. At room temperature, the area per molecule is about 60 sq. Å; as the pressure is increased, the molecules pack closer until the area occupied is 42 Å, agreeing with that which should be given by a film in which two parallel paraffin chains are packed closely together.

The Function of the Phospholipins

In 1920, Meigs, Blatherwick, and Cary (56) described experiments on the mammary gland which seemed to offer conclusive evidence that milk fat was derived from phospholipins, for the blood left the gland richer in inorganic phosphate and poorer in phospholipin in comparable amount. Jost (57) has now brought forward further evidence in support of the view previously advocated by Leathes (58) that the phospholipins act as intermediate substances in fat metabolism. In one set of experiments the organs perfused were "normal livers" from dogs well fed on a normal diet and subsequently starved for 24 hours; these livers contained from 0.5 to 1.5 per cent of glycogen and 3 per cent of fat. In the other set, "fatty livers" from dogs, previously treated with phlorhizin for four days, were used; these contained about 10 per cent of fat and were glycogen-free. When blood was perfused through them, its content of inorganic phosphate increased, the increase being 2 to 3 times as great in the "fatty" as in the "normal" livers; the lipin phosphate in the blood showed no significant change. The deduction was made that the breaking down of phospholipin was proceeding more actively in the fatty livers, phosphate being thrown into the blood stream. When a finely divided emulsion of heart kephalin was added to the perfusion fluid, it disappeared at first rapidly and then more slowly, the lipin phosphate of the blood corpuscles remaining practically unchanged. The fatty livers contained slightly less lipin phosphate after the perfusion than at the beginning of the experiment. The fatty livers always contained more inorganic phosphate than the normal ones and were richer in glycerophosphoric acid, a substance which is very easily broken down by the phosphatase known to be present in liver. In a study of the hydrolytic splitting of lecithin by tissue enzymes, King, King, and Page (59) found that liver extract and bone phosphatase were without action on lecithin, whereas extracts of the intestinal wall and of the kidney had a very marked action [King (60)]. Jost found that the breaking down of the lipin molecule appeared to be associated with the oxidation of its fatty acid, for when an emulsion of phospholipin was added to the circulating liquid a marked increase in the oxygen intake of the liver followed and the respiratory quotient fell from 0.95 to 0.62. The acetone and acetoacetic acid, however, increased only from 30 to 40–60 mg. per litre, an increase very much less than that corresponding to the increase in fat combustion. When glycogen-free livers from dogs starved for four days previously were perfused with blood the amount of acetone formed was 50 to 100 per cent more than in the glycogen-containing livers, while perfusion of the phlorhizinised "fatty livers" produced still larger amounts. The gas metabolism appeared, however, to furnish a better index of the increased fat oxidation of the isolated liver than the slight rise of acetone in the blood. Smedley-MacLean and Pearce (61) have pointed out that all available evidence points to the production of acetone from the four terminal atoms only of the carbon chain.

When the "fatty" livers were perfused with Ringer's solution, sugar appeared in the perfusion liquid, but the amount of sugar formed and of oxygen absorbed fell rapidly after the first half-hour, the respiratory quotient rising. If at the end of this time phospholipin was added to the perfusing fluid, the output of sugar and intake of oxygen rose sharply, while the respiratory quotient fell; the ketone bodies remained unchanged. Jost regarded this as definite evidence that sugar was formed from the fatty acids of the lipin molecule, the amount of glycerol being quite insufficient to account for the sugar formed. Heart kephalin was much more effective than lecithin, the addition of highly unsaturated acid being apparently necessary.

Sinclair (62) has furnished confirmatory evidence that the lipins are concerned in the absorption and metabolism of fat, for he found that during the absorption there was a pronounced change in the composition but none in the amount of the phospholipins of the liver and of the intestinal mucosa; on the other hand, the composition of the lipin fatty acids of both smooth and striated muscle showed no change. If the lipin feeding were continued for some days, the lipin fatty acids of all the tissues examined, liver, heart, kidney, smooth and striated muscle, intestinal mucosa, and brain, increased in unsaturation in animals fed on a more unsaturated diet. Beef kidney and beef muscle, respectively, were used as diets containing acids of different degrees of unsaturation. This result is in opposition to the finding of Terroine, Hatterer, and Roehrig (63, 64) who concluded that the composition and amount of the fatty acids was a fixed characteristic for each tissue, unaffected by diet. In Sinclair's experiments the amount of lipin fatty acid increased with the more unsaturated diet in the liver alone. Sinclair concluded that the fatty acids absorbed were transformed into phospholipins in the intestinal mucosa as an essential step in the resynthesis of neutral fat, and that the lipin either was an intermediary in the metabolism of fat or else that the phospholipins of the tissues underwent continual wear and tear and were replaced at the expense of the food fat. Boyd (46) working with a diet low in fat and rich in carbohydrate and using the micro-oxidative method of Bloor found abnormally low phospholipin values, e.g., 49 to 76 mg. per cent compared with values of 240 to 478 mg. for dogs fed on a normal diet. No similar variation was found in the lipin phosphate of the red blood corpuscles.

Sinclair (65) studied in young rats the ratio of the phospholipins to the tissue solids and found that they decreased rapidly after birth, the period of most rapid decline coinciding with that of most active growth. Bloor, Okey, and Corner (66) found that the percentage of lipin in the corpus luteum of the sow varied with the activity of the gland and before oestrus and during pregnancy was doubled or trebled. Bloor and his colleagues (67, 68) also showed that the amount of phospholipin per kilogram of liver tissue was approximately double that in other organs.

Changes in the Lipin Content of the Organs in Disease

Certain pathological conditions are characterised by marked increases or decreases in the amounts of lipins present in the blood or in various organs. Epstein and Lorenz (69) showed that in the case of Gauber's disease, the total lipin content of the spleen remained normal but a large proportion of kerasin was present. In the spleno-hepatomegaly of Neumann-Pick's disease there was a very marked increase in the phospholipin content of the spleen. In both these cases the cholesterol content of the spleen remained normal. Schmitz and Koch (70) found that in the lipaemia which follows venesection in dogs, the phospholipins were largely increased. In rabies, from the moment of infection of the animal until its death, there was a very characteristic steady increase in the lipin phosphorus of the blood [Zuwerkalow and Goldenberg (71)]. In lipoidic nephrosis, Macheboeuf, Wahl, and Sandon (72) found that the phospholipins of the serum might rise to six times their normal amount and a very much greater proportion of these was precipitated with the albumin fraction of the serum proteins. Eckstein and Wile (73) found the phospholipin content of a xanthematous tumour to be 200 times that present in the normal subcutaneous fat, and to be greatly increased in the tissue surrounding the tumour. A study of the livers of rats with tumours led Roffo and Correa (74) to the conclusion that as the tumour developed the phospholipin content of the liver fell much below the normal. In pneumonia, tuberculosis, and fatty degeneration, Theis (75) found that the proportion of liver phospholipin decreased. Milbradt (76), working on the avitaminosis of pigeons fed on polished rice, found that the phospholipin content fell in the brain and in all parenchymatous organs, as did the ratio $\frac{\text{phospholipin}}{\text{cholesterol}}$. The inorganic and nucleotidic phosphorus was increased. Milbradt ascribed this to a lessened synthesis of phospholipin, though it seems also possible that it may be due to an increased breaking down of the tissue lipins.

The lipins in tuberculosis.—The phospholipin fractions isolated by Anderson (*37 et seq.*) from various strains of tubercle bacilli when injected intraperitoneally into rabbits produced tubercle-like bodies with extensive infiltration of lymphocytes and with some diffuse epithelioid and giant Langerhans cells. Sabin and Doan (77) showed that there was a quantitative difference in the specificity of the phospholipins from the human, bovine, and avian strains which might be used to assist in identifying the type of organism causing any particular case of tuberculosis. Doan (78) showed that the phospholipin from the bovine type acted as an antigen in rabbits and was precipitated in high dilutions against the sera of tuberculous cattle. This particular property of the phospholipin seems to be derived from the liquid saturated fatty acid which it contains and for which possibly the lipin acts as a carrier.

LITERATURE CITED

1. SUEYOSHI, Y., *J. Biochem. (Japan)*, **13**, 145 (1931)
2. KLENK, E., AND SCHOENEBECK, O. VON, *Z. physiol. Chem.*, **194**, 191 (1931)
3. KLENK, E., *Z. physiol. Chem.*, **200**, 51 (1931)
4. LEVENE, P. A., AND ROLF, I., *J. Biol. Chem.*, **54**, 99 (1922)
5. HATEYAMA, T., *Z. physiol. Chem.*, **187**, 120 (1930)
6. RITTER, F., *Ber.*, **47**, 531 (1914)
7. MERZ, W., *Z. physiol. Chem.*, **196**, 10 (1931)
8. GRÜN, A., AND LIMPÄCHER, R., *Ber.*, **59**, 1350 (1926)
9. IWATA, M., *Biochem. Z.*, **224**, 430 (1930)
10. DELEZENNE, C., AND FOURNEAU, E., *Bull. soc. chim.*, **15**, 421 (1914)
11. SUZUKUI, B., AND YOKOYAMA, Y., *Proc. Imp. Acad. (Tokyo)*, **6**, 341 (1930)
12. ROSENFELD, G., *Biochem. Z.*, **218**, 48 (1930)
13. KLENK, E., *Z. physiol. Chem.*, **200**, 51 (1931)
14. LEVENE, P. A., AND ROLF, I., *J. Biol. Chem.*, **54**, 51 (1922)
15. BROWN, J. B., AND AULT, W. C., *J. Biol. Chem.*, **89**, 167 (1930)
16. GRÜN, A., AND LIMPÄCHER, R., *Ber.*, **60**, 151 (1927)
17. RUDY, H., AND PAGE, I. H., *Z. physiol. Chem.*, **193**, 251 (1930)
18. FABISCH, W., *Biochem. Z.*, **242**, 121 (1931)
19. MACLEAN, H., *"Lecithin and Allied Substances,"* Longmans, Green and Co., London, p. 81 (1917)
20. WADSWORTH, A., MALTANER, F., AND MALTANER, E., *Am. J. Physiol.*, **97**, 74 (1931)
21. REMESOW, I., *Biochem. Z.*, **218**, 86 (1930)
22. REMESOW, I., *Biochem. Z.*, **218**, 134 (1930)
23. THEORELL, H., AND WIDSTRÖM, G., *Z. ges. exptl. Med.*, **75**, 699 (1931)
24. SPRÄNGER, W., *Biochem. Z.*, **218**, 341; **221**, 315 (1930)
25. DEGKWITZ, R., *Klin. Wochschr.*, **9**, 2336 (1930)
26. DAHMLOS, J., AND SOLÉ, A., *Biochem. Z.*, **227**, 401 (1930)
27. DAHMLOS, J., *Biochem. Z.*, **242**, 88 (1931)
28. WENT, S., AND FARAGO, F., *Biochem. Z.*, **230**, 239 (1931)
29. MERKLEN, P., BRETON, E. LE, AND ADNOT, M. A., *Compt. rend.*, **192**, 1053 (1931)
30. MACHEBOEUF, A., *Compt. rend.*, **192**, 1413 (1931)
31. WADSWORTH, A., MALTANER, F., AND MALTANER, E., *Am. J. Physiol.*, **91**, 423 (1930)
32. PAGE, I. H., AND BÜLOW, M., *Z. physiol. Chem.*, **194**, 166 (1931)

33. KLENK, E., *Z. physiol. Chem.*, **185**, 169 (1929)
34. LAPWORTH, A., *J. Chem. Soc.*, **103**, 1029 (1913)
35. KLENK, E., AND DIEBOLD, W., *Z. physiol. Chem.*, **198**, 25 (1931)
36. MERZ, W., *Z. physiol. Chem.*, **193**, 59 (1930)
37. ANDERSON, R. J., AND ROBERTS, E. G., *J. Biol. Chem.*, **85**, 509 (1930)
38. ANDERSON, R. J., AND ROBERTS, E. G., *J. Biol. Chem.*, **85**, 519 (1930)
39. ANDERSON, R. J., AND ROBERTS, E. G., *J. Biol. Chem.*, **85**, 529 (1930)
40. ANDERSON, R. J., AND RENFREW, A. G., *J. Am. Chem. Soc.*, **52**, 1252 (1930)
41. ANDERSON, R. J., *J. Am. Chem. Soc.*, **52**, 1607 (1930)
42. ANDERSON, R. J., AND ROBERTS, E. G., *J. Biol. Chem.*, **89**, 599 (1930)
43. ANDERSON, R. J., AND ROBERTS, E. G., *J. Biol. Chem.*, **89**, 611 (1930)
44. PANGBORN, M. C., AND ANDERSON, R. J., *J. Biol. Chem.*, **94**, 465 (1931)
45. BLOOR, W. R., *J. Biol. Chem.*, **82**, 273 (1929)
46. BOYD, E. M., *J. Biol. Chem.*, **91**, 1 (1931)
47. OSATO, S., AND HEKI, M., *J. Biol. Chem.*, **87**, 541 (1930)
48. LINTZEL, W., AND FOMIN, S., *Biochem. Z.*, **238**, 452 (1931)
49. LINTZEL, W., AND MONASTERIO, G., *Biochem. Z.*, **241** (1931)
50. YASUDA, M., *J. Biol. Chem.*, **94**, 401 (1931)
51. KLENK, E., AND HÄRLE, R., *Z. physiol. Chem.*, **189**, 243 (1930)
52. ROSENHEIM, O., *Biochem. J.*, **10**, 142 (1916)
53. ROSENHEIM, O., *Biochem. J.*, **8**, 110 (1914)
54. PAGE, I. H., *Biochem. Z.*, **219**, 161 (1930)
55. TURNER, K., AND WATSON, M. M., *Biochem. J.*, **24**, 113 (1930)
56. MEIGS, E. B., BLATHERWICK, N. R., AND CARY, C. A., *J. Biol. Chem.*, **37**, 1 (1919)
57. JOST, H., *Z. physiol. Chem.*, **197**, 90 (1931)
58. LEATHES, J. B., *"The Fats,"* Longmans & Co., London (1910)
59. KING, H., KING, E. J., AND PAGE, I. H., *Z. physiol. Chem.*, **191**, 243 (1930)
60. KING, E. J., *Biochem. J.*, **25**, 799 (1931)
61. SMEDLEY-MACLEAN, I., AND PEARCE, M. S. B., *Biochem. J.*, **25**, 1252 (1931)
62. SINCLAIR, R. G., *J. Biol. Chem.*, **86**, 579 (1930)
63. TERROINE, E. F., HATTERER, CH., AND ROEHRIG, P., *Bull. soc. chim. biol.*, **12**, 657 (1930)
64. TERROINE, E. F., AND HATTERER, CH., *Bull. soc. chim. biol.*, **12**, 674 (1930)
65. SINCLAIR, R. G., *J. Biol. Chem.*, **87**, xxiii (1930)
66. BLOOR, W. R., OKEY, R., AND CORNER, G. W., *J. Biol. Chem.*, **86**, 291 (1930)
67. BLOOR, W. R., OKEY, R., AND CORNER, G. W., *J. Biol. Chem.*, **86**, 307 (1930)
68. BLOOR, W. R., AND SNIDER, R. H., *J. Biol. Chem.*, **87**, 399 (1930)
69. EPSTEIN, E., AND LORENZ, K., *Z. physiol. Chem.*, **192**, 145 (1930)
70. SCHMITZ, E., AND KOCH, F., *Biochem. Z.*, **223**, 257 (1930)
71. ZUWERKALOW, D., AND GOLDENBERG, I., *Biochem. Z.*, **226**, 278 (1930)

72. MACHEBOEUF, M. A., WAHL, R., AND SANDON, G., *Bull. soc. chim.*, 12, 504 (1930)
73. ECKSTEIN, H. C., AND WILE, U. J., *J. Biol. Chem.*, 87, 311 (1930)
74. ROFFO, A. H., AND CORREA, L. M., *Bull. soc. chim. biol.*, 12, 1247 (1930)
75. THEIS, E. R., *J. Biol. Chem.*, 82, 327 (1929)
76. MILBRADT, W., *Biochem. Z.*, 223, 278 (1930)
77. SABIN, E. R., AND DOAN, C. A., *J. Biol. Chem.*, 85, 521 (1930)
78. DOAN, C. A., *Proc. Soc. Exptl. Biol. Med.*, 26, 672 (1929)

LISTER INSTITUTE OF PREVENTIVE MEDICINE
CHELSEA BRIDGE ROAD
LONDON, S.W. 1, ENGLAND

THE CHEMISTRY OF THE AMINO ACIDS AND THE PROTEINS*

By Carl L. A. Schmidt

University of California

To cover adequately the literature of a field which is comprised by the title above in the space which is allotted is obviously impossible. The reviewer has therefore attempted to present briefly certain phases of the subject. It is hoped that glaring omissions in this year's review will be cared for in the review to be presented next year.

In a recent review dealing with the history of the discovery of the amino acids, Vickery and Schmidt (1) have adopted the following criteria as the basis for including an amino acid as a definite protein component which is obtained on hydrolysis of proteins: it must also have been isolated by some worker other than its discoverer, and, further, the constitution must have been established by synthesis and by demonstration of identity between the synthetic product and the racemized natural product or between the synthetic optical isomer obtained by resolution and the naturally occurring amino acid. On this basis, twenty-one amino acids are recognized. They are: alanine, aspartic acid, arginine, cystine, glutamic acid, glycine, histidine, β-hydroxyglutamic acid, hydroxyproline, iodogorgoic acid, isoleucine, leucine, lysine, methionine, phenylalanine, proline, serine, thyroxine, tryptophane, tyrosine, and valine.

This list does not include an almost equal number of amino acids which have at various times been reported as occurring either in protein hydrolysates or in plant extracts but which do not conform to all of the criteria which have been stated above. The following products are included in the latter group: aminobutyric acid, hydroxyaminobutyric acid, hydroxyvaline, hydroxylysine, norvaline, norleucine, citrullin, dibromotyrosine, dihydroxyphenylalanine, thiolhistidine, dihydroxypyrrole alanine, Dakin's tribasic amino acid from liver, protoctine, *tetratrisäure,* caseinic and *caseansäure,* a basic amino acid from jack bean, diaminoglutaric acid, diaminoadipic acid, dihydroxydiamino suberic acid, and possibly an amino acid occurring in casein,

* Received January 27, 1932.

some indications of which Rose (2) and his co-workers have obtained from feeding experiments.

Of this latter group, dibromotyrosine has the best claims to be considered as an accepted amino acid. Its identification as a constituent of the horny skeleton of the coral *Primnoa lepadifera* by Mörner (3) is so complete that very little room for doubt is left as to its identity. However, it would be desirable to have his results confirmed. Foreman (4) and Abderhalden and Weil (5) have brought forth evidence of the presence of aminobutyric acid in casein. Owing to lack of agreement between the natural and the synthetic product, as well as to the lack of experimental evidence, its existence must still be regarded as doubtful.

Considerable evidence for the occurrence of hydroxyamino butyric acid in proteins has been obtained by Schryver and Buston (6), Gortner and Hoffman (7), Rimington (8), and Czarnetzky and Schmidt (9). Confirmatory evidence of Schryver and Buston's (6) discovery of hydroxyvaline as a constituent of certain proteins has been afforded by the experiments of Brazier (10) and of Czarnetzky and Schmidt (11). The constitution of both of these amino acids needs to be established by synthetic methods.

Schryver and his co-workers (12) have reported the isolation of hydroxylysine and of protoctine. The work has not been confirmed, nor has the constitution of these products been established. Abderhalden and Bahn (13) and Abderhalden and Reich (14) have brought forth rather convincing evidence for the existence of norvaline (α-amino-n-valeric acid) among the hydrolytic cleavage products of globin and of casein. It is desirable that this work should be confirmed and extended by the use of other criteria. Further evidence of the distribution and identity of norleucine (α-amino-n-caproic acid), a product which was first described by Thudicum (15) and later obtained by Abderhalden and Weil (16), is desirable. A better method for separating this amino acid from valine and from other isomeric leucines is needed.

Citrullin was obtained from watermelon juice by Wada (17). He established its constitution as δ-carbamino-α-amino-n-valeric acid by synthesis. The substance has not as yet been shown to be a constituent of the protein molecule. Ackermann (17a) has obtained it by the action of bacteria on arginine.

Although dihydroxyphenylalanine (18) has repeatedly been isolated and its constitution established by synthesis, evidence of its being a constituent of the protein molecule is still lacking. Methods to prevent its destruction by oxidation during the process of hydrolysis and isolation will.have to be devised.

The synthesis of thiolhistidine by Ashley and Harington (19) makes an extensive study of the properties of this amino acid possible so that a search for its possible occurrence among the protein cleavage products may be more intelligently carried out. The occurrence of ergothionine in blood, especially when the animals are maintained on certain protein diets (20), points to the possibility that thiolhistidine may be a protein constituent.

Since the isolation of a substance by Van Slyke and Hiller (21) and by Van Slyke and Robson (22) which they believe to be dihydroxypyrrole alanine, no further work on this subject has appeared. The evidence presented by Fränkel and Monasterio (23) for the homogeneity of *tetratrisäure* is insufficient to warrant its being accepted as an established amino acid. Its constitution has not been proved.

The group of products comprising caseinic acid, *caseansäure*, diaminoadipic acid, hydroxyaminosuccinic (hydroxy aspartic) acid, and dihydroxydiaminosuberic acid, which Skraup (24) described as occurring in certain protein hydrolysates, remains up to now unsubstantiated in the literature. An intensive investigation to establish the presence of these substances among the accepted protein cleavage products or to eliminate them from the list of doubtful amino acids is highly desirable. The synthesis of hydroxyaspartic acid by Dakin (25) affords the possibility of comparing one of the products which Skraup described with a product of known constitution.

It may be remarked in this connection that altogether too little is known of the chemical behavior and properties of the basic amino acid which was isolated from jack bean extract by Kitagawa and Tomiyama (26) to warrant its serious consideration as an established amino acid. However, it is possible with respect to certain of the products which have been described as occurring in plant material that we may eventually have a repetition of the series of events which finally led to the recognition of arginine and other amino acids as constituents of the protein molecule.

Dakin and West's (27) discovery of a tribasic amino acid in liver extract is further evidence that probably not all of the units of protein molecules have yet been isolated. They believe that the structure of the amino acid is either

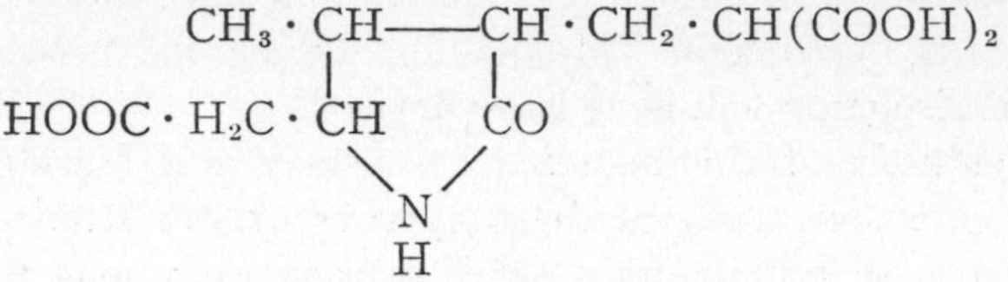

$$CH_3 \cdot CH{\rule{1.5em}{0.4pt}}CH \cdot CH_2 \cdot CH(COOH)_2$$

$$HOOC \cdot H_2C \cdot CH \qquad CO$$

$$\diagdown N \diagup$$

$$H$$

or

$$CH_3 \cdot CH{\rule{1.5em}{0.4pt}}CH \cdot CH_2 \cdot CH \cdot (COOH)_2$$

$$CO \qquad CH \cdot CH_2 \cdot COOH$$

$$\diagdown N \diagup$$

$$H$$

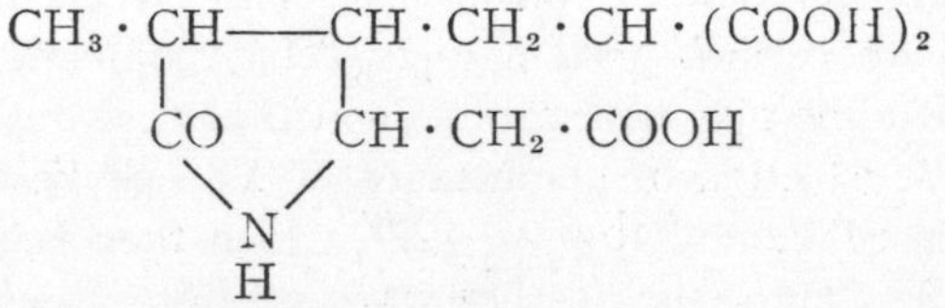

In order to account for the titration index of certain proteins, Simms (28) advanced the hypothesis that arginine exists "preformed" in the protein molecule, which may be interpreted as indicating that we are dealing with a substance which has not as yet been isolated or identified, but which, in the course of protein hydrolysis, yields arginine. Possible doubt is cast upon this hypothesis by the recent work of Greenstein (29). The evidence is, however, not quantitative. Greenstein determined the apparent dissociation constants for the peptids—histidyl-histidine and aspartyl-aspartic acid. He was able to show that the introduction of a second imidazole ring in the histidine compound led to a decided weakening of the acid and basic groups as compared with those of histidine itself. This was accompanied by a shift to a more acid range of one of the imidazole groups. This means that in order to correlate the nature of the titration curve of a protein with its content of amino acids, the position of the groups participating in the binding of acid and of base with respect to each other will have to be known.

For many purposes it is highly desirable that adequate supplies of amino acids should be available. This constitutes in itself a problem which must be met in nearly all investigations dealing with amino acids. Glutamic acid, which is used in the Orient in the form of its monosodium salt, is the only amino acid which is produced on an extensive commercial scale (30). It is marketed under such names as "Ajinomoto" and "Maywesuit." These commercial products afford a rapid and cheap source for the preparation of glutamic acid. It is highly desirable to have available rapid and standardized methods for the preparation of amino acids. Some work along this line has appeared in the last few years. The preparation of glycine has been studied in detail by Boutwell and Kuick (31) and by Robertson (32). The method of electrical transport described by Foster and Schmidt (33) and by Cox, King and Berg (34), together with the use of flavianic acid as a precipitant for arginine (35), permits the preparation of the hexone bases in large quantities by means of fairly inexpensive reagents. Proline can now be prepared with the aid of the method which has been described by Towne (36) and by Cox and King (37). Klabunde (38) has recently extended this method so as to include hydroxyproline. Dunn and Smart (39) have offered a new method for the synthesis of aspartic acid, and Dunn, Smart, Redemann and Brown (40) have devised a synthesis of glutamic acid which gives increased yields.

The isolation of methionine is still a somewhat unsatisfactory procedure. However, it may now be conveniently synthesized by the methods which have been described by Windus and Marvel (41) and by Barger and Weichselbaum (42). Du Vigneaud and Meyer (43) have isolated methionine from a pancreatic digest of casein. It would be highly desirable to have a better method for the preparation of β-hydroxyglutamic acid in large quantities. Dakin (44) is, apparently, the only worker who has obtained this amino acid in a crystalline state.[1]

Vickery (45) and his co-workers have contributed a great deal toward characterizing the properties of the basic amino acids, histidine, lysine, arginine, and the closely related ornithine. The first three mentioned were prepared in the free state. It is not quite clear why the last substance is unstable in the free state.

An inspection of the amino acid content of proteins, such as has been recently compiled by Cohn (46), shows considerable variability in the reported values. This is probably due in part to the inadequacy of our present analytical methods and in part to the variable purity and homogeneity of the preparations which have been submitted to analyses. Block and Vickery (47) have published figures

---

[1] C. R. Harington and S. S. Randall, *Biochem. J.*, **25**, 1917 (1931), have recently published an improved method for the synthesis of β-hydroxy glutamic acid. They were unable to obtain the naturally occurring amino acid in a crystalline state. They were unable to confirm certain of the tests given for this amino acid by Dakin.

for the content of certain of the amino acids in a number of keratins. They define a keratin as being a protein which (a) is resistant to digestion by pepsin and by trypsin, (b) is insoluble in dilute acids and alkalies, water, and organic solvents, and (c), on acid hydrolysis yields such quantities of histidine, lysine, and arginine that the molecular ratios of these amino acids are, respectively, approximately as 1:4:12. The cystine content varies greatly and bears no relationship to the proportions of basic amino acids. Brazier (48) has devised a new scheme for the fractionation of the amino acids into three groups which depends upon the solubility of the copper salts, viz., a group which is water-soluble and a group which is insoluble in water. The former can be further fractionated into a group which is soluble in methyl alcohol and a group which is insoluble in methyl alcohol.

A good deal of work has been carried out to characterize the amino acids from a physico-chemical standpoint. To that end the dissociation constants and certain thermodynamic data, such as the apparent change in free energy $\Delta F^{o\prime}$, the apparent entropy change $\Delta S'$, and heat of ionization $\Delta H'$, have been determined. These data have been summarized in tabular form by Kirk and Schmidt (49), Miyamoto and Schmidt (50), and by Cohn (46). It should be pointed out that the dissociation constants as well as the thermodynamic constants are apparent rather than true values. It was possible to calculate the apparent values only because of the lack of the activity-coefficient data. To elucidate this question, Hoskins, Randall and Schmidt (51) have determined from freezing-point measurements the activity coefficients of aspartic acid and of glutamic acid and their monosodium salts in solution. The amino acids and their salts were treated as uniunivalent electrolytes. The activity coefficients of the undissociated part of aspartic acid and of glutamic acid in solution were also determined. The data were interpreted as indicating that (a) the undissociated part of these amino acids exists to a considerable extent as neutral aggregates and (b) the ionized part of the monosodium salts exists to a slight extent as ionic aggregates or micelles. They have further shown that at 0° free glutamic acid and aspartic acid are but little ionized, while the monosodium salts are highly ionized. Using the data of Hoskins, Randall and Schmidt (51), Miyamoto and Schmidt (50) have carried out calculations which indicate that, in so far as the primary acid dissociation constants of aspartic and of glutamic acids are concerned, no appreciable error is introduced when the apparent dissociation constants of these acids are used instead of the true constants or, in other words, in the calculation of the dissociation constants concentration may be used in place of activity.

Fränkel (52) has carried out molecular weight estimations on certain of the amino acids, using for this purpose freezing- and boiling-point methods. He found that dihydroxyphenylalanine, arginine, asparagine, and glycine are appreciably polymerized in solution. Lewis (53) found that glycine in aqueous solution is polymerized to the extent of about 10 per cent. In the presence of sodium chloride and sucrose, osmotic abnormality was found in the freezing-point data.[2] It seems altogether probable that proteins in solution are also extensively polymerized. This may account for the very high molecular weights which have been determined by Svedberg and others for certain proteins. Lewis concludes that there is a decrease in the activity coefficient of glycine due to the presence of sucrose. Mr. Dalton of this laboratory has used the data of Fränkel and of Lewis for the purpose of calculating the activity coefficient of glycine. While the magnitude of the activity coefficient values in the two instances is the same, there are, nevertheless, sufficient differences to indicate that more accurate measurements will in the future have to be carried out in order to determine the activity coefficients of the amino acids with precision.

Mitchell and Greenstein (54) have brought out the fact that the dissociation constants of certain amino acids and peptids are functions of the hydrogen ion activity and of the ionic strength of the solutions. However, at equal ionic strengths the acid constants in the presence of KCl are greater than in the presence of K_2SO_4, the reverse holding true for the basic constants in alkaline solution. Apparently, we are dealing with phenomena which can at present be explained only on the basis of specific ion effects.

There are few good solubility data for the amino acids. Such measurements have usually been carried out for only one or possibly two temperatures rather than for a considerable temperature range. Moreover, a perusal of the literature reveals such facts as a differ-

---

[2] In the calculation of molecular weights of amino acids and proteins from freezing-point, boiling-point, and osmotic-pressure, etc., measurements, the assumption has been made that the laws of a perfect solution are obeyed. This is open to serious question and may affect the interpretation of the results which have been obtained in this manner. In this connection see Hildebrand, J. H., *Solubility*, New York (1924), p. 129.

ence in solubility between the d- and the l-form of the same compound. For this there is no theoretical justification. It is, however, possible on account of compound formation between the two isomeric forms, or the formation of imperfect solution, that the solubility of the racemic form of the amino acid might be different than the solubility of the individual isomers. Dalton, Kirk and Schmidt (55) determined that, between the limits of 273° and 320° absolute, the relationship between the solubility of diiodotyrosine and the temperature can be expressed by the equation

$$\log N_2 = 0.01923T - 10.329$$

where T = absolute temperature and N_2 = mol fraction of the solute. The solubility measurements are being extended by Mr. Dalton to include other amino acids. The solubility relationship for aspartic acid is expressed by the equation $\log N_2 = 0.01516T - 7.707$, and for glutamic acid the equation is $\log N_2 = 0.01610T - 7.795$.

While the idea that amino acids in solution exist in the form of zwitterions has never been disputed, direct experimental evidence for this has been lacking. Several recent papers have brought out evidence which strongly supports the zwitterion theory. Birch and Harris (56) have prepared titration curves of certain amino acids in the presence of increasing concentrations of formaldehyde. The formation of the methylene derivative resulted in a displacement of the NaOH curve and not of the HCl curve. This indicates that the acid and base titration curves of the amino acid represent replacement of COOH and of NH_2 by a stronger acid and a stronger base. Borsook and MacFadyen (57) have compiled the literature relating to the zwitterion theory. They also offer new experimental evidence to the effect that dilution of a phosphate solution with a glycine solution of greater ionic strength causes an increase in the hydrogen ion concentration of the mixture, while dilution with a glycine solution of lower ionic strength brings about a decrease in the hydrogen ion concentration. Similar results were obtained with alanine. The data can best be explained on the basis that the amino acids exist in solution as zwitterions. Emerson and Kirk's (58) titration curve of glycine ethyl ester likewise can be interpreted only on the basis of the zwitterion theory. In advancing the zwitterion concept, Bjerrum pointed out that there exists an equilibrium between the zwitterion and the classical form of the amino acid. Miyamoto and Schmidt (59) have recently made calculations which show that the amount of the classical form of the amino acid is negligibly small ($10^{-4.75}$ for glycine) as compared with the zwitterion form.

Considerable attention has in recent years been paid to the estimation of the molecular weights of the proteins. Svedberg (60) has presented a summary of the molecular weights of the more common proteins. He draws the conclusion that "The protein molecules containing more than one group of weight 34,500 are as a rule dissociated into molecules of lower number of groups of 34,500 when the pH of the solution is raised over a certain value . . . . At a sufficiently high alkalinity all proteins have the same molecular weight, viz., 34,500." This conclusion is open to serious question. Proteins are probably polymerized to a high degree. This probably accounts for the very high molecular weight which has been observed for certain proteins. It might well be conceived that, when the alkalinity is sufficiently high, depolymerization would take place with consequent reduction in molecular weight as postulated by Svedberg. Recent experimental work does not altogether bear out Svedberg's idea that the molecular weights of proteins are multiples of 34,500. Burk and Greenberg (61) and Burk (62) have attacked the problem in a novel way by determining the molecular weight of certain proteins in urea solutions. The advantage possessed by this method is that isoelectric proteins which are not soluble in water are soluble in aqueous urea solution. It is of interest to note that the molecular weight of hemoglobin in urea was found to be one-half that which has been determined in aqueous solution, indicating deaggregation. On the other hand, the molecular weight of egg albumin and of serum albumin is essentially the same in urea solution as in aqueous solution. Table I

TABLE I*

Protein	Minimum Molecular Weight Chemical Data	Molecular Weight in Aqueous Solution	Molecular Weight from Osmotic Pressure in Urea Solution
Casein	12,800	98,000 (62)	33,600
Edestin	29,000	212,000	49,500
Hemoglobin	16,660	67,000	34,300
Egg Albumin	33,800†	34,000	36,000
Serum Albumin ..	78,000	75,000	73,000

* A more recent compilation of data on molecular weight has been made by Vickery (115). His interpretation of Svedberg's hypothesis does not altogether agree with that given by the writer.

† See also Calvery (63a).

is a compilation of recent molecular weight data taken from the papers of Burk and Greenberg (61), Burk (62), and Carpenter (63).

If we accept the molecular weight of these proteins as being a minimum in urea solution, then the postulate of Svedberg becomes questionable. It is likewise not in accord with the molecular weights calculated from the chemical data. Hopkins (64) has shown that denaturation by urea probably involves changes in the sulfur linkages in the protein molecule. This phenomenon may be secondary to deaggregation. In the case of egg albumin and of serum albumin, denaturation by urea does not lead to a change in molecular weight (65). Some of the difference in molecular weight between that which can be calculated on the basis of amino-acid content and that which is determined experimentally is due to the fact that the protein in question is not a homogeneous molecule. Experimental work to date indicates that egg albumin and hemoglobin are the only naturally occurring proteins which can be considered as not being mixtures of several proteins.[3]

Adair and Robinson (65a) have studied the osmotic pressure of the serum proteins from the standpoint of Dalton's law of partial pressures. Their results indicate that serum protein is not a compound of albumins and globulins. The state of aggregation of the proteins in the untreated serum appears to be the same as their state of aggregation in the purified proteins.

Stadie and Sunderman (65b) have carried out studies on the osmotic coefficient of sodium in sodium hemoglobinate and of sodium chloride in hemoglobin solutions. They believe that their experiments show that NaHb cannot be regarded as a high valence salt of the type Na_nHb, in which ionic interaction would be marked and would produce pronounced effects on the osmotic properties with changes of concentration.

In present-day considerations of the properties of solutions, the dielectric constant is a factor of importance. It controls very largely the dissociation of dissolved electrolytes. It is one of the terms which enters into the solubility expression of Debye. It is concerned with the idea of activity coefficients. Very little work has been done on the estimation of the dielectric constants of the amino acids and of the proteins. Recently, Wyman (66) determined the dielectric constants

[3] For the literature relating to the subject of the non-homomolecularity of proteins consult 63b.

of alcohol-water mixtures and of zein in alcohol-water mixtures. The conclusion was reached that the zein molecules are highly polar. He found the value for the permanent electric moment of these molecules to be about 60×10^{-18} E.S.V. The values for the relaxation time were somewhat smaller than those calculated on the basis of Stokes's formula for the rotation of a spherical particle in a viscous medium. No change in the dielectric constant accompanying gelation was observed, suggesting that the viscosity of gels is not the ordinary viscosity which enters Stokes's expression.

The literature dealing with denaturation and coagulation of proteins has become so large that lack of space prevents a review. Such literature compilations have recently been presented by Lewis (67), Wu (68), and Meldrum (69). It appears that denaturation may be brought about under suitable conditions by drying, heat, pressure, light, shaking, sound, acid and alkali, alcohol, urea and related compounds, and possibly heavy metals. The work of Anson and Mirsky (70), Wu and Lin (71), and Meldrum (69) on hemoglobin, and of Spiegel-Adolf (72) on serum albumin, indicates the reversibility of the phenomenon of denaturation in these two instances at least. Denaturation is not necessarily accompanied by a change in molecular weight, nor is it characterized by any decided chemical change. The appearance of the nitroprusside reaction in denatured proteins is probably merely incidental to the phenomenon. Denaturation leads to increase in digestibility of egg albumin by trypsin and to a change in antigenic property. It is also accompanied by increase in viscosity. Wu, Liu and Chou (73) conclude that the ionization constants of some of the acidic and basic groups are changed in denaturation, but the total number of such groups remains unchanged.

According to Wu's (74) hypothesis, soluble protein possesses a compact structure rather than a flexible open chain of the polypeptide type which is held together by the force of attraction between the polar groups. The force which holds together different parts of the single protein molecule is the same as that which holds different molecules together in a single crystal. The difference between the "monomolecular crystal" of protein and an ordinary crystal is that a primary valence chain linking all atoms in the crystal exists in the former but not in the latter. In denaturation, not followed by coagulation, the compact and orderly structure is disorganized. In coagulation the molecules interpenetrate and are entangled. Considerably more information will have to be obtained about intramolecular forces as

well as the structure of the protein molecule before any theory dealing with denaturation can be accepted as proved.

In 1925 Cohn (75) showed that a linear relationship exists between the concentration of the added salt and the logarithm of the
solubility. In sufficiently concentrated solutions the relations can be
expressed by the equation

$$\log S = \beta - K's\mu$$

where S = solubility, μ = ionic strength, β = an intercept constant
and $K's$ = the salting-out constant. Florkin (76) found that the solubility of fibrinogen in concentrated salt solutions can be defined by
the equation above. He determined further that $K's$ is a constant for
a given protein and salt and is independent over wide ranges of temperature and of pH. Green (77) has ascertained that essentially the
same facts apply to carboxyhemoglobin and to oxyhemoglobin. She
found further that $K's$ varies with the salt, decreasing in the order
as given by the Hofmeister series. The term β depends upon the
nature of the protein and of pH. In a second paper, Green (78)
gives the results of her studies on the solubility measurements of
hemoglobin and of casein in salt solutions of varying hydrogen ion
activity. Both hemoglobin and casein behaved as though they were
divalent acids and bases. The total solubility, S, of hemoglobin was
found to be related to the solubility of the neutral molecule S_n, according to the equation

$$\frac{S}{S_n} = 1 + \frac{K_3'K_4'}{a_{H+}^2} + \frac{a_{H+}^2}{K_1'K_2'}$$

where $K_3'K_4'$ and $K_1'K_2'$ are the apparent dissociation constants of
the protein at constant ionic strength. The apparent dissociation constants and isoelectric point varied with the electrolyte concentration,
and the values of $pK_1'K_2'$ and of $pK_3'K_4'$ increased in value as the
salt concentration increased.

In order to throw further light upon the factors which determine
the behavior of proteins and amino acids in solution, Cohn, Mc-
Meekin, Edsall and Weare (79) have carried out solubility measurements of certain amino acids in alcohol-water mixtures containing
neutral salts. They have shown that the molecular forces between

amino acids, proteins, and salts depend upon their apparent valence, which, in turn, depends upon the number of charges and the distance between them, upon the electrical size, the contribution to the ionic strength, and the dielectric constants of the solutions.

A good deal of discussion has centered about the question as to the mode of combination which takes place between proteins and amino acids and acids and bases. In a larger sense this involves the question of the mode of combination of the inorganic elements with the first-named substances. Loeb's (80) experiments supported the view that proteins react stoichiometrically with acids and with bases rather than by adsorption and that there is no difference between the chemistry of the proteins and that of the crystalloids. Further evidence to favor this idea is furnished by the experiments of Chapman, Greenberg and Schmidt (81) and Rawlins and Schmidt (82) when they demonstrated stoichiometric combination between certain dyes and proteins. Since the dye-protein compounds formed insoluble precipitates, the usual equilibrium type of combination did not have to be considered. Moreover, it was found that the amount of dye which was taken up could be correlated with certain groups in the protein molecule, a correlation which has been shown by a number of individuals to hold for the amount of acids and bases which can be taken up as well. Hewitt (83) and Stearn (84, 85) have brought forth additional evidence that proteins combine with dyes in stoichiometric proportions. Miyamoto and Schmidt (86) have shown that certain basic amino acids can unite with the predominantly acidic amino acids to form compound amino acids. In fact, any two amino acids whose dissociation constants differ from each other will form compounds, although the stability of the compounds which are formed from amino acids whose dissociation constants are small or lie near to each other is necessarily not great.

Bancroft and his co-workers (87, 88) have studied the combination of gaseous ammonia and of hydrogen chloride with certain proteins and their hydrolytic products with the aid of the phase rule. They come to the somewhat puzzling conclusion that certain proteins adsorb ammonia but show no evidence of compound formation, while the hydrolytic products of this protein show chemical combination with ammonia to an extent, which in the case of gelatin can be accounted for on the combination of ammonia with the glutamic acid, aspartic acid, proline, hydroxyproline and histidine portions of the hydrolysate, after which adsorption of ammonia may still take place. On the other hand, proteins and their hydrolytic products were found to combine chemically with hydrogen chloride. However, they consider that the compound formed between gelatin and hydrogen chloride may adsorb further hydrogen chloride. They conclude further that, since zein does not show stoichiometric combination with hydrogen chloride, there are no peptide linkages present in this protein. Evidently they have overlooked the fact that since zein contains little or no lysine it contains no free amino nitrogen and hence possesses no acid-combining power. It is not desirable to criticize the conclusions of Bancroft and his co-workers without further data upon which to base criticism. It is strongly suspected, however, that they have not taken into account all of the factors which must be considered in the reactions which they were studying. Experiments to test their conclusions are in progress in this laboratory.

A great deal of experimental work points to the fact that proteins form complex ions with a number of the inorganic elements. The list includes members of the alkaline earth elements and the heavy metals. The literature bearing upon this subject has been presented by Smythe and Schmidt (89). These investigators have studied the mode of combination which takes place between certain proteins, amino acids, and related compounds. They showed that certain groups which are contained in hydroxymonocarboxylic acids, dicarboxylic acids, hydroxydicarboxylic acids, hydroxytricarboxylic acids, amino acids which are also hydroxy or dicarboxylic acids, and certain inorganic acids which contain hydroxy groups will hold iron as an undissociated compound. They offer an explanation, based on the residual charge of atoms, to account for the manner in which iron may be united. More recently Main and Schmidt (90) have published similar studies for manganous ions.

Greene and Power (91) have reported that certain of the alkali metals are bound to proteins in a non-diffusible form which suggests that these elements like those of the alkaline earth group may likewise exist to a certain extent as complex ions. The transference experiments of Greenberg and Schmidt (92), as well as unpublished experiments which have been carried out in this laboratory by Mr. Miyamoto, show within the limits of experimental error, which may be considered to be about 10 per cent, no evidence of complex ions containing alkali metals and protein.

With the aid of a cell without liquid junction, Hitchcock (93) has determined very accurately the titration curve of gelatin. He finds that it combines with a maximum of 9.58×10^{-4} equivalents of H^+ and 2.0×10^{-4} equivalents of Cl^-. The isoelectric point is 4.86 ± 0.01.

Considerable information has been gained from studies on the optical properties of proteins and amino acids. It is well known that the optical rotation of proteins and amino acids varies with the activity of the solution. Recently, Lutz and Jirgensons (94) have determined the variation in optical rotation of a large number of amino acids in solutions of varying acidities, and Almquist and Greenberg (95) have determined a similar relationship for egg albumin. Carpenter and Kucera (96) find that inorganic salts influence the optical activity of gelatin and that these salts may be arranged in a Hofmeister series with respect to their influence. Craig and Schmidt (97) have carried out titration curves of a number of amino acids and proteins with the aid of an interferometer. By assigning different values to the refractive index of the ions and the undissociated substances involved, it has been possible with the aid of the mass law to set up an equation connecting the refractive index of the solution with the amount of acid and base present and the dissociation constants of the substances involved. They also found a marked change in the value of the refractive index following the transition from the gel to the sol state.

Gelatin has been extensively employed for studies relating to the physical state of the protein. Straub (98) finds that gelatin consists of units of different degrees of association which are probably of the same or very similar molecular structure. Other workers, notably Krishnamurti and Svedberg (99) and Shepard and Houck (100), have obtained evidence along essentially similar lines. The findings of Greenberg and Mackey (101) that a difference exists in the conductivity between the gel and the sol state of gelatin indicating that the structural units of these two states are not identical, harmonize with Craig and Schmidt's refractivity studies. Northrup and Kunitz (102) have offered experimental data to show that various properties of gelatin such as swelling, osmotic pressure, and viscosity can be accounted for by assuming that gelatin sols or gels are two-phase, three-component systems. The solid phase consists of particles of an insoluble ingredient of the gelatin, and the liquid phase is an aqueous solution of the "insoluble fraction" and of a "soluble" fraction in water.

The unique suggestion has been made by McBain and Jameson (103) that the serum globulins are but three phases of a system of the same mother substance, dehydrated globulin, solutions of globu-

lin being the ordinary isotropic solution while euglobulin and pseudoglobulin are liquid crystalline phases or a liquid and glass which are
slightly doubly-refracting. These deductions should be checked by
other criteria before being accepted as proved.

The interesting observation has been made by von Muralt and
Edsall (104) that myosin is anisotropic. The problem arises to determine whether it is quantitatively possible to correlate the ani-
sotropy of the myosin particle with the double refraction in the living
muscle fiber, which, if it were found true, would be a conclusive
proof that the myosin particles are the long-sought "disdiaklasten"
of Brücke.

A number of reviews (105–115) of the status of various phases
of the chemistry of the proteins and amino acids have appeared in
recent years. A list is appended for the guidance of those who may
desire to gain ready access to the more detailed literature in this field.

LITERATURE CITED

1. VICKERY, H. B., AND SCHMIDT, C. L. A., *Chem. Rev.,* **9,** 169 (1931)
2. ROSE, W. C., ELLIS, R. H., WINDUS, W., AND CATHERWOOD, F., *Proc.
   Am. Soc. Biol. Chem.,* **7,** 66 (1931); WINDUS, W., CATHERWOOD, F. L.,
   AND ROSE, W. C., *J. Biol. Chem.,* **94,** 173 (1931)
3. MÖRNER, C. T., *Z physiol. Chem.,* **51,** 33 (1907); **88,** 138 (1913);
   ZEYNEK, R., *Z. physiol. Chem.,* **114,** 275 (1921)
4. FOREMAN, F. W., *Biochem. Z.,* **56,** 1 (1913)
5. ABDERHALDEN, E., AND WEIL, A., *Z. physiol. Chem.,* **81,** 207 (1912)
6. SCHRYVER, S. B., AND BUSTON, H. W., *Proc. Roy. Soc. (London),* B, **99,**
   476 (1925–26)
7. GORTNER, R. A., AND HOFFMAN, W. F., *J. Am. Chem. Soc.,* **47,** 580 (1925)
8. RIMINGTON, C., *Biochem. J.,* **21,** 1187 (1927)
9. CZARNETZKY, E. J., AND SCHMIDT, C. L. A., *Z. physiol. Chem.,* **204,** 129
   (1932)
10. BRAZIER, M. A. B., *Biochem. J.,* **24,** 1188 (1930)
11. CZARNETZKY, E. J., AND SCHMIDT, C. L. A., *J. Biol. Chem.,* **92,** 453 (1931)
12. SCHRYVER, S. B., BUSTON, H. W., AND MUKHERJEE, D. H., *Proc. Roy.
    Soc. (London),* B, **98,** 58 (1925); *ibid.,* **100,** 360 (1926); *ibid.,* **101,**
    519 (1927)
13. ABDERHALDEN, E., AND BAHN, A., *Ber.,* **63,** 914 (1930)
14. ABDERHALDEN, E., AND REICH, F., *Z. physiol. Chem.,* **193,** 198 (1930)
15. THUDICUM, J. L. W., *"Die chemische Konstitution des Gehirns des Men-
    schen und der Tiere,"* Tübingen (1901), p. 257
16. ABDERHALDEN, E., AND WIEL, A., *Z. physiol. Chem.,* **81,** 207 (1912);
    ibid., **84,** 39 (1913)

17. WADA, M., *Biochem. Z.*, **224**, 420 (1930)

17a. ACKERMANN, D., *Z. physiol. Chem.*, **203**, 66 (1931)

18. TORQUATI, T., *Arch. farmacol. sper.*, **15**, 213 (1913); GUGGENHEIM, M., *Z. physiol. Chem.*, **88**, 276 (1913); FUNK, C., *J. Chem. Soc.*, **99**, 554 (1911); MILLER, E. R., *J. Biol. Chem.*, **44**, 481 (1920); HARINGTON, C. R., *Biochem. J.*, **22**, 407 (1928); HIRAI, K., *Biochem. Z.*, **114**, 67 (1921)

19. ASHLEY, J. N., AND HARINGTON, C. R., *J. Chem. Soc.*, 2586 (1930)

20. EAGLES, B. A., AND JOHNSON, T. B., *J. Am. Chem. Soc.*, **49**, 575 (1927); EAGLES, B. A., AND VARS, H. M., *J. Biol. Chem.*, **80**, 615 (1928); NEWTON, E. B., BENEDICT, S. R., AND DAKIN, H. D., *J. Biol. Chem.*, **72**, 367 (1928); HUNTER, G., *Biochem. J.*, **22**, 4 (1928)

21. VAN SLYKE, D. D., AND HILLER, A., *Proc. Natl. Acad. Sci.*, **7**, 185 (1921)

22. VAN SLYKE, D. D., AND ROBSON, W., *Proc. Soc. Exptl. Biol. Med.*, **23**, 23 (1925)

23. FRÄNKEL, S., AND MONASTERIO, G., *Biochem. Z.*, **213**, 65 (1929)

24. SKRAUP, Z. H., *Z. physiol. Chem.*, **42**, 274 (1904); *see also* FISCHER, E., AND ABDERHALDEN, E., *Z. physiol. Chem.*, **42**, 540 (1904); FISCHER, E., *Z. physiol. Chem.*, **99**, 54 (1917)

25. DAKIN, H. D., *J. Biol. Chem.*, **48**, 273 (1921)

26. KITAGAWA, M., AND TOMIYAMA, T., *J. Biochem.* (*Japan*), **11**, 265 (1929); KITAGAWA, M., AND TOMITA, T., *Proc. Imp. Acad.* (*Tokyo*), **5**, 380 (1929)

27. DAKIN, H. D., AND WEST, R., *J. Biol. Chem.*, **92**, 117 (1931)

28. SIMMS, H. S., *J. Gen. Physiol.*, **12**, 231 (1928)

29. GREENSTEIN, J. P., *J. Biol. Chem.*, **93**, 479 (1931)

30. HAN, J. E. S., *Ind. Eng. Chem.*, **21**, 984 (1929); SCHMIDT, C. L. A., AND FOSTER, G. L., *Proc. Soc. Exptl. Biol. Med.*, **18**, 205 (1921)

31. BOUTWELL, P. W., AND KUICK, L. F., *J. Am. Chem. Soc.*, **52**, 4167 (1930)

32. ROBERTSON, G. R., *J. Am. Chem. Soc.*, **49**, 2889 (1927)

33. FOSTER, G. L., AND SCHMIDT, C. L. A., *J. Biol. Chem.*, **56**, 545 (1923)

34. COX, G. J., KING, H., AND BERG, C. P., *J. Biol. Chem.*, **81**, 755 (1929)

35. COX, G. J., *J. Biol. Chem.*, **78**, 475 (1928)

36. TOWNE, B. W., *Biochem. J.*, **22**, 1083 (1928)

37. COX, G. J., AND KING, H., *J. Biol. Chem.*, **84**, 533 (1929)

38. KLABUNDE, H. K., *J. Biol. Chem.*, **90**, 293 (1931)

39. DUNN, M. S., AND SMART, B. W., *J. Biol. Chem.*, **89**, 41 (1930)

40. DUNN, M. S., SMART, B. W., REDEMANN, C. E., AND BROWN, K. E., *J. Biol. Chem.*, **94**, 599 (1931)

41. WINDUS, W., AND MARVEL, C. S., *J. Am. Chem. Soc.*, **52**, 2575 (1930); *see also* EMERSON, O. H., KIRK, P. L., AND SCHMIDT, C. L. A., *J. Biol. Chem.*, **92**, 449 (1931)

42. BARGER, G., AND WEICHSELBAUM, T. E., *Biochem. J.*, **25**, 997 (1931)

43. DU VIGNEAUD, V., AND MEYER, C. E., *J. Biol. Chem.*, **94**, 641 (1932)

44. DAKIN, H. D., *Biochem. J.*, **12**, 290 (1918); **13**, 398 (1919); *Z. physiol. Chem.*, **130**, 159 (1923)

45. VICKERY, H. B., AND LEAVENWORTH, C. S., *J. Biol. Chem.*, **76**, 437, 701 (1928); VICKERY, H. B., AND COOK, C. A., *J. Biol. Chem.*, **94**, 393 (1931)

46. COHN, E. J., *Ergebnisse Physiol.*, **33**, 781 (1931)
47. BLOCK, R. J., AND VICKERY, H. B., *J. Biol. Chem.*, **93**, 105, 113 (1931);
    BLOCK, R. J., *J. Biol. Chem.*, **94**, 647 (1932)
48. BRAZIER, M. A. B., *Biochem. J.*, **24**, 1188 (1930)
49. KIRK, P. L., AND SCHMIDT, C. L. A., *Univ. Calif. Pub. Physiol.*, **7**, 57
    (1929)
50. MIYAMOTO, S., AND SCHMIDT, C. L. A., *J. Biol. Chem.*, **90**, 165 (1931)
51. HOSKINS, W. M., RANDALL, M., AND SCHMIDT, C. L. A., *J. Biol. Chem.*,
    88, 215 (1930)
52. FRÄNKEL, M., *Biochem. Z.*, **217**, 378 (1930)
53. LEWIS, W. C. M., *Chem. Rev.*, **8**, 81 (1931)
54. MITCHELL, P. H., AND GREENSTEIN, J. P., *J. Gen. Physiol.*, **14**, 255 (1931)
55. DALTON, J. B., KIRK, P. L., AND SCHMIDT, C. L. A., *J. Biol. Chem.*, **88**,
    589 (1930)
56. BIRCH, T. W., AND HARRIS, L. J., *Biochem. J.*, **24**, 1080 (1930); *see also*
    HARRIS, L. J., *Proc. Roy. Soc. (London), B*, **104**, 412 (1929)
57. BORSOOK, H., AND MACFADYEN, D. A., *J. Gen. Physiol.*, **13**, 509 (1930);
    see also PAULI, W., *Trans. Faraday Soc.*, **26**, 723 (1930)
58. EMERSON, O. H., AND KIRK, P. L., *J. Biol. Chem.*, **87**, 597 (1930)
59. MIYAMOTO, S., AND SCHMIDT, C. L. A., *Univ. Calif. Pub. Physiol.*, **8**, 1
    (1932); *see also* EBERT, L., *Z. physikal. Chem. A*, **121**, 385 (1926)
60. SVEDBERG, T., *Trans. Faraday Soc.*, **26**, 740 (1930); SVEDBERG, T., *Kolloid-Z.*, **51**, 10 (1930)
61. BURK, N. F., AND GREENBERG, D. M., *J. Biol. Chem.*, **87**, 197 (1930)
62. BURK, N. F., *Proc. Am. Soc. Biol. Chem.*, **7**, 40 (1931)
63. CARPENTER, D. C., *J. Am. Chem. Soc.*, **53**, 1812 (1931)
63a. CALVERY, H. O., *J. Biol. Chem.*, **94**, 613 (1932)
63b. LINDERSTRÖM-LANG, K., AND KODAMA, S., *Compt. rend. trav. lab. Carlsberg*, **16**, 48 (1925); FELIX, K., AND DIRR, K., *Z. physiol. Chem.*, **184**,
    111 (1929); SÖRENSEN, S. P. L., *Compt. rend. trav. lab. Carlsberg*, **15**,
    29 (1925); *ibid.*, **18**, 2 (1930); CARPENTER, D. C., AND HUCKER, G. J.,
    J. Infectious Diseases, **47**, 435 (1930)
64. HOPKINS, F. G., *Nature*, **126**, 328, 383 (1930)
65. HUANG, T. C., AND WU, H., *Chinese J. Physiol.*, **4**, 221 (1930)
65a. ADAIR, G. S., AND ROBINSON, M. E., *Biochem. J.*, **24**, 993 (1930)
65b. STADIE, W. C., AND SUNDERMAN, F. W., *J. Biol. Chem.*, **91**, 217 (1931)
66. WYMAN, J., *Physiol. Rev.*, **35**, 623 (1930); *J. Am. Chem. Soc.*, **53**, 3292
    (1931); *J. Biol. Chem.*, **90**, 443 (1931)
67. LEWIS, W. C. M., *Chem. Rev.*, **8**, 81 (1931)
68. WU, H., *Chinese J. Physiol.*, **5**, 321 (1931); *see also* BANCROFT, W. D.,
    AND RUTZLER, G. E., JR., *J. Phys. Chem.*, **35**, 144 (1931)
69. MELDRUM, N. V., *Biochem. J.*, **25**, 1498 (1931)
70. ANSON, M. L., AND MIRSKY, A. E., *J. Physiol.*, **60**, 50 (1925); *J. Gen.
    Physiol.*, **9**, 169 (1925); **13**, 133 (1929)
71. WU, H., AND LIN, K. H., *Chinese J. Physiol.*, **1**, 219 (1927)
72. SPIEGEL-ADOLF, M., *Biochem. Z.*, **170**, 126 (1926); *Naturwissenschaften*,
    15, 799 (1927)
73. WU, H., LIU, S. C., AND CHOU, C. Y., *Chinese J. Physiol.*, **5**, 309 (1931)

74. Wu, H., *Chinese J. Physiol.,* **5,** 321 (1931)
75. COHN, E. J., *Physiol. Rev.,* **5,** 413 (1925)
76. FLORKIN, M., *J. Biol. Chêm.,* **87,** 629 (1930)
77. GREEN, A. A., *J. Biol. Chem.,* **93,** 495 (1931)
78. GREEN, A. A., *J. Biol. Chem.,* **93,** 517 (1931)
79. COHN, E. J., MCMEEKIN, T. L., EDSALL, J. T., AND WEARE, J. H., *Proc. Am. Soc. Biol. Chem.,* **7,** 44 (1931)
80. LOEB, J., *"Proteins and the Theory of Colloidal Behavior,"* New York and London (1924)
81. CHAPMAN, L. M., GREENBERG, D. M., AND SCHMIDT, C. L. A., *J. Biol. Chem.,* **72,** 707 (1927)
82. RAWLINS, L. M. C., AND SCHMIDT, C. L. A., *J. Biol. Chem.,* **82,** 709 (1929)
83. HEWITT, L. F., *Biochem. J.,* **21,** 1305 (1927)
84. STEARN, A. E., AND STEARN, E. W., *Stain Tech.,* **4,** 111 (1929)
85. STEARN, A. E., *J. Biol. Chem.,* **91,** 325 (1931)
86. MIYAMOTO, S., AND SCHMIDT, C. L. A., *J. Biol. Chem.,* **87,** 327 (1930)
87. BANCROFT, W. D., AND BARNETT, C. E., *J. Phys. Chem.,* **34,** 449, 753, 1217, 1930, 2433 (1930)
88. BELDEN, B. C., *J. Phys. Chem.,* **35,** 2164 (1931)
89. SMYTHE, C. V., AND SCHMIDT, C. L. A., *J. Biol. Chem.,* **88,** 241 (1930) ; *see also* SMYTHE, C. V., *J. Biol. Chem.,* **92,** 233 (1931)
90. MAIN, R. K., AND SCHMIDT, C. L. A., *Proc. Soc. Exptl. Biol. Med.,* **28,** 830 (1931)
91. GREENE, C. H., AND POWER, M. H., *J. Biol. Chem.,* **91,** 183 (1931)
92. GREENBERG, D. M., AND SCHMIDT, C. L. A., *J. Gen. Physiol.,* **7,** 287 (1924)
93. HITCHCOCK, D. I., *J. Gen. Physiol.,* **14,** 685; **15,** 125 (1931)
94. LUTZ, O., AND JIRGENSONS, B., *Ber.,* **63,** 448 (1930) ; **64,** 1221 (1931)
95. ALMQUIST, H. J., AND GREENBERG, D. M., *J. Biol. Chem.,* **93,** 167 (1931)
96. CARPENTER, D. C., AND KUCERA, J. J., *J. Phys. Chem.,* **35,** 2619 (1931)
97. CRAIG, R., AND SCHMIDT, C. L. A., *Australian J. Exptl. Biol. Med. Sci. (Robertson Memorial Volume)* (in press) ; *see also* DONNAN, F. G., AND KRISHNAMURTI, K., *Colloid Symposium Monograph,* **7,** 1 (1930)
98. STRAUB, D., *J. Gen. Physiol.,* **14,** 643 (1931)
99. KRISHNAMURTI, F., AND SVEDBERG, T., *J. Am. Chem. Soc.,* **52,** 2897 (1930)
100. SHEPARD, S. E., AND HOUCK, R. C., *J. Phys. Chem.,* **34,** 273, 2187 (1930)
101. GREENBERG, D. M., AND MACKEY, M. A., *J. Gen. Physiol.,* **15,** 161 (1931)
102. NORTHRUP, J. H., AND KUNITZ, M., *J. Phys. Chem.,* **35,** 162 (1931)
103. MCBAIN, J. W., AND JAMESON, E., *Trans. Faraday Soc.,* **26,** 768 (1930)
104. VON MURALT, A. L., AND EDSALL, J. T., *Trans. Faraday Soc.,* **26,** 837 (1903) ; EDSALL, J. T., *J. Biol. Chem.,* **89,** 289 (1930)
105. COHN, E. J., *"The Physical Chemistry of the Proteins,"* *Physiol. Rev.,* **5,** 349 (1925) ; *"Die physikalische Chemie der Eiweisskörper (Erster Teil),"* *Ergebnisse Physiol.,* **33,** 781 (1931)
106. GREENBERG, D. M., *"Some Aspects of the Electrochemistry of the Proteins,"* *Trans. Am. Electrochem. Soc.,* **54,** 107 (1928)

107. HUNTER, A., "Protein Structure and Proteolysis in Some of Their Recent Aspects," *Trans. Roy. Soc. Can.,* III, **19,** 1 (1925)
108. KLARMANN, E., "Recent Advances in the Determination of the Structure of Proteins," *Chem. Rev.,* **4,** 51 (1927)
109. LEWIS, W. C. M., "The Crystallization, Denaturation, and Flocculation of Proteins with Special Reference to Albumin and Hemoglobin, Together with an Appendix on the Physico-Chemical Behavior of Glycine," *Chem. Rev.,* **8,** 81 (1931)
110. SPIEGEL-ADOLF, M., *Die Globuline,* Dresden and Leipzig (1930)
111. VICKERY, H. B., AND OSBORNE, T. B., "A Review of Hypotheses of the Structure of Proteins," *Physiol. Rev.,* **8,** 393 (1928)
112. VICKERY, H. B., AND SCHMIDT, C. L. A., "The History of the Discovery of the Amino Acids," *Chem. Rev.,* **9,** 169 (1931)
113. WASTENEYS, H., AND BORSOOK, H., "The Enzymatic Synthesis of Protein," *Physiol. Rev.,* **10,** 110 (1930)
114. WU, H., "A Theory of Denaturation," *Chinese J. Physiol.,* **5,** 321 (1931)
115. VICKERY, H. B., *Yale J. Biol. Med.,* **4,** 595 (1932)

UNIVERSITY OF CALIFORNIA MEDICAL SCHOOL
BERKELEY, CALIFORNIA

THE CHEMISTRY AND METABOLISM OF THE COMPOUNDS OF SULFUR*

By Howard B. Lewis

Department of Physiological Chemistry
University of Michigan

A new color reaction given by compounds of divalent sulfur doubly linked to a single non-metallic element has been described by Grote (1), which may be used for both qualitative and quantitative estimation of thiourea, thiosulfate, thiocyanate and related compounds of the C=S type. The active reagent is sodium aquoferricyanide, which is formed by treatment of sodium nitroprusside (nitroferricyanide) in sodium bicarbonate solution with hydroxylamine and subsequently with bromine. By means of this reagent organic compounds of type C—SH (e.g., cysteine), C—S—S—C (e.g., cystine), and C=S (e.g., thiourea) may be distinguished readily from other types and from one another. The importance of such a color reaction, particularly if satisfactory procedures for its use in quantitative determinations are developed, needs no comment.

METHIONINE

Barger and Weichselbaum (2) have described a new synthesis of this amino acid, which avoids the main difficulties of earlier syntheses, namely, the use of a rather inaccessible intermediate, acrolein, and the oxidation of the methylthiol group by bromination. A yield of 58 per cent based on the α-methylthiol-β-chloroethane employed, may be obtained. The resolution of the synthetic (*dl*) methionine has been effected by the utilization of the difference in the solubilities of the brucine derivatives of the optical isomers of formylmethionine (3). Specific rotations of $+8.7°$ and $-8.1°$ (at 25°), respectively, are reported for the *d* and *l* forms as compared with a value of $-6.87°$ ($\pm 0.5°$) at the same temperature for a sample of the natural isomer isolated from casein by Mueller's method. This method of isolation involves the use of alkali under conditions which probably lead to at least partial racemization. The apparent dissociation constants of methionine as recently determined (4), $pK'_a = 9.21$, $pK'_b = 11.72$

* Received December 21, 1931.

171

and $pI = 5.74$ at 25°, are characteristic of the monoaminomono-carboxylic amino acids, although the value of K'_a is slightly greater than for most of this group of amino acids.

The rôle of methionine in nutrition, hitherto largely unknown, has been studied in young white rats by Jackson and Block (5), who report in a preliminary communication that the addition of racemic methionine to diets deficient in their content of cystine results in an unmistakable increase in body weight, an increase similar to that which results from the addition of cystine to the diet. This utilization of methionine in the diet under conditions of a dietary cystine deficiency may help to explain the value of casein in nutrition, a biological value superior to that which would be expected in view of its low content of cystine as shown by chemical analyses.

CYSTINE AND CYSTEINE

Rimington and his associates have continued their important researches on the sulfur and cystine content of keratins of various origin. Within the limits of experimental error of the determinations, the entire sulfur content of rabbit fur (6) and wool (7) has been accounted for as cystine sulfur. In camel hair (7) more sulfur was present than the sulfur calculated from the content of cystine. It has been suggested that this may be due to the presence of a sulfur-containing pigment in camel hair. It is interesting to note that in confirmation of older results with the rabbit and white rat, the birth coat of the Welsh lamb (7) contained less sulfur than did wool of adult animals.

By a combination of histological and chemical methods, both porcupine quills and sheep wool have been studied to determine the localization of sulfur (and cystine) in structures composed primarily of scleroproteins (albuminoids) (8). The results have confirmed the view previously advanced that "medulla cells are substantially devoid of sulfur and that keratinization, so far as scleroproteins such as wool are concerned, is characteristically the result of incorporation of the cystine nucleus."

Data on the preparation and properties of the salts of the cystine anion with the alkali metals have not been available previously. Toennies and Lavine (9) have prepared the lithium, sodium, and potassium salts of l-cystine in crystalline form by precipitation of alkaline cystine solutions with acetonitrile and have furnished valuable data concerning their properties. The reaction of various heavy metals with cystine has been further investigated. It has been shown by Simonsen (10) that the reaction of mercuric sulfate in sulfuric acid solution with cystine is similar to that already reported for silver sulfate in a weakly acid medium, i.e., $3RS-SR + 3 H_2O = RSO_3H + 5RSH$. With the mercuric salt, the reaction proceeded to the extent of at least 75 per cent and cysteine was precipitated as a complex with mercury, while the sulfonic acid (cysteic acid) was isolated from the filtrate in amounts up to 68 per cent of the theoretical amount. Preisler in a preliminary report (11) has applied this same reaction to dithio acids $(RS-SR)$ and has shown that the reaction of dithiohydracrylic acid with mercuric bromide in the presence of hydrobromic acid proceeded similarly to the extent of at least 75 per cent and that the reaction appeared to occur with salts of other metals closely related to silver in the periodic system, i.e., copper, cadmium, thallium.

Owing to the symmetry of the cystine molecule and the presence of two asymmetric carbon atoms, two optically inactive forms, the internally compensated meso form and the racemic (dl) form, are possible. The separation of these two forms (12) has now been effected, the two isomeric inactive cystines differing in solubility, in crystalline form, and in the properties of certain derivatives. The brucine salt of the diacetyl derivative of racemic cystine has been prepared and by its resolution the isolation of both enantiomorphs has been accomplished (13). Dextrorotatory cystine was obtained in hexagonal crystals with a rotation of $[\alpha]_D^{26} = +212°$.

Pirie (14) has prepared and studied in detail the cuprous derivatives of a large number of cysteine derivatives[1] including glutathione and has pointed out the suitability of such cuprous derivatives for use in the isolation and purification of sulfhydryl compounds in general. Earlier studies on the preparation and properties of the complexes of cysteine with cobalt have been extended (15, 16).

Gerwe has described in detail the preparation of iron-free cysteine (17). The optical activity of such a preparation, stored, as cysteine hydrochloride, for one year in a desiccator over calcium chloride, had changed only from $+6.16°$ to $+6.05°$. These data emphasize the stability of purified dry cysteine hydrochloride even when exposed to oxygen.

[1] The cuprous salt of acetylcysteine is reported to exhibit a gel-forming capacity of the same order as that of dibenzoylcystine, a rigid jelly being formed in a concentration of only 0.15 per cent.

Pure cysteine was shown to oxidize spontaneously at a very slow rate (18), which could be accelerated by the addition of very small amounts of iron. Since the rate of oxygen uptake of pure cysteine was many times greater than could be attributed to the traces of iron present, pure cysteine free from iron is believed to be autoxidizable. Autoxidation (19) of iron-free cysteine was not inhibited by cyanides. The addition of iron salts greatly accelerated the oxidation of pure cysteine, but if cyanides were added to a cysteine-iron system, the rate of oxidation was similar to that of a system containing iron-free cysteine alone. It was considered probable that the inhibitory action of cyanides on iron catalysis of the oxidation of cysteine was due to the formation of the ferro- or ferri-cyanide compounds. No catalytic effect on the oxidation of pure cysteine was obtained with pure cystine. These conclusions of Gerwe (18) have been criticized (20) on the ground that the absence of metals other than iron which might catalyze the oxidation of cysteine, e.g., copper or manganese, has not been proved. It is believed that the rate of autoxidation of cysteine reported by Gerwe may well be too high.

Nicolet (21) has suggested that the removal of sulfur from cystine or cysteine by alkali is due primarily to the presence of sulfur in the position β- to the carboxyl group and that the reaction takes place as 1, 4-elimination of hydrogen sulfide from an intermediary enolized form according to the following scheme.

$$\underset{\displaystyle CH_2CH(NH_2)COH}{\overset{\displaystyle SH \qquad\qquad O}{|\qquad\qquad\quad \|}} \quad \longleftarrow \quad \underset{\displaystyle CH_2C(NH_2):COH}{\overset{\displaystyle SH \qquad\qquad OH}{|\qquad\qquad\quad |}}$$

$$\underset{\displaystyle CH_2C(NH_2):COH}{\overset{\displaystyle SH \qquad\qquad OH}{|\qquad\qquad\quad |}} \quad \longrightarrow \quad \underset{\displaystyle CH_2:C(NH_2)COH + H_2S}{\overset{\displaystyle O}{\|}}$$

β-ketonic sulfides were synthesized and were split by alkali with extreme ease to give mercaptans and α, β-unsaturated ketones. The analogy in structure and behavior between these compounds and cystine or cysteine has been pointed out, and various references to the older literature on the alkaline decomposition of cystine which support such a theory are cited. The problem of "labile" sulfur in protein and in insulin is of much importance in this connection.

The rate of destruction of cystine and cysteine under the influence of light from a quartz mercury vapor lamp or diffuse daylight has been studied by Lieben and Molnar (22). Subsequently the rate of liberation of ammonia from cystine and other amino acids by the action of light from a quartz mercury vapor lamp was determined (23). The rate of deamination after two hours' exposure of solutions containing equivalent amounts of amino acids was greatest with histidine (88 per cent of the α-amino nitrogen liberated) and with cystine (32.7 and 36 per cent in two series).

Rôle of Cystine and Its Derivatives in Nutrition

Sullivan (24) has determined the rate of absorption of cystine from the intestine of the young white rat by the procedure of Cori and with the use of the highly specific Sullivan reaction for the determination of the cystine. An absorption rate of 50 mg. of cystine per 100 gm. rat per hour was found, a figure nearly double that recorded earlier (30 mg.) and confirmed by Sullivan in experiments in which the Folin-Looney method was used for the determination of cystine. Since the latter method usually gives values higher than those of the Sullivan method, the interpretation of these data is not clear. In the same animals, increases of approximately 50 per cent were observed in the glutathione content of the liver after cystine feeding.

A comparative study of the oxidation of cystine and various derivatives (25) has been made by a study of the partition of urinary sulfur in the dog after oral or subcutaneous administration of these compounds. The extent of oxidation and excretion varied little with the mode of administration. A summary of the principal results is presented below in tabular form.

Substance	Percentage of Sulfur Administered Excreted in 2 Days	
	As Sulfate Sulfur	As Organic Sulfur
Cystine and cysteine	69.7	3.7
Racemic cystine and cysteine	66.0	16.2
Acetylcysteine	42.7	40.7
Chloroacetylcysteine and dichloroacetylcystine	22.0	81.3
Glycylcysteine	56.5	19.5
Glutathione	72.0	10.5

The figures are averages of several series of experiments and represent the percentages of the total sulfur administered excreted as sulfate and organic sulfur, respectively, during the two-day period immediately following administration of the experimental substances.

The oxidation and excretion in the amounts employed (in most cases the equivalent of 320 mg. of sulfur) showed little variation with the mode of administration. In view of the early statements concerning the stability of glutathione, its ease of oxidation is most surprising. From the point of view of oxidation of the sulfur, there was no difference between the behavior of glutathione and that of cystine in the dog. Of all the cystine-containing peptides studied, glutathione would appear to be the most completely oxidized. This is not unexpected in the experiments in which glutathione was administered orally since it has been shown (26) that glutathione in aqueous solution may be hydrolyzed completely by erepsin. In the injection experiments, however, the oxidation was as complete as in the feeding experiments. It is of interest also that a confirmation of older work was obtained in the diminished ease of oxidation when the α-amino group of cystine was "blocked" (acetylcysteine, etc.). In a brief footnote, it is stated that glutathione (3 gm.) fed to a cystinuric patient was oxidized as readily as was cystine. The theory that cystine is absorbed from the intestine as some complex peptide, which is not utilized normally by the cystinuric, has been previously advanced. In view of the ease of oxidation of glutathione by the cystinuric, this peptide can hardly be concerned.

Mitchell (27) has shown by the paired feeding method that cysteine may improve the growth-promoting value of a cystine-deficient diet for young white rats as effectively as does cystine. He concludes that cysteine "is therefore convertible into cystine in anabolism." Until it is definitely proved that cysteine does not exist and function as such in the animal organism rather than as cystine, such a conclusion must be accepted with reservations. In similar experiments with taurine, no evidence could be obtained that taurine could substitute for cystine in promoting growth.

In a limited number of experiments with rats, the value of dithioethylamine (cystine amine) as a substitute for cystine in diets deficient in their content of cystine has been demonstrated (28). Both cystine and cystine amine when added to the basal diet caused increased growth of the rats as compared with the rate of growth of animals on the basal diets, the increased gain in weight due to the addition of the cystine amine being 64.2 per cent of that due to the addition of cystine. Unfortunately no records of food intake are recorded. This is the first investigation in which the successful replacement of cystine or cysteine in the diet by a related sulfur compound has occurred.

Attention should again be called to the preliminary paper (5) in which it is reported that addition of methionine to the diet resulted in the promotion of growth of rats on a cystine-deficient diet.

By the use of paired feeding experiments with rats, another group of proteins, the mixed proteins of the alfalfa plant (29), has been added to the list of those in whose nutritive value cystine is the limiting factor.

Bonsma (30) in a study of the seasonal and individual variations in the sulfur content of the wool of South African sheep has concluded that although the sulfur content of sheep's wool is largely an individual character inherent or inheritable, this characteristic figure may be altered by environmental variations, as for example, limitation of the cystine supply in the natural diet. As long as the cystine requirements for the production of wool are adequately met by the food, wool with normal cystine content is produced, but under conditions of inadequate supply of cystine in the diet, a reduction in the sulfur content of the wool produced results. Bonsma believes that such nutritive factors are operative upon sheep grazing under typical sheep-farming conditions on the South African veld and that these variations in the nutritive value of the pasture are reflected in the varying composition of the wool grown during the different seasons of the year. The problem of the relation of cystine content of the diet to the growth of hair, wool, and related structures thus acquires a new importance from the standpoint of practical animal husbandry.

Earlier work from the laboratory of Karl Thomas had shown that the processes of endogenous protein catabolism did not result in the production of cystine or cysteine available for the detoxication of the monohalogen derivatives of benzene, since no mercapturic acids could be isolated from the urine when bromobenzene was fed to fasting dogs or to dogs on a protein-free diet. Abderhalden and Wertheimer (31) have criticized these experiments because of the large amounts of the relatively toxic benzene derivative fed to dogs weakened by prolonged fasting. In their own experiments, smaller doses of bromobenzene were used and the preliminary periods of fasting were short (1.5–2.5 days). Under these conditions, mercapturic-acid synthesis could be demonstrated in both fasting dogs and dogs fed a protein-free diet. In a subsequent investigation (32) after longer preliminary periods of fasting (3–5 days) dogs were fed rice, meat, or bread with moderate amounts of bromobenzene. No mercapturic acid could be isolated from the urine on the first day, despite the presence of protein in the diet; while in the one experiment in which cystine was also fed the mercapturic acid was obtained. The synthesis occurred readily on subsequent feeding days. Similar results were obtained with dogs previously fasted and phlorhizinized. The authors believed that these results were to be interpreted not as due to a lack of the ability to synthesize mercapturic acid, but rather to a lack of available cystine for synthesis. It is suggested that in conditions of hunger or cystine-deficient diets, any cystine available must be used for the more essential reactions, such as synthesis of insulin or glutathione, or for the renewal of body protein and that the conjugation with bromobenzene cannot occur till these requirements for cystine are met. Such a view would seem more logical than the assumption that the endogenous catabolism of protein does not yield cystine or cysteine.

It has been shown by Lawrie (33) in Hele's laboratory that the young white rat readily effects the synthesis of mercapturic acid but that the rabbit is able to convert a very small fraction only of injected iodobenzene into the corresponding mercapturic acid. Neither of these animals can oxidize p-iodophenylmercapturic acid to ethereal sulfate. Lawrie has also suggested a modification of the usual method of isolation of the mercapturic acid from urine which should prove of value.

CONJUGATED SULFURIC ACIDS

A new conjugated derivative of protein with sulfuric acid has been prepared from beef spleen (34) in which all the sulfur present in the molecule was in the form of an ester of sulfuric acid, the total sulfur content being equal to the total sulfate sulfur obtained after hydrolysis.

Neuberg and Hofmann (35) have summarized our knowledge of sulfatases and have added a new enzyme of this type, a chondrosulfatase (36). This enzyme which was able to effect the hydrolysis of chondrotin-sulfuric acid was present in the cultures of certain bacteria belonging to the fluorescens non-liquefaciens group and was also observed in cultures of *Bacillus proteus* and *pyocyaneus*. An enzyme (glucosulfatase) which is able to effect the hydrolysis of glucose-monosulfate (37) has been found in the autolysates of certain Japanese snails (*Eulota*). This enzyme was unable to hydrolyze other sulfuric-acid esters as phenylsulfuric acid, ethylsulfuric acid, etc. Hommerberg (38) has compared the activity of phosphatase and sulfatase (phenosulfatase) from various animal tissues and has shown that, in desiccated tissue, the activity of the two types of enzymes runs parallel. No greater content of sulfatase was found in pig brain than in pig kidney. It was impossible to extract the sulfatase from the tissue since autolysis or elution resulted in loss of activity in the material obtained.

Studies of the distribution of urinary sulfur have shown that, when isobarbituric acid was fed to a dog in moderate amounts (1.8–2.5 gm.), from 22 to 30 per cent of the compound fed appeared in the urine as a sulfuric-acid ester (39). A substance was isolated from the urine, which, although not pure, appeared to be isobarbituric-acid sulfate. After the oral administration of alloxan to dogs (40), a distinct drop in the output of inorganic sulfate sulfur of the urine was noted. Inasmuch as this decrease was not compensated for by the rise of any other sulfur fraction of the urine, the assumption was made that alloxan may be partially excreted in the bile, possibly as an ethereal sulfate.

Non-protein Sulfur of Blood

Total non-protein sulfur has been determined in trichloroacetic acid filtrates of blood, plasma, and serum by St. Lorant and his co-workers (41). The organic sulfur compounds of the filtrates are converted to sulfates by an alkaline oxidizing mixture (42), and the sulfates are reduced to hydrogen sulfide which is distilled off and determined colorimetrically as methylene blue by the highly specific Caro's reaction (43). The values obtained for whole blood (human) while remarkably constant (6.8 mg. per 100 cc.) were somewhat higher than those previously recorded, while the average value for human serum or plasma (2.5 mg. per 100 cc.) was slightly lower than the values of most other observers, as for example, the figures 3.2–5.6 mg. recently obtained by Chatron (44).

St. Lorant has also calculated the glutathione content of blood (41) on the assumptions that (a) the cellular elements contain no sulfur compounds other than glutathione and the plasma only other forms of sulfur and that (b) the cellular elements contain not only glutathione sulfur but also the sulfur-containing constituents of the plasma in the same concentrations as the plasma. He considered that the true content of glutathione sulfur of whole blood was approximately the average of the values calculated on the foregoing two assumptions, or 4.86 (men) and 4.80 (women) mg. These figures check well with the glutathione sulfur as calculated from the gluta-thione determinations made by the Tunnicliffe (45) or Gabbe (46) methods.

Modifications of the benzidine method for the determination of inorganic sulfate sulfur in small amounts of blood have been pro-posed (44, 47, 48). Values of 0.5–1.5 mg. (47) and of 0.1–0.5 mg. (48) for human plasma and of 0.8–2.2 mg. (44) for human serum have been obtained. In nephritis and cardio-renal disease, an increased retention of inorganic sulfate sulfur was observed (48, 49) coincident with the increased retention of urea and non-protein nitrogen (48).

GLUTATHIONE

A substance designated as "glutathion(?)" (50), from which cys-teine could be split readily by bacteria or dilute hydrochloric acid, has been isolated in small amounts from dried peas (0.1 gm. from 2.5 kgm. of dry material). This isolation of glutathione from the seeds of one of the higher forms of plants is of particular interest in view of the fact that among the earliest studies of the nitroprusside reaction were those of Gola on plant tissues, made in 1902 before the full signifi-cance of this reaction was recognized.

Mason (51) has shown that on aëration at a pH of 7.6, reduced glutathione may be quantitatively converted into oxidized glutathione without loss of either sulfur or nitrogen. The purified product con-tained two molecules of alcohol which were so firmly bound that they could not be removed despite the use of means which are usually effective for their removal. The preparation of the copper salt of oxidized glutathione has also been described (52).

Fleming (53) has described an adaptation of the nitroprusside reaction for the quantitative determination of glutathione. When applied to top yeast, the results by this method were higher (0.34 per cent) than those obtained by the same author by the iodine-titration method (0.22 per cent). According to King and Lucas (54) accurate values in the iodometric determination (starch indicator) of glutathione are to be obtained only in solutions relatively strongly acid (optimum pH, 5.0) and at a temperature not exceeding 25° Gavrilescu (55), on the other hand, in a comparative study of the use of starch and the nitroprusside reaction in glutathione estimations, obtained high figures with starch as indicator when the determinations were carried out in acid solution and in the absence of potassium iodide, while under the same conditions but in the presence of an excess of potassium iodide, low values were obtained. With a neutral reaction (litmus) and in the presence of an excess of iodide, the values obtained with the use of the starch indicator were comparable to those obtained using the nitroprusside end-point. On the basis of these findings the author proposes an accurate modification of Tunnicliffe's method with the use of starch as indicator. Kühnau (56) has described a modification of the iodometric method[2] for micro determination of the content of reduced and total glutathione in liver. A modification of Sullivan's method (57) has been proposed, which makes possible the accurate determination of cysteine in the presence of glutathione.

With the more recent development of improved methods for glutathione determinations in blood and tissues, the values obtained assume more significance. Since the glutathione of the blood is believed to exist chiefly if not entirely in the corpuscles, a definite relationship between the glutathione content of the blood and erythrocyte count might be anticipated. Bach and Bach (58) have shown that normal human blood contains 30 to 44 mg. per cent of glutathione with a glutathione quotient (mg. GSH per 100 cc./millions of erythrocytes per cmm.) of 7 to 8.6. In true pernicious anemia, there was observed a parallel increase in the GSH quotient and catalase quotient, while in secondary anemias no such increases in blood catalase or glutathione were found. Platt (45) has also studied the variations in disease (normal values, 30 to 50 mg. per cent) and has shown that, in the majority of pathological conditions, the values were within the limits of normal variations, but that, in anemia and in some cyanotic conditions, the amount of glutathione relative to the number of corpuscles was increased. Glutathione was also found in pus and in leucocytes. Fetal blood has been shown to contain more catalase and glutathione than maternal blood (59), an increased amount which may be compensatory for the purpose of overcoming the oxygen deficiency of the fetus. At high altitudes (1,300 to 1,500 m. above sea-level), the glutathione content of the blood has been shown to be increased above the normal values (60). After one hour's irradiation with natural Alpine sunshine, however, the glutathione content of the blood decreased as did also the GSH quotient (60). Yokota (61) has studied the changes in the glutathione content of various tissues

[2] Hopkins and Elliott (62) in their studies of glutathione in relation to oxidation in the liver have used the conditions for titration defined by Kühnau with satisfactory results.

of rats and guinea pigs on irradiation, but observed little change. Although slight increases in the values for lung tissues and decreased values for the spleen are reported, the variations between individuals were so extreme that the results would seem of doubtful significance.

Hopkins and Elliott (62) have determined the relative capacity of various mammalian tissues to reduce the disulfide form of glutathione under anaërobic conditions and have followed the course of the oxidation of the thiol group during the survival respiration of the hepatic tissue.

The influence of the presence of small amounts of various metallic salts on the rate of oxidation of crystalline glutathione in phosphate buffer solutions at a pH of 7.27 has been studied by Voegtlin and his associates (63). Of the metallic salts studied, copper was by far the most effective catalyst, while iron and manganese, other metals of physiological importance, were without any accelerating effect on oxidation. A method for the preparation of glutathione of low copper content is described, a product which shows a very low rate of oxidation in the absence of a metallic catalyst. The authors believe that blood serum contains sufficient copper to explain the rapid oxidation previously observed when crystalline glutathione was added to blood serum (64). In contrast to the oxidation of cysteine, the oxidation of glutathione was not catalyzed by the other heavy metals of physiological significance, e.g., iron and manganese. The possible physiological relationship between copper and glutathione has been discussed (63). The same authors (64) have also studied the influence of glutathione on the oxygen consumption of living cells and have extended previous work concerning the relationship between arsenic compounds and glutathione (65).

Sulfhydryl Groups and Cellular Activity

Hammett, Reimann, and their associates have presented additional data in support of the hypothesis previously advanced that the sulfhydryl group is a specific stimulus to cell proliferation by increase in cell numbers. These studies have included the investigation of the reaction of the skin to sulfhydryl groups and its significance both physiologically (66) and pathologically (67), as well as further application to the problem of the healing of wounds (68). Evidence has also been presented to demonstrate that gross regeneration in the foot of the hermit crab (69) may be stimulated by the sulfhydryl group, i.e., that the chemical equilibrium regulative of growth by increase in cell number is a determinant of the rate of regeneration as it has been in all other types of cell multiplication so far studied by them. On the other hand, Morgulis and Green (70) were unable to obtain any acceleration of the process of regeneration in *Podarke obscura* by the influence of a number of sulfhydryl compounds and have criticized both the experiments of Hammett and the interpretations drawn from the data. Gaunt (71) in summarizing the results of studies of the influence of cysteine solutions on the rate of development of the eggs of fresh-water snails concluded that the sulfhydryl group is not invariably a stimulus to cell division.

The significance of sulfhydryl groups in the skin (72) and in the tissues as a whole (73) has also been discussed by Giroud. Randoin and Fabre (74) have studied the changes in sulfhydryl derivatives in the tissues of the normal rat and under conditions of undernutrition and deprivation of vitamin B.

INSULIN AND SULFUR

The problem of the sulfur content of insulin and the relation of the sulfur to its physiological activity is still unsolved. Scott (75) has compared the sulfur content of crystalline insulin prepared from beef, sheep, hog, and fish pancreas. The sulfur contents of these crystalline products from different animal sources showed a very close agreement with each other (3.06 to 3.38 per cent) but were slightly higher than the values previously reported. A sample of beef insulin, obtained after ten recrystallizations, did not show on analysis a sulfur content different from the other products (3.13 per cent). Cysteine or glutathione was able to completely inactivate crystalline insulin (76). The inactivated material was not reactivated either by reoxidation or by treatment with alkali. DuVigneaud and his associates point out that while the disulfide linkage alone can hardly be considered to be responsible for the insulin action, so far no one has split out or changed the disulfide grouping without destroying the potency of insulin. They believe that reduction of the disulfide linkage of insulin by glutathione or cysteine was the cause of the inactivation observed and that the sulfhydryl form of insulin is inactive.

THE RELATION BETWEEN NITROGEN AND SULFUR METABOLISM

The question of the nature of "deposit" or retained protein and the conditions under which it is deposited or catabolized has again been approached by a study of the N/S ratios both in normal individuals and in disease. Wilson (77) in experiments with a normal man has concluded that the organism may store protein of varying composition as evidenced by the N/S ratio of the material retained after feeding meat at various levels. He has suggested that the sulfur content of the retained protein may be the determining factor in its stability and that the higher the content of sulfur, the more stable the retained material. "Sulfur or a moiety containing sulfur appears to be the mobile unit both in anabolism and catabolism."

Cuthbertson (78) has added to his earlier studies of the changes in nitrogen and sulfur metabolism resulting from tissue injury (bone fractures, minor surgical operations). After such injury marked loss of nitrogen from the body, associated with increased excretion of sulfur, was observed. The increased sulfur excretion was due largely to increases in the inorganic sulfate fraction of the urine. Striking illustrations of the constancy of the excretion of organic sulfur despite marked variation in the nitrogen level are presented in his data. In earlier studies, Grabfield showed that in "nephrosis" with edema, a marked retention of sulfur, greater than that of nitrogen, was observed with a high N/S ratio of the urine and a low ratio of the "retained" protein. The relationship between the excretion of nitrogen and sulfur in nephritic patients without edema has now been studied (79). There has been observed a marked tendency for such patients to go into negative sulfur balance, while remaining in positive nitrogen balance. Remarkably low ratios of urinary nitrogen to sulfur were obtained (4.3–8.7). The contrast between these findings and the previous ones in nephrosis with edema has led to the suggestion that in Bright's disease there is exhibited a defect in the intermediary metabolism of sulfur.

FORMATION OF HYDROGEN SULFIDE

A hydrogenase has been demonstrated to be present in a typical sulfate-reducing organism isolated from river mud (80), which can reduce sulfates quantitatively to sulfide by molecular hydrogen, $H_2SO_4 + 4H_2 = H_2S + 4H_2O$. The conditions in the intestine under which sulfates are reduced to sulfides (81) have also been studied.

LITERATURE CITED

1. GROTE, I. W., J. Biol. Chem., 93, 25 (1931)
2. BARGER, G., AND WEICHSELBAUM, T. E., Biochem. J., 25, 997 (1931)
3. WINDUS, W., AND MARVEL, C. S., J. Am. Chem. Soc., 53, 3490 (1931)

4. EMERSON, O. H., KIRK, P. L., AND SCHMIDT, C. L. A., *J. Biol. Chem.*, **92**, 449 (1931)
5. JACKSON, R. W., AND BLOCK, R. J., *Science*, **74**, 414 (1931)
6. BARRITT, J., AND RIMINGTON, C., *Biochem. J.*, **25**, 1072 (1931)
7. RIMINGTON, C., *Biochem. J.*, **25**, 71 (1931)
8. BEKKER, J. G., AND KING, A. T., *Biochem. J.*, **25**, 1077 (1931)
9. TOENNIES, G., AND LAVINE, T. F., *J. Biol. Chem.*, **90**, 203 (1931)
10. SIMONSEN, D. G., *J. Biol. Chem.*, **94**, 323 (1931)
11. PREISLER, P. W., *J. Biol. Chem.*, **92**, xxxvi (1931)
12. LORING, H. S., AND DuVIGNEAUD, V., *Proc. Soc. Exptl. Biol. Med.*, **29**, 41 (1931)
13. HOLLANDER, L., AND DuVIGNEAUD, V., *J. Biol. Chem.*, **94**, 243 (1931)
14. PIRIE, N. W., *Biochem. J.*, **25**, 614 (1931)
15. SCHUBERT, M. P., *J. Am. Chem. Soc.*, **53**, 3851 (1931)
16. KENDALL, E. C., AND HOLST, J. E., *J. Biol. Chem.*, **91**, 435 (1931)
17. GERWE, E. G., *J. Biol. Chem.*, **91**, 57 (1931)
18. GERWE, E. G., *J. Biol. Chem.*, **92**, 399 (1931)
19. GERWE, E. G., *J. Biol. Chem.*, **92**, 525 (1931)
20. ELVEHJEM, C. A., *Science*, **74**, 568 (1931)
21. NICOLET, B. H., *J. Am. Chem. Soc.*, **53**, 3066 (1931)
22. LIEBEN, F., AND MOLNAR, E., *Biochem. Z.*, **230**, 347 (1931)
23. LIEBEN, F., AND URBAN, F., *Biochem. Z.*, **239**, 250 (1931)
24. SULLIVAN, M. X., AND HESS, W. C., *U.S. Pub. Health Reports*, Supplement No. 89, 16 pp. (1931)
25. HELE, T. S., AND PIRIE, N. W., *Biochem. J.*, **25**, 1095 (1931)
26. MASON, H. L., *J. Biol. Chem.*, **90**, 25 (1931)
27. MITCHELL, H. H., *J. Nutrition*, **4**, 95 (1931)
28. SULLIVAN, M. X., HESS, W. C., AND SEBRELL, W. H., *U.S., Pub. Health Reports*, **46**, 1294 (1931)
29. HAAG, J. R., *J. Nutrition*, **4**, 363 (1931)
30. BONSMA, F. N., *J. Text. Inst.*, **22**, T 305 (1931)
31. ABDERHALDEN, E., AND WERTHEIMER, E., *Z. physiol. Chem.*, **198**, 18 (1931)
32. ABDERHALDEN, E., AND WERTHEIMER, E., *Z. physiol. Chem.*, **201**, 267 (1931)
33. LAWRIE, N. R., *Biochem. J.*, **25**, 1037 (1931)
34. EBEL, A., *Biochem. Z.*, **231**, 306 (1931)
35. NEUBERG, C., AND HOFMANN, E., *Naturwissenschaften*, **19**, 484 (1931)
36. NEUBERG, C., AND HOFMANN, E., *Biochem. Z.*, **234**, 345 (1931)
37. SODA, T., AND HATTORI, C., *Proc. Imper. Acad. (Japan)*, **7**, 269 (1931)
38. HOMMERBERG, C., *Z. physiol. Chem.*, **200**, 69 (1931)
39. STEKOL, J. A., AND CERECEDO, L. R., *J. Biol. Chem.*, **93**, 275 (1931)
40. CERECEDO, L. R., *J. Biol. Chem.*, **93**, 283 (1931)
41. ST. LORANT, I., HAJDU, N., AND WEIL, W., *Z. physiol. Chem.*, **200**, 121 (1931)
42. ST. LORANT, I., AND BLOBNER, F., *Z. physiol. Chem.*, **199**, 112 (1931)
43. ST. LORANT, I., AND KOPETZ, L., *Biochem. Z.*, **238**, 67 (1931)
44. CHATRON, M., *Bull. soc. chim. biol.*, **13**, 300 (1931)
45. PLATT, R., *Brit. J. Exptl. Path.*, **12**, 139 (1931)

46. BACH, E., AND BACH, E., *Biochem. Z.*, **236**, 174 (1931)
47. COPE, C. L., *Biochem. J.*, **25**, 1183 (1931)
48. CUTHBERTSON, D. P., AND TOMPSETT, S. L., *Biochem. J.*, **25**, 1237 (1931)
49. DE MICHELIS, V., *Minerva Med.*, **1**, 318 (1931); *Chem. Abst.*, **25**, 3062 (1931)
50. KOZLOWSKI, A., *Biochem. Z.*, **241**, 407 (1931)
51. MASON, H. L., *J. Biol. Chem.*, **90**, 409 (1931)
52. KOZLOWSKI, A., *Biochem. Z.*, **241**, 403 (1931)
53. FLEMING, R., *Compt. rend. soc. biol.*, **106**, 259 (1931)
54. KING, E. J., AND LUCAS, C. C., *Biochem. Z.*, **235**, 66 (1931)
55. GAVRILESCU, N., *Biochem. J.*, **25**, 1190 (1931)
56. KÜHNAU, J., *Biochem. Z.*, **230**, 353 (1931)
57. SULLIVAN, M. X., AND HESS, W. C., *U.S. Pub. Health Reports*, **46**, 390 (1931)
58. BACH, E., AND BACH, E., *Biochem. Z.*, **236**, 174 (1931)
59. ANSELMINO, K. J., AND HOFFMANN, F., *Arch. Gynäkol.*, **143**, 505 (1931)
60. DESCHWANDER, J. VON, *Strahlentherapie*, **39**, 278 (1931)
61. YOKOTA, S., *Biochem. Z.*, **239**, 303 (1931)
62. HOPKINS, F. G., AND ELLIOTT, K. A. C., *Proc. Roy. Soc. (London), B*, **109**, 58 (1931)
63. VOEGTLIN, C., JOHNSON, J. M., AND ROSENTHAL, S. M., *J. Biol. Chem.*, **93**, 435 (1931)
64. ROSENTHAL, S. M., AND VOEGTLIN, C., *U.S. Pub. Health Reports*, **46**, 521 (1931)
65. VOEGTLIN, C., ROSENTHAL, S. M., AND JOHNSON, J. M., *U.S. Pub. Health Reports*, **46**, 339 (1931)
66. HAMMETT, F. S., *Protoplasma*, **13**, 331 (1931)
67. REIMANN, S. P., *Am. J. Cancer*, **15**, 2149 (1931)
68. REIMANN, S. P., *Ann. Surgery*, **93**, 624 (1931)
69. HAMMETT, F. S., AND SMITH, D. W., *Protoplasma*, **13**, 261 (1931)
70. MORGULIS, S., AND GREEN, D. E., *Proc. Soc. Exptl. Biol. Med.*, **28**, 797 (1930–1931)
71. GAUNT, R., *Proc. Soc. Exptl. Biol. Med.*, **28**, 660 (1930–1931)
72. GIROUD, A., AND BULLIARD, H., *Bull. soc. chim. biol.*, **13**, 138 (1931)
73. GIROUD, A., *Bull. soc. chim. biol.*, **13**, 141 (1931)
74. RANDOIN, L., AND FABRE, R., *Compt. rend.*, **192**, 815 (1931)
75. SCOTT, D. A., *J. Biol. Chem.*, **92**, 281 (1931)
76. DUVIGNEAUD, V., FITCH, A., PEKAREK, E., AND LOCKWOOD, W. W., *J. Biol. Chem.*, **94**, 233 (1931)
77. WILSON, H. E. C., *J. Physiol.*, **72**, 327 (1931)
78. CUTHBERTSON, D. P., *Biochem. J.*, **25**, 236 (1931)
79. GRABFIELD, G. P., *J. Clin. Investigation*, **10**, 309 (1931)
80. STEPHENSON, M., AND STICKLAND, L. H., *Biochem. J.*, **25**, 215 (1931)
81. ZÖRKENDÖRFER, W., *Arch. exptl. Path. Pharmakol.*, **161**, 437 (1931)

DEPARTMENT OF PHYSIOLOGICAL CHEMISTRY
UNIVERSITY OF MICHIGAN
ANN ARBOR, MICHIGAN

THE CHEMISTRY AND METABOLISM OF THE COMPOUNDS OF PHOSPHORUS*

By H. D. Kay

Department of Biochemistry
University of Toronto

While it is convenient to consider in a separate review the chemistry and metabolism of the compounds of phosphorus, the line of separation between this field and those which perhaps more properly belong to other reviewers is not easy to draw. Compounds of phosphorus are present in every cell and fluid of the body; they are concerned with carbohydrate metabolism, with lipins and lipin metabolism, with certain types of protein synthesis, with the synthesis and breakdown of nucleic acids, with calcium metabolism, with the buffering power of blood and other tissues, with the growth and maintenance of bone, with muscular contraction, with the functioning of the central nervous system, and suffer changes in a large variety of diseased conditions. Any discussion of recent work on these compounds must inevitably abut on one or other of these fields, with some risk of trespass into other sections of this volume, though a small degree of overlapping is not, perhaps, entirely deplorable.

Recent Reviews

Among books and reviews which have been published lately, the following dealing with certain aspects of phosphorus metabolism and forming a background for the discussion of the most recent work may be cited: Peters and Van Slyke's article on phosphorus in *Quantitative Clinical Chemistry* (1); the chapter on the biochemistry of phosphorus compounds in Pryde's *Recent Advances in Biochemistry* (2); Meyerhof's (3) and Aubel and Cahn's (4) reviews on the rôle of phosphorus compounds in muscle; Euler's (5, 6) summaries of recent work on yeast fermentation and co-zymase; Roche's (7) account of work on the phosphatases of blood; Hunter's (8) review on calcium, phosphorus, and the parathyroids in health and disease; Milroy's (8a) article on the chemistry of skeletal muscular contraction.

* Received January 6, 1932.

Phosphorus Compounds Occurring Naturally

A list of phosphorus compounds known to occur or believed to occur in living organisms, or to be produced by the activity of living organisms, may prove useful at the outset. The following are known to occur:

a) *Inorganic phosphate*

b) *Phosphites and hypophosphites* (9)

c) *Hexose diphosphate* (γ fructose 1,6-diphosphoric acid), by dried yeast or yeast juice fermentation of several hexoses (10)

d) *Hexose monophosphate* ("Robison ester," mainly glucose-6-phosphoric acid) from same source as hexose diphosphate (10, cf. p. 193)

e) *Hexose monophosphate* ("Neuberg ester," fructose-6-phosphoric acid) enzymic hydrolysis of hexose diphosphate (11, 12)

f) *Hexose monophosphate,* by action of dried galactose-fermenting yeast on galactose (13)

g) *Trehalose monophosphate* from same source as hexose phosphate (14)

h) *Disaccharide monophosphate,* by action of *B. delbrücki* on hexose diphosphate (15)

i) *Diphospho l-glyceric acid* in red blood corpuscles (16)

j) *Adenylic acid* (adenine pentose phosphate) in red blood corpuscles, muscles, etc. (see pages 197 *et seq.*)

k) *Inosinic acid* in muscle extracts, probably derived from adenylic acid by deamination

l) *Adenylic acid pyrophosphate,* in muscle (see page 198)

m) *Creatine phosphate,* "phosphagen," in mammalian muscle (17, 18)

n) *Arginine phosphate,* "phosphagen," in crustacean muscle (19)

o) *Lecithin, kephalin, and sphingomyelin* (20)

p) *Nucleo-proteins, nucleic acids, and nucleotides* other than adenylic acid and inosinic acid (21)

q) *Phospho-proteins; casein, vitellin, ichthulin, ranovin,* and other similar compounds from the eggs of invertebrates (22)

r) Many *proteins,* not phosphoproteins, containing minute quantities of phosphate as an essential ingredient (23)

The following phosphorus compounds are believed to occur:

a) Pentose phosphoric esters

b) Free glycerophosphate in liver tissue (24)

c) The diphosphoric ester of an α-ketotrihydroxyadipic acid in the
  red blood cells (25).

d) A monophosphoglyceric acid in yeast fermentation (13)

e) Two non-reducing phosphoric esters from action of dried *B. casei*
  on glucose, one probably containing an oxidised, the other a
  reduced derivative of glucose (26)

Some recent methods of preparation of naturally occurring phosphoric esters.—Materials and methods employed in the preparation
and separation of the several phosphoric esters obtained by the action
of yeast juice, dried yeast, or zymin on glucose or fructose have been
described by Robison and Morgan (27). They have studied the
effect on the relative proportions of the different esters of varying
the rate of addition of phosphate. Hexose monophosphate is obtained
in maximum yield when the fermentation is rapid, with inorganic
phosphate in considerable excess. Trehalose monophosphate, on the
other hand, increases in amount when the fermentation is allowed to
continue for some time after the addition of phosphate, but again
decreases if fermentation is too prolonged. Veibel (28) also discusses
the quantitative relationships, at various times during the fermentation process, between the various phosphoric esters. He finds the
pure Robison ester (glucose-6-phosphate, see pp. 193 *et seq.*), to be
the main constituent of the monophosphate fraction in the earlier
stages of fermentation, but later it diminishes in quantity, whilst the
Neuberg ester (fructose-6-phosphate) and trehalose monophosphate
increase.

The method of isolation of adenyl pyrophosphate from muscle is
described by Lohmann (29).

The Chemical Composition of Bone

Bone, though highly mineralised, is a living, organised tissue in
dynamic equilibrium with the tissue fluids. That its mineral composition would be constant would therefore seem, *a priori,* a little unlikely. Nevertheless analytical findings are almost unanimous that
bone, derived from any part of the skeleton, or taken from any
species of vertebrate animal, has on the whole an astonishingly constant mineral composition. These findings have led to several endeavours to give to this compound of apparently constant composition
a chemical formula and to compare it with naturally occurring minerals of similar composition.

If a true compound is present in bone ash, it is of considerable importance that its exact chemical nature be determined. Otherwise the relationship which exists between the blood plasma, the tissue fluids, and bone, with its direct bearing on the problems of bone formation and disease, cannot be properly assessed.

During the past two or three years, knowledge of the chemical composition of the solid phase in bone has been accumulating from two main sources, (*a*) chemical and (*b*) physical.

a) *Chemical analyses.*—From chemical analyses it has hitherto been taken for granted that tricalcium phosphate $Ca_3(PO_4)_2$ either mixed or in loose chemical combination with calcium carbonate is the principal mineral salt of bone. Gassmann (30), for example, has held for some time that the bone substance is to be formulated, on Werner's system, as follows:

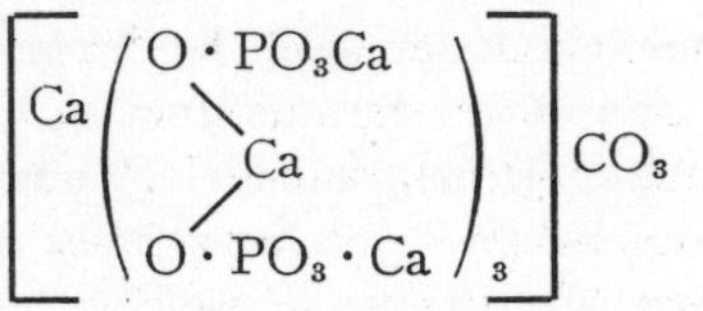

$$\left[Ca \left(\begin{array}{c} O \cdot PO_3Ca \\ \diagdown \\ Ca \\ \diagup \\ O \cdot PO_3 \cdot Ca \end{array} \right)_3 \right] CO_3$$

i.e., a phosphato-calcium carbonate. He believes he has obtained support for this view by recent experiments *in vitro* during which he has prepared a glycine compound of related structure. Klement (31, 32) has criticised Gassmann's formula on the grounds that it does not fit the analytical data, and that calcium carbonate is present only in small and variable amounts.

Shear and Kramer (33, 34) have brought forward evidence that is not in accord with the usually accepted views, and suggest that the presence of $CaHPO_4$ in bone should not be dismissed as an impossibility.

In normal adult bone the main inorganic constituents are calcium, phosphate, carbonate, and magnesium. Assuming that the carbonate is present as calcium carbonate, and the magnesium as phosphate, there is some 85 per cent of calcium phosphate and 14 per cent of calcium carbonate present. Of the 1 per cent remaining, the greater part is magnesium[1] phosphate with very small amounts of potassium,

---

[1] Some of the Mg may be, and probably is, present as $MgCO_3$, but even if the whole of the Mg is present as carbonate, the calculation of the residual Ca/P ratio is not materially affected.

combined either as carbonate or phosphate, and traces of other mineral substances. The residual Ca/P ratio, after correcting for the carbonate and the Mg present, works out at 2.00 ± 0.01 for rat's bone (33) and from 1.99 to 2.04 for a group of mammals (35). For $Ca_3(PO_4)_2$ the ratio would be 1.94; for $CaHPO_4$, 1.29. The belief that the principal component of bone is $Ca_3(PO_4)_2$, possibly chemically combined in some complex with $CaCO_3$, is thus not without a quantitative basis, although it is to be remembered that $Ca_3(PO_4)_2$ itself can only exist, if it exists at all, under conditions which are absent in bone (36, 37). The close approximation between the experimental figure for bone and the theoretical value for $Ca_3(PO_4)_2$ does not completely exclude the possibility that $CaHPO_4$ combined with $Ca(OH)_2$, i.e., a basic secondary phosphate, may be present.

Klement (32) finds that if pure solid $CaHPO_4$ is shaken up with frequently renewed phosphate buffer solution, the composition of the solid phase changes, at first rapidly and then more slowly till, after several weeks at $37°$, equilibrium is attained when the solid has the composition $6Ca_3(PO_4)_2 \cdot Ca(OH)_2$ ("semi-basic calcium phosphate"). The composition of the final reaction product is, within certain limits, independent of the pH of the phosphate buffer mixture used. If pure $CaHPO_4$ is shaken with bicarbonate solution (Tyrode's or even $NaHCO_3$) a similar equilibrium product is eventually obtained which contains, however, a relatively small quantity of $CaCO_3$. Whether or not it is possible, from results obtained by such *in vitro* experiments, to draw any conclusions with regard to the salts of bone, Klement's suggestion is not without interest, that the first substance laid down in growing bone is $CaHPO_4 \cdot 2H_2O$, which is then rapidly hydrolysed to $6(Ca_3PO_4)_2 \cdot Ca(OH)_2$. He further supposes that a small and variable quantity of $CaCO_3$ is also deposited, not in chemical combination with the "semi-basic phosphate." The presence in bone ash of Na, K, Mg, Cl, and CO_3 is due in part to the presence of blood serum imprisoned within the bone. (In the case of Mg at least, when one considers the paucity of this metal in the serum, it is evident that only a very small part of the bone Mg could be accounted for in this way.)

Recent work of Morgulis (35) on carefully prepared mineral matter of bone, obtained from vertebrae by Gabriel's method, which consists in dissolving out the entire organic matrix with 3 per cent KOH in glycerol at 200–250°C. without ashing, agrees with previous findings that the bone contains definitely more calcium than can be accounted for on the basis of phosphate and carbonate, and furthermore that this excess of calcium is present as a basic complex. Morgulis points out that if the bone ash contained $CaHPO_4$ it would be converted into pyrophosphate on incineration, and could not be determined until it had been changed back to orthophosphate by acid hydrolysis. Such a change does not occur.

From his analyses he concludes that the ratio between $CaCO_3$ and the calcium-phosphate-containing complex is not the same for all bones. Thus in analyses of the bone ash of marine fishes much less $CaCO_3$ (only about 7 per cent) is found, as against 11 to 12 per cent for mammalian bones. This difference may be correlated with the low bicarbonate content of the blood of these fishes. It would be expected, if the principal bone salt were a definite crystalline compound of calcium phosphate and carbonate, that the composition of this crystal would not be altered by changes in the amounts in solution in blood plasma of the essential components of the crystal, although its rate of deposition might be affected thereby. It is also well known that other conditions, such as the state of nutrition and the age of the animal, affect the phosphate/carbonate ratio. On the other hand, there is usually a fairly constant ratio between $Ca_3(PO_4)_2$ and the excess calcium of 6/1, which is the same for both marine and terrestrial bone. This finding receives corroboration from some of Shear and Kramer's analytical data for whole (unincinerated) bone material. Morgulis believes that the chemical evidence points strongly to the possibility that the principal component of bone ash is a complex salt of the probable composition $Ca[\{Ca_3(PO_4)_2\}_6](OH)_2$.

The results of Klement and of Morgulis with regard to the chemical composition of the ash of adult bone are thus in fairly close agreement.

b) Physical analyses.—The physical findings depend on determinations of refractive indices and of X-ray spectra. Taylor and Sheard (38) have compared the refractive indices of a number of samples of thoroughly dried bone with those of various known minerals containing calcium carbonate or phosphate. They find values of 1.56 for bone, 1.58 for dentine, 1.62 for dental enamel. This is the reverse order of the organic content of these materials, which is highest for bone and least for enamel. Of the crystalline minerals containing calcium phosphate and carbonate, two (dahlite, $CaCO_3 \cdot 2[Ca_3(PO_4)_2]$ and podolite, $CaCO_3 \cdot 3Ca_3[PO_4]_2$) have refractive indices near to that of dental enamel. Dahlite has a calcium carbonate/phosphate ratio which is near to that of bone.

DeJong in 1926 (39) made a series of X-ray diffraction photographs of modern and fossil bones and found lines characteristic of fluorapatite $CaF_2 \cdot 3Ca_3(PO_4)_2$, although all the apatite series in which F_2 may be replaced by Cl_2, $(OH)_2$, O, SO_4, give very similar diffraction patterns. Taylor and Sheard (38) have repeated this work with the same samples of bone material they used for refractive index determinations, and also observe patterns indicative of an apatite structure, although there are minor variations possibly ascribable to the presence in bone of magnesium compounds in small amounts, or to traces of alkali salts. They conclude from the refractive index and X-ray studies that the solid inorganic phase in bone consists essentially of very small crystals of apatite minerals, and they believe that brushite, $CaHPO_4 \cdot 2H_2O$, is not present to any extent in either normal or pathological bone.

A further contribution is that of Roseberry, Hastings, and Morse (40). From their X-ray spectrograms of bone, of naturally occurring minerals and of artificially produced calcium phosphates, they conclude (a) that bone has a crystalline structure which is fundamentally the same as that of other members of the apatite series; (b) that since chemical analysis and X-ray spectrograms agree as to the close similarity of untreated bone and dahlite, the calcium salts of bone and enamel may be represented by the formula $CaCO_3 \cdot nCa_3(PO_4)_2$ where n is not less than 2 nor greater than 3; (c) that there is no evidence of the presence of either free $CaHPO_4$ or free $CaCO_3$ in bone.

The interpretation of the physical findings is still, therefore, distinctly at variance with that of the chemical findings.

The Structure of Hexosemonophosphoric Ester ("Robison Ester")

This ester, first shown by Harden and Robison (41) to be present in the products of fermentation of glucose and fructose by yeast juice, was considered by Robison (42), from the properties and behaviour on hydrolysis of the isolated compound, to be a mixture of isomers, probably the monophosphoric esters of glucose and fructose.

To the phosphoric-acid radicle of the more or less pure aldose component of this mixture one group of workers (43) gave position 3 and another group (44) gave position 5 in the hexose molecule. These possible positions of the phosphate group in the Robison ester are given below:

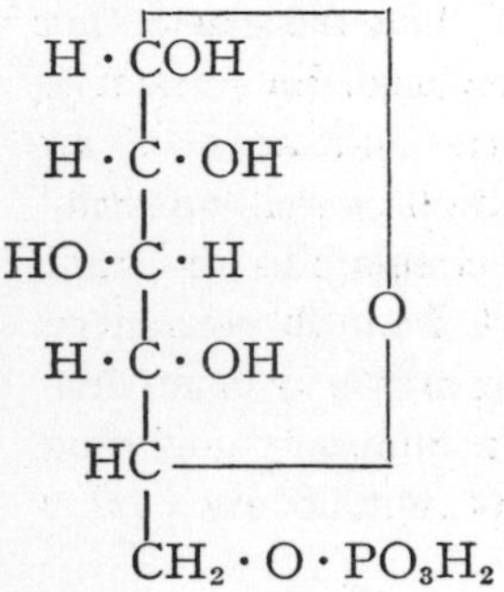

$$
\begin{array}{ccc}
\text{H·COH} & \text{H·C·OH} & \text{H·C·OH} \\
\text{H·C·OH} & \text{HC·OH} & \text{H·C·OH} \\
\text{HO·C·H} \quad \text{O} & \text{H}_2\text{PO}_3\text{·O·CH} \quad \text{O} & \text{HO·CH} \quad \text{O} \\
\text{H·C·OH} & \text{H·C·OH} & \text{HC} \\
\text{HC} & \text{HC} & \text{HC·O·PO}_3\text{H}_2 \\
\text{CH}_2\text{·O·PO}_3\text{H}_2 & \text{CH}_2\text{OH} & \text{CH}_2\text{OH} \\
\text{Position 6} & \text{Position 3} & \text{Position 5}
\end{array}
$$

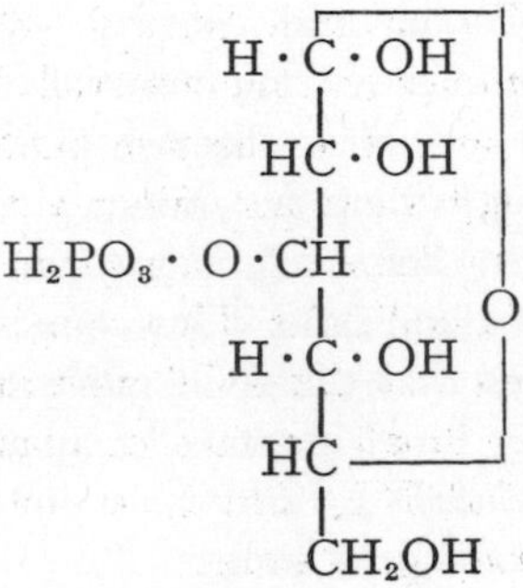

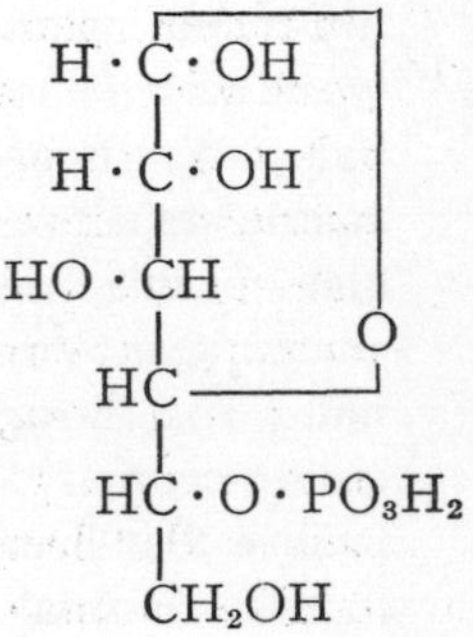

It will be observed that position 5 requires the presence of some other type of ring than the normal 1,5 (pyranose) ring, and an unstable 1,4 (furanose) ring, as shown above, was postulated for this ester (44). Both those who suggested position 3 and those who suggested position 5 founded their argument in part on the apparent difference between the phosphorus-containing osazone of the Robison ester and the not remotely dissimilar substance derived from the Neuberg ester, which was known with some certainty to be fructose-6-monophosphate. If these two osazones were not identical, the 6-position for the phosphoric-acid group in Robison's ester seemed to be excluded.

During the period under review, Levene and Raymond (45) further investigated the synthetic hexosemonophosphoric ester prepared by the phosphorylation of diacetone glucose (46) which appears to be definitely glucose-3-phosphate. This substance was shown to differ from the Robison ester in several ways; it formed an osazone which contained no phosphorus, had a different rate of fermentation and had different physical properties. Josephson and Proffe (47) also prepared and examined this synthetic ester, found that it differed markedly from the Robison ester, and had good reason for believing that it was the glucose-3 compound. Hence position 3 was excluded for the phosphoric-acid group of the latter. From the work of King and Morgan (43) position 5 now seemed untenable also.

The synthesis of glucose-6-phosphate by Levene and Raymond (45, 48) by phosphorylation of monoacetone glucose yielded a substance which gave an osazone, as would be expected, identical with that obtained from Harden and Young's and from Neuberg's ester. In addition the new ester had a high fermentation rate, practically identical with that of the Robison ester, and, with the exception of the melting-point of the osazone, which was 151° as against 139° reported for the osazone of the latter, had very similar properties. Levene and Raymond evidently believed that the two esters were identical and that the Robison ester, if purified, would prove to be the glucose-6-phosphate.

This purification has been achieved by Robison and King (49), who have separated the aldose monophosphoric ester from the mixture obtained after fermentation. The method employed is fractional crystallisation of the brucine salt first from 20 per cent ethyl alcohol, then from 90 or 95 per cent methyl alcohol, and finally from absolute methyl alcohol. The iodometric value (Willstätter and Schudel method) of the barium salt obtained in the final crystallisation indicates 100 per cent aldosemonophosphate. It gives only 0.5 per cent fructose by Seliwanoff's reaction, which is not appreciably greater than that given by glucose under similar conditions. Its reducing power (Hagedorn and Jensen) is 80 per cent of that of glucose.

The properties of the sugar obtained from it by acid hydrolysis as well as those of the hexonic acid (gluconic) formed from it by oxidation with bromine followed by enzymic removal of the phosphoric acid group by bone phosphatase show that the aldose is d-glucose. The phenyl hydrazine salt of the osazone prepared from the pure aldosemonophosphate has been found to have the same melting-point and rate of hydrolysis as that of the osazone of fructose monophosphoric ester (Neuberg), prepared from Harden and Young's diphosphoric ester, in which the phosphoric acid group is almost certainly in position 6 (50, 51, 52). The constitution of the pure aldomonophosphoric ester would therefore appear to be glucose-6-monophosphate. Nevertheless, the specific rotations of the free aldose ester and of its barium salt differ somewhat from those reported by Levene and Raymond for the synthetic ester and its barium salt prepared from monoacetone glucose. Robison and King have also obtained from the fermentation products a ketosemonophosphoric ester, similar in most respects to Neuberg's fructosemonophosphoric ester. They believe that the Robison ester, as separated originally from the fermentation of glucose and fructose by yeast juice, is a mixture of glucose-6-monophosphate and fructose-6-monophosphate (Neuberg) in which the glucose ester is present to the greater extent (55 to 70 per cent).

King, McLaughlin, and Morgan (53) have methylated a purified sample of the aldosemonophosphate by Fischer's method at 18° and at 60°, and have obtained two distinct forms of the methyl hexoside monophosphate, one, produced at 18°, being very sensitive to hydrolysis by $0.1\ N$ HCl, the other being much more stable. They consider the former to contain the unstable furanose ring structure, the latter the more stable pyranose ring. Their results support the view that the aldose component of the original hexosemonophosphate is glucose-6-phosphoric acid.

The phosphoaldonic acids of the Robison ester, and of the synthetic glucose-3-, and glucose-6-phosphates have recently been prepared by Levene and Raymond (48) by cautious oxidation of the esters with barium hypoiodate. The acid derived from the synthetic glucose-6-ester has been shown to have similar physical properties and rate of lactone formation in presence of HCl to those of the acid obtained from the Robison ester, but the corresponding properties of the acid from the glucose-3-ester are markedly different. The melting-point of the osazone of their synthetic glucose-6-phosphate is the same as that of the osazone of the purified (aldose) Robison ester. The same workers (54) have also synthesised glucose-6-phosphate in a different way—from 1,2,3,4-tetracetyl glucose—and have found its phosphosazone to have the same melting-point as the Robison phosphosazone, and to suffer no change in melting-point on admixture with it. Their purest synthetic glucose-6-phosphate has the same optical rotation as the purified aldose monophosphate of yeast fermentation, and both the synthetic esters have the same effect as the natural ester in diminishing the induction period of zymin fermentation.

There is, therefore, a general agreement as to the constitution of the Robison ester, the main (aldose) component being glucose-6-phosphate, the other (ketose) component being fructose-6-phosphate. This agreement brings to a conclusion a very interesting chapter in the chemistry of the naturally occurring phosphoric esters.

The Biochemistry of Adenylic Acid (Adenosine Phosphoric Acid, Adenine Nucleotide)

Of the several nucleotides obtainable by the fission of nucleic acids of animal or plant origin, it is a matter of considerable interest that apparently only one, an adenine nucleotide (which, indeed, may not be a constituent of any nucleic acid), is at all widely distributed in the tissues or tissue fluids. It was shown some years ago by Jackson (55) to be present in blood. Embden and Zimmermann (56) isolated it from muscle. It has also been shown to be present in heart, brain (57), goats' milk (58), and kidney (59). With regard to the nucleotide of muscle, Lohmann (60) and Fiske and Subbarrow (61) are agreed that this substance is present combined with a molecule of pyrophosphoric acid. The ammonia produced by a short autolysis of muscle is derived (56, 56a, 62) from adenylic acid and can be increased in amount by the addition of fresh adenylic acid to the tissue.

During the period under review, the part played by adenylic acid in at least three biologically important activities, namely, the fermentation of the hexoses by dried yeast or yeast extract, the breakdown of glycogen and other substances to lactic acid by muscle extracts, and the production of certain vascular changes in animals, has been investigated. (See also p. 204, *infra,* for the possible rôle of adenylic acid in glycolysis in blood.)

Adenylic acid and co-zymase.—Harden and Young (63) showed that a thermostable dialysable co-enzyme ("co-zymase") was necessary for the fermentation of hexoses by yeast juice. Euler and co-workers (64, 65, 66, 67, 68, 69), who have recently defined co-zymase as that substance which brings about the typical carbohydrate cleavage in an otherwise inactive mixture of sugar, phosphate, hexosediphosphate, "apozymase" (Neuberg), and Mg salts (see below) have, during the past few years, armed themselves with a reliable micro-method for the determination of co-zymase in various tissues and tissue fluids, and tracked down the identity of this "bio-catalyst" until it is now known to be adenylic acid or some very closely related substance.[2]

Starting from highly active, boiled yeast-extracts, Euler and Myr-

[2] For suggested nomenclature of the catalysts of alcoholic fermentation see Neuberg and Euler (69a).

back (64) precipitate the co-enzyme from the dialysate with lead acetate, free it from lead, adsorb on aluminium hydroxide, wash with water, elute with phosphoric acid, precipitate in turn with mercuric nitrate, phosphotungstic acid, and ammoniacal silver solution. Freed from silver, the co-zymase now shows activity values of 100,000 to 160,000 (in arbitrary units) per gram dry weight, as against some 200 only in the original yeast extract. Preparations of this degree of activity are apparently composed of a single substance, the chemical composition of which is that of an adenine nucleotide or very closely related compound with a $P/N/pentose$ ratio of $1/5/1$ (64, 65). A good yield of the characteristic adenine picrate, accounting for most of the nitrogen of the nucleotide, has been obtained from it. The co-zymase activity of the preparation is rapidly lost when the latter is treated with a phosphatase preparation, or is heated with dilute acid at 100°. The rate of hydrolysis with acid puts co-zymase into the same group of compounds as muscle adenylic acid and inosinic acid, and separates it from the adenylic acid derived by fission of yeast nucleic acid. The chemical properties of co-zymase also differentiate it sharply from the nucleotides of yeast nucleic or of pancreas nucleic acids.

Nevertheless, in spite of the similarity between co-zymase and muscle adenylic acid, the latter (66) does not activate apozymase. Thus the addition of 0.03 mg. of co-zymase of an activity of 100,000 to the test mixture led to the production of 4.3 cc. of CO_2 in 1.5 hours, whereas the addition of 1.0 mg. of pure muscle adenylic acid gave no observable activation. Only in the presence of a large quantity of hexosediphosphate was a slight co-enzyme effect shown by the muscle nucleotide. In muscle, however (see above), the adenylic acid exists as a complex with pyrophosphate—"adenyl pyrophosphate" or "adenosine triphosphate" (65a). Euler and Myrback (66) find that whilst this compound in very small quantities shows no co-zymase effect, in larger quantities it has a definite activity. Thus the addition of 0.8 mg. of adenyl pyrophosphate to the apozymase mixture produced 4.0 cc. of CO_2 in 1.5 hours, whereas the addition of only 0.04 mg. of pure co-zymase produced 3.7 cc. in the same time. On the whole the activity of the muscle compound was from 6 to 10 per cent of that of the same quantity of pure co-zymase. The possibility arises that this activity of adenyl pyrophosphate is due to co-zymase present as an impurity. The slight co-zymase effect of muscle adenylic acid may also be due to such contamination, in this case with less than 0.02 per cent of the pure co-zymase. It is to be remembered that these preparations are made from muscle which contains large quantities of co-zymase (67). There seems to be little doubt that adenyl pyrophosphate is not identical with co-zymase.

Adenylic acid and lactic acid production in muscle.—In muscle, Lohmann (70, 71, 72) and Meyerhof, Lohmann, and Meyer (73) have found that the enzyme system which produces lactic acid from glycogen (and from hexosediphosphate and hexosemonophosphate) is, in a general way, similar to the zymase system in yeast. They have found that it consists of a thermolabile enzyme, and three thermostable, dialysable co-enzymes, one of which is, and the other two are not, destroyed on autolysis of the muscle. By dialysing muscle extract for several hours at 0° against KCl solutions, they find that the non-dialysable portion of the muscle extract has lost its power to transform glycogen into lactic acid. If boiled muscle-juice is now added to this non-dialysable portion, the system is restored to activity only if the muscle-juice has been boiled when fresh; if the juice is kept for an hour at 37° before being boiled it will not restore activity to the non-dialysable residue.

On adding adenyl pyrophosphate to the juice boiled after autolysis, its co-enzymic quality is fully restored. The autolysable co-enzyme is probably adenyl pyrophosphate, which is known to be rapidly hydrolysed if muscle-juice containing it is allowed to stand. If, however, pure adenyl pyrophosphate or muscle adenylic acid is added to the thoroughly dialysed muscle extract there is little or no activation. It is necessary to add also Mg ions and inorganic phosphate before lactic acid formation begins. Thus the system in muscle which hydrolyses glycogen to lactic acid is dialysed muscle extract + inorganic phosphate + adenyl pyrophosphate (or muscle adenylic acid) + a magnesium salt. This finding recalls the interesting discovery of Erdtman (74), which has been further investigated recently (75, 76), that Mg ions are necessary for the activation of dialysed kidney phosphatase.

Lohmann (72) has also found that magnesium is necessary for the fermentative activity of the dialysed yeast juice + co-zymase system or the dried yeast + co-zymase system. In the latter system the yeast must be washed with dilute acid (KH_2PO_4 solution) to remove the magnesium sufficiently. Euler, Nilsson, and Auhagen (77) agree that magnesium is essential for the fermentation of glucose, fructose, or sucrose by dried, washed yeast, but find that it is not necessary for the activity of the oxidation-reduction system in this material.

Quite recently Lohmann (78) has shown that purified co-zymase is similar to muscle adenylic acid in its power to act as co-enzyme for lactic acid production in muscle extracts inactivated by keeping at 20°, but dissimilar in its inability to reactivate extracts inactivated by dialysis. He agrees with Euler that purified co-zymase is a much more active co-enzyme for alcoholic fermentation than adenyl pyrophosphate (the limited activity of which as a co-enzyme for alcoholic fermentation Lohmann was the first to show), but points out that, whereas reactivation of the inactive apozymase system by co-zymase requires the presence of hexosediphosphate, reactivation of this system by adenyl pyrophosphate does not. A mixture of co-zymase and adenyl pyrophosphate has a greater activity in stimulating the apozymase system than the sum of their separate activities. Whether or not these findings are capable of extension to other tissues which rapidly metabolise carbohydrate remains to be investigated.

Adenyl pyrophosphate does not appear to be the co-enzyme for methyl glyoxalase or for carboxylase (71), and Mg is also unnecessary for the activity of these two enzymes.

Zuckerkandl and Klebermass (79) have suggested that the activity of co-zymase is due, at least in part, to the presence in its molecule, of the group

$$-N = C - NH_2 \rightleftarrows HN - C = NH,$$

which assists the cleavage of the sugar molecule into two C_3 compounds by splitting off a molecule of H_2O from the sugar.

Definite differences have been reported between the adenine nucleotide from yeast nucleic acid and that from muscle (80, 81, 82) toward both enzymic and chemical reagents. Steudel and Wohinz (83) believe the differences to be due to positional isomerism, the phosphoric acid group being attached to different carbon atoms in the pentose chain [see also Levene (21)].

Adenine nucleotide and the vascular system.—Previous work (84) showing that trichloroacetic extracts of tissues would produce heart-block in guinea pigs and that this heart-block is due to adenylic acid present in such extracts has been confirmed and extended by Bennet and Drury (85). They have found that the duration of the heart-block may be used as an approximate measure of the amount of adenylic acid present in such extracts, and presumably present in the original tissues. In investigating by this means the distribution of adenylic acid in the body they have found the greatest quantity in heart and striated muscle (60 to 70 mg. of adenylic acid per 100 g. of tissue) and lowest in the blood serum (less than 2 mg. per 100 g.). The distribution of the nucleotide is similar, on the whole, to that found by Sym, Nilsson, and Euler (86) for co-zymase. Heart-block can, however, be produced equally by adenosine, the phosphorus-free nucleoside, but not by guanylic acid or guanosine. Bennet and Drury describe the various effects of adenylic acid and adenosine on several different organs. It is to be noted that pharmacologically, adenosine is as active, if not more active, than adenylic acid, and that here also there is no sharp distinction between yeast and muscle adenylic acid. The nucleotide seems to be liberated from muscle on injury, and may play some part in traumatic shock. Honey, Ritchie, and Thompson (87) find that adenosine given intravenously to humans may produce arrhythmia and heart-block but has no beneficial effect on auricular fibrillation. On the other hand, Rothmann (88) notes beneficial effects in clinical cases of mitral insufficiency when adenosine-phosphoric acid is given intravenously. Gard (89) finds that co-zymase and adenyl thiomethyl pentose (90, 91) have effects similar to those of adenylic acid on blood pressure and cardiac activity in the rabbit, and confirms Drury's finding that the lowering of the blood pressure is a non-specific effect of adenosine derivatives.

The Phosphorus Compounds of Blood

Qualitative.—There is an experimental basis, sometimes sound, sometimes not quite so sound, for the belief that the following phosphorus-containing substances are present in mammalian blood: (*a*) inorganic phosphate; (*b*) hexose phosphate (92, 93, 94); (*c*) diphospho-*l*-glyceric acid (95, 96); (*d*) adenine nucleotide (97, 98); (*e*) diphospho-α-ketotrihydroxyadipic acid (99); (*f*) nucleic acid in traces; and (*g*) lecithin, kephalin, sphingomyelin (100).

Recent work of Roche (101) has added to these pyrophosphate, isolated as the sodium salt from pig's blood by Lohmann's (65*a*) method. Since adenine nucleotide may be isolated from blood, it seems probable that a part, if not all, of the pyrophosphate may, in the fresh blood, be combined with the nucleotide, as it is in muscle

(65a). Roche has also obtained, from a substance precipitable by baryta from deproteinised blood filtrates, phosphorus-containing osazones, which he considers may possibly indicate the presence of a hexosephosphoric acid. This hexosephosphate fraction, if such it be, represents at the most not more than 5 per cent of the total acid-soluble phosphorus of the blood (pig's). Another unidentified phosphoric ester, having a barium salt insoluble in 10 per cent HCl, is stated to be present in the acid-soluble fraction. Roche believes that one and perhaps more of the phosphoric esters contribute to the reducing power of the blood. Phosphagen appears to be absent from blood.

Quantitative.—Methods for the determination of the partition of the phosphorus of blood into various fractions, inorganic P, acid-soluble P, lipin P, etc., are by no means new. During the period under review various methods of phosphorus determination have been applied to the compounds in blood and different schemes for dividing the blood phosphorus compounds into significant fractions have been advised (102 to 109). The reviewer has the impression that in some cases at least it has not been realised sufficiently that blood is a tissue composed of cells and plasma, the cells containing almost the whole of the acid-soluble phosphorus. Changes in the acid-soluble phosphorus of whole blood after the administration of physiologically active substances or in disease may, unless corpuscle volume (hematocrit) determinations are carried out and plasma phosphorus determinations also performed on the same sample of blood, provide a rather elaborate expression of the degree of anaemia present, but may have no other physiological or clinical significance.

Javillier and Fabrykant find nucleoprotein to be a constant constituent of human blood (104), the amount expressed as nucleoprotein P averaging 2.6 mg. of P per 100 cc. of blood. This value is increased in certain diseases. In conditions in which there is a rise in the reticulocyte count, Kay (110) finds an increase in the nucleoprotein P of the red cells.

The findings of Meier and Thoenes (111) confirm those of Byrom (112) that there is a marked decrease in the esterified phosphorus of blood in untreated diabetes, most noticeable in diabetic coma. Insulin treatment raises the value to the normal. These results may perhaps be correlated with the observations of Goertz (113) that in diabetes with acidosis there is a marked increase in the 24-hour excretion of phosphorus in the urine, which disappears after insulin treatment. Advanced diabetes appears to be the only disease in which the ester phosphorus of the red cells is definitely diminished.

It is hoped to discuss recent work on changes in the phosphorus compounds of the blood and of other tissues in disease in a subsequent review. For the present the reader is referred to Peters and Van Slyke (1), particularly pp. 1111–36.

PHOSPHATASES OF BLOOD

That normal blood contains a phosphatase has been known for some time, but it is only within the last two years that the properties of this enzyme in blood have been investigated in some detail. The enzyme is present in blood in relatively minute amounts; compared with human kidney tissue, for example, human blood plasma has only about 1/300 of the phosphatase activity (114).

Both the leucocytes and the red cells of blood contain phosphatase (114, 115), and it is necessary to avoid as far as possible admixture with either red or white cells in order to be certain that any given effect is due to the plasma enzyme. Using the necessary precautions it has been found by Kay (114) that, like the phosphatases of bone, kidney, and intestinal mucosa, that of plasma has a pH optimum for its action on sodium β-glycerophosphate (and on most other substrates) between 8.8 and 9.1. Mg ions act as a powerful stimulant to the hydrolysis of a variety of substrates (α and β glycerophosphates, pyrophosphate, glyco-phosphate, and nucleotide) by the plasma enzyme. Roche (115) finds that all mono-substituted phosphoric esters examined are attacked by this enzyme, but that the rate of hydrolysis varies with the nature of the substituting group. Disubstituted esters are not appreciably hydrolysed. Like the phosphatases of bone (116), kidney (117), and intestine (118), both the phosphatase of plasma and that of red blood cells will synthesise as well as hydrolyse phosphoric esters under suitable conditions (115). Roche believes that red-cell phosphatase, with an optimum pH of 6.0 to 6.8 and other specific properties, is quite distinct from that of plasma or of leucocytes.

Interesting changes have been demonstrated to take place in the phosphatase activity of the blood in disease, particularly in generalised bone disease (119, 120, 121). In osteitis deformans (Paget), generalised osteitis fibrosa, osteomalacia, and rickets (infantile, adolescent, and renal) there is almost invariably a marked increase in plasma phosphatase, the value rising in some cases to twenty or more times the normal average value. This abnormality is confined almost exclusively to cases of bone disease, and in a general way varies in extent with the severity of the disease. It suggests a definite correlation between bone disease and abnormal phosphatase distribution in the body, a finding which is of interest in connection with the suggested rôle (122) of phosphatase in bone formation and maintenance.

A clinical method for the determination of plasma phosphatase, in which duplicate determinations may be made on a total volume of 1 cc. of blood plasma, is described (123).

PHOSPHORUS COMPOUNDS OF BLOOD AND GLYCOLYSIS

Recent work of Engelhart, Engelhart and Ljubimova, and Barrenscheen and collaborators has definitely shown the intimate connection which has been long suspected between glycolysis and the phosphatase–phosphoric ester system in the red cells. From one species to another, the glycolytic power of the erythrocytes is found to be approximately proportional to their phosphoric ester content (124, 125). There is a close connection also between phosphatolysis, glycolysis, and cellular respiration. Inhibition of respiration of avian erythrocytes leads to a very rapid liberation of inorganic phosphate (126), which appears to be due not so much to an increased rate of breakdown of phosphoric ester but to the cessation of esterification of inorganic phosphate, which seems to be essentially an aërobic process. Non-nucleated red cells show similar, though not so striking, changes.

The following findings (127, 128) indicate that a marked similarity exists between the processes of glycolysis and of fermentation by dried yeast or yeast juice: (a) During aërobic glycolysis inorganic phosphate diminishes in blood, and phosphoric ester increases; (b) The induction period of glycolysis may be caused to disappear by the addition of hexosediphosphate to the red cells; (c) The glycolytic process is independent of cell structure; (d) The pyrophosphate fraction of the red cell phosphoric ester contains either the co-enzyme for glycolysis or the activator of the co-enzyme; (e) This fraction has itself some co-zymase properties.

METHODS

Determination of orthophosphoric acid, "inorganic phosphate."—
Kuttner and Lichtenstein (129) describe minor improvements in
extension of the elegant method of Kuttner and Cohen (130) for
the colorimetric determination of very small quantities (down to
0.005 mg. or less) of inorganic P. The use of ammonium molybdate
in this method instead of sodium molybdate is advised (131) and
is said to give more flexibility as regards concentration of molybdate.
The Kuttner-Cohen method has been adapted (132) for the determination of various phosphorus fractions in blood. The preparation
of permanent blue standards for use with this and similar colorimetric phosphorus methods is described (133, 134). It has been
shown (135) that the molybdenum-blue reaction on which the
Kuttner-Cohen method is founded, is specific, amongst all the acids
of phosphorus studied, for free orthophosphoric. The simultaneous
determination of phosphorus, sugar, and lactic acid in 3 cc. of blood,
using the Kuttner-Cohen method for phosphorus, the Hagedorn and
Jensen method for reducing substance, and the Friedemann-Cotonio-
Shaffer method for lactic acid, is described (136).

Inorganic phosphorus and calcium (137, 138) and inorganic
phosphorus, calcium, and cholesterol (139) may be determined on
the same small sample of blood serum. A method for determining
inorganic phosphate on 0.12 cc. of serum is described (140). The
phosphate is precipitated as strychnine phosphomolybdate and dissolved in NaOH. K_4FeCN_6 and HCl are then added, and the colour
produced compared with appropriate standards. An accuracy of ± 2
per cent with quantities of phosphorus of the order of 0.01 to 0.05
mg. is claimed (141) for a method in which the depth of blue colour
developed in Fiske and Subbarrow's (142) procedure is determined
spectrophotometrically. A novel colorimetric method is described
(143) in which inorganic P is precipitated as manganese ammonium
phosphate, the precipitate oxidised with $NaBiO_3$ in HNO_3 solution
and the permanganate ion determined colorimetrically. Monomethyl
p-aminophenol is recommended (144) as a reducing agent to replace
hydroquinone in the Briggs or Fiske and Subbarrow method, since
it gives stable colours over a wide range of acidity. A method of
separating ortho- and pyrophosphates from a mixture of several
phosphoric esters is described (145), together with the quantitative
determination of the first two compounds.

Several methods of determination which are not colorimetric have been described. A titrimetric method for inorganic phosphorus in 1 cc. of serum, avoiding deproteinisation, is suggested (146). A potentiometric titration of phosphate with $AgNO_3$ while maintaining a constant low $[H^+]$ is described (147). The antimony electrode (148) and the quinhydrone electrode (149) have been applied to the electrometric titration of inorganic phosphate. An oxidimetric method, using $KMnO_4$ in the final titration, has been used for phosphate determination (150). Inorganic phosphate may be determined volumetrically by adding excess of a standard solution of ammonium molybdate, and titrating back with lead acetate, using tannic acid as an outside indicator (151); an error of less than 2 per cent is obtainable with quantities of phosphorus ranging from 1 to 10 mg. A micro-titration method requiring much smaller quantities of phosphorus is described (152), on the basis of the Neumann technique; the phosphorus content of tissues containing only 0.05 to 0.2 mg. of phosphorus may be determined, and the simultaneous estimation of calcium is also possible. Another micro modification of the Neumann method is recommended (153), a tartaric acid–ammonium molybdate reagent being employed. The dried ammonium phosphomolybdate (containing 3.55 per cent P_2O_5) is weighed.

Advantage is taken of the insolubility of benzidine phosphate in neutral or weakly acid solution (154) to develop a method for inorganic phosphate determination similar to the well-known method for inorganic sulphate. Other acids of phosphorus do not interfere.

The direct titration of one, two, or three hydrogens of H_3PO_4, using various indicators, is described (155, 156). The separation of phosphate as bismuth phosphate is recommended (157). Nitric acid is added to the phosphate solution to $2N$ strength, and solid $BiONO_3$ is introduced. On diluting to $0.5N$ HNO_3, only 0.1 mg. of P_2O_5 per 100 cc. remains unprecipitated.

Determination of organically combined phosphorus.—A micro method in common use in biochemistry—oxidation with H_2O_2 and sulphuric acid followed by colorimetric determination by a phosphomolybdate reduction technique—has been applied (158) to the determination of phosphorus in alkyl phosphines. The destruction of organic matter preliminary to phosphorus determination, by electrolysis in HNO_3 solution, is described (159). Methods for estimating phosphatides in blood and other tissues by determination of inorganic phosphorus after oxidation of the phosphatide fraction are described by two investigators (160, 161). The former estimates the phosphatide in 2 cc. of serum by pipetting on plaster of paris, extracting the solid with ether, oxidising the ethereal extract with H_2O_2 and sulphuric acid, and, finally, after adding Embden's reagent, weighing the strychnine phosphomolybdate. The latter mixes the blood with alcohol and benzene, distils off the water as the ternary mixture, takes up the residue with ether, and finally oxidises with H_2SO_4 and HNO_3. The phosphate is precipitated with magnesia mixture, and the precipitate, dissolved in acetic acid, is submitted to Bell and Doisy's procedure for inorganic phosphorus determination.

The analysis of tissues for nucleoprotein phosphorus may be carried out (162) by extracting the tissue very thoroughly with alcohol and ether, then with NaCl solution. On treating the NaCl extract cautiously with acid, nucleic acid is quantitatively precipitated and may be oxidised in any convenient way before determining the phosphate colorimetrically.

LITERATURE CITED

RECENT REVIEWS

1. PETERS, J. P., AND VAN SLYKE, D. D., *Quantitative Clinical Chemistry,* I (Baltimore, 1931)
2. PRYDE, J., *Recent Advances in Biochemistry* (third edition, London, 1931)
3. MEYERHOF, O., *Lancet,* **II**, 1415 (1930)
4. AUBEL, E., AND CAHN, T., *Bull. soc. chim. biol.,* **11**, 903 (1929)
5. EULER, H. VON, *Biokatalysatoren* (Stuttgart, 1930)
6. EULER, H. VON, *Z. angew. Chem.,* **44**, 583 (1931)
7. ROCHE, J., *Bull. soc. chim. biol.,* **13**, 841 (1931)
8. HUNTER, D., *Quart. J. Med.,* **24**, 393 (1931)
8a. MILROY, T. H., *Physiol. Rev.,* **11**, 515 (1931)

PHOSPHORUS COMPOUNDS OCCURRING NATURALLY

9. RUDAKOV, K. I., *Biedermann's Zentr.,* **59**, 543 (1930)
10. HARDEN, A., *Alcoholic Fermentation* (London and New York, 1923)
11. NEUBERG, C., *Biochem. Z.,* **88**, 432 (1918)
12. NEUBERG, C., AND LEIBOWITZ, J., *Biochem. Z.,* **187**, 481 (1927)
13. NILSSON, R., *Arkiv Kemi, Mineral., Geol., A,* **10**, No. 7, 135 pp. (1930)
14. ROBISON, R., AND MORGAN, W. T. J., *Biochem. J.,* **22**, 1277 (1928)

15. NEUBERG, C., AND LIEBOWITZ, J., *Biochem. Z.*, **193**, 237 (1928)
16. GREENWALD, I., *J. Biol. Chem.*, **63**, 339 (1925)
17. FISKE, C. H., AND SUBBARROW, Y., *J. Biol. Chem.*, **81**, 629 (1929)
18. EGGLETON, P., AND EGGLETON, M. G., *Biochem. J.*, **21**, 190 (1927)
19. MEYERHOF, O., AND LOHMANN, K., *Biochem. Z.*, **195**, 22, 49 (1928)
20. MACLEAN, H., AND MACLEAN, I. S., *Lecithin and Allied Substances, the Lipins* (London and New York, 1927)
21. LEVENE, P. A., *Nucleic Acids* (New York, 1931)
22. JUKES, T. H., AND KAY, H. D., *J. Nutrition*, **5**, 81 (1932)
23. SORENSEN, S. P. L., *J. Chem. Soc.*, 2995 (1926)
24. FISKE, C. H., AND SUBBARROW, Y., *Science*, **70**, 381 (1929)
25. POSTERNAK, S., *Compt. rend.*, **187**, 1165 (1928)
26. VIRTANEN, A. I., AND TIKKA, J., *Biochem. Z.*, **228**, 407 (1930)
27. ROBISON, R., AND MORGAN, W. T. J., *Biochem. J.*, **24**, 119 (1930)
28. VEIBEL, S., *Biochem. Z.*, **239**, 350 (1931)

CHEMICAL COMPOSITION OF BONE

29. LOHMANN, K., *Biochem. Z.*, **233**, 460 (1931)
30. GASSMANN, T., *Z. physiol. Chem.*, **192**, 61 (1930)
31. KLEMENT, R., *Z. physiol. Chem.*, **184**, 133 (1929)
32. KLEMENT, R., *Z. physiol. Chem.*, **196**, 140 (1931)
33. SHEAR, M. J., AND KRAMER, B., *J. Biol. Chem.*, **79**, 105, 125 (1928)
34. SHEAR, M. J., AND KRAMER, B., *J. Biol. Chem.*, **86**, 677 (1930)
35. MORGULIS, S., *J. Biol. Chem.*, **93**, 455 (1931)
36. DANEEL, H., AND FRÖHLICH, K. W., *Z. anorg. Chem.*, **188**, 14 (1930)
37. DANEEL, H., AND FRÖHLICH, K. W., *Z. Electrochem.*, **36**, 302 (1930)
38. TAYLOR, N. W., AND SHEARD, C., *J. Biol. Chem.*, **81**, 479 (1929)
39. DEJONG, W. F., *Rec. trav. chim.*, **45**, 445 (1926)
40. ROSEBERRY, H. H., HASTINGS, A. B., AND MORSE, J. K., *J. Biol. Chem.*, **90**, 395 (1931)

STRUCTURE OF HEXOSE MONOPHOSPHORIC ESTER ("ROBISON ESTER")

41. HARDEN, A., AND ROBISON, R., *Proc. Chem. Soc.*, **30**, 16 (1914)
42. ROBISON, R., *Biochem. J.*, **16**, 809 (1922)
43. KING, E. J., AND MORGAN, W. T. J., *J. Soc. Chem. Ind.*, **48**, 143, 296 (1929)
44. LEVENE, P. A., AND RAYMOND, A. L., *J. Biol. Chem.*, **81**, 279 (1929)
45. LEVENE, P. A., AND RAYMOND, A. L., *J. Biol. Chem.*, **89**, 479 (1930)
46. RAYMOND, A. L., AND LEVENE, P. A., *J. Biol. Chem.*, **83**, 619 (1929)
47. JOSEPHSON, K., AND PROFFE, S., *Ann.*, **481**, 91 (1930)
48. LEVENE, P. A., AND RAYMOND, A. L., *J. Biol. Chem.*, **91**, 751 (1931)
49. ROBISON, R., AND KING, E. J., *Biochem. J.*, **25**, 323 (1931)
50. MORGAN, W. T. J., AND ROBISON, R., *Biochem. J.*, **22**, 1270 (1928)
51. LEVENE, P. A., AND RAYMOND, A. L., *J. Biol. Chem.*, **80**, 633 (1928)

52. MORGAN, W. T. J., *J. Soc. Chem. Ind.*, **48**, 143 (1929)
53. KING, E. J., McLAUGHLIN, R. R., AND MORGAN, W. T. J., *Biochem. J.*, **25**, 310 (1931)

BIOCHEMISTRY OF ADENYLIC ACID

54. LEVENE, P. A., AND RAYMOND, A. L., *J. Biol. Chem.*, **92**, 757 (1931)
55. JACKSON, H., *J. Biol. Chem.*, **59**, 529 (1924)
56. EMBDEN, G., AND ZIMMERMAN, M., *Z. physiol. Chem.*, **167**, 114, 137 (1927)
56a. EMBDEN, G., et al., *Z. physiol. Chem.*, **179**, 149 (1928)
57. POHLE, K., *Z. physiol. Chem.*, **185**, 9 (1929)
58. KAY, H. D., AND MARSHALL, P. G., *Biochem. J.*, **22**, 416 (1928)
59. EMBDEN, G., AND DEUTICKE, H. J., *Z. physiol. Chem.*, **190**, 62 (1930)
60. LOHMANN, K., *Naturwissenschaften*, **17**, 624 (1929)
61. FISKE, C. H., AND SUBBARROW, Y., *Science*, **70**, 381 (1929)
62. PARNAS, J. K., *Biochem. Z.*, **206**, 16 (1929)
63. HARDEN, A., AND YOUNG, W. J., *Proc. Roy. Soc. (London), B*, **78**, 369 (1906)
64. EULER, H. VON, AND MYRBÄCK, K., *Z. physiol. Chem.*, **198**, 219 (1931)
65. MYRBÄCK, K., AND EULER, H. VON, *Z. physiol. Chem.*, **198**, 236 (1931)
65a. LOHMANN, K., *Biochem. Z.*, **202**, 466 (1929).
66. EULER, H. VON, AND MYRBÄCK, K., *Z. physiol. Chem.*, **199**, 189 (1931)
67. EULER, H. VON, AND MYRBÄCK, K., *Z. physiol. Chem.*, **190**, 93 (1930)
68. EULER, H. VON, *Z. angew. Chem.*, **44**, 583 (1931)
69. EULER, H. VON, AND NILSSON, R., *Arkiv Kemi, Mineral., Geol., B*, **10**, No. 14 (1931) [quoted by von Euler (68)]
69a. NEUBERG, C., AND EULER, H. VON, *Biochem. Z.*, **240**, 245 (1931)
70. LOHMANN, K., *Naturwissenschaften*, **8**, 180 (1931)
71. LOHMANN, K., *Biochem. Z.*, **237**, 445 (1931)
72. LOHMANN, K., *Biochem. Z.*, **241**, 50 (1931)
73. MEYERHOF, O., LOHMANN, K., AND MEYER, K., *Biochem. Z.*, **237**, 437 (1931)
74. ERDTMAN, H., *Z. physiol. Chem.*, **172**, 182 (1927); **177**, 211 (1928)
75. HOMMERBERG, C., *Z. physiol. Chem.*, **185**, 123 (1929)
76. JENNER, H. D., AND KAY, H. D., *J. Biol. Chem.*, **93**, 733 (1931)
77. EULER, H. VON, NILSSON, R., AND AUHAGEN, E., *Z. physiol. Chem.*, **200**, 1 (1931)
78. LOHMANN, K., *Biochem. Z.*, **241**, 67 (1931)
79. ZUCKERKANDL, F., AND MESSINER-KLEBERMASS, L., *Biochem. Z.*, **239**, 172 (1931)
80. EMBDEN, G., AND SCHMIDT, G., *Z. physiol. Chem.*, **181**, 130 (1929)
81. MROCZKIEVICZ, V., *Biochem. Z.*, **235**, 267 (1931)
82. DEUTICKE, H. J., *Z. physiol. Chem.*, **192**, 193 (1930)
83. STEUDEL, H., AND WOHINZ, R., *Z. physiol. Chem.*, **200**, 82 (1931)
84. DRURY, A. N., AND SZENT-GYÖRGYI, A., *J. Physiol.*, **68**, 213 (1929)
85. BENNET, D. W., AND DRURY, A. N., *J. Physiol.*, **72**, 288 (1931)
86. SYM, E., NILSSON, R., AND EULER, H. VON, *Z. physiol. Chem.*, **190**, 228 (1930)

87. HONEY, R., RITCHIE, W., AND THOMPSON, W., *Quart. J. Med.*, **23**, 485 (1930)
88. ROTHMANN, H., *Arch. exptl. Path. Pharmakol.*, **155**, 129 (1930)
89. GARD, S., *Z. physiol. Chem.*, **196**, 65 (1930)
90. SUZUKI, U., ODAKE, S., AND MORI, T., *Biochem. Z.*, **154**, 278 (1924)
91. LEVENE, P. A., AND SOBOTKA, H., *J. Biol. Chem.*, **65**, 551 (1925)

PHOSPHORUS COMPOUNDS OF BLOOD

92. LAWACZEK, H., *Biochem. Z.*, **145**, 351 (1924)
93. LAWACZEK, H., *Klin. Wochschr.*, **8**, 1858 (1925)
94. GOODWIN, H. W., AND ROBISON, R., *Biochem. J.*, **18**, 1161 (1924)
95. GREENWALD, I., *J. Biol. Chem.*, **63**, 339 (1925)
96. JOST, H., *Z. physiol. Chem.*, **165**, 171 (1927)
97. JACKSON, H., *J. Biol. Chem.*, **59**, 529 (1924)
98. HOFMANN, W. S., *J. Biol. Chem.*, **63**, 675 (1925)
99. POSTERNAK, S., *Compt. rend.*, **187**, 1165 (1928)
100. BÜRGER, M., AND BEUMER, H., *Biochem. Z.*, **56**, 446 (1913)
101. ROCHE, J., *Bull. soc. chim. biol.*, **12**, 636 (1930)
102. YOUNGBURG, G. E., AND YOUNGBURG, M. V., *J. Lab. Clin. Med.*, **16**, 3, 253 (1930)
103. WALKER, B. S., AND HUNTSINGER, M. E., *J. Lab. Clin. Med.*, **10**, 247 (1930)
104. JAVILLIER, M., AND FABRYKANT, M., *Bull. soc. chim. biol.*, **13**, 687 (1931)
105. MEIER, R., AND THOENES, E., *Arch. exptl. Path. Pharmakol.*, **161**, 119 (1931)
106. MAYNARD, L. A., AND McCAY, C. M., *J. Biol. Chem.*, **92**, 273 (1931)
107. SOKOLOVITCH, M., *Arch. Disease Childhood*, **6**, 183 (1931)
108. ESAU, J. N., AND STOLAND, O. O., *Am. J. Physiol.*, **92**, 1 (1930)
109. PARHON, C. I., AND WERNER, G., *Compt. rend. soc. biol.*, **104**, 228 (1930)
109a. ROCHE, A., AND ROCHE, J., *Bull. soc. chim. biol.*, **11**, 549 (1929)
110. KAY, H. D., *Brit. J. Exptl. Path.*, **11**, 148 (1930)
111. MEIER, R., AND THOENES, E., *Arch. exptl. Path. Pharmakol.*, **161**, 119 (1931)
112. BYROM, F. B., *Brit. J. Exptl. Path.*, **10**, 10 (1929)
113. GOERTZ, S., *Bibliotek f. Laeger*, **122**, 159 (1930) [quoted from *Chem. Abstr.*, **25**, 147 (1931)]

PHOSPHATASES OF BLOOD

114. KAY, H. D., *J. Biol. Chem.*, **98**, 235 (1930)
115. ROCHE, J., *Biochem. J.*, **25**, 1724 (1931)
116. MARTLAND, M., AND ROBISON, R., *Biochem. J.*, **21**, 665 (1927)
117. KAY, H. D., *Biochem. J.*, **22**, 855 (1928)
118. KAY, H. D., *J. Chem. Soc.*, 524 (1929)
119. KAY, H. D., *Brit. J. Exptl. Path.*, **10**, 253 (1929)
120. ROBERTS, W. M., *Brit. J. Exptl. Path.*, **11**, 90 (1930)

121. KAY, H. D., *J. Biol. Chem.*, **89**, 249 (1930)
122. ROBISON, R., *Biochem. J.*, **17**, 286 (1923)
123. JENNER, H. D., AND KAY, H. D., *Brit. J. Exptl. Path.*, **13**, 22 (1932)

PHOSPHORUS COMPOUNDS OF BLOOD AND GLYCOLYSIS

124. ENGELHART, W. A., AND LJUBIMOVA, M., *Biochem. Z.*, **227**, 6 (1930)
125. BARRENSCHEEN, H. K., AND VASARHELYI, B., *Biochem. Z.*, **230**, 330 (1931)
126. ENGELHART, W. A., *Biochem. Z.*, **227**, 16 (1930)
127. BARRENSCHEEN, H. K., AND HUBNER, K., *Biochem. Z.*, **229**, 329 (1930)
128. BARRENSCHEEN, H. K., AND BRAUN, K., *Biochem. Z.*, **231**, 144 (1931)

ANALYTICAL METHODS

129. KUTTNER, T., AND LICHTENSTEIN, L., *J. Biol. Chem.*, **86**, 671 (1930)
130. KUTTNER, T., AND COHEN, H. R., *J. Biol. Chem.*, **75**, 517 (1927)
131. RANGANATHAN, S., *Indian J. Med. Research,* **18**, 109 (1930)
132. YOUNGBURG, G. E., AND YOUNGBURG, M. V., *J. Lab. Clin. Med.*, **16**, 3 (1930)
133. MEYER, A. H., *Science,* **72**, 174 (1930)
134. CHAPMAN, H. D., *Ind. Eng. Chem., Anal. Ed.*, **3**, 282 (1931)
135. DUNAEV, A., *Z. anal. Chem.*, **80**, 252 (1930)
136. MORGULIS, S., AND PINTO, S., *J. Lab. Clin. Med.*, **16**, 60 (1930)
137. LOWENBERG, C., AND MATTICE, M. R., *J. Lab. Clin. Med.*, **15**, 598 (1930)
138. GRENDEL, F., *Pharm. Weekblad,* **67**, 536 (1930)
139. BARIL, G. H., AND LABARRE, J., *Trans. Roy. Soc. Can.*, V, **24**, 185 (1930)
140. POPOVICIU, G., *Bull. soc. chim. biol.*, **13**, 548 (1931)
141. TEORELL, T., *Biochem. Z.*, **230**, 1 (1931)
142. FISKE, C. H., AND SUBBARROW, Y., *J. Biol. Chem.*, **66**, 375 (1925)
143. ISHIBASHI, M., *Anniversary volume dedicated to M. Chikashige,* 1 (1930) [quoted from *Chem. Abstr.*, **25**, 2663 (1931)]
144. LEIBOFF, S. L., *J. Lab. Clin. Med.*, **16**, 495 (1931)
145. HINSBERG, K., AND LASZLO, D., *Biochem. Z.*, **217**, 346 (1930)
146. CANNAVO, L., *Biochem. Z.*, **237**, 136 (1931)
147. BEDFORD, M. H., LAMB, F. R., AND SPICER, W. E., *J. Am. Chem. Soc.*, **52**, 583 (1930)
148. VOGEL, J. C., *J. Soc. Chem. Ind.*, **49**, 297 (1930)
149. SANFOURCHE, A., *Compt. rend.*, **192**, 1225 (1931)
150. BRESTAK, L., AND DAFFERT, O. A., *Z. angew. Chem.*, **43**, 216 (1930)
151. BIAZZO, R., *Ann. chim. applicata,* **21**, 75 (1931) [quoted from *Chem. Abstr.*, **25**, 2939 (1931)]
152. WIDMARK, G., AND VAHLQUIST, B., *Biochem. Z.*, **230**, 245 (1931)
153. ENDRÉDY, A. VON, *Z. anory. allgem. Chem.*, **194**, 239 (1930)
154. DEL CAMPO, A., *Anales soc. españ. fís. quim.*, **28**, 1153 (1930)
155. SMITH, W., *Quart. J. Pharm. Pharmacol.*, **2**, 238 (1929)

156. VILLARD, P., *Compt. rend.,* **191,** 1101 (1930)
157. KEŠĀNS, A., *Acta Univ. Latviensis Kim. Fakult. Serija,* 1, 4–5, Fasc. 2 (1930) [quoted from *Chem. Abstr.,* **25,** 2075 (1931)]
158. DAVIS, W. C., AND DAVIS, D. R., *J. Chem. Soc.,* 1207 (1931)
159. HELLER, K., *Mikrochemie,* **7,** 208 (1929)
160. KOCH, K., *Biochem. Z.,* **227,** 334 (1930)
161. CRUTO, A., *Biochim. terap. sper.,* **17,** 242 (1930)
162. JAVILLIER, M., AND ALLAIRE, H., *Bull. soc. chim. biol.,* **13,** 678 (1931)

UNIVERSITY OF TORONTO
TORONTO, CANADA

THE CHEMISTRY OF THE CARBOHYDRATES AND THE GLYCOSIDES*

By P. A. Levene and A. L. Raymond

The Rockefeller Institute

The large number of publications on the chemistry of the sugars makes a review of them almost impossible in the space allotted by this *Annual*. The reviewers were therefore confronted with the alternative of selecting the most important publications from each special field or of restricting the review to one field. The selection of the most significant contributions is often a difficult problem, and frequently the less comprehensive work contains more important suggestions for future investigations. In view of these considerations, the reviewers have chosen for the present discussion the year's progress in the study of the monosaccharides.

I. General Properties

The problem of mutarotation was exhaustively discussed by Lowry and Smith in a long general review. Lowry and Krieble have studied the mutarotations of galactonic acid and lactone and have also measured the rotatory dispersion of sodium galactonate and galactonic acid. The dispersion of the salt is complex and anomalous, while that of the acid is complex but normal.

Several papers have been published on the subject of optical activity and configuration. Votoček, Valentin, and Leminger have studied the optical properties of certain substituted benzyl hydrazones of sugars. They conclude that the benzyl hydrazone residue so exalts the effect of the α-carbon atom that its hydroxyl determines the direction of the rotation of the whole molecule. The hydrazone is dextrorotatory if this hydroxyl is to the left and levorotatory if to the right. The rule of Levene and of Hudson is thus generalized for all benzyl hydrazones. Ettel measured the rotatory values of the triacetyl and tribenzoyl acetals of mannitol in 100 solvents of all types but was unable to find any general mathematical relationships, although general conclusions were drawn. Darmois and Martin have studied the effect of alkaline molybdates on the mutarotation of glucose, and conclude that both anion and cation have their individual effects. More-

* Received March 22, 1932.

over, they believe that at equilibrium, at low temperature, the solution may contain the labile γ- form to the extent of several per cent of the total and that this form may combine very rapidly with the molybdates.

The number of isomers (ring isomers and the aldehydic form) in an aqueous solution of a sugar has been the subject of several investigations in recent years. Minsaas (1) prepared fucose from sea tang and re-crystallized the purified material several times. Different samples of the final material, however, behaved irregularly in dilatometric and optical respects. For any particular sample an equation with two exponentials was found to hold. The author concludes that the final material is a mixture of at least three modifications of the sugar. Isbell (1) has studied the rotation and mutarotation of gulose as the crystalline $CaCl_2$-addition compound and in the solution obtained by removing the $CaCl_2$ with silver oxalate. Mutarotation constants for the two were found to be almost identical, but the equilibrium was affected by the presence of the $CaCl_2$. The rate of mutarotation was close to that of mannose.

Stearn has studied the alkali binding capacity of the common sugars by the conductivity method and finds that the sugars in $2 N$ alkali behave as polybasic acids. Dissociation constants were calculated.

The correlation of reducing power and configuration has been studied by Sobotka and Reiner (1) who have determined the reducing power of various sugars as measured by the Hagedorn-Jensen method.

A paper dealing with the subject of osazone-forming groups was published by Votoček. It is generally known that, on heating sugars with phenylhydrazine, the primary or secondary alcoholic group adjacent to the carbonyl group is oxidized, leading to the formation of osones. The product thus formed then combines with aromatic hydrazines to form osazones. The author describes other groupings which also may lead to osazone formation. These groups are

CH_2ClCO, $CHClCO$, $CHCl_2CO$, $COCH_2NH_2$, $COCH(NH_2)C$, $C(:NOH)C(:NOH)$.

Micheel and Micheel continued their work on the action of trimethylamine on bromoacetylmonoses in anhydrous solution. Acetohalogen sugars in which the hydroxyl groups of carbon atoms 1 and 2 are situated in the *cis* position, form quaternary bases under the conditions of the experiment. This reaction does not take place when the two hydroxyls are in the *trans* position. Thus, in the case of mannose, the acetobromomannose is recovered unchanged; in the case of rhamnose, there were obtained diacetyl anhydrorhamnose, triacetyl rhamnose and an unsaturated compound the exact structure of which is not yet determined. The authors suggest that this reaction may serve to determine the configurations of carbon atoms 1 and 2 in sugars of unknown configuration.

Several papers were devoted to topics of rather special character. Thus, the peculiar conduct of the salts of mannosaccharic acid toward Fehling's solution was the topic of a new discussion by Kiliani. The reduction of Fehling's solution by these salts had been explained by Kiliani on the assumption of the formation of a keto-acid. Evidence in favor of this assumption was furnished by the interreaction of potassium cyanide and the salts of mannosaccharic acid. The resulting substance was a butanetricarboxylic acid. To this Kiliani assigned the structure of levulose carboxylic acid, in which two carboxyl groups are attached to carbon atom 2, the mechanism of the reaction being expressed as follows:

$$C_6H_{10}O_8 - H_2 + H \ldots \ldots CO_2H = C_7H_{10}O_{10} \text{ (tribasic acid)}.$$

Kiliani now modifies his view and assigns to the substance the structure of 1,1,4-butanetricarboxylic acid. The principal argument in favor of this view is the fact that on reduction with HI the substance forms a dicarboxylic and not a tricarboxylic acid. The article also discusses other peculiarities of the mannosaccharic acid and of the new tricarboxylic acids.

It has been claimed that uronic acids on treatment with mineral acids lose carbon dioxide and pass into pentoses.

$$\text{COOH} \cdot \text{CH} \cdot \text{CH(OH)} \cdot \text{CH(OH)} \cdot \text{CH(OH)} \cdot \text{CHOH}$$
$$\underline{\qquad\qquad\qquad O \qquad\qquad\qquad}$$
$$\downarrow$$
$$\text{CH}_2 \cdot \text{CH(OH)} \cdot \text{CH(OH)} \cdot \text{CH(OH)} \cdot \text{CHOH}$$
$$\underline{\qquad\qquad\qquad O \qquad\qquad\qquad}$$

Conrad tested this possibility experimentally by hydrolyzing the barium salt of galacturonic acid with 4 per cent sulfuric acid but could not detect arabinose in the reaction product, whereas added arabinose was easily detected. Pectin, on the other hand, hydrolyzed under the same conditions, yielded arabinose, thus showing that this pentose is a primary constituent of pectin.

Helferich and Bigelow have determined the rate of reaction of trityl chloride with α-methyl glucoside in pyridine. They found the reaction to be of second order and concluded that only the terminal OH reacts with trityl chloride.

Despite the large amount of work which has been done on the cycloses, only 7 of the 50 that are theoretically possible with 4, 5, or 6 hydroxyl groups have been found. To explain this fact, Patterson suggests that all these cycloses are derived from glucose and possess the configuration of this sugar. All the known cycloses appear to have structures compatible with this assumption and only 7, as yet unknown, are predicted.

X-ray studies among the sugars include agreeing determinations of space group and cell size and number for mannitol (Marwick, McCrea) and a determination of these values for dulcitol and mannose (Marwick).

II. STRUCTURE

A. RING STRUCTURE

The articles published last year by Hudson (1, 2, 3) on ring structure as deduced from the theory of optical superposition have aroused considerable controversy. In a long general introduction to a series of papers on this subject, Haworth and Hirst consider in detail several objections to the theories of Hudson. They point out that many of the anomalies observed in the mannose type arise from the rotations having been made only in water, and find that they may vanish or become accentuated if other solvents are employed.[1] They also call attention to the fact that Hudson at times accepts the results of methylation experiments and uses these results to disprove other conclusions resulting from the application of the same method.

Inasmuch as Hudson (1) has accepted the conversion of glucosido-glucose into glucosido-mannose as proceeding without change in the position of union and agrees that this is position 4, Haworth (1, 2) has used this as the basis for a critical test of the views of Hudson. He prepared 4-glucosido- and 4-galactosido-mannose [also Isbell (2)] and found that they both exhibit anomalous properties similar to those observed for mannose and not in agreement with the conclusions of Hudson. Moreover, 4-glucosido- and 4-galactosido-α-methyl mannosides are both hydrolyzed by emulsin

[1] This was shown several years ago by Levene and Bencowitz, *J. Biol. Chem.*, **73**, 679 (1927).

(Haworth, Hirst, Streight, Thomas and Webb; Haworth, Hirst, Plant, and Reynolds) and in each case ordinary α-methyl mannoside is formed. Inasmuch as Hudson claims no ring change in similar cases, Haworth concludes that α-methyl mannoside must possess the <1,5> ring. For even greater rigor Haworth, Hirst, and Streight first methylated the glucosido- and galactosido-mannosides and then hydrolyzed them, giving the known 2,3,6-trimethyl mannose. Haworth, Hirst, and Plant, and Haworth, Hirst, and Streight also oxidized glucosido- and galactosido-mannose to the corresponding mannonic acids, completely methylated these, and hydrolyzed the product, yielding 2,3,5,6-tetramethyl mannonic acid. In addition, an extensive study of the rotations of the methylated lactones in several solvents was made (Haworth, Hirst, and Smith) and it was found that the members of the mannose series exhibit enormous variations in rotation in individual solvents. It was concluded from this that no valid deductions can be made from observations in a single solvent and that Hudson's own rules fail when applied to the rotations as measured, for example, in chloroform.

With regard to the ring structure of fructose, the views formulated on the basis of the isorotation principle of Hudson are also in disagreement with those arrived at by the chemical methods. Hersant and Linnell (1, 2) attempted a solution of the question of the ring structure of fructose by a synthetic method. They prepared a 4-methyl d-fructose by the condensation of 2-methyl glyceraldehyde with dihydroxyacetone. This 4-methyl 2-ketohexose formed a glycoside which on hydrolysis behaved like a pyranoside. The authors, therefore, interpret this as additional evidence in favor of the pyranoside structure for the normal fructosides. It may be mentioned that the new methyl-hexose is reported to be fermentable, the fermenting solution showing initially a dextrorotation increasing progressively for a time and subsequently decreasing. It seems to the reviewers that this statement is in need of confirmation. Incidentally, in the paper new methods for the preparation of dihydroxyacetone and 2-methoxy glyceraldehyde are described.

In a similar manner Levene and Dillon have argued against the possibility of a propyleneoxidic ring as the structure of γ- glucosides. They have found that 3-methyl glucose forms a γ- glucoside with about the same velocity as does glucose, and also that this γ- glucoside on methylation gives the known tetramethyl methylglucofuranoside. They conclude from these facts that position 3 is not (as assumed by

Hudson, to explain certain discrepancies of his theory) involved in the ring formation of γ- glucosides.

The disagreement between the views of Hudson and of other workers as to the ring structure of the α- and β- mannoses was the subject of an investigation by Levene and Tipson (1). These authors converted β-mannose pentacetate into acetobromomannose. From this bromo derivative and silver acetate the α-pentacetate was formed, yet when the bromo derivative was converted into the tetracetate and further acetylated, the β-pentacetate was obtained. It was therefore concluded that the ring structure of the α- and β- mannoses is identical. In addition, it was concluded that the ring structures of mannose and glucose pentacetates are identical inasmuch as acetobromoglucose and acetobromomannose lead to the same triacetylglucal (which is known to be pyranoid).

The problem of the abnormal conduct of the mannose series with respect to the isorotation principle was discussed by Brauns in connection with his investigations on halogenoacetyl mannoses. Continuing his work on the halogen derivatives of the sugars, Brauns has prepared the iodo-, bromo-, chloro-, and fluorotetracetyl mannoses. This preliminary note points out that the ratios of differences in specific rotation observed in other sugars do not hold in the case of mannose. Brauns attributes the irregularity to the *cis* position of the hydroxyls of carbons 2 and 3.

The ring structure of β-methyl galactoside was investigated by A. Müller, who prepared β-methyl galactose 5,6-enide from β-methyl galactoside through the trityl derivative. From the fact that this substance does not reduce Fehling's solution until after acid hydrolysis, Müller concludes that it possesses a pyranoid structure, and not the furanoid assigned by Hudson.

From monoacetone galactose Levene and Meyer have prepared the trimethyl derivative. This was hydrolyzed to trimethyl galactose and oxidized to the corresponding aldonic acid. From the rate of lactone formation and from the direction of rotation of the lactone a $<1,5>$ ring was assigned to the trimethyl galactose and a pyranoid structure was attributed to diacetone galactose. By analogy of configuration it was concluded that diacetone arabinose is also of the pyranose type.

The differences in stability of pyranose and furanose forms of the sugars are discussed by Hibbert, who suggests that the normal valence angle of an oxygen atom attached to two carbon atoms is 32° as against a carbon angle of 109° 28′. On this assumption it is found that strainless, "puckered" rings can be constructed for the pyranose forms, while the furanose ring is under considerable strain and might be expected to rearrange into the strainless pyranose form.

Pryde and Williams have isolated glucuronic acid from human and canine urine after administration of borneol, and have subjected it to methylation and oxidation. From the nature of the oxidation products they conclude that glucuronic acid has in all probability the pyranose ring. In a similar manner the structure of synthetic theophylline arabinoside was investigated and it was concluded that the glycoside and the acetobromoarabinose from which it was prepared are both probably pyranose in form.

The formulation of the ring structure of sugars was frequently based on the properties of the normal and γ- lactones of the simple sugar acids. The hydrolysis of such lactones was previously studied by means of polarimetric measurements and the results have now been confirmed (Carter, Haworth, and Robinson) by repeating the studies but using conductivometric methods. The lowest rate observed for any of the δ- lactones was considerably greater than that observed for the fastest of the γ- lactones.

In extending their studies on simple hydroxy aldehydes, Helferich and Sparmberg (1) have prepared a 6-hydroxy aldehyde by ozonization of pure, optically active citronellol. This hydroxy aldehyde is apparently a mixture of the open chain and lactal forms in which the equilibrium may be displaced toward one or the other form by varying the solvent. It gives a non-reducing lactolide (hemiacetal) which can be easily hydrolyzed by acids to the original hydroxyaldehyde. The aldehyde also gives [Helferich and Sparmberg (2)] a crystalline 2,4-dinitrophenylhydrazone, and this same hydrazone is obtained from the product resulting from the hydrolysis of the lactolide, showing that there has been no migration of the hydroxyl group during lactolide formation. Thus the simple hydroxy aldehydes (unlike the ordinary sugars) can apparently form <1,6> rings.

B. NON-CYCLIC SUGARS

Continuing the work on the open-chain form of the sugars, Wolfrom and Thompson present evidence that the oxime of aldehydoglucose pentacetate is much more reactive than is the pentacetate of glucose oxime. They conclude that the ring form of glucose oxime changes, at least in part, to the open-chain form in undergoing nitrile formation.

A further paper in this series (Wolfrom and Christman) deals with the possibility of true hydrazone structures or open-chain forms in the sugar series. It is shown that galactose phenylhydrazone on acetylation gives the same product as that prepared from aldehydo-galactose pentacetate and phenylhydrazine. It is concluded from this evidence that galactose phenylhydrazone possesses a true hydrazone, or open-chain structure. Similar results were secured with secondary phenylhydrazines.

The mutarotation of the alcoholates and hydrates of aldehydo-galactose pentacetate was investigated (Wolfrom) and it was found that the curve for the ethanol compound is quite complex. This is claimed to indicate the presence of three substances with different rotations, corresponding to the free aldehyde and two alcoholates, epimeric with respect to carbon atom 1. The curve for the aldehydrol, on the other hand, corresponds to a simple monomolecular decomposition of the aldehydrol to the free aldehyde.

The rotatory dispersion of several aldehydo sugar acetates has been investigated (Wolfrom and Brode) and the dispersions were found in each case to be normal. The dispersion of the glucose compound is complex, while those of the galactose and arabinose compounds are simple.

Continuing previous work, Amadori (1) has condensed p-toluidine with glucose and has found that, as with the other aryl bases tried, either a cyclic glucoside or an open-chain Schiff's base may be obtained depending upon whether the reaction is done in the wet or dry way. The same author [Amadori (2)] has also investigated the formation of the glucosides from o-phenetidine, anisidine, and toluidine.

C. GLYCALS AND DESOXY SUGARS

Four possible ring structures may be considered for the glycals, namely, the <1,3>, <1,4>, <1,5>, and <1,6>. The first of these is excluded on the basis of the observations of Levene and Raymond (1) that 3-methyl glucose forms an ordinary glucal, and the <1,4> and <1,6> structures are excluded by Bergmann and Freudenberg (1) as glycals are formed from both 4-glucosidoglucose and 6-glucosidoglucose. Hence, the <1,5> structure may be assigned to triacetylglucal. Hirst and Woolvin have confirmed this deduction by methylating glucal. This trimethylglucal was converted into 2,3,4,6-tetramethyl glucopyranose.

A publication by Bergmann and Freudenberg (2) deals with the structure of the pseudoglycals. Pseudoglycals are formed on heating an aqueous solution of acetylglycals. Triacetylglucal forms a di-acetylpseudoglucal the aldehydic group of which does not reduce Fehling's solution. A double bond exists between carbon atoms 2 and 3. On oxidation the substance is decomposed, giving rise to glyoxal. On hydrogenation 2,3-*bis* desoxyglucose is formed. The pyranoid ring structure of pseudoglycals is evidenced as follows. Pseudocellobial on treatment with orthoformic methylester forms a lactolide of pseudocellobial. In this substance position 4 is substituted, but on enzymatic cleavage with emulsin it yields the lactolide of pseudoglucal. All the pseudoglycals which were investigated behave similarly.

The self-evident identity of the glycals of epimeric sugars was demonstrated experimentally by Gehrke and Obst, who prepared the identical glycal from acetobromoxylose and from acetobromolyxose, and confirmed the identity of the glucose and mannose derivative.

The fact that acetoglucal on oxidation with perbenzoic acid gave rise to a glucose and not a mannose derivative was observed by Tanaka and by Levene and Raymond (1). The latter also found that 3-methyl glucal was converted to 3-methyl glucose and ascribed the abnormality to the substituent on carbon 3. Hirst and Woolvin have now found a similar behavior in the case of trimethyl glucal which was oxidized to 3,4,6-trimethyl glucose but they also observed as much as 20 per cent of a mannose derivative in the product from the oxidation of acetoglucal.

The 2-hydroxyglucals of Maurer may be regarded as intermediary between glycals and sugars. In many respects they differ in their reaction from glycals. Maurer claimed that on treatment with phenyl-hydrazine the tetracetyl hydroxyglucal lost all the acetyl groups and formed a glucosazone. Repeating this experiment, Bergmann and Zervas (1) obtained a monoacetylosazone of a dicarbonyl substance, $C_6H_8O_4$, having one of the structures

$$CH_2 \cdot CO \cdot CO \cdot CH_2 \cdot CH \cdot CH_2OH \text{ or}$$
$$\underset{\mathstrut}{\rule{1pt}{8pt}\underline{\hspace{3em}}O\underline{\hspace{3em}}\rule{1pt}{8pt}}$$

$$CH(OH) \cdot CO \cdot CH = CH \cdot CH \cdot CH_2OH.$$
$$\underset{\mathstrut}{\rule{1pt}{8pt}\underline{\hspace{4em}}O\underline{\hspace{4em}}\rule{1pt}{8pt}}$$

The allocation of the hydroxyl group in position 6 and not in position 4 was based on the fact that the same derivative was obtained from both glucose and galactose.

In a later publication, Bergmann and Zervas (2) revised their view on the structure of the substance and assigned to the osazone the following structure.

$$CH_2 \cdot C(:N_2C_6H_5) \cdot C(:N_2C_6H_5) \cdot CH(OH) \cdot CH \cdot CH_2OH$$
$$|\underline{\hspace{3.5cm}}O\underline{\hspace{5cm}}|$$

Maurer had previously described the conversion of tetracetyl 2-hydroxyglucal to kojic acid (2-hydroxymethyl 5-hydroxy γ-pyrone). Maurer and Müller now describe the preparation of the tetracetyl 2-hydroxygalactal. This substance, through the intermediary of di-chlorotetracetyl 2-hydroxygalactal, was converted into the hydrate of the tetracetylgalactosone. The latter on treatment in pyridine solution with acetic anhydride yielded kojic acid.

The pyranose structure of desoxyglucose was demonstrated by Levene and Mikeska, who obtained two forms of methylated glu-codesonic lactones, one from glucodesonic lactone and the other from the methylated methylglucodesoside. This has been confirmed by Hirst and Woolvin, who converted 3,4,6-trimethyl glucal, on the one hand, into 2,3,4,6-tetramethyl glucose, and on the other, into 3,4,6-trimethyl 2-desoxy glucose. The great instability of the lactolides of all desoxy sugars has been noted by Bergmann and Freudenberg (2) and the stability of the ordinary glycosides therefore is attributed to the stabilizing effect of the hydroxyl of carbon 2.

D. STRUCTURE OF DERIVATIVES

1. *Orthoacetates.*—In the case of rhamnose, three isomeric tri-acetyl methylglycosides had been discovered by Fischer, Bergmann, and Rabe. The third form was characterized by the resistance of one acetyl group to saponification and by the great instability of the methyl group to dilute acids. It was subsequently found that the peculiarity of forming a similar acetylglycoside is common to other sugars having the hydroxyls of carbon atoms 2 and 3 in the *cis* position. In papers which afford a very striking demonstration of the importance of physical methods for the elucidation of chemical struc-ture, Braun (1, 2) explains the resistance of the one acetyl group by the assumption of its being linked to carbon atoms 1 and 2 in cyclic form as an orthoacetic ester, the methoxy group being located on the carbon atom of the orthoacetate and not on a carbon atom of the sugar. The evidence for this assumption was furnished by analysis of the ultra-violet absorption bands. The group $C = O$ has an absorp-

tion band nearer the visible than has orthoacetic acid. Actually, the absorption band of the monoacetyl methylrhamnoside was found in the same region as that of monoacetone glucose, whereas that of ordinary triacetyl methylrhamnoside had its absorption band in the neighborhood of methyl acetate.

Freudenberg, and Freudenberg and Scholz formulated the structure of the third form of heptacetyl chloromaltose in a similar manner, by assuming a cyclic structure for one acetyl group. The heptacetyl methylmaltoside prepared from the third chloro-derivative contained an alkali-stable acetyl group which could not be saponified by boiling in an alcoholic solution of potassium stearate. This acetyl group was removed only by hydrolysis with tolylsulphonic acid. Incidentally, the authors have observed that on long contact with pyridine the chloro- compound loses HCl from the chloro-orthoacetic acid radicle giving rise to a ketene.

If a *cis* configuration of the hydroxyls on carbon atoms 2 and 3 is the requirement for the formation of the cyclic acetates, then ribose likewise should yield a cyclic acetate. This expectation was realized by Levene and Tipson (2). They suggest that in sugars of this type the halogen of carbon atom 1 in the stable forms of the halogenoacetates is in *cis* position to the hydroxyl of carbon atom 2. These same authors have prepared the cyclic acetylmethylmannoside in good yield by reacting the acetobromo- compound with dry sodium methylate in toluene.

Isbell (3) furnished further evidence in favor of the cyclic (orthoacetic) structure of the uncommon form of tetracetyl methylmannoside and of the analogous derivatives of other sugars. He succeeded in replacing the methoxyl group of heptacetyl 4-glucosidomethylmannoside with a hydroxyl group and thus obtained a heptacetate. As distinct from the ordinary glucosidomannose heptacetates, the new form shows no mutarotation. This phenomenon is adduced by the author as evidence that the hydroxyl is attached not to the first carbon atom but to the carbon atom of the orthoacetic acid residue on carbon atoms 1 and 2.

2. *Partially methylated sugars.*—Through the work of Anderson, Charlton, and Haworth, doubt arose as to the structure of the 6-methyl *d*-glucose of Helferich, for they found that the osazones of Helferich's methyl ether and of 3-methyl glucose had identical properties. In view of the importance which the intermediate tritylglucose played in the interpretation of the structure of natural and synthetic

disaccharides and trisaccharides, Helferich and Günther reinvestigated the 3- and 6-methyl glucoses and found them distinctly different. The evidence was the following: First, on purification, the melting-point of the 6-methyl glucosazone was raised to 184°–187° and the rotation was $[\alpha]_D^{16} = -69°$. These constants differed from those of the osazone of 3-methyl glucose. Second, the mixed melting-points of the β-tetracetate of Helferich's substance and β-tetracetyl 3-methyl glucose showed a depression of that of the former by 10°–5°. Third, the 6-methyl β-methyl glucoside (prepared through the aceto-bromo-derivative) is identical with that from levo-glucosan.

A new and simpler preparation of 2-methyl glucose is given by Brigl and Schinle using tetrabenzoyl diethylmercaptan. It is of interest that heating the sugar with excess phenylhydrazine leads to loss of the methyl group and production of some glucosazone.

In view of the importance of possessing 4-methyl glucose for the study of the ring structure of the γ- and normal glucosides, the substance described by Pacsu as 4-methyl glucose was prepared by Levene, Meyer, and Raymond. However, it was found to be identical with the 2-methyl d-glucose of Brigl and Schinle described above. It was also concluded that the derivative to which Pacsu attributed the structure of 4-methyl d-mannose has the structure of 2-methyl d-mannose inasmuch as it forms, according to Pacsu, the same osazone as does the 2-methyl glucose.

3. *Apiose.*—For this substance the branched-chain structure has been generally accepted, as Vongerichten had succeeded in reducing apionic acid to what he claimed to be isovaleric acid (3-methylbutanoic acid). Schmidt considered the evidence of Vongerichten inconclusive and in need of substantiation. In a general way the older plan of establishing the structure was followed. The sugar was converted into apionic acid, this time by the method of Willstätter-Schudel-Goebel, and this was reduced by means of hydriodic acid to the isovaleric acid, which was identified as the p-bromo-phenacyl ester. Inasmuch as apionic acid contains only one asymmetric carbon atom, the configuration of the carbon atom suffices to determine the entire structure of the substance. On the basis of the differences in the rotations of the free acid and its salt, and of its phenylhydrazide, the conclusion was reached that apionic acid has the configuration of d (−) lactic acid.

4. *Formose.*—The formose of Butlerow and of Löw is known to consist of a mixture of different condensation products of formalde-

hyde. Karrer and Krauss undertook the task of separating the individual components. They acetonylated the entire mixture and fractionated the product by distillation. Each fraction was analyzed and its reducing power was determined by the methods of Bertrand and of Willstätter and Schudel. It was concluded that the mixture consisted of pentoses, hexoses, and possibly heptoses. Both aldoses and ketoses were present. The surprising peculiarity of the acetone derivatives was their low reducing power. The presence of polyhydric carbinols was considered but could not be demonstrated experimentally by formation of the benzal derivatives.

5. *Acid amides.*—The structures of the two previously known crystalline amides of tetramethyl hexonic acids were formulated prior to the more recent work on the ring structure of the γ- and normal methylglycosides. Humphreys, Pryde, and Waters have now prepared three pairs of isomeric tetramethyl amides from glucose, galactose, and arabinose. All six amides were dextrorotatory whereas four of the parent lactones were dextrorotatory and two (those related to galactopyranose and arabopyranose) were levorotatory. By the action of alkaline hypochlorite, isocyanate derivatives were formed. To the urethane previously described (Irvine and Pryde) a six-membered ring structure had been assigned. This conclusion should now be revised in favor of a seven-membered ring structure. Two new urethanes were prepared from the two isomeric trimethyl arabonamides. The urethane derived from the 2,3,5-trimethyl arabonamide on standing in 1 per cent methyl alcoholic hydrogen chloride suffered a change in rotation from $[\alpha]_D = +5.0°$ to $[\alpha]_D = -178°$. This change was attributed to enolization. Treatment of the final product with dilute alkali reduced the specific rotation to $-30.8°$. On the other hand, treatment of the original urethane $[\alpha]_D = +5.0°$ with alkali apparently formed a dimethyltetrose.

III. REACTIONS

A. MIGRATION OF SUBSTITUENTS

Helferich and Klein had observed that 1,2,3,4-tetracetyl β-*d*-glucopyranose on treatment with dilute alkali undergoes isomerization into a tetracetyl glucopyranose having a distribution of the acetyl groups different from that of the parent substance. Helferich attributed to the new substance the structure of 1,2,3,6-tetracetyl β-*d*-glucopyranose. One of the arguments in favor of this theory was the formation of a tetracetyl *p*-tolylsulfoglucose, in which the *p*-tolylsulfo group was assumed to occupy position 4. Haworth, Hirst, and Teece questioned the correctness of the conclusions of Helferich and suggested for the new isomer the structure of 2,3,4,6-tetracetyl β-*d*-glucopyranose. In the present article Helferich and Müller refute the views of Haworth on theoretical grounds. The weight of the arguments of Helferich centers on the properties of the tolylsulfo derivative. An unexpected peculiarity was observed in the case of the triacetyl tolylsulfo β-methyl *d*-glucopyranose which, on saponification, lost not only the acetyl groups but also the tolylsulfo group and gave rise to an anhydro sugar, which was provisionally assumed to be a 2,4-anhydro. To the reviewers it seems that the problem requires further investigation.

A case of simultaneous isomerization and acyl migration was observed by Ohle and Lichtenstein. Through the action of ammonia on 5-tolylsulfo 6-benzoylmonoacetone glucofuranose, two interesting products were obtained; first, a 6-aminohexose and second, a di-*p*-tolylsulfohexose. The properties of the first differed from those of the 6-aminoglucose of Fischer and Zach; the structure of 6-amino-idose was therefore tentatively assigned to the new aminohexose. The second substance is important as representing the first case in the sugar series of an intermolecular migration of an acyl group.

The rearrangement of 3-acetyl monoacetone glucose to 6-acetyl monoacetone glucose has been previously reported by Josephson (1). A new paper [Josephson (2)] gives a more thorough study of this reaction and shows that at 20° and pH 7.19 the monomolecular constant shows a progressive variation. This is interpreted by Josephson as being due to formation of an intermediate of unknown rotation. The effects of pH and of temperature were also determined and are discussed.

B. WALDEN INVERSION

Schneider, Fischer, and Specht were concerned with the structure of the mustard-oil glucosides and were thus led to inquire into the α- and β-isomerism of the natural glucosides. In the absence of a direct method the authors took advantage of the observations of Schlubach on dextro 1-bromotetracetyl glucose. When this substance was treated with silver chloride, a levorotatory 1-chloro-tetracetyl-glucose was formed which on standing passed into the more stable dextro- form. Schlubach considered the primary reaction of substitution of a halogen atom on carbon atom 1 to be accompanied by Walden Inversion. Schneider, Fischer, and Specht found that the levo-mustard-oil glucosides and the levo 1-thiol glucosides on hydrolysis with silver nitrate or mercuric chloride yielded a glucose with a high dextro-rotation which gradually passed into the equilibrium form. Accepting a Walden Inversion in this reaction the authors assigned to the levo-mustard-oil glucosides and to the levo 1-thiol d-glucosides the β-structure. In a later publication Schneider and Specht made use of the same method for the elucidation of the α- and β-glucosidic structure of the dextro alkyl 1-thioglucosides. The glucose formed on hydrolysis of methyl, ethyl, and propyl 1-thioglucosides had a rotation of about $[\alpha]_D = +46$–$48°$ which on standing reached a value of $[\alpha]_D = +53$–$55°$. Accepting again a Walden Inversion in the process of hydrolysis, and accepting the glucose formed on hydrolysis as predominatingly β-d-glucose, the authors arrive at the conclusion that the alkylthioglucosides in question are α-glucosides. To the reviewers the conclusions regarding the structure of the alkylthioglucosides do not seem convincing, as substitution on carbon atom 1 need not be regarded as substitution on a purely static atom.

C. DISMUTATION

A very interesting dismutation of glyceric aldehyde was observed by Strain and Spoehr. These authors found that glyceric aldehyde is readily converted by organic amines into methylglyoxal which was identified as its m-nitrobenzoyl osazone. The reagent was added to the reaction mixture and the osazone settled out in course of the reaction. Glyceric aldehyde does not form an insoluble osazone. Dihydroxyacetone does not undergo dismutation under the same conditions.

Another important paper by Spoehr and Strain deals with the properties of the three simple trioses with a view to devising methods for the estimation of each of the possible dissociation products of glucose in the presence of the other. For details the reader is referred to the original.

Bernhauer and Tschinkel reported on the formation of methylglyoxal from various monosaccharides, γ- and normal glycosides, inulin and lactose, by hydrogen peroxide in the presence of ferrous sulfate. All sugars examined form methylglyoxal in the presence of ferrous sulfate, whereas acids are formed in its absence. The methylglyoxal was demonstrated in the distillate as a p-nitrophenyl osazone.

The best yield was obtained from γ- glycosides. The authors argue that the furanose structure is essential for methylglyoxal formation. They assume that methylglyoxal formation is preceded by the formation of methylglyoxal aldol.

Parrod studied the products of dissociation of fructose and glucose, obtained by passing air through a mixture of water, the sugar, cupric oxide, and ammonia. The author isolated various imidazol derivatives. The formation of these substances was explained on the assumption of the dissociation of the sugar into smaller hydroxyaldehydes, hydroxyketones, and formaldehyde; the aldoses and ketoses are then oxidized to α-keto aldehydes, which combine with ammonia and formaldehyde to form imidazols.

An important observation on the action of alkali on xylose and on trimethyl xylose was published by Gross and Lewis. Acting on unsubstituted xylose with 0.004 N calcium hydroxide solution at 35° the authors found in the reaction product 52.9 per cent of xylose, 8.3 per cent of lyxose, and 9.8 per cent of a crystalline condensation product of 2-ketoxylose. In addition, an acid which they regard as d-saccharinic acid was found to the extent of 3 per cent of the total pentose. No stable enolic compounds were detected. On the other hand, trimethyl xylose by similar treatment was transformed into trimethyl lyxose and a substance which the authors regard as a cyclic enol. The reaction is accompanied by the liberation of methyl alcohol in the proportion of one mole for each mole of the enol. On treatment of the reaction product with acid, two additional equivalents of alcohol are liberated with simultaneous formation of furfural.

A conversion of glucose into fructose by means of organic bases is reported by Danilov, Danilova, and Shantarovich. In quinoline and pyridine, glucose was transformed only into fructose, and neither mannose nor saccharinic acid could be detected in the reaction product. In aqueous solutions of the organic bases, however, the formation of mannose and of saccharinic acid was also observed.

Stimulated by the fact that glucose, mannose, and fructose ferment at approximately the same rate and that in the process of fermentation the three sugars form the same hexosediphosphate, Evans and Hockett have compared the effect of alkali on the hexosediphosphate obtained in fermentation. Comparing the curves of lactic-acid formation, the authors observed that the curve of hexosediphosphate resembles that of fructose and not of glucose. The slight deviation is accounted for by the time required to hydrolyze the phosphoric acid groups. This course of events was to have been expected inasmuch as the hexosephosphate is a derivative of fructose.

D. OXIDATION

The subject of active glucose was the topic of two investigations, the one by Ort and the other by Roepke. In an earlier paper, Clifton and Ort reported results on the reduction potential of a solution of glucose to which an oxidant was added at intervals. In this manner the proportion of sugar which was undergoing oxidation was measured. The conclusion in the authors' words was as follows: "There exists in solutions of glucose a small but definite amount of a very powerful reductant or 'active glucose' which alone is responsible for the reduction intensities developed in these solutions. This active form is almost instantly destroyed by even a mild oxidant and exists in dynamic equilibrium with the main bulk of inactive or ordinary glucose since it is in time replaced when so destroyed. Under the conditions of the experiment reported by the author, the amount of the active glucose was found to be one part in 266,000 parts + 10 per cent." In the more recent paper Ort develops a mathematical formula which permits the calculation of the actual amount of active glucose at any pH. For this calculation it is necessary to know the rate of formation of active glucose and to make three determinations of the reduction potential in a given interval. Roepke measured the effect of the pH on the rate of formation of the active forms of glucose, mannose, maltose, and lactose. No linear relationship could be found between the pH and the rate of formation of the active sugar.

The oxidation of glucose with potassium permanganate at the pH at which glucose is oxidized by bromine to gluconic acid was studied by Louisa Ridgway. The object was to develop a convenient method for the preparation of gluconic acid. However, gluconic acid could not be isolated from the reaction product. Incidentally, it was found that in acid solution, oxidation proceeds very rapidly to a certain point and then continues at a much slower rate. The decrease in velocity is attributed to the formation of more stable oxidation products on one hand and the formation of a more stable oxidant on the other.

The oxidation of carbohydrates and fats by air in the presence of yellow phosphorus was studied by Chakrabarti and Dhar. It has long been known that many organic substances, among them carbohydrates, retard the oxidation of phosphorus by a current of air. On the basis of theoretical considerations, Dhar expected the inhibitor to undergo oxidation. This expectation was in a measure realized. Incidentally, it was observed that, contrary to expectations, colloidal phosphorus was the poorest inductor of oxidation.

The process of oxidation of glucose at low pH was studied by Fischler and Reil. The principal object of the investigation was to find conditions that would lead to a linear relationship between the oxidized glucose and the reduced copper. Conditions were found under which the relation approached the linear only to a certain extent. The product of the action of dilute alkali on glucose in the presence of an abundant supply of oxidant has a composition different from that formed by alkali treatment under the usual conditions. In addition to methylglyoxal, acetaldehyde, and formaldehyde, there are formed carbonic, formic, and acetic acids. The authors found that methylglyoxal yields the same products as does glucose, and in this fact they see additional evidence for accepting methylglyoxal formation as the initial step in the alkaline oxidation of glucose.

Continuing his work on the oxidation of glycols and unsaturated substances with lead tetracetate, Criegee has reported the almost quantitative oxidation of monoacetone glucose, yielding formaldehyde. Inasmuch as the reagent attacks only substances which have at least two free hydroxyls on adjacent carbon atoms, the ready oxidation of monoacetone glucose is taken as further evidence for a furanoid ring in this derivative.

Mention may be made of the work by Ochi on the oxidation of several sugars by bleaching powder and of the article by Schwartz on the reducing capacity of a solution containing a mixture of two sugars in equal concentration.

The studies on the theory of alcoholic fermentation based on the conduct of a "model" are being continued by Ohle. In previous publications Ohle and co-workers have shown that β-diacetonefructose-1-sulfuric acid on oxidation with permanganate forms a dicarboxylic acid which Ohle named 2,3-monoacetone β-1-furtondiacid-1-sulfuric acid. [This is the sulfate of monoacetone (dihydroxyacetonyl) malonic acid, formed by the migration of one carbon atom to carbon atom 4, thus having the structure of a ketodisaccharinic acid.] Hydrolysis of this substance yielded acetone, carbonic acid, methylglyoxal, and glycolic acid. The authors (Ohle and Coutsicos) now find that α-diacetonefructose-3-sulfuric acid on oxidation with permanganate gives the corresponding furtondiacid-sulfuric acid, which on hydrolysis likewise yields sulfuric acid, acetone, carbon dioxide, methylglyoxal, and glycolic acid. The authors consider the fructuronic acids to be the precursors of the diacid, and postulate the transformation of glucose into fructose as the first step in alcoholic fermentation.

A further attempt to obtain an insight into the mechanism of alcoholic fermentation was made by Ohle and García y González through the study of the effect of oxidizing agents on phosphoric esters of β-diacetone fructose. Specifically, the authors desired to prepare *bis*-(β-diacetone fructose-1) phosphoric acid. They encountered many difficulties but finally obtained a crystalline sodium salt. The oxidation of this substance with sodium permanganate proceeded at the same rate as that of the corresponding sulfuric-acid ester, the two oxidation curves being practically identical. In addition, the products obtained on treatment of the oxidation products with mineral acids were the same for the phosphoric and the sulfuric esters. The intermediate product was postulated to be *bis*-(β-monoacetone-1-furtondiacid-1) phosphoric acid. In place of the postulated substance, however, a singly substituted phosphoric acid was obtained, namely, β-monoacetone-1-furtondiacid-1-phosphoric acid.

An attempt to find a model for animal combustion of carbohydrates was made by Zuckerkandl and Messiner-Klebermass. Glucose is not affected by heating with charcoal. Aromatic bases, on the other hand, are hydrogenated under the same conditions and pass into imines of quinonoid structure. These substances can then act as hydrogen receptors and therefore serve as models for respiration enzymes. Actually, in the presence of *p*-phenylene diamine, glucose is almost completely destroyed, appearing partly as carbon dioxide and partly in the form of a condensation product with the base, adsorbed on the charcoal. Other aromatic bases may replace *p*-phenylene diamine. Aliphatic bases and amino acids act to a lesser degree.

IV. METHODS AND PREPARATIONS

In a study of degradations in the sugar group Deulofeu has converted arabinose and xylose to erythrose, rhamnose to methyl erythrose, galactose to lyxose, and mannose to arabinose. Several methods were used and the yields by the different methods were determined.

The preparation of lyxose from xylal by oxidation with perbenzoic acid is described by Gehrke and Obst.

Photosynthesis of aldehydes and reducing sugars from carbon dioxide and water by ultra-violet light has been studied by Mezzadroli and Vareton and by Mezzadroli and Giordano who find that the extent of the reaction is increased by $CaCO_3$ and by magnesium, particularly in finely divided or colloidal state. They also report a considerably increased yield as the result of ionizing the carbon dioxide with electric discharges or by radium.

The excellent solvent possibilities of dioxan have been studied by Helferich and Masamune, who report the solubilities of several sugars and derivatives at different temperatures. It is of interest that they apparently formed acetaldehyde from the dioxan in an experiment in which they attempted to condense acetobromoglucose with β-methyl glucoside by means of silver oxide. As the dioxan had been well purified, the reason for the presence of acetaldehyde seems a little obscure.

The preparation of α- and β-methyl mannosides (the latter in about 20 per cent yield) from mannose in methyl-alcoholic hydrogen chloride, has been described by Bott, Haworth, Hirst, and Tipson.

By intermediate preparation of their crystalline $CaCl_2$- addition compounds Isbell (4) was able to secure crystalline α- and β-methyl-gulosides, although the syrupy mixture of the two forms could not be crystallized. Regeneration of the $CaCl_2$- compounds from the crystalline gulosides afforded a check on their purity.

The application of mercury salts as condensing agents was extended by Zemplén and co-workers to a new series of glucosides. Thus a mixture of α- and β-2,3,6-trimethylglucose (obtained by hydrolysis of methylated cellobiose) was condensed in benzene with acetobromoglucose [Zemplén and Bruckner (1)]. In a further paper Zemplén and Gerecs (1) describe conditions which permit the selective preparation of either the α- or the β- forms of the ethyl-glycosides of cellobiose. Prior to that Zemplén and Gerecs (2) had no difficulty in preparing, by the mercury method, the α- forms of phenol or cyclohexanol glycosides of cellobiose acetate, but failed to prepare the corresponding α-ethyl glycoside. Systematic experiments in which all conditions save the concentration of alcohol were kept constant have shown that when the concentration of alcohol is low, both the α- and β- forms result, and when it is high the β- form is obtained. Zemplén, Bruckner, and Gerecs tested the applicability of the rule to the case when the alcohol used was 2,3,4-triacetyl β-methyl glucoside. (The latter was prepared from triacetyl levoglucosan by the interaction with titanic chloride to form the chloro-derivative, which with silver carbonate and methyl alcohol formed the glucoside.) Acetobromo-cellobiose was used as the halogenoacetyl derivative. It was again found that either the α- or β- glycoside was formed depending upon the concentration of the triacetyl glucoside. Subsequently, Zemplén and Gerecs (3) have shown that the above-mentioned 1-chlorotriacetyl glucose can be condensed in the presence of mercuric acetate with either acetobromoglucose or with acetobromocellobiose and gives a chloro-disaccharide and trisaccharide respectively.

Finally, Zemplén and Bruckner (2) investigated the possibility of the formation of 6-α-glucosido-β-methylglucoside under the conditions leading to the synthesis of α- glucosides by the mercury method. Under conditions previously employed, the experiment was unsuccessful. However, when the quantity of catalyst (mercuric acetate) was decreased, the desired substance was obtained without difficulty.

Zemplén and Csürös have also confirmed the experiments on the use of sublimed ferric chloride as a condensing agent for syntheses in the sugar group. This reagent has a great advantage, inasmuch as it permits condensation without resorting to the acetobromo derivatives. However, the yields of α- cellobiosides by this method were very small in the earlier experiments. Profiting by the experience with mercuric acetate as a catalytic agent, they made an effort to improve the yield by varying the concentration of the catalyst. The best yield (20 per cent of α-ethyl-heptacetyl-cellobioside) was obtained when exactly 1 mole of ferric chloride per mole of octacetyl cellobiose was used. Beyond this the yield could not be improved.

Robertson and Waters (1) continue their work on synthetic glycosides and describe the preparation of certain phenolic glucosides by reacting the bromo-derivative with the phenol in quinoline and in the presence of "active" silver oxide. The same authors describe (2) the synthesis of 6-bromoindican and several related products, and of several salicyl glycosides (3) including monotropitoside.

Continuing the work on the synthetic nucleosides Levene and Cortese describe the synthesis of theopylline-d-glucodesoside.

Extending the series of the β-halogenoses, Schlubach and Gilbert described β-acetochloro-galactose and -xylose. They also improved the preparation of the glucose compound and purified it rigorously to make certain that it really constituted an exception to the rules of Hudson. The galactose and xylose derivatives were also found to be exceptions. The β-acetochloro-galactose was converted into a hitherto unknown tetracetyl-α-galactose.

Derivatives of galactofuranose are described by Schlubach and Prochownick who prepared γ-galactose pentacetate and from this the β-acetochloro compound previously described by Hudson and Johnson. Also from the γ-pentacetate they were able to prepare a bromo compound by the action of liquid hydrogen bromide. This substance is unique in that it possesses two bromine atoms, each of which has the reactivity of a bromine atom in position 1. It will be of interest to determine the position of the second bromine.

An improved preparation of bromoacetyl sugars and acetoglucals has been described by Levene and Raymond (2), who use toluene for extraction and distil with this solvent until the other reagents have been removed.

Brauns and Frush have studied the action of free hydrogen fluoride on fructose pentacetate and have found that, while brief action of hydrogen fluoride leads to the replacement of only the acetyl on carbon 2, prolonged action hydrolyzes the acetyl of carbon 1 and leads to the production of 2-fluoro-triacetylfructose. In order to ascertain the position of the removed hydroxyl, they subjected the product to methylation and compared the methylated derivative with the synthetically prepared 1-methyl-fructose and 2-fluoro-3-methyl-triacetyl fructose. Brauns found no osazone formation in the case of 1-methyl fructose. (Ohle had recorded the formation of a trace of glucosazone.)

The condensation of acetone with sugars by means of phosphorus pentoxide in place of other catalysts has been studied by Smith and Lindberg, who find that the reaction is rapid, the yields are frequently good, and the isolation is not difficult. A similar study by Pette indicates the utility of P_2O_5 for reactions of this type. The preparation of diacetone glucose in good yield from β-glucose is described by Minsaas (2), but the procedure appears to be too tedious to compare favorably with other methods which have been proposed for this product.

Helferich and Appel have made studies on the formation of ethylidene derivatives by employing paraldehyde in the presence of very little sulfuric acid as used by Hill and Hibbert. They describe several ethylidine derivatives prepared in good yield by this means and assign structures to them. The accidental preparation of ethylidine-β-methylglucoside is described by Helferich and Masamune.

They were working with a solution of β-methylglucoside in dioxan, and the solvent apparently suffered decomposition forming acetalde-hyde, which then reacted with the glucoside.

From monoacetone-6-bromohydrin, Freudenberg, Toepffer, and Zaheer prepared the anhydride.

This anhydride on condensation with acetobromoglucose unexpectedly gave a 6-bromo-5-glucosidoglucose derivative and the bromine atom could not be replaced by a hydroxyl group. The only bromine-free substance was a derivative of a 5-glucosido 3,6-anhydro monoacetone glucose.

The preparation and properties of β-glucothiose, its pentacetate, and certain derivatives of the latter are described by Schneider and Bansa.

The phenylcarbimide and thiocarbimide of aminoglucose have been prepared by Shmuk and found to differ from the corresponding derivatives of glucosamine.

Bergmann and Zervas (3), resuming work started several years ago, condensed anisaldehyde with the amino group of glucosamine and used this product as starting material for the preparation of several derivatives of glucosamine.

Bertho and co-workers have described the formation of peptide-like derivatives of glucosamine, using a number of acyl bromides and con-verting these products in some cases to the corresponding amino acids.

The preparation of the d- and l-rhamnitols, as their trihydrates, by reduction of the corresponding rhamnoses is given by Valentin.

A study of the different factors in the formation of levulinic acid from sucrose has been made by Thomas and Schuette and the best procedure for its preparation is described.

The synthesis of a number of 1,1-dialkyl fructoses by acting on β-diacetone-2-ketogluconic acid or on its methyl ester with Grignard derivatives, is described by Ohle and Hecht. The monoacetone de-rivatives were prepared from certain of these by mild hydrolysis and the completely deacetoneated product by further hydrolysis. One of the intermediates was β-diacetone 1-methyl d-glucosone. Ohle and Dambergis oxidized diacetone galactose to galactonic acid and then treated this with Grignard reagents as above to obtain 6,6-dialkyl derivatives of galactose and 6-methyl 6-keto d-galactose.

In view of the possible biological significance of glucosone, Maurer and Petsch have endeavored to prepare crystalline esters of this substance. A tetracetate hydrate had been described previously and the authors now record the preparation of a triacetyl glucosone and of its hydrate. All these acetates in pyridine or in aqueous pyridine solution were found to change with measurable velocity into diacetyl kojic acid. This reaction is the cause of the anomalous results in acetyl determinations by the Zerevitinov method. No epimerization of the osones by alkali was observed.

Work on the preparation of crystalline sugar acids has been continued by Rehorst, using his method of concentrating the solution of the acid with ethyl alcohol and a higher boiling alcohol so that the water is removed during the distillation. Crystalline arabonic acid has thus been prepared but attempts to prepare crystalline rhamnonic acid in the same manner yielded only the crystalline lactone. The author has also studied the lactone formation of arabonic acid and has observed changes in the direction of optical rotation corresponding to the formation of two lactones. He concludes from this that the terminal hydroxyl group acts in a position *trans* to that of the γ-hydroxyl and expects this to be the case for all the pentoses.

The electrolytic oxidation of sugars to the corresponding acids has been described by Isbell and Frush. The method consists in an electrolysis in the presence of calcium carbonate and a small amount of a bromide, being essentially an ordinary bromine oxidation but one in which the bromine is regenerated so that only little is required. The isolation is thus facilitated and the calcium salts of the acids are prepared with ease. The oxidation of glucose, galactose, mannose, rhamnose, arabinose, lactose, and maltose is described.

The purification of commercial dihydroxyacetone to give a pure crystalline product is described by Reeves and Renbom, and from this the monomolecular form is prepared in the usual manner by distillation under reduced pressure.

Inasmuch as she was unable to methylate dihydroxyacetone, Neuberg has prepared the α-methyl ether by starting from α-methyl glycerol and oxidizing this to the ketone, isolated as the dinitrophenylhydrazone.

A simple preparation of methylglyoxal solutions is given by Hofmann and Neuberg, who carefully decompose the oxime with HSO_3NO_2.

An enol derivative of β-hydroxy propionaldehyde has been prepared from 2-*p*-toluenesulfonyl 1,3-benzal glycerol by Fischer, Ahlström, and Richter, and used by them for a new synthesis of glyceraldehyde.

The purification of methylglyoxal and a measurement of its absorption spectrum are described by Fischler, Hauss, and Täufel. The same absorption maxima are observed for glucose in dilute alkaline solution but are dissipated almost completely on acidification. The effect of dilute alkali on methylglyoxal and attempts to prepare this substance from lactates are also described.

The production of methylfurfuraldehyde oxide as a by-product in the preparation of hydroxymethylfurfuraldehyde from sucrose with oxalic acid is reported by Chandrasena.

V. NATURAL SUBSTANCES

A. GLYCOSIDES

The structure of esculin has been investigated by Head and Robertson, who conclude that it is not 7-glucosidoxy 6-hydroxy coumarin as had been previously supposed but is instead 6-glucosidoxy 7-hydroxy coumarin. This conclusion is confirmed by Macbeth in a preliminary paper. From methylation experiments he concludes that the glucose is present in the pyranose form and as a β-derivative.

Hesperidin is the subject of a study by King and Robertson, who confirm the view of Asahina and Inubuse that the glycoside is a rhamnoglucoside of hesperidin, analogous to naringin.

Robertson and Waters (4) have studied the structure of euxanthic acid by means of methylation experiments and have shown the glucuronic acid to have the pyranoside ring-form.

Gluco-*m*-hydroxybenzaldehyde was synthesized by Mauthner and was found to be not identical with picein.

Among the naturally occurring glycosides which have been reported during the year may be mentioned the preparation of frangularoside from alder by Bridel and Charaux (1, 2). This is a rhamnoside and on hydrolysis may give as much as 40 per cent of rhamnose. Bridel and Rabaté describe the preparation of piceoside from black willow bark, and Rabaté reports the preparation of rutoside. Thevetin, a glucoside obtainable from the seed kernels of the yellow oleander, is described by Ayyar. Unedoside is a new glucoside found by Bridel and Bourdouil, which is hydrolyzable by emulsin. The authors claim that the hydrolyzed material has a lower reducing power than the original glycoside. Vicioside, from vetch seeds, has been investigated by Hérissey and Cheymol (1, 2). The authors, having overlooked all recent work on the substance, have corroborated all the findings of the preceding workers and have added a new fact, namely, that the substance is hydrolyzed by emulsin. The glycoside asphodeloholoside has been isolated from asphodel tubers by Neyron and is found to be hydrolyzable to fructose and an aldose, probably glucose. It is hydrolyzed partly by sucrase and is fermented by *Aspergillus niger*.

A report on certain cyanogenetic glucosides has been made by Finnemore and Cox, who have studied the occurrence of the glucosides sambunigrin and prunasin as well as the presence of the corresponding hydrolytic enzymes. They report also that these glucosides are much more easily hydrolyzed by the enzymes of plants than is amygdalin.

B. ENZYMES

Weidenhagen advanced a theory regarding the mechanism of the action of the enzymes which operate in disaccharide cleavage. According to this author (1) the separation of maltase from invertase described by Willstätter and Bamann is really a separation of α-glucosidase from β-fructofuranosidase. The former enzyme is considered to be capable of hydrolyzing all α-glucoside linkages, and therefore both maltose and sucrose, while the latter enzyme can hydrolyze sucrose but not maltose. The paper describes the separation of the two enzymes and the preparation of α-glucosidase free from β-fructofuranosidase. A second paper [Weidenhagen (2)] suggests that the term "maltase" is not well chosen inasmuch as α-glucosidase hydrolyzes sucrose twice as rapidly as it does maltose and also has twice as great a combining capacity for the former sugar. The author also believes that the relation found by Michaelis and Menten was purely accidental, and points out the complexities which arise when yeast or yeast autolysates are considered as being a mixture of two enzymes attacking essentially different linkages. Continuing the work this author [Weidenhagen (3)] finds that mushroom extract accomplishes the cleavage of sucrose but not of maltose and he therefore describes it as a β-fructofuranosidase. In agreement with this conclusion he finds that this enzyme hydrolyzes raffinose to fructose and melibiose, but that melezitose is not hydrolyzed. This is contrary to the results of Ivanov.

Karström, on the other hand, finds that a particular strain of *B. coli* which ferments maltose, glucose, and fructose but not sucrose possesses an α-glucosidase which does not hydrolyze sucrose. Weidenhagen (4), repeating the experiments with material supplied by Karström, obtains opposite results. Myrbäck agrees with Karström in finding that *B. coli I* splits maltose in 7 hours but not sucrose, while in contrast, Weidenhagen (5) finds splitting of neither maltose nor sucrose with extracts of dried *B. coli I*. He also thinks that yeast is a better material for settling the question than is *B. coli*. In this connection may be mentioned the paper by Narasimhamurty and Sreenivasaya recommending maltase as a means of determining the maltose content of materials. It is evident that if Weidenhagen's contentions are correct, the presence of sucrose would introduce an error.

The hydrolysis of the levo-rotatory glucosides asebotin and phloridzin by emulsin (contrary to the results of earlier workers) is described by Bridel and these glucosides are therefore classified as β- glucosides.

A number of synthetic experiments with enzymes have been reported during the year: Bridel and Joanid describe syntheses of β-methyl glucoside using the same sample of enzyme repeatedly. Although the activity of the enzyme constantly decreased, still it was quite active at the end of three months and during that time had acted on 350 times its own weight of glucose and had converted 77 per cent of it to β-methyl glucoside. A synthesis is also reported for glucose in allyl alcohol (Olive) and glucose in propyl alcohol (Gollan), emulsin being the enzyme used in each case. The synthesis of β-5-iodosalicyl glucoside with emulsin is also reported (Delauney).

A study of the enzymic synthesis of sucrose has been made by Oparin and Kurssanov. These authors conclude that previous failures to obtain such synthesis are due to the fact that the necessary γ-fructose changes to ordinary β-fructopyranose faster than it is synthesized to sucrose. Inasmuch as sucrose phosphate (prepared by the method of Neuberg and Pollak) was found to be hydrolyzed by emulsin to the extent of only 40 per cent, these authors were led to study the reverse reaction in the presence of phosphates. Formation of a polysaccharide was observed and, although it was not isolated, the authors consider it to be sucrose.

The apparent synthesis of the trisaccharide, raffinose, is reported by Blagoveshchenskii, who effected the synthesis from sucrose and galactose by means of the enzyme emulsin.

Other enzymes which have been described include glucosulfatase, from certain kinds of Japanese snails, which hydrolyzes glucose-monosulfate but not galactose sulfate or similar compounds (Soda and Hattori). Glucoseoxidase from *Aspergillus niger* oxidizes glucose to glucuronic acid but acts upon sucrose only because of preliminary hydrolysis to glucose (D. Müller). Maltose is oxidized directly but by the separate enzyme, maltoseoxidase. Further properties of the enzyme are given. The preparation of alginic acid from brown algae and an enzyme which causes its liquefaction is given by Oshima.

C. YEASTS, MOLDS, AND BACTERIA

The problem of selective fermentation by yeasts has received some attention recently, Ivekovic pointing out that certain of the conclusions of Hopkins on this subject were similar to or derivable from earlier work of Ivekovic. Sobotka and Reiner (2) studied the selective action of several yeasts and found that they all preferred glucose to fructose, whether separately or in mixtures of the two sugars. The effect of added mannose was also studied. A second paper (3) on the subject deals with Sauterne yeast, which was found to prefer fructose to glucose in mixtures. Hopkins concludes from these and similar results that most yeasts are specific for that form of fructose which is present in small amount but which increases with temperature (such as a γ-form), whereas Sauterne yeast is specific for the normal form of the sugar.

The action of *Aspergillus oryzae* and *Aspergillus niger* on sugar is the subject of a paper by Challenger, Klein, and Walker. These authors find that kojic acid is produced by the former of these molds when grown on dihydroxyacetone or glycerol but not on ethylene glycol, calcium gluconate, potassium acid saccharate, potassium citrate or glyceric acid. The authors conclude that it is not necessary that pentoses be converted to hexoses as a preliminary to kojic-acid formation, but that instead it is more likely that the triose, dihydroxyacetone, is first formed and then condensed to the kojic acid. May, Moyer, Wells, and Herrick, however, find as much as 55 per cent of consumed dextrose converted into kojic acid by *Aspergillus flavus*. These authors also give the optimum conditions for growth and acid production.

Continuing earlier work, Takahashi and Asai investigated gluconic (1) and glucuronic acid (2, 3) formation by bacteria. One variety of bacteria which was employed produced glucuronic acid and oxy-gluconic acid (ketogluconic acid) not only from glucose, but also from gluconic acid. Gluconic acid formation by certain molds has been studied by Angeletti and Cerruti who find relatively large amounts formed from glucose, less from mannose, and none from galactose.

Two "glauconic" acids are reported as being formed from sucrose by *Pencillium glaucum* (Wijkman), and itaconic acid and mannitol from the same substrate by a new fungus, *Aspergillus itaconicus* (Kinoshita).

The formation of 2-hydroxymethylfuran-5-carboxylic acid, probably from chitin, is reported by Sumiki.

The formation of propionic acid from pentoses is the subject of one paper (Werkman, etc.), while another deals with the various products formed in pentose fermentations (Foote, Fred, and Peterson).

Formation of lactic acid and mannitol from sucrose has also been studied (Virgilio).

A study of saccharic-acid formation (Bernhauer, Siebenäuger, and Tschinkel) by molds leads to the conclusion that saccharic acid is not an intermediate in citric-acid formation, although several molds convert it into oxalic acid.

D. SUGARS IN PLANTS

The carbohydrates of the *Laminariae* and their seasonal variations were studied by Ricard. Mannitol was found to become maximum in amount at the time of sporulation, while fucose and glucose were not found at any time. A paper on the same subject by Bird and Haas describes the cell wall as consisting of fucoidin and alginic acid. The former is a complex, the calcium salt of a sulfuric ester of a non-reducing polymerized uronic acid with a methylpentosan. Alginic acid is a polymerized mannuronic acid.

Among papers studying metabolism of plants may be mentioned one by Neuberg and Kobel demonstrating the formation of methylglyoxal by the enzymes from germinating seeds. It is concluded that this substance is an intermediate in the metabolism of both plants and animals. Another paper by Szent-Györgyi describes an enzyme, occurring in the cabbage leaf, hexoxidase, which in the presence of oxygen oxidizes hexuronic acid to a reversible oxidation product. It is concluded that hexuronic acid plays an important part in the respiration of the cabbage leaf. Finally, the paper by Sreenivasaya may be mentioned showing mannitol to occur to the extent of 2 to 3 per cent in the spike disease of sandal. It is concluded that mannitol is one of the metabolic products of the virus.

LITERATURE CITED

AMADORI, M. (1), *Atti accad. Lincei*, 13, 72 (1931)
AMADORI, M. (2), *Atti accad. Lincei*, 13, 195 (1931)
ANDERSON, C. G., CHARLTON, W., AND HAWORTH, W. N., *J. Chem. Soc.*, 1329 (1929)
ANGELETTI, A., AND CERRUTI, C. F., *Ann. chim. applicata*, 20, 424 (1930)
ASAHINA, Y., AND INUBUSE, M., *J. Pharm. Soc. Japan*, 49, 128 (1929)
AYYAR, P. R., *Proc. 15th Indian Sci. Cong.*, 1928, 161 (1928)
BERGMANN, M., AND FREUDENBERG, W. (1), *Ber.*, 62, 2783 (1929)
BERGMANN, M., AND FREUDENBERG, W. (2), *Ber.*, 64, 158 (1931)
BERGMANN, M., AND ZERVAS, L. (1), *Ber.*, 64, 1434 (1931)
BERGMANN, M., AND ZERVAS, L. (2), *Ber.*, 64, 2032 (1931)
BERGMANN, M., AND ZERVAS, L. (3), *Ber.*, 64, 975 (1931)
BERNHAUER, K., SIEBENÄUGER, H., AND TSCHINKEL, H., *Biochem. Z.*, 230, 466 (1931)
BERNHAUER, K., AND TSCHINKEL, H., *Biochem. Z.*, 230, 484 (1931)
BERTHO, A., HÖLDER, F., MEISER, W., AND HÜTHER, F., *Ann.*, 485, 127 (1931)
BIRD, G. M., AND HAAS, P., *Biochem. J.*, 25, 403 (1931)
BLAGOVESHCHENSKII, A. V., *Biochem. J.*, 24, 1337 (1930)
BOTT, H. G., HAWORTH, W. N., HIRST, E. L., AND TIPSON, R. S., *J. Chem. Soc.*, 2653 (1930)
BRAUN, E. (1), *Naturwissenschaften*, 18, 393 (1930)
BRAUN, E. (2), *Ber.*, 63, 1972 (1930)
BRAUNS, D. H., *J. Am. Chem. Soc.*, 53, 2004 (1931)
BRAUNS, D. H., AND FRUSH, H. L., *Bur. Standards J. Research*, 6, 449 (1931)
BRIDEL, M., *J. pharm. chim.*, [8]12, 385 (1930)
BRIDEL, M., AND BOURDOUIL, C., *J. pharm. chim.*, [8]12, 241; *Bull. soc. chim. biol.*, 12, 910 (1930)
BRIDEL, M., AND CHARAUX, C. (1), *Compt. rend.*, 191, 1151 (1930)
BRIDEL, M., AND CHARAUX, C. (2), *Compt. rend.*, 191, 1374 (1930)
BRIDEL, M., AND JOANID, N., *J. pharm. chim.*, [8]12, 337 (1930)
BRIDEL, M., AND RABATÉ, J., *Bull. soc. chim. biol.*, 12, 332 (1930)
BRIGL, P., AND SCHINLE, R., *Ber.*, 63, 2884 (1930)
CARTER, S. R., HAWORTH, W. N., AND ROBINSON, R. A., *J. Chem. Soc.*, 2125 (1930)
CHAKRABARTI, S. N., AND DHAR, N. R., *J. Phys. Chem.*, 35, 1114 (1931)
CHALLENGER, F., KLEIN, L., AND WALKER, T. K., *J. Chem. Soc.*, 16 (1931)
CHANDRASENA, J. P. C., *J. Chem. Soc.*, 2035 (1930)
CLIFTON, C. E., AND ORT, J. M., *J. Phys. Chem.*, 34, 855 (1930)
CONRAD, C. M., *J. Am. Chem. Soc.*, 53, 2282 (1931)
CRIEGEE, R., *Ber.*, 64, 260 (1931)
DANILOV, S., VENUS-DANILOVA, E., AND SHANTAROVICH, P., *J. Russ. Phys.-Chem. Soc.*, 62, 494 (1930); *Ber.*, 63, 2269 (1930)
DARMOIS, E., AND MARTIN, J., *J. chim. phys.*, 28, 149 (1931)

DELAUNEY, P., *Compt. rend.*, **191,** 57 (1930)

DEULOFEU, V., *J. Chem. Soc.*, 2602 (1930)

ETTEL, V., *Collection Czechoslov. Chem. Communications,* **2,** 457 (1930)

EVANS, W. L., AND HOCKETT, R. C., *J. Am. Chem. Soc.*, **52,** 4065 (1930)

FINNEMORE, H., AND COX, C. B., *J. Proc. Roy. Soc. N.S. Wales,* **63,** 172 (1930)

FISCHER, E., BERGMANN, M., AND RABE, A., *Ber.*, **53,** 2375 (1920)

FISCHER, E., AND ZACH, K., *Ber.*, **44,** 132 (1911)

FISCHER, H. O. L., AHLSTRÖM, L., AND RICHTER, H., *Ber.*, **64,** 611 (1931)

FISCHLER, F., HAUSS, H., AND TÄUFEL, K., *Biochem. Z.*, **227,** 156 (1930)

FISCHLER, F., AND REIL, J., *Biochem. Z.*, **227,** 140 (1930)

FOOTE, M., FRED, E. B., AND PETERSON, W. H., *Zentr. Bakt. Parasitenk, II Abt.,* **82,** 379 (1930)

FREUDENBERG, K., *Naturwissenschaften,* **18,** 393 (1930)

FREUDENBERG, K., AND SCHOLZ, H., *Ber.*, **63,** 1969 (1930)

FREUDENBERG, K., TOEPFFER, H., AND ZAHEER, S. H., *Ber.*, **63,** 1966 (1930)

GEHRKE, M., AND OBST, F., *Ber.*, **64,** 1724 (1931)

GOLLAN, J., *Bull. soc. chim. biol.*, **13,** 403 (1931)

GROSS, C. E., AND LEWIS, W. L., *J. Am. Chem. Soc.*, **53,** 2772 (1931)

HAWORTH, W. N. (1), *J. Am. Chem. Soc.*, **52,** 4168 (1930)

HAWORTH, W. N. (2), *Nature,* **126,** 238 (1930)

HAWORTH, W. N., AND HIRST, E. L., *J. Chem. Soc.*, 2615 (1930)

HAWORTH, W. N., ·HIRST, E. L., AND PLANT, M. M. T., *J. Chem. Soc.*, 1354 (1931)

HAWORTH, W. N., HIRST, E. L., PLANT, M. M. T., AND REYNOLDS, R. J. W., *J. Chem. Soc.*, 2644 (1930)

HAWORTH, W. N., HIRST, E. L., AND SMITH, J. A. B., *J. Chem. Soc.*, 2659 (1930)

HAWORTH, W. N., HIRST, E. L., AND STREIGHT, H. R. L., *J. Chem. Soc.*, 1349 (1931)

HAWORTH, W. N., HIRST, E. L., STREIGHT, H. R. L., THOMAS, H. A., AND WEBB, J. I., *J. Chem. Soc.*, 2636 (1930)

HAWORTH, W. N., HIRST, E. L., AND TEECE, E. G., *J. Chem. Soc.*, 1405 (1930)

HEAD, F. S. H., AND ROBERTSON, A., *J. Chem. Soc.*, 2434 (1930)

HELFERICH, B., AND APPEL, H., *Ber.*, **64,** 1841 (1931)

HELFERICH, B., AND BIGELOW, N. M., *J. prakt. Chem.*, **131,** 259 (1931)

HELFERICH, B., AND GÜNTHER, E., *Ber.*, **64,** 1276 (1931)

HELFERICH, B., AND KLEIN,. W., *Ann.*, **455,** 173 (1927)

HELFERICH, B., AND MASAMUNE, H., *Ber.*, **64,** 1257 (1931)

HELFERICH, B., AND MÜLLER, A., *Ber.*, **63,** 2142 (1930)

HELFERICH, B., AND SPARMBERG, G. (1), *Ber.*, **64,** 104 (1931)

HELFERICH, B., AND SPARMBERG, G. (2), *Ber.*, **64,** 1151 (1931)

HÉRISSEY, H., AND CHEYMOL, J. (1), *Compt. rend.*, **191,** 387 (1930)

HÉRISSEY, H., AND CHEYMOL, J. (2), *Bull. soc. chim. biol.*, **13,** 29 (1931)

HERSANT, E. F., AND LINNELL, W. H. (1), *Nature,* **126,** 844 (1930)

HERSANT, E. F., AND LINNELL, W. H. (2), *Quart. J. Pharm. Pharmacol.*, **4,** 52 (1931)

HIBBERT, H., *Science,* **73,** 500 (1931)

HILL, H. S., AND HIBBERT, H., *J. Am. Chem. Soc.*, **45,** 3108, 3124 (1923)

HIRST, E. L., AND WOOLVIN, C. S., *J. Chem. Soc.*, 1131 (1931)

HOFMANN, E., AND NEUBERG, C., *Biochem. Z.*, **226**, 489 (1930)

HOPKINS, R. H., *Biochem. J.*, **25**, 245 (1931)

HUDSON, C. S. (1), *J. Am. Chem. Soc.*, **52**, 1680 (1930)

HUDSON, C. S. (2), *J. Am. Chem. Soc.*, **52**, 1707 (1930)

HUDSON, C. S. (3), *Dixième conf. union intern. chim.*, **1930**, 59

HUMPHREYS, R. W., PRYDE, J., AND WATERS, E. T., *J. Chem. Soc.*, 1298 (1931)

IRVINE, J. C., AND PRYDE, J., *J. Chem. Soc.*, **125**, 1045 (1924)

ISBELL, H. S. (1), *Bur. Standards J. Research*, **5**, 741 (1930)

ISBELL, H. S. (2), *Bur. Standards J. Research*, **5**, 1179; *Proc. Nat. Acad. Sci.*, **16**, 704 (1930)

ISBELL, H. S. (3), *J. Am. Chem. Soc.*, **52**, 5298 (1930)

ISBELL, H. S. (4), *Proc. Nat. Acad. Sci.*, **16**, 699 (1930)

ISBELL, H. S., AND FRUSH, H. L., *Bur. Standards J. Research*, **6**, 1145 (1931)

IVANOV, N., DODONAWA, E. W., AND TSCHASTUCHIN, W. J., *Fermentforschung*, **11**, 433 (1930)

IVEKOVIC, H., *Biochem. J.*, **24**, 4 (1930)

JOSEPHSON, K. (1), *Svensk. Kemi. Tid.*, **41**, 99 (1929)

JOSEPHSON, K. (2), *Ber.*, **63**, 3089 (1930)

KARRER, P., AND KRAUSS, E. VON, *Helv. Chim. Acta*, **14**, 820 (1931)

KARSTRÖM, H., *Biochem. Z.*, **231**, 399 (1931)

KILIANI, H., *Ber.*, **64**, 2018 (1931)

KING, F. E., AND ROBERTSON, A., *J. Chem. Soc.*, 1704 (1931)

KINOSHITA, K., *J. Chem. Soc. Japan*, **50**, 583 (1929)

LEVENE, P. A., AND CORTESE, F., *J. Biol. Chem.*, **92**, 53 (1931)

LEVENE, P. A., AND DILLON, R. T., *J. Biol. Chem.*, **92**, 769 (1931)

LEVENE, P. A., AND MEYER, G. M., *J. Biol. Chem.*, **92**, 257 (1931)

LEVENE, P. A., MEYER, G. M., AND RAYMOND, A. L., *J. Biol. Chem.*, **91**, 497; *Science*, **73**, 291 (1931)

LEVENE, P. A., AND MIKESKA, L. A., *J. Biol. Chem.*, **88**, 791 (1930)

LEVENE, P. A., AND RAYMOND, A. L. (1), *J. Biol. Chem.*, **88**, 513 (1930)

LEVENE, P. A., AND RAYMOND, A. L. (2), *J. Biol. Chem.*, **90**, 247 (1931)

LEVENE, P. A., AND TIPSON, R. S. (1), *J. Biol. Chem.*, **90**, 89 (1931)

LEVENE, P. A., AND TIPSON, R. S. (2), *J. Biol. Chem.*, **92**, 109 (1931)

LOWRY, T. M., AND KRIEBLE, V. K., *Z. physik. Chem.*, *Bodenstein-Festband.* 881 (1931)

LOWRY, T. M., AND SMITH, G. F., *Dixième conf. union intern. chim.*, **1930**, 79

MACBETH, A. K., *J. Chem. Soc.*, 1288 (1931)

MARWICK, T. C., *Nature*, **127**, 11 (1931)

MAURER, K., *Ber.*, **63**, 25 (1930)

MAURER, K., AND MÜLLER, A., *Ber.*, **63**, 2069 (1930)

MAURER, K., AND PETSCH, W., *Ber.*, **64**, 2011 (1931)

MAUTHNER, F., *J. prakt. Chem.*, **129**, 278 (1931)

MAY, O. E., MOYER, A. J., WELLS, P. A., AND HERRICK, H. T., *J. Am. Chem. Soc.*, **53**, 774 (1931)

McCREA, G. W., *Nature*, **127**, 162 (1931)

MEZZADROLI, G., AND VARETON, E., *Chimie & industrie*, Special No. 778 (March, 1931)

MEZZADROLI, G., AND GIORDANO, G., *Ind. saccar. ital.*, **22**, 207 (1919)

MICHAELIS, L., AND MENTEN, M. L., *Biochem. Z.*, **49**, 333 (1913)

MICHEEL, F., AND MICHEEL, H., *Ber.*, **63**, 2862 (1930)

MINSAAS, J. (1), *Rec. trav. chim.*, **50**, 424 (1931)

MINSAAS, J. (2), *Kgl. Norske Videnskab. Selskabs Forh.*, 1926, **I** (Medd., No. 2), 113 (1929)

MÜLLER, A., *Ber.*, **64**, 1820 (1931)

MÜLLER, D., *Biochem. Z.*, **232**, 423 (1931)

MYRBÄCK, K., *Z. physiol. Chem.*, **198**, 196 (1931)

NARASIMHAMURTY, N., AND SREENIVASAYA, M., *Biochem. J.*, **24**, 1734 (1930)

NEUBERG, C., AND KOBEL, M., *Biochem. Z.*, **229**, 433 (1930)

NEUBERG, I. S., *Biochem. Z.*, **238**, 459 (1931)

NEYRON, C., *Bull. sci. pharmacol.*, **38**, 38 (1931)

OCHI, S., *Proc. World Eng. Congr., Tokyo, 1929*, **31**, 537 (1931)

OHLE, H., *Ber.*, **58**, 2581 (1925)

OHLE, H., AND COUTSICOS, G., *Ber.*, **63**, 2912 (1930)

OHLE, H., AND DAMBERGIS, C., *Ann.*, **481**, 255 (1930)

OHLE, H., AND GARCÍA Y GONZÁLEZ, *Ber.*, **64**, 1759 (1931)

OHLE, H., AND HECHT, O., *Ann.*, **481**, 233 (1930)

OHLE, H., AND LICHTENSTEIN, R., *Ber.*, **63**, 2905 (1930)

OLIVE, M., *Bull. soc. chim. biol.*, **13**, 254 (1931)

OPARIN, A., AND KURSSANOV, A., *Biochem. Z.*, **239**, 1 (1931)

ORT, J. M., *Proc. Staff Meetings Mayo Clinic*, **6**, 295 (1931)

OSHIMA, K., *J. Agr. Chem. Soc. Japan*, **7**, 332; *Bull. Agr. Chem. Soc. Japan*, **7**, 17 (1931)

PARROD, J., *Compt. rend.*, **192**, 1136 (1931)

PATTERSON, A. L., *Nature*, **126**, 880 (1930)

PETTE, J. W., *Ber.*, **64**, 1567 (1931)

PRYDE, J., AND WILLIAMS, R. T., *Nature*, **128**, 187 (1931)

RABATÉ, J., *Bull. soc. chim. biol.*, **12**, 974 (1930)

REEVES, H. G., AND RENBOM, E. T., *Biochem. J.*, **25**, 411 (1931)

REHORST, K., *Ber.*, **63**, 2279 (1930)

RICARD, P., *Bull. soc. chim. biol.*, **13**, 417 (1931)

RIDGWAY, S. LOUISA, *J. Phys. Chem.*, **35**, 1985 (1931)

ROBERTSON, A., AND WATERS, R. B. (1), *J. Chem. Soc.*, 2729 (1930)

ROBERTSON, A., AND WATERS, R. B. (2), *J. Chem. Soc.*, 72 (1931)

ROBERTSON, A., AND WATERS, R. B. (3), *J. Chem. Soc.*, 1881 (1931)

ROBERTSON, A., AND WATERS, R. B. (4), *J. Chem. Soc.*, 1704 (1931)

ROEPKE, M. H., *Proc. Staff Meetings Mayo Clinic*, **6**, 371 (1931)

SCHLUBACH, H. H., *Ber.*, **59**, 840 (1926)

SCHLUBACH, H. H., AND GILBERT, R., *Ber.*, **63**, 2292 (1930)

SCHLUBACH, H. H., AND PROCHOWNICK, V., *Ber.*, **63**, 2298 (1930)

SCHMIDT, O. T., *Ann.*, **483**, 115 (1930)

SCHNEIDER, W., AND BANSA, A., *Ber.*, **64**, 1321 (1931)

SCHNEIDER, W., FISCHER, H., AND SPECHT, W., *Ber.*, **63**, 2787 (1930)

SCHNEIDER, W., AND SPECHT, W., *Ber.*, **64**, 1319 (1931)

SCHWARTZ, P., *Biochem. Z.*, **224**, 193 (1930)

SHMUK, A. A., *J. Russ. Phys.-Chem. Soc.*, **61**, 1759 (1929)

ANNUAL REVIEW OF BIOCHEMISTRY

SMITH, L., AND LINDBERG, J., *Ber.,* **64,** 505 (1931)
SOBOTKA, H., AND REINER, M. (1), *Biochem. J.,* **24,** 394 (1930)
SOBOTKA, H., AND REINER, M. (2), *Biochem. J.,* **24,** 926 (1930)
SOBOTKA, H., AND REINER, M. (3), *Biochem. J.,* **24,** 1783 (1930)
SODA, T., AND HATTORI, C., *Proc. Imp. Acad. (Tokyo),* **7,** 269 (1931)
SPOEHR, H. A., AND STRAIN, H. H., *J. Biol. Chem.,* **89,** 503 (1930)
SREENIVASAYA, M., *Nature,* **126,** 438 (1930)
STEARN, A. E., *J. Phys. Chem.,* **35,** 2226 (1931)
STRAIN, H. H., AND SPOEHR, H. A., *J. Biol. Chem.,* **89,** 527 (1930)
SUMIKI, Y., *J. Agr. Chem. Soc. Japan,* **6,** 1153; *Bull. Agr. Chem. Soc. Japan,*
  6, 105 (1930)
SZENT-GYÖRGYI, A., *J. Biol. Chem.,* **90,** 385 (1931)
TAKAHASHI, T., AND ASAI, T. (1), *Proc. Imp. Acad. (Japan),* **6,** 348 (1930)
TAKAHASHI, T., AND ASAI, T. (2), *J. Agr. Chem. Soc. Japan,* **7,** 1 (1931)
TAKAHASHI, T., AND ASAI, T. (3), *Proc. Imp. Acad. (Japan),* **7,** 5 (1931)
TANAKA, C., *Bull. Chem. Soc. Japan,* **5,** 214 (1930)
THOMAS, R. W., AND SCHUETTE, H. A., *J. Am. Chem. Soc.,* **53,** 2324 (1931)
VALENTIN, F., *Collection Czechoslov. Chem. Communications,* **2,** 689 (1930)
VIRGILIO, B., *Ind. saccar. ital.,* **22,** 427 (1929)
VOTOČEK, E., *Collection Czechoslov. Chem. Communications,* **2,** 681 (1930)
VOTOČEK, E., VALENTIN, F., AND LEMINGER, O., *Collection Czechoslov. Chem.
  Communications,* **3,** 250 (1931)
WEIDENHAGEN, R. (1), *Z. Ver. deut. Zucker-Ind.,* **80,** 155 (1930)
WEIDENHAGEN, R. (2), *Z. Ver. deut. Zucker-Ind.,* **80,** 374 (1930)
WEIDENHAGEN, R. (3), *Z. Ver. deut. Zucker-Ind.,* **80,** 569 (1930)
WEIDENHAGEN, R. (4), *Biochem. Z.,* **233,** 318 (1931)
WEIDENHAGEN, R. (5), *Z. physiol. Chem.,* **200,** 279 (1931)
WERKMAN, C. H., HIXON, R. M., FULMER, E. I., AND RAYBURN, C. H.,
  Proc. Iowa Acad. Sci., **36,** 111 (1929)
WIJKMAN, N., *Ann.,* **485,** 61 (1931)
WILLSTÄTTER, W., AND BAMANN, E., *Z. physiol. Chem.,* **151,** 273 (1926)
WOLFROM, M. L., *J. Am. Chem. Soc.,* **53,** 2275 (1931)
WOLFROM, M. L., AND BRODE, W. R., *J. Am. Chem. Soc.,* **53,** 2279 (1931)
WOLFROM, M. L., AND CHRISTMAN, C. C., *J. Am. Chem. Soc.,* **53,** 3413 (1931)
WOLFROM, M. L., AND THOMPSON, A., *J. Am. Chem. Soc.,* **53,** 622 (1931)
ZEMPLÉN, G., AND BRUCKNER, Z. (1), *Ber.,* **63,** 1820 (1930)
ZEMPLÉN, G., AND BRUCKNER, Z. (2), *Ber.,* **64,** 1852 (1931)
ZEMPLÉN, G., BRUCKNER, Z., AND GERECS, A., *Ber.,* **64,** 744 (1931)
ZEMPLÉN, G., AND GERECS, A. (1), *Ber.,* **63,** 2720 (1930)
ZEMPLÉN, G., AND GERECS, A. (2), *Ber.,* **62,** 990 (1929)
ZEMPLÉN, G., AND GERECS, A. (3), *Ber.,* **64,** 1545 (1931)
ZEMPLÉN, G., AND CSÜRÖS, Z., *Ber.,* **64,** 993 (1931)
ZUCKERKANDL, F., AND MESSINER-KLEBERMASS, L., *Biochem. Z.,* **226,** 395
  (1930)

THE ROCKEFELLER INSTITUTE
SIXTY-SIXTH STREET AND YORK AVENUE
NEW YORK CITY

CARBOHYDRATE METABOLISM*

By Philip A. Shaffer and Ethel Ronzoni

School of Medicine, Washington University

Within the period here surveyed—roughly the years 1929 to 1931 —the additions to the subject of carbohydrate metabolism consist not only of the ever-increasing volume of new experimental work but also of a number of authoritative and detailed summaries of existing knowledge in various regions of this field. As more and more facts accumulate it becomes increasingly difficult, without these critical and synthetic reviews, to comprehend the subject as a whole, or to appreciate the bearing of new facts upon current ideas and hypotheses. We shall first, therefore, draw attention to the following recent publications which collectively set forth in detail the present status of carbohydrate metabolism as related especially to the processes in animal tissues.

C. F. Cori, "Mammalian Carbohydrate Metabolism," *Physiol. Rev.,* **11**, 143 (1931)

H. B. Richardson, "The Respiratory Quotient," *Physiol. Rev.,* **9**, 61 (1929)

D. Rapport, "The Interconversion of the Major Foodstuffs," *Physiol. Rev.,* **10**, 349 (1930)

H. Chr. Geelmuyden, "Theories of Metabolism in Diabetes (An Epilog)," *Ergebnisse Physiol.,* **31**, 1 (1931)

O. Meyerhof, *Die Chemischen Vorgänge im Muskel* (Berlin, J. Springer, 1930)

O. Meyerhof, "Neuere Versuche zur Energetik der Muskel Kontraktion," *Naturwissenschaften,* **19**, 923 (1931)

T. H. Milroy, "The Present Status of the Chemistry of Muscular Contraction," *Physiol. Rev.,* **11**, 515 (1931)

P. Eggleton, "The Position of Phosphorus in the Chemical Mechanism of Muscular Contraction," *Physiol. Rev.,* **9**, 432 (1929)

A. V. Hill, "The Revolution in Muscle Physiology," *Physiol. Rev.,* **12**, 56 (1932)

* Received February 24, 1932.

With these available it will perhaps suffice to sketch what seem to be the more active problems of the day. The equally fundamental processes in plants, photosynthesis, respiration, and intermediary transformations, are not considered here. Work in these large fields, judged by results achieved as well as by number of workers, is small in relation to the biochemical importance of the subjects.

MUSCULAR CONTRACTION

The most dramatic discoveries during the period concern the chemical reactions related to muscular contraction. The "revolution" which has occurred is explained in the papers above cited by Milroy, Hill, and Meyerhof and is pointedly commented upon in an earlier critique by Bethe. The subject is treated in the chapter by Parnas in this volume, and only a hasty outline in relation to our topic need be given here.

The chief result of the new facts is the removal of lactic acid from the central rôle it has long been supposed to occupy, wherein the energy of its formation was the source of the work of contraction. With the demonstration by Lundsgaard that frog muscle when poisoned with iodo- or bromo-acetic acid contracts normally for a time without formation of lactic acid, Meyerhof and Hill were at last forced to agree with the contention of Embden, reiterated since 1924 (Lehnartz), that a part—and now all—of the lactate is formed after the contraction is over. So all the fine balance sheets heretofore thought to demonstrate a quantitative time-energy relation between the initial heat of contraction and lactic-acid formation from glycogen must now be set aside. The idea of a chemical coupling of the various reactions set off by stimulation, never very clearly defined but always implied, now seems impossible since the reactions are separate in time, and Meyerhof now regards the relations as only energetically coupled through cellular activity. Hahn (1931) has criticized this concept.

Lactic-acid formation is, however, retained in the new scheme for contraction. The rôle of furnishing the energy for contraction is now assigned to creatine-phosphate, and it is inferred that in normal muscle the formation of lactic acid furnishes energy for the endothermic resynthesis of phosphagen. The algebraic sum of the energies of the overlapping reactions is claimed to conform with and account for the old heat and energy balance of the initial plus delayed heat periods. Lactic acid is formed as formerly believed, only more slowly, and its removal is still supposed to determine and be responsible for the "recovery" heat, the cost of restoration of the whole system by the oxidation of lactate, carbohydrate, or something else. So the problem of the relation of carbohydrate metabolism to muscular contraction is not very essentially changed. That relation still revolves around the fate of lactic acid.

On the other hand, it might be argued from the new facts that muscular contraction is only incidentally and not of necessity related to carbohydrate metabolism. Since muscle treated with iodoacetic acid not only contracts without lactate formation but recovers (for a time) in oxygen (Lundsgaard) without lactate or carbohydrate oxidation (Meyerhof and Boyland), the previously assumed necessity for carbohydrate participation falls out. The respiration of the poisoned muscles is increased like the normal by stimulation and contraction, but the R.Q. (0.7 to 0.8) indicates that little or no carbohydrate is oxidized. Frog muscles rendered low in glycogen by insulin convulsions likewise do more work on stimulation than can be accounted for by carbohydrate oxidation (Ochoa). Meyerhof, and Witting, Markowitz, and Mann report that rabbit hearts perfused with glucose-free Ringer-Locke's solution beat as long when the glycogen content has been lowered (0.06 to 0.2 per cent) by fasting and strychnine convulsions as when the initial glycogen content is normal. Such observations would seem to remove a former difficulty of accepting the view that the work of muscular contraction may be performed by oxidation of fat as well as carbohydrate. This long-disputed question, the source of energy for muscular work, has been again studied by Rapport with dogs and by Carpenter and Fox with human subjects, and is reviewed briefly by Carpenter. Their results confirm the present majority opinion that *any foodstuff may be used for the restoration energy.* Best, Furusawa, and Ridout hold a different opinion—that carbohydrate is the fuel, formed when necessary from fat. After severe exercise they find high quotients, sometimes much above 1, the significance of which is not clear. The R.Q. after exercise depends upon the length of the recovery period; unless it includes complete recovery, erroneously high quotients are obtained, and at best the values are variable and of doubtful significance (Gemmill).

Other progress now discernible from the work of the last few years relates chiefly to (*a*) the behavior of liver and muscle glycogen under the influence of insulin and adrenalin, and the clearer formulation of a glucose-lactate cycle between liver and muscles as a chemical-physiological system; (b) elaboration of further details concerning the enzyme complex of muscle (and yeast) which converts glycogen or sugar to lactic acid; and (c) further details of the metabolism of isolated tissues, particularly as regards the influence of respiration on glycolysis, the notable stimulating effect of lactate upon respiration, and the material undergoing oxidation as indicated by the respiratory quotient. The fundamental questions, such as the chemical mechanism of insulin or adrenalin action on glycogen formation and hydrolysis, and on carbohydrate oxidation; by what steps glucose and glycogen are formed from lactate, or from glycerol or other small molecules; whether lactate is directly oxidized and thus represents the pathway of carbohydrate combustion or is first reconverted to glucose or glycogen—these problems still seem to defy direct attack. All of these last-named phenomena now appear to be inseparable from the activity of respiring intact cells, and cease when their physiological functions are much disturbed.

CARBOHYDRATE TRANSPORT AND BLOOD SUGAR REGULATION

The accompanying diagram is intended to represent in outline the relations concerned with carbohydrate transport and storage as regulated by adrenalin and insulin. Growing out of a long series of investigations dating from Claude Bernard and before, this system has been developed in the hands of recent workers—among whom C. F. and G. T. Cori are leaders—until it represents the best-known example of that physiological co-ordination through chemical agents first emphasized by Bernard and recently described by Cannon under the term "Homeostasis." Into this physiological scheme of regulation the chemical mechanisms must ultimately fit, though their intermediary reactions are still quite obscure. Beside a number of the arrows on the diagram will be found the mark "$\times$" to indicate the fact that the processes so designated have not yet been observed to occur except in consequence of the activity of respiring intact tissue. Where to insert on this diagram the reactions concerning carbohydrate oxidation, it is still impossible to decide. One view is that a portion (not over one-fourth) of the lactate is oxidized via pyruvate, and perhaps acetaldehyde and acetate to CO_2; another is that lactate formation is only a closed cycle serving other purposes, that all of the lactate

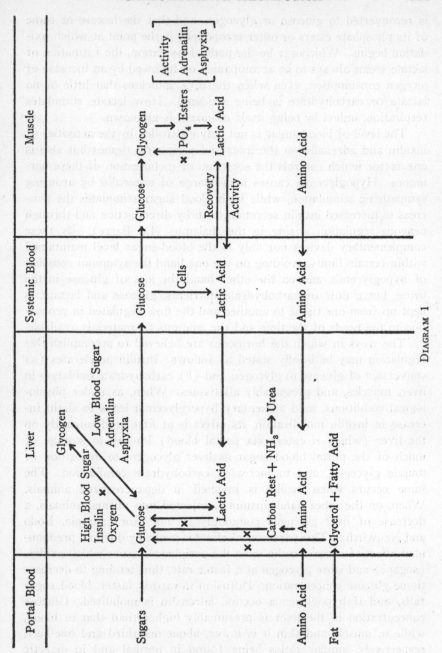

DIAGRAM 1

is reconverted to glucose or glycogen, and that the hexose or some of its phosphate esters or other compounds is the point at which oxidation begins. Whichever be the path of oxidation, the formation of lactate seems always to be accompanied or followed by an increase of oxygen consumption, even when the R.Q. indicates that little or no lactate or carbohydrate is being oxidized. How lactate stimulates respiration, unless by being itself oxidized, is unknown.

The level of blood sugar is not only controlled by the activities of insulin and adrenalin on the liver and peripheral tissues but also is one factor which controls the secretion or mobilization of these hormones. Hypoglycemia causes a discharge of adrenalin by arousing sympathetic stimulation, while high blood sugar stimulates the pancreas to increased insulin secretion, both by direct action and through nervous regulation arising in the thalamus (La Barre). By these complementary devices not only is the blood-sugar level maintained within certain limits, avoiding on the one hand the symptom complex of hypoglycemia and on the other hand the loss of glucose in the urine, but a flow of carbohydrate nutrients, glucose and lactate, is kept up from one tissue to another and the flow regulated in proportion to the needs of the time and the amounts of materials available.

The ways in which the hormones are believed to accomplish this regulation may be briefly stated as follows: Insulin accelerates (a) conversion of glucose to glycogen and (b) carbohydrate oxidation in liver, muscles, and presumably all tissues. When, as under physiological conditions, mild alimentary hyperglycemia leads to slight increase in insulin mobilization, its effect is at first predominantly on the liver (which it enters via portal blood) leading to storage of much of the portal blood sugar as liver glycogen, to deposition of muscle glycogen, and to increased carbohydrate combustion. The same occurs when insulin is injected in depancreatized animals. When, on the other hand, insulin is injected into normal animals, a decrease of liver glycogen commonly results (for example, Bodo and Neuwirth). This paradoxical effect is probably due to a predominant effect of excess insulin upon the peripheral tissues which oxidize (sugar?) and store glycogen at a faster rate, thus tending to decrease tissue glucose concentration. Diffusion inward is faster, blood sugar falls, and if hypoglycemia occurs, adrenalin is mobilized. Glucose concentration in the liver is presumably higher than that in blood, while in muscle and skin it is lower, about one-third and one-half, respectively, similar ratios being found in normal and in diabetic tissues (Trimble and Carey). These relative concentrations are consistent with the fact (Mann and Magath), now repeatedly confirmed, that only liver glycogen, not muscle glycogen, can directly support blood-sugar concentration.

The effects of adrenalin are primarily two: (*a*) increase in the rate of hydrolysis of liver glycogen to glucose, an effect counteracted by insulin, and (*b*) increase in the conversion of muscle glycogen to lactate accompanied by hexose monophosphate formation [Cori and Cori (3)]. Both these effects are produced also by asphyxia and by many anaesthetics, and it has often been supposed that the adrenalin action was the consequence of vasoconstriction. This possibility appears to be disposed of by recent work of Cori and Buchwald (1) showing that adrenalin further increases the *anaërobic* formation of glucose (from liver glycogen) and of lactate (from muscle glycogen) in intact frogs kept for three hours in nitrogen, and that even under anaërobic conditions insulin inhibits the adrenalin action on lactate as well as glucose formation.

To these adrenalin effects the Coris (1) added a third, retardation of absorption of sugar by the peripheral tissues. Colwell and Bright, and Colwell find that continuous injection of adrenalin with glucose virtually abolishes sugar oxidation as indicated by the R.Q. and suggest the relation of this effect to human diabetes. G. T. Cori finds that amytal (used in these experiments) exaggerates the depressing effect of adrenalin on sugar oxidation. Corkhill and Marks observed no effect of adrenalin on the rate of blood sugar decline in eviscerated cats, suggesting that adrenalin may act through inhibiting insulin secretion. It thus appears that adrenalin not only relieves hypoglycemia by accelerating liver glycogenolysis but (in excess) may also retard the absorption and oxidation of sugar by peripheral tissues. Accompanying these influences is still another, demonstrable by adrenalin injection, its calorigenic action of increasing the total metabolism. This effect also appears to be independent of asphyxia or vasoconstriction or of increased muscular activity, and is thought to be due to the increased lactate formation caused by adrenalin in muscles [Cori and Buchwald (2)].

THE GLUCOSE-LACTATE CYCLE

These effects of adrenalin together with the conversion of lactate to glucose and glycogen in the liver, again well-demonstrated by Cori and Cori (2) with the rat, explain earlier confusion as to the behavior of liver glycogen and form the basis for the glucose-lactate cycle between liver and muscles. Adrenalin had been found by some workers to increase and by others to decrease liver glycogen. Luck and Sahyun were the first to show with rabbits that the difference is due to the time of analysis after adrenalin injection and that the rise of liver glycogen is from muscle glycogen. Both liver and muscle glycogen being mobilized under its influence, the first to glucose and the other to lactate [and hexose phosphate, Cori and Cori (3)], time and insulin activity will determine where the material not oxidized or otherwise transformed in the meantime will come to rest as glycogen. At first the liver glycogen falls sharply, only to rise again as lactate from muscle glycogen appears in the blood and is removed by the liver. Cori, Cori, and Buchwald followed the changes of liver glycogen, blood sugar and lactate following adrenalin injection in fed rats, in which the decrease of liver glycogen lasted only fifteen minutes. Both groups of authors showed also that insulin inhibits liver glycogenolysis by adrenalin, though insulin did not inhibit lactate production. Eadie believes that species differences are responsible for the varying results as to rise or fall of liver glycogen under adrenalin noted by different observers.

Evans, Tsai, and Young find that after decapitation or decerebration under ether the liver glycogen of cats at first falls greatly, only to rise again after a few hours. The rise fails to occur in previously depancreatized animals. In normal (decapitated) animals the rise is hampered by overventilation, accelerated by respiring oxygen with 5 per cent carbon dioxide, and is only slightly favored by glucose infusion. The authors lean toward the view that glycogen is formed from fat and suggest that "liver glycogen is a primary product formed from non-carbohydrate sources, from which the blood sugar is formed as a secondary product." Anderson and Macleod compare the rate of glycogen decrease to lactate formation in isolated muscle, and conclude that glycogen is not alone the source of lactate. The analytical difficulties must be further improved before deciding this question.

The operation of the cycle between muscles and liver is demonstrated in a series of papers by Himwich and associates, in which glucose and lactate concentrations of arterial and venous bloods are compared, in normal, depancreatized, and phlorhizinized dogs. The differences are usually in the direction that liver gives up glucose and absorbs lactate from the blood, the latter occurring in the diabetic as in the normal animal.

As regards glycogen formers beside sugar and lactate, Catron and Lewis show that glycerol by mouth to rats increases liver glycogen. The high liver glycogen observed with rats on fat diets (Burn and Ling; Greisheimer and Johnson) may perhaps be thus accounted for. Wilson and Lewis find a rise of liver glycogen in fasting rats fed alanine, casein, gelatine, and butter, not when fed leucine or glycine, and doubtful with glutamic acid.

Glycogen resynthesis from lactate after muscular work was studied in fasted rats by Long and Grant. The blood lactate falls to normal in about two hours after work without a comparable increase of liver or muscle glycogen. In 24 hours the muscle glycogen had risen above the initial values. Similar experiments were performed by Eggleton and Evans using dogs and cats under amytal. In both eviscerated and intact animals some slight rise of muscle glycogen accompanied the fall of blood lactate during the recovery from exercise. They were not able to demonstrate a rise of muscle glycogen after r-lactate injection, and they question its formation from blood lactate. The same authors as well as Bornstein and Schmutzler, nevertheless, demonstrate that muscles (hind limbs and eviscerated preparations), as well as liver, absorb lactate. In this absorption of lactate by tissues (and its conversion to glucose at least in the liver) insulin seems to play no part; for its storage as glycogen, however, insulin seems to be essential. G. Debois finds that restoration of glycogen in muscle after work is dependent upon insulin, and also that for the mobilization of insulin, vagus stimulation is necessary. Markowitz, Mann, and Bollman confirm earlier observations that muscle glycogen is deposited from glucose even in dehepatized dogs, but not when the pancreas has been removed previously. To secure an increase of muscle glycogen in depancreatized animals very large doses of insulin as well as glucose were required. Nevertheless it must be remembered that muscle glycogen is present, although in smaller amounts, in skeletal muscles of depancreatized dogs, and even in abnormally large amounts in diabetic heart muscle. It may well be that high blood sugar compensates in some measure for insulin deficiency, and that the rate of sugar storage and perhaps oxidation is related to the product of sugar concentration and insulin activity. This is suggested by the observations of Bayliss, Müller, and Starling on heart-lung preparations.

The influence of lactate formation upon the total metabolism has been restudied by several workers. It will be recalled that the Meyerhof-Hill theory postulated that the energy cost of oxidative removal of lactate is about one-fifth the caloric value of the lactate removed, this being the work done in its reconversion to glycogen, and that this is the cause of the increase of oxygen consumption following muscular work. Then the consumption or restoration of lactate, whatever its origin, should be accompanied by a similar increase of oxygen consumption. Several years ago Abramson, Eggleton, and Eggleton found about the same increase in oxygen consumption after injecting r-lactate in amytalized dogs as after $NaHCO_3$ injection, and implied that the stimulating effect of lactate upon metabolism was small. Martin, Field, and Hall have compared the extent and duration of increase in oxygen consumption with the rate of decrease of blood lactate in dogs having a high lactate concentration as a consequence of 15 minutes of muscular activity brought about by electric stimulation through electrodes implanted under the skin in mid-cervical and sacral regions. The animals were either under amytal or had brain-stem transection. Oxygen consumption and blood lactate were determined before, during, and for 90 minutes following, the work period. There appeared to be no quantitative relation between the increased oxygen consumption and the amount of lactate which disappeared from the blood, and the authors doubt the existence of the relation postulated by Hill and Meyerhof. Terroine, Bonnet, and Zagami find that sodium lactate and pyruvate injected intraperitoneally in rabbits causes no more increase of oxygen consumption than that produced by the same volume of Ringer's solution, and conclude that the utilization of these substances produces no change of total metabolism. Virtually the same problem is approached with a different result by Cori and Buchwald (2) in a study of the calorigenic action of adrenalin. With frogs, the oxygen consumption of which was determined in an enlarged Warburg manometer vessel and by determining the glucose and lactate content of the whole body, these authors appear to show that the increase in oxygen consumption caused by adrenalin injection is about the quantity required to oxidize one-fourth of the excess of lactate formed by adrenalin in nitrogen, and conclude that the calorigenic action of adrenalin is due to the lactate formed and is a measure of its oxidative removal with a Meyerhof quotient of about 4. These papers also contain data on a number of other points, one of which is that the calorigenic effect of adrenalin is not dependent upon the presence of the liver, indicating again that other tissues beside the liver may remove lactate. Despite contradictory evidence, the trend of opinion appears to be that lactate, whether formed by stimulation, adrenalin, or asphyxia, is oxidatively removed only at a certain cost of increased respiration. How the lactate causes the increased respiration, whether by its own oxidation or as a stimulus to cell activity, is not clear.

The enzyme system for the hydrolysis of muscle glycogen to lactate has become more clearly defined. It may be recalled that Meyerhof found that the active constituent of muscle extracts in causing glycolysis might be separated, like the Harden-Young zymase preparations, into an enzyme and heat-stable co-enzyme parts, the latter being replaceable by yeast "Kochsaft," while muscle juice was likewise supplementary in zymin fermentation. Lohmann (3) now shows that the co-ferment of both muscle and yeast enzyme systems consists of adenylic acid pyrophosphate, free phosphate, and magnesium. Kay confirms the earlier observation of Erdtmann that phosphatase hydrolysis of glycerophosphate is likewise activated by Mg ions, and that the enzyme activity is inhibited by some of the same agents which prevent lactate formation—citrate, oxalate, and tartrate. It seems not unlikely that these inhibitors act through setting aside the magnesium ions, perhaps by complex formation. The inhibition is apparently located at the hydrolysis of phosphate esters. On comparing the Euler-Myrbäch yeast co-ferment with muscle co-ferment, Lohmann finds that they are in a measure replaceable, though differences exist, apparently in the adenylic acid of the two sources of origin; and that the lactic acid co-ferment is not concerned with glyoxalase activity and is not the co-ferment of respiration. Hexose diphosphate and monophosphate are more readily acted upon than glycogen, and this faster than hexose. A trihexose appears to be first formed from glycogen (Barbour). Only hexose monophosphate has yet been found in normal muscle, though the chief product in muscle extract is diphosphate. Lohmann (1, 2) also finds in frog muscle, under the influence of iodo acetate and fluoride, a diphosphate, apparently the same formed in muscle extract.

HEXOSE PHOSPHATE

Cori and Cori (3) have developed an improved method for estimating hexose monophosphate in muscle, with which they study the influence of insulin and adrenalin on its formation. The normal resting values represent about 53 mg. per cent as hexose. Immediately after killing the animal this rises to even 200 (hexosephosphate formation from glycogen), owing apparently to adrenalin stimulation, since adrenalin injection causes a similar rise. Insulin also produces an increase, but not if hypoglycemia is avoided or the adrenals have been previously removed. A part of the product of glycogenolysis set off by adrenalin, the authors think, is sidetracked and stabilized as the Embden monoester. Glucose feeding and glycogen storage appear not to be associated with a rise of hexosephosphate, which is, therefore, perhaps not an intermediate in glycogen formation but only in its glycolysis. Since hexosephosphate ultimately forms lactate, this substance must be included in attempts to balance carbohydrate migrations from muscle to liver as well as combustion or sugar excretion. Inability to do so may well account for many discrepancies noted in the past.

There is thus increasing evidence that esterification with phosphoric acid is an essential step both in yeast fermentation and lacticacid formation. A number of these esters are now known, some having been synthesized by Levene (Levene and Raymond). The chemical properties of the group have been brought together in a review by Lohmann (1). The trend of opinion seems to be that methyl glyoxal is an intermediate between hexosephosphate and lactic acid. In confirmation of the earlier work of Toennissen and Fischer and of Ariyama, Neuberg and Kobel—Vogt, and Inoue find methyl-glyoxal formation during hexosephosphate glycolysis by tissue hash.

Blood glycolysis in relation to phosphate esters has been studied by Barrenscheen, Hübner, and Braun, by Englehardt, and by Roche. Kraut and Bumm find acceleration of glycolysis by sarcoma extract, and Case that muscle extract accelerates glycolysis by brain or kidney tissue. Harrison and Mellanby, and Barrenscheen, Braun, and Dreguss have studied the inhibition of tissue glycolysis by iodoacetate, and Dickens and Simer (1) by fluoride. Very interesting results are reported by Wendel and by Warburg and co-workers concerning blood glycolysis and respiration under the influence of methylene blue and methemoglobin.

CARBOHYDRATE TOLERANCE

The effect of continuous intravenous injection of sugars has been studied with dogs by Wierzuchowski and co-workers. At a rate of 2 gm./kg.hr. with glucose, the blood sugar first rises and then falls below the initial value (owing to insulin mobilization by initial hyperglycemia), the blood lactate rises to high values, and is further increased by insulin (owing to adrenalin mobilization by hypoglycemia?). Insulin injection increases the fraction oxidized, that of galactose and fructose more than that of glucose. Deuel and Gulick report that acidosis from NH_4Cl does not decrease carbohydrate tolerance of dogs. Deuel gives further support to the view that phlorhizin does not fundamentally destroy the ability to oxidize carbohydrate, by showing that, although fasting phlorhizinized dogs (like normal ones) show typical "diabetic" blood-sugar curves after a first dose of glucose, they respond normally by a lower curve to a second dose of sugar.

The well-known effect of fasting in temporarily decreasing the ability to oxidize or store carbohydrate has been again demonstrated by Dann and Chambers, who studied in Lusk's respiration-calorimeter the metabolism of dogs given 50 gm. of glucose after 15- to 30-day fasts. There was no immediate rise of the R.Q. above 0.72, the level before sugar administration. A restoration of tolerance followed this dose of sugar and persisted for some days of a subsequent fast. The temporary loss of ability to oxidize glucose after fasting is a strong argument against the view that during fasting sugar is being formed (and burned) from fat; if that were the case, glucose should be promptly oxidized when given to a fasting man or animal.

Improvements in methods for determination of glycogen are described by Sahyun, and Sahyun and Alsberg, of the total carbohydrate in muscle by Kerly, for blood sugar by West, Scharles, and Peterson; by Herbert and Bourne; Folin; Somogyi; and Benedict.

The nature of blood sugar has been studied by Power and Greene and by Somogyi, the latter finding that the optical rotation, reduction of copper, rate of oxidation, and rate of fermentation by yeast all agree with the view that it is ordinary *d*-glucose.

Less seems now to be written about special active or "gamma" forms of sugars in relation to carbohydrate metabolism. The chemistry of these substances is reviewed by Lüdke and Neuberg under the name "Alloimorphic sugars."

ISOLATED TISSUES

Study of the respiration and anaërobic lactate formation of tissue fragments continues to yield important results, and may yet be the means of deciding the fundamental problems of carbohydrate oxidation. So far it has hardly done so. Almost always it is found that respiration markedly inhibits the rate of lactate formation by the same tissue in nitrogen, and except in poisoned tissues the amount of lactate inhibited is 2 to 10 (usually 3 to 6) times the amount which would be oxidizable (to CO_2) by the oxygen absorbed. Strangely enough this same ratio—the Meyerhof oxidationquotient or the "Pasteur reaction"—holds even with finely hashed muscle (Hahn and co-workers; Boyland), in which the oxygen uptake is for a time much increased, lactate production continues (at a slower rate) in oxygen, and no synthesis of glycogen is either demonstrable or assumed. Frog muscles (or hash) poisoned by fluoride or iodoacetate, although little or no lactate is formed even in nitrogen, respire in oxygen at almost the normal rate, with low R.Q. Stimulation of the intact poisoned muscle increases the oxygen uptake almost as much as normal; so the increased oxidation is not dependent upon lactate formation. But on adding lactate or pyruvate to chopped as well as to intact iodoacetate muscles, the respiration rises as does the R.Q., and on the assumption that the whole of the oxygen absorbed is used for the purpose (i.e., all other oxidation suppressed) the lactate and pyruvate are oxidized; if only the excess oxygen is credited to lactate, some is oxidatively restored, presumably to glycogen (Meyerhof and Boyland). The data on the last point scarcely permit much confidence in the conclusions.

Tissues of warm-blooded animals, normal and depancreatized, have been studied by Richardson, Shorr, and Loebel (1) (dogs and rats), who believe the rate of respiration of their tissue fragments (kidney, testes, and muscle) to be of the same order as of the organs *in situ*. Their results indicate low R.Q. with diabetic and higher with normal tissues; added glucose increases the oxygen uptake of normal fed, but not of normal fasted or diabetic kidney slices; added lactate increases the oxygen uptake of both normal and diabetic tissue to about the same maximum, but is greater with normal; the R.Q. is raised by lactate and by glucose, much with normal, less with fasted, and least with diabetic tissue. The same in general holds for sternomastoid and other muscles from the neck. The authors conclude that little carbohydrate oxidation occurred in the diabetic tissue. In a later report (2) they find that the amount of lactate, the formation of which is inhibited by oxygen, or the amount which disappears from the fluid during respiration of normal tissue gives the usual Meyerhof quotient. With tissues (kidney and testes) of normal and phlorhizin-treated rats, normal R.Q.'s were obtained, which were raised to the same degree by glucose. Phlorhizin added to the Ringer's solution in which normal tissues were suspended depressed respiration but caused no fall of R.Q. The authors conclude that phlorhizin does not interfere with sugar oxidation. Laser found the R.Q. of normal fowl muscle to be 0.83 and of the depancreatized tissue 0.73. Insulin added to the diabetic muscle was thought to increase its (depressed) oxygen uptake with a rise of R.Q., indicating either an increase in rate of lactate oxidation or its reconversion. Anaërobic glycolysis was not affected by insulin. The data seem too irregular and the amount of lactate change too small to permit satisfactory interpretation.

In a series of papers Dickens and Simer (2, 3, 4) describe improved methods for measurement of tissue respiration and anaërobic glycolysis and present data from various tissues, from which they conclude that among normal tissues those with high glycolytic power generally have high R.Q. and hence oxidize largely carbohydrate, and vice versa; tumors, on the other hand, have low R.Q. in spite of high glycolytic power, and are characterized by a defect in power to oxidize carbohydrate. Pyruvate and lactate increase the oxygen uptake and R.Q. of tissues as much as or more than glucose. They conclude that the failure of carbohydrate oxidation in tumors is at a point subsequent to the conversion of hexose to a 3-carbon state. The effect of insulin was indecisive. Dickens reviews the respiratory behavior of isolated cancer tissue.

Krebs finds the respiratory activity of various tissues, after being more or less abolished by iodoacetate, to be regained when lactate is added, as do also Meyerhof and Boyland, l-lactate being without effect. The Bernheims report a similar effect with washed liver in presence of pyrrol as catalyst, the oxygen absorbed corresponding to oxidation of lactate to pyruvate (no chemical analysis reported).

Khouvine, Aubel, and Chevillard find pyruvate to increase oxygen uptake of liver hash, and consider specific dynamic action related to this stimulation. Utevski has studied the fate of pyruvate with muscle hash.

The metabolism of isolated nervous tissue, from the point of view of carbohydrate changes, has been studied especially by Holmes and co-workers. Respiration of the gray matter of the brain is increased more by lactate than by glucose. The increase of respiration by lactate is not prevented by NaF, which does prevent a rise from glucose.

It is concluded that "glucose must be converted into lactate before it can be oxidized by gray matter." Meyerhof quotients are observed, though no synthesis of carbohydrate is demonstrable. They find no evidence of pyruvate or acetaldehyde formation.

The respiration metabolism of tubercle bacilli has been studied by Loebel, Shorr, and Richardson using Warburg manometer vessels. The oxygen consumption varies with the surrounding medium, but is about "twice as much as the resting muscle of the dog, and about one-third that of dog's kidney, a very active tissue." In media containing glycerol, asparagin, and ammonium citrate, respiration is much greater than in NaCl solution, by 2 to 10 times, the glycerol furnishing about $\frac{4}{5}$ of the increase and being effective in as little as 0.02 per cent, which is below that at which growth occurs. Glucose also supports respiration but not growth. Lactate stimulates respiration, again more than does glucose, and permits some growth.

An important bearing of many of these observations is upon the question whether carbohydrate oxidation in the animal body proceeds via lactic acid. If lactic acid is directly oxidized, the diabetic defect and the point at which insulin acts must be at or beyond lactate oxidation. In view of the notable effect of lactate and pyruvate in stimulating the oxygen uptake of isolated tissues, to a greater extent even than by glucose, as first observed some years ago by Meyerhof and co-workers, the presumption would seem strong that lactate is readily oxidized. That view would seem acceptable if it were not for the facts that lactate fails to relieve symptoms of insulin hypoglycemia, and that so far it has not been shown that insulin favors or accelerates the absorption of lactate from the blood or its disappearance in tissues. When hypoglycemia and consequent adrenalin mobilization is avoided, the increased carbohydrate combustion after insulin injection seems not to be accompanied by increase of lactate formation, nor is the rate of lactate disappearance from the blood hastened by insulin. For these reasons it would still seem premature, in spite of the presumptive evidence cited, to conclude that carbohydrate oxidation is mainly via lactate oxidation. The question remains unanswered. Continued study of the behavior of lactate and pyruvate with isolated tissues may in time decide it.

Two novel and interesting schemes of carbohydrate oxidation may be cited. Toennissen and Brinkmann propose a cycle involving condensation of pyruvate to succinate plus formic, malic, oxalacetic, and pyruvate, oxidation occurring at each cycle. The chief basis is their claim of demonstrating conversion of pyruvate to succinate on perfusion of rabbit muscles. Hahn and co-workers, in a series of papers, advocate a somewhat 'similar plan by which succinate is converted to pyruvate. They demonstrate considerable amounts of pyruvate to be formed when muscle hash is incubated in the presence of semi-carbazid, not without it. The oxidation of lactate to pyruvate, and no farther, by blood cells in presence of methylene blue or methemoglobin, studied by Wendel and by Warburg, is cited earlier. Whether or not this is related to the normal process of carbohydrate oxidation is not decided.

LITERATURE CITED

ABRAMSON, H. A., AND EGGLETON, P., *J. Biol. Chem.*, **75**, 763 (1927)

ANDERSON, I. A., AND MACLEOD, J. J. R., *Biochem. J.*, **24**, 1408 (1930)

BARBOUR, A. D., *J. Biol. Chem.*, **85**, 29 (1929)

BARRENSCHEEN, H. K., BRAUN, K., AND DREGUSS, M., *Biochem. Z.*, **232**, 165 (1931)

BARRENSCHEEN, H. K., HÜBNER, K., AND BRAUN, K., *Biochem. Z.*, **229**, 329; **230**, 330 (1930); **231**, 144 (1931)

BAYLISS, L. E., MÜLLER, E. A., AND STARLING, E. H., *J. Physiol.*, **65**, 33 (1928)

BENEDICT, S. R., *J. Biol. Chem.*, **92**, 141 (1931)

BERNHEIM, F., AND BERNHEIM, M. L. C., *J. Biol. Chem.*, **92**, 461 (1931)

BEST, C. H., FURUSAWA, K., AND RIDOUT, J. H., *Proc. Roy. Soc. (London), B*, **104**, 119 (1929)

BETHE, A., *Naturwissenschaften*, **18**, 678 (1930)

BODO, R. C., AND NEUWIRTH, ISAAC, *J. Biol. Chem.*, **92**, xxv (1931)

BORNSTEIN, A., AND SCHMUTZLER, E., *Arch. ges. Physiol.*, **221**, 395 (1929)

BOYLAND, E., *Biochem. Z.*, **237**, 418 (1931)

BURN, J. H., AND LING, H. W., *J. Physiol.*, **65**, 191 (1928)

CANNON, W. B., *Physiol. Rev.*, **9**, 399 (1929)

CARPENTER, T. M., *J. Nutrition*, **4**, 281 (1931)

CARPENTER, T. M., AND FOX, E. L., *Arbeitsphysiol.*, **4**, 532, 570 (1931)

CASE, E. M., *Biochem. J.*, **23**, 210 (1929)

CATRON, L. F., AND LEWIS, H. B., *J. Biol. Chem.*, **84**, 553 (1929)

COLWELL, A. R., *Endocrinology*, **15**, 25 (1931)

COLWELL, A. R., AND BRIGHT, E. M., *Am. J. Physiol.*, **92**, 543, 555 (1930)

CORI, C. F., AND BUCHWALD, K. W. (1), *J. Biol. Chem.*, **92**, 355 (1931)

CORI, C. F., AND BUCHWALD, K. W. (2), *J. Biol. Chem.*, **92**, 367 (1931)

CORI, C. F., AND CORI, G. T. (1), *J. Biol. Chem.*, **79**, 343 (1928)

CORI, C. F., AND CORI, G. T. (2), *J. Biol. Chem.*, **81**, 389 (1929)

CORI, C. F., AND CORI, G. T. (3), *J. Biol. Chem.*, **94**, 561, 581 (1931)

CORI, C. F., CORI, G. T., AND BUCHWALD, K. W., *J. Biol. Chem.*, **86**, 375 (1930)

CORI, G. T., *Am. J. Physiol.*, **95**, 285 (1930)

CORKILL, A. B., AND MARKS, H. P., *J. Physiol.*, **70**, 67 (1930)

DANN, M., AND CHAMBERS, W. H., *J. Biol. Chem.*, **89**, 675 (1930)

DEBOIS, G., *Arch. intern. pharmacodynamie*, **41**, 65 (1931)

DEUEL, H. J., JR., *J. Biol. Chem.*, **89**, 77 (1930)

DEUEL, H. J., JR., AND GULICK, M., *J. Biol. Chem.*, **89**, 93 (1930)

DICKENS, F., *Cancer Review*, **6**, 57 (1931)

DICKENS, F., AND SIMER, F. (1), *Biochem. J.*, **23**, 210 (1929)

DICKENS, F., AND SIMER, F. (2), *Biochem. J.*, **23**, 936 (1929)

DICKENS, F., AND SIMER, F. (3), *Biochem. J.*, **24**, 905, 1301 (1930)

DICKENS, F., AND SIMER, F. (4), *Biochem. J.*, **25**, 973, 985 (1931)

EADIE, G. S., *Am. J. Physiol.*, **94**, 69 (1930)

EGGLETON, M. G., AND EVANS, C. L., *J. Physiol.*, **70**, 261, 269 (1930)

ENGLEHARDT, W. A., *Biochem. Z.*, **227**, 6, 16 (1930)

EULER, H. VON, AND MYRBÄCH, K., *Z. physiol. Chem.*, **198**, 219 (1931)

EVANS, C. L., TSAI, C., AND YOUNG, F. G., *J. Physiol.*, **73**, 67, 81 (1931)

FOLIN, O., *J. Biol. Chem.*, **86**, 173 (1930)

GEMMILL, C. L., *Am. J. Physiol.*, **98**, 135 (1931)

GREISHEIMER, E. M., AND JOHNSON, O. H., *Am. J. Physiol.*, **94**, 11 (1930)

HAHN, A., *Z. Biol.*, **91**, 446 (1931)

HAHN, A., AND FISCHBACH, E., *Z. Biol.*, **89**, 149, 563 (1930)

HAHN, A., AND HAARMANN, W., *Z. Biol.*, **87**, 107, 464 (1928) ; **89**, 159 (1930)

HAHN, A., AND HAARMANN, W., *Z. Biol.*, **90**, 231 (1930)

HAHN, A., FISCHBACH, E., AND HAARMANN, W., *Z. Biol.*, **88**, 89, 91, 516, 587 (1929)

HAHN, A., FISCHBACH, E., AND NIEMER, H., *Z. Biol.*, **91**, 53 (1930)

HARRISON, S. T., AND MELLANBY, E., *Biochem. J.*, **23**, 43, 770 (1931)

HERBERT, F. F., AND BOURNE, M. C., *Biochem. J.*, **24**, 291, 299, 1787 (1930)

HIMWICH, H. E., CHAMBERS, W. H., KOSKOFF, Y. D., AND NAHUN, L. H., *J. Biol. Chem.*, **90**, 417 (1931)

HIMWICH, H. E., KOSKOFF, Y. D., AND NAHUN, L. H., *J. Biol. Chem.*, **85**, 371 (1929)

HIMWICH, H. E., AND NAHUN, L. H., *Am. J. Physiol.*, **90**, 389 (1929)

HOLMES, E. G., *Biochem. J.*, **24**, 914 (1930)

HOLMES, E. G., AND ASHFORD, C, A., *Biochem. J.*, **24**, 1119 (1930). (See also the chapter by Holmes in this volume.)

HOLMES, E. G., AND GERARD, R. W., *Biochem. J.*, **23**, 738 (1929)

INOUE, H., *J. Biochem. (Japan)*, **13**, 369 (1931)

KAY, H. D., *J. Biol. Chem.*, **93**, 733 (1931)

KERLY, M., *Biochem. J.*, **25**, 671 (1931)

KHOUVINE, Y., AUBEL, E., AND CHEVILLARD, L., *Compt. rend.*, **189**, 1102 (1929) ; **190**, 1243; **191**, 162, 446 (1930)

KRAUT, H., AND BUMM, E., Z. physiol. Chem., 184, 196 (1929)

KREBS, H. A., Biochem. Z., 234, 278 (1931)

LA BARRE, J., Am. J. Physiol., 94, 13 (1930)

LASER, H., Biochem. Z., 241, 36 (1931)

LEHNARTZ, E., Z. physiol. Chem., 197, 55 (1931)

LEVENE, P. A., AND RAYMOND, A. L., J. Biol. Chem., 91, 751; 92, 757 (1931)

LOEBEL, R. O., SHORR, E., AND RICHARDSON, H. B., Natl. Tuberculosis Assoc. Trans. (1930)

LOHMANN, K. (1), Handb. Biochem. (Oppenheimer's), Supplement, p. 133 (1930)

LOHMANN, K. (2), Biochem. Z., 222, 324 (1930); 236, 444 (1931)

LOHMANN, K. (3), Biochem. Z., 237, 445; 241, 50, 67 (1931)

LONG, C. N. H., AND GRANT, R., J. Biol. Chem., 89, 553 (1930)

LUCK, J. M., AND SAHYUN, M., J. Biol. Chem., 85, 1 (1929)

LÜDKE, M., AND NEUBERG, C., Handb. Biochem. (Oppenheimer's) Supplement, p. 117 (1930)

LUNDSGAARD, E., Biochem. Z., 217, 162; 220, 1, 8; 227, 51 (1930); 230, 10; 233, 322 (1931)

MANN, F. C., AND MAGATH, T. B., Arch. Internal Med., 30, 73 (1922)

MARKOWITZ, J., MANN, F. C., AND BOLLMAN, J. L., Am. J. Physiol., 87, 566 (1929)

MARTIN, E. G., FIELD, J., II, AND HALL, V. E., Am. J. Physiol., 88, 407 (1929)

MEYERHOF, O., Biochem., Z., 237, 427 (1931)

MEYERHOF, O., AND BOYLAND, E., Biochem. Z., 237, 406 (1931)

NEUBERG, C., AND KOBEL, M., Biochem. Z., 207, 232 (1929)

OCHOA, S., Biochem. Z., 227, 116 (1930)

POWER, M. H., AND GREENE, C. H., J. Biol. Chem., 94, 281, 295 (1931)

RAPPORT, D., Am. J. Physiol., 91, 238 (1929)

RICHARDSON, H. B., SHORR, E., AND LOEBEL, R. O. (1), J. Biol. Chem., 86, 529, 551 (1930)

RICHARDSON, H. B., SHORR, E., AND LOEBEL, R. O. (2), Am. J. Physiol., 97, 559 (1931)

ROCHE, J., Bull. soc. chim. biol., 12, 636 (1930)

SAHYUN, M., J. Biol. Chem., 93, 227 (1931)

SAHYUN, M., AND ALSBERG, C. L., J. Biol. Chem., 89, 33 (1930)

SOMOGYI, M., J. Biol. Chem., 90, 725 (1930)

SOMOGYI, M., J. Biol. Chem., 92, xxii (1931)

TERROINE, E. F., BONNET, R., AND ZAGAMI, V., Bull. soc. chim. biol., 13, 326 (1931)

TOENNISSEN, E., AND BRINKMANN, E., Z. physiol. Chem., 187, 137 (1930)

TRIMBLE, H. C., AND CAREY, W. C., J. Biol. Chem., 90, 655 (1931)

UTEVSKI, A., Biochem. Z., 228, 135 (1930)

VOGT, M., Klin. Wochschr., 8, 793 (1929)

WARBURG, O., AND CHRISTIAN, W., Biochem. Z., 242, 206 (1931)

WARBURG, O., KUBOWITZ, F., AND CHRISTIAN, W., *Biochem. Z.*, **227**, 245 (1930)

WENDEL, W. B., *Proc. Soc. Exptl. Biol. Med.*, **26**, 865 (1929); **27**, 624 (1930)

WEST, E. S., SCHARLES, F. H., AND PETERSON, V. L., *J. Biol. Chem.*, **82**, 137 (1929)

WIERZUCHOWSKI, M., PIESKOW, W., AND OWSIANY, E., *Biochem. Z.*, **230**, 146, 173, 187 (1931)

WILSON, R. H., AND LEWIS, H. B., *J. Biol. Chem.*, **85**, 569 (1931)

WITTING, V., MARKOWITZ, J., AND MANN, F. C., *Am. J. Physiol.*, **94**, 35 (1930)

LABORATORY OF BIOLOGICAL CHEMISTRY,
WASHINGTON UNIVERSITY SCHOOL OF MEDICINE,
ST. LOUIS, MISSOURI

FAT METABOLISM*

By W. R. BLOOR

Department of Biochemistry, University of Rochester School of Medicine and Dentistry

In the last few years there has been a renewed interest in the fatty substances in animal and plant economy and many significant contributions have been made. The following review is confined largely to the last three years, that is, 1929, 1930, and 1931. Several topics belonging in this field have been purposely omitted because of lack of space and also because it was felt that they would be dealt with better under other headings.

Chemistry and methods.—Acquaintance with the chemistry of the fatty substances and particularly with the methods employed for their chemical examination and analysis is the first essential in understanding the metabolism of these substances, and considerable progress has been made in promoting it. In the determination of cholesterol in blood and tissues, two general procedures are available. First, the colorimetric method depending on the Liebermann-Burchard reaction, which is used only for micro determinations, and the digitonin precipitation of Windaus (1), which has until recently been used only for macro determinations. Regarding this latter procedure it is widely believed that the digitonin precipitation is more accurate for cholesterol than the colorimetric method. It should be noted, however, that digitonin is not specific for cholesterol. Windaus (1) in his original article on the subject states that all previously investigated naturally occurring sterols behave like cholesterol toward digitonin. Other interfering substances have been mentioned by Okey in her discussion (2) preliminary to the use of this method as a micro method. Anderson (3) in an examination of the unsaponifiable material from beef plasma found a considerable portion which was precipitable by digitonin and was not cholesterol. While the digitonin methods probably give more accurate values for cholesterol than the colorimetric method, the latter method is much easier and more convenient, and is not likely to be immediately displaced. As a matter of fact, in the great majority of samples it gives values closely com-

* Received February 2, 1932.

parable with those obtained by the use of digitonin. With pure cholesterol both methods give accurate values. The fact that methods and modifications of methods for the colorimetric determination of cholesterol continue to appear indicates that the procedure as at present carried out is not satisfactory. Some reasons for the difficulties with the colorimetric method have been discovered very recently.

Cholesterol has been considered a relatively stable substance, but recent work has shown that it is fairly easily altered by procedures such as are used in its separation and examination, as a result of which it does not react quantitatively with either of these procedures. It is changed by even gentle heating. Scheffer (4) has reported that dry-warming of the blood extract may cause as much as 100 per cent error in the determination and that the high temperature of the mixture toward the end of the saponification procedure may also result in abnormal values.

Dam (5) found that sodium ethylate changes cholesterol so that it is less precipitable with digitonin. Okey (2) finds that cholesterol is changed by strong alkali, giving a product which is not quantitatively precipitable by digitonin; a fact which has been confirmed many times in this laboratory.

The effect of higher temperatures on cholesterol has been investigated. Blix and Löwenheim (6) found that temperatures slightly above its melting-point in the presence of air changes cholesterol into oxycholesterol when impurities are present. Pure cholesterol is not changed.

Irradiation has been found by Beumer (7) to produce changes in cholesterol which affect its properties. If the irradiation by ultra-violet light be continued long enough in the presence of oxygen the cholesterol changes to oxycholesterol and then to a tarry mass. Cholesterol so irradiated is no longer precipitable quantitatively by digitonin. Irradiation of cholesterol in nitrogen colors it but it retains its precipitability by digitonin. Reinhard and Buchwald (7a) report that X-ray and γ-ray irradiation produce a definite chemical change in cholesterol dissolved in chloroform or absolute alcohol. That part of the molecule which is responsible for the ultra-violet absorption and for the chemical reaction is changed more than the part which is optically active.

Shear and Kramer (8) find that irradiation produces a yellow oil, of which 40 per cent is not precipitable by digitonin.

Roffo and DeGiorgi (9) found that X-rays destroyed the color-producing properties of cholesterol with the Liebermann-Burchard reagent in chloroform. Similar destruction takes place in blood plasma but is much slower.

Methods.—A method for the micro determination of cholesterol has been provided by Okey (2), based on the digitonin precipitation with measurement of the precipitate by the oxidation procedure of Bloor (10). Improvements on Okey's procedure (2) have been made by Yasuda (11). Mühlbock and Kaufmann (150) have a gravimetric micro method based on the digitonin precipitation.

A micro method for the iodine-number determination of fatty materials has been developed by Yasuda (12). Reindel and Niederländer (13) have shown that the ordinary solutions used for determining the iodine number of fats are unsuitable for sterols because they bring about substitution in the molecule resulting in too high values, confirming the work of some years before by McLean. Yasuda (12) has shown that the solution recommended by Rosenmund and Kuhnhenn (14), essentially a pyridin solution of the halogens, gives accurate values for the sterols when used in either micro or macro methods and he has worked out a method for the micro determination of the iodine number of various fatty substances including cholesterol.

A method for the determination of the pigment in blood is offered by Boeck and Yater (15). The extracted lipochrome of the blood is compared with a solution of dichromate as standard.

Methods for the micro determinations of fatty acids have been developed in considerable number and variety in the last two or three years. The chromic acid oxidation method of Bang (16) has been made the basis of a new method by Blix (17) who determines the fatty acid content by measuring the carbon dioxide given off, using the micro Van Slyke apparatus.

Bloor, also on the basis of the Bang chromic acid oxidation, has developed (18) methods for total lipid and for phospholipid. His procedure is to oxidize the separated fatty substances with an excess of a dichromate sulphuric acid mixture, using silver as a catalyst (Nicloux), and to determine the amount of material present by titration of the excess dichromate. The advantage claimed for this procedure over that of Bang is that the oxidation is complete and the results are therefore less subject to individual error than when an empirical end point is taken. On the other hand, Staub (19) claims that Bang's original procedure is adequate and that it has the advantage of being a real micro method and as such should not be discarded.

Titration methods for the determination of small amounts of fatty acid have been developed by Stewart and White (20) and also by Stoddard and Drury (21).

A colorimetric method using Nile blue sulphate has been worked out by Milroy (22).

Methods for the separation of the fatty acids found in animal tissues are much needed but up to the present are not available. Some of the reasons for the difficulty have been reviewed by Brown and Ault (25). The main difficulties are intersolubility and intra-molecular rearrangements.

Rancidity.—Studies on the rancidity of fat and its control by various substances have been made by Mattill and co-workers (23). They find that there is always an induction period in the production of rancidity which is prolonged by moisture. Hydroxyl compounds retard the change, unsaturated fatty acids catalyze it. Peroxides allow oxidation even in vacuum. Ultra-violet irradiation shortens the induction period. These changes are accompanied by destruction of the fat-soluble vitamines. A more detailed study of the antioxidants brought out the following points. Anti-oxidative properties of the phenols reside in the two hydroxyl groups in their ortho or para position. In the meta position they are inactive. The hydroxyl groups must be directly attached to the ring. Fully hydroxylated inosite is inactive. In the naphthols one hydroxyl group is sufficient. Quinone is effective.

Oxidation.—The biological oxidation of the fatty acids has received attention from Smedley-MacLean and Pearce (153), who worked with oleic acid, oxidizing it with hydrogen peroxide, with and without copper sulphate, and indicating a possible analogy with its oxidation *in vivo*. Under conditions of oxidation similar to those employed by Dakin they found a diketo stearic acid, a dihydroxystearic, and some evidence of a keto derivative of nonoic or decoic acid. Five to ten per cent was completely oxidized. Cupric salt greatly increased the extent of complete oxidation, up to 70 per cent complete oxidation being obtained at 95°.

Other information regarding the chemistry of the fatty substances will be given under the headings "Blood" and "Tissues."

Fat absorption.—New possibilities as to the way in which the fatty acids pass through the intestinal wall are provided by the work

of Verzár and Kúthy (26). They found that sodium glycocholate
and taurocholate dissolve oleic, palmitic, and stearic acids to form
clear solutions. In this way the fatty acids are made diffusible and
the combinations are stable with buffers at pH 6.2. These findings
seem to dispose of the difficulty of reconciling the presence of a soap
emulsion in intestinal contents which are regularly acid and also the
difficulty of explaining the passage of the fatty acids through the
intestinal wall. This is an application of Wieland's (27) choleic acid
principle. Gardner and Gainsborough (28) think that this type of
absorption is important in cholesterol-ester synthesis, since when bile
is excluded from the intestine the cholesterol-ester content of the
blood falls.

The possibility of the absorption of fat directly into the blood
stream is raised again by results obtained by Cantoni (29). He found
that the fatty acid content of the portal blood was always higher than
that of the carotid after a meal of fat. For example: 3 hours after a
meal of fat the total fatty acids in the carotid blood were 0.414 per
cent, while the content of portal blood was 0.592 per cent. Twenty-
four hours after, the values of the two samples of blood were the
same. Cholesterol under the same conditions gave values for carotid
blood of 0.131, and portal blood, 0.109. d'Errico (30) had obtained
similar results long before, but repetition of the experiment by Zucker
(31) had given negative results. The absorption of fat directly into
the blood stream connects up with other findings as to the part which
the liver plays in fat absorption. The blood from the intestine ordinarily passes through the liver, and any fat which had been absorbed
into the intestinal blood would naturally pass through the liver by
way of the portal circulation.

Joannovics and Pick (32), Leathes and Meyer-Weddell (33),
and, recently, Sinclair (34), have contributed experiments which
relate to the absorption of fat directly into the portal system and the
part played by the liver in its metabolism. Joannovics and Pick (32)
found that after feeding cod liver oil the fat of the liver had a higher
iodine number than that of the cod liver oil fed. They found also
that the phospholipids of the liver, while not changed in percentage,
had fatty acids with a much higher iodine number than those found
in the liver phospholipids in the fasting state. Leathes and Meyer-
Weddell (33) found also that the fatty acids of the liver after absorption of a fat with a high iodine number always had a higher
iodine number than that of the fat fed. This was one of the facts

which led Leathes to the conclusion that the liver desaturates the fatty acids. Sinclair (34), in his experiments on fat absorption, obtained results essentially the same as those of Joannovics and Pick. These results taken together with the evidence of direct absorption of fat into the portal system indicate that the liver may remove from the portal blood which reaches it those fatty acids of very high iodine number. Joannovics and Pick found further that an Eck fistula prevents these changes in the fatty acids of the liver, indicating that these changes are directly referable to fat reaching the liver by the portal vein and cannot be referred to fat which is in the general circulation. Joannovics and Pick found also that in the course of 24 hours the iodine numbers of the fatty acids of the liver had again reached the low values found in fasting, indicating that the liver had disposed of these very unsaturated acids either by distribution to the tissues or, as they suspected, by a process of saturation. Iodized fat when fed was scarcely detectable in the liver phospholipid, indicating that saturated fatty acids are not removed from the portal circulation by the liver. Sinclair (34) found that the intestinal mucosa and the liver responded promptly to the absorbed fat by changes in the iodine number of their phospholipid fatty acids, while the other tissues responded much more slowly, indicating that not only the intestinal mucosa but also the liver has a part in fat absorption.

The question of changes in the fats during absorption is again brought up by work done by Bodansky (35). He found that after feeding olive oil the increase of saturated acids in blood plasma was proportionately much greater than the increase in unsaturated acids. It was also found by McClure and Huntsinger (36) that the increase of blood lipids, after oleic acid feeding, was not entirely due to oleic acid, suggesting desaturation of the absorbed oleic acid or mobilization of saturated acid from the fat depots. Similar changes in fat during absorption were reported by me some time ago (37). Other workers who report on possible changes in the fatty acids during absorption are Long and Fenger (38), who give experiments to show that triolein and tristearin may be changed to highly unsaturated fatty acids by the action of bile and pancreatic juice *in vitro,* and Tangl and Behrend (39), who report *in vivo* work which reaches essentially the same conclusion.

Davis (40) has studied the absorption of low-molecular fatty acids and their glycerides. He finds that tributyrin is utilized to about 90 per cent by chickens but is toxic. In rats there was no storage of tributyrin after feeding but some evidence of storage after giving it parenterally.

Eckstein (41) and Powell (42) review the results of feeding low-molecular fats and give results to show that trilaurin produces a depot fat containing as much as 25 per cent lauric acid, while tricapryllin is deposited only in traces. Feeding this fat causes a lowering of the iodine number of the body fat without changing the saponification number, which means that higher fatty acids are formed from it.

The participation of the corpuscles in the changes in blood of absorbed fat which was found by me in 1915 and confirmed by Knudson, is elaborated by work by Bodansky (43). He calculates that the relative increase of total fatty acids in the corpuscles is much greater than in the plasma; similarly that there is a greater increase of lecithin and cholesterol esters in the corpuscles than in the plasma. The increases noted in "acute" lipemia are in contrast to the findings in persistent lipemia where the content of the corpuscles is not markedly higher than normal. For this reason it is interesting to note that Vahlquist (151) has not been able to confirm the findings above. Examining the separated corpuscles by a method different from that used above (comparison of whole blood and plasma), he finds no changes in the corpuscles during fat absorption. It is hardly possible that the difference in method is responsible and his results indicate rather that the participation of the corpuscles may be occasional only.

Absorbed fat reaches the blood in the form of tiny globules. These have been given various names, such as "hemaconia" and most recently by Gage "chylomicrons." Gage found, as was to be expected, that the chylomicrons increased during fat absorption. It was found by Bloor, Gillette and James (44) and later by MacArthur (45) that the determination of absorbed fat by counting chylomicrons gave results comparable to those obtained by chemical methods. Hotta (46) found that the chylomicron count was an accurate measure of parenteral fat absorption, paralleling chemical analysis. A study of the nature of the chylomicrons has recently been made by Ludlum, Taft and Nugent (47). Chylomicrons are fat-droplets of about 1 micron and smaller in diameter and their properties indicate that they are surrounded by a protective protein layer because: (a) the maximum flocculation point is at pH 4.8 and 5.2; (b) reversal of charge takes place at pH 4.8 to 5.0; and (c) coalescence to larger droplets takes place at a point in acid or alkali where the protein would be salted out. The protective coat behaves like a mixture of albumin and globulin.

Page, Pasternak and Burt (48) have furnished results bearing on the effect of absorbed fat on the blood lipids of human beings. They find that cholesterol shows the greatest increase at about the third hour. Phospholipids increase, but irregularly. The iodine number is unchanged by the absorption. The absolute changes in content were relatively small, which perhaps explains the lack of difference in iodine number.

Rony and Levy (49) have studied the absorption of fat in obese individuals (90 lbs. or more over weight) and have found a considerable difference in behavior. Some did not react at all, some gave responses greater than normal individuals, and others behaved just like normals. The total fatty acid content of blood was only slightly higher in these obese individuals than in normals. They found a close relation between alimentary lipemia and sugar tolerance: the greater the sugar tolerance the less the effect of absorbed fat on the level of the blood fatty acid.

Work bearing more directly on this latter point was carried out by Rony and Ching (50) on dogs. They found that fat-feeding experiments on dogs, 15 hours post absorptive, gave a marked variance in response, but that a 7- to 14-day fasting period rendered the responses the same in all. The state of nutrition of the animal therefore affected the response to the dose of fat fed. Ordinarily the amount of fat fed (2 cc. of olive oil per pound body weight) gave a good alimentary lipemia. The lipemia was much reduced by giving at the same time a solution of dextrose, 1 gram per pound of body weight, either intravenously or parenterally. Insulin reduced the alimentary lipemia. Insulin sufficient to lower the blood sugar to about 30 milligrams produced no effect on the fasting blood lipids but prevented alimentary lipemia. They conclude that the process of removal of carbohydrates from the blood favors the removal of fat.

Results similar in kind had been reported several years ago by Bang (51). He found that the feeding of bread along with the fat inhibited the lipemia, and that a liver rich in glycogen prevented the accumulation of fat in the blood.

The relation of cholesterol to the intermediary metabolism of fat has been examined by Shope (52), who found that fasting causes a hypercholesterolemia, which is reduced by feeding any type of food—

fat, carbohydrate, or protein. A straight fat diet for 48 hours produced no increase of blood cholesterol. From these experiments he concludes that the participation of cholesterol in the early stages of fat metabolism is doubtful.

Fat digestion and absorption in the hen has been studied by Güntherberg (53), who reports that they digest and absorb fat very well up to a maximum of about 4.7 gm. per day. Of the grains, the fat of maize is best absorbed, followed by that of oats, then of barley, then of wheat.

INTERMEDIARY METABOLISM OF FATS

Terroine (54) and his collaborators give results to show that the degree of unsaturation of the fatty acids of the tissue phospholipids is a constant quantity of the same nature as the percentage of cholesterol and phospholipid (element constant). Sinclair (55), on the other hand, finds, by the use of suitable diets, that the iodine number of these fatty acids may be markedly changed, and a further study of these changes gave a considerable insight into the intermediary metabolism of the fatty acids. For example, the degree of unsaturation of the phospholipid fatty acids of cat tissues and organs was higher on a beef-kidney diet than on a diet of beef muscle. The phospholipid fatty acids of the intestinal mucosa and the liver of rats responds promptly to the feeding of cod liver oil, while those of the other tissues and organs respond definitely but only slowly. Small doses produce a disproportionately great effect, indicating a selection by the tissue phospholipids of the more highly unsaturated acids. Any fat will cause an increase in iodine number of the phospholipids of animals raised on a fat-free diet, but cod liver oil is most effective and linseed and olive oils are less potent. No regular proportionality between iodine number of food fat and its effect on the phospholipid could be noted. Doses of cod liver oil large enough to produce the maximum effect on the phospholipids may have no effect on the stored fat, while linseed oil seems to have a more marked effect on the stored fat. As the result of these and other findings and a study of the rate of turn-over of the phospholipid fatty acids, Sinclair concludes that the phospholipids of the muscles and presumably also of other tissues, with the possible exception of the liver and the blood, are not involved in the intermediary metabolism of the fatty acids. The "avidity" of the tissue phospholipids for certain fatty acids of a high degree of unsaturation remains to be explained, as also the rôle of the phospholipids in vital processes.

Formation of carbohydrate from fat.—Evidence on this obscure process continues to appear. Soskin (56) found a small positive excretion of sugar after fat feeding. The change of fat to carbohydrate by the surviving liver has been investigated by Jost (57). He finds evidence which leads him to believe that this change takes place in the liver. Hawley and Murlin (152) obtained very low R.Q.'s in human subjects after high fat feeding (down to 0.65). These values are much lower than could be explained otherwise than as a change of fat to carbohydrate.

Greisheimer (58) investigated the effect of fats on the liver glycogen. She found that as the percentage of fat (lard) was increased, the liver glycogen decreased and the liver lipids increased perceptibly. Although glycogen was readily formed by feeding the stock diet of sucrose, casein, or glycerol, only a small quantity was formed from lard. Maignon (154) on the contrary was not able to demonstrate any formation of glycogen from fat in the liver or muscles of dogs.

Fat storage.—The influence of the fat of the food on the stored fat in the animal body has been studied extensively in the last two or three years, partly because of its practical commercial importance in the matter of soft pork. Eckstein (59), reviewing the subject, finds that oleic, palmitic, and stearic acids can be formed from carbohydrate, that myristic and oleic acids may be deposited from the food when fed but butyric acid does not appear in the stores, apparently being synthesized to higher fatty acids. Arachidonic and linolic acids are present in the tissues no matter what the diet and are more or less independent of it, although the presence of triolein in the diet slightly increases the amount of both. The iodine number of the stored fat obtained after feeding myristic and butyric acids was the lowest found. Myristic acid displaced some of the palmitic, oleic, and stearic acids. The fat formed from protein was the same as that formed from carbohydrate; therefore it passes through a carbohydrate stage.

Much work has been done by Ellis and co-workers. Ellis and Zeller (60) raised hogs on brewers' rice, which contains only half of 1 per cent of ether extract, so that the fat which was stored must have been largely synthetic. One example will illustrate their findings: Hog 13 at 257 days had stored 124 pounds of fat or about one-half pound per day. The fat of this hog contained oleic acid 59 per cent, linolic acid 1.3 per cent, arachidonic 0.02 per cent, palmitic 24 per cent, stearic 10 per cent. The ratio, oleic acid to palmitic acid to stearic acid, was 4 : 2 : 1. The linolic acid is not synthesized but comes from the food, except possibly in the case of young animals.

Mendel and his pupils (61) have made significant advances. They have studied the factors influencing the distribution and character of adipose tissue in the rat. Their results may be summarized briefly as follows:

a) *Influence of diet.*—In every case more fat was stored by rats ingesting rations rich in fat than by those on a diet rich in carbohydrate. The distribution of the stored fat was the same regardless of the type of diet.

b) *Influence of weight.*—With increase in body weight more fat was stored in proportion to the body weight. The proportion of subcutaneous fat was largest in small rats. A typical distribution of reserve fat in a rat was as follows:

	Proportion of Total Fat
Subcutaneous	50 per cent
Genital	20 per cent
Peri-renal	12 per cent
Mesenteric	10 per cent
Inter-muscular	5 per cent
Omental	3 per cent

No change in the distribution of fat was observed under any conditions except forced exercise, nocturnal activity, and under-nutrition. Forced exercise and nocturnal activity increased the proportion of inter-muscular fat. Genital fat decreased following either forced activity or under-nutrition.

The degree of saturation of the stored fat was dependent on the diet and was practically the same in all depots. The chemical nature of the fat in any one depot was not changed by activity or the amount of food eaten.

Sterol metabolism.—Schönheimer (62), and Schönheimer, Behring and Hummel (63) have reported that sitosterol and other plant sterols are not absorbed by animals even when fed along with bile acids; neither is iso-cholesterol from lanolin. Allo-cholesterol is absorbed somewhat less readily than cholesterol. Saturation of the double bond prevents absorption. Coprosterol is not absorbed. Ergosterol is absorbed when irradiated but not otherwise. Cholesterol oxalate is not absorbed as such. Only cholesterolase is to be found in tissues.

Bürger and Winterseel (64) examined the sterols from human feces and found them to consist of 50 per cent coprosterol and the rest cholesterol; 10 to 30 per cent were present as esters. This ratio was constant for normal individuals on a milk or mixed diet or even after a dose of 5 grams of cholesterol in olive oil.

Among the factors influencing the absorption of cholesterol are the bile acids, as shown by work done by Loeffler (65) and by Hummel (66). Bile acids in the food result in greater absorption and greater storage in the liver. Glycocholic acid is most effective, then choleic, desoxycholic, and apocholeic.

Although earlier work had pretty definitely shown that cholesterol could be synthesized by the animal organism, workers continue to experiment on this subject. A good review is given by Pfeiffer (67). His own work on calves would seem to indicate that the synthesis was improbable.

Dam (68) studied the changes in cholesterol in young chickens. He found that in the first two weeks there was a decrease in total cholesterol but in two months there was an increase.

A fat deficiency disease.—A possible new deficiency disease has become manifest through the work of Burr and Burr (69) and McAmis, Anderson and Mendel (70). They found that the total exclusion of the neutral fat from the diet even if all known vitamins are supplied in adequate amounts is incompatible with growth and well-being. Burr and Burr found that the disease could be prevented and cured by feeding linoleic acid, and they propose the explanation that warm-blooded animals cannot synthesize appreciable quantities of linoleic acid and possibly of some of the other more highly unsaturated acids.

As was to be expected, results differing from those of Burr and Burr as at first reported have begun to appear. Sinclair (71) agrees with them as far as growth is concerned but is unable to find the other symptoms.

Other evidence of the same kind is supplied by Graham and Griffith (72); also by Hume and Smith (73); and by Funk, Caspe and Caspe (74).

FAT EXCRETION

Significant work in this field has been done by Sperry and co-workers (75). He found (a) that there is a definite endogenous excretion of fatty material in dogs; (b) that bile is not the source of this lipid; (c) that the bacteria found in the feces do not account for over 40 per cent of the material; and (d) that desquamation of intestinal epithelium is not significant as a source of the excreted lipids. Sperry also showed, and in this he has been confirmed by Schönheimer (76), that the sterol portion of the excretion is passed out mainly into the large bowel.

Previously Beumer and Hepner (77) had found much higher cholesterol in the colon than in the ileum. In a bile-fistula dog after a lipid-free meal, there was found an even more marked difference between the two portions of the intestine. The dried content of the ileum contained 0.21 per cent of cholesterol as compared with 1.21 per cent in the colon. Bürger and Oeter (78) found a greater cholesterol content in the sigmoid of cadavers than in sections of the small intestine. Angevine (79) found a definite secretion of lipids into intestinal loops. Sperry and Angevine (80) found a higher excretion from the small intestine than was obtained from the whole intestinal tract of the dog, which indicates an absorption in the large intestine. Schönheimer and Behring (81) examined the sterile secretion in the large intestines in dogs and found 80 per cent of the collected lipids to be unsaponifiable matter. Beumer and Hepner (82) report that cholesterol introduced intravenously is not excreted by way of the bile but directly into the intestinal tract.

Gardner and Gainsborough agree with Schönheimer that plant sterols cannot be changed into cholesterol in the animal body. Carnivora and omnivora have a good excretory mechanism for cholesterol, largely as coprosterol and cholestanol, while the herbivora do not excrete cholesterol readily, so that it piles up in their blood and tends to deposit in the tissues. The fat excretion in birds has been studied by Güntherberg (53), who finds that they excrete fat much as do higher animals.

LIPIDS OF TISSUES

Liver.—The lipids of the liver have been given considerable attention during the last two or three years. In this country Theis (83) has reported the finding in normal livers of a definite balance between phospholipid and fat, the normal ratio being in the neighborhood of 55 of phospholipid to 45 of fat. He finds that in abnormal conditions this ratio is changed, the phospholipid becoming less and the fat becoming greater.

Treating rabbits with various active substances resulted in great changes in the phospholipid-to-fat ratio. For example, insulinizing and phosphorus poisoning reduced the phospholipid very greatly, also phosphorous poisoning.

Bloor and Snider (84) found a much higher ratio of phospholipid to fat than Theis, averaging about 86 to 14. It is possible that this difference in values on the same organ obtained by different workers may be due to differences in treatment before slaughtering, especially as regards food intake. Bloor and Snider found that the neutral fat of beef liver was considerably more unsaturated than that of the fat depots, which supports Leathes' conception of the liver as a desaturating organ for the fatty acids but the possibility cannot be excluded that the presence of more highly unsaturated fats in this organ may be due to selection of these substances from the blood, possibly as part of the protective function of the liver.

Brain.—Studies of the fatty acids in combination in the brain lipids have been made by several workers. Brown and Ault (25) examined the highly unsaturated fatty acids of the brain and find that the ether-insoluble bromides of the acids from hog brains consist mainly of arachidonic acid, although the melting-point was too high. From sheep and beef brains there is obtained more of a still more unsaturated acid than arachidonic—tetracosapentenoic acid.

Merz (85) examined the ether-insoluble lecithin from brain and found that it contains mainly palmitic acid, very little stearic, and about 21 per cent of oleic acid. Fifty-eight per cent of the glycerophosphoric acid of this lecithin was of the beta form. He discusses the probability of the natural occurrence of a lecithin containing only saturated acids. He also examined the sphingomyelin of brain and found three fatty acids contained in it—stearic, lignoceric, and nervonic—from which he concludes that there are three sphingomyelins differing from each other only by their fatty acid component. Their structure is similar to that of the cerebrosides except that they contain a phosphoric-acid-cholin residue in place of galactose.

Klenk in 1929 (86) found that the brain fatty acids were mainly either C_{18} or C_{24} acids, therefore multiples of 6, which he refers to their probable origin in carbohydrates. The present research shows that sphingosine has the formula $C_{18}H_{36}NHO_2$, also a multiple of 6. The fatty acids of the cerebroside molecule are all C_{24} acids (lignoceric, $C_{24}H_{48}O_2$; cerebronic, $C_{24}H_{48}O_3$; nervonic, $C_{24}H_{46}O_2$; and oxynervonic, $C_{24}H_{46}O_3$), which indicates that the cerebroside molecule is composed entirely of compounds containing multiples of 6 carbon atoms.

In a later communication Klenk (87) reported that the saturated acids were palmitic and stearic, the latter predominating; but no higher homologs were found. Of the unsaturated acids several members of the series were represented, with the C_{18} and C_{24} acids predominating. Since the latter are multiples of 6 it is suggested that they may be derived from sugar. The C_{20} and C_{22} acids are best accounted for as β-oxidation and hydrogenation products of the C_{24} acids. The latter probably originate in the cerebrosides and sphingomyelins exclusively. The former occur only in the ether-soluble lecithins and cephalins.

Klenk and Schoenebeck (88) reported that the highly unsaturated C_{22} acid found in the cephalin fraction in brain occurs also in the lecithin fraction and in the phospholipids of beef liver.

Attempts have been made to connect function and composition of the brain—localization of the fatty substances in different areas and changes in composition during development and degeneration. R. M. May (89) has made a study of degeneration in brain and nerve tissue. Studies on autopsy material have shown that degenerative changes in brain consist largely in lowering of the phospholipid content. May, in his first paper, studied the sulphur and phosphorus content of the two hemispheres of the guinea-pig brain and found that they were the same. In a second paper he produced traumatic encephalitis of one hemisphere and determined total nitrogen, water content, sulphur, and phosphorus during the first eight days of disintegration and then 29 days after. He found that the main changes were in the phospholipid, which diminished greatly. His third paper has to do with degeneration of the sciatic nerve of the rabbit. The nerve was cut and allowed to degenerate. The main changes were found to be degradation of the phospholipids and nucleo-proteins.

Gorodisskay (90) has made a laudable attempt to connect function and chemical composition in her study of the distribution of the various lipids in different areas of the human brain. She found that the percentage of cholesterol differs considerably in the different areas, the saturated phospholipids are next in variability, and the unsaturated phospholipids are least variable. Calculated in terms of the total nitrogen of the tissue the lowest cholesterol values are found in the sphere of the higher psychic functions and the highest values in the motor areas. The two sides of the brain have different composition. In general, the more important and more active the portion of the nervous system the less lipid and the more protein it contains. The highest lipid is found in the peripheral nerves, less in the spinal cord, still less in the brain. In the gray matter the lipids constitute one-third and in the white matter two-thirds of the dry substance. The gray matter of the cerebrum is poorer in lipids and higher in protein than the gray matter of the subcortical ganglia. The highest lipid content is found in the motor centers, the lowest in the association centers. Especially low values are found here for cholesterol, cerebrosides, and saturated phospholipids. The effects of age were also studied, and it was found that up to 45 years there was no definite relation of age to composition but that after that there were definite changes. The unsaturated phospholipids and proteins diminished, cholesterol increased, and the saturated phospholipid and cerebrosides did not change. The changes with age are most marked in association centers.

Eric Backlin (91) has contributed a study of the changes in the lipids of rabbit brain during development. He found, as did practically all workers, that at birth the cerebrosides are lacking in the brain and that their appearance and increase parallel the growth of the myelin sheath. During extra-uterine development the dry substance of the brain increases, total lipid increases in terms of dry matter, and all lipid fractions increase in terms of moist weight, the increase being least for the phospholipids. The most notable change is in the cerebrosides, which at birth are almost zero and increase greatly. The unsaturated phospholipids probably do not increase in percentage, while the saturated phospholipids do. The saturated phospholipids and cholesterol and cerebrosides increase much more than the unsaturated.

General.—A difference of opinion has developed with regard to the constancy of composition of the phospholipids of animal tissues and organs. Terroine and co-workers (92) have found that the fatty acids of tissue phospholipids are constant as regards their degree of unsaturation and are independent of the nutritional conditions or nature of food of the animal; in other words, the nature of the fatty acids of the tissue phospholipids is constant. On the other hand,

Sinclair has found that the fatty acids of the tissue phospholipids may be made to undergo considerable changes, depending on the fat of the food. Whether it is possible to reconcile these opposite findings remains to be seen, but it is possible that the nature of the fat fed may be responsible.

Terroine and co-workers (92) have made a study of the degree of unsaturation of the fatty acids in cold-blooded animals. They find that the fatty acid content of the phospholipids of the tissues of these animals is always low, about 60 per cent, and that the iodine number of the phospholipid fatty acids is not as constant as in the warm-blooded animals. The phospholipid fatty acids have an iodine number generally below that of the stored fat (in warm-blooded animals the reverse is the case) and always higher than in the corresponding tissue of the warm-blooded animals. They give a review of the relation between environmental temperature and the degree of unsaturation of fatty acids in plants.

The relation between the lipid content of muscles and their fatigability has been examined by Sorg (93). He found that slowly fatiguing muscle has a higher cholesterol value than rapidly fatiguing muscle and that the heart has the highest cholesterol content of all the muscles. He found a parallelism between phospholipid content and non-fatigability. Here again the heart had the highest phospholipid of all the muscles.

Brown (94) has studied the fatty acids found in the lipids of various tissues and finds that in most tissues arachidonic is the only highly unsaturated one. He discusses some of the difficulties of working with this fatty acid; the fact that as normally found it is probably a mixture of isomers and that in the processes of isolation and purification the proportion of these isomers changes, resulting in changes in properties. These changes make it extremely difficult to determine the amount present.

Tumors.—The relation of the lipids to tumor formation and growth has engaged the attention of several workers. It has been found by Bierich, Detzel and Lang (95) that malignant tumors have a higher content of phospholipid and cholesterol than benign tumors or than that of the tissue surrounding the tumor. The same has been found in this laboratory by Yasuda (96). In the tumors examined by him, which included those of humans and rats and mice, the phospholipid and cholesterol content averaged about twice as great in the malignant tumors as in the benign. Roffo (97) gives evidence to indicate that there is a relation between the cholesterol content of a tissue and its tendency to develop cancer. LeMay (98) finds an increase in the lipoids in tumor tissue and in the blood serum in the cancer.

The relation between arteriosclerosis and the presence of lipids in the vessel wall has been studied by Schönheimer (99). In sclerotic arteries he found a large accumulation of cholesterol esters. Whereas in the normal aorta the cholesterol and cholesterol esters amount by weight to 20 to 60 mg. per cent, in arteriosclerosis the values may reach 1 to 1⅛ gm. per cent. There was no relation between calcification and amount of cholesterol esters. The amount of phospholipid was quite small (maximum 5.7 per cent of the total lipid), and neutral fat was absent. The fatty acids in combination with cholesterol were stearic, palmitic, and oleic. Galactosides were present.

FAT OF BLOOD

General.—Channon and Collinson (100), as the result of a study of beef blood, conclude that calcium phosphatidate is the mother substance of the phospholipids of the blood and that it is a possible intermediate in the synthesis of fat in the intestine. They find that of the acetone-soluble fraction of beef blood the fatty acids are arachidonic, linoleic, stearic, and palmitic and that 55 per cent of the fatty acids are in combination as cholesterol ester and 25 per cent as fat. The phosphatide fatty acids have an iodine number of 71, while those of the cholesterol esters have a much higher iodine number, which is in agreement with the earlier findings of Bloor (101) for beef plasma.

Further information on the hemorrhagic lipemia of rabbits has been supplied by Schmitz and Koch (102). An important finding is that the cephalin in many cases reaches the maximum value as regards its effect on coagulation of the plasma. They believe that the increase of cephalin in this case is a protective mechanism. The extra lipid in this lipemia is believed by Fishberg (103) to act in place of the diminished protein in maintaining the colloidal osmotic pressure of blood.

Anesthesia.—The effect of ether anesthesia on blood cholesterol has been studied by Mahler (104). Ether anesthesia has been shown to produce a definite rise in total cholesterol of blood which is roughly parallel to the rise of glucose and the duration of the anesthesia. There was no rise if insulin was administered. There is therefore a close relation between insulin and the cholesterol content of the blood.

Hormone effects.—The effect of hormones and of nervous stimulation on the level of the blood lipids has come in for a good deal of attention in the last two or three years. Himwich and various workers with him (105, 106, 107) have experimented with the effect of emotional stimuli and of those hormones which are produced as the result of nervous stimulation. They find that adrenalin produces lipemia while insulin lowers the blood fat. Since Cannon showed that adrenalin secretion is increased by nocuous stimulation they tried the effect of such stimulation on the blood fat and found that the total fatty acids of the blood increased to the extent of about 20 per cent, while the glucose increased about 35 per cent as a result of the stimulation (24).

Bruhn and Himwich (107), knowing that parasympathetic effects are mediated by acetylcholin, made the experiment of determining whether or not acetylcholin would reduce the levels of blood fat and blood sugar. They found a lowering in both cases of about 25 per cent.

Lyons (108) found that emotional stimulation of cats produced increases in blood cholesterol of 25 to 30 per cent. The values returned to normal within an hour. Sympathectomized animals did not show this change, and it was demonstrated that the gall bladder had nothing to do with it.

Page, Pasternak and Burt (109) determined the effect of insulin on the blood lipids. They found in rabbits that insulin given to the point of convulsions definitely lowered all the fatty substances and especially lecithin. In one rabbit no trace of phospholipid could be found in the blood. The most certain effect of insulin was on the phospholipid, although the other lipids were generally also affected.

Exercise.—The effect of exercise in increasing the fat of blood has been demonstrated by Stewart, Gaddie and Dunlop (110), corroborating the earlier results of Patterson (111). Experiments made on man showed that the blood fat usually rose after about 8,000 kilogram-meters of work (at 800 to 1,200 kilogram-meters per minute) had been done, or earlier at greater rates of work. After recovery a second period of exercise produced the change more easily. The increase was in the glycerides only. The respiratory quotient for exercise and recovery was 1 for amounts of work up to 5,000 kilogram-meters but fell steadily with increasing rates of work. Protein was not used for the production of work, but carbohydrate was used in decreasing amounts and fat in increasing amounts as the work continued.

Cholesterol and its esters.—Additions to the knowledge of cholesterol ester in serum and plasma have been made by Shope (112). He finds that there is a cholesterolase present in blood serum which after death may cause the complete disappearance of cholesterol ester. Cholesterolase is also present in many animal tissues. Citrate or oxalate causes a small but definite hydrolysis of the cholesterol esters. Cholesterol ester is absent from the blood of calves at birth but increases rapidly during the early life of the animal and then declines slowly with advancing age. Total cholesterol increases after birth.

Lipids and plasma proteins.—The relation of cholesterol to plasma proteins has received attention from several investigators. The idea that cholesterol is combined with euglobulin was first suggested by Bang, who found that precipitation of the globulin precipitates part of the cholesterol.

Handovsky and Lobmann (113) found that the higher the euglobulin of blood the less cholesterol could be shaken out with ether. Twenty-five per cent of the cholesterol of ox serum was bound with globulin.

The question was studied by Gardner and Gainsborough (114), who found that the percentage of total plasma sterol retained in the proteins was 16.4; euglobulin retained 13.8 per cent, pseudo-globulin 1.03 per cent, albumin 1.5 per cent.

In the course of a discussion of the physico-chemical aspects of the blood lipids Theorell (115) mentions that cholesterol is held in combination with the globulin and fibrinogen and that at the isoelectric point of globulin all cholesterol can be extracted with ether. Fibrinogen holds cholesterol firmly except at pH 6. He finds that cholesterol can be added to plasma so as to give a clear solution, that cholesterol and lecithin are antagonistic as regards hemolysis of the red blood cells, and that both lecithin and cholesterol inhibit sedimentation of the corpuscles due to adsorption by the corpuscles of these negatively charged substances.

Compounds containing both protein and fatty substances have been separated from plasma by Macheboeuf (116). He was able to separate an albumin fraction very rich in lecithin and cholesterol esters which was soluble in neutral or alkaline water to a clear solution containing up to 5 per cent.

The lungs and the blood fat.—The destruction of fatty materials in its passage through the lungs, which has long been claimed, has been investigated in several laboratories.

Remond, Colombies and Bernardbeig (117) find that the blood of the right side of the heart is always richer in cholesterol than that of the left. It seems therefore that cholesterol is either fixed or destroyed in the lungs.

Bugnard (118) finds an actual difference in the ratio of cholesterol in plasma and corpuscles in blood before and after passage through the lungs. He believes that the so-called destruction of cholesterol in blood plasma is due to a shift from plasma to corpuscles. He states further that cholesterol is a regulating factor in the physicochemical equilibrium of the blood correlated with the changes in pH and its distribution between plasma and corpuscles depends on the pH. When the blood gives up its carbon dioxide in the lungs cholesterol passes from plasma to the corpuscles, while the reverse takes place in the tissues.

Markowitz and Mann (119) find no change in blood fat values in the passage of blood through the lung and they conclude that the lung plays no part in fat metabolism.

Scheffer (120) found no evidence that the saturation of the blood with carbon dioxide or oxygen had any effect on the distribution of cholesterol between the cells and plasma. The lowering of the cholesterol content of the red cells in the presence of carbon dioxide as compared with oxygen is attributed to dilution due to the absorption of water.

Menstruation.—The changes in the cholesterol and other fatty substances of the blood in the menstrual cycle have been examined by Okey and Boyden (121), who find that the most striking and consistent cyclic alteration in the blood lipids is the fall in cholesterol, which takes place almost invariably during or within a few days of the menstrual period. This is usually preceded or followed by blood cholesterol levels higher than the average for the individuals concerned. The menstrual rise and fall of the blood cholesterol is not consistently paralleled by a similar rise and fall in blood fatty acids and lecithin. It is suggested that the period of retrogression of the corpus luteum may correspond to that of the drop in blood cholesterol. Decreased levels of blood cholesterol have been observed intermenstrually associated with relatively slight acute respiratory infections, for example, colds.

These results have been confirmed by Kaufman and Mühlbock (122), who find a fall in blood cholesterol at the menstrual period of about 40 per cent. In the pre-gravid stage of the cycle there is a rise of 50 per cent. In disturbed ovarian function, there is no rhythmical variation. In lues the cholesterol metabolism is deranged and there is no rhythm. In the menopause there is no change. Later they confirmed their earlier findings of the fall of blood cholesterol at the menstrual period and added that blood lecithin is not affected by menstruation.

Eufinger and Spiegler (123) find that in 47 per cent of the cases there is a tendency to edema in the pre-menstrual and menstrual period, thus apparently connecting the cholesterol with the water balance.

Enzymes.—The presence of a lecithinase in tissues has been reported by King (124). It is present in kidney, small intestine, spleen, liver, testes, pancreas, large intestine, brain, ovaries, supra-renals, lung, blood vessels, cardiac muscle, skeletal muscle. The optimum reaction for the lecithinase is pH 7.5 (phosphatase 8.9). Optimum temperature is 38°. The lecithinase is stable and neutral in reaction but is destroyed by acid or alkali at 38°. The presence of cholesterolase in blood has been shown by Shope (112).

Liver.—The part played by the liver in early fat metabolism has been investigated by Artom (125). The livers of dogs killed after a large meal of fat were examined and it was found that the acetone-insoluble material and the purified phospho-amino lipids increased regularly and almost parallel to a maximum of 30 per cent at the 5th to 8th hour of digestion, then decreased rapidly, and 10 hours after the meal were normal. The acetone-soluble fatty acids generally increased, but their increase was variable and often slight. The unsaponifiable material changed little or not at all. Acetone-soluble phosphorous was regularly increased. These changes are favorable to the conception of participation of the phospholipids in fat metabolism in the liver.

Liver diseases.—In hepatic and biliary diseases Gardner and Gainsborough (28) observed two types of change in cholesterol metabolism as shown by the blood. In obstructive jaundice and in complete external fistula the free cholesterol remains the same, while the cholesterol ester falls to a low level. If the obstruction is complete, for a long time there is a hyper-cholesterolemia but the percentage of ester remains below 50. They found no high values in uncomplicated cholelithiasis and no evidence in humans that the cholesterol of the food influences the bile cholesterol or has any relation to gallstones. Hyper-cholesterolemia in nephritis or in pregnancy has no relation to cholelithiasis. They give a full discussion of the close relation between the sterols and the bile acids.

Mancke (126) found in simple icterus a marked hyper-cholesterolemia with normal ester concentration. In sub-acute atrophy of the liver the cholesterol was high and no esters were present. In cirrhosis of the liver the values were normal; in diabetic xanthosis the cholesterol level was high.

Epstein (127) has investigated in particular the cholesterol-ester partition in the plasma in liver diseases. He finds that the cholesterol-ester present in plasma runs parallel to the severity of the liver damage as shown by clinical condition and tests, almost disappearing in severe damage and increasing with improvement. The ability to esterify is lost in acute parenchymatous damage and is in general sensitive and easily disturbed. In chronic and slowly developing conditions the liver may retain or regain this power. The relation between these findings and those of Gardner and Gainsborough is not entirely clear, except that in both cases there may be a cessation of the flow of bile into the intestine and hence a lack of bile salts which have been found necessary for cholesterol absorption and esterification.

Nephrosis.—The phenomenon of high cholesterol values in the blood in nephrosis has been studied by several workers. Fishberg (128) offers a constructive hypothesis to explain the high values in this condition, in which also there is ordinarily a deficiency of blood proteins. She believes that the cholesterol acts vicariously for the blood protein in keeping up the colloidal osmotic pressure of the plasma.

Machebœuf and Sandor (129) add some interesting facts about this condition. In normal serum 1 gram of albumin combines with about 7 centigrams of fatty substance; in nephrotic serum 1 gram of albumin carries 70 to 80 centigrams. They think that the fatty substances may play a rôle, small but not negligible, in maintaining the colloidal osmotic pressure of the blood. They agree with Fishberg (128) that the increase of fatty substances in nephrosis is useful in contributing to the dynamic equilibrium of salts and water between plasma and tissues by its effect on the Donnan equilibrium.

Calvin and Goldberg (130) find that the cholesterol content of the blood during edema is higher than normal and may remain so after the edema disappears. Cholesterol values vary with the intensity of the edema, and cholesterol changes are preceded by the edema.

Lichtenstein and Epstein (131) find in nephrosis that the cholesterol ester is often markedly above normal. The total cholesterol as usual is very high, the phospholipid high but not often excessive. They find that thyroxin greatly increases the blood cholesterol, a fact, which is denied by Bonilla and Moya (132).

The hypothesis of Fishberg (128) that the blood lipids and especially the cholesterol can act vicariously for the diminished protein in keeping up the colloidal osmotic pressure of plasma in nephrosis is commented upon by Rabinowitsch (133). He points out that the edema of this condition may be due to other causes produced by the lipids, for example, changes in imbibition pressure or altered membrane permeability in the kidneys. He seeks to apply the hypothesis to conditions in the blood in diabetes, where the blood pressure is often high and which is thought by some to contribute to arteriosclerosis. He finds that the protein content in diabetic hypercholesterolemia is normal or higher and the albumin to globulin ratio is normal.

Epilepsy and water balance.—The relation of cholesterol to water balance with its effect in epilepsy and other conditions has received attention. Robinson, Brain and Kay (134) found that in the preconvulsive period in epileptics the cholesterol level in both blood and plasma falls and the seizure takes place at or almost at the lower point in the curve. Incidentally they find that the blood cholesterol is reduced in normal individuals by exercise but comes back promptly. They mention that it is low at the menstrual period, which corresponds to the times of most frequent epileptic attacks.

Gosden, Fox and Brain (135) report that the average cholesterol level in epilepsy is subnormal and that it is more variable at the time of seizure than at other times.

Haustein (136) found that the cholesterol content of the blood of eight children with disturbed water metabolism was 120 to 135 mg. per cent—definitely low. He makes the statement that increased water content, increased water binding power of tissues, decreased serum cholesterol, and lowering of immunity go hand in hand.

Thyroid.—Hunt, Mason and Hurxthal (137) found that the cholesterol content of blood was decreased in hyper-thyroidism and was lowest in acute toxemia. It was markedly increased in true myxedema.

Pernicious anemia.—The cholesterol in the blood in pernicious anemia has been studied by Muller (138), who found that, accompanying the rise in reticulocytes during remission, there is a sudden rise in blood cholesterol lasting for about 12 days, then a second rise to normal, which is maintained as the reticulocytes fall to normal. Lecithin phosphorous ran parallel to cholesterol, while the fatty acids remained at their high level throughout. The change in blood lipids is closely related to the extent of the remission, no matter in which way produced.

Infections.—The relation between infections and blood cholesterol has received attention from Achard, Grigaut, Leblanc and David (139), who report that the cholesterol in infectious fevers first falls, then, on convalescence, rises, often to values above normal. Lecithin behaves in much the same way, the cholesterol/lecithin ratio remaining fairly constant. The iodine number of the fatty material of blood falls at the beginning of the infection and rises with convalescence, but very slowly. In infectious diseases the power of the organism to desaturate fatty acids thus appears to be lowered. Even mild infections such as a common cold have been found by Okey and Boyden (121) to cause a fall in blood cholesterol.

Cancer.—The conditions in blood in cancer have been examined by several workers. Mattick and Buchwald (140) found the cholesterol higher in plasma than in whole blood in 85 per cent of cancer patients. In 80 per cent of normal it is higher in whole blood. They later reported a tendency to hypercholesterolemia in plasma with little change in corpuscles. Lecithin was slightly lower than plasma but not significantly so. Total fatty acids were considerably higher than plasma and slightly higher in corpuscles in cancer. They found a tendency in cancer for a hypercholesterolemia in the plasma, while lecithin values were little changed. Total fatty acids were markedly higher than normal in plasma, with a similar tendency in the corpuscles. Thus it would appear that in cancer either fat absorption is increased or its utilization decreased, with resulting accumulation of total fatty acids and fats, especially in the plasma.

Removal of organs.—Randles and Knudson (155) have found that in rats removal of the spleen, suprarenal glands, ovaries, or testes has no effect on the cholesterol content of the blood.

FAT IN MILK

A study has been made by Maynard, Harrison and McCay (141) of the changes in the blood lipids during the lactation cycle. The results of their experiments are as follows: Examining total fatty acids, phospholipid fatty acids, and cholesterol in the blood of four cows during the dry period and in the succeeding lactation, they find that, following parturition, there is a rapid and approximately parallel rise in all these constituents, succeeded by a gradual drop to the original levels as the next dry period approaches. It is shown that the parallelism between the blood lipids, which is recognized to exist in fasting and non-lactating animals, is also exhibited as these values rise and fall during lactation, at which time an intense fat metabolism is occurring. A close metabolic relationship among these lipids is thus suggested. In experiments with animals held at a constant level of food and fat intake during the dry period and the earlier weeks of lactation the same rise in the blood lipids occurs following the onset of milk secretion. This demonstrates that lactation has an influence upon the level of blood lipids independent of any effect which changes in the fat intake may exert.

McCay and Maynard (142) have examined the interrelationship between the dietary fat and the phosphorous distribution in the blood of lactating cows. They find that during the period of low fat intake the phospholipids and the total phosphorous of the plasma decrease. The phospholipids of the erythrocytes are unaffected, indicating that there is no compensation in the erythrocytes for the losses of the plasma. There is no appreciable change in the other phosphorous constituents of the blood. Cows that are secreting large quantities of milk and fat are unable to synthesize sufficient fat within their bodies to permit the maximum secretion by the mammary gland that takes place when a liberal amount of fat is allowed in the ration.

Studies on the relation between blood lipids and milk fat have been made by Maynard and McCay (143). They found that a ration low in fat produced a lowered milk yield with little effect on the fat percentage. There was a correspondingly lowered blood fat and cholesterol. Milk on a low fat diet had a lower iodine number than on the diet with more fat in it.

Buschmann (144) found that addition of fat to the food did not change the percentage of the fat in the milk, but that the fat of the food changed the chemical nature of the milk fat. The addition of from 0.4 to 1 kilo of oil per day per thousand kilos of body weight affected the milk fat as though 18 per cent of the added fat had gone directly into the milk.

Leroy and co-workers (145) have found that there exists a high coefficient of correlation between the total fatty acids in the blood and the butter fat content of the milk. It is suggested that the determination of fatty acids in the blood will furnish a value by which the future capacity of young cattle to produce butter may be estimated. Its use in the breeding of cattle for high butter fat is also suggested.

In 1924 Gage and Fish (146) carried out a fundamental research on the fate of fat in the animal organism. Among other projects studied was the relation between the fat of the food and the fat of milk. They found that in the cow and other purely herbivorous animals the fat of the food had very little direct effect on the milk fat. In carnivorous and omnivorous animals in which fat has a relatively important place in the natural diet, the milk fat is derived much more directly from the fat of the food. The fat of the stores is also apparently directly available for this purpose.

It had been shown earlier by Mendel and Daniels (147) that if fat is not present in the food of lactating rats it is taken from the fat reservoirs to supply the material for the milk fat, a fact which Gage and Fish were able to corroborate. The fact that the fat of milk has apparently a different origin in these two groups of animals is noteworthy. Apparently the herbivorous animal forms milk fat largely from carbohydrate and has difficulty in using the fat of the food directly for that purpose, while the carnivorous animal can use food and stored fat directly.

In line with these facts is the work of Meigs, Blatherwick and Cary (148), which indicates that in the cow, a typically herbivorous animal, the milk fat has its origin in the blood phospholipid and not in the fat of the blood. Nevertheless the work of Maynard and McCay (143) goes to show that the fat level of the food is important in affecting the output of fat in the milk.

Petersen, Palmer and Eckles (149) have made studies on the time of secretion of the fat of milk. Their method was to compare the milk obtained from parts of the same gland before and after slaughter of the animal. As much milk was obtained from the gland *post mortem* as in life, therefore the cow's udder contains all the liquid secreted at a milking; but the fat content is much lower in that taken from the gland *post mortem,* therefore fat is secreted at milking time. In milkings during life the fat rises to a maximum and then falls off toward the end of the milking. They found also that the nature of the fat in the lactating gland differs widely from that of the non-lactating gland. The fat of the lactating gland is intermediate in composition between butter fat and body fat. The fat of the non-lactating gland is much like that of the surrounding adipose tissue fat. The iodine number of the fat of the lactating gland is less than that of the adipose tissue around the gland, from which they conclude that the fat in the mammary gland of lactating cows is concerned in the synthesis of the fat of milk. The lecithin content of the moist gland, which is 0.170 per cent, they think is not high enough to be a factor in the immediate fat production. Perfusion of the surviving gland, either with salt solution or with emulsion of corn oil, did not give any significant information. Taken together with the preceding, these results indicate that the mammary gland in the cow takes a definite part in the formation of milk fat, which would go to explain the lack of direct connection between food-fat and milk-fat in herbivorous animals as compared with the direct connection noted in omnivorous and carnivorous animals.

LITERATURE CITED

1. WINDAUS, A., *Z. physiol. Chem.*, **65**, 110 (1910)
2. OKEY, R., *J. Biol. Chem.*, **88**, 367 (1930)
3. ANDERSON, R. J., *J. Biol. Chem.*, **71**, 407 (1927)
4. SCHEFFER, J., *Bratislav. Lekárske Listy*, **11**, 41 (1931) ; *Chem. Abst.*, **25**, 4901 (1931)
5. DAM, H., *Biochem. Z.*, **194**, 177 (1928)
6. BLIX, G., AND LÖWENHEIM, G., *Biochem. J.*, **22**, 1313 (1928)
7. BEUMER, H., *Klin. Wochschr.*, **5**, 1962 (1926)
7a. REINHARD, M. C., AND BUCHWALD, K. W., *J. Biol. Chem.*, **73**, 387 (1927)
8. SHEAR, M. J., AND KRAMER, B., *J. Biol. Chem.*, **71**, 213 (1926)
9. ROFFO, A. H., AND DeGIORGI, H., *Bull. soc. chim. biol.*, **11**, 1062 (1929)
10. BLOOR, W. R., *J. Biol. Chem.*, **77**, 53 (1928)
11. YASUDA, M., *J. Biol. Chem.*, **92**, 303 (1931)
12. YASUDA, M., *J. Biol. Chem.*, **94**, 401 (1931)
13. REINDEL, F., AND NIEDERLÄNDER, K., *Ann.*, **475**, 147 (1929)
14. ROSENMUND, K. W., AND KUHNHENN, W., *Z. Untersuch Lebensm.*, **46**, 154 (1923)
15. BOECK, W. C., AND YATER, W. M., *J. Lab. Clin. Med.*, **14**, 1129 (1929)
16. BANG, I., *Biochem. Z.*, **91**, 86, 235 (1918)
17. BLIX, G., *Skand. Archiv. Physiol.*, **48**, 267 (1926)
18. BLOOR, W. R., *J. Biol. Chem.*, **77**, 53 (1928)
19. STAUB, H., *Biochem. Z.*, **232**, 128 (1931)
20. STEWART, C. P., AND WHITE, A. C., *Biochem. J.*, **19**, 840 (1925)
21. STODDARD, J. L., AND DRURY, P., *J. Biol. Chem.*, **84**, 741 (1929)
22. MILROY, J. A., *Biochem. J.*, **22**, 1206 (1928)

23. CUMMINGS, M. J., AND MATTILL, H. A., *J. Nutrition,* **3,** 421 (1931); MATTILL, H. A., *J. Biol. Chem.,* **90,** 141 (1931)
24. FAZIKAS, J. F., SPÍERS, M. A., AND HIMWICH, H. E., *Proc. Soc. Exptl. Biol. Med.,* **29,** 236 (1931)
25. BROWN, J. B., AND AULT, W. C., *J. Biol. Chem.,* **89,** 167 (1930)
26. VERZÁR, F., AND KÚTHY, A. VON, *Biochem. Z.,* **205,** 369; **210,** 265 (1929)
27. WIELAND, H., *Z. physiol. Chem.,* **106,** 181 (1919)
28. GARDNER, J. A., AND GAINSBOROUGH, H., *Quart. J. Med.,* **23,** 465 (1930)
29. CANTONI, O., *Boll. soc. ital. biol. sper.,* **3,** 1278 (1928)
30. D'ERRICO, G., *Arch. fisiol.,* **4,** 513 (1906-7)
31. ZUCKER, T. F., *Proc. Soc. Exptl. Biol. Med.,* **17,** 89 (1920)
32. JOANNOVICS, G., AND PICK, E. P., *Wiener klin. Wochschr.,* **23,** 573 (1910)
33. LEATHES, J. B., AND MEYER-WEDDELL, L., *J. Physiol.,* **38,** xxxviii (1909)
34. SINCLAIR, R. G., *J. Biol. Chem.,* **82,** 117 (1929)
35. BODANSKY, M., *Proc. Soc. Exptl. Biol. Med.,* **28,** 630 (1931)
36. MCCLURE, C. W., AND HUNTSINGER, M. E., *J. Biol. Chem.,* **76,** 1 (1928)
37. BLOOR, W. R., *J. Biol. Chem.,* **16,** 517 (1913-14)
38. LONG, J. H., AND FENGER, F., *J. Am. Chem. Soc.,* **39,** 1278 (1917)
39. TANGL, H., AND BEHREND, N., *Biochem. Z.,* **220,** 234 (1930)
40. DAVIS, R. E., *J. Biol. Chem.,* **88,** 67 (1930)
41. ECKSTEIN, H. C., *J. Biol. Chem.,* **81,** 613 (1929)
42. POWELL, M., *J. Biol. Chem.,* **89,** 547 (1930)
43. BODANSKY, M., *Proc. Soc. Exptl. Biol. Med.,* **28,** 628 (1931)
44. BLOOR, W. R., GILLETTE, E. M., AND JAMES, M. S., *J. Biol. Chem.,* **75,** 61 (1927)
45. MACARTHUR, E. H., *J. Biol. Chem.,* **87,** 299 (1930)
46. HOTTA, S., *Tôhoku J. Exptl. Med.,* **16,** 311 (1930)
47. LUDLUM, S. D., TAFT, A. E., AND NUGENT, R. L., *J. Phys. Chem.,* **35,** 269 (1931)
48. PAGE, I. H., PASTERNAK, L., AND BURT, M. L., *Biochem. Z.,* **223,** 445 (1930)
49. RONY, H. R., AND LEVY, A. J., *J. Lab. Clin. Med.,* **15,** 221 (1929-30)
50. RONY, H. R., AND CHING, T. T., *Endocrinology,* **14,** 355 (1930)
51. BANG, I., *Biochem. Z.,* **91,** 104, 111, 224 (1918)
52. SHOPE, R. E., *J. Biol. Chem.,* **80,** 133 (1928)
53. GÜNTHERBERG, K., *Wiss. Arch. Landw. Abt. B (Tierernähr- u. Tierzucht),* **3,** 339 (1930)
54. TERROINE, E. F., HATTERER, C., AND ROEHRIG, P., *Bull. soc. chim. biol.,* **12,** 657, 682 (1930)
55. SINCLAIR, R. G., *J. Biol. Chem.,* **86,** 579; **88,** 575 (1930)
56. SOSKIN, S., *Biochem. J.,* **23,** 1385 (1929)
57. JOST, H., *Z. physiol. Chem.,* **197,** 90 (1931)
58. GREISHEIMER, ESTHER M., *J. Nutrition,* **4,** 411 (1931)
59. ECKSTEIN, H. C., *J. Biol. Chem.,* **81,** 613 (1929)
60. ELLIS, N. R., AND ZELLER, J. H., *J. Biol. Chem.,* **89,** 185 (1930)
61. REED, L. L., YAMAGUCHI, F., ANDERSON, W. E., AND MENDEL, L. B., *J. Biol. Chem.,* **87,** 147 (1930)
62. SCHÖNHEIMER, R., *Z. physiol. Chem.,* **180,** 1 (1929)

63. SCHÖNHEIMER, R., BEHRING, H. VON, AND HUMMEL, R., Z. physiol. Chem., **192**, 117 (1930)

64. BÜRGER, M., AND WINTERSEEL, W., Z. physiol. Chem., **181**, 255 (1929)

65. LOEFFLER, K., Z. physiol. Chem., **178**, 186 (1928)

66. HUMMEL, R., Z. physiol. Chem., **185**, 105 (1929)

67. PFEIFFER, G., Biochem. Z., **222**, 214 (1930)

68. DAM, H., Biochem. Z., **232**, 269 (1931)

69. BURR, G. O., AND BURR, M. M., J. Biol. Chem., **82**, 345 (1929)

70. McAMIS, A. J., ANDERSON, W. E., AND MENDEL, L. B., J. Biol. Chem., **82**, 247 (1929)

71. SINCLAIR, R. G., Proc. Soc. Exptl. Biol. Med., **27**, 1059 (1930)

72. GRAHAM, C. E., AND GRIFFITH, W. H., Proc. Soc. Exptl. Biol. Med., **28**, 756 (1931)

73. HUME, E M., AND SMITH, H. H., Biochem. J., **25**, 300 (1931)

74. FUNK, C., CASPE, S., AND CASPE, H., Proc. Soc. Exptl. Biol. Med., **28**, 816 (1931)

75. SPERRY, W. M., J. Biol. Chem., **68**, 357 (1926) ; **71**, 351 (1927) ; **81**, 299 (1929) ; **85**, 455 (1930)

76. SCHÖNHEIMER, R., Science, **74**, 579 (1931)

77. BEUMER, H., AND HEPNER, F., Z. ges. exptl. Med., **64**, 787 (1929)

78. BÜRGER, M., AND OETER, H. D., Z. physiol. Chem., **182**, 141 (1929)

79. ANGEVINE, R. W., J. Biol. Chem., **82**, 559 (1929)

80. SPERRY, W. M., AND ANGEVINE, R. W., J. Biol. Chem., **87**, xxii (1930)

81. SCHÖNHEIMER, R., AND BEHRING, H. VON, Z. physiol. Chem., **192**, 102 (1930)

82. BEUMER, H., AND HEPNER, F., Klin. Wochschr., **7**, 1470 (1928)

83. THEIS, E. R., J. Biol. Chem., **76**, 107 ; **77**, 75 (1928) ; **82**, 327 (1929)

84. BLOOR, W. R., AND SNIDER, R. H., J. Biol. Chem., **87**, 399 (1930)

85. MERZ, W., Z. physiol. Chem., **196**, 10 (1931)

86. KLENK, E., Z. physiol. Chem., **185**, 169 (1929)

87. KLENK, E., Z. physiol. Chem., **200**, 51 (1931)

88. KLENK, E., AND SCHOENEBECK, O., Z. physiol. Chem., **194**, 191 (1931)

89. MAY, R. M., Bull. soc. chim. biol., **12**, 934 (1930)

90. GORODISSKAY, H., Biochem. Z., **164**, 446 (1925)

91. BACKLIN, ERIC, (Inaug. Diss.) Upsala Läkareförenings Förhandl. N.F., **35**, 105 (1930)

92. TERROINE, E. F., AND HATTERER, C., Bull. soc. chim. biol., **12**, 674 (1930)

93. SORG, K., Z. physiol. Chem., **182**, 97 (1929)

94. BROWN, J. B., J. Biol. Chem., **83**, 777 (1929)

95. BIERICH, R., DETZEL, A., AND LANG, A., Z. physiol. Chem., **201**, 157 (1931)

96. YASUDA, M., Proc. Soc. Exptl. Biol. Med., **27**, 944 (1930)

97. ROFFO, A. H., J. physiol. path. gén., **27**, 541 (1929)

98. LEMAY, P., Néoplasmes, **10**, 158 (1931)

99. SCHÖNHEIMER, R., Z. physiol. Chem., **160**, 61 (1926) ; **177**, 143 (1928)

100. CHANNON, H. J., AND COLLINSON, G. A., Biochem. J., **23**, 1212 (1929)

101. BLOOR, W. R., J. Biol. Chem., **59**, 543 (1924)

102. SCHMITZ, E., AND KOCH, F., Biochem. Z., **223**, 257 (1930)

103. FISHBERG, E. H., *J. Biol. Chem.*, **81**, 205 (1929)
104. MAHLER, A., *J. Biol. Chem.*, **69**, 653 (1926)
105. HIMWICH, H. E., AND FULTON, J. F., *Am. J. Physiol.*, **97**, 533 (1931)
106. HIMWICH, H. E., AND SPIERS, M. A., *Am. J. Physiol.*, **97**, 648 (1931)
107. BRUHN, M. J., AND HIMWICH, H. E., *Proc. Soc. Exptl. Biol. Med.*, **29**, 234 (1931)
108. LYONS, C., *Am. J. Physiol.*, **98**, 156 (1931)
109. PAGE, I. H., PASTERNAK, L., AND BURT, M. L., *Biochem. Z.*, **231**, 113 (1931)
110. STEWART, C. P., GADDIE, R., AND DUNLOP, D. M., *Biochem. J.*, **25**, 733 (1931)
111. PATTERSON, J. W. T., *Biochem. J.*, **21**, 958 (1927)
112. SHOPE, R. E., *J. Biol. Chem.*, **80**, 125 (1928)
113. HANDOVSKY, H., AND LOBMANN, K., *Archiv. ges. Physiol.*, **210**, 59 (1925)
114. GARDNER, J. A., AND GAINSBOROUGH, H., *Biochem. J.*, **21**, 141 (1927)
115. THEORELL, H., *Biochem. Z.*, **223**, 1 (1930)
116. MACHEBŒUF, M. A., *Bull. soc. chim. biol.*, **11**, 268 (1929)
117. REMOND, A., COLOMBIES, H., AND BERNARDBEIG, J., *Compt. rend. soc. biol.*, **90**, 1029 (1924)
118. BUGNARD, L., *Compt. rend. soc. biol.*, **102**, 369 (1929)
119. MARKOWITZ, C., AND MANN, F. C., *Am. J. Physiol.*, **93**, 521 (1930)
120. SCHEFFER, J., *Biochem. Z.*, **235**, 451 (1931)
121. OKEY, R., AND BOYDEN, R. E., *J. Biol. Chem.*, **72**, 261 (1927)
122. KAUFMANN, C., AND MÜHLBOCK, O., *Arch. Gynäkol.*, **134**, 603 (1928); **136**, 478 (1929)
123. EUFINGER, H., AND SPIEGLER, R., *Arch. Gynäkol.*, **135**, 223 (1928)
124. KING, E. J., *Biochem. J.*, **25**, 799 (1931)
125. ARTOM, C., *Bull. soc. chim. biol.*, **13**, 975 (1931)
126. MANCKE, R., *Deut. Arch. klin. Med.*, **170**, 358 (1931)
127. EPSTEIN, E. Z., *Arch. Internal Med.*, **47**, 82 (1931)
128. FISHBERG, E. H., *J. Biol. Chem.*, **81**, 205 (1929)
129. MACHEBŒUF, M. A., AND SANDOR, G., *Bull. soc. chim. biol.*, **13**, 745 (1931)
130. CALVIN, J. K., AND GOLDBERG, A. H., *Am. J. Diseases Children*, **41**, 1066 (1931)
131. LICHTENSTEIN, L., AND EPSTEIN, E. Z., *Arch. Internal Med.*, **47**, 122 (1931)
132. BONILLA, E., AND MOYA, A., *Endokrinologie*, **9**, 171 (1931)
133. RABINOWITSCH, I. M., *Arch. Internal Med.*, **46**, 752 (1930)
134. ROBINSON, S. H. G., BRAIN, W. R., AND KAY, H. D., *Lancet*, **11**, 325 (1927)
135. GOSDEN, M., FOX, J. T., AND BRAIN, W. R., *Lancet*, **II**, 12 (1929)
136. HAUSTEIN, F., *Arch. Kinderheilk.*, **86**, 33 (1929)
137. MASON, R. L., HUNT, H. M., AND HURXTHAL, L., *New Engl. J. Med.*, **203**, 1273 (1930)
138. MULLER, G. L., *Am. J. Med. Sci.*, **179**, 316 (1930)
139. ACHARD, C., GRIGAUT, A., LEBLANC, A., AND DAVID, M., *J. physiol. pathol. gén.*, **26**, 415 (1928)

140. MATTICK, W. L., AND BUCHWALD, K. W., *J. Cancer Research,* 12, 236 (1928) ; 13, 157 (1929)
141. MAYNARD, L. A., HARRISON, E. S., AND McCAY, C. M., *J. Biol. Chem.,* 92, 263 (1931)
142. McCAY, C. M., AND MAYNARD, L. A., *J. Biol. Chem.,* 92, 273 (1931)
143. MAYNARD, L. A., AND McCAY, C. M., *J. Nutrition,* 2, 67 (1929)
144. BUSCHMANN, A., *Tierernähr.,* 1, 129 (1930) ; *Chem. Abst.,* 25, 1558 (1931)
145. LEROY, A., LECOQ, R., VELINE, M., VALISSANT, MME, AND BARJOT, G., *Lait,* 11, 12, 144, 234, 359 (1931) ; *Chem. Abst.,* 25, 5457 (1931)
146. GAGE, S. H., AND FISH, P. A., *Am. J. Anat.,* 34, 1 (1924)
147. MENDEL, L. B., AND DANIELS, AMY L., *J. Biol. Chem.,* 13, 71 (1912–13)
148. MEIGS, E. B., BLATHERWICK, N. R., AND CARY, C. A., *J. Biol. Chem.,* 37, 1 (1919)
149. PETERSEN, W. E., PALMER, L. S., AND ECKLES, C. H., *Am. J. Physiol.,* 90, 573, 582, 592 (1929)
150. MÜHLBOCK, O., AND KAUFMANN, C., *Biochem. Z.,* 233, 222 (1931)
151. VAHLQUIST, B., *Biochem. J.,* 25, 1628 (1931)
152. HAWLEY, E. E., AND MURLIN, J. R., *Am. J. Physiol.,* 97, 531 (1931)
153. SMEDLEY-MACLEAN, I., AND PEARCE, M. S. B., *Biochem. J.,* 25, 1252 (1931)
154. MAIGNON, F., *Bull. soc. chim. biol.,* 11, 943 (1929)
155. RANDLES, F. S., AND KNUDSON, A., *J. Biol. Chem.,* 76, 89 (1928) ; 82, 57 (1929)

UNIVERSITY OF ROCHESTER
ROCHESTER, NEW YORK

THE METABOLISM OF PROTEINS AND AMINO ACIDS*

By J. Murray Luck

Stanford University, California

Severe space restrictions have made it impossible to give adequate attention to all the questions of current interest embraced by this subject. Of those selected for review, exhaustive treatment has, likewise, proved impracticable. The reviewer has chosen what seemed to him the most significant contributions, but has undoubtedly overlooked a number of equally important papers. It is hoped that such omissions may be remedied in the future.

The present survey is concerned, primarily, with the literature of 1930 and the first 10 months of 1931.

Nitrogen Retention and Protein Storage

Little substantial progress may be reported in studies on the storage of protein, partly because of the lack of adequate experimental means of investigating the subject. The greatest difficulty, doubtless, is the absence of criteria for distinguishing chemically between hypothetical storage protein on the one hand, and the structural proteins of the tissues on the other.

From a study of the urinary S/N ratio during diets of differing nitrogen content Wilson (1) has concluded that there are three types of protein retention: (a) unstable circulating protein of low sulphur content, dependent in quantity on the protein intake; (b) transitional protein; and (c) body protein. His theory, somewhat related to that of Voit, is based upon the observation that diets of increased nitrogen content lead to higher urinary S/N ratios than diets of low nitrogen content. Similar changes in the urinary S/N ratios are to be found in Folin's classical paper on the "Laws Governing the Chemical Composition of the Urine" (2). Rubner's analysis (3) of Berry's experiments indicates, in contrast to these findings, that increase of protein intake decreases the S/N ratio.

Gautier and associates (4, 5) have cited evidence, gained from administration of high nitrogen diets to frogs, suggestive of protein storage in the liver and intestinal wall. The experiments are few in number and somewhat inconclusive. It should be mentioned that

* Received February 8, 1932.

MacKay and MacKay (6) failed to observe hypertrophy of the liver in rats on high protein diets, although pronounced increases in kidney weight were observed and found to be proportional to the nitrogen content of the diet. None of these experiments succeeds in discriminating fully between deposition of storage protein and simple organ hypertrophy.

After a long-continued diet low in protein (33 to 35 gm. per day), Susskind (7) found that almost two weeks were required to regain nitrogen equilibrium when the protein intake was increased to 52 gm. per day. For over a week on the new diet the excretion of nitrogen remained at the previous low protein level. The results suggest that protein reserves, previously exhausted, were being replenished. From studies of the nitrogen balance, total food nitrogen, and total body nitrogen, Lombroso and associates have concluded that under certain conditions, especially during growth (8), labile depots of nitrogen exist. In their judgment nitrogen retention is not necessarily accompanied by a corresponding increase in weight. Under special conditions (9) there are indications that nitrogen may be lost by new and undetermined routes (9–13). The nitrogen-sparing action of ammonium salts (14), according to the work of Lombroso and associates (15), is not due to diminished protein catabolism or to protein storage. In rats and pigs on N-free diets ammonium salts exert the recognized sparing influence on nitrogen loss without any correspondingly favorable effect on body weight or sulphur excretion. Like Lombroso and Di Frisco, Terroine and colleagues (16, 17) have been able to confirm Grafe's work on the nitrogen-sparing action of ammonium salts and have extended Gessler's observations (18) on the failure of ammonium salts to influence the rate of sulphur loss. They do not agree (19) with Lombroso that under these and other special conditions nitrogen is lost by new and undetermined paths (9, 20). Dohna-Schlobitten (21) after repeating Lombroso's experiments has also been unable to accept this conclusion. Terroine and Reichert (22) have been able to show that mixtures of inorganic salts, even though N-free, may have significant effects on the nitrogen balance.

UREA

Related to the question of nitrogen retention are the observations of Moore et al. (23), who report that urea administered to nephritic patients induced positive nitrogen balances. In normal subjects urea ingestion was followed by long-continued retention of nitrogen. A similar retention has been observed by Prüfer (24), who also found in experiments on dogs that much of the injected urea passed temporarily into the form of another substance. These facts along with the lag in urea formation reported by Kiech and Luck (25) may partly account for the delayed excretion of urea from administered amino acids.

Urea of autolytic origin arises exclusively from arginine according to Clementi (26) and Salaskin and Soloviev (27). Other amino acids are suggested as sources in the work reported by Kase (28).

The large amount of urea present in selachians does not appear to be of hepatic origin (29).

Ammonia

The work of Bornstein's laboratory has added further proof to the theory that ammonia formation during amino-acid deamination is localized in the liver. Bornstein (30), Kohn (31), and Nothhaas and Never (32) have shown that the liver forms ammonia from glycine and other amino acids. None is formed in the musculature (32, 33) or small intestine (34). On the other hand, perfusion of the kidney with glycine is accompanied by definite increases in the ammonia content of the perfusion fluid (35; but cf. 36). The failure of moderate injections of sodium cyanate to increase the ammonia content of the blood (37), despite the fact that amino acids under comparable conditions do so (30), strongly suggests that cyanic-acid formation is not an intermediate stage in deamination.

Although several interesting papers on the subject have appeared, no substantial progress can be reported in inquiries concerning the origin of the ammonia in the blood and urine. A significant portion of the blood ammonia may enter by diffusion from the kidney, the muscles (38–41), and the gastro-intestinal tract (42). Adenylic acid of blood is doubtless a direct precursor of some. A portion may originate in the extraordinarily labile autolytic systems of blood, and some possibly arises from amino acid deamination (30–32). The problem is complicated by the ureogenic activity of the liver, which opposes any tendency toward ammonemia. The blood ammonia content increases after hepatectomy (42).

Insulin has been found to lessen considerably the increases normally produced in blood ammonia by muscle work (39).

The precursors of the urinary ammonia, clearly of renal origin, are equally uncertain. Adenylic acid, amino acids, and urea (42–47) have been suggested.

The important studies of the Embden and Parnas laboratories on muscle ammonia as reported in detail in another chapter agree in showing that contraction, under defined conditions of stimulation, increases the ammonia content of muscle. It is also agreed that adenylic acid is the principal precursor (48, 49). The main point of controversy between the two schools is the reversibility or irreversibility of the process. According to Embden and associates it is reversible, while Parnas and colleagues have cited evidence to the contrary. Both laboratories agree that poisoning with monobromoacetic acid or monoiodoacetic acid increases greatly the ammonia content of the stimulated muscle (50–52). Whether this means that lactic acid or phosphagen (50) is necessary for the re-amination of inosinic acid or that some of the muscle elements are simply thrown into a state of rigor with enhanced ammonia production (52) is a second point of controversy.

The Parnas theory of irreversibility necessitates the simultaneous deamination of amino acids or the metabolism of other nitrogenous constituents to provide ammonia for the amination of inosinic acid. To this extent the question of muscle ammonia requires mention in this chapter.

The formation of ammonia from urea by gastric urease (53) has again been demonstrated (54, 55).

OTHER NITROGENOUS BASES

Trimethylamine oxide, $(CH_3)_3N:O$, is now recognized as an end product of metabolism in marine teleosts and selachians (56). In the cephalopods (*Octopus vulgaris*) neither trimethylamine nor trimethylamine oxide occurs. Urea is also absent. Betaine is reported by Hoppe-Seyler and Linneweh (57) to be the principal nitrogenous constituent of cephalopod urine. In confirmation of Langley's work (58) on the metabolism of trimethylamine, Kapeller-Adler and Krael (59) have shown that this base suffers 85 per cent destruction when fed to dogs.

The interesting substance "anserine," first described by Ackermann and associates (60) as a constituent of goose muscle, is now recognized as a derivative of carnosine. The following formula has been assigned to it by Keil (61):

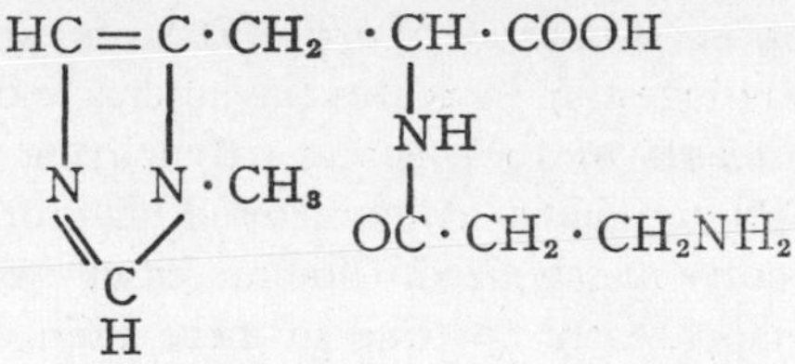

$$\begin{array}{ccc}
HC = C\cdot CH_2 & \cdot CH\cdot COOH \\
\;|\quad\;| & \;\;\;| \\
\;N\quad N\cdot CH_3 & \;\;NH \\
\;\;\backslash\!\!\backslash\;\;/ & OC\cdot CH_2\cdot CH_2NH_2 \\
\;\;\;C \\
\;\;\;H
\end{array}$$

It is a dipeptide of β-alanine and *l*-methyl histidine (62). The occurrence of carnosine and anserine in various vertebrates has been studied by Ackermann and Hoppe-Seyler (63).

A curious base named "arcaine" has been found in *Arca noae* by Kutscher, Ackermann, and Flössner (64). The formula (65) $H_2N(HN:)C\cdot NH(CH_2)_4HN\cdot C(:NH)NH_2$ suggests that α, Δ-diguanidino valerianic acid, at present unknown, may be its natural precursor (66). Various saprophytes act on arcaine to form putrescine and urea (67). Agmatine may be an intermediate in this decomposition.

INTERMEDIARY METABOLISM

Glycine.—Kohn (31) has confirmed the observation of Bornstein (30) on ammonia formation from glycine during perfusion of the liver. Methylamine also appears and reaches a maximum concentration of 0.1 to 0.5 mg. per 100 cc. The author suggests its origin from glycine by simple decarboxylation.

From studies of hippuric acid formation, Quick (68) has shown that the maximum rate of glycine synthesis in man is 0.009 gm. per kilo per hour. This may be compared with corresponding values of 0.0035, 0.015, and 0.025 for the dog, pig, and rabbit, respectively (69).

Histidine.—In the cleavage of histidine by histidase it is now agreed (70–73) that 30 to 40 per cent of the nitrogen is split off as ammonia. Part of this comes from the imidazole ring (70, 74). The residue is readily decomposed by dilute NaOH with the liberation of a second nitrogen atom as ammonia. Glutamic acid appears to be formed (75). Imidazole lactic acid cannot be regarded as the primary product of histidase action, because of its resistance both to histidase and NaOH. The enzyme has been found in the livers of all vertebrates examined and is highly specific.

The normal excretion of imidazole bodies by man is reported by Kauffmann and Engel (73) to be 150 to 600 mg. per day. In confirmation of the observations of Fürth (76) and of Koessler and Hanke (77) protein ingestion increases the imidazole output. Patients suffering from diseases of the hepatic parenchyma were found to excrete 800 to 1000 mg. daily. Administered histidine and imidazole lactic acid were poorly metabolized. The increased excretion of imidazole bodies was apparently not due to mere failure of liver histidase.

Best and McHenry (78) report the discovery of histaminase, an enzyme capable of inactivating histamine. The enzyme is most abundant in the kidney and intestine. Although its mode of action is not yet determined, the experimental findings suggest oxidative cleavage of the imidazole ring.

Tryptophane.—Kotake and associates have published a series of papers pertaining to their extensive studies on the intermediary metabolism of tryptophane. In confirmation of earlier work (79), a substance to which the name "kynurenin" is now given was isolated from the urine of rabbits receiving tryptophane (80). Under optimum conditions as much as 2.5 to 2.9 gm. of kynurenin (as the sulphate) and 1.3 gm. of kynurenic acid could be extracted after giving 3 to 4 gm. of tryptophane. From the analysis of kynurenin, kynurenin sulphate (both crystalline), the dibromide and diester dihydrochloride, and from the color reactions and alkaline decomposition of kynurenin (81, 82), the authors assign to it the formula

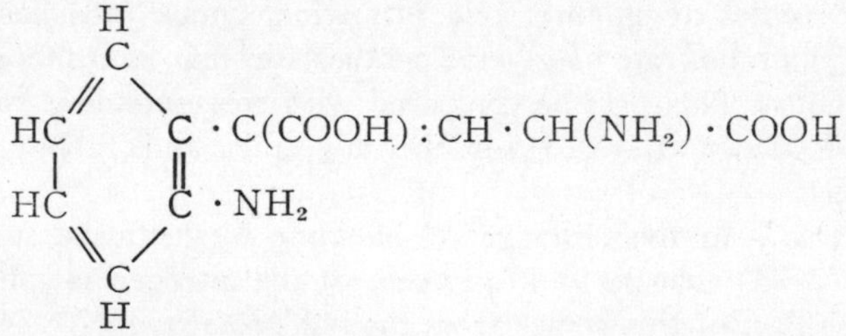

$$
\begin{array}{c}
\text{H} \\
\text{C} \\
\diagup \diagdown \\
\text{HC} \qquad \text{C} \cdot \text{C(COOH)} : \text{CH} \cdot \text{CH(NH}_2) \cdot \text{COOH} \\
| \qquad \qquad || \\
\text{HC} \qquad \text{C} \cdot \text{NH}_2 \\
\diagdown \diagup \\
\text{C} \\
\text{H}
\end{array}
$$

Injected into rabbits kynurenin suffered a 20 to 40 per cent conversion into kynurenic acid (80). In the light of these findings Kotake (83) has proposed a revision of the Ellinger-Matsuoka (84) theory of kynurenic acid formation. Unfortunately the mechanism proposed makes no provision for indole pyruvic acid, hitherto regarded by many as the primary product of tryptophane metabolism. An alternative scheme suggested by Kotake recognizes the formation of indole pyruvic acid but does not include kynurenin. The facts presumably necessitate a theory of kynurenic acid formation that will explain the relationship of both intermediates.

From observations on the fate of tryptophane in the hepatectomized dog and of kynurenin in the isolated perfused liver it is also concluded that kynurenic acid is formed only in the liver (85). Incidentally this paper describes briefly an ingenious technique for total hepatectomy in a single operation.

In dogs, a large percentage of kynurenic acid is found to be excreted in the bile (86). On the contrary, the biliary excretion of kynurenic acid by rabbits is negligible.

In 1925 Tani (87) showed that tryptophane ingestion increased the urochrome fraction of urine. By application of the Weiss method it is now found (88) that kynurenin in both rabbits and humans leads to great increases (sevenfold) in the diazo and urochrome values of urine and should be regarded as an important precursor of the urinary pigment.

That indolepyruvic acid may be regarded as a normal metabolite of tryptophane is demonstrated by the work of Berg, Rose, and Marvel (89), who have shown that it will adequately replace tryptophane as a dietary supplement in animal nutrition. Indole propionic acid, methylene tryptophane, and benzoyl tryptophane cannot be utilized (90). Acetyltryptophane and tryptophane ethyl ester hydrochloride are satisfactory, probably because of the ability of the animal organism to effect de-acetylation and ester hydrolysis. These observations have been confirmed by Berg (91), who studied the formation of kynurenic acid from the tryptophane derivatives mentioned above.

Ichihara and Iwakura (92) used d-indole lactic acid in tryptophane replacement studies on five rats. In contrast to the conclusions of Jackson (93) they regard it as an adequate dietary substitute for tryptophane. From two animals only they further conclude that indolepyruvic acid cannot be utilized.

Phenylalanine and tyrosine.—From observations on the fate of phenylalanine and tyrosine, Shambaugh, Lewis, and Tourtellotte (94) have found that rabbits to which phenylalanine had been administered excrete a substance which behaves in all respects like phenylpyruvic acid. The corresponding α-keto product was not obtained from tyrosine, suggesting that, if formed, it underwent immediate and further metabolism.

Two alcaptonuric subjects have been studied by Reinwein (95) and Sachs (96). The latter maintained his subject on a nitrogen-free diet for five days, during which the daily excretion of nitrogen and homogentisic acid fell sharply to minima of 2.18 gm. and 0.29 gm., respectively. Since food protein corresponding to 2.18 gm. of nitrogen would give rise to 1.09 gm. of homogentisic acid, the large discrepancy of 0.80 gm. suggests that homogentisic acid may not arise in significant quantities during endogenous protein metabolism.

Foster and Gutman (97) have studied the metabolism of diiodotyrosine in rabbits. Of the total urinary iodine, 10 per cent was inorganic iodide, 60 per cent was in the form of unchanged diiodotyrosine, and 18 per cent was present as 3,5-diiodo 4-hydroxy phenyllactic acid.

Arginine.—The synthesis of arginine by the growing rat is seemingly established by the work of Scull and Rose (98). When maintained upon diets of low and known arginine content for some weeks the tissue increment in arginine was found to be two to three times the amount ingested. Kiech, Luck, and Smith (99) have shown that three of the four nitrogen atoms in arginine are rapidly converted into urea when arginine is fed to rats. There is no transient accumulation of ornithine.

Glucogenesis from Amino Acids

In twenty-six experiments with glycine Wilson and Lewis (100) have shown that this amino acid administered orally to rats fails to increase the glycogen stores. Of the other amino acids investigated (*d*-, and *dl*-alanine, leucine, and glutamic acid) alanine alone produced significant quantities of glycogen. These findings have been confirmed by Greisheimer and Arny (101). Lundsgaard (102) now reports that glycine and glutamic acid produce hyperglycemia in rabbits only when injected subcutaneously in massive, toxic doses. Glycine administered by mouth fails to produce hyperglycemia. Intravenous glycine is also without effect (105). Lundsgaard's work fails to confirm the early observations of Pollak (103) and disagrees in several respects with those of Nord (104). Nevertheless, Nord's observations are best explained by regarding glycine as a stimulant of the adrenal medulla, without being directly glucogenetic itself.

Although the glucogenetic behavior of glycine in the diabetic organism is well recognized, the extent to which this amino acid normally participates in the formation of glucose and glycogen is possibly less than has hitherto been suspected.

Amino Acids in Nutrition

Sure's observations (106) on the indispensability of proline as a constituent of the diet have been confirmed by Adeline (107), who has also shown that hydroxyproline will serve as an adequate substitute for proline.

Rose and his associates have published several important papers (108–111) in which it is convincingly demonstrated that a new amino acid or essential dietary principle, at present of undetermined nature, is present in casein, gliadin, gelatin, and, presumably, other proteins also. The new substance is indispensable for animal maintenance and growth. Its presence was determined by the use of a synthetic diet, supposedly adequate, in which proteins were replaced by a mixture of the known amino acids, excepting β-hydroxy glutamic acid. For proper maintenance and growth it was found necessary to supplement the mixture with the proteins mentioned or with certain fractions of a casein hydrolysate. The work of Jones and Nelson (112) on the efficacy of casein and lactalbumin supplements in diets, otherwise adequate, seems to necessitate the same conclusion.

The Calorigenic Action of Amino Acids

The baffling problem of the calorigenic action of amino acids has received considerable attention during the period under review. The principal theories advanced in explanation of the phenomenon have been four in number: (a) the extra heat liberated after protein or amino acid administration arises from intermediate reactions associated with glucogenesis; (b) the amino acids themselves serve as metabolic stimuli and elevate the organism to a higher level of metabolism; (c) specific products formed in the course of amino-acid metabolism serve as stimulating agents; (d) extra work is thrown upon the kidney, for which additional energy must be provided. Only a portion of the energy potentially available in various metabolites can be so expended. A large fraction will necessarily be liberated as heat.

1. By reference to the Third Law of thermodynamics, Adams (113) has calculated that about 60×10^3 calories are required to effect the change of state indicated by the endothermic reaction

$$2CH_3 \cdot CH(NH_2) \cdot COOH + H_2O + CO_2$$
$$\rightarrow C_6H_{12}O_6 + CO(NH_2)_2$$

In the formation of glucose from glycine according to the equation

$$3CH_2(NH_2) \cdot COOH + \tfrac{3}{2}CO_2 + \tfrac{3}{2}H_2O$$
$$\rightarrow C_6H_{12}O_6 + \tfrac{3}{2}O_2 + \tfrac{3}{2}CO(NH_2)_2,$$

similar calculations indicate that 196×10^3 calories should be absorbed. Chambers and Lusk (114) see in these calculations of Adams and also in those of Aubel (115) an explanation of the phenomenon in question, concluding, so it would seem, that the energy required as a driving force in the reactions is the heat of specific dynamic action. By similar reasoning it is argued that glucose formation from glutamic acid would proceed without an elevation of metabolism, since the exothermic nature of the reaction

$$2C_5H_9NO_4 + 3O_2 \rightarrow C_6H_{12}O_6 + H_2O + CO(NH_2)_2 + 3CO_2$$

permits glucogenesis without the addition of energy to the system. Borsook and Winegarden (116) criticize this analysis of the problem by pointing out that estimates of the entropies of amino acids are not sufficiently reliable to permit application of the Third Law. By the use of accepted values for the molar heats of formation of the various reactants and by application of the First Law of thermodynamics they conclude that ΔH in the reactions postulated above is $-24,000$ calories per mol for alanine, $-66,000$ calories for glycine, and $+129,000$ calories for glutamic acid.

Though it be assumed that these reactions represent the actual paths of metabolism of glycine, alanine, and glutamic acid, it does not follow, however, that the thermal changes can be readily calculated. For the liberation of energy that must be supplied in the two endothermic reactions above there is required the driving force of accompanying exothermic reactions. The efficiency of energy transfer is unknown, but probably not more than 20 or 25 per cent of the energy liberated in the exothermic processes could be used in effecting the change of state of alanine and glycine. The remaining 75 per cent or more, liberated as heat, would seem to be the heat of specific dynamic action. So, too, the exothermic nature of the glutamic-acid reaction warrants the conclusion that much heat would necessarily be liberated in the course of glucogenesis from glutamic acid, even though it be conceded that accompanying exothermic reactions need not be postulated. This conclusion stands in contrast with the view of Chambers and Lusk. Lusk has restated his interpretation in a recent and interesting review of the subject (117).

These difficulties in lending a precise quantitative interpretation to the phenomenon are aggravated by disagreement in the experimental findings. Although Grafe (118), Rapport and Beard (119), and Terroine and collaborators (120, 121) have observed definite increases in heat output after glutamic acid administration, Lusk (122) and Aub, Everett, and Fine (123) concluded that it was without effect. In the work of Chambers and Lusk (114) there is some uncertainty as to whether a positive result was observed in the normal dog after glutamic acid administration. Lundsgaard reported positive effects with glutamic acid in normal dogs and in narcotized cats (124). In the former, difficulty was encountered through nausea. This has been frequently observed (25, 125, 126) in experiments with glutamic and aspartic acids and may lead to a pseudo specific dynamic action.

Aubel (115) has calculated the energy changes resulting from the metabolism of alanine after postulating a series of intermediate reactions involving pyruvic acid, lactic acid, and glucose. It is assumed that one-fourth of the latter undergoes complete oxidation. By summation of the whole, Aubel calculates that 113,375 calories would be given off as heat for each mol of alanine metabolized. This is regarded as the heat of specific dynamic action.

To the writer there seems no satisfactory basis for assuming that one-fourth of the glucose undergoes complete oxidation. The findings of Wilhelmj, Bollman, and Mann (127) and of Dock (128) prove that the liver is the seat of action and permit us to dissociate the entire process from events in muscle, where Aubel's scheme for oxidation of one-fourth of the glucose from lactic acid seems to originate. Indeed, as Terroine, Bonnet, and Zagami (129) have pointed out, if 25 per cent of the glucose were to burn, 21 per cent of the potential energy of the lactic acid would be appearing as heat, implying that the Meyerhof muscle law is directly applicable to this phenomenon. The point is undoubtedly important, since according to Aubel 75 per cent of the calculated output of heat arising from the metabolism of alanine would be given off at this stage.

The question has not escaped abundant investigation. Although Aubel, in three experiments on frogs, found that the heat of oxidation of sodium lactate closely approximated the value required by theory, various others have observed only negative results. Abramson, Eggleton, and Eggleton (130) found but a negligible elevation[1] of oxygen consumption in dogs injected intravenously with sodium lactate, an observation which received confirmation in the work of Martin, Field, and Hall (131). Lundsgaard (124) has reported only negative results with sodium lactate administered to dogs and urethanized rabbits. Likewise in five experiments of Terroine, Bonnet, and Zagami (129) on normal rabbits, sodium lactate induced no increase in oxygen consumption. Zagami (132) has studied the fate of other ternary substances in rabbits, with the result that succinic acid alone, of those investigated, had any positive effect on the respiratory metabolism. Malic acid, citric acid, dihydroxyacetone, and glycerol were without action. Pyruvic acid is also known to be without effect (124, 129).

It seems to the writer that Aubel's calculation of the theoretical respiratory quotient is also in question, for in arriving at the value 0.88 the complete oxidation of five mols of glucose is postulated, while the energy calculations assume that only one is burned.

In addition to glucogenesis it seems probable that an appreciable portion of an amino acid may undergo complete oxidation. This may or may not involve the intermediate formation of glucose. In view of the facts that the proportion undergoing complete oxidation is unknown, that the entropies of amino acids have not been satisfactorily estimated, and that the extent to which other endothermic and exothermic processes may be drawn into the metabolic picture remains undetermined, the possibility of giving a quantitative explanation of the calorigenic action of amino acids by the methods referred to above would seem to be remote. It should be added that little evidence is available that glycine, despite its high specific dynamic action, is glucogenetic in the normal animal (cf. p. 306).

2. Only one investigation seems to have been reported during the past two years which can be regarded as lending clear support to the theory of amino-acid stimulation. Von Kuthy (133) has shown that a close correlation exists between the amino-nitrogen content of the blood and the rate of oxygen consumption following the administration of raw meat to rats. The parallelism in the curves plotted by von Kuthy is continuous throughout the entire period of increased metabolism. The results are supported by those of Völker [(134); cf. Tables VI and VII] and are in general agreement with certain findings of Arvay and Nothhaas. Although this theory predicts that an

---

[1] No greater than that induced by $NaHCO_3$ injection.

increase in the concentration of amino acids in the blood will be attended by the liberation of heat, it throws no light on the nature of the thermogenic reactions. It has to recognize that they are probably centered in the liver (127, 128) and that other exothermic processes bearing no relation to the concentration of amino acids in the blood may participate in the liberation of heat.

3. No recent work has come to the attention of the writer in support of the theory that certain of the non-nitrogenous products of amino-acid metabolism serve specifically as sources of heat or stimulants of the respiratory metabolism following administration of protein or amino acids. The failure of lactic acid, pyruvic acid, malic acid, citric acid, dihydroxyacetone, and glycerol to influence oxygen consumption has already been mentioned. Glycollic acid also has little if any effect (124). In Zagami's experiments (132) succinic acid increased the oxygen consumption of rabbits, but the animals are reported to have been restless and active. The interesting papers of Lundsgaard (124) bring out the fact that sodium acetate and sodium propionate induce in narcotized cats and rabbits significant increases in oxygen consumption. In four experiments on urethanized rabbits the elevation in metabolism following sodium acetate administration was equally as great as that induced by glycine (15 per cent increase). Sodium propionate in four similar experiments gave increases in oxygen consumption of 20 to 30 per cent. The mechanism is probably different from that of glycine, since curare almost abolished the calorigenic action of glycine in rabbits without influencing that of sodium acetate. A curious species difference is here noted, curare failing to abolish the calorigenic action of glycine in cats.

Although sodium lactate had little if any influence on oxygen consumption, ammonium lactate increased it as much as alanine. So too did ammonium chloride. In unanaesthetized dogs the results for all three were quantitatively similar. In chloralosed cats similar results were obtained and found to persist after curare. The positive action of ammonium salts suggests that ammonia arising from amino-acid deamination may serve as a stimulant to thermogenic processes. Bornstein (30) has shown that increases in the ammonia content of the blood may be observed during the metabolism of glycine and alanine. At the same time the formation of urea from ammonia and carbon dioxide is an exothermic process, permitting one to anticipate that urea formation from the administered ammonium salts would necessarily give rise to extra heat. In addition to these possibilities, it has been pointed out, most recently by Borsook and Winegarden (116), that the excretion of urea, be it from amino acids or from ammonia, would require an expenditure of energy and would be attended by the liberation of heat. This brings us to the fourth theory under consideration.

4. Borsook and Winegarden (116) have inquired afresh into the theory, first proposed by Zuntz (135, 136), that a portion of the heat of specific dynamic action is associated with the work of nitrogen excretion. They conclude from the data of Rapport and associates, supported by the findings of Wishart (137), that a linear relationship exists between the excess metabolism in calories per hour and the rate of extra nitrogen excretion. They attribute this in part to the energy expended by the kidney in the work of urea concentration. Rapport and associates have not subscribed to this point of view, having considered hitherto that their results did not clearly demonstrate the suggested relationship. Borsook and Winegarden, it should be pointed out, conclude that not more than 25 to 60 per cent of the heat of specific dynamic action is due to work imposed upon the kidney, thereby leaving the way open for other interpretations. The theory is, doubtless, an attractive way of explaining the calorigenic effect of ammonium salts (14, 118, 124) and suggests that confirmatory experiments with urea would be of value. Glutamic acid, known to be quite rapidly metabolized (25), should likewise exert an appreciable effect. This is now a disputed point.

It should also be mentioned that the method, first proposed by Wilhelmj and Bollman (138), of expressing the excess metabolism in calories per millimol amino acid deaminized has given in actual practice a relationship between the extra calories evolved and the excess nitrogen excreted. This has come about through the necessity, imposed by the conditions of almost all experiments, of measuring the progress of deamination by the rate of nitrogen excretion. Nevertheless, the method is clearly based upon the assumption that deamination, urea formation, and urea excretion proceed with equal velocity. Actually, the results of Lusk (122), Wilhelmj and Bollman (138), Wilhelmj and Mann (139), and Ralli, Canzanelli, and Rapport (140) seem to indicate that a pronounced lag in the excretion of urea is manifest in short-period experiments. Lusk (141), recognizing the rate of nitrogen excretion as an inadequate index of the rate of deamination, chose to calculate the degree of amino-acid catabolism from Csonka's results (142) on the rate of sugar excretion by the phlorhizinized dog. The existence of an actual lag in urea formation is now demonstrated (25) by direct analysis of the whole animal. It is therefore apparent that the rate of extra nitrogen excretion observed in short-period experiments is not a reliable measure of the rate of amino-acid deamination. The important findings of Wilhelmj and Bollman (138), Wilhelmj and Mann (139, 143), and Wilhelmj, Bollman, and Mann (144) expressed in terms of amino-acid deamination should be more strictly regarded as relationships between excess metabolism in calories and the rate of extra nitrogen excretion. Although a superficial analysis of the results from this point of view might seem to lend added support to the theory revived by Borsook and Winegarden, this conclusion does not necessarily follow.

The rôle of osmotic phenomena in the calorigenic action of amino acids has never been clear and is again brought into consideration by the observation of Wilhelmj, Bollman, and Mann (144) that solutions of sodium chloride have a significant thermogenic effect. Under the conditions of their experiments "it would possibly be justified to conclude that from 30 to 50 per cent of the specific dynamic action of the solutions of amino acids was of a non-specific nature resulting from the effects of osmotic pressure."

It also seems to be established that the nutritional condition of the animal is an important factor. According to Wilhelmj and Mann (139, 143) prolonged fasting leads to an increase in the extra heat expressed in calories per millimol of amino acid administered. A subsequent period of carbohydrate feeding greatly reduces the effect induced by glycine.

Investigations of the last two years have given further support to the theory that the reactions incident to the calorigenic action of amino acids are resident in the liver. Dock (128) has shown that the extra oxygen consumed by animals when placed on high-protein diets is almost entirely used in the increased respiration of the viscera. The oxygen consumption of the musculature was found to be of practically equal magnitude in rats on high- and low-protein diets. The experiments of Rapport and Katz (145) on the calorigenic action of glycine in the perfused limb have frequently been cited in support of the opposing theory, viz., that the thermogenic action of amino acids is equally manifest in non-hepatic tissue. Bornstein and Roese (146) and Nothhaas and Never (32) now report only negative results in attempts to confirm the experiments of Rapport and Katz.

Many efforts have been made to analyze the phenomenon by perfusion of various organs (32, 146–148) and by the respiration of minced tissue (149–151), but it is difficult to relate the results to experiments *in vivo*. It seems established that glycine increases the oxygen consumption of the isolated liver but is without effect upon the respiration of fresh minced tissue. Alanine, asparagin, and glutamic acid, *per contra,* increase the oxygen consumption of the latter.

In view of the multiplicity of physical factors involved, it is a relief to learn that psychic conditions play no rôle (152).

The relationship of hormones and the sympathetic nervous system to the calorigenic action of amino acids is still too uncertain to warrant discussion at this time.

The effects of high protein diets on the kidney, the sulphur-containing amino acids, and the hematogenic properties of amino acids are reviewed elsewhere in the present volume. Recent work on the amino acids in relation to the origin and metabolism of creatine will be discussed by Professor Rose in the second volume of the *Review* (1933) under "Creatine and Creatinine." Consideration of the blood proteins is also proposed for inclusion in the next volume.

LITERATURE CITED

1. WILSON, H. E. C., *J. Physiol.,* 72, 327 (1931)
2. FOLIN, O., *Am. J. Physiol.,* 13, 66 (1905)
3. RUBNER, M., *Z. ges. exptl. Med.,* 72, 144 (1930)
4. GAUTIER, C., AND THIERS, H. P., *Bull. soc. chim. biol.,* 10, 537 (1928)
5. GAUTIER, C., *Bull. soc. chim. biol.,* 12, 1382 (1930); 13, 395 (1931)
6. MacKay, E. M., AND MacKay, L. L., *J. Nutrition,* 3, 375, 387 (1931)
7. SUSSKIND, B., *Z. ges. exptl. Med.,* 72, 119 (1930)
8. ZUMMO, C., *Arch. intern. physiol.,* 34, 349 (1931)
9. LOMBROSO, U., *Arch. intern. physiol.,* 34, 21 (1931)
10. LOMBROSO, U., AND DI FRISCO, S., *Boll. soc. ital. biol. sper.,* 3, 303 (1928)
11. LOMBROSO, U., AND DI FRISCO, S., *Arch. intern. physiol.,* 33, 92, 109 (1930)
12. PASQUALINO, G., *Arch. intern. physiol.,* 33, 185 (1930)
13. DI FRISCO, A., *Arch. intern. physiol.,* 33, 98, 137 (1930)
14. GRAFE, E., AND SCHLÄPFER, V., *Z. physiol. Chem.,* 77, 1 (1911); GRAFE, E., *Z. physiol. Chem.,* 78, 485 (1912); 86, 347 (1913)
15. LOMBROSO, U., *Arch. intern. physiol.,* 34, 229 (1931)
16. TERROINE, E. F., BONNET, R., CHOTIN, R., AND MOUROT, G., *Arch. intern. physiol.,* 33, 60 (1930)
17. GIAJA, A., *Arch. intern. physiol.,* 34, 222 (1931)
18. GESSLER, H., *Z. physiol. Chem.,* 109, 280 (1920)

19. TERROINE, E. F., *Arch. intern. physiol.*, **34**, 1 (1931)
20. LOMBROSO, U., *Arch. intern. physiol.*, **34**, 362 (1931)
21. DOHNA-SCHLOBITTEN, SIGMAR GRAF ZU, *Wiss. Arch. Landw. Abt. B (Tierernähr- u. Tierzucht)*, **6**, 415 (1931)
22. TERROINE, E. F., AND REICHERT, T., *Arch. intern. physiol.*, **32**, 337, 374, 391 (1930)
23. MOORE, D. D., LAVIETES, P. H., WAKEMAN, A. M., AND PETERS, J. P., *J. Biol. Chem.*, **91**, 373 (1931)
24. PRÜFER, J., *Z. klin. Med.*, **114**, 293 (1930)
25. KIECH, V. C., AND LUCK, J. M., *J. Biol. Chem.*, **94**, 433 (1931)
26. CLEMENTI, A., *Boll. soc. ital. biol. sper.*, **5**, 1142 (1930)
27. SALASKIN, S., AND SOLOVIEV, L., *Z. physiol. Chem.*, **192**, 28 (1930)
28. KASE, K., *Biochem. Z.*, **233**, 258, 271 (1931)
29. KISCH, B., *Biochem. Z.*, **225**, 197 (1930)
30. BORNSTEIN, A., *Biochem. Z.*, **212**, 137 (1929) ; **214**, 374 (1929)
31. KOHN, R., *Z. physiol. Chem.*, **200**, 191 (1931)
32. NOTHHAAS, R., AND NEVER, H. E., *Arch. ges. Physiol.*, **224**, 527 (1931)
33. BORNSTEIN, A., AND ROESE, H. F., *Biochem. Z.*, **212**, 127 (1929)
34. ROESE, H. F., *Arch. ges. Physiol.*, **226**, 190 (1930)
35. BORNSTEIN, A., AND BUDELMANN, G., *Biochem. Z.*, **218**, 64 (1930)
36. MANN, F. C., AND BOLLMAN, J. L., *Am. J. Physiol.*, **85**, 390 (1928)
37. BORNSTEIN, A., AND PANTKE, R., *Biochem. Z.*, **225**, 330 (1930)
38. PARNAS, J. K., MOZOLOWSKI, W., AND LEWINSKI, W., *Biochem. Z.*, **188**, 15 (1927)
39. SCHWARZ, H., AND TAUBENHAUS, M., *Biochem. Z.*, **236**, 474 (1931)
40. STANOYEVITCH, L., *Bull. soc. chim. biol.*, **13**, 579 (1931)
41. STANOYEVITCH, L., *Biochem. Z.*, **239**, 257 (1931)
42. BOLLMAN, J. L., AND MANN, F. C., *Am. J. Physiol.*, **92**, 92 (1930)
43. EMBDEN, G., AND SCHUMACHER, H., *Arch. ges. Physiol.*, **223**, 487 (1930)
44. EMBDEN, G., AND DEUTICKE, H. J., *Z. physiol. Chem.*, **190**, 62 (1930)
45. GYÖRGY, P., AND KELLER, W., *Biochem. Z.*, **235**, 86 (1931)
46. PATEY, A., AND HOLMES, B. E., *Biochem. J.*, **23**, 760 (1929)
47. HOLMES, B. E., AND PATEY, A., *Biochem. J.*, **24**, 1564 (1930)
48. EMBDEN, G., AND ZIMMERMAN, M., *Z. physiol. Chem.*, **167**, 137 (1927)
49. PARNAS, J. K., *Biochem. Z.*, **206**, 16 (1929)
50. EMBDEN, G., AND NORPOTH, L., *Z. physiol. Chem.*, **201**, 105 (1931)
51. MOZOLOWSKI, P., MANN, T., AND LUTWAK, C., *Biochem. Z.*, **231**, 290 (1931)
52. LUTWAK, C., *Biochem. Z.*, **235**, 485 (1931)
53. LUCK, J. M., *Biochem. J.*, **18**, 825 (1924)
54. SIMICI, D., VLADESCO, R., AND POPESCO, M., *Compt. rend. soc. biol.*, **101**, 199 (1929)
55. RIGONI, M., *Arch. sci. biol.*, **15**, 37 (1930) ; *Arch. ital. biol.*, **84**, 74 (1931)
56. HOPPE-SEYLER, F. A., *Z. Biol.*, **90**, 433 (1930)
57. HOPPE-SEYLER, F. A., AND LINNEWEH, W., *Z. physiol. Chem.*, **196**, 47 (1931)
58. LANGLEY, W. D., *J. Biol. Chem.*, **84**, 561 (1929)
59. KAPELLER-ADLER, R., AND KRAEL, J., *Biochem. Z.*, **235**, 394 (1931)

60. ACKERMANN, D., TIMPE, O., AND POLLER, K., *Z. physiol. Chem.*, **183**, 1 (1929)
61. KEIL, W., *Z. physiol. Chem.*, **187**, 1 (1930)
62. LINNEWEH, W., AND LINNEWEH, F., *Z. physiol. Chem.*, **189**, 80 (1930)
63. ACKERMANN, D., AND HOPPE-SEYLER, F. A., *Z. physiol. Chem.*, **197**, 135 (1931)
64. KUTSCHER, F., ACKERMANN, D., AND FLÖSSNER, O., *Z. physiol. Chem.*, **199**, 273 (1931)
65. KUTSCHER, F., ACKERMANN, D., AND HOPPE-SEYLER, F. A., *Z. physiol. Chem.*, **199**, 277 (1931)
66. ZERVAS, L., AND BERGMANN, M., *Z. physiol. Chem.*, **201**, 208 (1931)
67. LINNEWEH, F., *Z. physiol. Chem.*, **200**, 115 (1931)
68. QUICK, A. J., *J. Biol. Chem.*, **92**, 65 (1931)
69. Cited from the literature by QUICK (68)
70. ABDERHALDEN, E., AND BUADZE, S., *Z. physiol. Chem.*, **200**, 87 (1931)
71. KAUFFMAN, F., AND MISLOWITZER, E., *Biochem. Z.*, **226**, 325 (1930)
72. EDLBACHER, S., AND KRAUS, J., *Z. physiol. Chem.*, **195**, 267 (1931)
73. KAUFFMAN, F., AND ENGEL, R., *Z. klin. Med.*, **114**, 405 (1930)
74. MISLOWITZER, E., AND KAUFFMAN, F., *Biochem. Z.*, **234**, 101 (1931)
75. EDLBACHER, S., AND KRAUS, J., *Z. physiol. Chem.*, **191**, 225 (1930)
76. FÜRTH, O., *Biochem. Z.*, **96**, 269 (1919)
77. KOESSLER, K. K., AND HANKE, M. T., *J. Biol. Chem.*, **59**, 803 (1924)
78. BEST, C. H., AND MCHENRY, E. W., *J. Physiol.*, **70**, 349 (1930)
79. MATSUOKA, Z., AND YOSHIMATSU, N., *Z. physiol. Chem.*, **143**, 206 (1925)
80. KOTAKE, Y., AND IWAO, J., *Z. physiol. Chem.*, **195**, 139 (1931)
81. KOTAKE, Y., AND KIYOKAWA, M., *Z. physiol. Chem.*, **195**, 147 (1931)
82. KOTAKE, Y., AND SHICHIRI, G., *Z. physiol. Chem.*, **195**, 152 (1931)
83. KOTAKE, Y., *Z. physiol. Chem.*, **195**, 158 (1931)
84. ELLINGER, A., AND MATSUOKA, Z., *Z. physiol. Chem.*, **109**, 259 (1920)
85. ICHIHARA, K., OTANI, S., AND TSUJIMOTO, J., *Z. physiol. Chem.*, **195**, 179 (1931)
86. KOTAKE, Y., AND ICHIHARA, K., *Z. physiol. Chem.*, **195**, 171 (1931)
87. TANI, Y., *Mitt. med. Ges. Osaka*, **24**, 1457 (1925). Cited by Kotake and Sakata (88)
88. KOTAKE, Y., AND SAKATA, H., *Z. physiol. Chem.*, **195**, 184 (1931)
89. BERG, C. P., ROSE, W. C., AND MARVEL, C. S., *J. Biol. Chem.*, **85**, 219 (1930)
90. BERG, C. P., ROSE, W. C., AND MARVEL, C. S., *J. Biol. Chem.*, **85**, 207 (1930)
91. BERG, C. P., *J. Biol. Chem.*, **91**, 513 (1931)
92. ICHIHARA, K., AND IWAKURA, N., *Z. physiol. Chem.*, **195**, 202 (1931)
93. JACKSON, R. W., *J. Biol. Chem.*, **73**, 523 (1927)
94. SHAMBAUGH, N. F., LEWIS, H. B., AND TOURTELLOTTE, D., *J. Biol. Chem.*, **92**, 499 (1931)
95. REINWEIN, H., *Deut. Arch. klin. Med.*, **170**, 327 (1931)
96. SACHS, P., *Deut. Arch. klin. Med.*, **170**, 344 (1931)
97. FOSTER, G. L., AND GUTMAN, A. B., *J. Biol. Chem.*, **87**, 289 (1930)
98. SCULL, C. W., AND ROSE, W. C., *J. Biol. Chem.*, **89**, 109 (1930)

99. KIECH, V. C., LUCK, J. M., AND SMITH, A. E., *J. Biol. Chem.,* 90, 677 (1931)
100. WILSON, R. H., AND LEWIS, H. B., *J. Biol. Chem.,* 85, 559 (1930)
101. GREISHEIMER, E. M., AND ARNY, F. P., *Proc. Soc. Exptl. Biol. Med.,* 28, 894 (1931)
102. LUNDSGAARD, E., *Biochem. Z.,* 217, 125, 147 (1930)
103. POLLAK, L., *Biochem. Z.,* 127, 120 (1922)
104. NORD, F. F., *Acta med. Skand.,* 65, 1, 61 (1926) ; 70, 277 (1929)
105. COSTA, A., AND BARONE, V. G., *Boll. soc. ital. biol. sper.,* 6, 21 (1931)
106. SURE, B., *J. Biol. Chem.,* 59, 577 (1924)
107. ADELINE, M., *Z. physiol. Chem.,* 199, 184 (1931)
108. ROSE, W. C., ELLIS, R. H., WINDUS, W., AND CATHERWOOD, F. L., *J. Biol. Chem.,* 92, lxvi (1931)
109. ROSE, W. C., *J. Biol. Chem.,* 94, 155 (1931)
110. ELLIS, R. H., AND ROSE, W. C., *J. Biol. Chem.,* 94, 167 (1931)
111. WINDUS, W., CATHERWOOD, F. L., AND ROSE, W. C., *J. Biol. Chem.,* 94, 173 (1931)
112. JONES, D. B., AND NELSON, E. M., *J. Biol. Chem.,* 91, 705 (1931)
113. ADAMS, E. T., *J. Biol. Chem.,* 67, xxi (1926)
114. CHAMBERS, W. H., AND LUSK, G., *J. Biol. Chem.,* 85, 611 (1930)
115. AUBEL, E., *Biochem. Z.,* 225, 81 (1930)
116. BORSOOK, H., AND WINEGARDEN, H. M., *Proc. Natl. Acad. Sci.,* 17, 75 (1931)
117. LUSK, G., *J. Nutrition,* 3, 519 (1931)
118. GRAFE, E., *Deut. Arch. klin. Med.,* 118, 1 (1916)
119. RAPPORT, D. AND BEARD, H. H., *J. Biol. Chem.,* 73, 299 (1927) ; 80, 413 (1928)
120. TERROINE, E. F., TRAUTMANN, S., BONNET, R., AND JACQUOT, R., *Bull. soc. chim. biol.,* 7, 351 (1925)
121. TERROINE, E. F., AND BONNET, R., *Bull. soc. chim. biol.,* 8, 976 (1926)
122. LUSK, G., *J. Biol. Chem.,* 13, 155 (1912)
123. AUB, J. C., EVERETT, M. R., AND FINE, J., *Am. J. Physiol.,* 79, 559 (1926)
124. LUNDSGAARD, E., *Skand. Arch. Physiol.,* 62, 223, 243 (1931)
125. LEWIS, H. B., DUNN, M. S., AND DOISY, E. A., *J. Biol. Chem.,* 36, 9 (1918)
126. JOHNSTON, M. W., AND LEWIS, H. B., *J. Biol. Chem.,* 78, 67 (1928)
127. WILHELMJ, C. M., BOLLMAN, J. L., AND MANN, F. C., *Am. J. Physiol.,* 87, 497 (1928)
128. DOCK, W., *Am. J. Physiol.,* 97, 117 (1931)
129. TERROINE, E. F., BONNET, R., AND ZAGAMI, V., *Bull. soc. chim. biol.,* 13, 326 (1931)
130. ABRAMSON, H. A., EGGLETON, G., AND EGGLETON, P., *J. Biol. Chem.,* 75, 763 (1927)
131. MARTIN, E. G., FIELD, J., II, AND HALL, V. E., *Am. J. Physiol.,* 88, 407 (1929)
132. ZAGAMI, V. M., *Bull. soc. chim. biol.,* 13, 343, 354 (1931)
133. KUTHY, A. VON, *Arch. ges. Physiol.,* 225, 567 (1931)
134. VÖLKER, H., *Z. ges. exptl. Med.,* 75, 487 (1931)

135. MERING, J. VON, AND ZUNTZ, N., *Arch. ges. Physiol.,* 15, 634 (1877)
136. ZUNTZ, N., *Med. Klin.,* 1, 351 (1910)
137. WISHART, G. M., *J. Physiol.,* 65, 243 (1928)
138. WILHELMJ, C. M., AND BOLLMAN, J. L., *J. Biol. Chem.,* 77, 127 (1928)
139. WILHELMJ, C. M., AND MANN, F. C., *Am. J. Physiol.,* 93, 69 (1930)
140. RALLI, E. P., CANZANELLI, A., AND RAPPORT, D., *Am. J. Physiol.,* 96, 331 (1931)
141. LUSK, G., *J. Biol. Chem.,* 20, 555 (1915)
142. CSONKA, F., *J. Biol. Chem.,* 20, 539 (1915)
143. WILHELMJ, C. M., AND MANN, F. C., *Am. J. Physiol.,* 93, 258 (1930)
144. WILHELMJ, C. M., BOLLMAN, J. L., AND MANN, F. C., *Am. J. Physiol.,* 98, 1 (1931)
145. RAPPORT, D., AND KATZ, L. N., *Am. J. Physiol.,* 80, 185 (1927)
146. BORNSTEIN, A., AND ROESE, H. F., *Arch. ges. Physiol.,* 223, 498 (1930)
147. STAUB, H., *Arch. exptl. Path. Pharmakol.,* 162, 433 (1931)
148. MANSFELD, G., AND HORN, Z., *Biochem. Z.,* 234, 257 (1931)
149. MEYERHOF, O., LOHMANN, K., AND MEIER, R., *Biochem. Z.,* 157, 459 (1925)
150. REINWEIN, H., *Deut. Arch. klin. Med.,* 160, 278 (1928)
151. KISCH, B., *Biochem. Z.,* 238, 351 (1931)
152. GRASSHEIM, K., AND WITTKOWER, E., *Deut. med. Wochschr.,* 57, 141 (1931)

THE BIOCHEMICAL LABORATORY
STANFORD UNIVERSITY
CALIFORNIA

NUTRITION*

By Arthur H. Smith

Department of Physiological Chemistry
Yale University

Nutritional Anemia

Research in nutrition during the past year has been characterized by the large interest in nutritional anemia. Noted by Abderhalden at the beginning of the century, the question of the anemia following exclusive feeding with milk was reopened by Hart and his co-workers in 1925. The intense and widespread interest in this theme at the present time is probably due to the ready availability of the rat for experimental purposes and its susceptibility to the disease, together with a desire to explain, if possible, the disagreements which have arisen between certain of the investigators in this field relative to the effective methods of bringing about a remission of the anemia. At the end of 1930 disputed evidence had been recorded that iron alone would not cure the anemia but that copper was an effective supplement to iron; that manganese as well as copper served as an effective supplement to iron; that several other metals were as efficacious as copper and manganese; and that iron alone produced a remission of the anemia. Furthermore, there was evidence that investigation yielding a given result in certain laboratories could not be invariably duplicated under apparently similar conditions when carried on elsewhere. Now, at the end of 1931, the divergence of opinion and lack of reproducibility of experimental results in different laboratories is more evident than ever. Obviously there is needed a careful scrutiny of experimental details and a unification of procedure before the mass of apparently conflicting evidence can be correctly interpreted.

The influence of manganese as a supplement to iron in curing nutritional anemia has received considerable attention by investigators during the past year. Krauss (1) at the Ohio Experiment Station obtained copper sulfate, manganese chloride, and ferric chloride from the Wisconsin laboratories, where manganese had failed to give positive results, and manganous chloride and ferric chloride from the Kansas laboratories, where manganese was first reported to act as an

* Received January 11, 1932.

effective supplement to iron. It was found that, whereas iron from Kansas with copper from Ohio, as well as iron plus copper, both from Wisconsin, produced striking remissions of the anemia in the rat, manganese alone at 0.1 mg. per diem level or with 0.05 mg. of copper or with 0.5 mg. of iron, failed to influence the hemoglobin content of the blood to an appreciable degree. Results of an essentially similar nature were reported by Keil and Nelson (2) with 0.1 mg. of manganese added to 0.5 mg. of iron. Graded levels of manganese from 0.1 to 0.01 mg. daily in addition to different daily dosages of iron from 0.1 mg. to 0.5 mg. failed to elicit an increase in hemoglobin in anemic rats according to Mitchell and Miller (3). In striking contrast to the foregoing conclusions are those of Myers and Beard (4) in Cleveland, who observed that 0.1 mg. of manganese given as a daily supplement to various quantities of iron produced striking increases in both pigment and erythrocytes in less than three weeks. These investigators, like Mitchell and Miller (3), varied the amounts of iron with which the supplements were added. Furthermore they point out the fact that the response in red-cell production is usually more rapid than that of hemoglobin and emphasize the necessity of making determinations of both values.

The ability of other metals to stimulate hemopoiesis has also been investigated. Continuing their earlier work along this line, Myers and Beard (4) have demonstrated that when copper, nickel, germanium, arsenic, titanium, zinc, rubidium, chromium, vanadium, selenium, and mercury are given in certain favorable daily doses as a supplement to 0.5 mg. of iron, hemoglobin regeneration occurred in two to three weeks and erythrocytes returned to the normal level in a slightly shorter interval of time. According to Myers and Beard (4) there is a distinctly optimal concentration of the supplementary metals for given daily amounts of iron and the order of efficacy of the supplements varies with the iron concentration. In contrast to these favorable results are those of Keil and Nelson (2), who used the same series of metals (except rubidium and selenium) as supplements to iron in the form of ferric chloride; in these studies there was a failure of hemoglobin regeneration. Myers, Beard, and Barnes (5) also reported a marked increase of red cells and hemoglobin in adult normal rats when cobalt or vanadium was added to the stock diet and when germanium and iron were added to a whole milk ration.

That copper is specific as a supplement to iron in promoting a remission of nutritional anemia seems apparent from several studies which have reassessed this question during the past year. Of the several elements used by Keil and Nelson (2) copper was the only one to give unequivocal regeneration of hemoglobin. Underhill, Orten, and Lewis (6) investigated the curative effect on milk anemia of iron alone and of iron supplemented by copper, manganese, cobalt, nickel, and zinc, respectively, and came to the conclusion that of these the only potent combination is that of iron and copper. It should be noted, however, that the quantities of manganese, nickel, and zinc employed were much greater than those used by Myers and Beard. A contribution of considerable interest is that of McGhee (7) who observed a favorable response in hemoglobin regeneration when metallic copper and iron were suspended for twelve hours in the milk used as a ration. Copper alone was somewhat effective, but copper and iron proved most potent. Favorable results were likewise obtained in secondary anemia in man with metallic copper and iron. Cunningham (8) has criticized the use of the exclusive milk diet in the study of nutritional anemia largely because of its low calorie value per unit of weight. He has devised a solid ration very low in iron. With this food the striking effect of copper in supplementing iron in the cure of anemia was likewise demonstrated. With a milk diet, neither iron, cobalt, nor manganese was effective.

Investigations of the curative effect of iron alone in nutritional anemia by Krauss, Keil and Nelson, and McGhee have shown again that, without supplementary additions, this metal does not bring about regeneration of hemoglobin in depleted animals (albino rats). Contrasted to these observations are those of Mitchell and Miller (3) in Michigan, who demonstrated a definite but slow response of hemoglobin production with 0.1, 0.25, and 0.5 mg. of iron in daily additions to the milk. Furthermore, the extensive study of Beard and Myers (9) in Cleveland indicates that both the pigment and the red cells are regenerated in six weeks with 0.25 mg. of iron daily; with 2.0 mg. of iron the time required for the remission of the disease can be cut to less than two weeks. These results were obtained with electrolytic iron, with the filtrate from the H_2S precipitate of that iron, and with iron obtained from Krauss and from Elvehjem, both of whom had failed to cure the anemia with iron alone. Iron alone also prevented the appearance of anemia when added to the milk which formed the ration (10). It would appear that the copper content of the milk used by Beard and Myers (9) was somewhat high; no analysis is given for the sample collected in glass. The work of

McGhee (7) indicates that sufficient copper can be dissolved from the sheet metal to bring about a cure of anemia.

The cure of nutritional anemia has been reported with substances other than pure salts of metals. According to Drabkin and Miller (11), 100 mg. daily of arginine hydrochloride and 70 mg. of glutamic acid are very effective supplements to 0.2 mg. of iron, which in these studies was ineffective when fed alone in the milk. Tryptophane, sodium hydrogen aspartate, and pyrrolidonecarboxylic acid produced a temporary increase in hemoglobin, while alanine, alanine hydrochloride, histidine dihydrochloride, and hydrochloric acid alone were without influence on the anemia. Further experiments by Drabkin and Miller (12) indicated that succinic acid and succinimide are mildly effective, that leucine, cystine, glycine, α amino valeric acid, and glutaric acid are without effect and that sodium glutamate not only cures the anemia but, even in the absence of iron, is a prophylactic against its onset. All of the amino acid preparations except the histidine dihydrochloride were examined for copper, and none was found. Elvehjem, Steenbock, and Hart (13) repeated the experiments with both glutamic acid and the hydrochloride, feeding the former compound at a level of 70 mg. and the latter at 100 mg., both supplementing 0.5 gm. of iron daily in the milk ration. The amino acids failed to stimulate an accelerated production of hemoglobin in the anemic animals and the authors suggest the possibility that either the preparations found effective by Drabkin and Miller (11) contained copper or the experimental animals possessed unusual copper reserves.

Continuing the studies with phenylhydrazine anemia in dogs, Okagawa and Tatsui (14) observed that the usual accelerated recovery following subcutaneous injections of tryptophane was not obtained after splenectomy. The recovery from experimental anemia in guinea pigs is more rapid after subcutaneous injections of α methyltryptophane than with tryptophane (15). That this is independent of the ordinary metabolism of tryptophane is indicated by the fact that α methyltryptophane cannot compensate for a lack of tryptophane in the diet. According to Foster (16) ultraviolet light produces a slight but definite increase in hemoglobin, erythrocyte count, size of the cells, and saturation with pigment. It is not stated whether or not iron was added to the milk; furthermore, the degree of anemia initially produced was not as severe as has been customary in this type of study. Both carbon-arc and mercury-vapor irradiation brought about an increased rate of regeneration of pigment and red cells in acetylphenylhydrazine anemia, whereas in the anemia following severe hemorrhage similar treatment with radiant energy produced a marked response in erythrocytes and reticulocytes without altering the hemoglobin concentration (18).

Hemopoiesis during various vitamin deficiencies has received attention. Sure, Kik, and Smith (19) observed the development of anemia in rats consuming a diet lacking vitamin G but otherwise so constituted as to eliminate the probability of mineral deficiency. Removal of vitamins A or D from the ration, however, was not followed by anemia (20, 21).

Of considerable interest are the studies of Cunningham (8), who injected iron, hematoporphyrin, and protoporphyrin subcutaneously into rats exhibiting milk anemia. No demonstrable influence on hemoglobin concentration was produced with these compounds, although with similar technique iron and copper were highly effective. Food materials which have been found efficacious in curing experimental milk anemia doubtless owe their value in this regard largely to the character of the inorganic residue. Sheets and Frazier (22) have demonstrated a favorable effect of sorghum and sugar-cane syrup. In a study of the curative value of oysters in nutritional anemia in rats, Levine, Remington, and Culp (23) showed that 0.56 gm. of dried oyster increased the hemoglobin to the normal level in from two to three weeks. The hydrochloric acid extract of the oyster ash and an artificial mixture of copper, iron, and manganese containing the same quantities of the elements as the dried oyster gave similar results. The authors concluded that metals other than copper and manganese contained in the oyster are not effective supplements to iron in milk anemia.

The very recent work on nutritional anemia has been carried out in large part on rats. It is of interest to note the applications of the results obtained to other types of anemia and to other species of animals. Mendenhall (24) has reported that certain secondary anemias in children are helped by the use of copper. A report by Josephs (25) indicates an accelerating effect of copper and iron upon the rise in hemoglobin in premature infants and in those with secondary anemia. Copper apparently exerted little effect in initiating a reticulocyte response. On the contrary, with a varied diet containing added iron Parsons (26) noted little improvement with copper. Lewis (27) reported a better response with iron and copper than with iron alone. Both the adjuvants were given along with a varied diet. It appears that the clinical observations during the past year have added little convincing evidence that the therapy which has proved effective in experimental nutritional anemia can also be applied with similar results to human subjects. However, an application of iron-copper therapy which promises to be of considerable economic importance has been reported by Neal, Becker, and Shealy (28). Farm animals reared on certain soils in Florida suffer from a nutritional anemia not of milk origin but rather arising from the low iron and copper in the local vegetation. Growth is retarded, reproduction is impaired, and the mortality rate is high in untreated animals. Treatment with ferric ammonium citrate and copper sulfate results in a marked increase in hemoglobin, while a salt lick containing iron and copper is an effective preventive agent. Iron alone or with the amount of copper in reagents of "technical" grade is inadequate.

The physiology of the cure of nutritional anemia by the various methods has been discussed, and certain pertinent observations have been made. Mitchell and Miller (29) have described an anemia occurring normally in female rats which develops before parturition, progresses for two or three days after the birth of the young, and then slowly disappears. None of the measures found effective in nutritional anemia had an influence in preventing this phenomenon. On the basis of analyses for iron made on the spleen of rats given iron alone, copper alone, and both elements together, Cook and Spilles (30) conclude that the essential transformation of material in the relief of nutritional anemia with copper is the change of hemosiderin in the spleen to a form of iron utilizable for building hemoglobin. Cunningham (8) has observed that the proportion of organic to total iron in the liver of animals with milk anemia is increased by giving copper. The possibility is suggested that under these conditions there occurs a preliminary formation of copper porphyrin with the subsequent replacement of copper by iron. According to Beard, Baker, and Myers (31) nutritional anemia is characterized by moderately augmented production of reticulocytes but a failure of these to change to erythrocytes. Iron alone stimulates reticulocytosis but changes the reticulocytes to mature red cells very slowly. These authors state that other elements which were found effective in supplementing iron act by accelerating the maturation of the red cells. From a review of the available evidence it appears that the final explanation of the cure of nutritional anemia awaits the establishment of facts upon which investigators at large can agree.

METALS IN NUTRITION

The allegedly unique part played by certain metallic elements—notably iron, copper, and manganese—has doubtless been the factor promoting renewed interest in the metabolism of these substances. Miller and Forbes (32) observed that beef muscle, beef liver, beef kidney, and eggs were superior when fed as the sole source of iron in the diet, whereas milk was poor in this respect. The experimental rations were limited to sodium chloride and calcium carbonate for the added inorganic constituents, which fact might raise doubt as to their adequacy other than in iron. The presence of one hundred times the "normal" (0.05 mg. daily) amount of copper in the diet is not detrimental to growth of young rats nor toxic to adults according to Cunningham (8). In these studies reproduction was not disturbed by high levels of copper acetate (7.5 mg. daily) but was adversely influenced by the same dosage of verdigris.

The peculiarities of storage of iron in the newborn have been discussed by Lintzel and Radeff (33). Large stores of this element were found in the liver of newborn rabbits, while much less occurred in rats, dogs, hogs, and cattle. Guinea pigs, cats, and goats appeared to have no iron reserve in this organ. In spite of variations in accumulation of iron during the suckling period, all the species examined had approximately the same store of iron at the end of this time. Whereas the iron of suckling rats could be diminished by giving the mother a ration poor in iron, no increased storage occurred in the young of mothers given excessive amounts of iron.

The nutritive importance of manganese has received considerable attention during the past year. Richards (34) had indicated its significance in reproduction of both plants and animals. Studies carried out by McCollum and Orent (35, 36) showed that elimination of manganese from an otherwise adequate ration was followed by testicular degeneration in the male rats employed. In the females the oestrus cycle was not disturbed, but there was deficient lactation. No manganese was found in the organs of rats reared on a manganese-free ration. Skinner, Peterson, and Steenbock (37) have followed the content, loci of accumulation, and paths of excretion of manganese in rats under various conditions. The relative concentration of this element is highest at birth, though the total content increases progressively with age. The liver, muscle, bones, and skin are the outstanding depots and the amount stored can be increased by feeding manganese. Apparently the greater portion of the manganese excreted passes out by way of the gut. Studies with mice given only milk with iron and copper indicated better growth in the females when manganese was added [Kemmerer, Elvehjem, and Hart (38)]. Ovulation, ordinarily defective on a diet of milk, copper, and iron, was normal when 0.01 mg. of manganese was added daily.

As is to be expected, the recent suggestions of the potency of these mineral elements in the nutrition of experimental animals have led to new analyses of food materials used for human consumption. The content of iron, copper, and manganese in serving portions of some of the common foods has been determined by Hodges and Peterson (39). It was calculated that with rather well-planned menus the average daily intake of copper was 2.26 mg., of manganese 2.39 mg., and of iron, 15.44 mg. The largest proportion of manganese and copper in these diets was furnished by the cereals, whereas iron was supplied largely by vegetables and cereals. In some of the diets where milk was emphasized a large part of the iron was provided by this food material. Peterson and Skinner (40) have analyzed a large number of food materials for manganese. Sea foods, dairy products, and poultry products are poorest in this element, whereas nuts, cereals, and dried legume seeds are richest.

NUTRITION DURING THE REPRODUCTIVE CYCLE

The production of a new individual in the mammal raises many questions of great significance from the point of view of physiology; not the least of these arises from the consideration of the nutrition both of the fetus and of the maternal organism. The fetus is essentially a parasite and, unless the food supply to the mother is adequate, will draw upon her tissues for its sustenance. The quantity as well as quality of the ration, therefore, is important.

The question of augmented food intake by women in the various stages of the reproductive cycle has been considered in a report by Shukers, Macy, Donelson, Nims, and Hunscher (41). Three subjects were studied; they had been under observation repeatedly and their physiological processes were known to be adequate for the demands of reproduction. The total energy, protein, carbohydrate, fat, phosphorus, and calcium were determined in the food during pregnancy, lactation, and in post-reproductive rest. The demand for food materials was not accentuated by pregnancy; actually the food consumption tended to decrease toward the end of pregnancy. The requirements of lactation, however, resulted in a marked increase in food consumption over that during pregnancy; in these studies the average values for percentage increase of the various food materials were as follows: calories, 60; protein, 54; fat, 57; carbohydrate, 68; calcium, 77; and phosphorus, 73.

Sandiford, Wheeler, and Boothby (42) have pointed out that with an adequate diet pregnancy does not result in a loss to the maternal organism in so far as nitrogen is concerned; on the contrary, there may be a storage of nitrogen in addition to that of the developing fetus.

The necessity for an augmented food supply especially during lactation is emphasized in a study on dogs by Daggs (43). At the beginning of the ninth week of pregnancy the food was increased 20 per cent over the maintenance requirement; at parturition, 25 per cent; beginning second week of lactation, 50 per cent; third week of lactation, 75 per cent; and at the start of the fourth week of lactation, 100 per cent. Under these conditions there was a positive nitrogen balance at the ninth week of pregnancy, third week of lactation, and fifth week of lactation, though as the period of milk production progressed the magnitude of the balance decreased.

The storage and withdrawal of material in the maternal organism during pregnancy and lactation has received considerable attention at the hands of investigators in animal husbandry and latterly in human beings. Studying one case intensively, Macy, Donelson, Long, Graham, Sweeney, and Shaw (44) observed a storage of calcium, phosphorus, and nitrogen during the seventh and eighth months of pregnancy. The chemical analysis of the blood and urine showed no significant deviation from the normal values. Considering with these data the fact that food intake during this period changes relatively little, the conception that pregnancy under favorable nutritive conditions represents a net gain to the mother is given further weight. The situation is changed, however, once a vigorous milk flow occurs after parturition. The loss of relatively large quantities of calcium and phosphorus through the milk presents a serious problem to the maternal organism, especially as, thus far, those devices found efficacious in promoting better utilization of calcium and phosphorus under ordinary circumstances do not appear to bring about a favorable balance of these mineral elements during vigorous lactation. This timely theme has received the renewed attention of Donelson, Nims, Hunscher, and Macy (45), who investigated the calcium and phosphorus balances in three women over intervals covering the latter part of a lactation period and at three and twelve months after cessation of milk flow. The subjects produced relatively large volumes of milk (from 932 cc. to 3448 cc. daily) at the time of the study, and there was observed a loss of calcium in spite of an abundant intake in particularly favorable forms. The calcium balance had been positive during pregnancy and late in the preceding period of lactation. Not only was the heightened milk production reflected in the loss of this element during lactation, but the negative balance continued for relatively long periods after the flow of milk had ceased. In these studies the phosphorus balance was positive at all times.

During the past year further studies have been made upon the influence of diet upon reproduction, lactation, and subsequent growth. The interest in the anemia produced on a milk diet led to a reinvestigation of reproduction under these conditions by Waddell, Steenbock, and Hart (46). Milk supplemented either with copper alone or with iron and copper failed to serve as a satisfactory ration, both reproduction and lactation being below normal. Satisfactory growth likewise was not obtained. It was observed that a delayed sexual maturity and slow ovulation rhythm in the females was in part responsible for the poor reproduction. That the male is likewise affected by the milk diet was shown by Waddell (47). Disappearance of the germinal epithelium, loss in testicular tissue, and edema were observed after twenty-three to twenty-five weeks on a milk, iron, and copper ration. It was suggested in this paper that part of the difficulty in lactation and in growth of young arises from the inability to obtain sufficient energy from the milk.

Mitchell and Miller (48) studied the influence of variations in the acid-base balance of adequate rations upon the reproduction and growth of the rat. Acidity equivalent to 19.4 cc. of normal acid and alkalinities to 20.6 cc. normal alkali per 100 grams of dry food had no effect on reproduction, growth, or mineralization of the bones. In this connection might be mentioned the work of Kugelmass and Greenwald (49), who set out to suit the buffer value of the diet to the hydrogen-ion concentration of the gastric juice. They found that cereals, fruits, and vegetables have a low buffer action, while eggs, meat, and milk are high in this respect. Apparently, also, cooking resulted in a decrease in buffer value.

That the character of dietary protein may exert considerable influence upon the reproductive cycle is apparent from the study of

Daggs (43) carried out on dogs. Four sources of protein—muscle meat, liver, whole egg, and kidney—were employed in rations otherwise adequate. The number of young born, growth of the young, maternal nitrogen balance, blood and urine analysis of the mother, and the volume and analysis of the milk were determined. No young were born on the kidney diet. It appears that a more favorable nitrogen balance was obtained with liver as the protein of the diet than with egg or muscle meat. Liver, likewise, favored a larger quantity of milk with a higher percentage of fat than either of the other sources of protein. Furthermore the pups receiving milk from the mother on the liver diet grew definitely faster than did those on the egg and muscle meat experiments. These studies corroborate the earlier ones of Wilkinson and Nelson (50), who observed poor milk production on diets containing 10 and 20 per cent of soy beans together with 18 per cent casein. Liver added to this ration to the extent of 25 and 30 per cent rendered it satisfactory for lactation and superior growth. This favorable action of liver was destroyed by heating to 120°C. It appears from the foregoing observations that liver owes its favorable influence on lactation to some constituent other than protein.

In a study of the mechanism of milk production Gowan and Tobey (51) showed that during inanition in cows there occurs a rapid decrease in the quantity of milk produced. The relative content of solids is increased, the percentage of ash and calcium is augmented and the fat percentage increases. There is a moderate decrease in the lactose but the nitrogen is unchanged. The decrease in lactose in the milk is parallel to the diminution in blood sugar both in starvation and after insulin. It appears that with a diminution in lactose the osmotic pressure of the milk is maintained at the same value as that of the blood by an elevation of the concentration of inorganic salts. These studies are interpreted as additional evidence that the characteristic carbohydrate of milk has its origin in the blood sugar.

Although milk is a true secretion it has repeatedly been shown that, with experimental animals, certain changes in the maternal ration are followed by alteration in the quality and quantity of milk produced. The influence of feeding menhaden fish oil to lactating cows has been investigated by Brown and Sutton (52). After this adjustment of the ration had been in effect two weeks it was observed that the daily quantity of milk produced fell from 17 pounds to 10.4 pounds and that there was a concomitant decrease in the percentage of butter fat. Furthermore certain of the characteristic fatty acids of the fish oil appeared in the milk fat. Upon a return to the usual ration without the menhaden oil the concentration of fat returned to the normal value before the yield of milk did.

Variation in composition of different portions of milk withdrawn at a single milking is a well-recognized phenomenon in dairy practice. In a recent investigation by Macy, Nims, Brown, and Hunscher (53) the same observation was made in human subjects. Three women producing somewhat more than two liters of milk per diem were studied. The milk was withdrawn every four hours and the first, middle, and last portions analyzed separately. Under these conditions there was a tendency for the fat, total protein, total solids, casein-nitrogen, and phosphorus to increase from the first to the last milking.

Protein in Nutrition

One of the outstanding advantages in the use of the rat as an experimental animal is the short life cycle; problems involving not only reproduction but also "long distance" effects of nutritional deficiencies through several generations can be carried out with ordinary laboratory facilities. During the past year Slonaker (54) has reported upon a number of effects on the organism resulting from various levels of dietary protein. The experiments extended over the life span of the rats used and, where reproduction was involved, several generations were studied. The diets consisted of mixtures of so-called purified food substances combined with salts and ground grains and were satisfactory in their qualitative makeup. The protein contents of the various rations were 10.3 per cent, 14.2 per cent, 18.2 per cent, 22.2 per cent, and 26.3 per cent, respectively, and were adjusted mainly through the use of meat scrap. The groups were large enough to permit statistical evaluation. The most rapid growth was obtained in the individuals consuming the ration con taining 14.2 per cent protein, although the females grew well on the 18.2 per cent food. During the first 150 days of life the greatest amount of food was consumed by the group on the lowest-protein ration, although the animals given the diet with 26.3 per cent protein gained most rapidly during the first 120 days. When put into revolving cages the rats with the diet poorest in protein began to run sooner than the rest, but those consuming the rations containing 14.2 and 18.2 per cent protein showed the greatest spontaneous activity throughout the experiment. The animals on the 14.2 per cent food had the longest life span and those given the diet poorest in protein died earliest.

Slonaker (54) also demonstrated that a moderate concentration of dietary protein produced larger body weights than either extreme of protein content. The 14.2 per cent ration was correlated with the largest per cent of fertile males and females, while sterility was most marked on the diet with the greatest protein content. The same correlation held for the span of reproductive activity. The average number of litters and average number of young born per pair was greatest on the 14.2 per cent diet and least on the highest protein food. A larger number of young, which represented a greater percentage of young born, was reared on the ration with 14.2 per cent protein than on the other diets. The mother rats lost less weight while nursing, and the quantity and quality of the milk improved with increasing amounts of protein in the ration. No correlation was demonstrable between percentage of protein in the ration and the pulmonary infection which was the most frequent cause of death. This significant group of studies illustrates very well the wide possibilities of nutritional research with small animals, and the results should prove of considerable practical value.

The foregoing observations on the favorable growth response of young rats to moderately elevated concentrations of dietary protein were confirmed by Smith and Moïse (55) with rats after unilateral nephrectomy. These authors pointed out that maintenance, growth, and general well-being is obtained in animals (rats) of widely differing ages by rations containing either 12 or 38 per cent of the calories as protein. When 67 per cent of the energy was derived from protein, very young rats made moderately good growth, whereas maintenance and growth of older animals was not favored by this high concentration of protein.

The influence of the level of protein in the food upon the enlargement of the kidney has received further attention during the past year. Francis, Smith, and Moïse (56) investigated the alleged retarding action of vitamins B and G upon renal enlargement with protein-rich rations. Using both intact rats and others in which unilateral nephrectomy intensified the physiological strain on the remaining kidney, they concluded that the increase in size of the kidney under these conditions was neither lessened nor prevented by vitamin B, vitamin G, or any combination of these factors. The question of the ability of urea to stimulate increase in size of the kidney was reopened by MacKay, MacKay, and Addis (57), who employed as a criterion values obtained with an equation relating weight of kidney to dietary nitrogen. Using various combinations of casein and urea, they observed that the kidneys were too small if all the nitrogen was calculated as protein but too large for the actual amount of protein nitrogen in the ration. They therefore concluded that urea does cause the kidney to enlarge to some extent.

The controversy over the nephropathic action of protein has not been settled. Newburgh and Johnston (58) reported that the ease of producing renal injury and its severity depends on the character of the nitrogenous compounds in the diet. Liver apparently is unusually toxic, 40 per cent of the dried tissue in the ration producing injury to the kidney of rats. As little as 10 per cent of sodium nucleate caused noticeable lesions, while 20 per cent given over a period of eight months caused granular kidneys.

NUTRITION AND GROWTH

A recent contribution to the literature on the influence of nutrition on growth is that of Jackson and Smith (59). They studied the effect of restriction of water intake on the development of young rats. As a result of this deficiency, growth was arrested and food consumption fell off. Control animals given water *ad libitum* but limited in food to that amount eaten by the experimental rats gained a subnormal amount in body weight; the conclusion was drawn that limitation of water results in a retardation specific for this deficiency. Accompanying the desiccation there was an increase in fresh weight of some of the organs, a decrease in others, while the brain, stomach, and muscle remained unchanged. All the tissues lost water, the skin most, and the brain least.

A summary of certain phenomena correlated with retarded growth has been published by Smith (60). In it emphasis is placed on the point of view that a stunted animal is like neither a normal individual of the same size nor one of the same age when appearance, changes in structure, or behavior are used as criteria for comparison.

Bing and Mendel (61) demonstrated a striking correlation between food consumption and water intake in mice. Under ordinary conditions with an air-dried stock diet, 1.3 cc. of water per gram of food was drunk. This relation was maintained fairly uniformly under changed conditions of metabolism and even when the ration was qualitatively deficient. On the other hand, deprivation of water resulted in complete anorexia.

A statistical study of reproduction in rats as affected by the diet of the mother was made by Wan and Wu (62). The litters from females given an omnivorous ration were larger than those from mothers consuming a vegetarian diet and the individual young were heavier. It was also shown (63) by the use of the more satisfactory omnivorous ration and the poorer vegetarian food that, for satisfactory growth, favorable nutrition during lactation is more important than later in the life of the individual.

The importance of factors other than a deficiency in energy in rations effective in bringing about loss of weight in the obese has been investigated by Keeton, MacKenzie, Olson, and Pickens (64). Hogs were used as experimental animals and adjustments in the carbohydrate, protein, fat, and water were made in the rations. Little difference in the rate at which weight was lost was observed in the various experiments, the loss being parallel in each case to the calorie deficiency.

A searching critique of current methods of biological assay in nutrition was published by Palmer and Kennedy (65) early in 1931. On the basis of their own studies and of a review of the literature, these investigators point out that not only must the food consumption be controlled in experiments of this type but also an index of the utilization of the food by the experimental animal should be known. At present it appears that this ideal situation is not attainable. Mitchell (66) has presented a summary of the elements constituting a good nutrition experiment.

Nutrition and Pernicious Anemia

The etiology of pernicious anemia has been the subject of continued study by both physiologists and biochemists during the past year. That a disturbance of nutritional functions is an important causative factor is the opinion of Castle, Heath, Strauss, and Townsend (67). They point out that pernicious anemia is a deficiency disease resulting most obviously from a hypofunction of the bone marrow, which in turn occurs because there is a lack of some essential food substance due to a gastrointestinal disturbance. The characteristic achlorhydria is given considerable attention by Moschcowitz (68), who states that it is primary and not a result of the disease. On the other hand, pernicious anemia does not invariably follow the development of achlorhydria. West and Howe (69) indicate that the remission of pernicious anemia by liver and liver extracts is due to relatively simple organic compounds derived from these therapeutic substances. The suggestion is made that the active material either permits the union of existing pyrrole groups with iron or actually supplies some of the missing necessary pyrrole groups. These views receive support from the experiments of Dakin and West (70) in which a tribasic acid was obtained from the hydrolysis products of liver extract. This levorotatory acid was changed to a soluble monobasic pyrrolecarboxylic acid by heating with baryta at 120–130°C. In relatively large doses (800 mg.) the tribasic acid produced a mild reticulocyte response in a patient with pernicious anemia (69). However, the earlier statements as to the clinical efficacy of another acid obtained from liver, of peptide or diketopiperazine nature, yielding on hydrolysis α-hydroxyglutamic acid and γ-hydroxyproline (71) are erroneous according to a late report of West and Howe (72).

The therapeutic value of gastric mucosa has received considerable additional comment during the past year. Wilkinson (73) believes that hog stomach is superior to liver in the treatment of pernicious anemia. That intestinal mucosa is without effect is the conclusion of both Gutzeit and Herrmann (74) and Henning and Brugsch (75). However, the former investigators found that the mucous membrane of the fundus was active, whereas the best response was obtained by the latter authors with the mucosa of the antrum. The favorable action is not obtained with gastric muscle; the effective substance apparently is liberated from the mucosa by the action of tissue enzymes (76). This observation receives further support from the studies of Kandel (77), who obtained favorable results with ventriculin[1] in the absence of meat in the diet.

LITERATURE CITED

1. KRAUSS, W. E., *J. Biol. Chem.*, **90**, 267 (1931)
2. KEIL, H. L., AND NELSON, V. E., *J. Biol. Chem.*, **93**, 49 (1931)
3. MITCHELL, H. S., AND MILLER, L., *J. Biol. Chem.*, **92**, 421 (1931)
4. MYERS, V. C., AND BEARD, H. H., *J. Biol. Chem.*, **94**, 89 (1931)
5. MYERS, V. C., BEARD, H. H., AND BARNES, B. O., *J. Biol. Chem.*, **94**, 117 (1931)
6. UNDERHILL, F. A., ORTEN, J. M., AND LEWIS, R. C., *J. Biol. Chem.*, **91**, 13 (1931)
7. McGHEE, J. L., *Science*, **73**, 347 (1931)

[1] Ventriculin is desiccated whole hog stomach (78).

8. CUNNINGHAM, I. J., *Biochem. J.*, **25**, 1267 (1931)
9. BEARD, H. H., AND MYERS, V. C. (*et al.*), *J. Biol. Chem.*, **94**, 71 (1931)
10. BEARD, H. H., RAFFERTY, C., AND MYERS, V. C., *J. Biol. Chem.*, **94**, 110 (1931)
11. DRABKIN, D. L., AND MILLER, H. K., *J. Biol. Chem.*, **90**, 531 (1931)
12. DRABKIN, D. L., AND MILLER, H. K., *J. Biol. Chem.*, **93**, 39 (1931)
13. ELVEHJEM, C. A., STEENBOCK, H., AND HART, E. B., *J. Biol. Chem.*, **93**, 197 (1931)
14. OKAGAWA, Y., AND TATSUI, M., *Z physiol. Chem.*, **195**, 192 (1931)
15. MATSUOKA, Z., AND NAKAO, T., *Z. physiol. Chem.*, **195**, 208 (1931)
16. FOSTER, P. C., *J. Nutrition*, **4**, 517 (1931)
17. MAYERSON, H. S., AND LAURENS, H., *J. Nutrition*, **4**, 351 (1931)
18. LAURENS, H., AND MAYERSON, H. S., *J. Nutrition*, **4**, 465 (1931)
19. SURE, B., KIK, M. C., AND SMITH, M. E., *Proc. Soc. Exptl. Biol. Med.*, **28**, 498 (1931)
20. SURE, B., KIK, M. C., AND WALKER, D. J., *Proc. Soc. Exptl. Biol. Med.*, **28**, 495 (1931)
21. SURE, B., AND KIK, M. C., *Proc. Soc. Exptl. Biol. Med.*, **28**, 496 (1931)
22. SHEETS, O., AND FRAZIER, E., *J. Home Econ.*, **23**, 273 (1931)
23. LEVINE, H., REMINGTON, R. E., AND CULP, F. B., *J. Nutrition*, **4**, 469 (1931)
24. MENDENHALL, D. R., *Wisconsin Sta. Bull.*, **75**, No. 420 (1931)
25. JOSEPHS, H., *Bull. Johns Hopkins Hosp.*, **49**, 246 (1931)
26. PARSONS, L. G., *J. Am. Med. Assoc.*, **97**, 973 (1931)
27. LEWIS, M. S., *J. Am. Med. Assoc.*, **96**, 1135 (1931)
28. NEAL, W. M., BECKER, R. B., AND SHEALY, A. L., *Science*, **74**, 418 (1931)
29. MITCHELL, H. S., AND MILLER, L., *Am. J. Physiol.*, **98**, 311 (1931)
30. COOK, S. F., AND SPILLES, N. M., *Am. J. Physiol.*, **98**, 626 (1931)
31. BEARD, H. H., BAKER, R. W., AND MYERS, V. C., *J. Biol. Chem.*, **94**, 123 (1931)
32. MILLER, R. C., AND FORBES, E. B., *J. Nutrition*, **4**, 483 (1931)
33. LINTZEL, W., AND RADEFF, T., *Arch. Tierernähr. Tierzucht*, **6**, 313 (1931)
34. RICHARDS, M. B., *Biochem. J.*, **24**, 1572 (1930)
35. McCOLLUM, E. V., AND ORENT, E., *J. Maryland Acad. Sci.*, **2**, 33 (1931)
36. ORENT, E. R., AND McCOLLUM, E. V., *J. Biol. Chem.*, **92**, 651 (1931)
37. SKINNER, J. T., PETERSON, W. H., AND STEENBOCK, H., *J. Biol. Chem.*, **90**, 65 (1931)
38. KEMMERER, A. R., ELVEHJEM, C. A., AND HART, E. B., *J. Biol. Chem.*, **92**, 623 (1931)
39. HODGES, M. A., AND PETERSON, W. H., *J. Am. Dietetic Assoc.*, **7**, 6 (1931)
40. PETERSON, W. H., AND SKINNER, J. T., *J. Nutrition*, **4**, 419 (1931)
41. SHUKERS, C. F., MACY, I. G., DONELSON, E., NIMS, B., AND HUNSCHER, H. A., *J. Nutrition*, **4**, 399 (1931)
42. SANDIFORD, I., WHEELER, T., AND BOOTHBY, V. M., *Am. J. Physiol.*, **96**, 191 (1931)
43. DAGGS, R. G., *J. Nutrition*, **4**, 443 (1931)
44. MACY, I. G., DONELSON, E., LONG, M. L., GRAHAM, A., SWEENEY, M. E., AND SHAW, M. M., *J. Am. Dietetic Assoc.*, **6**, 314 (1931)

45. DONELSON, E., NIMS, B., HUNSCHER, H. A., AND MACY, I. G., *J. Biol. Chem.,* **91,** 675 (1931)
46. WADDELL, J., STEENBOCK, H., AND HART, E. B., *J. Nutrition,* **4,** 53 (1931)
47. WADDELL, J., *J. Nutrition,* **4,** 67 (1931)
48. MITCHELL, H. S., AND MILLER, L., *J. Home Econ.,* **23,** 1043 (1931)
49. KUGELMASS, I. N., AND GREENWALD, E., *Am. J. Diseases Children,* **41,** 1377 (1931)
50. WILKINSON, P. D., AND NELSON, V. E., *Am. J. Physiol.,* **96,** 139 (1931)
51. GOWAN, J. W., AND TOBEY, E. R., *J. Gen. Physiol.,* **15,** 45, 67 (1931)
52. BROWN, J. B., AND SUTTON, T. S., *J. Dairy Sci.,* **14,** 125 (1931)
53. MACY, I. G., NIMS, B., BROWN, M., AND HUNSCHER, H. A., *Am. J. Diseases Children,* **42,** 569 (1931)
54. SLONAKER, J. R., *Am. J. Physiol.,* **96,** 547, 557; **97,** 15, 322, 573, 626; **98,** 266 (1931)
55. SMITH, A. H., AND MOÏSE, T. S., *J. Nutrition,* **4,** 261 (1931)
56. FRANCIS, L. D., SMITH, A. H., AND MOÏSE, T. S., *Am. J. Physiol.,* **97,** 210 (1931)
57. MACKAY, L. L., MACKAY, E. M., AND ADDIS, T., *J. Nutrition,* **4,** 379 (1931)
58. NEWBURGH, L. H., AND JOHNSTON, M. W., *J. Clin. Investigation,* **10,** 153 (1931)
59. JACKSON, C. M., AND SMITH, V. D. E., *Am. J. Physiol.,* **97,** 146 (1931)
60. SMITH, A. H., *J. Nutrition,* **4,** 427 (1931)
61. BING, F. C., AND MENDEL, L. B., *Am. J. Physiol.,* **98,** 169 (1931)
62. WAN, S., AND WU, H., *Chinese J. Physiol.,* **5,** 53 (1931)
63. WAN, S., AND CHEN, T. T., *Chinese J. Physiol.,* **5,** 71 (1931)
64. KEETON, R. W., MCKENZIE, A., OLSON, S., AND PICKENS, L., *Am. J. Physiol.,* **97,** 473 (1931)
65. PALMER, L. S., AND KENNEDY, C., *J. Biol. Chem.,* **90,** 545 (1931)
66. MITCHELL, H. H., *J. Nutrition,* **4,** 525 (1931)
67. CASTLE, W. B., HEATH, C. W., STRAUSS, M. G., AND TOWNSEND, W. C., *J. Am. Med. Assoc.,* **97,** 904 (1931)
68. MOSCHCOWITZ, E., *Arch. Internal Med.,* **48,** 171 (1931)
69. WEST, R., AND HOWE, M., *J. Am. Med. Assoc.,* **97,** 685 (1931)
70. DAKIN, H. D., AND WEST, R., *J. Biol. Chem.,* **92,** 117 (1931)
71. WEST, R., AND HOWE, M., *J. Biol. Chem.,* **88,** 427 (1930)
72. WEST, R., AND HOWE, M., *J. Biol. Chem.,* **94,** 611 (1931)
73. WILKINSON, J. F., *Brit. Med. J.,* **1,** 85 (1931)
74. GUTZEIT, K., AND HERRMANN, J., *Münch. med. Wochschr.,* **78,** 266 (1931)
75. HENNING, N., AND BRUGSCH, H., *Deut. med. Wochschr.,* **57,** 757 (1931)
76. BURGESS, J. P., AND MORGAN, J. E., *Proc. Soc. Exptl. Biol. Med.,* **28,** 371 (1930–31)
77. KANDEL, E., *Proc. Soc. Exptl. Biol. Med.,* **28,** 385 (1931)
78. STURGIS, C. C., AND ISAACS, R., *J. Am. Med. Assoc.,* **93,** 747 (1929)

YALE UNIVERSITY
NEW HAVEN, CONNECTICUT

VITAMINS*

By Leslie J. Harris

Dunn Nutritional Laboratory
Cambridge, England

PART I. WATER-SOLUBLE GROUP

Vitamin B_1 (B)

1. *Symptoms of avitaminosis B_1 in rats.*—The conditions requisite for the production in rats of regular and consistent symptoms of polyneuritis are gradually becoming clarified. That the question should still be under discussion may cause some surprise, particularly when one recalls that polyneuritis was the first of the avitaminoses to be studied experimentally; that rats were the species employed from the start in work on "water-soluble B" and that the identity of the latter with the antineuritic vitamin was early taken for granted; and indeed that polyneuritis in vitamin-B–deficient rats was long ago duly described by Schaumann and by Hofmeister. One of the conditions, which of course until recently it was impossible to control with scientific understanding, is the provision of vitamin B_2. But this in itself is not sufficient, as was evident from the experiences of Chick and Roscoe, who only rarely observed symptoms of polyneuritis, or of those of Kinnersley, Peters, and Reader (1) who expressed doubt as to whether the rat test could be used to differentiate the B_1 factor (quoted by Sandels). A second and very important condition, which emerges in a number of recent papers (Sherman and Sandels; Sebrell and Elvove; Sandels), is the necessity of providing slight traces of vitamin B_1. Polyneuritis is seen not with an absolute deprivation of vitamin B_1—that results in early death without convulsions—but rather in hypovitaminosis B_1, i.e., in a state of chronic, long-standing, slight deficiency. No doubt much has been done to solve the puzzle, but one suspects that certain points still remain to be investigated. Unexpected irregularities are still liable to occur, judging from our own experience and from conversation with other workers. The nature of the basal diet appears to be one of the factors in question.

* Received January 19, 1932.

Peters supposes that the symptoms generally regarded as typical of polyneuritis are due in reality to a combination of the avitaminoses B_1 and "B_4" [Kinnersley, Peters, and Reader (2)]. This is clearly an issue of some importance, because the vitamin is commonly defined by the symptoms which it will cure, and if different workers accept varying definitions there is danger of argument at cross purposes.

2. *Concentration of vitamin B_1.*—An account of Jansen and Donath's isolation of a crystalline vitamin B_1 preparation [Jansen (1); Jansen and Donath] and re-investigations upon this or similar products [Williams, Waterman, and Gurin; Jansen, Kinnersley, Peters, and Reader; Seidell and Smith; and van Veen (1)] fall outside the scope of the year's report, for chronological reasons. In the year under review, however, Seidell and Birckner claim to have obtained a concentrate still far from pure but which has an activity apparently slightly greater even than that of Jansen's crystalline preparation. The latter they assume therefore to owe its activity to admixed vitamin. The steps in Seidell's new concentration method involve essentially: (a) the preparation of an "activated solid," as originally described by him fifteen years ago; (b) extraction of the activated solid in alkali, followed by neutralization, evaporation, and precipitation of impurities with alcohol; (c) benzoylation, followed by precipitation with acetone; (d) extraction with a propyl alcohol–HCl mixture, and, finally, (e) concentration by evaporation, and precipitation and re-precipitation with acetone. As the authors point out, their procedure makes no use of the precipitating agents which are usually employed in concentrating the vitamin.

Evans and Lepkovsky have described a simple procedure, involving no bulky precipitations, by which fairly active concentrates of vitamin B_1, free from vitamin B_2, may be obtained. Rice polishings are the raw material; the vitamin is extracted by 80 per cent alcohol and then adsorbed on clay. Guha (1) starting with brewer's yeast obtained a concentrate of which the pigeon day-dose is about 0.05 mg. This is about one-fifth of the activity of Jansen's crystals. The latter likewise are slightly more active than a preparation obtained by Peters from yeast, by a process similar to Jansen's. Jansen himself has improved his yield (2), although presumably not the actual activity of the final material, by incorporating methods based on the technique of Peters and of Seidell. Reports substantially confirming Jansen and Donath's concentration technique are recently to hand from Odake and from Freudenberg and Cerecedo. The latter workers used mice as test animals, following Bing and Mendel and others.[1]

3. *Chemistry of vitamin B_1.*—Investigations by electrical transference methods in the writer's laboratory have definitely proved the basic nature of vitamin B_1 (Birch and Guha). (The method of electrodialysis is shown also to afford a means of concentrating vitamin B_1 free from vitamin B_2.) That vitamin B_1 is a base is concluded again by Sherman and Whitsitt, who are the most recent workers to have re-investigated the action of nitrous acid upon it. They find that the vitamin is destroyed by the nitrous acid only if the treatment is "drastic," i.e., if the solution is "directly treated" instead of treated by aspiration.

Guha (1) obtained negative, or practically negative, results, testing vitamin B_1 for the following: cozymase activity; the ninhydrin, Adamkiewicz-Hopkins, and Pauly reactions; and precipitating with flavianic acid. It could not be replaced nutritionally by adenine, guanine, uracil, *dl*-thyroxin, histamine, or adrenalin. Veen (2) has investigated the nature of the substances which appear in the various fractions when vitamin B_1 is concentrated on the lines of Jansen and Donath's method. Among the bodies identified were xanthine, guanine, adenine, hypoxanthine, uracil, histidine, arginine, guanidine; and unknown picrolonates and picronates were separated. Peters has summarised his views as to the relative properties of vitamin B_1 as compared with "B_3", "B_4", and "B_5", in respect to the following: solubility of hydrochloride in alcohol and in lipoid solvents; stability to acid hydrolysis and boiling HNO_3; resistance to benzoylation, oxidation, reduction, and to HNO_2; inactivation by alkali; influence of pH upon the adsorption on charcoal; etc.

4. *Assay of vitamin B_1.*—A method was described by Smith in 1930 suitable for estimating the antineuritic potency of highly active watery concentrates, depending on intravenous injection into polyneuritic rats. The use of polyneuritic rats has been extended by Birch and Harris working for the conference on vitamin standardization convened by the League of Nations Health Organization, so as to permit the estimation of foodstuffs, which of course are fed instead of injected. This method is more specific and as delicate, if not more so, than the rat growth-promotion method. It is more accurate, rapid,

[1] Windaus' claim to the isolation of vitamin B_1 appeared after the foregoing had been sent to press. [A. Windaus, R. Tschesche, H. Ruhkopf, F. Laquer, and F. Schultz, *Z. physiol. Chem.*, **204**, 123 (1932).]

and convenient than the pigeon method and has the great advantage of permitting assays upon foods containing very small quantities of the vitamin. Sebrell and Elvove have confirmed the value of Smith's method as applied to aqueous concentrates, now employing also subcutaneous or intraperitoneal injections. They emphasize again the necessity of giving slight traces of vitamin B_1 in order to produce the necessary polyneuritic condition in the rat.

Chase and Sherman have made yet another study of the estimation of the vitamin by growth tests on rats, vitamin B_2 being provided as "standardized" autoclaved yeast. The importance of administering the test material separately, instead of incorporated in the diet, has been stressed [Roscoe (2)]. Randoin and Lecoq have discussed basal diets for pigeon tests.

The report of the London Conference has now appeared (*League of Nations Health Organisation,* 1931). The international standard chosen for the antineuritic vitamin is an adsorption product prepared in the medical laboratory at Java after the method of Seidell, and Jansen and Donath (viz., an H_2SO_4 extract of rice polishings adsorbed upon fuller's earth). One unit of the "antineuritic vitamin B" is defined as the antineuritic activity of 10 mg. of the adsorption product (i.e., the earth with the vitamin adsorbed upon it). The approximate vitamin value of the standard can be gauged from the relation that 10 to 20 mg. per day is needed to maintain normal growth in young rats, or 20 to 30 mg. for a pigeon curative day-dose. The standard is kept at the National Institute for Medical Research, Hampstead, London. From thence specimens are sent to other countries and issued to "suitable individuals and institutions under conditions defined by the Conference." The standard preparation appears to remain stable at room temperature for some years, but it must be kept dry. It is recommended that either prophylactic or curative tests, upon either rats or pigeons, may be employed.

The suggested use of mice in vitamin B_1 tests has already been alluded to.

5. *Occurrence of vitamin B_1.*—The distribution of vitamins B_1 and B_2 in leafy vegetables (watercress, lettuce, spinach, and cabbage) has been determined by Roscoe (1) by the rat-growth method. Owing to their high water content they are relatively poor sources of these vitamins but on a basis of dry weight have a B_1 value of about one-fourth of that of dry brewer's yeast (or between that of wheat-germ and egg-yolk). The onion bulb has only about one-third of the B_1

value of the above-mentioned green leaves. These vegetables were on the whole richer in vitamin B_1 than in B_2. In cooking spinach by the domestic process one-half of the vitamin B_1 was found to be lost. A second paper [Roscoe (2)] deals with vitamin B in root vegetables. The carrot on a dry-weight basis had only one-fifth the vitamin B_1 content of yeast, turnip was slightly poorer, and potato had only one-third the value of carrot.

By the pigeon weight-maintenance method Plimmer and coworkers [Plimmer, Raymond, and Lowndes (1)] have redetermined the "vitamin B" content of cereals. Strictly speaking, this method does not enable one to assay for a particular constituent of the complex, but there can be no doubt that the results represent essentially the relative antineuritic or vitamin B_1 values:

TABLE I

	Percentage in Diet for Maintenance	Comparative "Vitamin B" Value
Dried yeast	4	100
Marmite	6	67
Wheat germ ("bemax")	6 to 7	62
Middlings	10	40
Baker's yeast	12	33
Bran	20	20
Buckwheat	20	20
Millet	30	13
Oatmeal	35	11
Wheat	40	10
Barley	40	10
Malt	40	10
Rye	40	10
Dari	40	10
Brown rice	40	10

According to these figures cereals have a slightly lower value than pulses, which were previously found to have a comparative value of about 13. The same authors in a later paper [Plimmer, Raymond, and Lowndes (2)] have examined the vitamin B_1 values of fruits and vegetables, by the pigeon preventive method. The results are in corroboration of those of Roscoe and show that these foodstuffs are poor sources of the vitamin. They would have to comprise no less than 60 per cent of a diet to supply a sufficiency of vitamin B. Even on a dry-weight basis they have only one-fifth to one-tenth the value of dry yeast.

TABLE II

COMPARATIVE VITAMIN B_1 VALUE, DRY-WEIGHT BASIS

Orange juice	20
Orange peel	13
Tomatoes	20
Cabbage	13
Watercress	20
Artichokes	9
Leeks	10
Parsnips	12
Potatoes	7

Certain commercial liver extracts and stomach extracts are quite rich in vitamin B_1, but different brands vary considerably [Gilroy (1, 2) ; Salmon and Guerrant].

Further studies on the water-soluble portion of milk have served to confirm the impression that it is definitely poor in antineuritic potency but richer in growth-promoting or antipellagra activity (Supplee, Kahlenberg, and Flanigan). The workers at Detroit (McCosh, Macy, and Hunscher) have continued their studies on human milk. The vitamin B value seemed to vary inversely as the total volume secreted. The effect of giving the mothers 10 gm. daily of yeast was tested. On somewhat indirect grounds it was concluded that a substance distinct from vitamin B was carried over into their milk by such treatment. (The evidence was that the milk in question appeared to promote a better growth rate in rats with no concurrent increase in their appetite or food intake.)

6. *Physiology of the action of vitamin B_1.*—In the last year or two increasing attention has been paid to the importance of *lactic acid in avitaminosis B_1*. It was shown by workers in Japan that in patients with beriberi the lactic acid tends to accumulate in the body and reach abnormally high levels, most noticeably after exercise. Hayasaka has shown that the recovery process after muscular fatigue is more prolonged in beriberi than it is in normal individuals and that the CO_2 output during exercise is diminished. Using the dog as experimental animal, he has pointed out that even quite light exercise suffices to keep the blood lactic acid elevated above its normal value for a long period. He concludes that in beriberi there is some disturbance in the resynthesis of lactic acid. In good keeping with these conclusions, it was shown that when sodium lactate was injected into beriberi patients the resynthesis to glycogen was very much lower than it was

with normal controls or cured beriberi subjects. Also the rise in blood lactic acid was much greater. [See also earlier work by Bickel (1, 2); also Collazo.] Collazo and Bayo enumerate the abnormalities of carbohydrate metabolism brought about by vitamin B deficiency as follows: accumulation of lactic acid and H_3PO_4, hyperlacticacidemia, hyperglycemia, and glycogen shortage.[2] Kinnersley and Peters (1, 2) have demonstrated that when symptoms of opisthotonus are threatening in the pigeon there is an increase of lactic acid in the lower part of the brain. They are concerned to show that the defect in metabolism in the lower part of the brain is directly responsible for the symptoms, i.e., that they have a central rather than local origin. More recently Fisher, working in Peters' laboratory, has confirmed that there is quite definitely a general defect in lactic-acid metabolism in the polyneuritic pigeon as a whole, in addition to the defect in the brain as described by Kinnersley and Peters. Gavrilescu and Peters (2) find that brain tissue from beriberi pigeons gives a subnormal oxygen uptake *in vitro;* they conclude: "we feel that these results together with the observations upon lactic acid in the brain (Kinnersley and Peters, 1930) show finally that the symptoms are central in origin in the polyneuritic pigeon." The same authors [Gavrilescu and Peters (1)] were able to detect some evidence of improved oxygen uptake when vitamin B was added to a brain tissue preparation also *in vitro.*

In collaboration with Dr. A. N. Drury the writer has shown that deprivation of vitamin B$_1$ leads to a remarkable drop in heart rate in the rat. The bradycardia is due to the vitamin deficiency *per se* and not, like a number of the ill effects, to the loss of appetite and inanition. It was suggested that the low heart rate might well be due to the accumulation of lactic acid in the heart (Drury, Harris, and Maudsley).

In view of the importance now to be attached to the lactic-acid question, fresh significance is lent to earlier observations on the influence of the various dietary ingredients, including especially carbohydrate, on the course of avitaminosis B. Funk in 1914 showed that carbohydrate-rich diets bring about a more rapid production of polyneuritis in pigeons, and the matter has since been investigated by

[1] There is still, however, some uncertainty about the blood sugar level in avitaminosis B$_1$. Bell, working in Drummond's laboratory, finds no increase in vitamin-B–depleted rats but a rise in pigeons during the convulsive stage only, attributable perhaps to nervous stimulation.

many workers, some of whom have found that the vitamin B requirements are proportional to the carbohydrate intake (e.g., most recently,
Randoin). Others again have varyingly concluded that it is necessary to "balance" not only the carbohydrate but also the protein, or
the calories or the total food intake either with vitamin B_1 or with
one or another of the constituents of the complex. In conformity
with the recent developments alluded to above is the finding of Sure
and Smith that the glycogen content of the livers of polyneuritic
nursling rats fell to a small fraction of the normal. More negative
are the results of Lepkovsky, Wood, and Evans, who found that
glucose tolerance is normal in beriberi rats unless they be moribund;
of Roscoe (2), who concluded that vitamin B_1 requirements are unrelated to total food consumption; or of Guha (2), who found that
vitamin B_1 requirements are independent of the protein/carbohydrate
ratio or the nature of the dietary carbohydrate. The last-mentioned
writer had rather disappointing results with lactic acid: the ingestion
of sodium lactate did not hasten the appearance of symptoms in
vitamin-B_1–deficient rats, although it was claimed that the pH of the
urine was diminished, and that the lethal dose of injected sodium
lactate was lower in deficient than in control animals. With regard to
the food constituents other than carbohydrate, recent results have
mostly been negative. Thus Francis, Smith, and Morse were unable
by increasing the allowance of the vitamin B complex to alleviate the
ill effects of high-protein diets upon the kidney. Some years ago Evans
and Lepkovsky found that fat had a vitamin-B–sparing action. They
now conclude that the addition of fat to an almost fat-free diet is
still beneficial, even if the requirements for vitamin B are fully satis-
fied. Guha (2) believes that while lard has a definite vitamin-B–
sparing effect, other fats such as palm kernel oil and olive oil have
no such action. Hume and Henderson Smith suspect that the "fat-
deficiency disease" of Burr and Burr may be correlated rather with
a vitamin B deficiency.

It has long been known that vitamin-B–starved animals tend to
suffer from a general *laxity of the gastro-intestinal tract*. Gál has
found the absorption of glucose to be only one-third of normal, and
of nitrogenous substances only one-half. Radiograms showed a reduced motility and delayed emptying of the stomach. Julian and
Heller, in the contrary direction, find the digestibility of protein, fat,
and carbohydrate to remain unimpaired. Somewhat contradictory
results have been reached in measurements of the "efficiency" of the

food consumed in avitaminosis (Palmer and Kennedy; Sure and Walker; Sure, Smith, Kik, and Walker).

In the past it has often been suggested that vitamin B deficiency is associated with a lack of some enzyme, or hormone. Vogt-Møller considers that avitaminosis B_1 is an intoxication with methyl glyoxal, resulting from a shortage not so much of glyoxalase as of the coenzyme. His evidence is that methyl glyoxal could be demonstrated for vitamin-B–depleted animals but not for normal or starved controls in preparations of liver plus hexosephosphate. Abderhalden (2) states that the dehydrase content of the tissues is lowered in vitamin B deficiency in the pigeon and suggests that the high antineuritic activity of certain organ extracts has a special significance in this connection [Abderhalden (1)]. It has been claimed that the muscles and livers of vitamin-B–deficient pigeons are able to bring about an increased phosphate esterification although having a normal phosphatase activity (Bodnar and Karell). Another worker, again, finds that vitamin B invariably possesses phytase activity, that is, that it is able to split phytin into phosphoric acid and inositol (Cuboni).

The view that *beriberi can be aggravated by a toxic substance* present, e.g., in polished rice ("oryzatoxin") has not yet been abandoned (Teruuchi, Ohyama, and Wada). At this point we may recall that Harris and Moore found that an excess of cod-liver oil increased the need for vitamin B_1, an effect confirmed by Norris and Church, who attributed it to the presence of toxic substances such as choline and isoamylamine in the oil. Plimmer supposes that vitamin B_1 acts by preventing the formation of toxins from stagnant food in the gut [Plimmer, Raymond, and Lowndes (2)]. A difficulty which has to be faced before Plimmer's view can be accepted is that the feces, presumed toxic, of a polyneuritic rat have a remedial antineuritic action when ingested.

It is now well established that for successful lactation a greatly increased supply of the vitamin B complex is necessary, but it is uncertain whether the B_1 constituent (Evans and Burr) or the B_2 (Sure) is the more essential. Husseman and Hetler assume it to be the latter, but their evidence, a comparison of the action of autoclaved yeast with tikitiki, is somewhat inconclusive.

The detrimental effect of vitamin B shortage on higher nervous function is illustrated by the work of Maurer and Tsai, who have recorded a diminished maze-learning ability on the part of partially depleted rats.

Vitamin B_2 (G)

Before proceeding to a systematic report of the past year's publications on vitamin B_2 it seems right that the reviewer should draw attention here to an influence which, as he believes, tends to retard progress in this field and to render difficult any proper co-ordination of our knowledge. We refer to the fact that different workers may have somewhat divergent conceptions in mind when speaking of vitamin B_2. To one the term will denote, as though by definition, "the heat stable (or heat-alkali stable) component of the vitamin B complex"; to a second it indicates "the fraction or fractions needed for supplementing vitamin B_1 in order to procure adequate growth in rats"; to a third it is a dermatitis-curative or -preventive factor, and so on. It is by no means certain that these varying lines of approach will necessarily yield data relating exclusively to one and the same single factor, and until workers define more closely the sense in which they are using the term, or until a more exact official nomenclature is adopted, unnecessary confusion is being spread. We shall return to this question below (see section on "Additional B Vitamins").

1. *Pellagra and avitaminosis B_1.*—The available evidence fairly well supports the assumption that the B_2 vitamin, as measured by the rat growth-technique (vitamin B_1 provided), corresponds essentially with the pellagra-preventive factor for humans. Many aspects of the question, however, are still in the arena of controversy. Protagonists still support the old theory that pellagra is a matter of poor quality protein (e.g., Wilson). It is difficult to reconcile this view with the convincing experiments of Voegtlin and of Goldberger and their co-workers, which it may be in place to recall here. Voegtlin cured pellagra by protein-free (and amino-nitrogen free) extracts rich in vitamin B, while showing that other extracts equally rich in antineuritic vitamin were non-curative. Goldberger showed that pellagra could not be cured, e.g., by purified casein, but could be cured or prevented by meat, by small amounts of yeast and other foods rich in vitamin B. A pellagra-like condition was produced in rats and dogs (black-tongue), and it was shown that the protective substance differed from the antineuritic substance in (a) occurrence, (b) heat stability, and (c) solubility. High protein itself was not protective if purified. By these investigations of Goldberger, Funk's prophetic prediction, a decade and a half previously, of the existence of a specific antipellagra vitamin stood justified.

Recently several writers have suggested that pellagra in humans may represent a twofold deficiency. A pellagra-like disease prevalent in Sierra Leone appears to be a combined vitamin A and B_2 deficiency, since it has been shown that the mucous membrane lesions which it entails clear up very readily when vitamin A is exhibited (Wright). Again, Mellanby suggests that the sub-acute degeneration of the spinal cord sometimes observed in cases of pellagra may be due to lack of vitamin A and the skin lesions to lack of vitamin B_2. He has shown experimentally that deficiency of vitamin A can predispose to the former abnormality. That pellagra is an iron deficiency is postulated by Bliss (1, 2) from examination of the literature and from his own therapeutic results with humans, and experimentally with dogs and rats; reviewing the evidence Guha (3) feels that iron deficiency may indeed be a secondary or limiting factor, but that a deficiency of vitamin B_2 is the main factor.[3] It has been stated that the distribution of vitamin B_2, as worked out on the rat, leaves the association of pellagra with maize unexplained (Aykroyd); but perhaps insufficient emphasis has been laid on the point that the association is not so much with maize as with highly milled maize. The toxin theory of avitaminosis dies hard. Sabry assumes that pellagra is a toxaemia, adopts Bloch's views on pigment formation, applies them to the hyperpigmentation seen in pellagra, and assumes therefrom that pellagra must be an intoxication with dihydroxyphenylalanine. Although these premises seem insecure, this author states that on the practical side he has succeeded in aborting the skin lesions in pellagra by treatment with thiosulphate.

Turning to pellagra-like lesions in the rat, it has been concluded alternatively (a) that the dermatitis observed is of two different types, one resulting from vitamin B_2 deficiency proper and the other from the lack of some other and unidentified factor (Gurin, Eddy, Denton, and Ammerman), or (b) that the anti-dermatitis factor occurs in association with a separate growth-promoting factor possessing no anti-dermatitis activity (Sure and Smith; Thatcher, Sure,

---

[3] Indications of some association between the pellagra-preventive factor and a blood-regenerative factor are provided by the observations that anaemia is present in pellagra in humans (Anding and Sinani) and in vitamin B_2 deficiency in rats (Sure, Kik, and Smith), and that liver extracts are curative of black-tongue in dogs (Goldberger and co-workers) or of vitamin B_2 deficiency in rats (*vide infra*), but the blood-forming factor present in liver is said to be distinguished from the vitamin by its resistance to alkaline autoclaving (Guha and Mapson).

and Walker). The main pathological changes noted by the last-mentioned authors were alopecia, ulceration of the skin, atrophy of the spleen and the thymus, fatty changes in the liver, and hemorrhages and congestion of the intestines. Reminiscent of similar conditions which hold for the production of typical polyneuritic symptoms in avitaminosis B_1 is the finding of Sherman and Sandels that the characteristic pellagra-like symptoms of dermatitis develop best when the animal is suffering from a partial, or late, deprivation of vitamin B_2, which tends to lengthen the survival period and so permit the more gradual development of the lesions. The latter are described as consisting of red and inflamed paws, and saddle-like areas of baldness and dermatitis on the shoulders and back. The nitrogen balance, in vitamin B_2 deficiency in the rat, has been studied (Kon), but no definite conclusions were reached; the deficient animals grew less well than the controls having diet limited in quantity.

Pellagra is only very rarely encountered in England; two separate cases have recently been reported in seven-year-old children, one of them at Cambridge (Stannus; Whittle).

2. *Concentration of vitamin B_2.*—Chick, Copping, and Roscoe have shown that convenient concentrates of vitamin B_2, free from B_1, may be obtained from egg-white by simply removing the heat-coagulable proteins. Growth was restored and the skin lesions healed by doses corresponding to 5 to 10 gm. per rat per day of the original egg-white. Attempts at further purification were unsuccessful. Guha (2) uses aqueous extract of liver concentrate, autoclaved at pH 9 for half an hour at 124 to 125°, as a source of vitamin B_2 free from B_1.

3. *Chemistry of vitamin B_2.*—Reports published up to and including 1930 (which considerations of space preclude us from detailing here) yielded very conflicting results as to the precise solubility, and even more so as to the heat-stability, of vitamin B_2 or G. As already hinted, matters of definition were, we consider, largely responsible for the apparent discrepancies. Furthermore, some workers have been too ready to draw wide generalisations from experiments carried out under only quite limited conditions. During 1931 several further studies have been published. Guha (4, 5) found the heat-stability to vary with the source of the vitamin, which was more stable for example in marmite or commercial liver concentrate than in aqueous extract of yeast or in fresh ox-liver. On the other hand, Hunt and Wilder conclude that the "antipellagric factor (vitamin G) is stable under all the conditions tried," in acid and alkaline media.

Guha (4, 5) showed that the vitamin was : (*a*) adsorbed on norite charcoal at pH 4.6; (*b*) partially precipitated by neutral lead acetate and silver nitrate; (*c*) not precipitated by picric acid, benzoyl chloride, flavianic acid, baryta; (*d*) not effectively eluted by aqueous alcohol, 30 per cent propyl alcohol, or dilute saponin; (*e*) stable to treatment with trypsin, SO_2, H_2O_2, O_3; but (*f*) partially destroyed during esterification and by phosphotungstic acid. This evidence seems to indicate that the vitamin is not an acid, a base, or a peptide but is a neutral substance. Touching on the adsorbability of vitamin B_2, Hunt and Wilder have written "the antipellagra or anti-dermatitis factor is not the non-adsorbable fraction of yeast extract as previously reported, but it is probably an adsorbable fraction, different from the antineuritic fraction." We may conclude that much more work still needs to be done, and under conditions more closely standardised, and matched in various laboratories, before security is reached in our knowledge of the chemical behaviour of vitamin B_2. Examining the action of nitrous acid on vitamin B_2, Sherman and Whitsitt sum up their findings rather inconclusively : "the results of subsequent feeding tests were such as to indicate a partial destruction of vitamin G when the data are taken for an 8-week experimental feeding period, but not when they are taken for a week experimental feeding period." They throw out the suggestion that the apparent loss of activity may be related to "one of the newer and not yet clearly defined factors," or else that the reaction "may be one of oxidation rather than deamination in this case." Sherman and Sandels find that the apparent solubility of vitamin G in aqueous alcohol increases with the amount of water present, but that the alcohol partially destroys the vitamin (this corroborates earlier workers).

4. *Assay of vitamin B_2.*—Methods have been described for determining vitamin B_2 by the growth-rate of rats, with vitamin B_1 provided either as alcoholic extract of ground whole wheat (Bourquin and Sherman), or as 30 per cent of white corn (Munsell).

5. *Occurrence of vitamin B_2.*—A commercial liver extract, such as Eli Lilly's "No. 343," has a number of advantages over yeast as raw material for vitamin B_2; it is richer than yeasts are in B_2, while poorer in B_1; it is easily manipulated; and the vitamin is readily extractable with cold water [Guha (4, 5, 6)]. The daily dose is only 40 to 60 mg. per rat (Guha), the vitamin B_2 content being 4 to 5 times that of brewer's yeast, and the B_1 content only about one-fifth (Salmon and Guerrant). Different commercial liver—and also

stomach—extracts may, however, vary somewhat widely in their B_1 and B_2 values (Gilroy). The water-soluble fraction of milk is fairly rich in vitamin B_2, although not in B_1; casein preparations vary in growth-promoting power according to the methods of preparation and purification (Supplee, *et al.*). As to root vegetables, carrot has one-fifth the value of yeast, being about equal to milk or meat; turnip is less potent, being equal roughly to egg-yolk or wheat germ; while potato is low and comparable to cereals or pulses; nevertheless "the relatively large amounts of this vegetable eaten may render it an important source of both the B vitamins in ordinary diet" [Roscoe (2)]. Leafy vegetables (watercress, lettuce, spinach, and cabbage) are poor sources of vitamin B_2 owing to their high water content, and on a dry-weight basis have only one-fourth the value of dry brewer's yeast. Onion bulb is as low as 1/12 to 1/16. There seemed to be more vitamin B_2 in dark green leaves than in pale ones [Roscoe (1)]. Meats and certain meat products have been examined by Hoagland and Snider (1, 2). Beef or pork liver or beef kidney is 5 to 8 times richer than the muscle of beef, lamb, or pork, or than pork spleen, in vitamin B_2; the former material gave good growth responses in rats when fed at a level of 3 per cent (dry weight), or under, of the diet, and the latter at 20 per cent to 25 per cent (dry weight), while for commercial beef extract, the figure was 7.5 per cent (dry weight). Canned haddock prevented black-tongue in dogs if fed at high levels, but salt pork, lard, and dried peas were relatively ineffective (Goldberger, Wheeler, and Rogers). Other investigators have studied the vitamin B_2 content of the following: cereals (Aykroyd); egg-white, which as already mentioned is free from vitamin B_1 (Chick, Copping, and Roscoe); and various specimens of yeast (Quinn, *et al.*). The vitamin B_2 contents of the latter were relatively uniform, although the B_1 varied at least tenfold.

REPORTED ADDITIONAL B VITAMINS AND UNCLASSIFIED FACTORS

Up to the time of writing, something like a score of authors claim to have demonstrated the existence of new factors having mostly a distribution similar to vitamin B. In each case the new factor is said to be different from any previously described, although it is only rarely that a possible relationship to the various new factors of the other contemporary authors is considered. While it seems probable, with the weight of papers published, that the vitamin B complex does in fact contain other factors in addition to those concerned in preventing polyneuritis (in pigeon or rat) or dermatitis (in rat; or pellagra in man), yet any direct comparison or collation of results is rendered almost impossible by the fact that widely diverging definitions and basal assumptions are taken by the different investigators. Thus, the experimental observation that rats have failed to thrive on a diet supplemented with antineuritic concentrate plus autoclaved (or alkali-autoclaved) yeast is interpreted by one worker to mean a partial destruction of the vitamin B_2 during the autoclaving [e.g., Williams, Waterman, and Gurin; Chick and Roscoe (2)], but by a second to mean the deficiency of some new factor (a different definition now being taken for vitamin B_2, which is assumed to be *present* in the autoclaved yeast). Again determination of growth-rate on a diet supplemented with vitamin B_1 is a usual method of assaying for vitamin B_2, but it is used concurrently also for demonstrating the presence of new factors. We cannot in fact expect the position to become clarified until a more uniform system of definitions prevails; investigators in particular should specify in which of the different senses they are using the term vitamin B_2 (or G), i.e., whether it is defined (*a*) by antidermatitis action, (*b*) by growth promotion in presence of antineuritic supplement, or (*c*) as heat stable, *ex hypothesi*. As to the actual evidence offered for the new factors, it may be noted in the first place that more often than not it is indirect and circumstantial, namely a relatively low growth-rate has been observed in animals on a diet presumed to be adequate in the previously known factors. Generally there is no specific lesion or syndrome characteristic of the alleged deficiency, to serve as a criterion. Nor are there concentrates of the new factor free from contamination with the known vitamins, or vice versa, so that conclusive evidence is lacking that the "new" deficiency disease may not be due to partial shortage of a known factor and the cure to the provision of it. An unsatisfactory feature in many instances is that in order to produce the "new" deficiency disease the animals are first "run out" on a diet which is in fact lacking in the whole vitamin complex, the aim being subsequently to make good the deficiency of the better-known constituents: if, however, these are provided from the beginning the new deficiency disease fails to appear. Finally it may be observed that the possibility is sometimes overlooked that what at first sight appear to be symptoms of separate deficiency diseases are in reality different stages in the development of a single one; thus complete deprivation of vitamin B_1 in a young rat leads to a rapid loss in weight and early death without

TABLE III

ALLEGED ADDITIONAL "B" FACTORS

No. of Factor, Worker and Original Reference	Species of Experimental Animals	Special Features of Diet	Nature of Ill Effect Resulting	Source of Alleged New Curative Factor	Apparent Heat-Stability or -Lability	Comments
1. Williams and Waterman (1928)	Pigeon	B_1 as activated fuller's earth; B_2 as autoclaved yeast	Unsatisfactory growth	Unheated yeast, malt, wheat	Extremely labile	"Vitamin B_3"
2. Randoin and Lecoq (1928)	Pigeon	B_1 as activated fuller's earth extract	Unsatisfactory growth, etc.	Alkaline-auto-claved yeast extract	Heat- and alkali-stable (cf. No. 1)	Possible identity with B_3 (Lecoq, 1931)
3. Rosedale (1927, 1929)	Pigeon	Polished rice + B_1 concentrate	Intestinal stasis	Lead acetate ppt. from rice polishings	?	"Anti-stasis factor" (distinct from B_2)
4. Carter, Peters, and Kinnersley (1930)	Pigeon	B_1 as Peters' concentrate	Unsatisfactory growth	Alkalised mar-mite, alcoholic extracts of acti-vated charcoal	Heat- and alkali-stable	"Vitamin B_5" converts "falling" into "mainte-nance," not "ris-ing" nutrition (cf. B_3)
5. Carter (1930)	Pigeon	Polished rice	Heart block	Baker's yeast	Labile	"Heart block factor" (B_1 and B_2 not curative)

6. Reader (1929)	Rat	B_1 as Peters' concentrate; B_2 as autoclaved marmite (pH 9, 120°)	Unsatisfactory growth; symptoms hitherto included in polyneuritis	Unheated marmite, $HgSO_4$ ppt. from yeast extract	Labile	"Vitamin B_3"
7. Hunt (1928)	Rat	B_1 as activated fuller's earth; B_2 as activated fuller's earth filtrate	Unsatisfactory growth	Yeast fractionation residues. Autoclaved yeast fraction	Stable	[Cf., however, Hunt and Wilder (1931), as to heat stability, etc.]
8. Kennedy and Palmer (1928)	Rat	B_1 as wheat embryo	Unsatisfactory growth, etc.	Starch-free yeast, alcohol-extracted yeast, autoclaved yeast, residues from B_1 concentrate	Stable	Non-identity with B_2 later questioned (Kennedy and Palmer, 1929)
9. Hartwell (1921–1928); Drummond (1926–)	Rat	High protein + minimal allowance of B complex	Unsatisfactory growth, etc.	Alkaline autoclaved yeast	Heat- and alkali-stable	More alkali-stable than B_2 (cf. Sherman and Gloy, 1927)
10. Chick and Roscoe (1929); Chick and Copping (1930)	Rat	B_2 as egg-white; B_1 as Peters' concentrate	Unsatisfactory growth, without dermatitis	Alkaline-autoclaved yeast	Heat- and alkali-stable	"Y" factor (cf. Sure et al., below)

TABLE III (Continued)

ALLEGED ADDITIONAL "B" FACTORS (Continued)

No. of Factor, Worker and Original Reference	Species of Experimental Animals	Special Features of Diet	Nature of Ill Effect Resulting	Source of Alleged New Curative Factor	Apparent Heat-Stability or -Lability	Comments
11. Sure, Smith, and Kik (1931)	Rat	a) B_1 as irradiated rice polishings. B_2 as autoclaved yeast	a) Dermatitis without growth failure			a) Deficiency of a new "G" vitamin
		b) B_2-free diet	b) Growth failure without dermatitis			b) Deficiency of a new "F" vitamin
12. Williams and Lewis (1930)	Rat	Aqueous alcohol extract of yeast: B_1 adsorbed on earth, B_2 as the filtrate	Unsatisfactory growth	Extracted yeast (i.e., insoluble residue)	Stable	N. B. insolubility in alcohol and water
13. Guha (1931)	Rat	B_1 and B_2 concentrates and/or yeast	Unsatisfactory growth	Milk		Milk factor, different from third yeast factor; see also Supplee et al. (1931)

ALLEGED ADDITIONAL FACTORS, UNCLASSIFIED

14. Boas (1927); Fixen (1931)	Rat	Protein as desiccated egg-white + all known vitamins	Posture, etc.	Fresh egg-white, starches, milk, proteins, etc. (not in marmite)	Stable	? Analogue of pink disease (Findlay and Stern, 1929)
Parsons (1931)	Rat	Complete diet very rich in egg-white	Death, or later dermatitis	Beef liver (not yeast)		
15. Coward *et al.* (1929, 1930, 1931)	Rat	Protein as "Glaxo Casein" + all known vitamins	Unsatisfactory growth	B.D.H. "Light white casein," various foods, ether and alcoholic extracts	Stable ?	
16. Evans and Burr (1927)	Rat	Sugar, casein, salts + all known vitamins	Growth, ovulation, lactation; caudal necrosis	Lettuce, liver, lard		Later attributed to fat deficiency (Burr and Burr, 1929, 1930), but compare Funk, Caspe, and Caspe (1931) and Hume and Henderson Smith (1931)
17. Goettsch and Pappenheimer (1931)	Rabbit and guinea pig	Oats, bran, casein, lard, salts; cod liver oil, orange juice, vitamin E	Muscular dystrophy			

convulsions, while chronic shortage gives rise eventually to the characteristic convulsions; and certain of the symptoms yield more readily to treatment than do others. Among the better known of the new factors are Williams and Waterman's pigeon vitamin B_3, needed for supplementing a diet of polished rice plus antineuritic vitamin, and Reader's rat vitamin B_4 (first also called B_3), needed in addition to antineuritic vitamin and alkali-autoclaved marmite. Well authenticated too among the factors having a distribution somewhat different from vitamin B are: (a) the "light-white-casein factor" of Coward, present in certain specimens of casein but not in others more drastically treated during purification, and (b) the Boas factor, which protects against the toxic action of diets containing much desiccated egg white. Exigencies of space have excluded a discussion *seriatim* of the separate factors, but a tabulated summary is included to facilitate comparison of the conditions and conclusions in the various investigations.

GROWTH-PROMOTING FACTORS FOR MICRO-ORGANISMS; "BIOS"

At one time it was thought that "bios" was identical with vitamin B (Williams). Recent work by Williams and collaborators emphasises that just as vitamin B possesses a complex nature, so yeast growth-stimulants also are of a diverse character and, as is known, vary greatly with the type of yeast used. The bios originally investigated by Wildiers appears to have no relationship to vitamin B_1 and is not adsorbed by fuller's earth or precipitated by phosphotungstic acid, etc. On the other hand, the crystalline vitamin B_1 of Jansen can stimulate yeast growth to a remarkable extent under some conditions, and so can certain fractions discarded during the course of the preparation (Williams and Roehm; Williams and Bradway). Wildiers' bios is split into two components by fractional electrolysis (Williams and Truesdail). Narayanan cannot admit the claims of Eddy, or of Miller, Lucas *et al.*, to have isolated bios, having obtained still more active concentrates himself. The alleged activity of inositol could not be confirmed; and neither vitamin B_2 nor a large group of other substances tested had any bios action.

Of special interest in connection with the foregoing is the finding that the growth-promoting accessory factor for the fungus *Nematospora gossypii* consists of two components, one of which is inositol. The latter when added to a relatively inert substance, such as marmite, increased its activity. Nevertheless it is denied that inositol has any true bios activity, the growth-promoting factor in question being different from bios (Buxton and Pramanik).

Neither is the substance in peptone having a growth-promoting action on a *lacto-bacillus* identical with bios (Davis and Golding).

VITAMIN C

1. *Scurvy in man and experimental animals.*—Yet another instance to be added to the many existing accounts of scurvy among isolated populations in outlying areas is furnished by the report of an anthropological expedition to the Finke River district (Hermannsburg Mission Station) in Central Australia. The aborigines here subsist on a diet which is deficient in all the vitamins; scurvy is rife, with marked joint lesions, and 40 deaths occurred in the previous year (Cleland and Fry).

An ingenious method of measuring the lability to cutaneous capillary hemorrhages, and hence of indicating the presence of any scorbutic tendency, has been devised by a Swedish worker (Göthlin), and tested out on two human volunteers given diets low in vitamin C. The minimum protective dose of orange juice for the adult was found to be 0.7 cc. to 1 cc. per kg., so that the allowance for a 60-kg. man is about 14 to 20 times that for a guinea pig. The test was applied to a series of country school children, 11 to 14 years old, and it was found that 18 per cent of them were suffering from vitamin C under-nourishment.

Very significant are the observations of Hanke pointing to the lack of vitamin C as an important factor in the initiation of dental disease, and to the value of orange juice in the treatment of gingivitis.

Of interest to clinicians is the record of a case of severe scurvy in a patient with duodenal ulcer, for whom a diet of the usual restricted type, plus alkali, had been prescribed; the scurvy had already been mistakenly diagnosed as "rheumatism," "arthritis with pyorrhoea" (all teeth extracted), and as "rheumatism with purpura," and the writer concludes: "in view of the obscurity of the early symptoms it seems probable that slight undiagnosed cases of this type are not uncommon" (Martin).

A unique account has appeared of the spontaneous development of scurvy in a group of 39 monkeys (*Macacus rhesus*) shipped from India (Howitt). Attention has again been drawn to the intensified ill-effects of a vitamin-C–deficient diet upon the foetus and the pregnant female, in experimental animals (Wells; cf. Reyher and Walkoff).

2. Concentration of vitamin C.—Zilva has published further papers discussing various technical points in his procedure for concentrating vitamin C from lemon juice. In the first [Zilva (1)] it is emphasised that the amount of lead acetate to be added is not constant on each occasion; that lead acetate at pH 8 to 9 inactivates the vitamin, and that the phenolindophenol reduction test gives an arbitrary guide as to whether or not the vitamin is likely to have escaped oxidation. In the second paper [Zilva (2)] it is mentioned that the amount of acetic acid used for redissolving the active lead precipitate determines the pH at which further precipitates will appear and also the action of the latter. As we go to press accounts appear in the newspapers of the reported isolation of vitamin C by O. Rygh of Oslo.

3. Assay of vitamin C.—A helpful refinement of Höjer's method (which it will be recalled depends on an examination of a cross-section of the incisor teeth) has been worked out by Key and Elphick of the vitamin-testing section of the Pharmaceutical Society's laboratory in London. In outline the technique is as follows: A group of guinea pigs is allowed a given quantity of the "unknown," sufficient to afford partial protection from scurvy. After 14 days sections are prepared from which the average "degree of protection" can be determined. Four such degrees of protection are recognised, defined by the condition of the odontoblasts, the inner dentine, the predentine, and Tomes's canals. The amount of orange juice which is needed to afford the identical degree of protection being known, the antiscorbutic potency of the "unknown" can be expressed in terms of orange juice.

The London Conference on Vitamin Standards (League of Nations Health Organization) has chosen "fresh lemon juice" as the international standard. We are fortunate to possess, in the case of this vitamin, a ready-made standard which varies little from season to season or place to place. The unit of vitamin C is defined as the "vitamin C activity of 0.1 cc. of fresh juice of the lemon." That represents about 1/10 of the daily dose needed to prevent macroscopic scorbutic lesions in the guinea pig. The conference recommends that the juice may be prepared for feeding according to the following directions: decitrate with excess $CaCO_3$, stand for 1 hour, filter, and feed within 2 hours; the pH value of the juice thus decitrated should be about 6.

4. Occurrence of vitamin C.—The antiscorbutic activity of the orange has been shown to be independent of its country of origin (S. Africa, Palestine, or Honduras) or of the condition of cultivation, of the age of the tree, of the soil, etc. Grape fruit has a constant vitamin content whether from British Honduras or South Africa. The latter fruit is rather richer than the orange in the antiscorbutic factor (Bracewell and Zilva). Further studies have appeared on the antiscorbutic potency of the apple (Bracewell, Kidd, West, and Zilva). Tomatoes, it has been shown, are a better source of vitamin C when ripened on the vine than when picked green and ripened artificially with ethylene (Jones and Nelson). Judging from the reports published by the British Medical Association (Coward) little success has attended the efforts of manufacturers to provide stable sources of vitamin C in proprietary food preparations. Milk (which is, to begin with, a poor antiscorbutic) is said to lose 20 to 40 per cent of the vitamin during (aërobic) pasteurisation (Schwartze, Murphy, and Cox). Dried prunes and apricots retain vitamin C if lyed and then sulphured in the usual commercial fashion, but not if sulphured without lye or if unsulphured (Morgan, Field, and Nichols). As one might have anticipated, various brands of German coffee are equally devoid of the vitamin (Scheunert and Reschke).

5. *Action of vitamin C.*—But little light is shed by recent work on the mode of action of vitamin C in the animal organism. Apparently the digestibility of protein, fat, and carbohydrate (measured by the intake less the fecal excretion) is unimpaired in scurvy (St. Julian and Heller); and it is doubtful how much significance can be attached to the reports of an increased chloride content in the muscles (Randoin and Michaux; Michaux); of a diminished concentration of an adrenalin-like body in the suprarenals and blood serum (Ohata); or of increased oxygen uptake by the tissues with unchanged powers of dehydrogenation (Lio). The well-known cessation of growth in the bones in scurvy is accompanied by a failure of calcium deposition (Salter and Aub), but the calcium and phosphorus balance and the level in the blood appear to remain normal, at least until the final stages of the disease (Humphreys and Zilva).

LITERATURE CITED

REFERENCES TO VITAMIN B₁

ABDERHALDEN, E. (1), *Arch. ges. Physiol.*, **226**, 723 (1931)
ABDERHALDEN, E. (2), *Arch. ges. Physiol.*, **226**, 808 (1931)

BELL, M. E., *Biochem. J.*, **25**, 1755 (1931)

BICKEL, A., *Biochem. Z.*, **146**, 493 (1924)

BICKEL, A., *Biochem. Z.*, **166**, 251 (1925)

BING, F. C., AND MENDEL, L. B., *J. Nutrition*, **2**, 49 (1929)

BIRCH, T. W., AND GUHA, B. C., *Biochem. J.*, **25**, 1391 (1931)

BODNAR, J., AND KARELL, A., *Biochem. Z.*, **230**, 233 (1931)

CHASE, E. F., AND SHERMAN, H. C., *J. Am. Chem. Soc.*, **53**, 3506 (1931)

CHICK, H., AND ROSCOE, M. H., *Biochem. J.*, **21**, 698 (1927)

COLLAZO, J. A., *Biochem. Z.*, **136**, 278 (1923)

COLLAZO, J. A., AND BAYO, C. P., *Biochem. Z.*, **238**, 335 (1931)

CUBONI, E., *Boll. soc. intern. microbiol. Sez. ital.*, **3**, 161 (1931)

DRURY, A. N., HARRIS, L. J., AND MAUDSLEY, C., *Biochem. J.*, **24**, 1632 (1931)

EVANS, H. M., AND BURR, G. O., *J. Biol. Chem.*, **76**, 263 (1927)

EVANS, H. M., AND LEPKOVSKY, S., *J. Nutrition*, **3**, 353 (1931)

FISHER, R. B., *Biochem. J.*, **25**, 1410 (1931)

FRANCIS, L. D., SMITH, A. H., AND MORSE, T. S., *Am. J. Physiol.*, **97**, 210 (1931)

FREUDENBERG, W., AND CERECEDO, L. R., *J. Biol. Chem.*, **94**, 207 (1931)

GÁL, G., *Biochem. Z.*, **225**, 286 (1930)

GAVRILESCU, N., AND PETERS, R. A. (1), *Proc. Physiol. Soc., J. Physiol.*, **72**, 32P (1931)

GAVRILESCU, N., AND PETERS, R. A. (2), *Biochem. J.*, **25**, 1397 (1931)

GILROY, E. (1), *Lancet*, **220**, 1423 (1931)

GILROY, E. (2), *Lancet*, **221**, 1093 (1931)

GUHA, B. C. (1), *Biochem. J.*, **25**, 931 (1931)

GUHA, B. C. (2), *Biochem. J.*, **25**, 1367 (1931)

HARRIS, L. J., AND MOORE, T., *Biochem. J.*, **23**, 1114 (1929)

HAYASAKA, E., *Tôhoku J. Exptl. Med.*, **14**, 53, 72, 85, 283, 487 (1930)

HOFMEISTER, F., *Biochem. Z.*, **128**, 540 (1922)

HUME, E. M., AND HENDERSON SMITH, H., *Biochem. J.*, **25**, 300 (1931)

HUSSEMAN, D. L., AND HETLER, R. A., *J. Nutrition*, **4**, 127 (1931)

JANSEN, B. C. P. (1), *Rec. trav. chim.*, **48**, 984 (1929)

JANSEN, B. C. P. (2), *Nature*, **128**, 39 (1931)

JANSEN, B. C. P., AND DONATH, W. F., *Chem. Weekblad*, **23**, 201 (1926)

JANSEN, B. C. P., KINNERSLEY, H. W., PETERS, R. A., AND READER, V., *Biochem. J.*, **24**, 1824 (1930)

JULIAN, R. R. ST., AND HELLER, V. G., *J. Biol. Chem.*, **90**, 99 (1931)

KINNERSLEY, H. W., AND PETERS, R. A. (1), *Biochem. J.*, **24**, 711 (1930)

KINNERSLEY, H. W., AND PETERS, R. A. (2), *Proc. Physiol. Soc., J. Physiol.*, **69**, 11 (1930)

KINNERSLEY, H. W., PETERS, R. A., AND READER, V. (1), *Biochem. J.*, **22**, 276 (1928)

KINNERSLEY, H. W., PETERS, R. A., AND READER, V. (2), *Biochem. J.*, **24**, 1820 (1930)

LEPKOVSKY, S., WOOD, C., AND EVANS, H. M., *J. Biol. Chem.*, **87**, 239 (1930)

League of Nations Health Organization; Permanent Commission on Biological Standardization. *"Report of the Conference on Vitamin Standards,"* London, Geneva (1931)

McCosh, S. S., Macy, I. G., and Hunscher, H. A., *J. Biol. Chem.*, **90**, 1 (1931)

Maurer, S., and Tsai, L. S., *J. Nutrition*, **4**, 507 (1931)

Norris, E. R., and Church, A. E., *J. Biol. Chem.*, **89**, 437 (1930)

Odake, S., *Proc. Imp. Acad. (Tokyo)*, **7**, 102 (1931)

Palmer, L. S., and Kennedy, C., *J. Biol. Chem.*, **90**, 545 (1931)

Peters, R. A., *Nature*, **128**, 39 (1931)

Plimmer, R. H. A., Raymond, W. H., and Lowndes, J. (1), *Biochem. J.*, **25**, 691 (1931)

Plimmer, R. H. A., Raymond, W. H., and Lowndes, J. (2), *Biochem. J.*, **25**, 1788 (1931)

Randoin, L., *Bull. soc. sci. hyg. aliment.*, **18**, 231 (1930)

Randoin, L., and Lecoq, R., *Compt. rend.*, **192**, 444 (1931)

Roscoe, M. H. (1), *Biochem. J.*, **24**, 1754 (1930)

Roscoe, M. H. (2), *Biochem. J.*, **25**, 1205 (1931)

Salmon, W. D., and Guerrant, N. B., *Science*, **73**, 243 (1931)

Sandes, M. R., *J. Nutrition*, **2**, 409 (1930)

Schaumann, H., *Trans. Soc. Trop. Med.*, **58** (1911)

Sebrell, W. H., and Elvove, E., *U.S. Pub. Health Service, Pub. Health Repts.*, **46**, 917 (1931)

Seidell, A., and Birckner, V., *J. Am. Chem. Soc.*, **53**, 2288 (1931)

Seidell, A., and Smith, M. I., *U.S. Pub. Health Service, Pub. Health Repts.*, **45**, 3194 (1930)

Sherman, H. C., and Sandels, M. R., *J. Nutrition*, **3**, 395 (1931)

Sherman, H. C., and Whitsitt, M. L., *J. Biol. Chem.*, **90**, 153 (1931)

Supplee, G. C., Kahlenberg, O. J., and Flanigan, G. E., *J. Biol. Chem.*, **93**, 705 (1931)

Sure, B., *J. Biol. Chem.*, **80**, 297 (1928)

Sure, B., and Smith, M. E., *Proc. Soc. Exptl. Biol. Med.*, **27**, 861 (1930)

Sure, B., Smith, M. E., Kik, M. C., and Walker, D. J., *J. Biol. Chem.*, **92**, viii (1931)

Sure, B., and Walker, D. J., *J. Biol. Chem.*, **91**, 69 (1931)

Teruuchi, Y., Ohyama, T., and Wada, C., *Kitasato Arch. Exptl. Med.*, **8**, 60 (1931)

Veen, A. G. van (1), *Rec. trav. chim.*, **49**, 1178 (1930)

Veen, A. G. van (2), *Rec. trav. chim.*, **50**, 200 (1931)

Vogt-Møller, P. (1), *Biochem. J.*, **25**, 418 (1931)

Vogt-Møller, P. (2), *Biochem. Z.*, **233**, 248 (1931)

Williams, R. R., Waterman, R. E., and Gurin, S., *J. Biol. Chem.*, **87**, 559 (1930)

REFERENCES TO VITAMIN B₂

Anding, C., and Sinani, A., *Arch. Schiffs-Tropen-Hyg.*, **35**, 171 (1931)

Aykroyd, W. R., *Biochem. J.*, **24**, 1479 (1930)

Bliss, S. (1), *Science*, **72**, 577 (1930)

Bliss, S. (2), *Proc. Soc. Exptl. Biol. Med.*, **28**, 636 (1931)

BOURQUIN, A., AND SHERMAN, H. C., *J. Am. Chem. Soc.*, **53**, 3501 (1931)

CHICK, H., COPPING, A. M., AND ROSCOE, M. H., *Biochem. J.*, **24**, 1748 (1930)

GILROY, E., *Lancet*, **221**, 1093 (1931)

GOLDBERGER, J., *Medicine*, **5**, 79 (1926)

GOLDBERGER, J., WHEELER, G. A., AND ROGERS, L. M., *U.S. Public Health Service, Pub. Health Repts.*, **45**, 1297 (1930)

GUHA, B. C. (3), *Brit. Med. J.*, ii, 53 (1931)

GUHA, B. C. (4), *Biochem. J.*, **25**, 945 (1931)

GUHA, B. C. (5), *Nature*, **127**, 594 (1931)

GUHA, B. C. (6), *Lancet*, **220**, 864 (1931)

GUHA, B. C., AND MAPSON, L. W., *Biochem. J.*, **25**, 1674 (1931)

GURIN, S. S., EDDY, W. H., DENTON, J., AND AMMERMAN, M., *J. Exptl. Med.*, **54**, 421 (1931)

HOAGLAND, T., AND SNIDER, G. G. (1), *J. Agr. Research*, **40**, 977 (1930)

HOAGLAND, T., AND SNIDER, G. G. (2), *J. Agr. Research*, **41**, 205 (1930)

HUNT, C. H., AND WILDER, W., *J. Biol. Chem.*, **90**, 279 (1931)

KON, S. K., *Biochem. J.*, **25**, 482 (1931)

MELLANBY, E., *J. Am. Med. Assoc.*, **96**, 325 (1931)

MUNSELL, H. E., *J. Nutrition*, **4**, 203 (1931)

QUINN, E. J., et al., *J. Nutrition*, **3**, 257 (1930)

ROSCOE, M. H. (1), *Biochem. J.*, **24**, 1754 (1930)

ROSCOE, M. H. (2), *Biochem. J.*, **25**, 1205 (1931)

SABRY, I., *Lancet*, **221**, 1020 (1931)

SALMON, W. D., AND GUERRANT, N. B., *Science*, **73**, 243 (1931)

SHERMAN, H. C., AND SANDELS, M. R., *J. Nutrition*, **3**, 395 (1931)

SHERMAN, H. C., AND WHITSITT, M. L., *J. Biol. Chem.*, **90**, 153 (1931)

STANNUS, H. S., *Proc. Roy. Soc. Med.*, **24**, 1645 (1931)

SUPPLEE, G. C., et al., *J. Biol. Chem.*, **93**, 705 (1931)

SURE, B., AND SMITH, M. E., *Science*, **73**, 1887 (1931)

SURE, B., KIK, M. C., AND SMITH, M. E., *Proc. Soc. Exptl. Biol. Med.*, **28**, 498 (1931)

THATCHER, H., SURE, B., AND WALKER, D. J., *Arch. Path.*, **11**, 425 (1931)

VOEGTLIN, C., et al., *U.S. Pub. Health Service, Hyg. Lab. Bull.*, No. 116 (1920)

WHITTLE, H., *Proc. Roy. Soc. Med.*, **24**, 1645 (1931)

WILSON, W. H., *Proc. Intern. Congr. Med. (Cairo)*, **2**, 461 (1929)

WRIGHT, E. J., *"The A and B Avitaminosis Disease of Sierra Leone"* (London, 1930)

REFERENCES TO REPORTED ADDITIONAL B VITAMINS AND UNCLASSIFIED FACTORS

AYKROYD, W. R., *Biochem. J.*, **24**, 1479 (1930)

BOAS, M. A., *Biochem. J.*, **21**, 724 (1927)

BURR, G. O., AND BURR, M. M., *J. Biol. Chem.*, **82**, 364 (1929); **86**, 587 (1930)

CARTER, C. W., *Biochem. J.*, **24**, 1811 (1930)

CARTER, C. W., AND DRURY, A. N., *J. Physiol.*, **68**, proc. i (1929)

CARTER, C. W., KINNERSLEY, H. W., AND PETERS, R. A., *Biochem. J.*, **24**, 1833, 1844 (1930)

CHICK, H., AND COPPING, A. M., *Biochem. J.*, **24**, 1764 (1930) ; *Chemistry and Industry,* **49**, 1081 (1930)
CHICK, H., AND ROSCOE, M.˙H. (1), *Biochem. J.*, **23**, 498 (1929)
CHICK, H., AND ROSCOE, M. H. (2), *Biochem. J.*, **24**, 105 (1930)
COWARD, K. H., KEY, K. M., DYER, F. J., AND MORGAN, B. G. E., *Biochem. J.*, **25**, 551 (1931)
COWARD, K. H., KEY, K. M., AND MORGAN, B. G. E., *Biochem. J.*, **23**, 695 (1929)
COWARD, K. H., KEY, K. M., MORGAN, B. G. E., AND CAMBDEN, J. M., *Biochem. J.*, **23**, 913 (1929)
COWGILL, G. R., *Am. J. Physiol.*, **79**, 341 (1927)
EDDY, W. H., GURIN, S., AND KERESZTESY, J., *J. Biol. Chem.*, **87**, 729 (1930)
EVANS, H. M., AND BURR, G. O., *Proc. Soc. Exptl. Biol. Med.*, **25**, 41 (1927)
FINDLAY, G. M., AND STERN, R. O., *Arch. Disease Childhood,* **4**, 1 (1929)
FIXSEN, M. A. B., *Biochem. J.*, **25**, 596 (1931)
FUNK, C., CASPE, S., AND CASPE, H., *Proc. Soc. Exptl. Biol. Med.*, **28**, 816 (1931)
GOETTSCH, M., AND PAPPENHEIMER, A. M., *J. Exptl. Med.*, **54**, 145 (1931)
GUHA, B. C. (7), *Chemistry and Industry,* **48**, 1248 (1929)
GUHA, B. C. (8), *Biochem. J.*, **25**, 960 (1931)
HASSAN, A., AND DRUMMOND, C., *Biochem. J.*, **21**, 653 (1927)
HARTWELL, G., *Biochem. J.*, **15**, 140 (1921) ; **18**, 784 (1924) ; **19**, 1075 (1925) ; **22**, 1212 (1928)
HUME, E. M. AND SMITH, H. H., *Biochem. J.*, **25**, 300 (1931)
HUNT, C. H., *J. Biol. Chem.*, **79**, 723 (1928)
HUNT, C. H., AND WILDER, W., *J. Biol. Chem.*, **90**, 279 (1931)
HUTCHISON, R., *Lancet,* **221**, 979 (1931)
KENNEDY, D., AND PALMER, L. S. (1), *J. Biol. Chem.*, **76**, 591, 607 (1928)
KENNEDY, D., AND PALMER, L. S. (2), *J. Biol. Chem.*, **83**, 493 (1929)
LECOQ, R. (1), *J. pharm. chim.*, **6**, 289 (1927)
LECOQ, R. (2), *J. Biol. Chem.*, **91**, 671 (1931)
NARAYANAN, B. T., AND DRUMMOND, J. C., *Biochem. J.*, **24**, 19 (1930)
NORRIS, L. C., AND RINGROSE, A. T., *Science,* **71**, 643 (1930)
PARSONS, H. T., *J. Biol. Chem.*, **90**, 351 (1931)
PARSONS, H. T., *et al.*, *Arch. Path.*, **10**, 1 (1930)
PETERS, R. A. (1), *J. State Med.*, **37**, 683 (1930)
PETERS, R. A. (2), *Nature,* **128**, 39 (1931)
RANDOIN, L., AND LECOQ, R., *Compt. rend.*, **187**, 60 (1928)
READER, V. (1), *Biochem. J.*, **23**, 689 (1929)
READER, V. (2), *Biochem. J.*, **24**, 77 (1930)
READER, V. (3), *Biochem. J.*, **24**, 1827 (1930)
READER, V., AND DRUMMOND, J. C., *Biochem. J.*, **20**, 1256 (1926)
ROSEDALE, J. L. (1), *Biochem. J.*, **21**, 1266 (1927)
ROSEDALE, J. L. (2), *Indian J. Med. Research,* **17**, 216 (1929)
SHERMAN, H. C., AND GLOY, O. H. M., *J. Biol. Chem.*, **74**, 117 (1927)
SUPPLEE, G. C., KAHLENBERG, C. J., AND FLANIGAN, G. E., *J. Biol. Chem.*, **93**, 705 (1931)
SURE, B., SMITH, M. E., AND KIK, M. C., *Science,* **73**, 242 (1931)

WILLIAMS, G. Z., AND LEWIS, R. C., *J. Biol. Chem.,* **89,** 275 (1930)
WILLIAMS, R. J., AND WATERMAN, R. E., *J. Biol. Chem.,* **78,** 311 (1928)
WILLIAMS, R. J., WATERMAN, R. E., AND GURIN, S., *J. Biol. Chem.,* **83,** 321 (1929)

REFERENCES TO GROWTH-PROMOTING FACTORS FOR
MICRO-ORGANISMS; "BIOS"

BUXTON, H. W., AND PRAMANIK, B. N., *Biochem. J.,* **25,** 1656, 1670 (1931)
DAVIS, J. G., AND GOLDING, J., *Biochem. J.,* **24,** 1503 (1930)
NARAYANAN, B. T., *Biochem. J.,* **24,** 6 (1930)
WILLIAMS, R. J., *J. Biol. Chem.,* **38,** 465 (1919)
WILLIAMS, R. J., AND BRADWAY, E. M., *J. Am. Chem. Soc.,* **53,** 783 (1931)
WILLIAMS, R. J., AND ROEHM, R. R., *J. Biol. Chem.,* **87,** 581 (1930)
WILLIAMS, R. J., AND TRUESDAIL, J. H., *J. Am. Chem. Soc.,* **53,** 4171 (1931)

REFERENCES TO VITAMIN C

BRACEWELL, M. F., KIDD, F., WEST, C., AND ZILVA, S. S., *Biochem. J.,* **25,** 138 (1931)
BRACEWELL, M. F., AND ZILVA, S. S., *Biochem. J.,* **25,** 1081 (1931)
CLELAND, J. B., AND FRY, H. K., *Med. J. Australia,* **1,** 410 (1930)
COWARD, K. H., *Brit. Med. J.,* **ii,** 71 (1931)
GÖTHLIN, G. F., *Skand. Arch. Physiol.,* **61,** 225 (1931)
HANKE, M. T., *J. Am. Dent. Assoc.,* **17,** 957 (1930)
HOWITT, B. F., *Arch. Path.,* **11,** 574 (1931)
HUMPHREYS, F. E., AND ZILVA, S. S., *Biochem. J.,* **25,** 579 (1931)
JONES, D. B., AND NELSON, E. M., *Am. J. Pub. Health,* **20,** 387 (1930)
JULIAN, R. R. ST., AND HELLER, V. G., *J. Biol. Chem.,* **90,** 99 (1931)
KEY, K. M., AND ELPHICK, G. K., *Biochem. J.,* **25,** 888 (1931)
League of Nations Health Organization, Permanent Commission on Biological Standardization. *"Report of the Conference on Vitamin Standards,"* London, Geneva (1931)
LIO, G., *Sperimentale,* **85,** 99, 111 (1931)
MARTIN, H. E., *Lancet,* **221,** 293 (1931)
MICHAUX, A., *Bull. soc. sci. hyg. aliment.,* **19,** 117 (1931)
MORGAN, A. F., FIELD, A., AND NICHOLS, P. F., *J. Agr. Research,* **42,** 35 (1931)
OHATA, S., *J. Biochem. (Japan),* **12,** 419 (1930)
RANDOIN, L., AND MICHAUX, A., *Compt. rend.,* **192,** 108 (1931)
REYHER, E. W., AND WALKOFF, O., *Münch. med. Wochschr.,* **75,** 2087 (1928)
SALTER, W. T., AND AUB, J. C., *Arch. Path.,* **11,** 380 (1931)
SCHEUNERT, A., AND RESCHKE, J., *Klin. Wochschr.,* **31,** 1452 (1931)
SCHWARTZE, E. W., MURPHY, F. J., AND COX, G. J., *J. Nutrition,* **4,** 211 (1931)
WELLS, F. M., *Brit. Med. J.,* **ii,** 873 (1931)
ZILVA, S. S. (1), *Biochem. J.,* **24,** 1687 (1930)
ZILVA, S. S. (2), *Biochem. J.,* **25,** 594 (1931)

PART II. FAT-SOLUBLE GROUP*

Vitamin A

1*a*. *Clinical instances of avitaminosis A*.—That vitamin A deficiency in humans is not so rare as is commonly supposed suggests itself from a record of 17 cases of xerophthalmia, or night blindness, seen in one year in an ophthalmological department in a North of England hospital (Spence). An account has appeared of 13 cases of xerophthalmia noted among undernourished children in America (Weech). In many parts of India xerophthalmia is the chief cause of blindness in children, and is not infrequent in adults; 67 instances were seen in Madras alone among children under five and two-thirds of these became blind (Wright, R. E.). In Malaya the immigrant Indians suffer from vitamin A starvation, as evidenced by the high incidence of xerophthalmia and night blindness, and it may be responsible for their observed low resistance to infection (Field). In China also many cases have been noted by one observer (Chou) and several in Newfoundland (Aykroyd). The occurrence of a multiple vitamin A and vitamin B deficiency in Sierra Leone has already been alluded to (Wright, E. J.). Skin lesions attributed to vitamin A deficiency in a group of Chinese soldiers have been described by Frazier and Hu. A Dutch worker, pointing out the importance of vitamin A in the metabolism of cells of ectodermal origin, has advocated vitamin A therapy for infantile eczema, but his results seem rather indefinite (Kuipers). Urinary calculi are very prevalent over a large area of India, and McCarrison (3) has evidence that the principal causative factors are vitamin A deficiency, together with excess calcium over phosphate, and a high cereal intake.

1*b*. *Lesions in experimental avitaminosis A*.—The pathology of vitamin A deficiency has been examined for the albino mouse (Wolfe and Salter) and the monkey (Tilden and Miller): there is extensive epithelial keratinisation in both species but few evidences of infective troubles are seen. The tracheal mucous membrane in the vitamin-A–deficient rat undergoes proliferative inflammatory changes, and the thyroid gland shows hypertrophy and abnormal distention of the follicles [McCarrison (1)]. In hens, vitamin A deficiency is readily

* Received February 15, 1932.

produced and appears to be identical with the disease known to poultry experts as "visceral gout" (Capper, McKibbin, and Prentice; see also Henninger; McFarlane, Graham, and Richardson).

In vitamin A deficiency (in the rat) no noteworthy deviations from the normal are apparent in respect to the following: carbohydrate metabolism (Sure and Smith); hematopoietic function (Sure, Kik, and Walker; but compare the positive result of Binet and Strumza, on hematopoietic action of carotene in venesectioned dogs); blood chemistry and red cell count (Turner; but compare Turner and Loew); absorption of fats, proteins and carbohydrates (St. Julian and Heller).

Vitamin A deficiency in man has no unfavourable influence on the calcification and formation of the teeth (Bloch).

Apart from the better-known ill effects of vitamin A deprivation— respiratory diseases, xerophthalmia, stone [McCarrison (2, 4); McCarrison and Ranganathan; Ranganathan (1, 2)], infective conditions—all attributable presumably to mucous membrane degeneration, special attention has recently been drawn to the following: (a) periodontal disease; (b) night blindness; and (c) degenerative changes in the nervous system including the spinal cord. With regard to the first, it has been shown (May Mellanby) that a shortage of vitamin A in a puppy's diet leads in later life to hyperplasia of the subgingival epithelium and a resulting invasion by pathogenic organisms; a condition resembling pyorrhoea is thus set up. This observation opens up questions of possibly great clinical significance. The night blindness of vitamin A deficiency was shown some years ago, by Fridericia and Holm, to be correlated with a failure to regenerate the visual purple, and Tansley has developed this work and devised a photographic method of measuring the visual purple. In this connection also it is interesting to note that the retinal tissue appears to be particularly richly supplied with vitamin A (Yudkin, Kriss, and Smith; Smith, Yudkin, Kriss, and Zimmerman).

Marked nervous symptoms, characterised by impaired vision, inco-ordination and spasms, were noted by Hughes and co-workers in 1928 in vitamin A deficient animals—pigs, chickens, and cows. Histological examination showed degeneration of the nerve bundles in portions of the spinal cord, and optic, sciatic, and femoral nerves (Hughes, Lienhardt, and Aubel). E. Mellanby (1, 2, 3) has found that ergot and the germ of cereals, if given in the absence of vitamin A, will produce a degeneration in the spinal cord; administration of the vitamin led to a rapid cure. He points out that clinically a similar degeneration is found in the following conditions: (*a*) nervous ergotism, (*b*) lathyrism, (*c*) pellagra, and (*d*) pernicious anaemia. The causation of the first two of these is apparently the same as in Mellanby's experiments, viz., a diet containing ergotised rye and poor in animal fat. Pellagra is regarded as a joint deficiency of vitamin B_2 and vitamin A, the former responsible for the skin lesions and the latter for the nerve degeneration. In pernicious anaemia it is held that there is a deficiency (*a*) of the water-soluble substance from the liver, causing the blood changes, and (*b*) of vitamin A, causing the lesions in the central nervous system. Here again a fresh field of great interest and importance is opening up.

2. *Vitamin A and resistance to infections in humans.*—Much attention is being given to the therapeutic possibilities of vitamin A, following on Mellanby's preliminary report published two years back of its apparently successful use in puerperal septicaemia (Mellanby and Green). It had been known for many years that vitamin A deficiency in the rat leads to infective troubles, and Mellanby suggested renaming the factor the anti-infective vitamin, adding "it is difficult to avoid the conclusion that a large number of common infective conditions are due to a deficiency of this substance in the diet of many people" [Green and Mellanby (1)]. Commercial interests have not failed to exploit the idea to the utmost and vitamin A concentrates are being widely advertised "for the treatment of many acute infections." It is almost certain, however, that the actual possibilities of vitamin A in clinical practice are somewhat less general than suggested by such advertisements. As Mellanby himself has recently written (1931), "It is clear that vitamin A as a therapeutic agent in acute infective conditions like pneumonia is limited in its effect. As a prophylactic agent against infection and especially against chronic infection, it seems to me probable that it will be more effective." A number of arguments may be cited here in support of the view that vitamin A has a rather specialised action in relation to infectivity. In the first place the actual infections seen in vitamin A deficiency are not of an acute but of a sub-acute or chronic type, and they clear up readily when vitamin A is given. Secondly, it appears that these infections originate on the mucous membranes, which it will be recalled are keratinised and degenerated and in consequence, we may suppose, unable to prevent invasion by fortuitous micro-organisms: work in the writer's laboratory (1930–31) indicates that all of the various

infective processes which can be detected in avitaminosis A are in fact invariably associated with mal-functioning membrane. Furthermore we find (1929–30) that human subjects who have succumbed to the most varied types of acute infections may have fully normal vitamin A reserves, so that in such cases little could be gained by treatment aimed at rectifying a non-existing deficiency. These results, of course, in no way militate against the advantage of providing adequacy of vitamin A prophylactically, in order to insure mucous membrane functioning healthily. As Mellanby (1931) points out, "favourable results could be expected to ensue from vitamin A therapy in puerperal sepsis, since the disease is an infection of a mucous membrane."

Mellanby's original results with puerperal septicaemia were commented on by Cramer who wrote, "there is no evidence that vitamin A can cure infections once the barrier of the mucous membranes has been passed." However, Mellanby (1931) has since reported that "the results so far obtained in 19 cases are promising but not conclusive, the mortality being about 28 per cent, as compared with a usual mortality rate of 80 per cent." A difficulty in assessing these results is that normally the virulence and mortality may vary considerably from case to case. The foregoing relates to the curative treatment of puerperal septicaemia. Puerperal sepsis, as distinct from septicaemia, has also been attacked by preventive treatment with vitamin A (Green, Pindar, Davis, and Mellanby). Two hundred and seventy-five pregnant women attending ante-natal clinics at Sheffield were given vitamin A supplements, and 275 acted as the controls. The results are summarised below in Table IV.

TABLE IV

	Vitamin Group	Control Group
Number of cases	275	275
Morbid cases (notifiable standard)	11	15
Morbid cases (B.M.A. standard)	3	13
Puerperal pyrexia	53	85
Maternal mortality	0	1
Infant morbidity	13	9

As the authors point out, the results if analysed on the basis of the "notifiable" standard would indicate little or no benefit from the vitamin treatment; but, on the other hand, if expressed on the B.M.A. standard of morbidity or on the basis of duration of pyrexia, they indicate an increased resistance. A comparison of the results as expressed by the two standards suggests that the vitamin A delayed the onset of sepsis to a later stage in the puerperium. Burton and Balmain also investigated the influence of vitamin A and D administration during pregnancy on a group of 52 women, but were unable to obtain any evidence of increased streptococcal immunity as measured by the Dick test. Treatment of pneumonia by massive doses of vitamin A has been tested (Donaldson and Tasker) ; while it is admitted that mortality and clinical symptoms may vary so widely that no far-reaching conclusions are justified from a small series of cases, yet there appeared to be some evidence of lessened mortality and fewer instances of delayed resolution (Table V). There was no obvious difference in duration of pyrexia or of physical signs.

TABLE V

	Untreated	Vitamin A as Liver	Vitamin A as Concentrate
Total number of cases	100	99	100
Percentage of mortality	13	9	8
Percentage of delayed resolution	17	7	12

The incidence of common colds in infants under two years was not lessened by the administration of massive doses of vitamin A, added to the ordinary liberal diet (Wright, *et al.*).

It will be readily admitted, of course, that in many distant parts of the globe vitamin A deficiency is the rule, as it is also among some of the poorer sections of the community in England and America, and in such cases the provision of adequate sources of vitamin A is an urgent task awaiting the attention of the sociologist.

A striking example of the connection between diet and disease is furnished by a comparison of the incidence of infectious disorders in two neighbouring East African tribes, one consuming a one-sided cereal diet and the other on a mixed meat, milk, and raw blood diet (Orr, MacLeod, and MacKie, Table VI).

TABLE VI

INCIDENCE EXPRESSED AS PERCENTAGE OF ALL ILLNESS RECORDED

	On Cereal Diet	On Animal Diet
Bronchitis, and pneumonia, etc.	31	4
Tropical illness	33	3
Phthisis	6	1

On the animal diet the chief disease was rheumatoid arthritis, associated with chronic constipation. There is no proof of course that vitamin A deficiency was the only defect in the cereal diet, but it was almost certainly a principal factor.

3. *Vitamin A and experimental infections.*—Our view that the infections in vitamin A deficiency are purely secondary to xerotic changes is in keeping with the following findings: (*a*) that the inflammatory changes in the eye are preceded by a loss of transparency of the cornea (Mouriquand, Rollet, and Chaix), (*b*) that there is leucocytosis, and as the avitaminosis advances the lymphocyte count decreases and the polymorphonuclear count increases (Turner and Loew), and (*c*) that dietary changes in no way modify the resistance in mice to experimental epidemics caused by *B. aertrycke* (Topley, Greenwood, and Wilson); and (*d*) that in cases of scarlet fever in humans, or in normal pregnant women, the consumption of vitamin A has no effect on the Dick test for immunity (Burton and Balmain). Boynton and Bradford report a decreased resistance to an injected *mucosus capsulatus* organism in vitamin A deficient rats. Scrutiny of their paper, however, shows that this conclusion is deduced solely from the finding that the survival period is shorter in rats suffering from the infection with concurrent vitamin A deficiency than in those suffering from the infection alone—which itself was bordering on the lethal dose. It is possible therefore that the effect may have been merely additive, and so not indicative of any direct action of vitamin A upon the infective process. Further, the variation in the survival period in the inoculated controls receiving vitamin A is so great (e.g., 10 to 30 days in one group, but 20 to 50 or indefinitely greater in another) that the statistical significance of the results is necessarily low. Lassen found that resistance to *per os* (or subcutaneous) infection with paratyphoid was diminished in vitamin A deficiency in rats. He was unable, however, to demonstrate any fault in the gut wall or mucosa which could be held responsible. No final or conclusive evidence has yet been brought forward of any abnormality in the "immunological" reactions, in avitaminosis A. Lassen, it is true, had some evidence of lowered agglutinins but not of the immunising power of vaccination; and Euler reports that excess of carotene (provitamin A) administered to rabbits increased the amboceptor in their blood but did not affect haemolysis *in vitro* or react with amboceptor. In short we have no reason to suppose that vitamin A bears any relation to infectivity other than through its action

on dermal tissues. Several of the investigators mentioned above, like others before them, have endeavoured to demonstrate anti-infective properties for the other vitamins but always with substantially negative results.

4. *Absorption and excretion of vitamin A.*—Vitamin A administered with large amounts of mineral oil may be largely lost to the body if the amount of vitamin is very slight and of oil great [Rowntree (2)]; but there is little evidence of such loss when the oil and the vitamin are given separately [Jackson (1, 2)]. The presence of bile is not necessary for the absorption of vitamin A from the gastrointestinal tract of the rat (Schmidt and Schmidt). The vitamin is excreted to a marked extent in the faeces by children, the loss running parallel with the loss of fat [Rowntree (1)]. Carotene, like vitamin A, is less well absorbed in paraffin oil than in a vegetable fat [Moore (2)]; and better on a fat-rich than on a fat-free diet [Ahmad (2)].

The remarkable powers of vitamin A storage are illustrated by the observation that a quantity sufficient to protect a rat for several months may be given in a single dose (Nelson, Walker, and Jones). Vitamin A reserves are not depleted in vitamin B deficiency in the rat (Dann and Moore).

5. *Vitamin A and carotene.*—Work published during 1930–31 has brought further confirmation to the claim of Euler and co-workers (1928) that the pigment carotene possesses vitamin A activity (as first suggested several years previously by Steenbock), and to Moore's contention (3, 4) that carotene is not identical with the vitamin but is the pro-vitamin and is converted into the vitamin in the animal body. The vitamin A activity of carotene is abundantly demonstrated by the papers of Moore (1, 2), who carried out biological tests on carotene derived from carrot root or red-palm oil, demonstrated its freedom from vitamin D and showed that it was still efficacious even when given with fat-free diets; and (during the period under review) of Javillier and Emerique (1), who find that a specimen prepared 40 years ago is still potent, and that repeated re-purification does not lead to loss of activity provided oxidation is excluded (2, 3); of Euler and others (Euler, Demole, Karrer, and Walker) who demonstrate that the activity of the unsaponifiable matter from various plant substances runs parallel with the carotene content; of Olcovich and Mattill who find crystalline carotene from lettuce to have an activity equal to that from other sources; of van

Stolk and associates who still obtained positive results with carotene recrystallised 11 times; and of Green and Mellanby (1930) who demonstrated that the pigment has the same characteristic anti-infective action as vitamin A. The negative results first obtained by Dulière, Morton, and Drummond are to be attributed not to the use of a fat-free diet [Moore (2)] but to the destructive action on the carotene of the solvent employed (Hume and Smedley-MacLean; Drummond, Ahmad, and Morton). That carotene is not identical with the vitamin A of liver-oils is clear from the fact that vitamin A is colourless whereas carotene is intensely yellow (Dulière, Morton, and Drummond); that the physical properties and selective absorptions of the two substances differ [Moore (3); Drummond, Ahmad, and Morton], carotene being devoid of the intense band at 328 mμ deemed characteristic of vitamin A [Capper (1)] and giving a colour reaction with SbCl$_3$ at 590 mμ instead of 610 to 630 mμ [Moore (5)]; and, although this now seems in question, that weight for weight vitamin A concentrates may be 100 times more active than carotene (Dulière, et al.; Drummond, Ahmad, and Morton; Bezssonov, etc.). That carotene *is converted into vitamin A* in the animal organism, as suggested by Moore (4), has been proved by feeding it to depleted rats and showing that vitamin A then appears in the liver, as characterised by growth-promoting (or anti-xerotic) activity but differentiated from carotene [Moore (5)] by: (*a*) absence of yellow pigmentation [Moore (4)]; (*b*) SbCl$_3$ reaction at 610 to 630 mμ; (*c*) ultra-violet absorption at 328 mμ [Capper (2)]. Drummond and co-workers (1930) reached the same conclusion, working likewise with the rat, and this conversion of carotene to vitamin A in the animal organism has been shown to hold good also for the hen [Capper (3); Capper, McKibbin, and Prentice] and the rabbit (Wolff, Overhoff, and Eckelen).[1]   Euler and co-workers (1928) claimed that dihydro α-crocetin shared with carotene a vitamin A activity, but this has not been confirmed (Drummond, et al., 1930), nor are other carotenoids or their esters active, as, e.g., xanthophyll (Karrer, Euler, and Rydbom), or xanthophyll distearate and lutein distearate (Rydbom). The alleged activity of chlorophyll and its derivatives (Bürgi) lacks confirmation. Rubrene is inactive [Javillier and Emerique (4)].

Efforts to bring about the conversion of carotene into vitamin A

[1] These workers claim to be able to separate carotene from vitamin A by shaking a petrol-ether solution of the two with 90 per cent alcohol; the vitamin goes into the alcoholic layer.

in vitro, by incubation with liver tissue, and by the action of intestinal bacteria, have not succeeded [Ahmad (2)], but Euler thinks he has evidence that hen's serum can transform carotene into a substance similar to but not spectroscopically identical with vitamin A. He supposes that it is in the blood that the transformation occurs *in vivo;* whereas Moore (6) concludes that it is probably in the liver, since he found that carotene fed to rats could be detected unchanged in the alimentary canal and faeces while large amounts of vitamin A appeared as such in the liver. The storage-fats of the body contained much smaller traces of the vitamin, e.g., only 1/100,000 of the concentration in the liver, so that it was concluded that the organ plays a rôle in regulating the distribution of the vitamin throughout the body.[2]

The vitamin A activity of plant substances is presumably due principally to their carotene content rather than to the "liver-oil vitamin A" (Drummond, Ahmad, and Morton). The same has been shown to be true of the diatom, *Nitzschia closterium* [Ahmad (1)]. Butter contains both substances (Morton and Heilbron; Lundborg). The value of red-palm oil as a source of carotene (e.g., Moore, 1929) has been confirmed [Ahmad (2)]. Euler, Demole, Weinhagen, and Karrer found little carotene in chestnut leaves, nor any growth-promoting substances like vitamin A in wheat nuclei; they could not get evidence of the alleged toxic substance of wheat-embryo oil. A very interesting observation is that the genes for inheritance of yellow pigmentation in corn are also responsible for the formation of carotenoid pigments and vitamin A activity (Mangelsdorf and Fraps). It is stated that this is the first time that a direct relationship between different doses of the same gene and their chemical effect has been established (but cf. Hauge and Trost).

Many papers have appeared in the past few months dealing with the properties and constitution of carotene and its chemical relationship to vitamin A.[3] Its degradation by ozone (Pummerer, Rebman, and Reindel); its absorbability on norite and Lloyd's earth (Quinn and Hartley); and its bleachability and protection by hydroquinone (Olcovich and Mattill), have been studied. Smith has obtained fur-

---

[2] Since this MS was prepared for the press, the paper of Olcott and McCann has appeared. Carotene was incubated with liver tissue from depleted rats, or with aqueous extract of liver; the appearance of a band at 328 mμ was taken to indicate the transformation of carotene to vitamin A.

[3] Cf. also page 551 (Ed.).

ther evidence in favour of a structure for carotene previously proposed by him. The empirical formula $C_{40}H_{56}$ shows that there are thirteen unsaturated linkages in the molecule, and in order to determine whether these are double bonds, rings, or combinations of the two he employed the method of catalytic hydrogenation. The results suggest a system of nine conjugated double bonds, conjugated further with two other unsaturated linkages, either double bonds or cyclopropane rings. Karrer reached somewhat similar conclusions and put forward the following formula (Karrer, Helfenstein, Wehrli, and Wettstein) :

I. β carotene

Carotene has been shown to exist in two or more isomeric modifications, which are now being studied with some intensity [Kuhn and Lederer (1, 2, 3) ; Kuhn and Brockmann (1, 2) ; Karrer; Euler; Euler, Karrer, Hellström, and Rydbom; Rosenheim (2)].

It has been stated that partial reduction with aluminium amalgam yields a product more active than carotene. Hydrocarotene containing eight double bonds is more active biologically, and gives a more intense $SbCl_3$ coloration than carotene and has an absorption spectrum similar to but not identical with the liver vitamin A. The latter, it is suggested, may be a hydrogenated carotene, formed in the liver through the action of carotenase (Euler; Karrer, Euler, Euler, Hellström, and Rydbom; and Euler, Karrer, Hellström, and Rydbom), Dihydrocarotene differs from vitamin A in absorption spectrum, quality of blue coloration with $SbCl_3$, and ratio of intensity of the two (Morton).

6. *Chemistry of vitamin A.*—It has been concluded that vitamin A contains the same carbon ring system (pseudo-ionone) as carotene, since cod-liver oil concentrate resembles carotene in yielding geronic acid on ozonisation (Karrer). Karrer believes vitamin A to be hy-

droxy carotene, or a carotene oxidation product; whereas Euler, as mentioned above, has suggested that it may be a reduced derivative. An attempt has been made to measure the molecular weight of vitamin A by the diffusion method : the value obtained, however (molecular weight 330), would indicate no simple relationship to carotene, which has a molecular weight of 536 (Bruins, Overhoff, and Wolff).[4]

Several papers suggest the possibility that vitamin A can be derived from cholesterol. [It will be recalled that some years ago Rosenheim (1) concluded that the $SbCl_3$ test given by oxycholesterol differed from the true vitamin A reaction, in being inhibited by fats, and biological tests also were inconclusive. Similar negative results had been reported by Takahashi, *et al.,* in 1925.] Kerppola finds that by special treatment, including recrystallisation in absence of light and air, a "cholesterol fraction" can be obtained from cod-liver oil which differs from ordinary cholesterol and contains a substance apparently identical with vitamin A, which acts as a chromogen with $SbCl_3$, cures xerophthalmia, and restores the $SbCl_3$ reactivity to tissues of depleted rats. Seel, and Seel and Dannmeyer, report that cholesterol oxidised with benzoyl superoxide is partly transformed into a product resembling vitamin A in giving (*a*) ultra-violet absorption bands at 327 and 293 mμ, (*b*) $SbCl_3$ coloration, (*c*) biological activity. The minimum dose of the "synthetic" oxidised cholesterol, however, was as high as 0.1 mg. whereas a "natural" vitamin A preparation from shark-liver oil was active at 0.0001 mg. Seel concludes that vitamin A is a very highly labile partial oxidation product of cholesterol. A report on the absorption spectrum of Seel's preparation in the $SbCl_3$ test would have been of interest. It is conceivable that under suitable conditions vitamin A could be derived from cholesterol, as well as from carotene; but obviously further work will be needed to confirm or disprove these claims.

7. *Spectroscopic data.*—It has been found that the absorption bands exhibited by substances rich in vitamin A in the $SbCl_3$ blue coloration test may vary according to the source employed or can be

---

[4] Since this review was prepared for the press Karrer and co-workers (*Helv. Chim. Acta,* December, 1931) have announced the isolation of vitamin A, from halibut or mackerel-liver oil, as an alcohol with the formula $C_{20}H_{30}O$, or $C_{22}H_{32}O$; and possible structural formulae are suggested. Drummond, Heilbron, and Morton describe the isolation, also from halibut-liver oil, of a viscid oil with the composition $C_{20}H_{30}O$, probably vitamin A (Society of Chemical Industry, January 4, 1932).

shifted by experimental conditions. Which bands are characteristic of vitamin A is still under discussion. The Liverpool investigators believe that cod-liver oil contains two separate and distinct chromogens for the SbCl$_3$ coloration, one giving the maximum at 606 mμ and the other at 572 mμ. It is the latter which runs parallel with the ultra-violet absorption band at 328 mμ and is attributed to vitamin A. The 606 mμ band, which had often in the past been taken to relate to the vitamin [e.g., by these workers themselves in an earlier paper (Morton, Heilbron, and Thompson)] and which is mainly responsible for the blue colour, is now found to vary independently of the 572 mμ band and to be increased in intensity when oils are allowed to age or when they are treated with oxidising agents. "Hence it is concluded that the matching of blue colours with Lovibond glasses (for the SbCl$_3$ test) though it may act as a rough guide to vitamin A potency is theoretically unsound." Some of the principal data of these workers [Gillam, Heilbron, and Morton; Heilbron and Morton (1); Gillam, Heilbron, Hilditch, and Morton; Gillam and Morton; Heilbron, Gillam, and Morton; Heilbron and Morton (2)] we have summarised in Table VII. In support of the foregoing conclusions it has been found (Emmerie, Eckelen, and Wolff) that the 606 mμ band disappears in the presence of indol or furan and related substances, without effect on the 572 mμ band or the ultra-violet 328 mμ band, or the biological activity. The latter and not the 606 mμ band is therefore again supposed to correspond better with the vitamin. On the other hand Brode and Magill have defined conditions for the SbCl$_3$ test under which only the 606 mμ band is produced and not the 578 mμ; they mention incidentally that two new bands at 532 and 472 mμ appear when the test solution fades or becomes red, related to the original ones at 608 mμ and 578 mμ, respectively. That the problem is not so simple as at first sight appeared is shown also by one of the most recent of the papers in which Morton has collaborated, which reports that the 606 band, and not the 572, agrees best with the biological activity of different samples of cod-liver oils (Coward, Dyer, Morton, and Gaddum, *vide infra*). While this contribution tends if anything to restore the issue to its original position, the possibility should be borne in mind that there may well exist more than one labile transformation product closely similar to vitamin A or carotene, and, like these, varying in precise biological activity and position of absorption bands.

In turn the ultra-violet absorption of vitamin A-containing fats is

not restricted to the simple band at 328 mμ; there are others, e.g., at
260 to 295 mμ (Morton,.Heilbron, and Thompson), not specifically
due it seems to vitamin A, but yet absent from vitamin-A–free fats
or the fatty acids derived therefrom (Gillam, Heilbron, Hilditch, and
Morton). The complexity of the matter is illustrated by Woodrow
and Cunningham, who report that sources of vitamin A, such as cod-
liver oil, spinach juice, egg-yolk, and butter, had prominent bands at
310 and 326, with minor bands at 320, 330, and 337 mμ. These were
shifted 3 mμ toward shorter wave-lengths in the ether-extracted oils,
and disappeared after aëration or irradiation. Peanut oil, rich in
vitamin D, had bands at 270 to 290 but not at 326 mμ.

TABLE VII

VITAMIN A ABSORPTION SPECTRA DATA, FROM PAPERS OF
GILLAM, MORTON, AND HEILBRON

	Absorption Maxima in the Ultra-Violet mμ	Absorption Maxima in the SbCl$_3$ Test mμ
Liver oils	260–295, 328	572, 606
Concentrates	?, 328	583, 620
Concentrates decomposed with NaOEt	260, 271, 282, 302, 316, 330, 350, 375, 394	....
Natural fats free from vitamin A.....	....	....

The bands at 572 and 328 are attributed to vitamin A.

The bands at 583 and 620, for concentrates, correspond with 572 and 606,
respectively, for oils.

The band at 606 is increased in intensity by ageing, H_2O_2, O_3, etc.

(Band 328 is free from fine structure.)

(Band 606 is a sharp single band.)

8. *Stability, solubility, etc.*—It has been shown that vitamin A is
adsorbed on silica gel so tenaciously as to be unavailable to rats fed
thereon, although still extractable in toluene (Lachat, Dutcher, and
Honeywell); that various finely divided powders may inactivate the
vitamin (Marcus); and that hydroquinone can delay its destruction
in cod-liver oil-grain mixture (Huston and Hoppert). The destructive action of ultra-violet rays on vitamin A activity in butter (Steenbock and Wirick) and in petrol-ether extracts of plant tissues (Quinn,
Hartley, and Derow), has been investigated; the chromogen is destroyed by ultra-violet waves of length less than 500 mμ, which process is accelerated by the presence of oxygen [Norris and Church

(2)]. The unsaponifiable fraction can be extracted from saponified fats, without any loss of vitamin A activity, by means of solvents such as ether, ethylacetate, chloroform, or light petrol (Smith and Hazley), and vitamin A of plant tissues dissolves readily in vegetable oils (Quinn, *et al.*).

9. *Vitamin A assay.*—A careful study has recently been carried out by the Pharmaceutical Society workers in collaboration with the Liverpool group, on the relative merits of various methods of assaying for vitamin A in cod-liver oil, viz.: (*a*) biological; (*b*) SbCl$_3$ tintometric, on the oil direct, or (*c*) on the unsaponifiable fraction; (*d*) intensity of absorption in the oil-SbCl$_3$ blue solution, at 572 mμ, or (*e*) at 606 mμ; and (*f*) intensity of absorption, in the oil itself, at 328 mμ. Statistical examination of the results showed that best agreement with the biological method was obtained by the 328 mμ band or by the tintometer method on the unsaponifiable fraction (methods *f* and *c*). Notwithstanding the findings of Heilbron and others alluded to in the last section, the 572 mμ and 606 mμ bands (methods *d* and *e*) gave less good agreement. The least satisfactory result of all was given by the tintometric method on the oil itself (method *b*). The agreement noted between methods *a, c,* and *f* was not so good on stale as on fresh oils (Coward, Dyer, Morton, and Gaddum). Further information would be of interest as to the relative merits of determinations at 583 mμ and 620 mμ, carried out on the unsaponifiable fraction instead of on the whole oil.

The London Conference (League of Nations Health Organisation) have selected carotene as a provisional international standard of reference for vitamin A, with a selected sample of cod-liver oil as second provisional standard. The international unit is the vitamin A potency of 1γ (= 0.001 mg.) of a mixed specimen of carotene, 3 to 5 γ of which ought in practice to be sufficient to restore growth or cure xerophthalmia in vitamin A depleted rats. No special method of test is recommended by the conference, but it is suggested that further attention might be given to curative action on xerophthalmia or other lesions characteristic of vitamin A deficiency, as well as to weight increase.

The SbCl$_3$ tintometric method was found unreliable by some workers (e.g., Schmidt-Nielsen and Schmidt-Nielsen) ; in particular it was pointed out that the dilution curve is not linear [Norris and Church (1)] so that a direct comparison of different oils is not possible, except by working at low colour-values [Norris and Church

(2)] ; however, the difficulty is overcome by using the unsaponifiable residue (which is readily extracted by $CHCl_3$) instead of the oil itself (Smith and Hazley), a conclusion substantiated by the results of Coward and co-workers (*supra*). A sub-committee appointed by the Pharmacopoeia Commission has issued a report (General Medical Council) which sets out detailed technical directions for carrying out the test, and preparing the reagents, etc. As already indicated a series of papers has appeared showing that varying conditions may serve to intensify either the 606 mμ band or the 572 mμ band, and suggesting that one or the other is more specific for vitamin A; nevertheless the simple Lovibond tintometric method, carried out on the unsaponifiable fraction, still appears preferable to the more complicated spectrophotometric determination of the intensity of either of these bands.

The growth-rate method has received study. In order to save the use of extravagantly large numbers of experimental animals, as necessitated in the usual growth-test method (e.g., Accessory Food Factors Committee), in which groups of animals are put on various graded levels of both unknown and standard, and a comparison made between such supplements as will induce the same growth effect, Coward and her collaborators [Coward, Key, Dyer, and Morgan (1)], have worked out a method in which only two groups of animals are taken, one on a given dose of the unknown and the other on a given dose of the standard. Five or preferably ten animals are used in each group. The mean gains in weight with each of the two substances are worked out. Reference is then made to an existing curve which relates amount of vitamin fed (as standard cod-liver oil) to corresponding increases in body weight. In this way the relative values of the two substances are found, and can be expressed in terms of the standard cod-liver oil. The method has been applied to butter with satisfactory results (Morgan and Coward). Sherman has continued his studies on the growth effects of graded increments of vitamin A : when nine or more standardised depleted animals were used at each level, and all the improvements permitted by recent developments were adopted, a decrease of 25 per cent or increase of 33 per cent in vitamin content could be readily measured (Sherman and Batchelder) ; comparison was best made at growth gains of 3 to 4 gm. per week (Sherman and Stiebeling). The following sources of error in vitamin A assay have been discussed : the presence of vitamin A in the yeast used in the basal diet (Honeywell, Dutcher, and Ely) ; premature flattening of growth-curve, arising either from an inadequate supply of vitamin B [Norris and Church (3)] or from increased needs for vitamin A at puberty (Schmidt-Nielsen and Schmidt-Nielsen) or from overdoses of vitamin A (Schmidt-Nielsen and Schmidt-Nielsen) ; variety of casein employed [Coward, Key, Dyer, and Morgan (2)]. A diet for breeding rats for vitamin A work, said to eliminate seasonal variation, is given (Gudjónsson).

Other methods are advocated. Nelson, Walker, and Jones adopt a preventive test in place of the usual curative-growth method. The growth response and duration of life were found to be satisfactorily proportional to the amount of vitamin fed, even when the quantity ingested was sufficient to prolong the life of the rat for two months. Hume and Henderson Smith prefer to determine the smallest dose of the unknown on which all the animals in a group are able to survive; it is said that considerable accuracy is possible, and, of course, few animals are required, compared with the growth method. The cornified epithelium seen in the vaginal smears of vitamin-A-deficient spayed rats (*colpokeratosis*), is said to disappear within 24 to 72 hours once vitamin A is fed, which should provide a rapid and convenient test (Hohlweg and Dohrn) ; but it should be borne in mind that Steenbock and Wirick, and Coward, Morgan, and Dyer have questioned the value of the vaginal-smear method.

10. *Occurrence of vitamin A.*—An example of national patriotism in science is afforded by the rival claims, on the one hand, of Drummond and Hilditch working on behalf of the British Empire Marketing Board, who have "demonstrated beyond doubt the unrivalled medicinal value of the cod-liver oils produced in Scotland and Newfoundland," and, on the other, of Poulsson (2) who found that oil from Norwegian fish was superior, coming from spawning fish and possessing "twice the antirachitic potency of Newfoundland oil." Shark's-liver oil is eight times richer than cod's in vitamin A, although much poorer in D [Poulsson (2)]. The body oil of salmon was $\frac{1}{3}$ as potent as cod-liver oil in vitamin A, and sardine, Alaska herring and tuna oils were only $\frac{1}{10}$ as potent (Nelson and Manning). Drummond and Hilditch have obtained confirmatory evidence that the primary source of the vitamin A of cod-liver oil is the minute green plant life of the sea. Zoöplankton in contrast with phytoplankton gave negative results in assays for the vitamin (Drummond and Gunther). The association of vitamin A with greenness in plant tissue is examined further by Crist and Dye in a study on the vitamin A

content of asparagus grown under light of various qualities. They find that conditions which favour the production of chlorophyll appear also to favour vitamin A synthesis.

Watercress is very rich in vitamin A (Mendel and Vickery). Yellow corn or corn meal is richer than white (Fraps). Oat oil is a poor source (Meyer and Hetler). Tomato pulp is 32 times as potent as the clear serum (Steenbock and Schrader). Stored plant tissues lose vitamin A activity; more so in presence of rancid fat (Quinn, Hartley, and Derow). Artificially dried alfalfa is superior to the field-cured (Hauge and Aitkenhead; see also Smith and Lynott). Sulphured and dried peaches and prunes showed good retention of the vitamin (Morgan and Field). Animal margarines tend to be superior to the vegetable, but varying results are obtained (Fetter and Carlson; cf. Scheunert). Ghee (clarified milk fat, a staple article of Indian diet) is deficient (Bacharach). Heated, baked, or roasted butter is still appreciably active (Scheunert and Wagner). Very rapid sterilisation or heating of milk involves little loss (Fredericia and Hausen). Thin butter cookies retain ¾ or ⅘ of the vitamin content of the butter used (Parsons, Stevenson, Mullen, and Horn). Swiss milk chocolate, Peter's and Nestlé's "Gala" brands, had about ¼ to ⅕ the value of butter (Scheunert and Reschke). Two German proprietary foods were active (Mattis and Nolte). The observation that a specimen of cow-fat had 15 times the activity of one of bull-fat, and fat from a human female twice that from the male, is made the basis for a rather sweeping generalisation [Poulsson (1)].

Vitamin D

1. *Prevalence of rickets.*—Although rickets is now a preventable and a rapidly declining disease, an official report not long back showed that no less than 87 per cent of London elementary school children (aged 5) still showed evidence of having had some degree of rickets. In many parts of the world conditions are vastly worse, and juvenile rickets or adult rickets (osteomalacia) is rampant, e.g. in China; and in India, where Wilson's studies show that both dietary vitamin D deficiency and lack of exposure to sunlight are contributing causes [Wilson (1, 2); Wilson and Coombes; Wilson and Surie; Wilson and Patel]. The terribly high incidence in certain areas is illustrated by Table VIII.

The surprising prevalence of rickets among Finlanders and Lapps in a Norwegian fishing district in the Arctic Circle is shown by Kloster's figures. The diet is largely salt fish (Table IX).

TABLE VIII

INCIDENCE OF JUVENILE RICKETS AMONG SCHOOL GIRLS
(AGES 5 TO 17 YEARS) IN LAHORE [WILSON (1)]

Classification of Schools	Number Examined	Number of Cases
1. Intramural congested city..............	783	422
2. Extramural city	415	135
3. Well-planned suburb	284	50
Total	1,482	607

Adenoids are so often associated with rickets that the Board of Education Committee of Enquiry suggest the possibility of some definite relationship to vitamin D deficiency.

TABLE IX

INCIDENCE OF RICKETS AMONG CHILDREN IN NORWEGIAN FISHING DISTRICT

	Number Examined	Signs of Rickets	Percentage
Age 2 months to 7 years......................	376	163	43
Age 7 years to 17 years......................	451	60	13

2. *Treatment of rickets.*—The value of *irradiated ergosterol therapy* has become firmly established. A chief advantage is that it can be given at higher levels of antirachitic activity than would be tolerated with cod-liver oil, which sometimes fails to protect, especially with premature infants and twins (as may also be the case in osteomalacia; e.g., Gargill, Gilligan, and Blumgart). Several recent reports indicate that a given amount of vitamin D is less effective in the form of irradiated ergosterol ("viosterol") than as cod-liver oil, for curing rickets in infants [De Sanctis and Craig; Brady, Brady, and James; Holmes and Pigott (2); Holmes], or in hens [Massengale and Nussmeier (1)]. This, however, in our view, does not militate against the use of irradiated ergosterol. The most likely explanation is incomplete absorption, rather than the absence of vitamin A [Poulsson (2)] from the synthetic preparation. The dosage of irradiated ergosterol is now fairly well worked out [J. H. Hess, Poncher, Dale, and Klein; György (2); A. F. Hess, Lewis, and Rivkin (2); May;

Bamberger]. The amount at first recommended tended to be on the low side. In the other direction the possibility of hypervitaminosis has to be borne in mind, notwithstanding the advertisements of commercial houses that their preparations are incapable of producing ill effects. As suggested by the writer in 1928 the margin between therapeutic optimum and toxic overdose is not so wide for infants as it is for rats and some other species. The ill effects seen clinically, which are proving identical (Harris and Innes) with those produced in experimental animals, have included instances of: hypercalcaemia and excessive calcification of bone [A. F. Hess, Lewis, and Rivkin (1); György (1)]; single instances of calcification in kidney with fatal termination (Thatcher; Putschar); three instances of renal lesions after vigantol (Klaussner-Croheim); renal damage after three teaspoonsful of vigantol taken in error during one day (Tu Tungi); raised blood Ca or P in normal children or adults given 5 to 10 mg. (Hughes, *et al.*; Lasch; Ghirardi); and loss of Ca by way of the urine in normal children given very large overdoses [Hottinger (1)].

Actinotherapy brings about almost as rapid a recovery as irradiated ergosterol, and has been used successfully for tetany (Bakwin and Bakwin); results with heliotherapy depend largely on locality; e.g., there is a deficiency of ultra-violet rays in summer sunlight in California (Fawley) but not in Colorado (Stern and Lewis; Lewis, Frumess, and Stern); and winter sunlight at Boston, passed through "celoglass," had a definite antirachitic effect on children (Wyman, Drinker, and MacKenzie) and on rats (Wilder and Vack), and success has attended similar experiments with chickens (Russell and Howard).

Irradiated milk has been advocated in many quarters (e.g., Nabarro), and used with success (Hentschel and Fischer) or partial success (R. Hess; Hickman; Essig; Rau and Gruber: see also animal tests by Supplee, Flanigan, Kahlenberg, and Hess) but its activity varies considerably, at best one pint being equivalent to only 12 gm. of average cod-liver oil, and we regard it as more suited to prophylactic than to curative treatment.

Irradiated yeast is rich in vitamin D and has been proved to have clinical possibilities (Kon and Mayzner). Proprietary German preparations of irradiated meal and groats were shown to be devoid of vitamin D (Schwarz and Sieke). Milk from cows which had been fed on irradiated ergosterol, or better on irradiated yeast, was effective for prevention or cure; it relieves the mother of the responsibility of administering antirachitic supplements (A. F. Hess, Lewis, Mac-Leod, and Thomas).

The alleged benefits of *elementary phosphorus* added to cod-liver oil have again been canvassed (Compère) ; but it appears that the pathological "phosphorus band" to which it gives rise had been mistaken for evidence of healing calcification (A. F. Hess), and in practice it has no advantage over cod-liver oil (Leersum; Seel). Partially successful prophylactic results obtained with cod-liver oil (e.g. Crawford and Williamson) may be compared with J. H. Hess's splendid record with irradiated ergosterol (Hess, Poncher, Dale, and Klein). The British Pharmaceutical Committee (General Medical Council, 1931) have not thought it necessary to impose a test for vitamin D content on cod-liver oils; but a statement as to its vitamin A value (the $SbCl_3$ test), free acidity, and date of test is asked for (Drummond and Hilditch). "Malt and oil" sold under the "National Mark" scheme must contain 15 per cent by volume of the oil (Ministry of Agriculture and Fisheries).

Large amounts of vitamin A given concurrently with D are without effect on the cure of rickets clinically (Rohmer and Dubois).

3. *Vitamin D therapy for fractures, etc.*—Healing of fractures is delayed among vitamin-D–deficient individuals, or experimental animals (Roegholt) and heavy doses of irradiated ergosterol augment callus formation (Morelle; cf. Shelling) ; beneficial effects are also seen in certain types of pathological fractures if not in normal fracture patients (Cuthbertson). Recalcification of bones affected with tuberculosis was not accelerated by extra vitamin D (Pattison). Treatment of chilblains gave negative results (Hallan).

4. *Susceptibility of species in experimental rickets.*—The ill effects of vitamin D deficiency have been examined for the following species: rabbits (Moritz and Krenz), chickens [Russell, Howard, and Hess; Hart, Kline, and Keenan; King and Hall (2)], pigs (Peterson) ; typical rickets could not be produced in the guinea pig (Randoin and Lecoq).

5. *Various etiological factors in rickets.*—The rachitogenic influence of cereals, first demonstrated by Mellanby, has been confirmed, with the Ca/P factor fully controlled, for rats (Steenbock, Black, Thomas, and Riising; Fine) and for chickens (King and Hall) ; and an extract has been prepared from oatmeal which depresses the blood calcium (Mirvish).

An artificial diet low in pre-vitamin D (non-irradiated ergosterol) is less satisfactory than one richer in it, for preventing experimental rickets when restricted exposures to ultra-violet rays are permitted, which suggests that the body has only limited powers of synthesising the sterol (Hume and Henderson Smith). The absorbability of non-irradiated ergosterol has, however, been disputed [Schönheimer and von Behring; Schönheimer; but cf. results with the acetate: Page and Menschick (2)]. The seat of activation is presumably the sebaceous secretion of the skin, since irradiation of a thoroughly cleansed area is relatively ineffective (Hou), although the active rays are able to penetrate as far as the dermal capillaries (Lucas), and ergosterol has been detected in human skin (Hentschel and Schindel). The subcutaneous administration of irradiated ergosterol is relatively ineffective (Drummond); and vitamin D ingested *per os* is apparently partly lost by destruction within the organism (in the case of the chick) (Klein and Russell).

6. *Experimental "beryllium" rickets* is produced by substituting beryllium carbonate for calcium carbonate in Steenbock's diet (Branion, Guyatt, and Kay); vitamin D is unable to cure or prevent this condition. Magnesium carbonate increases the severity of rickets (Mouriquand, Leulier, and Roche); strontium carbonate has no effect (Mouriquand, Leulier, and Nogier).

7. *Phosphorus and calcium metabolism in rickets.*—That a low blood phosphate is necessarily an essential feature of rickets has been questioned by Hess and collaborators (Hess, Weinstock, Rivkin, and Gross) from measurements on rats; and by Park, who found that histological changes could be detected in bone before the fall in the blood phosphates. Hess's conclusions and his technique have, however, been called into question by Kramer, Shear, and Siegel (2); and recalcification in rachitic rat bone has been shown to be preceded by a rise in the blood Ca × P [Kramer, Shear, and Siegel (1)]. In the opinion of the reviewer there is overwhelming evidence that rickets is in fact associated with and directly due to a low Ca × P product. Clinical records published during the year under review have shown that in adult rickets the serum phosphate and/or calcium was invariably low and returned to normal on treatment (Maxwell; Wills). Rickets as observed clinically is generally of the low phosphate variety, but low calcium rickets is known, and in severe cases both calcium and phosphates may be considerably down. A low calcium is of course the cause of nutritional tetany; a current communication suggests that the diffusible calcium is a better criterion

than the total serum calcium. A figure of or below 3.5 gives rise to clinical symptoms (Gunther and Greenberg). Transient symptoms of tetany are produced in rats with low-phosphate rickets, by changing from the high-calcium diet to a normal mixed ration (Hess, Weinstock, Benjamin, and Gross), i.e., of course, with a lower Ca/P ratio.

Vitamin D has been demonstrated to aid a positive calcium or phosphorus balance in an extensive series of experiments on dogs (Skaar); and to conserve skeletal calcium in adult rats (Kleitzien, Thomas, Templin, and Steenbock), and in chicks (Holmes and Pigott). The shaft of the bones as well as the epiphyses are poorly mineralised in rickets (in rats) (Hess, Berliner, and Weinstock) and the calcium content of striated muscle is also sub-normal (Haury). The actual deposition of the calcium salts in the newly forming bone tissue has long been known to depend on the presence in the latter of the enzyme phosphatase; this is present in fully normal amounts in vitamin deficiency. It has now been shown that the phosphatase activity *in vitro* is also not influenced by irradiated ergosterol (Heymann).

8. *Miscellaneous factors in rickets.*—Vitamin D deficiency has no effect on the following: sugar concentration, alkaline reserve and glycogen content of liver (Sure and Smith), hematopoietic function (Sure and Kik); absorption of fat, protein and carbohydrate (St. Julian and Heller), pH of intestinal contents in children (confirming early work and in contrast with effect on rats with special diets) [Hottinger (2)]. Conflicting results are reported as to blood cholesterol (Lesné, Sylvestre, and Zizine; Dorlencourt and Seisoff). Evidence for acidosis in rickets is unconvincing, but certain types of tetany are associated with alkalosis (Shohl, Brown, Rose, Smith, and Cozad). Changes in the acid-base composition of the gastric and pancreatic juices, in clinical cases, of doubtful significance, are mentioned (Bauer, Marble, Maddock, and Wood). Chronaxie, in rabbits, is said to be raised (Morin and Boucomont).

9. *Hypervitaminosis and vitamin D action.*—Detailed investigations on hypervitaminosis in the writer's laboratory (Harris and Innes) have substantiated the view that the mode of action of vitamin D is to raise the blood calcium and/or phosphate, increasing "net absorption" of these elements from the gut; the raised blood figure automatically gives rise to increased calcification. Thus, a rational explanation is offered of the phenomenon of hypervitaminosis in place of the empirical pharmacological observation that irradiated

ergosterol in excess is toxic, noted by the original German observers Pfannenstiel and Kreitmair and Moll, who however were only able to suggest that the loss in weight of the experimental animals might indicate an increase in metabolic rate (an idea still retained by some authors). That hypercalcemia or hyperphosphatemia results when excess of vitamin D is administered to experimental animals (rats or rabbits) was first shown by Harris and Stewart, and has since been confirmed by many workers in all parts of the world. Hypervitaminosis thus stands in logical contrast with rickets. In the latter there is deficient net absorption of calcium and/or phosphate, hence hypocalcemia and/or hypophosphatemia, and resulting insufficient calcification; in the former there is increased net absorption, with hypercalcemia and/or hyperphosphatemia, and resulting excessive calcification. The contrast between the overcalcification of the growing end of bone seen in hypervitaminosis and the defective calcification characteristic of rickets is particularly striking. Likewise in the teeth there is overgrowth of the cement (essentially an inorganic material), and the teeth may even become ankylosed to the jaw bone. It is of significance that the sites in the soft tissues which are found to become calcified in hypervitaminosis are those which are, after the bones, the most richly provided with the calcifying enzyme, phosphatase. As was to be expected hypervitaminosis was increased in severity as more calcium was provided to be absorbed. Each increase in the vitamin D allowance was shown to favour increased net absorption of calcium and/or phosphate; except of course with maximal doses, when toxic symptoms had supervened and the animal had ceased to eat, and naturally all bodily functions were failing. This last secondary complication, however, has led to a great deal of misunderstanding in the interpretation of the results of metabolic tests in hypervitaminosis. So also has the fact that under similar circumstances, with very high levels of vitamin excess and with an insufficient source of available calcium in the gut, some of the extra calcium drawn into the blood is now found to come from the bony storehouse. The last-mentioned effect, together with the hypercalcemia, and the consequent increased excretion in the urine, resembles the effect of parathormone administration, but it was stressed that parathormone has never been found to increase the net absorption of calcium and/or phosphate from the gut, which normally is characteristic of vitamin D action. Parathormone so far as is known raises the calcium in the blood solely by withdrawing it from the bones.

The present writer (1930) first drew attention to the importance of the Ca/P intake as a controlling factor in hypervitaminosis, and this has been confirmed by Duguid, Duggan, and Gough; Shelling; Bills and Wirick; Jones, Rapoport, and Hodes (2); and others. Extended studies of the calcium and phosphate balance were undertaken by Brown and Shohl and by Watchorn (1, 2), and of the blood phosphate and urinary calcium and phosphate by Ashford, and the significance of various metabolic results was discussed at length in the paper of Harris and Innes already alluded to. The increase in gut absorption and in urinary excretion with large doses of vitamin D has recently been confirmed by Kern, Montgomery, and Still, and the influence upon the blood figure of the Ca/P intake by Warkany (1), Jones and Rapoport, and Massengale and Nussmeier (2) (the last-mentioned working on chickens). Heubner (1) has confirmed the high calcium content of the various organs; and bone analyses, showing almost normal figures, were done by Jones and Robson.

So many papers have appeared during 1930–31 describing the histopathology of hypervitaminosis, and reaching essentially similar conclusions or confirming earlier findings, that it is not feasible to discuss each individually [Shohl, Goldblatt, and Brown; Levaditi and Po; Warkany (1); Duguid; Vara-Lopez; Michelazzi; Pincherle and Nava; Light, Miller, and Frey; Innes]. Special aspects of the pathology have been discussed by the following: King and Hall (1, 2) (effects in fowls); Spies and Glover (kidney lesions); Brand and Holtz (local effects after subcutaneous injections); Fraser (lymphopenia); Heubner (2) (absence of after-effects on cure); Comel (2) (effect on offspring; cf. Bills and Wirick); Page and Residue (absence of effect on phosphate activity); Morelle (callus formation); Reed and Thacker (greater efficacy of subcutaneous and intraperitoneal injections); György (2), Sœur (studies on bone); Spies, Simmonet and Tanret (2), and Policard, Paupert-Ravault, and Barral, and Levaditi and Po (effect on tubercle).

The convincing proof which Hess at first believed he had obtained for the theory that vitamin D functions by stimulating the parathyroid, consisting of the evidence that vitamin D excess no longer raised the blood calcium once the parathyroid had been removed, was not confirmed by later work in which it was shown that the vitamin was in fact still effective if given in somewhat larger amounts (Hess, Weinstock, and Rivkin). A similar result has been obtained by other workers; but might be attributed, according to Comel (1), to the presence of accessory parathyroid tissue, not completely removed at the operation. Taylor, Branion, and Kay also concluded that vitamin D acts by stimulating the parathyroid; and in a later detailed study (Taylor, Weld, Branion, and Kay) they also advance this explanation of accessory tissue, and point out as further evidence: (a) that the effects of vitamin D excess closely resemble those of hyperparathyroidism, and (b) that the susceptibility of different species to vitamin excess and to hyperparathyroidism is approximately the same. Many workers on this question have succeeded in showing that the effects of vitamin D and parathormone are intensified when they are given together, or that to some extent they can replace each other. This, however, is to be expected, since both substances raise the blood calcium, but it is no evidence that the action may not be independent (*vide supra*). The following papers connecting parathyroid and vitamin D published during 1930–31 may also be consulted: Jones, Rapoport, and Hodes (1) ; Shelling ; Bischoff ; Pappenheimer and Buxton ; Comel (3, 5) ; Morgan and Garrison (1, 2) ; Jones and Rapoport.

Many workers have supposed that the ill effects of excess of irradiated ergosterol are due not to vitamin D but to some alleged toxic impurity. Thus Holtz and Schreiber found the degree of toxicity as measured on mice to vary independently of the antirachitic activity as determined prophylactically on rats, and postulated an independent "calcinosing" factor (see further Holtz, Laquer, Kreitmair, and Moll). Windaus at first leaned to this view, separate spectroscopic properties, etc., being ascribed to the calcinosing factor, but later papers stress that no success has attended efforts to prepare an antirachitic preparation free from concurrent toxicity [Windaus (1, 4) ; Windaus and Auhagen (2)].

In addition to the argument developed above that the ill effects are precisely those which would be logically anticipated for vitamin D excess (and were in fact predicted by the writer) ; and that toxicity ran parallel with vitamin D activity, as shown by Harris and Moore; we have now the further evidence that calciferol itself, i.e., purified crystalline vitamin D, has toxicity equal to crude irradiated ergosterol, activity for activity (*vide infra*).

In England, Hoyle and Dixon have been the principal protagonists of the "toxic impurity" theory. Being unable at first to confirm the harmfulness of irradiated ergosterol excess, they threw doubt on the theory of hypervitaminosis, and suggested that the ill effects which had been observed elsewhere must have arisen from the irradiation having been carried out in alcohol (the German commercial practice) instead of in oil (the English procedure). In a second experiment, however, in which a synthetic basal diet was now used, instead of bread and milk as previously, they were more successful and duly obtained ill effects. It was then postulated that toxic results can be produced only when animals are on a synthetic diet and that the bread and milk contains some unknown substance which protected from hypervitaminosis (Hoyle). However in yet a third experiment hypervitaminosis once again resulted, either on a bread diet, or on a milk diet. This would indicate that there are not one but two hypothetical protective substances, the one present in bread, the other in milk, which separately are ineffective but together are able to prevent hypervitaminosis from developing. In the view of the writer these variable results are more likely to be attributed to differences in the calcium and phosphorus content of the diets. Claims as to the antirachitic activity but non-toxicity of certain irradiated ergosterol preparations (e.g. Kisch and Reiter) have been disproved (Laquer; György and Popoviciu). On the other hand many writers claim to have proved that the toxic is not the antirachitic factor, having found an absence of parallelism between the following: rickets prevention, and calcium deposition in bone, or effect on blood phosphate (Schultz and Meyer); antirachitic action, calcification, and toxicity [Simmonet and Tanret (2, 3)]; toxicity and hypercalcemia (Reed and Thacker) or antirachitic action (Wendt); or from analyses of sterols from the calcified aorta [Page and Menschick (1)]. [Further references: Comel (4); Vara-Lopez; Heubner (3).] It is possible that the observed lack of parallelism may have been due to the unsatisfactory absorption of certain preparations.

McGown, Cunningham, and Auchinachie postulate that the cause of the calcium deposits in hypervitaminosis is the same as that of the calcified lesions in chloroform poisoning; further they postulate that in the latter case the chloroform acts "by setting free from the lipins of the body of inorganic phosphate"; and this is described accordingly also as the "Fundamental Mode of Action of Vitamin D." It may be pointed out, however, that calcium deposition in hypervitaminosis differs fundamentally from ordinary post-necrotic calcification, and that there is no evidence to warrant the supposed association with the calcification of chloroform poisoning in especial.

Vitamin D excess is said to inhibit the metamorphosis of larvae of *Bufo vulgaris* (Coccheri).

The toxic effect of cod-liver oil excess (due presumably to some constituent other than vitamin D) has been studied further as follows: Norris and Church (remedial action of vitamin B) ; Agduhr (effect on reproductive processes) ; and Wahlin (histological changes).

Examples of hypervitaminosis in humans were alluded to in an earlier section.

10. *Vitamin D and pregnancy and lactation.*—It has been realised for some years that pregnant and lactating women are liable to run into severely adverse calcium (or phosphate) balance, and this is again emphasised from a study of a series of subjects whose lactation had been unduly heavy and prolonged (Donelson, Nims, Hunscher, and Macy). It has been amply proved by earlier work and confirmed in the past year (Macy, Hunscher, McCosh, and Nims) that provision of ample vitamin D is of great benefit to the mother in stimulating adequate utilisation of calcium and phosphate. But attempts to show that such treatment improves also the vitamin D content of the mother's milk have generally been without convincing success, although a positive result is claimed for ultra-violet therapy (Lesné and Dreyfus-See). The futility of vitamin D medication without an abundant supply of calcium (milk) is clear from the work of Toverud and Toverud, according to whom no less than 1¾ pints per day of milk are necessary.

In the case of the cow several workers have at last succeeded in improving the antirachitic value of the milk, either by feeding irradiated ergosterol (Krauss and Bethke), or, better, irradiated yeast (Thomas and MacLeod), 14- to 16-fold increases in activity being obtained. It will be recalled that practical use has been made of the latter finding in infant feeding (A. F. Hess, Lewis, MacLeod, and Thomas). Hart, Steenbock, and Kline found irradiated yeast to have no effect on the calcium assimilation of the milch cow, or on the calcium and phosphate content of the milk, although it increased the vitamin D value of the latter. With a goat (Steenbock, Hart, Riising, Kleitzien, and Scott), but not with cows (Steenbock, Hart, Riising, Hoppert, and Basherov; cf. Falkenheim and Kirsch) irradiation improved the antirachitic activity of the milk. With breeding and lactating rats no improvement in calcium conservation could be observed to follow the provision of additional vitamin D to the stock diet (Kleitzien, Thomas, Templin, and Steenbock).

11. *Vitamin D and teeth.*—Clinical trials of the value of vitamin D in arresting dental decay in children have been strikingly successful. Eight hundred children in poor-law institutions were the subjects; they were arranged in groups of 65 to 86 receiving various dietary additions, and the experiment lasted two years. The rate of spread of caries in the group receiving extra vitamins A and D (cod-liver oil and radiostoleum) was found to be only one-third of that in the control group receiving vitamin-free additions of olive oil or treacle. Similarly beneficial results were obtained with the addition of vitamin D (radiostol) alone (Medical Research Council, *Special Report Series,* No. 159; see also *Minutes of the Dental Board of the United Kingdom,* 1930).

TABLE X

THE USE OF FAT-SOLUBLE VITAMINS IN THE PREVENTION OF DENTAL CARIES

	Percentage of Teeth Carious
Sheffield:	
Olive oil group	10.00
Cod-liver oil group	1.55
Vitamin D group	1.01
Birmingham:	
Olive oil group	7.63
Cod-liver oil group	2.97
Vitamin D group	2.09

It is important to note that the clinical investigation described above relates to the incidence and rate of spread of caries in teeth already formed. The influence of vitamin D in the formation of sound well-calcified teeth is now well known. Toverud and Toverud show how the feeding to a pregnant bitch of a diet deficient in calcium, phosphorus, and fat-soluble vitamins leads to badly calcified teeth in the offspring. Attempts, however, to produce experimental caries, in dogs or rats, have so far met with little success, although with rabbits results were more promising (Mellanby). Knowlton and Rosebury and Karnshan likewise were unable to produce experimental dental caries in rats. The second-mentioned describe histological abnormalities resulting from diets low in calcium and free from vitamin D, or—a surprising statement—deficient in vitamin C. Klein and Shelling on the other hand claim that they have succeeded in producing "frequent caries-like lesions" in the molars of rats fed for prolonged periods on unbalanced "rachitogenic" diets plus vitamin D. Hess and Abramson find some difficulty in reconciling the theory that vitamin D deficiency is the essential etiological factor of dental caries, with the clinical records of its occurrence in non-rachitic children and with the geographical distribution. Eddy discusses the separate effects of deficiencies of vitamins C, A, and D in giving rise to dental defects in guinea pigs.

A shortage of vitamin D results in defects in the alveolar bone, and "if a puppy's diet has been deficient in vitamins A and D during the early months of life, the dog is liable to develop periodontal disease at a later stage, whatever the subsequent diet" (Mellanby).

12. *Isolation of vitamin D.*—The outstanding event of the year has been the separation of crystalline preparations of vitamin D almost simultaneously by four different laboratories; and, more recently, the announcement by the London group of the further separation of their crystals into active and inactive constituents.

The first paper by Bourdillon and his group of collaborators describes the separation of a crystalline product by the fractional distillation and condensation of irradiated ergosterol in a high vacuum, followed by crystallisation from aqueous alcohol; the product was apparently not yet pure vitamin D, judging from its relatively low antirachitic activity [Askew, Bourdillon, Bruce, Jenkins, and Webster (1)]. A later paper describes the preparation of large amounts of the crystalline substance (which was named "calciferol"), and an examination of its activity, colour reactions, stability, etc. Attempts to separate a more active constituent from the calciferol had failed, but it was apparent that its activity was relatively low compared with the ordinary, crude, ergosterol irradiation mixture, and it was therefore supposed that the latter contained another form of the vitamin, still more active (Angus, Askew, Bourdillon, Bruce, Callow, Fischmann, Philpot, and Webster). However, a final communication to *Nature* (Askew, Bruce, Callow, Philpot, and Webster) describes the separation from the calciferol of an inactive contaminant, pyrocalciferol, a substance which forms when irradiated ergosterol is heated. As the authors point out, crystalline preparations obtained by the various workers had approximately the same antirachitic activity (20,000–25,000 units per milligram), but their varying optical rotations implied that they were not one and the same single substance. The impurity, pyrocalciferol, was separated from the active constituent, in the distilled crystalline product, by the fractional crystallisation of the 3,5-dinitrobenzoic acid esters. The active constituent comprises 50–70 per cent of the original distilled product and the name calciferol is retained for it. It has also been separated direct from the undistilled, crude irradiation product, again by way of the ester. It possesses an antirachitic activity of 40,000 units per mg., and its physical constants have been determined. Both calciferol and pyrocalciferol have the same empirical formula as ergosterol.

Pure calciferol, as separated from pyrocalciferol, is not identical with either the crystalline "Substance L" of Reerink and van Wijk, or the crystalline vitamin D_1, of Windaus, since it possesses higher antirachitic activity and absorption coefficient than either. It may be identical with Windaus' D_2, but has, apparently, a higher antirachitic activity (Askew, *et al., loc. cit.*). Calciferol can now be purchased commercially.

Concurrently, intensive investigations were being carried out by Windaus and his collaborators on the heat stability, and other properties of the various ergosterol isomers and derivatives, and on their identification by their absorption spectra. In 1930 Windaus described vitamin D as a low-melting oil having a slight negative rotation, absorption band at 270 mμ, and destroyed by heating at 150°. Later he found it possible to remove inactive products from crude irradiated ergosterol by treatment with maleic or citraconic anhyhride in ethereal solution, followed by extraction with KOH. Crystalline vitamin D was obtained by evaporation of the ethereal layer and its activity and properties were determined [Windaus (2, 3); see also Windaus, Gaede, Köser, and Stein; Windaus and Auhagen (1); Windaus, Dithmar, Murke, and Sukfüll].

Reerink and van Wijk believed that ergosterol could be converted by irradiation into one single transformation product, the active substance "L" (= vitamin D), provided certain conditions were complied with, viz., rays below 284 mμ to be excluded, oxygen absent, and the irradiation to be concluded before more than 50 per cent of the ergosterol was transformed. Although these theories are doubted, crystalline preparations were nevertheless made from the irradiated product, e.g., by recrystallisation at low temperature after treatment with digitonin *in vacuo* [Reerink and van Wijk (1, 2)].

13. *Chemistry of vitamin D.*—That vitamin D is an isomer of ergosterol is confirmed from the analyses of purified calciferol (Askew, Bruce, Callow, Philpot, and Webster) and from the observa-

tion that the heat of combustion of the two substances is the same (Bills, McDonald, BeMiller, Steel, and Nussmeier). Windaus (3) believes that, in the photochemical transference of ergosterol into vitamin D, the alcohol group and three double bonds remain unchanged, but that the spatial size of the molecule is increased. Castille, however, has suggested that the changes in absorption recall those of known *cis-trans* transformations. Selective absorption in a sterol, such as is given by ergosterol, appears to indicate the presence of two ethenoid linkages, one in the $\Delta^{1:13}$ (or $\Delta^{1:2}$) position and the Tortelli-Jaffé reaction indicates an "inert" $\Delta^{10:19}$ linkage (Heilbron and Spring). According to Rosenheim and Callow red coloration with a mercury reagent is a better test for the $\Delta^{1:13}$ (or $\Delta^{1:2}$) linkage, and ergosterol gives only a greenish blue or yellow with it. Distinctive color tests to distinguish irradiated and non-irradiated ergosterol have been described (Meesemaecker; Levine and Richman).

Certain new ergosterol derivatives and esters are shown to be activatable by ultra-violet rays (MacCorquodale, Steenbock, and Adkins) and the same is claimed for the lipoid, heliosterol (Mouriquand and Leulier). Chemical investigations have been made by Bills and his co-workers of the various isoergosterols and their relationship to vitamin D (Bills, McDonald, and Cox; Bills and McDonald; McDonald and Bills; Cox and Bills). Apparent differences in properties between the vitamin D of cod-liver oil and of irradiated ergosterol lead to the suggestion that they may not be identical (Loureiro). The same has been argued from differences in clinical efficacy (cf. page 382).

14. *Photochemistry of vitamin D formation.*—According to the theory of Reerink and van Wijk, an active substance "L" is formed on long-wave irradiation, and on short-wave irradiation (or on too prolonged long-wave irradiation) a substance "S," which is antirachitically inactive [Reerink and van Wijk (3); van Niekerk and Everse]. However, Marshall and Knudson found the production of vitamin D to be independent of the wave-length of the light used, and to be destroyed by the same wave-length as that which forms it. Similarly, Bourdillon and co-workers were unable to confirm the claim that long-wave irradiation (less than 280 mμ) gives rise to only one product. Nor did the 280 mμ band indicate vitamin D, since it was found that its intensity increased as the antirachitic activity decreased, when ergosterol previously activated with long waves was re-irradiated with short wave-lengths [Askew, Bourdillon, Bruce,

Jenkins, and Webster (2) ; Bourdillon, Jenkins, and Webster]. Purified calciferol is now found to have a band with a maximum at 265 mμ and pyrocalciferol a band with maxima at 296, 284, and 274 mμ (Askew, Bruce, Callow, Philpot, and Webster). It is of interest to note that already, in 1930, Windaus had described vitamin D as a substance with an absorption band at 270 mμ, and mentioned a derivative with a band at 280–290 mμ (as well as others with bands at 247 mμ [? toxic compound; cf. Cox and Bills], and at 240 mμ; and one having no bands above 240 mμ). Further accounts of his observations on the absorption spectra of various ergosterol isomers and derivatives will be found in the papers quoted earlier.

Ergosterol was more effectively activated in ether than in alcohol or cyclohexane (Bills, Honeywell, and Cox).

Theoretically it should be possible to activate ergosterol by rays of any length under 300 mμ, and this has been accomplished by means of soft X-rays (Shelow and Loofbourow), and by radium emanation (Maisin, Mund, Pourbaix, and Castille; Moore and DeVries). The infra-red absorption spectrum of vitamin D differs from that of non-irradiated ergosterol (Husch and Kellner).

15. *Vitamin D assay.*—A valuable report has appeared, discussing exhaustively the various aspects of vitamin D assay by the radiographic method (Bourdillon, Bruce, Fischmann, and Webster). A scale is given representing twelve degrees of healing of rickets, from complete healing to negligible effect. In carrying out an assay, ten animals with severe rickets are given the same dose of the unknown, and ten comparable litter mates are given another dose (of as far as can be gauged approximately equal activity) of the standard. Results are assessed by reference to the scale, and the scale number for each group is averaged. Numbers on the scale correspond with known ratios of vitamin D (for example, at the middle of the scale a difference of two points corresponds with doubling the dose of the vitamin), and hence the vitamin value of the unknown can be compared with the standard. The "probable error" is stated to have been reduced to as low as 8 per cent. The principal sources of error were found to be: (a) errors in estimation of degree of healing; (b) varying responses of litter mates; (c) varying responses of different litters; and others are also discussed.

A method similar to the foregoing has been described by Dutch workers; seven degrees of healing are recognised and these are related to the logarithm of the dose by an **S**-shaped curve (Everse and van Niekerk; van Niekerk and Everse). A preventive radiographic method is preferred by Holtz, Laquer, Kreitmair, and Moll, and by Schultzer, who suggests that it gives more uniform results, as well as being simpler. Schieblich, on the other hand, finds that the preventive dose bears no constant ratio to the curative.

The line-test method has been examined very thoroughly by Dyer at the Pharmaceutical Society's laboratory; six degrees of healing are represented, and a curve given connecting them with the dose. A similar study, with a statistical treatment of the degree of accuracy possible, has been published by Bills, Honeywell, Wirick, and Nussmeier. The Soames and Leigh-Clare method (growth test) has been tried, and its usefulness and limitations discussed (Crawford, Golding, Perry, and Zilva). Sherman and Strebling's method is to find the dose needed to induce under suitably controlled conditions a "midway degree of calcification, as measured by the ash content of the femur." Fresh maize meal as purchased may contain vitamin D, and should be ground and stored for six months before use (R. S. Harris and Bunker); indications of the possibility of such variations in the maize are apparent also from comments in Bourdillon's paper. Goldblatt thinks that variable results are due rather to the settling of the $CaCO_3$ and the diet may be made up as a gel to prevent this (Goldblatt). A modified McCollum diet is preferred by Rogozinski to either Steenbock's or Randoin and Lecoq's. No additional vitamin A need be added to the Steenbock diet (Bacharach, Allchorne, and Hazley).

The international standard of vitamin D (League of Nations Health Organisation) chosen by the London Conference is a solution of irradiated ergosterol, made under defined conditions, and of a strength corresponding with 1 mg. of the original ergosterol in 10 cc. of olive oil. The unit of vitamin is 1 mg. of this solution; and the activity is such that 1 mg. given daily to rachitic rats for 8 successive days should produce a wide calcium "line." As to the method of test, either the "line" test, X-ray examination, or determination of bone ash is permitted, but it is recommended that at least ten animals should be put on the standard and an equal number on the unknown.

Hypervitaminosis effects in rabbits—either urinary phosphate excretion [Warkany (2)], or hyperphosphatemia and hypercalcemia and weight loss (Naser)—are suggested for the assay of irradiated ergosterol preparations.

16. *Occurrence of vitamin D.*—Milk is normally a poor source of vitamin D, and sterilised or evaporated milks are still poorer (Honeywell, Dutcher, and Dahle). Milk which has been first irradiated and then dried may possess a definite antirachitic potency (Supplee, Flanigan, Kahlenberg, and Hess), as also does milk from cows fed on irradiated yeast (Steenbock, Hart, Hanning, and Humphrey). The whole of the vitamin A and D potency of the milk is found in the butter prepared from it (Crawford, Golding, Perry, and Zilva).

Rival claims have been made for the vitamin D content of Newfoundland and Norwegian cod-liver oils [Drummond and Hilditch; Poulsson (1, 3)]. Although its food is relatively deficient in the vitamin, the cod is probably unable to synthesise it and presumably accumulates it gradually in its liver (Drummond and Hilditch). Phytoplankton had no antirachitic activity, and that of zoöplankton was only vague (Drummond and Gunther). Burbot liver oil is eight times as rich in vitamin D as that of the cod (Poulsson). The vitamin D content of the liver oils of cartilagenous fishes is much lower than that of the bony fishes (Poulsson). Lampreys contain a moderate amount only (Callow and Fischmann). Body oils of tuna and sardine were equal to, or better than, cod-liver oil; but salmon, menhaden, and Alaska and Maine herrings were much inferior (Nelson and Manning). Pilchard oil is superior to dogfish oil although not quite up to cod-liver oil, but should have useful commercial applications (Brocklesby and Denstedt). A hardened cod-liver oil preparation, "Jemalt," was satisfactory (Mansfeld and Horn). A report stressing the superiority of certain animal to vegetable margarines has appeared (Fetter and Carlson).

As a supplement for infants' and childrens' diets, tomato with added irradiated ergosterol retains its activity well (Steenbock, Schrader, Riising, and Wirick). The vitamin D contents of animal feeds have been determined by Brouwer and de Ruyter de Wildt, of *Welpenkuchan* by Lössl, and of various green fodder grasses, etc.—which were found to vary according to the exposure to light—by Scheunert, and Scheunert and Reschke. The statement that vitamin D appears in germinating seeds (Schillenhelm and Eisler) is in conflict with earlier observations. Ultra-violet irradiated moulds or mycelia were active for rats in daily doses of 10 to 50 mg. (Preuss, Peterson, Steenbock, and Fred). Irradiated yeast is an exceptionally rich source of vitamin D as proved by tests on children (Kon and Mayzner) as well as on rats (Kon).

Vitamin E

Interesting information has been gained as to a relation between vitamin E and certain autoxidants or "anti-vitamins," as a result of work by Mattill and collaborators on the one hand, and Waddell, Steenbock, and others, on the other. Milk to which traces of iron and copper are added is thereby rendered satisfactory so far as the prevention of anemia is concerned (Waddell, Steenbock, Hart, and VanDonk); but it is found that, though not lacking vitamin E, it gives rise to total sterility in males, with disappearance of germinal epithelium and loss of testicular tissue (Waddell and VanDonk). The addition of the iron to the milk appears to antagonise the vitamin E; and an anti-vitamin can be extracted with ether from the iron-treated ration (Waddell and Steenbock). Cummings and Mattill show that the efficacy of a given source of vitamin E depends on the presence or absence of certain associated fats which function either as autoxidants or anti-oxidants. Thus fats like cotton-seed oil or butter, which take up oxygen relatively promptly, are satisfactory in preventing sterility, while others such as cod-liver oil or lard which take up oxygen after a longer period are unsatisfactory. The anti-oxidant in lettuce has been separated from the vitamin (Olcovitch and Mattill); and independent work has demonstrated the great vitamin E activity of this vegetable (Mendel and Vickery).

Injection of vitamin E in infantile rats induced hypertrophy of the uterus, resembling the action of pituitary hormone (Verzár), or incited oestrus (Szarka). Spontaneously occurring sterility in cows has been cured by vitamin E (Vogt-Møller and Bay), and its therapeutic application to habitual abortion in man is urged (Vogt-Møller). Juhasz-Schäffer has carried out some detailed work on the vitamin and confirmed many earlier results; the histology was examined fully, and the vitamin shown to be stored in the body, and present in small amounts in the faeces. Wheat-germ oil added to embryonic chicken tissue stimulated its growth *in vitro*. Sure has published a full recapitulation of work on vitamin E with eighty references.

Miscellaneous Studies on Vitamin Distribution

During the year have appeared Parts I and II of Volume VIII of Scheunert's treatise on the "Vitamin Value of German Foodstuffs," published by the German Ministry of Nutrition and Agriculture, and dealing respectively with fruits and vegetables, and flours and breads [Scheunert (2)]. With Schieblich he has written a comprehensive monograph on the vitamins in milk, for the "Handbuch der Milchwirtschaft," giving close on two hundred references (Scheunert and Schieblich). Other of his papers deal respectively with the vitamin values of: vegetables; conserves; egg-yolk extracts; staple foods; and mushrooms [Scheunert (1, 3, 4, 5); Scheunert and Reschke]. Other writers have examined yeast for B_1 and B_2 (Quinn, Whalen, and Hartley) and malted milks for A, B_1, and B_2 (Quinn and Brabec).

CONCLUSIONS

Perhaps the principal impression one gains in retrospect is the immense volume of work published. To keep pace with this has entailed several hours daily reading throughout the year, of a widely scattered literature. On vitamin D alone some 300 communications have appeared. The great majority of papers represent some definite addition to knowledge; and while, undeniably, communications vary considerably as to their fundamental significance, in no branch of science does ultimate progress seem more dependent on the cumulative effect of continual small advances. Striking progress has been made over a wide area, ranging from clinical medicine to chemical physics. It has seemed best therefore to attempt a comprehensive epitome of the year's work rather than choose certain aspects at random and ignore others of possibly equal value and interest. Among the more important developments we may note the following: The establishment of international standards and units of vitamin activity. Appreciation of the significance of lactic acid excess in avitaminosis B_1. Numerous papers on new B vitamins, but results not easily comparable for lack of uniformity in definitions. Rôle of carotene as pro-vitamin A substantiated. Question as to which absorption bands are characteristic of vitamin A. Physiology of night blindness; and vitamin A deficiency as cause of experimental periodontal disease and nerve degeneration. Preparation of crystalline vitamin D. Hypervitaminosis D and mode of action of vitamin D. Clinical value of vitamin D in arresting dental caries. Influence on vitamin E of associated autoxidants, iron, etc. Within the space of a week or two since the beginning of the new year have come reports of the isolation or identification of vitamins A, B_1, and C, by Karrer or Drummond, Windaus and Rygh respectively; discussion of these must be deferred until next year.

LITERATURE CITED

REFERENCES TO VITAMIN A

Accessory Food Factors Committee, *Lancet,* **214,** 148 (1928)

Ahmad, B. (1), *Biochem. J.,* **24,** 860 (1930)

Ahmad, B. (2), *Biochem. J.,* **25,** 1195 (1931)

Aykroyd, W. R., quoted by *Lancet,* **221,** 917 (1931)

Bacharach, A. L., *Brit. Med. J.,* **2,** 141 (1930)

Bezssonov, N., *Compt. rend.,* **190,** 529 (1930)

Binet, L., and Strumza, M. V., *Compt. rend.,* **192,** 1758 (1931)

Bloch, C. E., *Hospitalstidende,* **74,** 265 (1931)

Boynton, L. C., and Bradford, W. L., *J. Nutrition,* **4,** 323 (1931)

Bürgi, E., *Deut. med. Wochschr.,* **56,** 1650 (1930)

Brode, W. R., and Magill, M. A., *J. Biol. Chem.,* **92,** 87 (1931)

Bruins, H. R., Overhoff, J., and Wolff, L. K., *Biochem. J.,* **25,** 430 (1931)

Burton, A. H. G., and Balmain, A. R., *Lancet,* **218,** 1065 (1930)

Capper, N. S. (1), *Biochem. J.,* **24,** 453 (1930)

Capper, N. S. (2), *Biochem. J.,* **24,** 980 (1930)

Capper, N. S. (3), *Nature,* **126,** 385 (1930)

Capper, N. S., McKibbin, I. M. W., and Prentice, J. H., *Biochem. J.,* **25,** 265 (1931)

Chou, C. H., *Nat. Med. J. China,* **16,** 365 (1930)

Coward, K. H., Dyer, F. J., Morton, R. A., and Gaddum, J. H., *Biochem. J.,* **25,** 1102 (1931)

Coward, K. H., Key, K. M., Dyer, F. J., and Morgan, B. G. E. (1), *Biochem. J.,* **24,** 1952 (1930)

Coward, K. H., Key, K. M., Dyer, F. J., and Morgan, B. G. E. (2), *Biochem. J.,* **25,** 551 (1931)

Coward, K. H., Morgan, B. G. E., and Dyer, F. J., *J. Physiol.,* **69,** 349 (1930)

Cramer, W., *Lancet,* **218,** 1153 (1930)

Crist, J. W., and Dye, M., *J. Biol. Chem.,* **91,** 127 (1931)

Dann, W. J., and Moore, T., *Biochem. J.,* **25,** 914 (1931)

Donaldson, S., and Tasker, J., *Transvaal Mine Med. Officers' Assoc.,* Feb., March (1931)

Drummond, J. C., Ahmad, E., and Morton, R. A., *J. Soc. Chem. Ind.,* **40,** 291 (1930)

Drummond, J. C., and Gunther, E. R., *Nature,* **126,** 398 (1930)

Drummond, J. C., and Hilditch, T. P., *"The Relative Values of Cod-Liver Oils from Various Sources,"* Empire Marketing Board, Report **351,** London (1930)

Dulière, W., Morton, R. A., and Drummond, J. C., *J. Soc. Chem. Ind.,* **48,** 316 (1929)

Emmerie, A., Eckelen, M. van, and Wolff, L. K., *Nature,* **128,** 495 (1931)

Euler, H. von, *Nature,* **128,** 39 (1931)

Euler, H. von, et al., *Biochem. Z.,* **203,** 270 (1928)

Euler, H. von, Demole, V., Karrer, P., and Walker, O., *Helv. Chim. Acta,* **13,** 1078 (1930)

EULER, H. VON, DEMOLE, V., WEINHAGEN, A., AND KARRER, P., *Helv. Chim. Acta,* **14,** 831 (1931)

EULER, H. VON, KARRER, P., HELLSTROM, H., AND RYDBOM, M., *Helv. Chim. Acta,* **14,** 839 (1931)

FETTER, D., AND CARLSON, A. J., *Am. J. Physiol.,* **96,** 257 (1931)

FIELD, G. W., *Malayan Med. J.,* **6,** 46 (1931)

FRAPS, G. S., *Texas Agr. Sta. Bull.* No. **422** (1931)

FRAZIER, C. H., AND HU, C. K., *Arch. Internal Med.,* **48,** 507 (1931)

FREDERICIA, L. S., AND HAUSEN, A. P., *Dairy,* Supp. 73 (1931)

GENERAL MEDICAL COUNCIL, *Pharmacopoeia Commission Reports of Sub-Committees.* "3. Report of Cod-Liver Oil Colour Test Sub-Committee," March, 1931

GILLAM, A. E., HEILBRON, I. M., HILDITCH, T. P., AND MORTON, R. A., *Biochem. J.,* **25,** 30 (1931)

GILLAM, A. E., HEILBRON, I. M., AND MORTON, R. A., *J. Soc. Chem. Ind.,* **50,** 244 (1931)

GILLAM, A. E., AND MORTON, R. A., *Biochem. J.,* **25,** 1346 (1931)

GREEN, H. N., AND MELLANBY, E. (1), *Brit. Med. J.,* **2,** 691 (1928)

GREEN, H. N., AND MELLANBY, E. (2), *Brit. J. Exptl. Path.,* **11,** 81 (1930)

GREEN, H. N., PINDAR, D., DAVIS, G., AND MELLANBY, E., *Brit. Med. J.,* **2,** 595 (1931)

GUDJÓNSSON, S. V., *Biochem. J.,* **24,** 1591 (1930)

HARRIS, L. J., *et al., Medical Research Council, Ann. Rep.* (1930–31)

HAUGE, S. M., AND AITKENHEAD, W., *J. Biol. Chem.,* **93,** 657 (1931)

HAUGE, S. M., AND TROST, J. F., *J. Biol. Chem.,* **80,** 107 (1928)

HEILBRON, I. M., GILLAM, A. E., AND MORTON, R. A., *Biochem. J.,* **25,** 1352 (1931)

HEILBRON, I. M., AND MORTON, R. A. (1), *J. Soc. Chem. Ind.,* 50, 183T (1931)

HEILBRON, I. M., AND MORTON, R. A. (2), *Nature,* **128,** 842 (1931)

HENNINGER, E., *Arch. Geflügelkunde,* **5,** 137 (1931)

HOHLWEG, W., AND DOHRN, M., *Z. ges. exptl. Med.,* **71,** 762 (1930)

HONEYWELL, H. E., DUTCHER, R. A., AND ELY, J. O., *J. Nutrition,* **3,** 491 (1931)

HUGHES, J. S., LIENHARDT, H. F., AND AUBEL, C. E., *J. Nutrition,* **2,** 183 (1929)

HUME, E. M., AND HENDERSON SMITH, H., *Lancet,* **219,** 1362 (1930)

HUME, E. M., AND SMEDLEY-MACLEAN, I., *Lancet,* **218,** 290 (1930)

HUSTON, R. C., AND HOPPERT, C. A., *Division of Biological Chemistry, 80th Meeting, American Chemical Society* (1930)

JACKSON, R. W. (1), *J. Nutrition,* **4,** 171 (1931)

JACKSON, R. W. (2), *J. Biol. Chem.,* **92,** vii (1931)

JAVILLIER, M., AND EMERIQUE, L. (1), *Compt. rend.,* **190,** 655 (1930)

JAVILLIER, M., AND EMERIQUE, L. (2), *Compt. rend.,* **191,** 226 (1930)

JAVILLIER, M., AND EMERIQUE, L. (3), *Bull. Soc. Chem. Biol.,* **12,** 1355 (1930)

JAVILLIER, M., AND EMERIQUE, L. (4), *Bull. Soc. Chem. Biol.,* **12,** 1362; *Compt. rend.,* **191,** 862 (1930)

KARRER, P., *Nature,* **128,** 842 (1931)

Karrer, P., Euler, B., Euler, H. von, Hellström, H., and Rydbom, M., *Arkiv Kemi, Mineral. Geol.,* **10B,** No. 12 (1931) (Quoted by *Chem. Abst.,* **25,** 1876 [1931])

Karrer, P., Euler, H. von, and Rydbom, M., *Helv. Chim. Acta,* **13,** 1059 (1930)

Karrer, P., Helfenstein, A., Wehrli, H., and Wettstein, A., *Helv. Chim. Acta,* **13,** 1084 (1930)

Kerppola, W., *Skand. Arch. Physiol.,* **60,** 311 (1930)

Kuhn, R., and Brockmann, H. (1), *Z. physiol. Chem.,* **200,** 255 (1931)

Kuhn, R., and Brockmann, H. (2), *Ber.,* **64B,** 1859 (1931)

Kuhn, R., and Lederer, E. (1), *Naturwissenschaften,* **14,** 306 (1931)

Kuhn, R., and Lederer, E. (2), *Z. physiol. Chem.,* **200,** 246 (1931)

Kuhn, R., and Lederer, E. (3), *Ber.,* **64B,** 1349 (1931)

Kuipers, F. C., *Nederland. Tijdschr. Geneeskunde,* **75,** 1108 (1931)

Lachat, L. L., Dutcher, R. A., and Honeywell, H. E., *Penn. Agr. Exptl. Sta. Bull.,* **258,** 43d Annual Report of Director (1930)

Lassen, H. C. H., *J. Hyg.,* **30,** 300 (1930)

League of Nations Health Organisation, Permanent Commission on Biological Standardisation. *Report of the Conference on Vitamin Standards,* London, Geneva (1931)

Lundborg, M. L., *Biochem. Z.,* **235,** 1 (1931)

McCarrison, R. (1), *Indian J. Med. Research,* **17,** 693 (1930)

McCarrison, R. (2), *Indian J. Med. Research,* **18,** 903 (1930–31)

McCarrison, R. (3), *Brit. Med. J.,* **1,** 1009 (1931)

McCarrison, R. (4), *Indian J. Med. Research,* **19,** 51 (1931)

McCarrison, R., and Ranganathan, S., *Indian J. Med. Research,* **19,** 55 (1931)

McFarlane, W. D., Graham, W. R., and Richardson, F., *Biochem. J.,* **25,** 358 (1931)

Mangelsdorf, P. C., and Fraps, G. S., *Science,* **73,** 241 (1931)

Marcus, J. K., *J. Biol. Chem.,* **90,** 507 (1931)

Mattis, H., and Nolte, E., *Arch. Pharm.,* **269,** 22 (1931)

Mellanby, E. (1), *Medical Research Council, Ann. Rep.* (1929–30)

Mellanby, E. (2), *J. Am. Med. Assoc.,* **96,** 325 (1931)

Mellanby, E. (3), *Brit. Med. J.,* **1,** 89 (1931)

Mellanby, E., and Green, H. N., *Brit. Med. J.,* **1,** 984 (1929)

Mellanby, May, *Medical Research Council, Special Report Series,* No. 153

Mendel, L. B., and Vickery, H. B., *J. Home Econ.,* **22,** 581 (1930)

Meyer, C. R., and Hetler, R. A., *J. Agr. Research,* **42,** 501 (1931)

Moore, T. (1), *Biochem. J.,* **23,** 803 (1929)

Moore, T. (2), *Biochem. J.,* **23,** 1267 (1929)

Moore, T. (3), *Lancet,* **216,** 499 (1929)

Moore, T. (4), *Lancet,* **217,** 380 (1929)

Moore, T. (5), *Biochem. J.,* **24,** 692 (1930)

Moore, T. (6), *Biochem. J.,* **25,** 275 (1931)

Morgan, A. F., and Field, A., *J. Biol. Chem.,* **88,** 9 (1930)

Morgan, B. G. E., and Coward, K. H., *Lancet,* **221,** 758 (1931)

Morton, R. A., *Nature,* **128,** 39 (1931)

Morton, R. A., and Heilbron, I. M., *Biochem. J.*, 24, 870 (1930)
Morton, R. A., Heilbron, I. M., and Thompson, A., *Biochem. J.*, 25, 20 (1931)
Mouriquand, G., Rollet, J., and Chaix, Mme, *Bull. histol.*, 8, 72 (1931)
Nelson, E. M., and Manning, J. R., *Ind. Eng. Chem.*, 22, 1361 (1930)
Nelson, E. M., Walker, R., and Jones, D. B., *J. Biol. Chem.*, 92, vi (1931)
Norris, E. R., and Church, A. E. (1), *J. Biol. Chem.*, 87, 139 (1930)
Norris, E. R., and Church, A. E. (2), *J. Biol. Chem.*, 89, 421 (1930)
Norris, E. R., and Church, A. E. (3), *J. Biol. Chem.*, 89, 589 (1930)
Olcott, H. S., and McCann, D. C., *J. Biol. Chem.*, 94, 185 (1931)
Olcovich, H. S., and Mattill, H. A., *J. Biol. Chem.*, 91, 105 (1931)
Orr, J. B., MacLeod, J. J. R., and MacKie, T. J., *Lancet*, 220, 1177 (1931)
Parsons, H. T., Stevenson, I., Mullen, I., and Horn, C., *J. Home Econ.*, 23, 366 (1931)
Poulsson, E. (1), *Deut. med. Wochschr.*, 56, 1688 (1930)
Poulsson, E. (2), *Norsk. Mag. Laegevidenskap.*, 92, 125 (1931)
Pummerer, R., Rebman, L., and Reindel, W., *Ber.*, 64B, 492 (1931)
Quinn, E. J., and Hartley, J. G., *J. Biol. Chem.*, 91, 633 (1931)
Quinn, E. J., Hartley, J. G., and Derow, M. A., *J. Biol. Chem.*, 89, 657 (1931)
Ranganathan, S. (1), *Indian J. Med. Research*, 19, 1 (1931)
Ranganathan, S. (2), *Indian J. Med. Research*, 19, 55 (1931)
Rosenheim, O. (1), *Biochem. J.*, 21, 386 (1927)
Rosenheim, O. (2), *Nature*, 128, 39 (1931)
Rowntree, J. I. (1), *J. Nutrition*, 3, 265 (1930)
Rowntree, J. I. (2), *J. Nutrition*, 3, 345 (1930)
Rydbom, M., *Biochem. Z.*, 227, 482 (1930)
St. Julian, R. R., and Heller, V. G., *J. Biol. Chem.*, 90, 99 (1931)
Scheunert, A., *Klin. Wochschr.*, 9, 1247 (1930)
Scheunert, A., and Reschke, J., *Z. Untersuch. Lebensm.*, 61, 337 (1931)
Scheunert, A., and Wagner, E., *Biochem. Z.*, 236, 29 (1931)
Schmidt, W., and Schmidt, C. L. A., *Univ. Calif. Pub. Physiol.*, 7, No. 13, 211 (1930)
Schmidt-Nielsen, S., and Schmidt-Nielsen, S., *Chem. Abst.*, 24, 5798, 5799 (1930)
Seel, H., *Arch. exptl. Path. Pharmakol.*, 159, 93 (1931)
Seel, H., and Dannmeyer, F., *Strahlentherapie*, 39, 499 (1931)
Sherman, H. C., and Batchelder, E. L., *J. Biol. Chem.*, 91, 505 (1931)
Sherman, H. C., and Stiebeling, H. K., *J. Biol. Chem.*, 88, 683 (1930)
Smith, A. H., Yudkin, A. M., Kriss, M., and Zimmerman, H., *J. Biol. Chem.*, 92, xcii (1931)
Smith, E. L., and Hazley, V., *Biochem. J.*, 24, 1942 (1931)
Smith, J. H. C., *J. Biol. Chem.*, 90, 597 (1931)
Smith, M., and Lynott, M. L., *J. Agr. Research*, 42, 421 (1931)
Spence, J. C., *Arch. Diseases Childhood*, 6, 17 (1931)
Steenbock, H., and Schrader, I. M., *J. Nutrition*, 4, 267 (1931)
Steenbock, H., and Wirick, A. M., *J. Dairy Sci.*, 14, 229 (1931)
Stolk, D. van, Guilbert, J., Penau, H., and Simmonet, H., *Compt. rend.*, 192, 1499 (1931)

SURE, B., KIK, M. C., AND WALKER, D. J., *Proc. Soc. Exptl. Biol. Med.,* **28,** 495 (1931)

SURE, B., AND SMITH, M. E., *Proc. Soc. Exptl. Biol. Med.,* **28,** 439 (1931)

TAKAHASHI, K., NAKAMIYA, Z., KAWAKAMI, K., AND KITASATO, T., *Sci. Papers Inst. Phys. Chem. Research (Tokyo),* **3,** 81 (1925)

TANSLEY, K., *J. Physiol.,* **71,** 442 (1931)

TILDEN, E. B., AND MILLER, E. G., *J. Nutrition,* **3,** 121 (1930)

TOPLEY, W. W. C., GREENWOOD, M., AND WILSON, J., *J. Path. Bact.,* **34,** 163 (1931)

TURNER, R. G., *Proc. Soc. Exptl. Biol. Med.,* **27,** 1006 (1930)

TURNER, R. G., AND LOEW, E. R., *Proc. Soc. Exptl. Biol. Med.,* **28,** 506 (1931)

WEECH, A. A., *Am. J. Diseases Children,* **39,** 1153 (1930)

WOLFE, J. M., AND SALTER, H. P., *J. Nutrition,* **4,** 185 (1931)

WOLFF, L. K., OVERHOFF, J., AND ECKELEN, M. VAN, *Deut. med. Wochschr.,* **56,** 1428 (1930)

WOODROW, J. W., AND CUNNINGHAM, H. L., *Physiol. Rev.,* **35,** 125 (1931)

WRIGHT, E. J., *"The A and B Avitaminosis Disease of Sierra Leone,"* London (1930)

WRIGHT, H. P., *et al., Can. Med. Assoc. J.,* **25,** 412 (1931)

WRIGHT, R. E., *Lancet,* **220,** 800 (1931)

YUDKIN, A. M., KRISS, M., AND SMITH, A. H., *Am. J. Physiol.,* **97,** 611 (1931)

REFERENCES TO VITAMIN D

AGDUHR, E., *Proc. 2d Internat. Congr. Sex Research (London)* (1930)

ANGUS, T. C., ASKEW, F. A., BOURDILLON, R. B., BRUCE, H. M., CALLOW, R. K., FISCHMANN, C. F., PHILPOT, J. ST. L., AND WEBSTER, T. A., *Proc. Roy. Soc. (London), B,* **108,** 340 (1931)

ASHFORD, C. A., *Biochem. J.,* **24,** 661 (1930)

ASKEW, F. A., BOURDILLON, R. B., BRUCE, H. M., JENKINS, R. G. C., AND WEBSTER, R. A. (1), *Proc. Roy. Soc. (London), B,* **107,** 76 (1930)

ASKEW, F. A., BOURDILLON, R. B., BRUCE, H. M., JENKINS, R. G. C., AND WEBSTER, R. A. (2), *Proc. Roy. Soc. (London), B,* **107,** 91 (1930)

ASKEW, F. A., BRUCE, H. M., CALLOW, R. K., PHILPOT, J. ST. L., AND WEBSTER, T. A., *Nature,* **128,** 759 (1931)

BACHARACH, A. L., ALLCHORNE, E., AND HAZLEY, V., *Biochem. J.,* **25,** 639 (1931)

BAKWIN, H., AND BAKWIN, R. M., *J. Am. Med. Assoc.,* **95,** 396 (1930)

BAMBERGER, P., *Deut. med. Wochschr.,* **57,** 57, 104 (1931)

BAUER, W., MARBLE, A., MADDOCK, S. J., AND WOOD, J. C., *Am. J. Med. Sci.,* **181,** 399 (1931)

BILLS, C. E., HONEYWELL, E. H., AND COX, W. M., *J. Biol. Chem.,* **92,** 601 (1931)

BILLS, C. E., HONEYWELL, E. M., WIRICK, A. M., AND NUSSMEIER, M., *J. Biol. Chem.,* **90,** 619 (1931)

BILLS, C. E., AND McDONALD, F. G., *J. Biol. Chem.,* **88,** 337 (1930)

BILLS, C. E., McDONALD, F. G., BeMILLER, L. N., STEEL, G. E., AND NUSS-MEIER, M., *J. Biol. Chem.,* **93,** 775 (1931)

BILLS, C. E., McDONALD, F. G., AND COX, W. M., *J. Biol. Chem.,* **87,** liii (1930)

BILLS, C. E., AND WIRICK, A. M., *J. Biol. Chem.*, **86**, 117 (1930)

BISCHOFF, G., *Z. physiol. Chem.*, **188**, 247 (1930)

BOARD OF EDUCATION, *Committee on Adenoids and Enlarged Tonsils. 2d Interim Report* (H. M. Stationery Office, 1931)

BOURDILLON, R. B., BRUCE, H. M., FISCHMANN, C., AND WEBSTER, T. A., *Medical Research Council, Special Report Series,* No. 158 (London, 1931)

BOURDILLON, R. B., JENKINS, R. G. C., AND WEBSTER, T. A., *Nature,* **125,** 635 (1930)

BRADY, D. J., BRADY, M. J., AND JAMES, E. M., *Am. J. Diseases Children,* **39,** 45 (1930)

BRAND, T. VON, AND HOLTZ, F., *Z. physiol. Chem.*, **195**, 241 (1930)

BRANION, E. D., GUYATT, B. L., AND KAY, H. D., *J. Biol. Chem.*, **92**, xi (1931)

BROCKLESBY, H. N., AND DENSTEDT, O. F., *Can. Chem. Met.*, **14**, 29 (1930)

BROUWER, E., AND DE RUYTER DE WILDT, J. C., *Landbouwk Tijdschr.*, **43,** 337 (1931)

BROWN, H. B., AND SHOHL, A. T., *J. Biol. Chem.*, **86**, 245 (1930)

CALLOW, R. K., AND FISCHMANN, C. F., *Biochem. J.*, **25**, 1464 (1931)

CASTILLE, A., *Bull. acad. roy. med. Belg.*, **10**, 319 (1931)

COCCHERI, P., *Biochim. terap. sper.*, **17**, 372 (1930)

COMEL, M. (1), *Boll. soc. ital. biol. sper.*, **5**, 729 (1930)

COMEL, M. (2), *Boll. soc. ital. biol. sper.*, **5**, 738 (1930)

COMEL, M. (3), *Atti. accad. Lincei,* [6]**11**, 857 (1930)

COMEL, M. (4), *Arch. isti. biochim. ital.*, **2**, 281 (1930)

COMEL, M. (5), *Arch. ital. biol.*, **84**, 118 (1931)

COMPÈRE, E. L., *Am. J. Diseases Children,* **40**, 941, 1177 (1931)

COX, W. S., AND BILLS, C. E., *J. Biol. Chem.*, **88**, 709 (1930)

CRAWFORD, H. E. F., GOLDING, J., PERRY, E. O. V., AND ZILVA, S. S., *Biochem. J.*, **24**, 682 (1930)

CRAWFORD, R., AND WILLIAMSON, G. R., *New Orleans Med. Surg. J.*, **83**, 219 (1930)

CUTHBERTSON, D. P., *Biochem. J.*, **24**, 1244 (1930)

DE SANCTIS, A. G., AND CRAIG, J. D., *J. Am. Med. Assoc.*, **94**, 1258 (1930)

DENTAL BOARD, *Minutes of the Dental Board of the United Kingdom.* Appendix IX, p. 12 (1930)

DONELSON, E., NIMS, B., HUNSCHER, H. A., AND MACY, I. G., *J. Biol. Chem.*, **91**, 675 (1931)

DORLENCOURT, J., AND SEISOFF, C., *Bull. soc. sci. hyg. aliment.*, **19**, 296 (1930)

DRUMMOND, J. C., *Lancet,* **221**, 904 (1931)

DRUMMOND, J. C., AND GUNTHER, E. R., *Nature,* **126**, 398 (1930)

DRUMMOND, J. C., AND HILDITCH, T. P., "The Relative Values of Cod-Liver Oils from Various Sources." *Empire Marketing Board, Report 35* (London, 1930)

DUGUID, J. B., *J. Path. Bact.*, **33**, 697 (1930)

DUGUID, J. B., DUGGAN, M. M., AND GOUGH, J., *J. Path. Bact.*, **33**, 353 (1930)

DYER, F. J., *Quart. J. Pharm. Pharmacol.*, **4**, 503 (1931)

EDDY, W. H., *J. Dental Research,* **11**, 349 (1931)

ESSIG, B., *Münch. med. Wochschr.*, **78**, 273 (1931)

EVERSE, J. W. R., AND NIEKERK, J. VAN, *Nederland. Tijdschr. Geneeskunde,* 75, 1101 (1931) .

FALKENHEIM, C., AND KIRSCH, W., *Z. Zücht. Reihe B. (Tierzücht. Züchtungs-biol.),* 21, 514 (1931)

FAWLEY, J. M., *Am. J. Diseases Children,* 41, 751 (1931)

FETTER, D., AND CARLSON, A. J., *Am. J. Physiol.,* 96, 257 (1931)

FINE, M. S., *Cereal Chem.,* 7, 456 (1930)

FRASER, A. C., *Compt. rend. soc. biol.,* 103, 461 (1930)

GARGILL, S. L., GILLIGAN, D. R., AND BLUMGART, H. L., *Arch. Internal Med.,* 45, 879 (1930)

GENERAL MEDICAL COUNCIL, *Pharmacopoeia Commission Reports of Sub-Committees.* "3. Report of Cod-Liver Oil Colour Test Sub-Committee" (1931)

GHIRARDI, G. E., *Biochim. terap. sper.,* 16, 241 (1929)

GOLDBLATT, H., *Science,* 73, 494 (1931)

GUNTHER, L., AND GREENBERG, D. M., *Arch. Internal Med.,* 47, 660 (1931)

GYÖRGY, P. (1), *Klin. Wochschr.,* 8, 684 (1929)

GYÖRGY, P. (2), *Chem. Zentr.,* 1, 998 (1930)

GYÖRGY, P. (3), *Klin. Wochschr.,* 9, 102 (1930)

GYÖRGY, P., AND POPOVICIU, G., *Jahr. Kinderheilk,* 132, 34 (1931)

HALLAM, R., *Brit. Med. J.,* 1, 215 (1931)

HARRIS, L. J., *Lancet,* 218, 236 (1930)

HARRIS, L. J., AND INNES, J. R. M., *Biochem. J.,* 25, 367 (1931)

HARRIS, R. S., AND BUNKER, J. W. M., *Science,* 73, 95 (1931)

HART, E. B., KLINE, O. L., AND KEENAN, J. A., *Science,* 73, 710 (1930)

HART, E. B., STEENBOCK, H., AND KLINE, O. L., *J. Biol. Chem.,* 86, 145 (1930)

HAURY, V. G., *J. Biol. Chem.,* 89, 467 (1930)

HEILBRON, I. M., AND SPRING, F. S., *Biochem. J.,* 24, 133 (1930)

HENTSCHEL, H., AND FISCHER, W., *Klin. Wochschr.,* 9, 1761 (1930)

HENTSCHEL, H., AND SCHINDEL, L., *Klin. Wochschr.,* 9, 262 (1930)

HESS, A. F., *Am. J. Diseases Children,* 41, 1081 (1931)

HESS, A. F., AND ABRAMSON, H., *Dental Cosmos,* 849 (1931)

HESS, A. F., BERLINER, F. S., AND WEINSTOCK, M., *J. Biol. Chem.,* 94, 9 (1931)

HESS, A. F., LEWIS, J. M., MACLEOD, F. L., AND THOMAS, B. H., *J. Am. Med. Assoc.,* 97, 370 (1931)

HESS, A. F., LEWIS, J. M., AND RIVKIN, H. (1), *J. Am. Med. Assoc.,* 91, 783 (1928)

HESS, A. F., LEWIS, J. M., AND RIVKIN, H. (2), *J. Am. Med. Assoc.,* 94, 1885 (1930)

HESS, A. F., WEINSTOCK, M., BENJAMIN, H. R., AND GROSS, J., *J. Biol. Chem.,* 90, 737 (1931)

HESS, A. F., WEINSTOCK, M., AND RIVKIN, H., *Proc. Soc. Exptl. Biol. Med.,* 27, 298 (1930)

HESS, A. F., WEINSTOCK, M., AND GROSS, J., *J. Biol. Chem.,* 87, 37 (1930)

HESS, J. H., PONCHER, M. G., DALE, M. L., AND KLEIN, R. I., *J. Am. Med. Assoc.,* 95, 316 (1930)

HESS, R., *Chem. Zentr.,* 1, 998 (1930)

HEUBNER, W. (1), *Chem. Zentr.*, 1, 1000 (1930)

HEUBNER, W. (2), *Klin. Wochschr.*, 9, 775 (1930)

HEUBNER, W. (3), *Nachr. Ges. Wiss. Göttingen, math.-phys. Klasse*, No. 2, 149 (1930)

HEYMANN, W., *Biochem. Z.*, 227, 1 (1930)

HICKMAN, J. O., *J. State Med.*, 38, 476 (1930)

HOLMES, A. D., *New Engl. J. Med.*, 204, 211 (1931)

HOLMES, A. D., AND PIGOTT, M. G. (1), *Ind. Eng. Chem.*, 23, 190 (1931)

HOLMES, A. D., AND PIGOTT, M. G. (2), *New Engl. J. Med.*, 203, 220 (1930)

HOLTZ, F., LAQUER, F., KREITMAIR, H., AND MOLL, T., *Biochem. Z.*, 237, 247 (1931)

HOLTZ, F., AND SCHREIBER, E., *Z. physiol. Chem.*, 191, 1 (1930)

HONEYWELL, H. E., DUTCHER, R. A., AND DAHLE, C. D., *J. Nutrition*, 2, 251 (1930)

HOTTINGER, A. (i), *Z. Kinderheilk.*, 47, 341 (1929)

HOTTINGER, A. (2), *Chem. Zentr.*, 1, 997 (1930)

HOU, H. C., *Chinese J. Physiol.*, 4, 345 (1930)

HOYLE, J. C., *J. Pharmacol.*, 38, 271 (1930)

HUGHES, T. A., *et al., Indian J. Med. Research*, 17, 461 (1929)

HUME, E. M., AND HENDERSON SMITH, H., *Biochem. J.*, 25, 292 (1931)

HUSCH, W., AND KELLNER, L., *Biochem. Z.*, 235, 162 (1931)

INNES, J. R. M., *Proc. Roy. Soc. Med.*, 24, 24 (1931)

JONES, J. H., AND RAPOPORT, M., *J. Biol. Chem.*, 93, 153 (1931)

JONES, J. H., RAPOPORT, M., AND HODES, H. P. (1), *J. Biol. Chem.*, 86, 267 (1930)

JONES, J. H., RAPOPORT, M., AND HODES, H. P. (2), *J. Biol. Chem.*, 89, 647 (1930)

JONES, J. H., AND ROBSON, G. M., *J. Biol. Chem.*, 91, 43 (1931)

KERN, R., MONTGOMERY, A. F., AND STILL, E. V., *J. Biol. Chem.*, 93, 365 (1931)

KING, E. J., AND HALL, G. E. (1), *Biochem. Z.*, 229, 315 (1930)

KING, E. J., AND HALL, G. E. (2), *Poultry Sci.*, 10, 332 (1931)

KISCH, E., AND REITER, T., *Deut. med. Wochschr.*, 48, No. 6 (1931)

KLAUSSNER-CROHEIM, I., *Deut. med. Wochschr.*, 56, 1566 (1930)

KLEIN, D., AND RUSSELL, W. C., *J. Biol. Chem.*, 93, 693 (1931)

KLEIN, H., AND SHELLING, D. H., *J. Dental Research*, 11, 151 (1931)

KLEITZIEN, S. W. F., THOMAS, B. H., TEMPLIN, V. H., AND STEENBOCK, H., *J. Biol. Chem.*, 92, ix (1931)

KLOSTER, J., *Acta Paediatrica*, 12, Supp. iii (1931)

KNOWLTON, G. C., *Proc. Soc. Exptl. Biol. Med.*, 27, 757 (1930)

KON, S. K., *Lancet*, 220, 579 (1931)

KON, S. K., AND MAYZNER, M., *Lancet*, 218, 794 (1930)

KRAMER, B., SHEAR, M. J., AND SIEGEL, J. (1), *J. Biol. Chem.*, 91, 271 (1931)

KRAMER, B., SHEAR, M. J., AND SIEGEL, J. (2), *J. Biol. Chem.*, 91, 723 (1931)

KRAUSS, N. E., AND BETHKE, R. M., *J. Biol. Chem.*, 92, x (1931)

LAQUER, F., *Klin. Wochschr.*, 10, 1072 (1931)

LASCH, F., *Klin. Wochschr.*, 7, 2148 (1928)

LEAGUE OF NATIONS HEALTH ORGANISATION, Permanent Commission on Biological Standardisation. *Report of the Conference on Vitamin Standards.* London and Geneva (1931).

LEERSUM, E. C. VAN, *Nederland. Tijdschr. Geneeskunde,* 74, I, 2854 (1931)

LESNÉ, E., AND DREYFUS-SEE, G., *Lait,* 11, 155 (1931)

LESNÉ, E., SYLVESTRE, MISS, AND ZIZINE, P., *Bull. soc. sci. hyg. aliment.,* 18, 295 (1930)

LEVADITI, C., AND PO, L. Y., *Presse médi.,* 38, 168 (1930)

LEVADITI, C., AND PO, L. Y., *Compt. rend. soc. biol.,* 106, 169 (1931)

LEVINE, V. E., AND RICHMAN, E., *Proc. Soc. Exptl. Biol. Med.,* 27, 832, 833, 1010 (1930)

LEWIS, R. C., FRUMESS, G. M., AND STERN, H. B., *Am. J. Diseases Children,* 41, 71 (1931)

LIGHT, R. F., MILLER, G. E., AND FREY, C. N., *J. Biol. Chem.,* 92, 47 (1931)

LÖSSL, H., *Z. Hungerforschung,* 1, Nos. 3 and 4 (1931)

LOUREIRO, J. A. DE, *Compt. rend. soc. biol.,* 106, 555 (1931)

LUCAS, N. S., *Biochem. J.,* 25, 27 (1931)

MACCORQUODALE, D. W., STEENBOCK, H., AND ADKINS, H., *J. Am. Chem. Soc.,* 52, 5212 (1930)

McDONALD, F. G., AND BILLS, C. E., *J. Biol. Chem.,* 88, 601 (1930)

McGOWN, J. P., CUNNINGHAM, I. J., AND AUCHINACHIE, D. W., *Biochem. J.,* 25, 1295 (1931)

MACY, I. B., HUNSCHER, H. A., McCOSH, S. S., AND NIMS, B., *J. Biol. Chem.,* 86, 59 (1930)

MAISIN, J., MUND, W., POURBAIX, Y., AND CASTILLE, A., *Compt. rend. soc. biol.,* 103. 534 (1930)

MANSFELD, G., AND HORN, Z., *Deut. med. Wochschr.,* 57, 1452 (1931)

MARSHALL, A. L., AND KNUDSON, A., *J. Am. Chem. Soc.,* 52, 2304 (1930)

MASSENGALE, O. N., AND NUSSMEIER, M. (1), *J. Biol. Chem.,* 87, 423 (1930)

MASSENGALE, O. N., AND NUSSMEIER, M. (2), *J. Biol. Chem.,* 87, 415 (1930)

MAXWELL, J. P., *Proc. Roy. Soc. Med.,* 23, 639 (1930)

MAY, E. W., *J. Am. Med. Assoc.,* 96, 1376 (1931)

MEDICAL RESEARCH COUNCIL, *Special Report Series,* No. 159. London (1931)

MEESEMAECKER, R., *Compt. rend.,* 190, 216 (1930)

MELLANBY, M., *Medical Research Council, Special Reports Series,* No. 153. London (1930)

MICHELAZZI, L., *Arch. ital. biol.,* 84, 111 (1931)

MINISTRY OF AGRICULTURE AND FISHERIES, *Lancet,* 219, 672 (1930)

MIRVISH, L., *Biochem. J.,* 24, 233 (1930)

MOORE, R. B., AND DEVRIES, T., *J. Am. Chem. Soc.,* 53, 2676 (1931)

MORELLE, J., *Rev. belge sci. med.* (Paris), 2, 226 (1930)

MORGAN, A. F., AND GARRISON, E. A. (1), *J. Biol. Chem.,* 85, 687 (1930)

MORGAN, A. F., AND GARRISON, E. A. (2), *J. Biol. Chem.,* 92, xciv (1931)

MORIN, G., AND BOUCOMONT, J., *Compt. rend.,* 192, 509 (1931)

MORITZ, A. R., AND KRENZ, C., *J. Nutrition,* 2, 257 (1930)

MOURIQUAND, G., AND LEULIER, A., *Paris Méd.,* 19, 409; *Bull. soc. sci. hyg. aliment.,* 18, 294 (1930)

MOURIQUAND, G., LEULIER, A., AND NOGIER, *Compt. rend. soc. biol.,* 106, 18 (1931)

MOURIQUAND, G., LEULIER, A., AND ROCHE, A., *Compt. rend. soc. biol.*, 107, 676 (1931)

NASER, H., *Arch. exptl. Path. Pharmakol.*, 158, 201 (1931)

NEBARRO, D., *Lancet*, 218, 127 (1930)

NELSON, E. M., AND MANNING, J. R., *Ind. Eng. Chem.*, 22, 1361 (1930)

NIEKERK, J. VAN, AND EVERSE, J. W. R., *Strahlentherapie*, 40, 733 (1931)

NORRIS, E. R., AND CHURCH, A. E., *J. Biol. Chem.*, 89, 437 (1930)

PAGE, I. H., *Biochem. Z.*, 220, 420 (1930)

PAGE, I. H., AND MENSCHICK, W. (1), *Naturwissenschaften*, 18, 585 (1930)

PAGE, I. H., AND MENSCHICK, W. (2), *Biochem. Z.*, 221, 6 (1930)

PAGE, I. H., AND RESIDUE, D. M., *Biochem. Z.*, 223, 171 (1930)

PAPPENHEIMER, A. M., AND BUXTON, C. L., *J. Exptl. Med.*, 52, 805 (1930)

PARK, E. A., *Am. J. Diseases Children*, 39, 1351 (1930)

PATTISON, C. L., *Brit. Med. J.*, 2, 178 (1930)

PETERSON, C., *Wiss. Arch. Landw. Abt. B (Tierernähr. u. Tierzucht)*, 5, 554 (1931)

PINCHERLE, M., AND NAVA, V., *Riv. chim. pedriatica*, 28, No. 3 (1930)

POLICARD, A., PAUPERT-RAVAULT, AND BARRAL, P., *Compt. rend. soc. biol.*, 104, 633 (1930)

POULSSON, E. (1), *Chem. Zentr.*, 1, 997 (1930)

POULSSON, E. (2), quoted by *Brit. Med. J.*, 1, 853 (1931)

POULSSON, E. (3), *Norsk. Mag. Laegevidenskap.*, 92, 125 (1931)

PREUSS, L. M., PETERSON, W. H., STEENBOCK, H., AND FRED, E. B., *J. Biol. Chem.*, 90, 369 (1931)

PUTSCHAR, W., *Z. Kinderheilk.*, 48, 269 (1929)

RANDOIN, L., AND LECOQ, R., *Compt. rend.*, 191, 732 (1930)

RAU, H., AND GRUBER, A., *Münch. med. Wochschr.*, 78, 274 (1931)

REED, C. I., AND THACKER, E. A., *Am. J. Physiol.*, 96, 21 (1931)

REERINK, E. H., AND WIJK, A. VAN (1), *Nederland. Maandschr. Geneeskunde*, 17, 1 (1930)

REERINK, E. H., AND WIJK, A. VAN (2), *Biochem. J.*, 25, 1001 (1931)

REERINK, E. H., AND WIJK, A. VAN (3), *Strahlentherapie*, 40, 728 (1931)

ROEGHOLT, M. N., *Nederland. Tijdschr. Geneeskunde*, 74, 1028 (1930)

ROGOZINSKI, F., quoted by *Nutrition Abst. Rev.*, 1, 73 (1931)

ROHMER, P., AND DUBOIS, R., *J. Am. Med. Assoc.*, 96, 305 (1930)

ROSEBURY, T., AND KARNSHAN, M., *J. Dental Research*, 11, 121 (1931)

ROSENHEIM, O., AND CALLOW, R. K., *Biochem. J.*, 25, 74 (1931)

RUSSELL, W. C., AND HOWARD, C. H., *J. Biol. Chem.*, 91, 493 (1931)

RUSSELL, W. C., HOWARD, C. H., AND HESS, A. F., *Science*, 72, 506 (1930)

ST. JULIAN, R. R., AND HELLER, V. G., *J. Biol. Chem.*, 90, 99 (1931)

SCHEUNERT, A., *Berlin. Tier. Wochschr.*, 40, 746 (1930)

SCHEUNERT, A., AND RESCHKE, J., *Tierernähr.*, 2, 262 (1930)

SCHIEBLICH, M., *Biochem. Z.*, 230, 312 (1931)

SCHILLENHELM, A., AND EISLER, B., *Z. ges. exptl. Med.*, 75, 737, 745, 758; *Klin. Wochschr.*, 10, 1014 (1931)

SCHÖNHEIMER, R., *J. Biol. Chem.*, 92, v (1931)

SCHÖNHEIMER, R., AND BEHRING, H. VON, *Klin. Wochschr.*, 9, 1308 (1930)

SCHULTZ, O., AND MEYER, W., *Klin. Wochschr.*, 9, 1360 (1930)

SCHULTZER, P., *Biochem. J.*, **25**, 1745 (1931)

SCHWARZ, L., AND SIEKE, F., *Münch. med. Wochschr.*, **77**, 1801 (1930)

SEEL, H., *Arch. exptl. Path. Pharmakol.*, **140**, 194 (1929)

SHELLING, D. H., *Proc. Soc. Exptl. Biol. Med.*, **28**, 298, 301, 303, 306 (1930)

SHELOW, E., AND LOOFBOUROW, J. R., *Bull. Basic Sci. Research*, **3**, 47 (1931)

SHERMAN, H. C., AND STREBLING, H. K., *J. Biol. Chem.*, **88**, 683 (1930)

SHOHL, A. T., BROWN, H. B., ROSE, C. S., SMITH, D. N., AND COZAD, F., *J. Biol. Chem.*, **92**, 711 (1931)

SHOHL, A. T., GOLDBLATT, H., AND BROWN, H. B., *J. Clin. Investigation*, **8**, 505 (1930)

SIMMONET, H., AND TANRET, G. (1), *Bull. soc. chim. biol.*, **12**, 371 (1930)

SIMMONET, H., AND TANRET, G. (2), *Compt. rend.*, **190**, 1526 (1930)

SIMMONET, H., AND TANRET, G. (3), *Compt. rend.*, **192**, 586 (1931)

SKAAR, T., *Acta Paediatrica*, **12**, Supp. i (1931)

SŒUR, R., *Arch. intern. med. exptl.*, **6**, 365 (1931)

SPIES, T. D., *Am. J. Path.*, **6**, 337 (1930)

SPIES, T. D., AND GLOVER, E. C., *Am. J. Path.*, **6**, 485 (1930)

STEENBOCK, H., BLACK, A., THOMAS, B. H., AND RIISING, B. M., *J. Biol. Chem.*, **85**, 585 (1930)

STEENBOCK, H., HART, E. B., HANNING, G., AND HUMPHREY, G. C., *J. Biol. Chem.*, **88**, 197 (1930)

STEENBOCK, H., HART, E. B., RIISING, B. M., HOPPERT, C. A., AND BASHEROV, S., *J. Biol. Chem.*, **87**, 103 (1930)

STEENBOCK, H., HART, E. B., RIISING, B. M., KLEITZIEN, S. W. F., AND SCOTT, H. T., *J. Biol. Chem.*, **87**, 127 (1930)

STEENBOCK, H., SCHRADER, I. M., RIISING, B. M., AND WIRICK, A. M., *J. Nutrition*, **4**, 267 (1931)

STERN, H. B., AND LEWIS, R. C., *Am. J. Diseases Children*, **41**, 62 (1931)

SUPPLEE, G. C., FLANIGAN, G. E., KAHLENBERG, C. J., AND HESS, A., *J. Biol. Chem.*, **91**, 773 (1931)

SURE, B., AND KIK, M. C., *Proc. Soc. Exptl. Biol. Med.*, **28**, 496 (1931)

SURE, B., AND SMITH, M. E., *Proc. Soc. Exptl. Biol. Med.*, **28**, 440 (1931)

TAYLOR, N. B., BRANION, H. D., AND KAY, H. D., *J. Physiol.*, **69**, xxv (1930)

TAYLOR, N. B., WELD, C. B., BRANION, H. D., AND KAY, H. D., *Can. Med. Assoc. J.*, **24**, 763; **25**, 20 (1931)

THATCHER, L., *Edinburgh Med. J.*, **38**, 457 (1931)

THOMAS, B. H., AND MACLEOD, F. L., *Science*, **73**, 618 (1931)

TOVERUD, K. U., AND TOVERUD, G., *Acta Paediatrica*, **12**, Supp. ii (1931)

TU TUNGI, D. F., *Lancet*, **220**, 53 (1931)

VARA-LOPEZ, R., *Klin. Wochschr.*, **9**, 1072 (1930)

WAHLIN, B., *Acta Med. Scand.*, **74**, 430 (1931)

WARKANY, J. (1), *Klin. Wochschr.*, **9**, 63 (1930)

WARKANY, J. (2), *Klin. Wochschr.*, **9**, 2152 (1930)

WATCHORN, E. (1), *Biochem. J.*, **24**, 631 (1930)

WATCHORN, E. (2), *Biochem. J.*, **24**, 1560 (1930)

WENDT, G. VON, *Klin. Wochschr.*, **4**, 166 (1930)

WILDER, T. S., AND VACK, C., *Am. J. Diseases Children*, **39**, 930 (1930)

WILLS, L., *Indian Med. Gaz.*, **66**, 75 (1931)

WILSON, D. C. (1), *Lancet,* **220,** 10 (1931)
WILSON, D. C. (2), *Indian J. Med. Research,* **18,** 951, 963, 969, 979 (1931)
WILSON, D. C., AND COOMBES, W. K., *Indian J. Med. Research,* **18,** 959 (1931)
WILSON, D. C., AND PATEL, G. P., *Indian J. Med. Research,* **17,** 889 (1930)
WILSON, D. C., AND SURIE, E., *Indian J. Med. Research,* **17,** 899 (1930)
WINDAUS, A. (1), *Nachr. Ges. Wiss. Göttingen, Math.-physik. Klasse,* No. 1, 36 (1930)
WINDAUS, A. (2), *Nature,* **128,** 39 (1931)
WINDAUS, A. (3), *Proc. Roy. Soc. (London), B,* **108,** 568 (1931)
WINDAUS, A. (4), *Deut. med. Wochschr.,* No. 16 (1931)
WINDAUS, A., AND AUHAGEN, E. (1), *Z. physiol. Chem.,* **196,** 108 (1931)
WINDAUS, A., AND AUHAGEN, E. (2), *Z. physiol. Chem.,* **197,** 167 (1931)
WINDAUS, A., DITHMAR, K., MURKE, H., AND SUKFÜLL, F., *Ann.,* **488,** 91 (1931)
WINDAUS, A., GAEDE, J., KÖSER, I., AND STEIN, G., *Ann.,* **483,** 17 (1930)
WYMAN, E. T., DRINKER, P., AND MacKENZIE, K. H., *Am. J. Diseases Children,* **39,** 969 (1930)

REFERENCES TO VITAMIN E

CUMMINGS, M. J., AND MATTILL, H. A., *J. Nutrition,* **3,** 421 (1931)
JUHASZ-SCHÄFFER, A., *Arch. path. Anat. (Virchows),* **281,** 3, 34, 46, 53 (1931)
MENDEL, L. B., AND VICKERY, H. B., *J. Home Econ.,* **22,** 581 (1930)
OLCOVITCH, H. S., AND MATTILL, H. A., *J. Biol. Chem.,* **92,** xxxi–xxxii (1931)
SURE, B., *Arkansas Agr. Exptl. Sta. Bull.,* **250,** (1931)
SZARKA, A., *Arch. ges. Physiol.,* **223,** 657 (1930)
VERZÁR, F., *Arch. ges. Physiol.,* **227,** 499 (1931)
VOGT-MØLLER, P., *Hospitalstidende,* **1931,** 567 (1931)
VOGT-MØLLER, P., AND BAY, F., *Vet. J.,* **87,** 165 (1931)
WADDELL, J., AND STEENBOCK, H., *J. Nutrition,* **4,** 79 (1931)
WADDELL, J., STEENBOCK, H., HART, E. B., AND VANDONK, E., *J. Nutrition,* **4,** 53 (1931)
WADDELL, J., AND VANDONK, E., *J. Nutrition,* **4,** 67 (1931)

REFERENCES TO MISCELLANEOUS STUDIES ON VITAMIN DISTRIBUTION

QUINN, E. J., AND BRABEC, L. B., *J. Home Econ.,* **22,** 123 (1930)
QUINN, E. J., WHALEN, F. B., AND HARTLEY, J. G., *J. Nutrition,* **3,** 257 (1930)
SCHEUNERT, A. (1), *Z. ärtz. Fortbild.,* **27,** 221 (1930)
SCHEUNERT, A. (2), *"Der Vitamin Gehalt der deutschen Nahrungsmittel,"* Berlin (1930)
SCHEUNERT, A. (3), *Deut. med. Wochschr.,* No. 20 (1931)
SCHEUNERT, A. (4), *Ärtz. Rundschau,* No. 17 (1931)
SCHEUNERT, A. (5), *Margarine-Industrie,* No. 18 (1931)
SCHEUNERT, A., AND RESCHKE, J., *Deut. med. Wochschr.,* No. 9 (1931)
SCHEUNERT, A., AND SCHIEBLICH, M., *Handb. Milchwirt.,* **1930,** 87 (1930)

DUNN NUTRITIONAL LABORATORY
UNIVERSITY OF CAMBRIDGE
CAMBRIDGE, ENGLAND

THE HORMONES*

By D. L. THOMPSON AND J. B. COLLIP

McGill University

So enormous has the literature of endocrinology become that it was found impossible to cover the publications of a single year, even superficially, in the space allotted. We have therefore dealt only with those topics in which general interest is, to judge by the number of articles surveyed, at present chiefly focused, and to postpone to some future occasion[1] a discussion of other fields. The subjects dealt with are the sex hormones, the suprarenal cortex, sympathin, and in part thyroxin and insulin; even in this limited field, however, we have found space to discuss only a fraction of the mass of papers which were read for the purposes of this review. We wish to express our thanks to those who lightened our task by sending reprints of their articles, and our regret that some of these have unavoidably been passed over on this occasion.

Oestrin.—The crystalline substance obtained from pregnancy urine by Doisy and Butenandt independently in 1929 has been further examined by these workers. Butenandt (1) ascribes to it the formula $C_{18}H_{22}O_2$, and gives the melting-point as 250° (corrected) and $[\alpha]_D^{18}, + 156°$, in chloroform. He has prepared a monoacetate (m.p. 126°), a monobenzoate (m.p. 211°), an oxime (m.p. 230°), and a perhydroderivative $C_{18}H_{30}O$ (m.p. 104°), the two first-named retaining biological activity; he concludes that the original substance contains three double bonds and four hydro-aromatic rings (less probably, one benzene ring), one hydroxyl group, probably alcoholic, and one keto-group, which may show tautomerism to an enol form. Thayer, Levin, and Doisy (2) now accept the same formula, and place the melting-point and specific rotation (in alcohol) slightly higher; they have also obtained the acetate and the oxime, and also a monomethyl ether (m.p. 165°); iodine is taken up at only one double bond. De Jongh, Kober, and Laqueur have proved the identity, both chemically and biologically, of this product with one isolated from the urine of pregnant mares, and Kober has found that a modi-

* Received January 14, 1932.
[1] Volume 2, 1933.

fied Salkowski test constitutes a specific colour reaction for the substance, which may be estimated in this way colorimetrically in amounts of the order of 50 units.

The substance obtained in 1930 by Marrian and later by Doisy has also received further study. Butenandt finds it to be $C_{18}H_{24}O_3$, confirming Marrian, and to have m.p. 269° (uncorrected) and $[\alpha]_{5461} = + 38°$ It forms a triacetate (m.p. 122°). Butenandt (1) has further shown that this substance, when sublimed from $KHSO_4$, yields the above-mentioned $C_{18}H_{22}O_2$, and believes that in this reaction the elements of water are withdrawn from adjacent carbon atoms, between which a double bond is left; no oxime could be obtained, hence apparently the enol form is stabilised in this case. Doisy and Thayer separate this substance from the preceding one by distribution between ether and alkali, the more polar trihydroxyform being more soluble in the latter. Thayer, Levin, and Doisy (1) give the melting-point of the new compound as 274° and $[\alpha]_D^{27}, + 61°$ in alcohol; they obtained the triacetate and a monomethyl ether (m.p. 155°), and the iodine number reveals one double bond. Slawson has described the crystallographic properties.

Doisy refers to these two substances as theelin and theelol; Marrian calls them dihydroxy- and trihydroxy-oestrin. Neither pair of names is perfectly logical, perhaps, yet we consider that Doisy's are the more acceptable. Undoubtedly there is still room for a group-name such as oestrin to designate substances, for example those in the placenta, amniotic fluid, and follicular fluid, of which little is known save that they evoke the phenomena of oestrus in castrate animals, theelin and theelol then being two examples of the oestrin group of substances, a group whose size is unknown. Butenandt believes that theelin and theelol are both present in human pregnancy urine; Doisy considers that, although the yields of theelol are five or ten times greater than those of theelin, the former may be an artefact arising in the course of purification. Butenandt finds that the amount of theelin required to produce oestrus in 75 per cent of a group of castrate mice, when injected as a single dose in oil, is about 0.11γ; theelol is only one-fifth as active.[2] Curtis and Doisy, who give three doses in aqueous solution in one day to castrate rats, find that 0.3γ theelin, or 0.5γ to 0.6γ theelol, gives 75 per cent oestrus response;

[2] Butenandt and Hildebrandt, however, find their purest preparations (melting-point 276°) much less active, possibly because contaminating theelin has been removed.

orally, theelol is effective in amounts twice or thrice as large as the subcutaneous dose. Skarzynski, who further subdivides the dose, finds the mouse unit of theelin to be of the same order as Butenandt's. Dodds has insisted on the great difference between divided doses and single doses, where aqueous solutions are concerned, the latter being relatively ineffective, while single doses in oil have intermediate efficacy. He believes that the mouse unit is only one-tenth of the rat unit; but Becker, Mellish, D'Amour, and Gustavson found them identical (possibly this relation too depends on the division of the dose). Curtis and Doisy also studied the effect of these substances in immature rats, defining the unit as the minimum quantity that causes establishment of the vaginal orifice within 10 days in three out of five animals receiving the hormone in six doses in three days, beginning when the animal is 18 days old; they found this unit to weigh 1.08γ for theelin but only 0.16γ for theelol—that is, the former was much less and the latter much more effective than in the adult castrate. Theelin was as effective orally as subcutaneously; theelol was active orally in amounts of 0.25 to 0.3γ. It is clear that there has been much misconception in the past concerning the efficacy of oestrin administered orally, and the view of Schoeller, Dohrn, and Hohlweg that oral activity decreases as purification proceeds does not seem to be justified by Doisy's results.

The fact that oestrin has an "antimasculine" effect, confirmed this year by de Jongh and Laqueur, Brouha and Simonnet, Neumann, Reiprich, Wade and Doisy, and Spencer, Gustavson, and D'Amour, is plausibly interpreted by the attractive hypothesis presented by Moore, that the internal secretions of the gonads tend to prevent the production of the gonad-stimulating hormone of the anterior pituitary, for lack of which in turn the gonads fail to develop normally. Thus even in the female animal frequent injections of oestrin retard the development of the gonad and the appearance of ovulation, according to Doisy, Curtis, and Collier, and Leonard, Meyer, and Hisaw. But it is pushing the theory far to assert that any observed retardation in somatic growth is due to failure of growth-hormone production by the anterior pituitary, under the influence of oestrin injections. Neither Zondek and Berblinger nor Fluhmann and Kulchar could confirm the view of Schoeller, Dohrn, and Hohlweg that injections of oestrin can prevent the appearance of "castration cells" in the anterior pituitary of the öophorectomized animal. According to David, oestrin may increase the oxygen consumption of the immature mouse uterus; Reynolds has shown that the uterus of the rabbit *in situ* passes into a quiescent state and becomes refractory to histamine and pituitrin after öophorectomy, or after copulation (this quiescence is noted even before ovulation has taken place); in the first case, but not in the second, the normal condition may be restored by injections of oestrin. Using very pure preparations, neither Deanesly nor Levin, Katzman, and Doisy could confirm the finding of Kelly and others, that oestrin readily produces abortion; it was noted by Whitehead and Huddleston that impure preparations may contain some unknown oxytocic substance. Juhn, Faulkner, and Gustavson have studied the experimental production of pale (female type) feathers in Brown Leghorn capons and cocks injected with oestrin. Parkes and Zuckermann conclude that the amounts of oestrin required to induce full oestrus in the hamadryad baboon and in the mouse, respectively, agree with the ratio of the weights of the two animals (400/1). Birch has brought forward some clinical evidence for the attractive suggestion that the hereditary character of haemophilia fails to become manifest in females because ovarian hormones suppress the "disease."

Testicular hormone.—Many of the papers which have appeared in the period under review and deal with the testicular hormone are concerned with the methods of assaying the activity of fractions; in spite of the great advances that have been made, the assay is still far from satisfactory. The increase in size of the comb of the capon (Hardesty has shown that this is due to mucin formation and increased blood flow rather than actual growth) is, according to Blyth, Dodds, and Gallimore, subject to great individual variations and is not proportional to the dose. Their conclusions agree in general with those of Gallagher and Koch, who, however, are less pessimistic. Voss and Loewe believe that the cytological changes in the seminal vesicles of the castrate rodent form a more accurate if less convenient test; but Laqueur *et al.* point out that fractions active in the capon may be relatively inactive in the rat, and vice versa, and tentatively suggest that two different substances may be represented. Lendle observes that even in small doses testicular extracts inhibit ovulation (this has also been noted by Ihrke and D'Amour and is probably due to suppression of anterior pituitary hormone), and suggests this as a means of assay, though its specificity remains to be proved. Womack, Koch, Domm, and Juhn find that the hormone is badly absorbed from the alimentary tract, but is not quite inactive when given orally. That the hormone is produced by interstitial (Leydig's) cells of the testis is supported by the observations that the organs on which it acts are not influenced when the spermatogenetic tissues atrophy as a result of exposure to X-rays (Mirskaia and Crew) or of experimental cryptorchidism (Jeffries). Dingemanse *et al.* have found that the comb-growth-promoting substance is not extracted from benzol by alkaline alcohol, and may thus be separated from oestrin. Moreover, it distils over at a lower temperature than theelin and theelol at very low pressures, and in this way preparations have been obtained which were active in amounts as small as 8γ, far less than any previously reported preparation. Recently, however, Butenandt (2) has obtained the substance in pure crystalline form (melting-point 178°) by separation as a crude oxime followed by distillation. The yield was 15 mg. from 25,000 liters of male urine. In divided doses, a quantity as small as 1γ causes distinct growth of the comb of the capon. The composition $C_{18}H_{26}O_2$ is suggested.

Corpus luteum.—Hisaw has stated his belief that there are three hormones of the corpus luteum, one ("progestin" or "corporin") which causes progestational proliferation in the uterus sensitized by oestrin; one ("relaxin") more widely distributed, which causes relaxation of the pubic ligaments in the guinea pig; and one which causes the appearance of high mucous cells in the vagina of the rat or mouse.[3] This last effect has been proposed as a means of assay by Harris and Newman, but Robson and Wiesner (though the Edinburgh group formerly laid great emphasis on the phenomenon) say that this histological picture can be produced by doses of oestrin too small to produce cornification. Robson and Illingworth, however, have shown clearly that extracts of corpus luteum can be separated into a fraction soluble in acidified 50 per cent alcohol and a fraction soluble in petroleum ether, the latter giving progestational proliferation and the former making the rabbit uterus insensitive to pitocin and pitressin (Knaus effect). In its wider distribution this latter fraction appears to resemble "relaxin," but of course identity cannot be assumed. Fellner, however, regards the Knaus effect as nonspecific, and, according to Siegert, in the rat uterus oestrin displays this property. Moreover, the well-known effect of corpus luteum extracts in suppressing oestrus cycles, recently confirmed by Graber and Cowles, has to be fitted into the picture. One must also ascribe to

[3] Fevold, Hisaw, and Leonard (2) describe the separation of these fractions. The first is ether-soluble, the last alcohol-soluble, while "relaxin" is insoluble in absolute alcohol or ether.

the corpus luteum the power of causing the cat's uterus to respond to epinephrine by contraction, as in pregnancy, rather than by relaxation; Gustavson and van Dyke have shown that the corpora lutea produced by injections of urine of pregnancy are active in this respect.

Anterior pituitary material, etc.—The assumption that the active principles in human pregnancy urine or blood or placenta are identical with those present in the anterior lobe of the pituitary is so confidently made that not a few authors fail to define the source of the material with which their experiments are carried out. For this reason we propose in this review to lay great emphasis upon such differences between the various sources and methods of application as have come to light.

Intramuscular implants of anterior pituitary material in immature female rats lead to precocious puberty and ovulation. Repetition of such treatment leads, as Collip, Thomson, McPhail, and Williamson have shown, to great hypertrophy of the ovaries; in the male the seminal vesicles and prostate are enlarged, in immature males the testis also (cf. also Moore and Price). Emanuel has confirmed the view that the apparent hormone content of the tissue is increased after castration, while it is reduced by oestrin administration (according to Leonard, Meyer, and Hisaw), and greatly reduced in pregnancy in women (Philipp) though not in the cow or sow [Zondek (2)], where the circulation and excretion of large amounts of the same or a similar substance in the urine do not appear.

Alkaline extracts of bovine anterior lobes are rich in growth-promoting substances; Evans and Simpson, in an important paper, have pointed out that females respond to such extracts better than males, a sex-difference which partly persists even after castration. Such extracts, however, have no power to induce premature oestrus in immature rats; the ovaries may be luteinized but are not hypertrophied (Reiss, Selye, and Balint; Brouha and Simonnet; Leonard). Yet, according to Leonard, these extracts do lead to ovulation in the rabbit; and Wiesner and Marshall state that they become oestrogenic in the rat when proteins are removed with sulphosalicylic acid. Bugbee, Simond, and Grimes find that sheep glands more readily yield oestrogenic extracts; Wallen-Lawrence and van Dyke concur with this view, and have described a careful series of experiments on the effect of various preparations on the weights of the ovaries and the seminal vesicles in young rats. Fevold, Hisaw, and Leonard (1) obtained active extracts in pyridine, and fractionated them into a water-soluble portion, which caused moderate enlargement of immature ovaries and was presumably oestrogenic, and a water-insoluble portion which, inactive by itself, combined with the former fraction to produce greatly enlarged, luteinized ovaries. Hisaw, Fevold, and Leonard also found these extracts potent in immature monkeys, though luteinization was not seen. Claus obtained and purified alcohol-soluble oestrogenic and luteinizing substances from anterior pituitary and various other organs; her results are not in line with other recent work and have not been confirmed. Loeser finds intraperitoneal injection of acetone-dried anterior lobe powder to be effective in immature female rats (though Wallen-Lawrence and van Dyke do not confirm this), and Janssen and Loeser obtained indecisive evidence of its activity by oral administration.

Loeb and Friedman find that extracts of anterior pituitary increase thyroid weight and activity (as judged from the histological appearance) in the guinea pig, and Larionov, Woitkewitsch, and Novikow, like Riddle and Polhemus, have noted similar effects in the dove. Closs, Loeb, and Mackay find that the amount of alcohol-insoluble iodine is decreased in the gland but increased in the blood by this treatment, though Paal and Huber find the hormone content of the gland, estimated by the Reid-Hunt reaction, increased. Closs points out that certain commercial "anterior pituitary" preparations are rich in iodine and therefore untrustworthy in such experiments. Charles finds that, in the toad, hypophysectomy leads to a fall in metabolic rate and in serum calcium. Houssay and Biasotti have reviewed the evidence for their theory that the anterior pituitary has an endocrine rôle in carbohydrate metabolism as an antagonist to insulin, and Cowley has shown that the blood of hypophysectomized dogs has marked hypoglycaemic properties.

Zondek (2) regards human placenta as a poor source of gonad-stimulating substances. Wiesner and Marshall made active extracts with sulphosalicylic acid, and regard them as physiologically equiva-lent to their extracts from pregnancy urine. Collip, Thomson, McPhail, and Williamson extracted with acetone (a procedure which does not yield active preparations from anterior pituitary material) and precipitated active substances from the filtrate by adding alcohol. The fraction so obtained is quite distinct from the alcohol-soluble "emmenin" (Collip). They point out that continued administration of these extracts to immature rats does not lead to the excessive ovarian hypertrophy (beyond normal adult size) obtainable with pituitary implants, nor to testicular hypertrophy, though they are oestrogenic in the female and in the male lead to great development of the seminal vesicles and prostate. Hill and Parkes found that placental extracts were active in hypophysectomized as well as in normal rabbits.

Injections of human pregnancy urine, or of the alcohol-insoluble fraction thereof, produce changes in young rats and mice similar to those which follow the implantation of anterior pituitary tissue. Zondek (1) has collected his experience with these reactions in a valuable monograph. According to Reiss, Selye, and Balint, these effects are partly prevented by the simultaneous injection of alkaline extracts of bovine anterior lobes. In the male, there is little increase in testis size and spermatogenesis may be deranged, while the interstitial tissue shows great development and the accessory organs are enlarged (Borst and Gostimirovic; Kraus; Boeters; Moore and Price; de Jongh). Bourg has described analogous effects in the cat. Urine from öophorectomized or postmenopausal human subjects has but little tendency to cause luteinization of the ovaries, and Zondek (1) supposes that it contains an ovary-stimulating "Prolan A," while pregnancy urine contains also the luteinizing "Prolan B." This view is supported by the observations of Leonard, who notes that either type of urine will provoke ovulation in the rabbit. Urine from pregnant animals of other species is inert in the rabbit as in the rat (Snyder and Wislocki).

Reichert *et al.* affirm that pregnancy urine preparations are quite ineffective in hypophysectomized puppies and rats. Evans, Meyer, and Simpson say that the response (measured by change in ovarian weights) is proportional to the dose when pituitary preparations are employed, but not in the case of pregnancy urine. Wallen-Lawrence and van Dyke find that pregnancy urine preparations, unlike pituitary preparations, are as effective in males as in females. All these findings suggest a marked difference, or even the possibility that the substances in pregnancy urine stimulate, not the gonad directly, but the anterior lobe of the pituitary; thus Zondek and Berblinger state that the pituitary shows "maturation" in Prolan-treated animals. But Hill and Parkes, though misled by their first experiments, find that pregnancy urine causes ovulation even in hypophysectomized rabbits. Moreover, Friedman has shown that pregnancy-urine extracts produce local luteinization when injected into mature follicles.

Most recent workers agree that the active principles do not dialyse. Reiss, Schäffner, and Haurowitz find them to be destroyed by activated trypsin but not by polypeptidases, which argues for a high molecular weight. A great deal of inert matter has been got rid of by Wiesner and Marshall, who precipitate impurities with sulphosalicylic acid and throw down the active fraction with phosphotungstic acid or alcohol; Dickens, using saturated ammonium sulphate and tannic acid as precipitants, and Fischer and Ertel, who make use of adsorption, seem to have carried purification further, but the most active preparations are those of Katzman, Levin, and Doisy, obtained by an undescribed process. In no case is there clear evidence of separation into fractions such as "Prolan A" and "Prolan B."

Several laboratories have used birds as subjects for experiments in this field. Noether finds that injection of acetone-dried pituitary powder interrupts the cycle of ovulation in the hen, while Gutowska, giving similar material orally, finds the size and number of eggs increased. Riddle and Polhemus found that almost any anterior pituitary extract, especially a commercial one in glycerol, caused great increase in the weight of the testes and (less markedly) the ovaries of immature doves and pigeons (Schockaert obtained similar results in ducks), but preparations from pregnancy urine were ineffective or even retarded gonad growth. In pigeons, while the eggs are being incubated, there occurs in both sexes a great glandular development of the crop, from which arises the nutritive "milk" (studied chemically by Carr and James) on which the young are partly fed; Riddle and Braucher find that this growth of the crop can be obtained even in immature birds of either sex by injecting extracts of ox or sheep anterior lobes, but not by pregnancy urine extracts.

Wolfe has shown that the hormone content of the anterior pituitary gland of sows apparently varies in a manner parallel to the oestrus cycle. But there is also evidence that the oestrus rhythmicity is inherent in the ovary; thus Friedman and Nice doubled the frequency of oestrus by grafting two extra ovaries into normal female rats. Collip, Thomson, Browne, McPhail, and Williamson point out that the immature rat ovary responds in a rhythmic manner to daily administration of their placental extract (whereas continued administration of Zondek's "Prolan A" or of the purified urine preparations of Wiesner and Marshall, or of Katzman, Levin, and Doisy, leads to continued vaginal cornification, without rhythm, but giving place finally to persistent anoestrus). Wallen-Lawrence and van Dyke observe that hypophysectomized rats treated with pituitary extracts may show several oestrus *cycles* after the treatment has been discontinued. Genther has been unable to confirm the claim that oestrus rhythm may proceed undisturbed when follicular maturation has been abolished by X-rays.

Substances giving the "Aschheim-Zondek reaction" have been found by Trancu-Rainer in the saliva of pregnant women, by Heim in human milk, by Huddleston and Whitehead in human amniotic fluid, by various authors in the fluid from ovarian cysts and hydatid moles, and by Zondek (2) and Goss and Cole in the blood (not the urine) of pregnant mares.

Suprarenal cortex.—Swingle and Pfiffner have described in detail their procedure for obtaining active extracts of the cortical hormone. The acetone-soluble, benzene-soluble fraction of an alcohol extract of the whole gland is distributed between alcohol and petroleum ether ; the alcohol-soluble portion is freed from the last traces of epinephrine either by filtering through permutit, or by extracting a solution in ether with dilute alkali. The final product contains less than one part of epinephrine in four million, and contains about 0.03 per cent of the total solids of the gland. It is made up so that 1 cc. represents 30 gm. of fresh gland, and a dose of 0.5 cc. per kg. per day is probably sufficient to maintain bilaterally adrenalectomized cats in good condition. Larger doses will restore to health cats in which adrenal insufficiency has progressed to the stage of prostration. These striking demonstrations of potency have been confirmed by Wilson, and by Britton and Silvette, from whose paper it appears, however, that the first rapid improvement may possibly be due to the epinephrine content, though the permanent gain is undoubtedly ascribable to cortical hormone. Britton, Flippin, Silvette, and Kline believe that the extract is active orally in doses three to five times as large as those effective intraperitoneally. Britton and Silvette believe that the extract lowers blood non-protein nitrogen and raises blood sugar, not merely in adrenalectomized cats with a return toward normal blood chemistry but also in normal cats, if sufficiently large doses are given. Zwemer, Agate, and Schroeder have described the preparation of a less pure extract (the freedom of which from epinephrine was established only by colour test), which according to Zwemer and Sullivan shows the above-mentioned effects on blood chemistry and also raises the CO_2 combining power. Kutz has also described a simplification of the Swingle-Pfiffner procedure in which the extraction is made with acetone in the first place. The equivalent of 5 gm. of fresh gland administered daily was found by Kutz to maintain life and sub-normal growth in immature rats bilaterally adrenalectomized, which almost invariably die when untreated. It is clear from a number of recent papers, such as those of Britton, of Carr, and of Freed, Brownfield, and Evans, that the ability of rats to survive adrenalectomy has been overestimated by many earlier workers. Rowntree, Greene, Swingle, and Pfiffner have described the effects of treating cases of Addison's disease with these cortical extracts, and their view of the results as highly promising is confirmed by Simpson and others.

The extract to which Hartman and Brownell have given the name "cortin" is also unquestionably potent, and capable of maintaining adrenalectomized cats and rats and permitting growth. According to Hartman and Thorn it increases muscular efficiency, as measured by the ergometer, even in normal subjects and in Addison's disease. Hartman and Lockwood have published striking figures showing how readily a simple reflex arc (or the muscle itself) becomes fatigued in adrenalectomized rats, and the restorative power of cortin is clearly demonstrated. Hartman, Brownell, and Crosby find that the adrenalectomized rat has a low resistance to cold, since unless it is treated with cortin it cannot greatly increase its metabolic rate. Swingle, Pfiffner, and Webster also noted that their extract restored the falling basal metabolic rate of the adrenalectomized or thyroidectomized cat. Cortin restores to normal the lowered resistance of adrenalectomized rats to typhoid vaccine [Scott and Hartman; Perla and Marmorston-Gottesman (1)] and to histamine (Marmorston-Gottesman and Perla). It was found by Perla and Marmorston-Gottesman (2) that a benzene extract of human urine (from normal adults) also protected adrenalectomized rats against histamine, suggesting that each litre of urine contains as much activity as 200 gm. of fresh suprarenal, though it may be too early to assume that the essential cortical hormone is present in both cases. Wyman and tum Suden consider that the medulla is more important than the cortex in resistance to histamine.

Nice and Schiffer found that implants of cortical tissue led to precocious puberty in young female rats, and Corey and Britton found that injections of the Swingle-Pfiffner extract had the same effect. Connor, however, could not confirm this, and another cortical extract was found to retard sexual development in females by Müller and in males by Amson. Freed, Brownfield, and Evans describe degenerative changes in the testis of the adrenalectomized rat.

"Sympathin."—Newton, Zwemer, and Cannon find that the rate of the denervated heart of the cat is increased by struggling even in animals deprived of the suprarenal medullae and all chromophil tissue, with denervated liver, pancreas, stomach, and small intestine, and after castration, thyroparathyroidectomy, or hypophysectomy, but not after complete removal of the sympathetic chains. Cannon and Bacq show that stimulation of the peripheral end of the sympathetic chain, cut on the sacral promontory, accelerates the denervated heart and stimulates the denervated submaxillary gland. From this and other ingenious experiments they conclude that an unknown epinephrine-like substance, "sympathin," is set free into the circulation when the smooth muscle of the abdominal viscera receives sympathetic impulses. Rosenblueth and Schlossberg found that cocaine sensitized the vascular system to this substance, as to epinephrine, so that a distinct pressor response could be obtained; 30 seconds of light tetanizing stimulation of the lower end of the sympathetic chain has a pressor effect comparable to that of 5γ of epinephrine injected at a decreasing rate during five minutes. This speaks in favour of the resemblance of sympathin to epinephrine, since Burn and Tainter find that cocaine does not increase but rather abolishes the action of tyramine and ephedrine. Sakussow reported that cocaine sensitized intestinal muscle to epinephrine, but neither Rosenblueth, nor Burn and Tainter, found clear evidence of this synergism except in vasomotor effects.

Thyroid.—The relation between the thyroid gland and the heart has received much attention in the period under review. It was shown by Lewis and McEachern, and by Yater, that the heart of the thyroid-treated rabbit beats abnormally fast even when removed from the body. Priestley, Markowitz, and Mann made the same observation for the dog, and showed that when a second heart was transplanted into the neck of a dog it could be accelerated by administration of thyroxin, while the animal's own heart, under nervous control, showed no change. Rake and McEachern showed that clinical or experimental hyperthyroidism does not produce any specific lesion in the heart. From the work of Defauw, and of Lawrence and McCance, it appears that thyroxin has an almost specific action in reducing the heart's glycogen content; Stockheim, however, did not observe this in the dog.

Henschel and Steuber discovered the remarkable fact that the heat production of adult frogs is not affected either by thyroidectomy or by the administration of large quantities of thyroxin, even in experiments lasting many weeks.

Insulin.—Scott has shown that insulin crystals obtained from ox, fish, sheep, and hog agree in potency (27 units per mg.) and sulphur content (3.3 per cent), both these figures being rather higher than previous reports have set them. Sjögren and Svedberg found the molecular weight of crystalline insulin to be 35,000, by means of the ultracentrifuge. But Freudenberg and Dirscherl take the stand that even in crystalline insulin the molecules may be similar but not identical (since X-ray analysis reveals no structure in the crystals) and that the mother liquors may contain active molecules too divergent in size or configuration to enter into the crystal lattice. On this theory it is not so hard to accept the claim of the Amsterdam laboratory, which Dirscherl has partly confirmed, that an insulin preparation four times more potent than the crystals may be obtained by fractional adsorption.[4] Freudenberg and Dirscherl adopt the view that the activity resides in a comparatively small and simple group incorporated, probably by peptide linkage, in the insulin molecule, and have made ingenious deductions as to the nature of this active group. The reversible inactivation by acetylation suggests a hydroxyl (or imino) group, since acetyl-amino combinations are relatively stable; moreover, the primary amino groups may be destroyed by HNO_2 without inactivation taking place; then the reversible inactivation with formaldehyde must be ascribed to combination with an acid-amide group. There may, indeed, be two such $CONH_2$ groups, since in inactivation with alkali two molecules of ammonia are apparently split off (on this basis the minimal molecular weight is roughly half that found by Svedberg), since sodium-amalgam splits off only half as much, and oxidizing agents such as *o*-chlorobenzaldehyde halve the amount of alkali-labile nitrogen (Freudenberg, Dirscherl, and Eyer). Changes in optical activity suggest that these acid-amide groups are attached to asymmetric carbon atoms. Inactivation by diazomethane, or by esterification, suggests the presence of a free carboxyl group; but the first-named is hardly a specific reagent, and Charles and Scott have shown that in the treatment of insulin with acid alcohol there is

---

[4] According to Dingemanse, such preparations may produce extreme hypoglycaemia without convulsions.

evidence of inactivation by alkylation of nitrogen rather than by esterification. Freudenberg and Dirscherl find no evidence of carbonyl groups, and consider that the "labile sulphur" of insulin is not related to the active group; but du Vigneaud, Fitch, Pekarek, and Longwood ascribe the inactivation of insulin by cysteine to the reduction of a disulphide linkage. The inactivation by ultra-violet light, studied by Kuhn, Eyer, and Freudenberg, suggests that the active group may have an absorption spectrum similar to that of tyrosine. Freudenberg, Dirscherl, Eichel, and Weiss, studying the effect of proteolytic enzymes on insulin (a question which has also been discussed by Cornell), note the remarkable fact that crystalline insulin treated with papain loses only two-thirds of its potency, which certainly suggests some heterogeneity in the substrate.

LITERATURE CITED

AMSON, K., *Endokrinologie,* 2, 241 (1931)

BECKER, T. J., MELLISH, C. H., D'AMOUR, F. E., AND GUSTAVSON, R. G., *J. Pharmacol.,* 43, 693 (1931)

BIRCH, C. L., *Proc. Soc. Exptl. Biol. Med.,* 28, 752 (1931)

BLYTH, J. S. S., DODDS, E. C., GALLIMORE, E. J., *J. Physiol.,* 73, 136 (1931)

BOETERS, H., *Arch. path. Anat. (Virchow's),* 280, 215 (1931)

BORST, M., AND GOSTIMIROVIC, D., *Münch. med. Wochschr.,* 78, 19 (1931)

BOURG, R., *Compt. rend. soc. biol.,* 106, 926 (1931)

BRITTON, S. W., AND SILVETTE, H., *Am. J. Physiol.,* 99, 15 (1931)

BRITTON, S. W., FLIPPIN, J. C., SILVETTE, H., AND KLINE, R., *Am. J. Physiol.,* 99, 44 (1931)

BROUHA, L., AND SIMONNET, H., *Ann. med.,* 29, 305 (1931)

BUGBEE, E. P., SIMOND, A. E., AND GRIMES, H. M., *Endocrinology,* 15, 41 (1931)

BURN, J. H., AND TAINTER, M. L., *J. Physiol.,* 71, 169 (1931)

BUTENANDT, A. (1), *Abhandl. ges. Wiss. (Göttingen),* 3, 1 (1931)

BUTENANDT, A. (2), *Z. angew. Chem.,* 44, 905 (1931)

BUTENANDT, A., AND HILDEBRANDT, F., *Z. physiol. Chem.,* 199, 243 (1931)

CANNON, W. B., AND BACQ, Z. M., *Am. J. Physiol.,* 96, 392 (1931)

CARR, J. L., *Proc. Soc. Exptl. Biol. Med.,* 29, 128 (1931)

CARR, R. H., AND JAMES, C. M., *Am. J. Physiol.,* 97, 227 (1931)

CHARLES, A. F., AND SCOTT, D. A., *J. Biol. Chem.,* 92, 289 (1931)

CHARLES, E., *Proc. Roy. Soc. (London), B,* 107, 486 (1931)

CLAUS, P. E., *Physiol. Zoöl.,* 4, 36 (1931)

CLOSS, K., *J. Pharmacol.,* 43, 131 (1931)

CLOSS, K., LOEB, L., AND MACKAY, E., *Proc. Soc. Exptl. Biol. Med.,* 29, 170 (1931)

COLLIP, J. B., *Proc. Calif. Acad. Med.,* 1, 38 (1930)

COLLIP, J. B., THOMSON, D. L., BROWNE, J. S. L., McPHAIL, M. K., AND WILLIAMSON, J. E., *Endocrinology,* 15, 315 (1931)

COLLIP, J. B., THOMSON, D. L., MCPHAIL, M. K., AND WILLIAMSON, J. E., *Can. Med. Assoc. J.,* **24,** 201, (1931)

CONNOR, C. L., *Proc. Soc. Exptl. Biol. Med.,* **29,** 131 (1931)

COREY, E. L., AND BRITTON, S. W., *Am. J. Physiol.,* **99,** 33 (1931)

CORNELL, W., *Z. physiol. Chem.,* **199,** 217 (1931)

COWLEY, R. J., *J. Pharmacol.,* **43,** 287 (1931)

CURTIS, J. M., AND DOISY, E. A., *J. Biol. Chem.,* **91,** 647 (1931)

DAVID, J. C., *J. Pharmacol.,* **43,** 1 (1931)

DEANESLY, R., *J. Physiol.,* **72,** 62 (1931)

DEFAUW, J., *Compt. rend. soc. biol.,* **105,** 228 (1930)

DICKENS, F., *Biochem. J.,* **24,** 1507 (1930)

DINGEMANSE, E., *Arch. néerland. physiol.,* **16,** 295 (1931)

DINGEMANSE, E., FREUD, J., KOBER, S., LAQUEUR, E., LUCHS, A., AND MÜNCH, A. P. W., *Biochem. Z.,* **231,** 1 (1931)

DODDS, E. C., *Am. J. Obstet. Gynecol.,* **22,** 520 (1931)

DOISY, E. A., CURTIS, J., AND COLLIER, W. D., *Proc. Soc. Exptl. Biol. Med.,* **28,** 885 (1931)

DOISY, E. A., AND THAYER, S. A., *J. Biol. Chem.,* **91,** 641 (1931)

EMANUEL, S., *Ugeskr. Laeger,* **1,** 535 (1931)

EVANS, H. M., MEYER, K., AND SIMPSON, M. E., *Proc. Soc. Exptl. Biol. Med.,* **28,** 845 (1931)

EVANS, H. M., AND SIMPSON, M. E., *Am. J. Physiol.,* **98,** 511 (1931)

FELLNER, O. O., *Med. Klinik,* **2,** 1317 (1931)

FEVOLD, H. L., HISAW, F. L., AND LEONARD, S. L. (1), *Am. J. Physiol.,* **97,** 291 (1931)

FEVOLD, H. L., HISAW, F. L., AND LEONARD, S. L. (2), *J. Am. Chem. Soc.,* **54,** 254 (1932)

FISCHER, F. G., AND ERTEL, L., *Z. physiol. Chem.,* **202,** 83 (1931)

FLUHMANN, C. F., AND KULCHAR, G. V., *Proc. Soc. Exptl. Biol. Med.,* **28,** 417 (1931)

FREED, S. C., BROWNFIELD, B., AND EVANS, H. M., *Proc. Soc. Exptl. Biol. Med.,* **29,** 1 (1931)

FREUDENBERG, K., AND DIRSCHERL, W., *Z. physiol. Chem.,* **202,** 192 (1931)

FREUDENBERG, K., DIRSCHERL, W., AND EYER, H., *Z. physiol. Chem.,* **202,** *Chem.,* **202,** 151 (1931)

FREUDENBERG, K., DIRSCHERL, W., AND EYER, H., *Z. physiol. Chem.,* **202,** 128 (1931)

FRIEDMAN, J. L., AND NICE, L. B., *Am. J. Physiol.,* **95,** 40 (1930)

FRIEDMAN, M. H., *Am. J. Physiol.,* **99,** 332 (1932)

GALLAGHER, T. F., AND KOCH, F. C., *Proc. 2d Internat. Congr. Sex Research (London),* 312 (1931)

GENTHER, I. T., *Am. J. Anat.,* **48,** 99 (1931)

GOSS, H., AND COLE, H. H., *Endocrinology,* **15,** 214 (1931)

GRABER, H. T., AND COWLES, R. A., *Proc. Soc. Exptl. Biol. Med.,* **28,** 977 (1931)

GUSTAVSON, R. G., AND VAN DYKE, H. B., *J. Pharmacol.,* **41,** 139 (1931)

GUTOWSKA, M., *Quart. J. Exptl. Physiol.,* **21,** 197 (1931)

HARDESTY, M., *Am. J. Anat.,* **47,** 277 (1931)

HARRIS, R. G., AND NEWMAN, D. M., *Science,* **74**, 182 (1931)
HARTMAN, F. A., AND BROWNELL, K. A., *Am. J. Physiol.,* **97**, 530 (1931)
HARTMAN, F. A., BROWNELL, K. A., AND CROSBY, A. A., *Am. J. Physiol.,* **98**, 674 (1931)
HARTMAN, F. A., AND LOCKWOOD, J. E., *Proc. Soc. Exptl. Biol. Med.,* **29**, 141 (1931)
HARTMAN, F. A., AND THORN, G. W., *Proc. Soc. Exptl. Biol. Med.,* **29**, 48 (1931)
HEIM, K., *Klin. Wochschr.,* **10**, 357 (1931)
HENSCHEL, H., AND STEUBER, M., *Arch. exptl. Path. Pharmakol.,* **160**, 401 (1931)
HILL, M., AND PARKES, A. S., *J. Physiol.,* **71**, 36; **72**, 15P (1931)
HISAW, F. L., *J. Am. Med. Assoc.,* **97**, 1865 (1931)
HISAW, F. L., FEVOLD, H. L., AND LEONARD, S. L., *Proc. Soc. Exptl. Biol. Med.,* **29**, 204 (1931)
HOUSSAY, B. A., AND BIASOTTI, A., *Endocrinology,* **15**, 511 (1931)
HUDDLESTON, O. L., AND WHITEHEAD, R. W., *J. Pharmacol.,* **42**, 274 (1931)
IHRKE, I. A., AND D'AMOUR, F. E., *Am. J. Physiol.,* **96**, 289 (1931)
JANSSEN, S., AND LOESER, A., *Arch. exptl. Path. Pharmakol.,* **159**, 737 (1931)
JEFFRIES, M. E., *Anat. Record,* **48**, 131 (1931)
JONGH, S. E. DE, *Arch. ges. Physiol.,* **226**, 547 (1931)
JONGH, S. E. DE, KOBER, S., AND LAQUEUR, E., *Biochem. Z.,* **240**, 247 (1931)
JONGH, S. E. DE, AND LAQUEUR, E., *Arch. ges. Physiol.,* **227**, 57 (1931)
JUHN, M., FAULKNER, G. H., AND GUSTAVSON, R. G., *J. Exptl. Zoöl.,* **58**, 69 (1931)
KATZMAN, P. A., LEVIN, L., AND DOISY, E. A., *Proc. Soc. Exptl. Biol. Med.,* **28**, 873 (1931)
KELLY, G. L., *Surg. Gynecol. Obstet.,* **52**, 713 (1931)
KOBER, S., *Biochem. Z.,* **239**, 209 (1931)
KRAUS, E. J., *Arch. Gynäkol.,* **145**, 524 (1931)
KUHN, W., EYER, H., AND FREUDENBERG, K., *Z. physiol. Chem.,* **202**, 97 (1931)
KUTZ, R. L., *Proc. Soc. Exptl. Biol. Med.,* **29**, 91 (1931)
LAQUEUR, E., DINGEMANSE, E., FREMERY, P. DE, FREUD, J., JONGH, S. E. DE, KOBER, S., LUCHS, A., AND MÜNCH, A. P. W., *Nederland. Tijdschr. Geneeskunde,* **75**, 1648 (1931)
LARIONOV, W. T., WOITKEWITSCH, A., AND NOVIKOW, B., *Z. vergl. Physiol. (Z. wiss. Biol. Abt. C),* **14**, 546 (1931)
LAWRENCE, R. D., AND MCCANCE, R. A., *Biochem. J.,* **25**, 570 (1931)
LENDLE, L., *Arch. exptl. Path. Pharmakol.,* **159**, 463 (1931)
LEONARD, S. L., *Am. J. Physiol.,* **98**, 406 (1931)
LEONARD, S. L., MEYER, R. K., AND HISAW, F. L., *Endocrinology,* **15**, 17 (1931)
LEVIN, L., KATZMAN, P. A., AND DOISY, E. A., *Endocrinology,* **15**, 207 (1931)
LEWIS, J. K., AND MCEACHERN, D., *Proc. Soc. Exptl. Biol. Med.,* **28**, 504 (1931)
LOEB, L., AND FRIEDMAN, H., *Proc. Soc. Exptl. Biol. Med.,* **29**, 14 (1931)
LOESER, A., *Arch. exptl. Path. Pharmakol.,* **159**, 657 (1931)

Marmorston-Gottesman, J., and Perla, D., *Proc. Soc. Exptl. Biol. Med.*, **28**, 1022 (1931)

Mirskaia, L., and Crew, F. A. E., *Quart. J. Exptl. Physiol.*, **21**, 135 (1931)

Moore, C. R., *Proc. 2d Internat. Congr. Sex Research (London)*, 293 (1931)

Moore, C. R., and Price, D., *Am. J. Physiol.*, **99**, 197 (1931)

Müller, C., *Endokrinologie*, **8**, 5 (1931)

Neumann, H. O., *Zentr. Gynäkol.*, **55**, 1639 (1931)

Newton, H. F., Zwemer, R. L., and Cannon, W. B., *Am. J. Physiol.*, **96**, 377 (1931)

Nice, L. B., and Schiffer, A. L., *Endocrinology*, **15**, 205 (1931)

Noether, P., *Arch. exptl. Path. Pharmakol.*, **160**, 367 (1931)

Paal, H., and Huber, W., *Arch. exptl. Path. Pharmakol.*, **162**, 521 (1931)

Parkes, A. S., and Zuckermann, S., *J. Anat.*, **65**, 272 (1931)

Perla, D., and Marmorston-Gottesman, J. (1), *Proc. Soc. Exptl. Biol. Med.*, **28**, 648 (1931)

Perla, D., and Marmorston-Gottesman, J. (2), *Proc. Soc. Exptl. Biol. Med.*, **28**, 1024 (1931)

Philipp, E., *Zentr. Gynäkol.*, **55**, 929 (1931)

Priestley, J. T., Markowitz, J., and Mann, F. C., *Am. J. Physiol.*, **98**, 357 (1931)

Rake, G., and McEachern, D., *J. Exptl. Med.*, **54**, 23 (1931)

Reichert, F. L., Pencharz, R. I., Simpson, M. E., Meyer, K., and Evans, H. M., *Proc. Soc. Exptl. Biol. Med.*, **28**, 843 (1931)

Reiprich, W., *Proc. 2d Internat. Congr. Sex Research (London)*, 367 (1931)

Reiss, M., Selye, H., and Balint, J., *Endokrinologie*, **8**, 15; **9**, 81 (1931)

Reiss, M., Schäffner, A., and Haurowitz, F., *Endokrinologie*, **8**, 22 (1931)

Reynolds, S. R. M., *Am. J. Physiol.*, **97**, 706; **98**, 230 (1931)

Riddle, O., and Braucher, P. F., *Am. J. Physiol.*, **97**, 617 (1931)

Riddle, O., and Polhemus, I., *Am. J. Physiol.*, **98**, 121 (1931)

Robson, J. M., and Illingworth, R. E., *Quart. J. Exptl. Physiol.*, **21**, 93 (1931)

Robson, J. M., and Wiesner, B. P., *Quart. J. Exptl. Physiol.*, **21**, 217 (1931)

Rosenblueth, A., *Am. J. Physiol.*, **98**, 186 (1931)

Rosenblueth, A., and Schlossberg, T., *Am. J. Physiol.*, **97**, 365 (1931)

Rowntree, L. G., Greene, C. H., Swingle, W. W., and Pfiffner, J. J., *J. Am. Med. Assoc.*, **96**, 231 (1931)

Sakussow, W. W., *Arch. exptl. Path. Pharmakol.*, **160**, 393 (1931)

Schockaert, J., *Arch. intern. pharmacodynamie*, **41**, 23 (1931)

Schoeller, W., Dohrn, M., and Hohlweg, W., *Am. J. Med. Sci.*, **182**, 326 (1931)

Scott, D. A., *J. Biol. Chem.*, **92**, 281 (1931)

Scott, W. J. M., and Hartman, F. A., *Proc. Soc. Exptl. Biol. Med.*, **28**, 649 (1931)

Siegert, F., *Klin. Wochschr.*, **10**, 734 (1931)

Simpson, S. L., *Quart. J. Med.*, **1**, 99 (1932)

Sjögren, B., and Svedberg, T., *J. Am. Chem. Soc.*, **53**, 265 (1931)

Skarzynski, B., *Z. physiol. Chem.*, **196**, 19 (1931)

Slawson, C. B., *J. Biol. Chem.*, **91**, 667 (1931)

Snyder, F. F., and Wislocki, G. B., *Bull. Johns Hopkins Hosp.*, **48**, 362 (1931)

Spencer, J., Gustavson, R. G., and D'Amour, F. E., *Proc. Soc. Exptl. Biol. Med.*, **28**, 500 (1931)

Stockheim, W., *Arch. ges. Physiol.*, **228**, 469 (1931)

Swingle, W. W., and Pfiffner, J. J., *Am. J. Physiol.*, **96**, 153; **98**, 144 (1931)

Swingle, W. W., Pfiffner, J. J., and Webster, B., *Proc. Soc. Exptl. Biol. Med.*, **28**, 728, 1021 (1931)

Thayer, S. A., Levin, L., and Doisy, E. A. (1), *J. Biol. Chem.*, **91**, 655 (1931)

Thayer, S. A., Levin, L., and Doisy, E. A. (2), *J. Biol. Chem.*, **91**, 791 (1931)

Trancu-Rainer, M., *Compt. rend. soc. biol.*, **106**, 1001 (1931)

Vigneaud, V. du, Fitch, A., Pekarek, E., and Longwood, W. W., *J. Biol. Chem.*, **94**, 233 (1931)

Voss, H. E., and Loewe, S., *Arch. exptl. Path. Pharmakol.*, **159**, 532 (1931)

Wade, N. J., and Doisy, E. A., *Proc. Soc. Exptl. Biol. Med.*, **28**, 714 (1931)

Wallen-Lawrence, Z., and van Dyke, H. B., *J. Pharmacol.*, **43**, 93 (1931)

Whitehead, R. W., and Huddleston, O. L., *J. Pharmacol.*, **42**, 197 (1931)

Wiesner, B. P., and Marshall, P. G., *Quart. J. Exptl. Physiol.*, **21**, 147 (1931)

Wilson, A. T., *J. Physiol.*, **72**, 9P (1931)

Wolfe, J. M., *Am. J. Anat.*, **48**, 391 (1931)

Womack, E. B., Koch, F. C., Domm, L. V., and Juhn, M., *J. Pharmacol.*, **41**, 173 (1931)

Wyman, L. C., and tum Suden, C., *Am. J. Physiol.*, **99**, 285 (1932)

Yater, W. M., *Am. J. Physiol.*, **98**, 338 (1931)

Zondek, B. (1), *"Hormone des Ovariums und des Hypophysenvorderlappens,"* Berlin (1931)

Zondek, B. (2), *Zentr. Gynäkol.*, **55**, 1 (1931)

Zondek, B., and Berblinger, W., *Klin. Wochschr.*, **10**, 1061 (1931)

Zwemer, R. L., Agate, F. J., and Schroeder, H. A., *Proc. Soc. Exptl. Biol. Med.*, **28**, 721 (1931)

Zwemer, R. L., and Sullivan, R. C., *Proc. Soc. Exptl. Biol. Med.*, **28**, 723 (1931)

McGill University
Montreal, Canada

THE CHEMISTRY OF MUSCLE*

By J. K. Parnas

Department of Medical Chemistry
The University, Lwow, Poland

During the first period[1] in the modern development of muscle chemistry, from 1906 until 1926, chief consideration was given to the metabolism of carbohydrate and lactic acid. Since 1926, however, unforeseen constituents in new rôles of metabolic interest have been discovered: phosphocreatine and phosphoarginine, and their cleavage and resynthesis; adeninenucleotide and its relation to inosinic acid and ammonia formation; pyrophosphate and adenosinetriphosphoric acid, and new hexosephosphoric esters. The discovery of these constituents falls in the period from 1926 to 1929 and is summarized in the monograph by O. Meyerhof (153*b*).[2]

In an appendix to this monograph, a most important event is reported—the discovery, by Einar Lundsgaard, of muscular contractions without lactic-acid formation in muscles poisoned with iodoacetic acid. Since this discovery the knowledge of the chemistry of muscular activity has been fully revised, not without the renunciation of certain fundamental beliefs; more understanding has been attained, and many difficulties and contradictions have been cleared away. The task of reviewing the work of these two years means, however, dealing with some two hundred papers, with results sometimes contradictory or for other reasons hardly acceptable without confirmation. The reviewer feels that he ought to emphasize what he thinks important and true, setting aside at present what he believes insufficiently supported,

---

* Received January 26, 1932.

[1] The contents of this review will be limited strictly to the period 1930–31, and to the normal muscle chemistry and chemical energetics; general metabolism, interaction with other organs, pathology and pharmacology, exercise, and related subjects will be entered into only for points of general interest.

[2] This is the best source of information; for shorter accounts cf. 153*c* and 177*a*. Cf. also Bethes' critical treatment (8). The review by Milroy (163*a*) extends into the period covered by this review; so does also the quite recent review by Meyerhof (153*a*). The chemical sections of the papers concerned with muscle physiology, published before 1926, are today obsolete. The literature which has been compiled is given thoroughly only for the period covered by this review; but the space allowed makes it impossible to refer in the text to every author and every paper.

less relevant, or of no general interest; but he cannot avoid some important points of controversy.

The chemistry of muscle activity is studied mainly by differential experiments, in which the percentage of constituents is estimated before and after some experimentally produced or spontaneous change; but the differences found are not always significant, in the sense of the theory of errors. The constituents of muscle tissue are subject, more than those of any other tissue, to changes produced in a very short time by functional and experimental conditions; they are affected by a multiplicity of factors not always under control, by errors inherent in the experimental procedures, and by individual and functional variations inherent in the object. Statistical analysis is therefore necessary, and where such treatment of the quantitative data is neglected, and the figures are consistent neither in their absolute value, nor in the differences, there the confidence placed by the authors in their results is often illusory,[3] and the conclusions must be accepted as suggestions rather than as facts (178).

Treatment of muscles prior to chemical analysis.—Attention is usually paid to the prevention of traumatic and postmortem changes, and additional precautions are taken (such as suitable anaesthesia), in the case of the muscles of homoeotherms. Freezing in liquid air is much employed for stopping the changes in muscle. On the other hand, irritation by freezing is also used to produce contractions, followed immediately by fixation. Contraction of a tetanic character, accompanied by action currents and development of considerable tension, follows dipping of muscles into liquid air, and persists, in gastrocnemii of frogs up to 10 seconds. The contraction in liquid air is weaker but not abolished after a preceding strong direct tetanic stimulation. Preceding indirect stimulation does not change the reaction of fresh muscle to liquid air [Manigk (144)]. Experimental evidence has been built up, at times, upon the belief that muscles do not react to irritation by freezing when previously stimulated; this belief must now be discarded. Freezing remains, nevertheless, a convenient method of stopping the chemical changes in the tissue, but its effectiveness must not be overestimated [cf. Meyerhof (163)].

The proteins of muscle.—Material progress has been attained in

---

[3] Cf., for instance, the example given by R. A. Fisher (82) on page 110 of his book; in dealing with differences Fisher takes cases in which the precision of the measurements is beyond doubt; this is not so in most of the chemical estimations in muscle.

the chemistry of muscle proteins, and contact seems established, at last, between the achievements of the advanced chemical and morphological researches. The rod-like structural elements of the anisotropic disks can be correlated now on the basis of the wonderful work of Edsall and von Muralt (61, 168, 169), H. H. Weber (203), and Boehn and Signer (16), with the muscle globulin *myosin*.[4] When extracted from fresh ground mammalian muscle by cold alkaline salt solutions (potassium chloride; potassium phosphate; ionic strength 1.3; pH 7.85), it can be purified by repeated precipitation (dilution or lowering of pH) and redissolving. The chemical characteristics are admirably presented in the paper by Edsall and in the note by H. H. Weber; the solubility as a function of the ionic strength and pH is important, especially in work concerned with changes in muscle proteins.

Solutions of myosin are optically void and isotropic, but when the liquid is set in motion, they show the phenomenon of *fluxional birefringence;* this double refraction of the solution in flow means the presence of rod- or needle-shaped molecules, and this must therefore be the form of the myosin molecules. From the quantitative study of the birefringence, *monodisperse* molecules of about 1,000 Å can be deduced; they are needle-shaped [Fadenmoleküle (Boehn and Signer)], independent of the reaction in shape and size, and not subject to ageing and association; their parallel position in the flowing liquid determines the double refraction. The fluxional birefringence is irreversibly lost by action of acid, alkali, and all reagents producing denaturation. Myogen (the water-soluble protein of muscle) and the soluble myogen-fibrin, resemble in solubility myosin, but do not show at all the double refraction of flow, and must consist of rather spherical molecules with no distinctly eccentric axis.

Myosin solutions set into gels, which show the distinct features of *thixotropy;* though transformed by shaking into sols, they set again when resting. The anisotropic disks in muscle fibres have possibly the consistency of such thixotropic gels; thus may be explained an old observation by Kühne (1863), who saw a nematode crawling through the disks of a muscle fibre, which reappeared, however, when the worm had passed.

The birefringent system of the "disdiaclast" has been extracted as a muscle protein in monodisperse form. Weber supposes 70 to

[4] Myosin (Kühne) = Paramyosinogen (Halliburton) = Myostromin (Danilewski).

75 per cent of the muscle proteins to be myosin, but only 25 to 30 per cent can be extracted; what remains has the acid-base-binding properties of myosin and the positive birefringence of this protein. The very soluble myogen can be extracted completely, and amounts to 25 to 30 per cent. Myogen can be the material neither of the external membranes nor of the fibrillae, and must be located in the sarcoplasm; myosin is indicated as the probable material of the fibrillae by its quantity, its birefringence, and its tendency to form strong structures. For the membranes of the muscle fibres a protein, *sui generis,* must be supposed. Myosin has, between the physiological limits of pH 6.4 and 7.3 a threefold larger acid-base-binding capacity than myogen, and could actually neutralize half of the lactic acid formed in fatigue.

The molecular size and form of a different protein preparation from muscle juice has been measured by de Caro (25); the coagulation of muscle plasma, its nature, and the rôle of salts have been investigated by Smith (188). The postmortem changes in the solubility of proteins in minced muscle have been investigated by H. J. Deuticke (52) and by J. Hensay (104); on the whole, the proteins gradually lose their solubility in alkaline salt solutions, and this reduction of solubility proceeds at a higher rate at higher temperatures. The solubility in acid salt solutions, pH 4, is, however, increased. Rigor, fatigue, and insulin also lead to a reduction of solubility in alkaline salt solutions.

Heart proteins have been the object of extensive studies by Galvialo and Keines (86) and Wladimirow (209); muscle hemoglobin has been investigated by Dirken and Mook (55) and by Ray and Paff (181, 182).

The state of water and the molar concentration in muscle tissue.— A new accurate thermal method of measuring vapour pressures (108) of aqueous solutions led A. V. Hill to a reinvestigation of the "free water" in fluids and tissues, and of the molar concentrations (106, 110). Free water means the weight of water in one gram of tissue or fluid, in which dissolved substances produce a normal depression of vapour tension; it amounts, in muscle at rest or in rigor, to little less than the total water. The depression of vapour pressure in frog's blood is that of a 0.725 per cent solution of NaCl; this must be considered as the true isotonic solution. The molar concentration is accounted for by the known soluble constituents in the muscle, dissolved in the free water. In the exhausted muscle the depression is as great as if 0.35 per cent NaCl has been added to the isotonic solution; this cannot be accounted for by the formation of lactate ions, creatine, and the minor constituents produced in muscular activity; in the alactacid activity of the muscle, when the increase of the molar concentration is equivalent to the addition of 0.147 per cent of NaCl, and lactic acid is not produced, the increase is larger than the increase of known constituents. In thermoelectric cryoscopic determinations also [Meyerhof and Grollmann (152, 156)], an increase of the molar concentration by 30 per cent more than could be accounted for was observed in fatigue and rigor of frog muscles. This suggests that some unknown changes may occur during activity and development of rigor. [The permeability of the muscle and activity: cf. 164 and 75; diffusibility of creatine and urea (62); of potassium (44); the state of potassium (24).]

The nitrogenous extractives.—The recently discovered anserin:

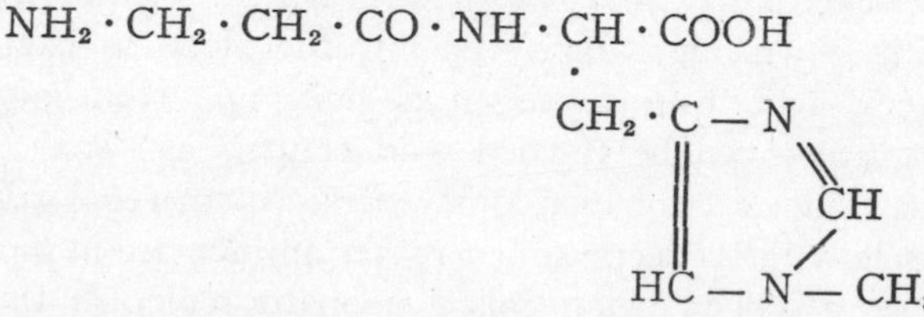

$$NH_2 \cdot CH_2 \cdot CH_2 \cdot CO \cdot NH \cdot CH \cdot COOH$$

$$CH_2 \cdot C - N$$

$$CH$$

$$HC - N - CH_3$$

or β-alanyl methylhistidine (120, 125, 180) occurs not only in avian muscle, but also in dog muscle [Wilson and Wolff (211)]. The extractives of fish muscle have also been extensively investigated [Kapeller-Adler and Krach (118, 119)]. Creatine in human muscles has been determinated by Bodansky (14); the effect of fasting on the distribution of creatine in the rat by Chanutin and Shearer (30); and the relation of creatine to glycogen in rabbits by Masayama and Riesser (148). For purine derivatives, nucleosides, nucleotides, and their distribution, cf.: Dmochowski (56), Jaworska (117), Ostern (174); for their transformation during autolysis in rabbit muscle, M. Buell (23). The phosphorus compounds of creatine and adenosine will be treated below.

The carbohydrates of muscle.—The carbohydrates of muscle have been carefully investigated by M. Kerly (121); the total of glucides in frog muscle, after hydrolysis, is in excess of the sum of glycogen and alcohol-soluble sugar. Figures for the amount of glycogen in warm-blooded animals are given by G. T. Cori (40); in rats killed by stunning, serious losses of glycogen occur, which can be prevented when the muscles are extirpated during amytal anaesthesia. The presence of a reducing dialysable saccharide probably smaller than a trisaccharide in muscle is referred to by Sahyun (186). It seems improbable that the trisaccharide of Lohmann and Barbour should be a normal intermediary in physiological glycogenolysis [Case (27)]. An alcohol-insoluble, non-reducing, non-ultrafiltrable, but non-opalescent polysaccharide is reported by Sahyun (187).

For recent developments of the knowledge concerning carbohydrate metabolism in mammalian muscle reference must be made to the admirable review by C. F. Cori (34). Glycogenolysis in living muscle means, as the Coris and other workers have demonstrated, the formation of lactic acid from muscle glycogen, with an intermediate formation of hexosemonophosphoric ester [Cori and Cori (34a, 34b)]; this transformation is accelerated by epinephrine [see also Corkill and Marks (42)]. The Coris have shown that the muscle glycogen is not locked away, and that it does not pass through glucose when breaking down but is delivered into the blood as lactic acid. From the lactic acid, liver glycogen is built up; from glycogen of the liver, glucose can be formed, and returns as blood glucose to the muscle. The effect of insulin is inverse: increased oxidation of sugar in muscle with no decrease but rather an increase in muscle glycogen, the liver glycogen being called upon to replenish the blood sugar which is withdrawn by the muscle. This picture, as drawn by the Coris for the rat, holds equally well for the frog, as Geiger (87, 88) states.

The way in which glycogen formation in mammalian muscle depends on hormonal and nervous factors is demonstrated in the lucid experiments of Debois. The recovery of glycogen in muscles is attained in decerebrated cats with intact vagi, but not in spinal animals or after vagotomy and not after pancreatectomy with intact vagi; but in all these cases reconstitution of glycogen takes place after injection of insulin. Thus the reconstitution of glycogen lost in activity must be a function of the islets and depends on innervation by the vagi. The left vagus only, however, is of importance; its stimulation in vagotomized animals induces the recovery of muscle glycogen. The depletion of glycogen in muscle is shown, in these experiments, as an adrenal function (46, 47, 48, 49, 50, 51, 112).

Muscle sugar and its depletion by adrenalin has been the object of careful work [Bischoff and Long (10, 10a, 11)]. The muscle sugar appears at an intermediary stage in the anabolic change between blood sugar and glycogen and not in the catabolic glycogen-olysis. The distribution of glycogen in rats after starvation, and of phlorhizin, epinephrine, pituitrin, and thyroid substance has been studied by Lawrence and McCance (123). Thyroid substance lowers the glycogen of the heart muscle so that the latter may become unable to regain its glycogen content. This statement is confirmed by Abderhalden and Wertheimer (1). For the influence of epinephrine in the starved rabbit, cf. Matsui and Inouye (149); in cats, cf. Evans, Tsai, and Young (77), and for the muscle-liver cycle, cf. Himwich, Koskoff, and Nahum (113); for distribution of glycogen, as influenced by epinephrine and insulin, cf. Corkill and Marks (41, 42); for diurnal variations, cf Ågren, Wilander, and Jorpes (2); for postmortem changes in rat muscle, cf. Anderson and Macleod (3) (this very important paper states a number of criticisms of experiments with carbohydrates in mammalian muscle, and makes it probable that lactic-acid formation may occur before glycogen is actually significantly broken down); for distribution of glycogen in frog muscle, cf. Sahyun (187); for influence of epinephrine in absence of the liver, cf. Firor and Eadie (79); for seasonal variations in the glycogen of toad muscle, cf. Iino (116); and for a method for determination of glycogen, cf. Sahyun (186).

The phosphorus compounds of muscle.—The hexosephosphoric esters and their behaviour in muscle have been thoroughly investigated by Lohmann and Lipmann (135a, 134, 127). Four such esters have been found to occur in fresh muscle, or to be produced in postmortem experimental changes in muscle pulp, juice, or extracts: (a) the hexosemonophosphoric ester (Embden's ester), which is the only hexosephosphoric ester found, until now, in normal muscle tissue; (b) the diphosphoric ester of Harden and Young, produced in muscle extracts from starch or fructose together with Embden's ester, but also in the tissue during alactacid rigor; (c) the diphosphoric ester (Lohmann's ester I), resistant to hydrolysis by normal hydrochloric acid; and (d) another resistant diphosphoric ester II (Lohmann and Lipmann). The last two are formed in muscle extracts from carbohydrates of the muscle tissue or from added glycogen, starch, or the Embden, Neuberg, or Robison ester, by taking up phosphate, or by transformation of the Harden-Young ester. Lohmann's ester I is produced in the presence of fluorides, oxalates, or citrates, ester II in attenuated or diluted frog muscle extracts. The diphosphoric ester, described previously as "lactacidogen" by the school of Embden, appears during the preparation of muscle juice [Embden, Jost, and Lehnhartz (67)]. There are obviously conditions under which synthesis of different hexosephosphoric esters, of various stability, takes place in muscle extracts; but there is no reason to attribute to any one of them, except the Embden monoester (which occurs in normal muscle), a special function in the intermediary metabolism of carbohydrates in muscle.[5] Each of the esters can be transformed into lactic acid when incubated with muscle extract containing the enzyme and coenzyme, and it seems that the esters containing two phosphoric-acid groups undergo this fermentation in the presence of less coenzyme than the monoesters. The amount of the Embden ester increases, when the muscle (frog, rat) is stimulated or when glycogenolysis, i.e., lactic-acid formation, is produced. The understanding of the intermediary function of phosphoric ester formation in the breakdown of glycogen is still difficult without the hypothesis, expressed by Meyerhof in his work on the lactic-acid-forming enzymes of muscle; namely, that an intermediary labile ester is formed, which is transformed into lactic acid and the known stable esters. The Embden ester found in muscle tissue may possibly be this stable ester.

The belief held formerly that cleavage of this ester must occur during the very contraction of muscle was founded upon a mistaken interpretation of experiments with two symmetrical muscles dipped into liquid air; the one muscle previously exhausted was supposed to be in a condition close to that of a fresh one, while the other, fresh muscle was supposed to possess at the moment of freezing the maximum concentration of transient substances produced by the contraction. This mistake was suspected by the Eggletons and recently corrected by Lohmann (133). The accumulation of the monoester and its relatively long persistence in tetanized muscles of frogs was proved by the significant values of Lohmann (133); and the same view was reached by the Coris (34b, 36), in very conclusive experiments on rat muscles tetanized or under the action of epinephrine. The question was reinvestigated recently by Embden and Jost (66). Although abandoning the validity of the previous demonstration of the cleavage of hexosemonophosphoric ester (cf. also 207), they made

[5] For this reason the designation "lactacidogen" for the hexosemonophosphoric ester (Embden's ester) is not used in this review. This designation has been used since 1927 by Embden and others, but it is rather misleading. Embden and his co-workers have recently postulated a breakdown of this ester, during muscle contraction, into hexose and phosphoric acid (65).

an attempt to find new evidence for the same assertion. Two symmetrical muscles were stimulated in a similar way to fatigue; one was then dipped into liquid air after a short rest (30 to 60 seconds), and the other was frozen during a supplementary strong direct tetanus. The muscle frozen during contraction contained in the majority of experiments less hexosemonophosphoric ester (mean, 38 mg. per cent H_3PO_4) than the muscle frozen in relaxation (mean, 45 mg. per cent H_3PO_4). The authors are convinced that this is a conclusive demonstration of cleavage of the monophosphoric ester during contraction, agreeing, however, that longer activity leads to accumulation of the ester (cf. also 207). From another series of experiments Embden (65) was led to conclusions as to the fate of the pyrophosphates and the nucleotides in the various stages of muscular contraction. The synthesis of pyrophosphates during the oxidative recovery, after previous breakdown in fatigue, was demonstrated by significant differences between gastrocnemii in fatigue and after recovery. The behaviour of pyrophosphates during contraction was compared on symmetrical muscles both frozen in liquid air, one having been weighted with 25 to 50 g., and the other having carried no load. The weighted muscle was supposed to have performed more work, and to have undergone greater chemical changes; but this assumption was not tested on any well-known chemical transformation. In the majority of experiments the muscle under load contained somewhat more pyrophosphate than the unweighted; the differences showed great dispersion. In trichloroacetic extracts from frog muscle, after removal of phosphorus compounds, alcohol precipitation, and drying of supernatant fluid and yeast fermentation, an orcin reaction for pentoses was obtained, and this reaction was more pronounced in the extracts from weighted or exhausted muscles than from unweighted or fresh ones. From these experiments Embden and Lehnhartz (69) infer and consider it as demonstrated that phosphoric acid (and purine) are split off from the adeninenucleotide during contraction. The largest amounts of pentose which they find do not exceed, however, more than one and a half per cent of the total pentose bound in the muscle as adeninenucleotide and inosinic acid.

Embden's view of what is going on during muscular contraction and recovery may be summarized as follows: I, Contraction: (a) synthesis of pyrophosphates; (b) breakdown of monophosphoric ester into hexose and phosphoric acid; (c) splitting of adeninenucleotide into ammonia, phosphoric acid, pentose, and a purine; II, Relaxation:

(*a*) breakdown of pyrophosphate; (*b*) synthesis of monophosphoric ester; III, Recovery: (*a*) synthesis of pyrophosphates; (*b*) no change in monophosphoric ester. In the reviewer's opinion only III (*a*) (synthesis of pyrophosphates) is demonstrated by the evidence presented. The other conclusions are far beyond the experimental and analytical technique available and can be taken at present only as more or less suggestive.

Adeninepyronucleotide.—This name[6] will designate the compound of the animal adeninenucleotide with the pyrophosphoric group, discovered by Lohmann, and by Fiske and Subbarow (1929) in trichloroacetic acid extracts of muscle. The following formula may, for the present, be assigned to this substance:

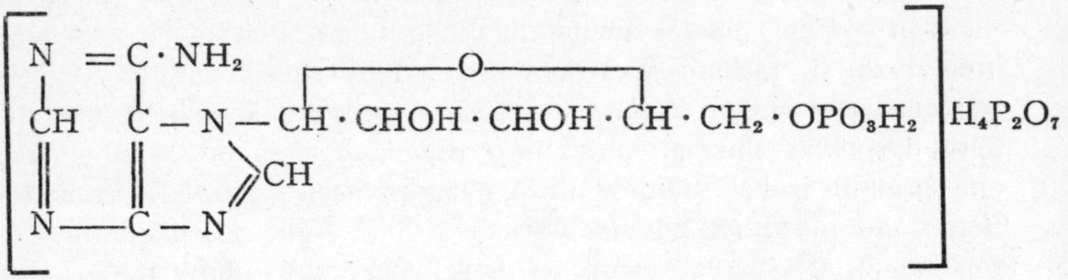

$$\left[\begin{array}{l} N = C \cdot NH_2 \qquad\qquad\;\; O \qquad\qquad \\ \;|\qquad\;| \qquad\qquad\quad | \qquad\qquad\qquad | \\ CH \quad C - N - CH \cdot CHOH \cdot CHOH \cdot CH \cdot CH_2 \cdot OPO_3H_2 \\ \;\|\qquad\| \qquad\;\; {\diagdown}CH \\ \;N \!-\!\!-\! C - N \diagup \end{array} \right] H_4P_2O_7$$

The kind of linkage between the pyrophosphoric group and the nucleotide is not known, and the formula should indicate only that the two phosphate groups can be split off together by acid, as pyrophosphate. The pyronucleotide is a primary constituent of fresh resting muscle, and inosinetriphosphoric acid, adeninenucleotide, inosinic acid, phosphate, and ammonia are its physiological decomposition products. The preparation and the properties of the pyronucleotide are described in detail by Lohmann (130). Its decomposition with $Ca(OH)_2$ is a convenient method for preparing adeninenucleotide. Another method for preparing Embden's ester and adeninenucleotide from meat is reported by Hahn (96). The same adeninepyronucleotide was found in invertebrate muscle, but a somewhat different preparation was obtained from the mammalian heart (130). The pyronucleotide can be isolated from yeast also.

The pyronucleotide has probably some general cellular function; e.g., there are in plant seeds specific dehydrases, reducing methylene blue only in the presence of this body [Deuticke (53); Thunberg

---

[6] Adenosinetriphosphoric acid and adenylpyrophosphoric acid are alternative designations.

(196)]. Considerable interest was aroused in medicine by the discovery of the physiologieal activity of the adeninenucleotide, by Drury and Szent-Györgyi and others; this substance ranks with epinephrine, histamine, and acetylcholine as one of the most active endogenous constituents of the animal body, and has been extensively investigated in these two years. Adenine nucleotide as well as adenosine and pyronucleotide can be detected and estimated by biological methods: by their action upon the heart of the guinea pig, in which they produce a heart block [Bennett and Drury (7)], and by the even more sensitive test on the isolated atropinized frog heart, in which a transitory stoppage of the auricles and ventricle is produced by about 10^{-6} gm. of the nucleotide, nucleoside, or pyronucleotide [Parnas and Ostern (179)].

Adeninenucleotide is ubiquitous in the animal tissues. The adeninenucleotide of pig blood, where this body was first discovered, is identical with the adeninenucleotide of muscle (166), but is different from the nucleotide of yeast nucleic acid.

The function of the adeninepyronucleotide in the metabolism of muscle has been demonstrated recently by Lohmann (131, 132) and Meyerhof, Lohmann, and Meyer (158); it is the organic constituent of the coenzyme in the enzymic system concerned with lactic-acid formation in muscle extracts. In muscle extracts inactivated by autolysis and dialysis the lactic-acid-producing activity returns after addition of adeninepyronucleotide, phosphates, and magnesium salts; these three components suffice and are indispensable. The pyronucleotide substitutes for the organic component lost during autolysis; the magnesium salts and the phosphates substitute for the parts lost during dialysis.

Adeninepyronucleotide itself is synthesized from the nucleotide and orthophosphate by muscle extracts at an alkaline reaction: this synthesis of pyrophosphate was first observed by E. Lehnhartz. Splitting off of orthophosphate and restitution of the pyrophosphate group from orthophosphates is therefore possible in muscle extracts as well as in intact muscle, when energy for this change is available. This cycle may be involved in the formation of hexosephosphoric esters; the formation of lactic acid from glycogen by inactivated muscle extracts requires the addition of the full coenzyme system; the cleavage of the Harden-Young di-ester does not require the presence of phosphate, but the Embden monoester undergoes fermentation only in the presence of phosphate. The diphosphoric ester requires for its fermentation to lactic acid less pyronucleotide than the monoester. In the absence of magnesium salts only dephosphorylation of the di-ester may occur, without formation of lactic acid. In this way, the rôle of the pyronucleotide can possibly be associated with the linking of phosphoric groups to the hexoses and with the formation of the intermediary labile ester. The system pyronucleotide-magnesium is not the coenzyme of respiration, nor is it concerned with the glyoxalase, which changes synthetic pyruvic aldehyde into lactic acid.

The pyronucleotide may also be supposed to play a rôle in the synthesis of phosphocreatine from its cleavage products; this reaction, which occurs in alkaline muscle extracts, requires at least 0.12 calories for each milligram of phosphoric acid bound. When the simultaneous formation of lactic acid from glycogen is near an end and cannot provide the necessary energy, the synthesis goes on at the expense of energy liberated by the breakdown of pyronucleotide into phosphates, inosinic acid, and ammonia;[7] possibly the deamination *per se* is not an essential stage in this liberation of energy.

Ammonia formation in muscle.—Deamination of the pyronucleotide by mechanical destruction of the muscle tissue leads to hypoxanthinepyronucleotide (130). What has been found regarding the deamination of adeninenucleotide in muscle applies probably also to pyronucleotide; the share of the two substances in ammonia formation cannot, however, be estimated.

In the question of ammonia formation and of its reversibility, and also of the absolute values of ammonia contained or formed in muscle tissue, the controversy between Embden and Parnas remains as sharp as before; both parties have stated their cases (178 and 63), and can be judged only from evidence contained in the original papers and from the reader's own experience with muscle—and ammonia. It would be much easier to picture the part of ammonia formation in muscle metabolism if it could be proved to be a reversible change; but unfortunately no significant fact indicates such a reversibility, and to postulate reversibility without, or even against, direct evidence seems rather hazardous.

The function of the adeninepyronucleotide as coenzyme is bound to the presence of its amino-group; but this function is not associated with deamination (with the related cozymase of alcoholic fermenta-

7 This change sets free 17 calories per mol.

tion no deamination occurs). After deamination the pyronucleotide is rendered inactive until its amino-group is replaced in the oxidative recovery of the intact muscle. In the reviewer's opinion the deamination of pyronucleotide during muscular activity is related to the rhythm of the chemical changes, and is concerned with putting out of action, until oxidative recovery takes place, of certain quantities of the coenzyme, after certain quantities of lactic acid have been produced; but this cannot be proved at present.

Phosphocreatine (phosphagen, creatinephosphoric acid).—An understanding of the function of phosphocreatine was attained in this biennium, with the discovery of the alactacid activity of muscle; much knowledge was accumulated, however, in the earlier period. Many figures for phosphocreatine distribution may be found in Palladin's review (176); data for the phosphocreatine content of smooth muscle have been published by Zanghi (212).

The alactacid activity of skeletal muscle.—Frogs poisoned by injection of 40 mg. of iodoacetic acid or bromoacetic acid become completely rigid after one hour; but if their sciatic plexus be severed before poisoning, the limbs will appear normal after one hour, while the innervated extremities will be rigid. When nerve-muscle preparations from such frog limbs are stimulated, 60 to 100 twitches are produced, which could not be told from normal contractions by their mechanical, thermal, and electrical [Henriques and Lundsgaard (103)] responses (Stage I). Then, the contractions become weaker, and a contracture begins to appear (Stage II), finally the twitches come to an end, and contracture develops rapidly; after a few minutes the muscle is in full rigor (Stage III). *During all these changes no lactic acid is produced in the muscle, either during the periods of activity or when rigor develops.* This is the portentous discovery by Einar Lundsgaard (138).[8]

During the alactacid contractions phosphocreatine is decomposed at a rate strictly proportional to the tension developed and to the heat set free, ammonia is produced in amounts slightly larger than in the

---

[8] Bromoacetic rigor without lactic-acid production and with an increase of the phosphate content in resting frog muscle had been previously noticed by Schwartz and Oschmann (194). Credit must be given, however, to Lundsgaard for having recognized the full importance of his observation and for having investigated the alactacid contraction carefully and in detail, but the co-operation of Meyerhof and his co-workers, of Henriques, and of Hill must also be mentioned.

normal muscle, and phosphate is liberated from the pyronucleotide. The phosphates very soon become combined with sugar, and both Embden's monoester and Harden and Young's di-ester are formed. This change belongs probably to the second and third stages, in which rigor develops; during the last stage very large amounts of ammonia are formed,[9] glycogen is broken down, and esterification proceeds [Lundsgaard (136, 138); Kerly (121); Mozolowski, Mann, and Lutwak (165); Lutwak (142); Mozolowski, unpublished; Parnas (177)]. In the crustacean muscle the cleavage of phosphoarginine takes the place of the breakdown of phosphocreatine in vertebrate muscle [Lundsgaard (140)]. The rigor and accompanying chemical changes follow after the exhaustion of phosphocreatine, which is completely broken down when the contracture sets in. In muscles poisoned with fluorides similar changes occur [Lipmann (126)].[10]

In consequence of this discovery a fundamental belief has had to be discarded—the belief that lactic-acid formation is the principal change in muscular contraction. In the period preceding the discovery this opinion was generally held and supported, but it was also opposed, by arguments both good and poor. It is obviously contrary to the old conception that muscle can work without lactic-acid formation; the formation of lactic acid must now be considered, however, as a factor in recovery; it prevents the exhaustion of phosphocreatine and the consequent development of rigor; it becomes a remoter link in the chain of events, a first or second factor in the anaërobic recovery, just

[9] On this point, as on every one concerning ammonia in muscle, the results and conclusions of Embden and his co-workers are incompatible with those of Parnas. For Embden's opinions, see literature cited (64, 71, 171); for the other side, see Parnas (177); Mozolowski, Mann, and Lutwak (165); and Lutwak (142).

[10] The nature of the changes produced in the muscle tissue by the iodoacetic acid is not yet explained. The poisoning is a slow reaction, not instantaneous, as with fluoride; this has been demonstrated with muscle extracts [Lohmann 141a)] and with sartorii [Meyerhof and Boyland (154)]. Iodoacetic acid probably acts on the lactic-acid-forming enzyme (Lohmann). Embden and Metz have published experiments in which they find the solubility of muscle proteins in salt solutions [cf. Deuticke (52); Hensay (104)] greatly reduced by bromoacetic acid poisoning, and consider this as a primary change [Embden (64); Embden and Metz (70)]. This change must be considered rather as the effect of the chemical transformations following the disintegration of the poisoned muscle (unpublished), and as identical with that of a muscle in rigor. Rigor develops rapidly around every injury of a muscle poisoned with iodoacetic acid.

as in a former period of physiology the oxidations lost their direct relation to muscle contraction, and became a factor in recovery. The demonstration that lactic-acid formation outlasts a tetanic stimulation in normal muscle was made a little later [Lehnhartz (124); Meyerhof and Schulz (163, 151)]; this view, held by Embden *contra* Meyerhof, has been proved correct.

We must assume now, with Lundsgaard, that the cleavage of phosphocreatine is the primary change in the normal contraction, as it is the primary and final change in the anaërobic twitch of the iodoacetic muscles; and that this change is followed, in the normal muscle, by restitution of phosphocreatine, depending on the chemical changes of the anaërobic recovery, viz., lactic-acid formation from glycogen and the splitting off of phosphate from the pyronucleotides.

This recovery is quite admirably achieved; the energy liberated by the lactic-acid formation in a fresh normal muscle is so completely used up for the recovery of phosphocreatine that the ratio, tension/heat, of a contraction, is identical with or without lactic-acid formation; it is immaterial whether the energy is ultimately derived from the splitting of phosphocreatine only, or from lactic-acid formation through the intermediary reconstruction of phosphocreatine [Fischer (80); Meyerhof, Lundsgaard, and Blaschko (159); Hill and Parkinson (112)]. Owing to this reconstruction of phosphocreatine the normal muscle is able to perform in anaërobic activity four times as much work as the iodoacetic-acid-poisoned muscle without going into rigor. The origin of the delayed heat production in anaërobic contractions has also been discovered [Blaschko (13)]; the anaërobic recovery heat is the balance between the exothermic lactic-acid formation and the endothermic resynthesis of phosphocreatine.

The very important question of the changes in reaction during contraction cannot be treated here at the length which it deserves; but the reader will find a full account in Milroy's review (163a). In the physiological zone of pH 5 to 7.5 phosphocreatine neutralizes more basic equivalents than its cleavage products, and its cleavage must set free equivalents of base. This buffering action was observed by Mackler, Olmsted, and Simpson (143) with minced mammalian muscle. This problem was investigated thoroughly by Meyerhof and Lipmann (128, 157) on anaërobic contractions of sartorii of frogs, the manometric method of Warburg being used. The absorption or liberation of CO_2 into an atmosphere of CO_2-N_2 equilibrated with Ringer bicarbonate solution was measured; this absorption or liberation depends on changes in the acid-base equilibrium of the immersed tissue. *In muscles poisoned with iodoacetic acid the reaction becomes distinctly alkaline during activity:* this agrees with the fact that phosphocreatine breakdown is the major change, accompanied by pyronucleotide cleavage. In normal anaërobic contractions changes of reaction are also revealed by the manometric method. Cleavage of phosphocreatine prevails at the onset of a series of contractions and lactic-acid formation predominates at a later stage. The change toward alkalinity is the more pronounced the more acid the muscle is at the onset; it is very distinct at pH 6.07 and is scarcely demonstrable at pH 7.93. When the lactic-acid formation comes into prominence, the CO_2 bound in the previous period is set free again; by the time this is completed and the previous pH of the muscle is again attained, the lactic acid must have neutralized the basic equivalents set free by the breakdown of phosphocreatine and pyronucleotide; the acid base changes can be shown to be in good agreement with the changes in the components enumerated above.

Another important point which should be emphasized is that the reaction of the muscle can become more acid, or more alkaline, or remain almost unchanged, especially if the reaction at the onset of anaërobic activity is that of the body fluids (pH 7.4). The idea that the formation of lactic acid in the tissue, by virtue of its being an acid, is the factor inducing contraction was held and developed in the previous period coincident with increasing refinement of physicochemical knowledge; and such attempts extend, in a very tempting form, into the period under consideration [Meyer and Marks (150)]. They have, however, been strongly opposed, chiefly by Bethe (8) and Wöhlisch (210). The view that acid production or a change of reaction itself is a factor inducing the contraction must be considered as disproved and the same applies to recent attempts in which the function hitherto attributed to acidification is ascribed to the change toward alkalinity [Embden (64)]. This means, of course, that changes toward acidity or alkalinity of the muscle tissue as a whole cannot be the factors determining its contraction or relaxation; and it makes it less likely that liberation of alkali or acid in restricted regions of the muscle structure could be the essential point in this process. The present situation certainly indicates that it would be wiser, for the moment, to defer speculation until additional information is obtained.

It was formerly impossible to understand why the ratio of tension developed to heat set free remained constant during a series of anaërobic contractions in isolated muscle, while the ratio of tension to lactic-acid formation was decreasing, and the ratio of tension to phosphocreatine decomposed was increasing infinitely. This is perfectly clear now. In a fresh isolated muscle the energy is furnished by the cleavage of phosphocreatine; but of its components only a part is rebuilt by the utilization of the energy liberated by lactic-acid formation; as fatigue proceeds, little phosphocreatine remains, but the contractions still result from the breakdown of this substance, which is continually rebuilt. The resynthesis depends on the extent of lactic-acid formation; the latter, therefore, is the limiting factor [Meyerhof and Schulz (163); Lundsgaard (141)].

Since it has been demonstrated by Neuberg and M. Vogt that pyruvic aldehyde is produced from hexosediphosphoric ester by the muscle enzyme deprived of its coenzyme (muscle apozymase), it is legitimate to consider this aldehyde as a possible intermediary stage in lactic-acid formation; further evidence is added by the work of Sym (193), with pike muscle powder. The entire dephosphorylation products are accounted for in Sym's experiments by the lactic-acid and pyruvic-aldehyde formation. Inhibition of the dismutation of phenylglyoxal in fowl muscle poisoned with iodoacetic acid is reported [Dudley (57)]; but less inhibition of the transformation of synthetic pyruvic aldehyde than of lactic-acid formation by frog muscle extracts is found by Lohmann (141a), and this inhibition is probably not the essential disturbance in iodoacetic poisoning. Experiments of Barrenscheen (4, 5, 6) are referred to in which the formation of pyruvic aldehyde was observed in rigor of spontaneous origin, or induced by iodoacetic intoxication; the aldehyde was produced in the intact tissue itself; or after mincing and incubation with hexosediphosphoric ester. This constitutes a further demonstration of the intermediary rôle of pyruvic aldehyde, as stated by Neuberg and Vogt. The adeninepyronucleotide is deaminized under the conditions of spontaneous or iodoacetic rigor and so the coenzyme is destroyed; the transformation of the carbohydrate, starting at hexosephosphate, is stopped in the absence of coenzyme, at the stage of pyruvic aldehyde. Formation of pyruvic acid in frog and rabbit muscle along with the aldehyde is reported by Case and Cook (28), and under their experimental conditions was independent of the oxygen supply; Barrenscheen (4) has made a similar observation.

The sequence of changes in the anaërobic part of the contraction cycle.—The energy of the contraction is supplied by the decomposition of phosphocreatine; this decomposition is the change closest to the contraction yet discovered. The phosphocreatine is rebuilt immediately, possibly by the intermediary cleavage of the adenine pyronucleotide into orthophosphate and nucleotide. Ultimately, the energy of phosphocreatine resynthesis is supplied by lactic-acid formation from glycogen. The reactions involved in muscle contraction are hydrolytic cleavages, but distinguished from the bulk of such decompositions by the large energy liberations and, as shown by Dean Burk for glycogenolysis in muscle, by free energy changes, probably larger than the heat production. The reversion of these reactions seems possible only in association with certain exothermic reactions, possibly in strict chemical linkage; the total chemical energy change is certainly exothermic. The particular character of the energy-supplying reactions is shown by the fact that the cleavage of phosphocreatine is able to furnish the energy of contraction in muscle until it is nearly completely exhausted. Speculation concerning the postulated linkage of these reactions may be better left to some future number of the *Review*.

Oxidative recovery.—I take from Milroy's review (163a) the lucid summary of the changes occurring during the oxidative recovery: (*a*) the completion of the synthesis of the phosphocreatine; (*b*) the entire removal of lactic acid which was formed in the contraction, and the synthesis of glycogen associated with increased oxygen intake so that the amount of carbohydrate in the muscle after recovery is the same as before the contraction minus the equivalent of lactic acid, which has undergone oxidation; (*c*) the reamination of the nucleotide (or pyronucleotide) deaminized, at the expense of oxidative deamination of amino acids,[11] and the resynthesis of the pyronucleotide from orthophosphate.

Investigations of the dehydrogenations in muscle tissue have been made by Hahn (93, 96, 98, 99) and to the substances considered previously (94) propionic, citric, glycerophosphoric, and hexosephosphoric acids were added, which undergo dehydrogenation and are transformed into pyruvic acid, in the presence or absence of methylene blue. The origin and the fate of succinic acid was supposed by Thunberg to be related to the oxidative carbohydrate metabolism in

[11] The attempt by Embden and Lehnhartz (68) to invalidate this concept may be dealt with in another volume of this *Review*, by which time a paper concerned with this question will have been published. It is now in press.

muscle: in the pathway from succinic acid to pyruvic acid as traced in Hahn's scheme, pyruvic acid is decomposed to acetic aldehyde and acetic acid. From acetic acid, succinic acid is supposed to be built up by the dehydrogenation of two mols of acetic acid for each mol of succinic acid formed. In a recent investigation [Toenniessen and Brinkmann (197, 198)] succinic and formic acid formation is observed after addition of pyruvic acid to blood perfused through rabbit muscles; the formation of a hypothetical α, Δ- diketoadipinic acid from two molecules of pyruvic acid is suggested, from which succinic acid could arise when formic acid is split off.

$$2CH_3 \cdot CO \cdot COOH + 0 = COOH \cdot CO \cdot CH_2 \cdot CH_2 \cdot CO \cdot COOH \\ + H_2O \qquad (a)$$

$$COOH \cdot CO \cdot CH_2 \cdot CH_2 \cdot CO \cdot COOH + 2H_2O = 2H \cdot COOH \\ + COOH \cdot CH_2 \cdot CH_2 \cdot COOH \qquad (b)$$

The origin of succinic acid from aspartic and glutamic acid, acting together on muscle tissue, is suggested by the work of D. M. Needham (170); the addition of these precursors produces, anaërobically, succinic, fumaric, and malic acid in muscle pulp, without increase of ammonia or amino nitrogen. For the dehydrogenation of succinic acid, reference is also made to the papers by Broman (20) and Wieland and Lawson (206).

Experiments on muscles poisoned with iodoacetic acid have brought important information also into this field. The poisoned muscle is able to perform more work in oxygen than without it [Lundsgaard (136); Hill and Parkinson (112); Cattell, Feng, Hartree, Hill, and Parkinson (29)]; respiration is raised by the addition of lactates or pyruvates [Meyerhof and Boyland (154)]. In myothermic experiments delayed heat in normal relation to the initial heat can be observed at the onset of activity and recovery-heat after exhaustion, but the functional recovery in oxygen is not quite regular and is probably impaired by the poisoning. In any case, recovery oxidation without the intermediate formation of lactic acid is demonstrated in the poisoned muscle, and there must be some direct linkage between combustion and the resynthesis of phosphocreatine.

It is also seen now that the isolated normal frog muscle is able to draw the energy for aërobic contractions from sources other than carbohydrate metabolism [Ochoa (172); Meyerhof (153)]. When containing more than 0.5 per cent of glycogen, the muscle draws the energy almost exclusively from this source, but when less than 0.3 per cent is present, it draws energy from some other source.[12] The decrease of fatty acids in the legs of frogs in poor nutritional condition, when performing prolonged exercise, is confirmed by Buchwald and Cori (22a). Thus the results obtained with isolated muscles are beginning to show better agreement with the results of investigations in general metabolism.

The validity of experiments on isolated amphibian muscles has been doubted at various times. A statement by A. V. Hill may be interesting in this respect. "An isolated sartorius in oxygenated Ringer-glucose solution may give more than ten thousand twitches, oxidise more than 1 per cent of its weight of carbohydrate, may develop a tension of more than six tons per square cm. of its cross section, without sign of failure. This corresponds, in man, to a walk of more than 14 kilometres. The muscles of a man who can walk 14 kilometres without obvious signs of failure are not so abnormal that a physiologist need despair of investigating them."

Rigor.—Rigor has nothing whatever to do with lactic-acid formation or with changes brought about by the acidification of the tissue. This had been made probable by previous observations on post-insulinic rigor (Hoet and Marks) ; by the mechanical properties of muscle in contractures produced by acids (Bethe, Wöhlisch) ; and by observations on muscles without connective tissue (*Ciona* larva), where rigor was brought about by chloroform, but no similar changes were produced by acid (Paul Weiss). Now it is certain. It may be repeated that rigor develops in iodoacetic-poisoned muscle only when the phosphocreatine is broken down. What kind of changes in the proteins are essential in rigor we do not know ; and what relationship should be postulated between the exhaustion of phosphocreatine, preceding the rigor, and the simultaneous chemical changes in phosphates and ammonia,[13] we cannot at present perceive.

The heart.—The metabolism of the isolated heart has been the subject of many papers, and some substantial results obtained by Clark, Gaddie, and Stewart may be reported here (31, 32). Oxygen

[12] No very significant changes in the nitrogenous extractives after work, in the muscles of rats low in carbohydrate, are reported by Blaettler (12).

[13] The chemical changes during various forms of contractures with iodoacetic poisoning and without have been investigated since the discovery of iodoacetic alactacid rigor: cf. Bethe, Norpoth, and Huf (9) ; Martini (147) ; Lippay (129).

consumption, CO_2 output, carbohydrate metabolism, ammonia and urea production, and fat oxidation were investigated simultaneously. No carbohydrate oxidation was demonstrable in the first 6 hours; after 24 hours it became appreciable, but it accounted only for 15 per cent of the total metabolism; when insulin and blood were added the metabolism of carbohydrate accounted for 30 per cent of the total. No evidence of fat oxidation was obtained, but the formation of ammonia and of urea accounted for one-third of the metabolism. Thus, one-half of the metabolism remained unexplained. Addition of amino acids increased the ammonia formation. The formation of ammonia in the frog heart was also investigated by Ostern (173); it cannot be accounted for by the decomposition of adeninenucleotides, and its origin is thought to be rather in a cyclic recovery of the adenine-compound in oxidative reaminations, as suggested by Parnas.

The heart muscle seems in its metabolism a less specialized tissue than the skeletal muscle; its metabolism rather resembles that of the whole organism.

I thank Dr. W. Mozolowski and Dr. P. Ostern for their valuable help.

LITERATURE CITED

1. ABDERHALDEN, E., AND WERTHEIMER, E., *Z. ges. exptl. Med.*, **72**, 472 (1930)
2. ÅGREN, G., WILANDER, O., AND JORPES, E., *Biochem. J.*, **25**, 777 (1931)
3. ANDERSON, J. A., AND MACLEOD, J. J. R., *Biochem. J.*, **24**, 1408 (1930)
4. BARRENSCHEEN, H. K., BRAUN, K., AND DREGUSS, M., *Biochem. Z.*, **232**, 165 (1931)
5. BARRENSCHEEN, H. K., *Biochem. Z.*, **240**, 381 (1931)
6. BARRENSCHEEN, H. K., FREY, L., AND RENTH, O., *Biochem. Z.*, **240**, 394 (1931)
7. BENNET, D. W., AND DRURY, A. N., *J. Physiol.*, **72**, 288 (1931)
8. BETHE, A., *Naturwissenschaften*, **12**, 678 (1930)
9. BETHE, A., NORPOTH, L., AND HUF, E., *Klin. Wochschr.*, **10**, 1175 (1931)
10. BISCHOFF, F., AND LONG, L., *J. Biol. Chem.*, **87**, 47 (1930)
10a. BISCHOFF, F., AND LONG, L., *Am. J. Physiol.*, **95**, 403 (1931)
11. BISCHOFF, F., AND LONG, L., *J. Nutrition*, **3**, 201 (1930)
12. BLAETTLER, E., *Biochem. Z.*, **221**, 359 (1930)
13. BLASCHKO, H., *J. Physiol.*, **70**, 96 (1930)
14. BODANSKY, M., *J. Biol. Chem.*, **91**, 147 (1931)
15. BODNAR, I., AND TANKO, B., *Biochem. Z.*, **230**, 228 (1931)
16. BOEHN, G., AND SIGNER, R., *Helv. Chim. Acta*, **14**, 1370 (1931)
17. BOLLMAN, J. L., MANN, F. C., AND WILHELMY, C. M., *J. Biol. Chem.*, **93**, 83 (1931)
18. BOYLAND, E., *Biochem. Z.*, **237**, 418 (1931)

19. BRENTANO, C., RIESSER, O., AND MASAYAMA, T., *Klin. Wochschr.*, **10**, 840 (1931)
20. BROMAN, T., *Skand. Arch.*, **59**, 25 (1930)
21. BROWN, M., AND IMRIE, C. G., *J. Physiol.*, **71**, 214 (1931)
22. BUCHWALD, K. W., AND CORI, C. F., *J. Biol. Chem.*, **92**, 355 (1931)
22a. BUCHWALD, K. W., AND CORI, C. F., *Proc. Soc. Exptl. Biol. Med.*, **28**, 737 (1931)
23. BUELL, M., *J. Biol. Chem.*, **85**, 435 (1930)
24. CALLISON, W. E., *J. Biol. Chem.*, **90**, 665 (1930)
25. CARO, L. DE, *Arch. sci. biol. (Italy)*, **14**, 247 (1930)
26. CARO, L. DE, *Atti. acad. Lincei*, **11**, 98 (1930)
27. CASE, E., *Biochem. J.*, **25**, 561 (1931)
28. CASE, E., AND COOK, R. P., *Biochem. J.*, **25**, 1319 (1931)
29. CATTELL, McK., FENG, T. P., HARTREE, W., HILL, A. V., AND PARKINSON, J., *Proc. Roy. Soc. (London), B*, **108**, 279 (1931)
30. CHANUTIN, A., AND SHEARER, L. D., *J. Biol. Chem.*, **91**, 475 (1931)
31. CLARK, A. J., GADDIE, R., AND STEWART, C. P., *J. Physiol.*, **70**, vii (1930)
32. CLARK, A. J., GADDIE, R., AND STEWART, C. P., *J. Physiol.*, **72**, 443 (1931)
33. COLE, V. V., *J. Biol. Chem.*, **92**, 15 (1931)
34. CORI, C. F., *Physiol. Rev.*, **11**, 143 (1931)
34a. CORI, G. T., AND CORI, C. F., *J. Biol. Chem.*, **94**, 561 (1931)
34b. CORI, C. F., AND CORI, G. T., *J. Biol. Chem.*, **94**, 581 (1931)
35. CORI, C. F., AND BUCHWALD, K. W., *J. Biol. Chem.*, **92**, 367 (1931)
36. CORI, C. F., AND CORI, G. T., *J. Biol. Chem.*, **92**, 52 (1931)
37. CORI, E. F., AND CORI, G. T., *Proc. Soc. Exptl. Biol. Med.*, **27**, 934 (1930)
38. CORI, E. F., CORI, G. T., AND BUCHWALD, K. W., *Am. J. Physiol.*, **93**, 273 (1930)
39. CORI, G. T., *Am. J. Physiol.*, **95**, 285 (1930)
40. CORI, G. T., *Am. J. Physiol.*, **94**, 557 (1930)
41. CORKILL, A. B., *Biochem. J.*, **24**, 779 (1930)
42. CORKILL, A. B., AND MARKS, H. P., *J. Physiol.*, **70**, 67 (1930)
43. McCULLAGH, D. R., AND CASE, E. M., *Biochem. J.*, **25**, 1220 (1931)
44. DAMBOVICEANU, A., SAGER, O., AND ROTH, E., *Compt. rend. soc. biol.*, **103**, 1371 (1930)
45. DAVENPORT, H. A., DAVENPORT, H. K., AND RANSON, S. W., *J. Biol. Chem.*, **87**, 295 (1930)
46. DEBOIS, G., *Compt. rend. soc. biol.*, **103**, 546 (1930)
47. DEBOIS, G., *Compt. rend. soc. biol.*, **103**, 944 (1930)
48. DEBOIS, G., *J. Physiol.*, **70**, 2 (1930)
49. DEBOIS, G., *Arch. intern. pharmacodynamie*, **41**, 65 (1931)
50. DEBOIS, G., *Arch. intern. pharmacodynamie*, **41**, 129 (1931)
51. DEFAUW, J., *Compt. rend. soc. biol.*, **105**, 228 (1930)
52. DEUTICKE, H. J., *Arch. ges. Physiol.*, **224**, 1 (1930)
53. DEUTICKE, H. J., *Z. physiol. Chem.*, **192**, 193 (1930)
54. DILL, D. B., AND EDWARDS, H. T., *J. Biol. Chem.*, **92**, 87 (1931)
55. DIRKEN, M. N. J., AND MOOK, H., *J. Physiol.*, **69**, 210 (1930)
56. DMOCHOWSKI, A., *Acta Biol. Exptl. (Warsaw)*, **4**, 51 (1930)
57. DUDLEY, H. W., *Biochem. J.*, **25**, 139 (1931)

58. DUNN, H. L., *Physiol. Rev.*, **9**, 276 (1929)
60. EADIE, G. S., *Am. J. Physiol.*, **94**, 69 (1930)
61. EDSALL, J. T., *J. Biol. Chem.*, **89**, 291 (1930)
62. EGGLETON, P., *J. Physiol.*, **70**, 294 (1930)
62a. EGGLETON, P., *Physiol. Rev.*, **9**, 432 (1929) (Review)
63. EMBDEN, G., *Z. physiol. Chem.*, **196**, 23 (1931)
64. EMBDEN, G., *Klin. Wochschr.*, **9**, 1337 (1930)
65. EMBDEN, G., HEFTER, J., AND LEHNHARTZ, M., *Z. physiol. Chem.*, **187**, 45 (1930)
66. EMBDEN, G., AND JOST, H., *Z. physiol. Chem.*, **203**, 48 (1931)
67. EMBDEN, G., JOST, H., LEHNHARTZ, M., *Z. physiol. Chem.*, **189**, 261 (1930)
68. EMBDEN, G., AND LEHNHARTZ, M., *Z. physiol. Chem.*, **200**, 273 (1931)
69. EMBDEN, G., AND LEHNHARTZ, M., *Z. physiol. Chem.*, **200**, 149 (1931)
70. EMBDEN, G., AND METZ, E., *Z. physiol. Chem.*, **192**, 132 (1931)
71. EMBDEN, G., AND NORPOTH, L., *Z. physiol. Chem.*, **200**, 104 (1931)
72. EMBDEN, G., AND SCHMIDT, G., *Z. physiol. Chem.*, **197**, 191 (1931)
73. EMBDEN, G., AND SCHMIDT, G., *Z. physiol. Chem.*, **186**, 205 (1930)
74. ERNST, E., AND TAKACS, I., *Biochem. Z.*, **224**, 145 (1930)
75. ERNST, E., *Arch. ges. Physiol.*, **226**, 243 (1931)
76. EULER, H. VON, AND NILSSON, R., *Z. physiol. Chem.*, **194**, 260 (1931)
77. EVANS, L. C., CHIAO TSAI, AND YOUNG, F. C., *J. Physiol.*, **71**, 30 (1931)
78. FERDMANN, D., *Z. physiol. Chem.*, **187**, 160 (1930)
79. FIROR, W. M., AND EADIE, G. S., *Am. J. Physiol.*, **94**, 615 (1930)
80. FISCHER, E., *Arch. ges. Physiol.*, **226**, 500 (1931)
81. FISCHER, R. B., *Biochem. J.*, **25**, 1410 (1931)
82. FISHER, R. A., *"Statistical Methods,"* 3d edition (London), (1930)
83. FLEISCHMANN, W., *Biochem. Z.*, **219**, 7 (1930)
84. FOA, C., *Arch. farmacol. sper.*, **48**, 187 (1930)
85. FREEMAN, N. E., *Am. J. Physiol.*, **92**, 107 (1930)
86. GALVIALO, M. J., AND KEINES, C. J., *Biochem. Z.*, **222**, 123 (1930)
87. GEIGER, E., *Biochem. Z.*, **223**, 190 (1930)
88. GEIGER, E., SCHMIDT, E., *Arch. exptl. Path. Pharmakol.*, **143**, 321 (1929)
89. GELLHORN, E., *Biol. Bull.*, **60**, 397 (1931)
90. GOLDBERGER, S., *Arch. sci. biol. (Italy)*, **15**, 505 (1930)
91. GROLLMANN, A., *Biochem. Z.*, **238**, 488 (1931)
92. HAHN, A., *Z. Biol.*, **91**, 444 (1931)
93. HAHN, A., *Ges. Morph. Physiol.* (München), **39**, 23 (1930)
94. HAHN, A., *Am. J. Physiol.*, **90**, 373 (1929)
95. HAHN, A., BELMONTE, H., AND NIEMER, H., *Z. Biol.*, **91**, 491 (1931)
96. HAHN, A., FISCHBACH, E., AND HAARMAN, W., *Z. Biol.*, **91**, 315 (1931)
97. HAHN, A., FISCHBACH, E., AND NIEMER, H., *Z. Biol.*, **91**, 53 (1930)
98. HAHN, A., AND HAARMAN, W., *Z. Biol.*, **89**, 563 (1930)
99. HAHN, A., AND HAARMAN, W., *Z. Biol.*, **91**, 231 (1930)
100. HARRISON, D. C., *Biochem. J.*, **25**, 1011 (1931)
101. HARRISON, S. T., AND MELLANBY, E., *Biochem. J.*, **24**, 141 (1930)
102. HAURY, V. G., *J. Biol. Chem.*, **89**, 467 (1930)
103. HENRIQUES, V., AND LUNDSGAARD, E., *Biochem. Z.*, **236**, 219 (1931)
104. HENSAY, J., *Arch. ges. Physiol.*, **224**, 43 (1930)

105. HERRIN, R. C., *Am. J. Physiol.*, **93**, 657 (1930)

106. HILL, A. V., *Proc. Roy. Soc. (London) B*, **109**, 267 (1931)

107. HILL, A. V., *Proc. Roy Soc. (London) B*, **106**, 477 (1930)

108. HILL, A. V., *Proc. Roy. Soc. (London) B*, **127**, 9 (1930)

109. HILL, A. V., *Proc. Roy. Soc. (London) B*, **107**, 115 (1930)

110. HILL, A. V., KUPALOV, P. S., *Proc. Roy. Soc. (London) B*, **106**, 445 (1930)

111. HILL, A. V., AND KUPALOV, P. S., *Proc. Roy. Soc. (London) B*, **105**, 313 (1929)

112. HILL, A. V., AND PARKINSON, J. L., *Proc. Roy. Soc. (London) B*, **108**, 148 (1931)

113. HIMWICH, H. E., KOSKOFF, Y. D., AND NAHUM, L. H., *J. Biol. Chem.*, **85**, 571 (1930)

114. HORTON, H. V., *J. Physiol.*, **70**, 389 (1930)

115. HUKUDA, J., *J. Physiol.*, **72**, 438 (1931)

116. IINO, Y., *Mitt. med. Akad. Kioto*, **3**, 249 (1929)

117. JAWORSKA, J., *Biochem. Z.*, **221**, 71 (1930)

118. KAPELLER-ADLER, R., AND KRACH, J., *Biochem. Z.*, **221**, 437 (1930)

119. KAPELLER-ADLER, R., AND KRACH, J., *Biochem. Z.*, **224**, 364 (1930)

120. KEIL, W., *Z. physiol. Chem.*, **187**, 1 (1930)

121. KERLY, M., *Biochem. J.*, **25**, 671 (1931)

122. KERNOT, J. C., KNAGGS, J., AND SPEER, N. E., *Biochem. J.*, **24**, 379 (1930)

123. LAWRENCE, R. D., AND McCANCE, R. A., *Biochem. J.*, **25**, 580 (1931)

124. LEHNHARTZ, E., *Z. physiol. Chem.*, **197**, 55 (1930)

125. LINNEWEH, W., AND LINNEWEH, F., *Z. physiol. Chem.*, **189**, 80 (1930)

126. LIPMANN, F., *Biochem. Z.*, **227**, 110 (1930)

127. LIPMANN, F., AND LOHMANN, K., *Biochem. Z.*, **222**, 389 (1930)

128. LIPMANN, F., AND MEYERHOF, O., *Biochem. Z.*, **227**, 84 (1930)

129. LIPPAY, F., *Klin, Wochschr.*, **10**, 889 (1931)

130. LOHMANN, K., *Biochem. Z.*, **233**, 460 (1931)

131. LOHMANN, K., *Biochem. Z.*, **241**, 50 (1931)

132. LOHMANN, K., *Biochem. Z.*, **241**, 67 (1931)

133. LOHMANN, K., *Biochem. Z.*, **227**, 39 (1930)

134. LOHMANN, K., *Biochem. Z.*, **222**, 324 (1930)

135. LOHMANN, K., *Biochem. Z.*, **237**, 445 (1931)

135a. LOHMANN, K., "Die Zuckerphosphorsäureester und ihre Bedeutung für den Stoffwechsel der Hefe und des Muskels," Oppenheimer, O., *Handbuch der Biochemie*, Supplement, 133 (1930) (Review)

136. LUNDSGAARD, E., *Biochem. Z.*, **227**, 51 (1930)

137. LUNDSGAARD, E., *Biochem. Z.*, **220**, 1 (1930)

138. LUNDSGAARD, E., *Biochem. Z.*, **217**, 162 (1930)

139. LUNDSGAARD, E., *Biochem. Z.*, **220**, 8 (1930)

140. LUNDSGAARD, E., *Biochem. Z.*, **230**, 10 (1931)

141. LUNDSGAARD, E., *Biochem. Z.*, **233**, 322 (1931)

141a. LOHMANN, K., *Biochem. Z.*, **236**, 444 (1931)

142. LUTWAK, C., *Biochem. Z.*, **235**, 485 (1931)

143. MACKLER, H., OLMSTED, J. M. D., AND SIMPSON, W. W., *Am. J. Physiol.*, **94**, 626 (1930)

144. MANIGK, W., *Arch. ges. Physiol.*, **224**, 722 (1930)

145. MANN, T., *Biochem. Z.*, **231**, 33 (1931)
146. MARTIN, E. G., FIELD II., J., AND HALL, V. E., *Proc. Soc. Exptl. Biol. Med.*, **28**, 162 (1930)
147. MARTINI, E., *Klin. Wochschr.*, **10**, 1031 (1931)
148. MASAYAMA, T., AND RIESSER, O., *Biochem. Z.*, **234**, 323 (1931)
149. MATSUI, K., AND INOUYE, T., *Nagasaki Zassi*, **8**, 1178 (1930)
150. MEYER, K. H., AND MARKS, H., *"Der Aufbau hochpolymerer Naturstoffe,"* Leipzig, 239 (1930)
151. MEYERHOF, O., *Klin. Wochschr.*, **10**, 214 (1931)
152. MEYERHOF, O., *Biochem. Z.*, **226**, 1 (1930)
153. MEYERHOF, O., *Biochem. Z.*, **237**, 427 (1931)
153a. MEYERHOF, O., *Naturwissenschaften*, **19**, 923 (1931, Appendix) (Review)
153b. MEYERHOF, O., *"Die chemischen Vorgänge im Muskel,"* Berlin (1930) (Review)
153c. MEYERHOF, O., "The Chemistry of Muscular Contraction," *Lancet*, 1415 (1930) (Review)
154. MEYERHOF, O., AND BOYLAND, E., *Biochem. Z.*, **237**, 406 (1931)
155. MEYERHOF, O., McCULLAGH, D. R., AND SCHULZ, W., *Arch. ges. Physiol.*, **224**, 230 (1930)
156. MEYERHOF, O., AND GROLLMANN, A., *Biochem. Z.*, **241**, 23 (1931)
157. MEYERHOF, O., AND LIPMANN, F., *J. Physiol.*, **69**, 21 (1930)
158. MEYERHOF, O., LOHMANN, K., AND MEYER, K., *Biochem. Z.*, **237**, 437 (1931)
159. MEYERHOF, O., LUNDSGAARD, E., AND BLASCHKO, H., *Biochem. Z.*, **236**, 326 (1931)
160. MEYERHOF, O., LUNDSGAARD, E., AND BLASCHKO, H., *Naturwissenschaften*, **11**, 787 (1930)
161. MEYERHOF, O., AND MEYER, K., *Naturwissenschaften*, **19**, 180 (1931)
162. MEYERHOF, O., AND NACHMANNSOHN, D., *Biochem. Z.*, **222**, 1 (1930)
163. MEYERHOF, O., AND SCHULZ, W., *Biochem. Z.*, **236**, 54 (1931)
163a. MILROY, T. H., "The present status of the chemistry of skeletal muscle metabolism," *Physiol. Rev.*, **11**, 515 (1931) (Review)
164. MOND, R., AND NETTER, H., *Arch. ges. Physiol.*, **224**, 702 (1930)
165. MOZOLOWSKI, B., MANN, T., AND LUTWAK, C., *Biochem. Z.*, **231**, 290 (1931)
166. MROCZKIEWICZ, U., *Biochem. Z.*, **235**, 267 (1931)
167. MURALT, A. L. VON, AND EDSALL, J. T., *J. Biol. Chem.*, **89**, 315 (1930)
168. MURALT, A. L. VON, AND EDSALL, J. T., *J. Biol. Chem.*, **89**, 349 (1930)
169. MURALT, A. L. VON, EDSALL, J. T., *Trans. Faraday Soc.*, **26**, 837 (1930)
169a. NACHMANNSOHN, D., *Die Guanidophosphorsäeuren des Muskels;* OPPENHEIMER, O., *Handbuch der Biochemie*, Supplement, 163 (1930) (Review)
170. NEEDHAM, D., *Biochem. J.*, **24**, 208 (1930)
171. NORPOTH, L., *Z. physiol. Chem.*, **200**, 133 (1931)
172. OCHOA, S., *Biochem. Z.*, **227**, 116 (1930)
173. OSTERN, P., *Biochem. Z.*, **228**, 401 (1930)
174. OSTERN, P., *Biochem. Z.*, **221**, 64 (1930)
175. OZORIO DE ALMEIDA, M., AND MARTINS, T., *Compt. rend. soc. biol.*, **104**, 684 (1930)

176. Palladin, A., *Bull. soc. chim. biol.*, **13**, 13 (1931)
177. Parnas, J. K., *Naturwissenschaften*, **18**, 916 (1930)
177a. Parnas, J. K., *"Le metabolisme des muscles en activité,"* *Compt. rend. soc. biol.*, Réunion plénière (1929) (Review)
178. Parnas, J. K., Lewinski, W., Jaworska, J., and Umschweif, B., *Biochem. Z.*, **228**, 366 (1930)·
179. Parnas, J. K., and Ostern, P., *Biochem. Z.*, **234**, 307 (1931)
180. Pymann, F. L., *J. Chem. Soc.*, Part I, 183 (1930)
181. Ray, G. B., and Paff, G. H., *Am. J. Physiol.*, **94**, 521 (1930)
182. Ray, G. B., and Paff, G. H., *Am. J. Physiol.*, **93**, 683 (1930)
183. Ronzoni, E., *Proc. Soc. Exptl. Biol. Med.*, **28**, 712 (1931)
184. Rothschild, P., *Biochem. Z.*, **217**, 365 (1930)
185. Rowinsky, P., *Boll. soc. ital. biol. sper.*, **5**, 899 (1930)
186. Sahyun, M., *J. Biol. Chem.*, **93**, 227 (1931)
187. Sahyun, ·M., *J. Biol. Chem.*, **94**, 29 and 253 (1931)
188. Smith, E. C., *Proc. Roy. Soc. (London) B*, **105**, 579 (1930)
189. Smith, E. C., and Meren, T., *Proc. Roy. Soc. (London) B*, **106**, 122 (1930)
190. Smith, P. W., and Visscher, M. B., *Am. J. Physiol.*, **95**, 130 (1930)
191. Smith, P. W., *Proc. Soc. Exptl. Biol. Med.*, **28**, 415 (1931)
192. Smith, P. W., *Proc. Soc. Exptl. Biol. Med.*, **27**, 502 (1930)
193. Sym, E., *Biochem. Z.*, **233**, 251 (1931)
194. Schwartz, A., and Oschmann, A., *Compt. rend. soc. biol.*, **91**, 275 (1925); **92**, 169 (1925)
195. Stiven, D., *Biochem. J.*, **24**, 169, 172 (1930)
196. Thunberg, T., *Kungl. Fysiografiska Sällskapets Handlinger*, N.F., **42**, 10, 3 (1931)
197. Toenniessen, E., *Klin. Wochschr.*, **9**, 211 (1930)
198. Toenniessen, E., and Brinkmann, E., *Z. physiol. Chem.*, **187**, 137 (1930)
199. Trimble, H. C., and Carcy, B. W., *J. Biol. Chem.*, **90**, 655 (1930)
200. Utewski, A., *Biochem. Z.*, **228**, 135 (1930)
201. Visscher, M. B., and Mulder, A. J., *Am. J. Physiol.*, **94**, 630 (1930)
202. Visscher, M. B., and Smith, P. W., *Am. J. Physiol.*, **95**, 121 (1930)
203. Weber, H. H., *Ber. ges. Physiol. exptl. Pharmakol.*, **61**, 382 (1931)
204. Weber, H. H., *Biochem. Z.*, **217**, 430 (1930)
205. Wertheimer, E., *Arch. ges. Physiol.*, **221**, 429 (1930)
206. Wieland, H., and Lawson, A., *Ann.*, **485**, 193 (1931)
207. Wilhelmi, D., *Z. physiol. Chem.*, **203**, 34 (1931)
208. Witting, V., Markowitz, J., and Mann, F. C., *Am. J. Physiol.*, **94**, 35 (1930)
209. Wladimirow, G. E., *Biochem. Z.*, **222**, 135 (1930)
210. Wöhlisch, E., *Naturwissenschaften*, **18**, 931 (1930)
211. Wolff, W. A., and Wilson, D. W., *J. Biol. Chem.*, **92**, 60 (1931)
212. Zanghi, G., *Arch. fisiol.*, **28**, 372 (1930)

Department of Medical Chemistry
The University, Lwow, Poland
Piekarska, 52

LIVER AND BILE*

By Jesse L. Bollman and Frank C. Mann

*Division of Experimental Surgery and Pathology,
The Mayo Foundation*

In presenting this review of the work done in the last two years
with regard to the liver and the bile, we desire at the outset to clarify
what we have attempted to accomplish. We have repeatedly pointed
out that the functions of the liver are so numerous and hepatic
activity so varied that there are few physiologic processes which are
not in some manner affected physiologically by the presence of this
organ. Probably no better illustration of this statement can be found
than may be observed by a consideration of the subjects to be reviewed in this publication. It will be seen that more than half are
pertinent to hepatic activity. Therefore, it is obvious that there is
considerable overlapping of the material of other reviewers and ours.
In the selection of our material we have attempted to present only
those subjects which appeared to be specifically pertinent to the liver
and to leave for other reviewers those touching on hepatic activity
which appeared to us to be a more integral part of their subject. We
recognize that, by doing this, isolated articles may be omitted from
reviews altogether. This defect, if it exists, can be remedied in the
future.

We have tried to make a comprehensive yet readable review of
the subject. Many articles have not been included which are probably
equal in importance to some of those reviewed. This is mainly because even with the most careful search we have failed to find some
articles the titles of which did not permit proper indexing. We have
also omitted some work because we could not make it fit the general
treatment. However, we have included a list of many such articles
for reference.

Although no outstanding discovery has been made in regard to
the biochemical knowledge of the liver during the last two years,
many significant advances have been made and valuable data presented.

* Received February 19, 1932.

Rhythmic Activity in the Liver

One of the most interesting observations in regard to hepatic activity concerns a daily change of rhythm in the size and some of the important constituents of the liver.

Forsgren, in 1928, described cyclic activity in the livers of rabbits that concerned the functions of formation of glycogen and secretion of bile. By histochemical methods he learned that the secretion of bile alternated with the formation of glycogen, and that these two functions were independent of nutritional conditions to a great extent. Early in the day glycogen may disappear in spite of an ample supply of food, whereas at night there is an accumulation of glycogen even though food is withheld. Correspondingly, the secretion of bile maintains alternating periodicity in that a maximal amount is produced during the day when glycogen content is low and a minimal amount at night when the glycogen content is high. These two alternating functions have been well designated "assimilatory" and "secretory" phases.

The susceptibility of the animal organism to insulin is dependent on the state of metabolism in connection with the rhythmic activity of the liver (6). The liver displays a rhythmic activity which is independent of nutritional factors, and is correlated with its functions of assimilation and secretion. During assimilation the liver is a consumer of glucose in that glycogen is laid down; during the secretory phase it is a producer of glucose. The susceptibility to insulin is greatest if it is administered during the final phase of secretory activity when the glycogen has disappeared. The body is least susceptible to insulin if assimilated when the glycogen content is high.

The nonprotein nitrogen of the blood is periodic in its manifestation and may be correlated with the rhythmic functions of the liver (3). The twenty-four-hour periodicity of the nonprotein nitrogen of the blood bears no relation to the time of taking food. In the morning, after a night's fast, the nitrogen in the blood may or may not be at a peak for that twenty-four-hour period. It may even be at the lowest level for that given interval, and is thus wholly unrelated to diet. Accordingly, this nonprotein nitrogen of the blood may in some manner be associated with the known assimilatory and secretory rhythm in the liver.

The relation between sleep and hepatic function differs in men and rabbits (5). In both, however, there is a maximal amount of glycogen and minimal amount of bile at night, but rabbits are most active at night and least active at midday. Sleep may be governed by some substances produced within the liver, for drowsiness has been induced in lively animals by the subcutaneous injection of a watery extract of livers of rabbits killed at midday. Sleep in man, however, is psychic rather than bodily and may or may not be correlated with hepatic function.

The secretion of bile corresponds, in a measure, to the rhythmic activity of the liver (4). During its assimilatory phase the liver takes in glycogen and water, whereas during the secretory phase it is freed of them. The assimilatory phase is more marked at night; the secretory phase occurs during the day. The maximal amount of urine is secreted between 12:00 M. and 2:00 P.M. at the height of the hepatic secretory phase, whereas the minimal quantity is produced between 2:00 and 4:00 A.M. when the glycogen content is highest. These actual times, however, may vary with the activity of the individual.

Ågren, Wilander, and Jorpes (1) noted that cyclic changes also occur in the content of the liver and the muscles of rats and mice. These authors sustain Forsgren (3) in his contention that glycogen in the liver is independent of intake of food and that it accumulates at night and disappears in the day. These changes occur even if the subject is fasting. Similar periodic changes appear, although to a minor extent, in skeletal muscle. By using insulin, Ågren, Wilander, and Jorpes have shown that the resistance to the hormone coincided with the amount of glycogen in the liver. In the evening a smaller number of animals had convulsions, after insulin had been given, than at noon, whereas during the night the dose had to be doubled to secure the same effect. The output of nitrogen in the urine at night increased about 20 per cent over that in the day. This would indicate that an increased deamination of amino acids occurred at night, and that the formation of glycogen of the assimilatory phase takes place partly at the expense of the body proteins.

BILIRUBIN

Numerous reviews have been written concerning the site of formation of bilirubin. Ernst and Hallay (12), continuing their studies of perfused organs, found that the formation of bilirubin in the surviving spleen of the dog was not dependent on the number of erythrocytes in the splenic parenchyma, since alteration of the formation of bilirubin was not produced by increasing the arterial pressure and producing venous stasis of the organ. Cultures of embryonic splenic tissue of the chick and of the frog are able to produce bilirubin, which gives only the indirect diazo reaction when hemoglobin is added to such cultures, according to the observations of Sümegi and Csaba (30). Ascoli, Fioretti, and Malago (9) made simultaneous determinations of the content of bilirubin of arterial and venous blood of various organs of the dog, and concluded that the liver is the chief but not the only site of formation of bilirubin. The retention of bilirubin in the blood appears to depend on the condition of the liver. Mjassnikow and Ssamarin (26) found that the increased hemolysis following the injection of distilled water or laked blood into dogs did not give rise to an increased content of bilirubin in the blood. Following small doses of phosphorus, which were of themselves insufficient to cause jaundice, repetition of the administration of distilled water or hemoglobin caused considerable bilirubinemia. Anselmino and Hoffmann (7), however, attributed icterus neonatorum to excessive destruction of hemoglobin that occurred following the increased availability of oxygen after birth. Hinglais and Govaerts (18) found that the cholesterol content of the blood of infants at birth is low, and bears no relation to the bilirubin content of the blood as it decreases a few days after birth. Jordan and Greene (23) found that the degree of bilirubinemia of dogs with experimental obstructive jaundice depended on the amount of blood being regenerated rather than on the amount of hemoglobin in the circulation. Whipple and his associates (17, 29), in quantitative studies on dogs with biliary fistula, found that normal animals excreted 90 to 95 per cent of the amount of bilirubin calculated to be derived from hemoglobin following the intravenous injection of this substance. Anemic dogs, however, gave 100 per cent return of bile pigment from hemoglobin injected, and also formed 100 per cent of new hemoglobin. This appears to be definite proof that the nucleus of bilirubin as found in hemin is readily synthesized in the body to form new hemoglobin provided the globin and iron portions are available.

Verzár and his associates (9a) have continued their work showing that bilirubin acts as a regulator for formation of hemoglobin in the body. They state their belief that under normal conditions the amount of bilirubin liberated from the destruction of erythrocytes stimulates the hemopoietic system to a degree comparable to the amount of bilirubin liberated. They found that intravenous or oral administration of small amounts of bilirubin increases the number of erythrocytes in circulation. Popper (27), however, contended that the hemo-globin content of the blood but not the erythrocyte content is in-volved in this transient increase.

The nature of two types of diazo reactions of bilirubin continues to excite comment. Griffiths and Kaye (14) and M'Gowan (25) called attention to the effect of hydrogen-ion concentration on the van den Bergh reaction for bilirubin. They also contended that pure bilirubin in serum gives only the indirect diazo reaction, but that since bile contains a pigment (not bilirubin) which gives the direct reaction, serums giving a direct reaction contain this substance normally present in bile which is not bilirubin. Hunter (19, 20, 21) stated that the direct reaction is due to the presence of sodium acid bilirubinate, and that serums or exudates giving the indirect reaction contain free bilirubin in an unknown solvent which is probably a lipoid or sterol. This bilirubin is probably in combination with its solvent, so that it resists salt formation and oxidation and is not dializable or extractable with chloroform. Bollman and Mann (10a) found that the indirect reacting bilirubin of the serum of liverless dogs passed through the kidney of the dog, differing from that of man, to give the direct reac-tion in the urine, and that the liver was necessary for the conversion of the indirect reacting bilirubin to that giving the direct reaction in the serum. The differential solubilities of bilirubin in tissue were shown by Rosenthal (28) and by Gassmann (13), who found that with the exception of the liver and kidney more bile pigment was dissolved in those tissues containing most elastin, such as the lungs, arteries, and skin. De Castro (11) found considerably less bilirubin in the spinal fluid than in the blood. Billaudot and Matthieu (10) and Matthieu (24) found that injections of cholesterol greatly increased the amount of bile pigment found in the Kuppfer cells of the liver in jaundiced animals.

BILE ACIDS

Smith and Whipple (45) have continued their studies on the efficiency of various substances for the production of bile acids in the dog with a bile fistula. Dogs on the standard diet of salmon bread give a constant excretion of about 100 mg. of taurocholic acid for each kilogram of body weight every 24 hours. Liver, kidney, or beef muscle yield 200 to 300 mg. of taurocholic acid for each kilo-gram of body weight every 24 hours. Casein produces 125 to 190 mg. of taurocholic acid, ovalbumin 50 mg., and the endogenous output of 30 to 40 mg. is unaltered by the feeding of sugar. The feeding of whole beef blood increases the formation of taurocholic acid, whereas beef erythrocytes alone cause a slight decrease. Sweetbreads give about the same effect as the standard diet. Tryptic digestion of beef muscle reduces its potency in the formation of bile acids, probably because of the loss of some important amino acids during digestion. The addition of proline to the standard diet increases the excretion of taurocholic acid 50 per cent but increases the efficiency of ovalbumin 100 per cent. Tryptophane is without effect except when added to gelatine diet, when an increase of 150 per cent is obtained. Additions of glycine increased the low output that followed the feeding of ovalbumin. Proline and tryptophane were found to have cholagoic effects but glycine had not. Indine and isatin contain the indine ring of the cholic-acid formula, and both compounds are powerful cholagogues. Isatin gave a slight increase in the excretion of bile salt, but indine and hyrindenedicarboxylic acid were without effect. Mild injury of the liver by chloroform immediately reduces the output of taurocholic acid, which returns to normal in a few days as the liver recovers from the degeneration produced by the chloroform. Substances that stimulate the formation of hemoglobin, such as the hepatic fractions active in pernicious anemia and secondary anemia, ferric citrate, and apricots, are all inactive in increasing the output of bile salt of animals on the standard diet of salmon bread. Daily refeeding of all bile secreted increased the output of the bile salt to a high level. The surplus bile salts gradually disappear, but they are not found in the urine. The output of bile salt of dogs with both the Eck fistula and a bilary fistula is reduced lower than in a normal dog on the standard diet of salmon bread. Refeeding of bile does not increase the output to such a high level as in the normal dog, and considerably reduces the sensitivity to the action of cholagogues. The output of bile salt is unaffected by feeding liver, iron salts, or ovalbumin with or without glycine, and is reduced by the feeding of a tryptic digest of meat. Marked reduction follows the inhalation of chloroform in these animals. Jenke's (36) observations of dogs with bile fistulas were similar to those of Whipple in that he found the output of bile salt was greatest when the animals were fed meat, less when the food was mixed, and least when carbohydrates were fed. From these studies it would appear that the liver is the site of formation of the bile acids. Thannhauser and Fromm (47) found that the unsaponifiable fraction of liver after the removal of cholesterol contains some highly unsaturated hydrocarbons which are not present in bile and which appear to be precursors of cholesterol and bile acids.

Ries and Still (40) investigated the toxicity of bile salts and found that they were only slightly toxic for muscle and did not materially affect conduction through the nerve fibres. The neuromuscular juncture and the reflex centers of the cord were the structures they found to be the most susceptible to the toxic effects of bile salts. Rewbridge (39) found that fat necrosis of the pancreas was caused by the local action of bile salts. Thomas (48) found that neither glycocholates nor taurocholates affected cardiac rhythm, and could not be responsible for the development of icteric bradycardia. Walker (50) denied the presence of bile salts in normal blood, although Jenke and Steinberg (37) found 0.025 mg. for each 100 cc. in normal blood and 2 to 8 mg. in the presence of jaundice. Fuentes, Apolo, and Esculies (32) found values to 20 mg. for each 100 cc. in the first few days of obstructive jaundice in the dog, with a subsequent decline to about 6 mg. Sekitoo (43, 44) claimed that there was a decrease in serum calcium of rabbits with bile fistulas which could be remedied by the administration of bile salts. Sanford, Crane, and Leslie (41) found that the erythrocytes of children were more resistant to hemolysis by bile salt, and that there was no difference in this effect in the presence of idiopathic icterus, congenital syphilis, or hemorrhagic disease. Eufinger, Wiesbaden, and Focsaneau (31) found the erythrocytes more resistant during pregnancy, and that the serum of eclampsia showed increased power in protecting erythrocytes from hemolysis by bile salts.

Henriques (35) found that the dissociation constants of the various bile acids gave pH values ranging between 2.46 and 3.23, which groups them among the strongest organic acids. Langecker (38) found that bile salts inhibited the precipitation of proteins by alkaloids and that they inhibited the absorption of dyes, epinephrine, and so forth, by charcoal. The effect of bile salts on absorption from the intestine may be due to their power to increase solubility and decrease adsorption as well as to increase the permeability of the intestine. Verzár and Kúthy (49) found that bile salts played a large part in the solution of substances insoluble in water due to their hydrotropic effect. They also found that bile acids become absorbed on the intestinal epithelium in much greater concentration than in the lumen of the intestine. The fatty acids are thus passed through the mucosa. Fürth and Scholl (34) found that both saponified and unsaponified fats require bile for their absorption from the intestine, probably because of the increased solubility of fatty acids and fat in the presence of bile acids. Lipoid-soluble substances diffuse into gelatin, agar, filter paper, or clay much more quickly if bile salts are present because of this increased solubility in water. Lecithin is soluble in bile salts and greatly enhances (10 to 15 times) the solubility of olive oil in bile salts. Fürth and Minibeck (33) found that the increased solubility of fat in bile as compared to pure bile salts is probably due to the lecithin content of the bile and not to its mucin content. The increased resorption under the influence of bile salts was demonstrated by the adsorption of iodolecithin from the subcutaneous tissue of rabbits, and also on the increased toxicity of injections of camphor with bile salts in mice. Sperry (46) found increased excretion of lipid in the feces of dogs with bile fistulas, which was two or three times as great as that of normal dogs on diets free from lipid. Schmidt and Schmidt (42) found vitamine A to be well absorbed from the intestine of the rat in the presence of obstructive jaundice.

CHOLESTEROL

Pfeiffer (58) found that young beef liver has a high content of oxycholesterol and cholesterol ester. This appeared to be due to the action of the esterifying enzymes of the liver and to its excretory function. There appears to be little evidence of true endogenous formation of cholesterol by the liver, although it is probably able to extract cholesterol from destroyed erythrocytes and also from the cholesterol compounds absorbed from food of plant origin. Schönheimer and Hummel (59, 60) found that feeding mice for fourteen days with cholesterol oxalate gave a 5 per cent increase in the cholesterol in the liver. Oxalate was not found in the liver, but oxalates were excreted in the urine. Hydrolysis of the ester occurred in the intestine and both the cholesterol and the oxalate were absorbed. Cantoni (51) found that the surviving hepatopancreatic preparation removed cholesterol from the blood independent of its fat content. Merkulow (56) examined histologic sections of liver following the injection of cholesterol esters into the portal vein, and found that they disappeared and that there was an increase in the glycogen content of the liver.

Gardner and Gainsborough (53) found two types of change of cholesterol content of the plasma in biliary and hepatic disease. When bile was absent from the intestine there was a sudden fall in the cholesterol esters of the blood with no change in the free cholesterol content. In obstructive jaundice of long duration there is a gradual rise in the free cholesterol content of the blood, but the content of cholesterol esters remains low. Hypercholesterolemia does not occur in cases of uncomplicated cholelithiasis, and there is no evidence that the cholesterol of the diet influences cholesterol in the blood or the formation of gallstones, which is corroborated by Pecco (57). Epstein (52) found a reduction of the cholesterol esters in the blood during acute parenchymatous hepatic injury and normal cholesterol partitions in the presence of hepatic cirrhosis. Mancke (55) reported similar observations. Leites and Golbitz-Katschan (54) believed that patients with hepatic disease did not show the hypercholesterolemia found in normal subjects following test meals of 50 gm. of olive oil with or without the addition of 2 or 3 gm. of cholesterol.

Excretion in the Bile

It is becoming recognized that many substances besides the usual biliary constituents, heavy metals, and certain dyes may be excreted in the bile. Hermann, Caujolle, and Jourdan (64) found that quinine, nicotine, strychnine, genestrychnine, atropine, and genatropine could be found in the bile after their intravenous injection. Caujolle (61, 62) reiterated these observations as regards quinine, strychnine, atropine, and nicotine, although he found that more quinine was eliminated in the urine than in the bile. Halpert, Hanke, and Curtis (63) did not find sodium salicylate in the bile of patients with biliary disease after oral administration. Ivanov (65) found that epinephrine increased the excretion of sucrose in the bile during its continued ingestion, whereas insulin decreased its elimination.

Cholagogues

The search for an effective agent to stimulate the liver to secrete bile still goes on. The salicylates, benzoates, and bile salts remain the substances of choice. Surmont and Dumont (73a) considered that salicylate of magnesia produces an increase in discharge of bile by acting on the bile ducts and gallbladder. Maximin and Bocquentin (72) found that sodium benzoate and para-oxybenzoate did not cause an increase in the flow of bile in the dog. They found experimentally that sodium salicylate had a variable effect on the secretion of bile, whereas meta-oxybenzoate had a strong cholagogic action. The diphenol acids, catechuic and caffeic, were also excellent cholagogues.

Vanillic acid produced increased secretion of bile. Maximin and Bocquentin stated their belief that the metahydroxyl group favors the development of cholagogic properties and that the phenol group, although of value, was not essential. Chabrol (66–70) noted that the administration of phenol doubled the secretion of bile. Diphenol, pyrocatechin, resorcin, and hydroquinone had a marked cholagogic action. Pyrogallol and phloroglucin as well as alpha and beta naphthol also increased the secretion of bile. Gantt (71) observed that magnesium sulphate increased flow of bile when given by stomach tube but not when it was passed directly into the duodenum. Pera (73) investigated the effect of certain carbohydrates, fats, and protein on the secretion of bile in the dog. He found that the subcutaneous injection of lactose and raffinose in small amounts was followed by an increased flow of bile, whereas if large amounts were injected a decrease occurred. Peptone produced its usual decrease in flow of bile, whereas a slight increase occurred after olive oil.

GLYCOGEN

The storage of glycogen in the liver continues to attract considerable attention. Since variations of this glycogen are directly or indirectly involved in the metabolism of carbohydrate, protein, and fat, complete knowledge of the formation and variations of hepatic glycogen is essential to our understanding of these processes. Greisheimer and Johnson (78–80) determined the glycogen content of livers of rats maintained on diets which varied in the percentage composition of fat, carbohydrate, and protein. From their results it could be concluded that carbohydrate in the diet formed glycogen, and that the more readily assimilable sugars were the more efficient. Protein formed glycogen under conditions of extremely low intake of carbohydrate, and appeared to diminish the formation of glycogen from larger amounts of carbohydrate. Fat in the diet gave opposite results from protein; that is, addition of fat decreased formation of glycogen from diets extremely low in carbohydrate and protein, but allowed somewhat greater formation of glycogen from diets rich in carbohydrate. The results of Hynd and Rotter (81), and Krantz and Corr (82) are in agreement with these observations. Eckstein (76) obtained formation of glycogen from propionic acid but not from oral administration of the sodium salts of butyric, valeric, or caproic acids. Bridge and Bridges (75) found no relation between the glycogen content of the liver and the storage of water in that organ.

Popper and Wozasek (84) found considerably larger amounts of glycogen in the liver of human beings after sudden death than after death from wasting diseases, such as diphtheria (89) and yellow fever (92). Wakeman and Morrell (92) showed that in yellow fever produced experimentally in monkeys, absorption of dextrose was poor, that dextrose injected intravenously disappeared more slowly than normally, and that hypoglycemia developed about twenty-four hours before death, when the glycogen content of the liver was low, that epinephrine was ineffective in raising the level of the sugar in the blood at this time. Wachsmuth (90, 91) found that hepatic injury in dogs with Eck fistula delayed the sugar-tolerance curve, but that the administration of sodium bicarbonate improved this condition. Rewbridge and Andrews (87) found that injections of calcium chloride increased the content of sugar in the blood of both jaundiced and normal dogs, and concluded that there was a reciprocal relation between the calcium and glucose content of the blood. Roncato (87a) found that curare increased the threshold of formation of glycogen in the liver. Abelin and Spichtin (74) found that feeding thyroid extract diminished the creatinine as well as the glycogen content of the liver of rats. Fuss (77), and also Mekie (83), found that ether liberates glycogen from the liver, probably by its direct action on the hepatic cell. Rathery, Kourilsky, and Laurent (85, 86) determined the glucose content of the liver of dogs. In twenty-five of twenty-eight dogs sugar was being added to the blood by the liver. The addition of sugar under these circumstances appeared to be independent of the glycogen content of the liver, since it also occurred in fasting dogs with varying amounts of glycogen in the liver, and also in depancreatized and in phlorhizinized dogs with extremely low glycogen content. Rosenfeld (88) found that the administration of phosphorus to dogs did not prevent fatty liver following the administration of phosphorus as it did after phlorhizin.

LACTIC ACID

The relation of the liver to the metabolism of lactic acid has assumed particular significance according to the magnitude of publications dealing with this subject. Khouvine, Aubel, and Chevillard (100) found that isolated liver converted pyruvic acid to lactic acid under aërobic or anaërobic conditions. Rosenthal (104) studied the lactic-acid fermentation of a variety of sugars by livers of rats, finding that methylglyoxal formed lactic acid about four times faster than did glucose, fructose, hexose diphosphate, hexosemonophosphate, glycericaldehyde, or dihydroxyacetone. Glycogen, sucrose, maltose, lactose, galactose, and mannose caused practically no formation of lactic acid. Bornstein and Mayer (95) found the production of acetaldehyde from liver and glycogen, levulose, alanine, and dihydroxyacetone. Ethyl alcohol and pyruvic acid were the most efficient in forming acetaldehyde, whereas glycine, glucose, and methyl alcohol produced none. Loeper, Degos, and Tonnet (101) found oxalic acid increased by incubation of liver with glycogen.

Carruthers (96) did not obtain carbohydrate synthesis from perfusion of isolated liver with lactic acid in oxygenated buffered Ringer's solution. Schneider and Widmann (105) found that the liver of dogs retained 150 cc. of 0.1 per cent optically inactive lactic acid injected into the portal vein. The lactic acid content of the hepatic veins was unaltered and showed no change in its optical activity. Anderson, Cleghorn, Macleod, and Peterson (93) found that lactic acid accumulated in the blood and tissues after the removal of the abdominal viscera. Eggleton and Evans (98) studied the lactic acid of the blood under experimental conditions and concluded that the liver removed lactic acid from the blood, but was not the only organ involved in its removal. Himwich, Chambers, Koskoff, and Nahum (99) found that the liver removed lactic acid from the blood and added glucose in depancreatized animals as well as in the normal animal. Long and Grant (102), however, found that exercise in the rat did not greatly alter the glycogen content of the liver, so that if glycogen was formed from the lactic acid of exercise it was liberated with about equal rapidity. Anselmino and Hoffmann (94) found that the liver is able to remove injected lactic acid from pregnant as well as it does from normal women, so that the increased values for lactic acid in the blood during pregnancy are probably due to the muscles and to the activity of the thyroid gland. Mossobrio and Michailoff (103) found that parenchymatous injury to the liver increased the lactic-acid content of the blood, and that the liver did not remove injected lactic acid as well under these conditions. Diaz and Cuenca (97) reported similar observations.

EPINEPHRINE

The action of epinephrine on carbohydrate metabolism plays an important part in the formation of hepatic glycogen and in the utilization of lactic acid. Complete understanding of this process is essential, since many of the experimental results of studies of lactic acid and glycogen metabolism are probably colored by variations in secretion of epinephrine due to experimental or physiologic conditions. Cori, Cori, and Buchwald (107) found that fifteen minutes after injections of epinephrine in rats the liver glycogen was lower, after one hour it was higher, and after three hours the same as in control animals. Lactic acid in the blood was increased in fifteen minutes and was normal in one hour, whereas the sugar in the blood was still elevated at three hours. Since the sugar set free by the liver is only a fourth of the amount utilized by the rat in one hour, Cori concluded that decreased utilization of glucose plays an important part in the hyperglycemia of epinephrine. Insulin prevented the loss of glycogen from the liver after epinephrine had been administered, but did not influence the increase in lactic acid of .the blood. Eadie (109) found that small doses of epinephrine increased glycogen in the liver and decreased it in muscle, although larger doses caused a fall in both. In the cat both large and small doses of epinephrine caused a decrease of glycogen in the liver with no change in the content of the muscles. Sacks (114) reported similar observations in the cat, except that with large doses of epinephrine he obtained slightly decreased glycogen content of the muscles. Geiger (111) found that epinephrine liberated lactic acid from the glycogen of the muscles of frogs in normal and in liverless animals. Extirpation of the liver did not alter the glycogen content of the muscles of frogs three or four days after operations. In perfused isolated muscle from the frog or dog, epinephrine increased the output of lactic acid but did not alter the output of glucose, and a further rise in lactic acid was not obtained after exhaustion of the glycogen content of the muscles. Epinephrine did not cause glycosuria in dehepatized frogs but did increase the excretion of lactic acid. Similar results were obtained in normal hibernating frogs, which appear to be unable to resynthesize lactic acid to hepatic glycogen because of the depleted state of the glycogen content of the liver. Cori and Buchwald (106) obtained similar results with dehepatized frogs, but found that the calorigenic action of epinephrine was present in these animals. Corkhill and Marks (108) found that epinephrine lowered glycogen in the muscle in decapitated eviscerated cats and liberated lactic acid. Firor and Eadie (110) found epinephrine to be ineffective in liberating glycogen from the muscles of dehepatized cats. Loeb, Reeves, and Glasier (112) found that the response to epinephrine was altered in hepatic disease. They obtained a less marked rise in the content of sugar in the blood, but this was found not to be indicative of the extent of the hepatic lesion. The original content of lactic acid in the blood was frequently higher in hepatic disease, and fewer alterations were produced by injections of epinephrine. Nannini (113) and also Sucksdorff (115) reported low responses of glucose values in the blood after epinephrine was administered to patients with hepatic disease.

INSULIN

Corkhill (120) calls attention to the influence of epinephrine secreted after the injection of insulin. He found that insulin increased the glycogen content of the liver and decreased the glycogen of the muscles. Rathery, Kourilsky, and Gibert (122) made similar observations on the dog, but found that early after the administration of insulin the glycogen content of the liver decreased. Rathery and Kourilsky (121) were inclined to minimize the significance of glycogen in the liver in the regulation of the sugar of the blood, since they found sugar being added to the blood passing through the liver under varying circumstances. Root, Hall, and Gray (123, 124) found insulin to decrease the glycogen in the liver and to increase the glycogen in the muscle of fish. Althausen and his associates (116, 117, 118) proposed administration of insulin, dextrose, and water as a functional test in hepatic disease. Collazo and Rubino (119) found 100 per cent increase in the glycogen in the liver of rabbits three hours after the administration of glucose and insulin. Schmidt and Saatchian (125) found that liver inactivated insulin more than did any other tissues when incubated with insulin.

FRUCTOSE

Bollman and Mann (126) found that fructose was rapidly converted to glucose in the dehepatized dog, and that the disappearance of injected fructose was not greatly dissimilar from that in the normal animal. If the intestines and liver were removed from dogs, conversion of fructose to glucose was not observed. Removal of the intestines alone permitted the conversion of fructose to glucose as in the normal animal. From these experiments it appeared that the liver and the intestines were able to convert fructose to glucose but that the other tissues of the body were unable to do so. Heinicke and

Peters (127), and Peters, Heinicke, and Del'Espine (128) advocated oral administration of fructose as a test for hepatic function.

GALACTOSE

Petow, Kosterlitz, and Naumann (135), Elmer and Scheps (133), Bode (131), Fiessinger and Dieryck (134), Shay, Schloss, and Bell (137), and Rowe and McManus (136) found that tolerance tests with galactose afforded clinical information as to the functional capacity of the liver. Blöch (130) found that glycine, alanine, or aspartic acid when added to galactose improved the tolerance test in hepatic disease. Bauer and Wozasek (129) found that administration of ergotamine of a diet of liver altered the response to administration of galactose, but that it was utilized less in hepatic disorders. Bollman, Power, and Mann (132) found no evidence of utilization of galactose by liverless dogs. After the intravenous administration of galactose, about 80 per cent of it was recovered in the urine unchanged, whereas normal animals excreted only 25 per cent. Following the oral administration of galactose larger amounts of galactose disappeared, but evidence of the conversion of galactose to glucose could not be obtained.

PROTEIN

Gautier (144, 145) was unable to increase the percentage of protein in the liver of hibernating frogs, although the total protein and the total weight of the liver could be increased by administration of various foodstuffs. He contended that the reserve of protein in the liver is exceedingly slight as compared to its content of fat and glycogen. Martens (146), in presenting evidence of the formation of the polypeptide nitrogen of the blood, believed that synthesis of protein is a function of the liver. Fractionation of the nonprotein nitrogen of the blood under pathologic conditions demonstrated to Christomanos (141) that the amino-acid nitrogen, ammonia nitrogen, and undetermined nitrogen of the blood were increased in severe hepatic disease. Paschkis (148) found an abnormal increase in the amino acids of the blood following peroral administration of amino acids in severe toxic jaundice. Alzona (138) used this method to study the degree of hepatic injury in cardiac disease. Wakeman and Morrell (152) found impairment of this function in experimental yellow fever in monkeys only in the last few hours of life.

Salaskin and his associates (149–151) have a new series of studies on the formation of urea in the body. They found, as did Clementi (142), that almost all of the formation of urea in surviving liver and in juice pressed from the liver was the result of arginine-arginase reaction. Liver perfused with physiologic solutions yields little urea from added ammonium carbonate. The addition of serum to the perfusing fluid somewhat increases the formation of urea, and great increases are obtained when defibrinated blood, erythrocytes, or oxyhemoglobin are added. It would appear that the transformation of ammonium carbonate to urea by the liver is dependent on the presence of oxygen. Cantoni (140) observed considerable formation of urea in the surviving hepatopancreatic preparation. Nothhaas and Never (147) added glycocol to the blood perfusing the liver and observed an increase in the oxygen consumption which was not found when muscle was perfused. Dock (143) also found that most of the extra heat of specific dynamic action of protein was liberated in the liver when he studied the microrespiration of the isolated tissues of the rat.

Bollman and Mann (139) found that complete removal of the liver of dogs did not directly affect the formation of ammonia, and definite alterations of the ammonia of the urine followed alterations in the acid-base equilibrium of the liverless animal. Urea was not formed from administrations of ammonium compounds and almost quantitative recovery of the ammonia administered was found in the blood, tissues, and urine of the animal many hours after removal of the liver. Because of the absence of urea, the urea content of the blood and tissues decreases from the excretion of urea in the urine until the urea of the blood reaches an extremely low level. At this point the urea content of the urine becomes greatly reduced or may be entirely absent, and only traces of ammonia are found in the urine. Administration of urea restores the content of ammonia of the urine as long as urea is available.

FAT

Bloor and Snider (155) found that the neutral fat of beef liver is more unsaturated than that of the other organs and depots. Müller (164), reporting similar observations on human beings, added that the arachidonic acid content of the liver was independent of the total fat and total iodine number of the liver. He considered that the total fat content of the liver affords little information concerning the activity of fat metabolism, but believes that the level of arachidonic acid is an index of the fat-splitting activity of the organ. Orestano

(165) found the total fat of the liver to be little varied by the action of drugs which allowed considerable variation in the fat of the blood. Page and Pasternak (166) found the total fat of the liver of rabbits to be increased by repeated injections of epinephrine. Monasterio (163) produced fatty degeneration of the liver with an increase of its neutral fat content by subjecting animals to reduced atmospheric pressure; Berg and Zucker (153), by deprivation of the external pancreatic secretion, and Blatherwick and his co-workers (154), by feeding rats food containing dried whole liver, produced similar results. Cantoni (158, 159) found that circulating fats in the surviving hepatopancreatic preparation were decreased but that the liver desaturated a considerable portion of the fat, since the iodine number of the circulating fat increased. Dulière and Raper (160) found that the perfused liver converted ketohexoic acid to acetone bodies as further evidence of beta oxidation of fatty acids.

Cannavò (156, 157) found the formation of ketone bodies from several fatty acids of the aliphatic series both in diabetic patients and in patients suffering with hepatic disease. Steppun and his associates (167) state their belief that the depletion of glycogen in the liver allows fat to come to the liver with subsequent formation of ketone bodies. Hirsch (161), in observing the absence of alimentary lipemia in patients with cirrhosis of the liver, attributed the absence to failure of fat absorption since it is also absent in many other kinds of disturbances of fat absorption. Jost (162) perfused the livers of dogs with lecithin or keratin, and in livers rich in glycogen obtained diacetic acid and an increase in the oxygen consumption with a decreased respiratory quotient. In fatty livers taken from dogs after phlorhizination, for four days, formation of acetone bodies was already at its maximal, but on perfusion with phosphatides an increased consumption of oxygen and a decreased respiratory quotient were observed. The sugar content of the circulating fluid showed an increase over that of similar control experiments without phosphated perfusion. These experiments would be of much greater significance if the total carbohydrate content of the livers used had been determined on specimens of the organ before and after the increased formation of sugar was observed.

Coagulation of Fibrinogen of the Blood

Considerable evidence has accumulated indicating that the process of coagulation of the blood is dependent in some manner on hepatic activity. Most of the facts observed in this regard can be explained on the basis that the fibrinogen originates in the liver. The results of the experiments of Jones and Smith (173) can be interpreted as substantiating this point of view. They removed the liver from dogs, employing the modified technic of Mann, and noted that there was a gradual decrease in the fibrinogen content of the blood (from 20 to 50 per cent in twelve to twenty hours). Jones and Smith also considered that the utilization of fibrinogen was variable. In their method of estimating fibrinogen they added pure cephalin to promote complete clotting of the blood. Canto (168) also studied the proteins in the plasms after hepatectomy. He concluded that the liver plays an important part in the regulation of the proteins of the blood. There was diminution in the fibrinogen content of the blood after removal of the liver, and the process of coagulation of the blood was slowed. The proportion of globulin was increased, and the albumin-globulin ratio was diminished. He estimated that the total protein of the blood decreased 28 per cent.

The manner in which peptone makes the blood incoagulable has been in dispute. De Nicola (170) found that 0.05 gm. peptone for each kilogram of body weight made the blood incoagulable in normal dogs, but that 0.3 gm. for each kilogram did not make the blood of liverless dogs incoagulable. Falkenhausen (171, 172) obtained only a fleeting increase in antiprothrombin in dehepatized geese after the injection of peptone. Cranston and Caillet (169) noted a delay and reduction of the anticoagulant action of peptone during the mechanical constriction of the hepatic veins.

The Detoxicating Function of the Liver

Priestley, Markowitz, and Mann (193) found that liverless dogs and frogs were more susceptible to strychnine poisoning than were the normal animals. The liver is able to remove strychnine from the blood, thereby reducing the amount remaining which produces symptoms by its effect on nerve tissue. Numerous clinical tests of hepatic function have been based on the detoxicating function of the liver. Voit and Wendt (200) found an increase in the carbon compounds of the urine following administration of menthol in hepatic disease. Marsh (189) recommended administration of 40 mg. sodium salicylate, none of which appears in the urine of normal individuals, but positive tests with ferric chloride are obtained from patients with impaired hepatic function. Schour and Rosengarten (198) noted an increase in indoles and urosein and decreased indicanuria in hepatic disease accompanied by intestinal putrefaction. Kauffmann and Engle (186) noted an increase in the derivatives of imidazole in the urine in hepatic diseases. Bechner (176) noted an increase in the phenols of the blood and the appearance of free phenols in the blood in cirrhosis of the liver. Sauer (197) found increased excretion of glucuronic acid. Lichtman (188) found that patients with hepatic diseases excreted more than 7 to 21 per cent (normal) of 0.45 gm. cinchophen as hydroxycinchophen in the urine following its administration orally.

Bischoff and Long (177, 178) found that it was possible to deplete the glycogen reserves of the liver and destroy the power of the organ to store glycogen by administration of compounds of guanidine. This could be accomplished without destroying the power of the muscles to utilize glucose or store glycogen. Insulin increased and epinephrine decreased the utilization of glucose under these circumstances. Ellsworth (183) found slight increases in the guanidine content of the blood in cirrhosis and splenic anemia, and marked increases in the toxic jaundice of arsphenamine. Patients with diffuse hepatic injury showed increases in the concentration of guanidine in the blood which were not present in normal subjects following oral administration of 200 mg. methylguanidine sulphate. Cutler (182) reported increased guanidine content of the blood following experimental acute hepatic injury by carbontetrachloride, chloroform, arsenic, or phosphorus. Findlay and Hindle (184) found increased substances resembling guanidine in the blood in yellow fever produced experimentally. The guanidine content of the blood could be reduced by administration of calcium lactate, but this procedure had no effect on the fatal outcome of the disease. Hepler and Simonds (185) produced hepatic injury and death from hepatic necrosis by mechanical obstruction of the hepatic veins without altering the guanidine content of the blood.

Marshall, Aydelotte, and Barbour (190), continuing their studies on heat regulation and water exchange, found that the liver retains water at the onset of experimentally produced fevers and is responsible at least for a large part of the dehydration that occurs with fever. Abe (174) found that the urinary excretion of water after oral administration was delayed in both patients and dogs with injured livers.

Numerous studies have been made on the action of toxic substances on the liver. Rosenthal (194) found that administration of alcohol by stomach tube did not injure the liver of normal dogs or of dogs with previously injured livers. Dogs receiving alcohol were made more susceptible to chloroform poisoning. Yokota (201) found that the livers of pregnant rabbits were more susceptible to the toxic action of chloroform, carbontetrachloride, or phosphorus. M'Gowan (191) believed that in chloroform poisoning the cell lipoid is converted to fat which is rapidly removed in the form of sodium salts, and that the more insoluble calcium salts remain in the liver cells. Kaczander (187) found avertin to be without toxic effect on the liver, but Bourne and Raginsky (179) found toxic injury to livers previously impaired by the administration of chloroform. Rosenthal and Lillie (195) found slight impairment of hepatic function following the excessive ingestion of fat. Callaway (180) produced focal necrosis in the liver by acute passive congestion. Polson (192) experimentally produced necrosis of the liver and cirrhosis by intraperitoneal injections of shale oil in rats and rabbits. Sherwood and Sherwood (199), Ross (196), and Beaver and Robertson (175) reported acute toxic hepatitis and cirrhosis following the administration of atophan. Churchill and Van Wagoner (181) produced similar changes in dogs.

ENZYMES

Many important observations have been added concerning the activity of various enzymes found in the liver. Since most of this work is more specifically concerned with the nature of enzymes and enzyme action, we are including it here only by reference.

THE ADMINISTRATION OF LIVER FOR PERNICIOUS ANEMIA

This very important phase of the chemistry of the liver has progressed and received ample verification. Since most of the work on this subject is included in the many excellent reviews, the reader is referred to the appended references.

CHEMICAL COMPOSITION OF THE LIVER

Owing to the interest in the relation of copper to the development and treatment of anemia, and owing to the relation of copper to the development of hemochromatosis and cirrhosis, this element has been extensively studied. Morrison and Nash (280) found about six times the amount of copper in the livers of infants than in those of adults. Andrianoff and Ansbacher (273) report similar observations, and

Loeschke (278) found that the copper content of embryonic livers of chicks was twelve to twenty times greater than that of the remaining portions of the egg. Mallory and Parker (279), Santesson (281), and Hall and MacKay (275) found that the feeding of copper produced necrosis of hepatic cells with subsequent formation of hemochromatosis and cirrhosis in rabbits. Schönheimer and Herkel (282), Herkel (277), Haurowitz (276), and Funk and St. Clair (274) found increased amounts of copper in the liver in cirrhosis and hemochromatosis.

COMMENT

The studies on the liver and bile during 1930 and 1931 have afforded us a wealth of material. Because of the magnitude of the work that has been recorded in the literature we have refrained from adding comments which would involve reference to the accomplishments of other years. Instead of criticism, we have attempted, by arrangement and correlation of the material, to create a readable continuity. We regret the omission of many articles, and feel particularly unfortunate in being unable to incorporate any of the interesting and important details of these studies.

The concept of rhythmic activity of the liver, more or less independent of the nutritional state, has added many new problems to the already complicated field of physiology and chemistry of the liver. In most of the previous studies in this field the nutritive state of the liver has been carefully considered, particularly in regard to the changes in glycogen, fat, and protein content under the different conditions. Unfortunately, many studies, involving the chemical composition of the liver, regarding compounds and functions which are not so well understood, have not been sufficiently correlated with its nutritional state. Since the liver has been found to vary in activity, size, and composition, it is not unlikely that divergent results might be obtained by similar experiments and analyses performed at different stages in the hepatic cycle. This does not mean that studies made without reference to the hepatic cycle should be considered invalidated, since most changes that have been accepted as being of significance have been well beyond the range of changes produced by cyclic periodicity of the liver. Future advances in chemical and physiologic technic may be anticipated which will be exact enough to allow us to investigate and understand the constantly varying chemistry and physiology of the liver.

LITERATURE CITED

RHYTHMIC ACTIVITY IN THE LIVER

1. ÅGREN, G., WILANDER, O., AND JORPES, E., *Biochem. J.*, **25**, 777 (1931)
3. FORSGREN, E., *Acta med. Scand.*, **73**, 213 (1930)
4. FORSGREN, E., *Skand. Arch. Physiol.*, **59**, 217 (1930)
5. FORSGREN, E., *Skand. Arch. Physiol.*, **60**, 299 (1930)
6. FORSGREN, E., HOLMGREN, H., WILANDER, O., AND AGREN, G., *Acta med. Scand.*, **73**, 60 (1930)

BILIRUBIN

7. ANSELMINO, K. J., AND HOFFMANN, F., *Klin. Wochschr.*, **10**, 97 (1931)
8. ANSELMINO, K. J., AND HOFFMANN, F., *Arch. Gynäkol.*, **143**, 477, 500 (1931)
9. ASCOLI, M., FIORETTI, A., AND MALAGO, G. B., *Bull. Atti. Accad. med. Roma*, **54**, 6 (1930)
9a. BENCSIK, F. GÁSPAR, VERZÁR, F., AND ZIH, A., *Biochem. Z.*, **225**, 278 (1930)
10. BILLAUDOT, M., AND MATTHIEU, J., *Compt. rend. soc. biol.*, **103**, 878 (1930)
10a. BOLLMAN, J. L., AND MANN, F. C., *Arch. Surg.*, **24**, 675 (1932)
11. CASTRO, U. DE, *Deut. Arch. klin. Med.*, **170**, 176 (1931)
12. ERNST, Z., AND HALLAY, E., *Biochem. Z.*, **228**, 354 (1930)
13. GASSMANN, F. K., *Z. klin. Med.*, **114**, 476 (1930)
14. GRIFFITHS, W. J., AND KAYE, G., *Brit. J. Exptl. Path.*, **11**, 441 (1930)
15. GRIFFITHS, W. J., AND KAYE, G., *Biochem. J.*, **24**, 1400 (1930)
16. HARROP, G. A., AND BARRON, E. S. G., *J. Clin. Investigation*, **9**, 577 (1931)
17. HAWKINS, W. B., SRIBHISHAJ, K., ROBSCHEIT-ROBBINS, F. S., AND WHIPPLE, G. H., *Am. J. Physiol.*, **96**, 463 (1931)
18. HINGLAIS, H., AND GOVAERTS, J., *Gynéc. obstét.*, **22**, 137 (1930); *J. Am. Med. Assoc.*, **95**, 1870 (1930)
19. HUNTER, G., *Brit. J. Exptl. Path.*, **11**, 415 (1930)
20. HUNTER, G., *Brit. J. Exptl. Path.*, **11**, 407 (1930)
21. HUNTER, G., *Can. Med. Assoc. J.*, **23**, 823 (1930)
22. ITCH, T., *Beitr. path. Anat.*, **86**, 488 (1931)
23. JORDAN, F. M., AND GREENE, C. H., *Am. J. Physiol.*, **91**, 409 (1930)
24. MATTHIEU, J., *Compt. rend. soc. biol.*, **105**, 180 (1930)
25. M'GOWAN, J. P., *Edinburgh Med. J.*, **37**, 28 (1930)
26. MJASSNIKOW, A. L., AND SSAMARIN, G. A., *Z. ges. exptl. Med.*, **71**, 40 (1930)
27. POPPER, L., *Klin. Wochschr.*, **9**, 1770 (1930)
28. ROSENTHAL, F., *Klin. Wochschr.*, **9**, 1909 (1930)
29. SRIBHISHAJ, K., HAWKINS, W. B., AND WHIPPLE, G. H., *Am. J. Physiol.*, **96**, 449 (1931)
30. SÜMEGI, I., AND CSABA, M., *Magyar Orvosi Arch.*, **31**, 473 (1930)

BILE ACIDS

31. EUFINGER, H., WIESBADEN, H., AND FOCSANEAU, L., *Arch. Gynäkol.,* **140,** 21 (1930)

32. FUENTES, B. V., APOLO, E., AND ESCULIES, J., *Z. ges. exptl. Med.,* **73,** 412 (1930)

33. FÜRTH, O., AND MINIBECK, H., *Biochem. Z.,* **237,** 139 (1931)

34. FÜRTH, O., AND SCHOLL, R., *Biochem. Z.,* **222,** 430 (1930)

35. HENRIQUES, O. M., *Acta Path. Microbiol. Scand.,* Suppl., **111,** 141 (1930)

36. JENKE, M., *Arch. exptl. Path. Pharmakol.,* **163,** 175 (1931)

37. JENKE, M., AND STEINBERG, F., *Arch. exptl. Path. Pharmakol.,* **153,** 244 (1930)

38. LANGECKER, H., *Arch. exptl. Path. Pharmakol.,* **154,** 1 (1930)

39. REWBRIDGE, A. G., *Arch. Path. Lab. Med.,* **12,** 70 (1931)

40. RIES, F. A., AND STILL, E. U., *Am. J. Physiol.,* **91,** 609 (1930)

41. SANFORD, H. N., CRANE, M., AND LESLIE, E. I., *Am. J. Diseases Children,* **40,** 1039 (1930)

42. SCHMIDT, W., AND SCHMIDT, C. L. A., *Univ. Calif. Pub. Physiol.,* **7,** 211 (1930)

43. SEKITOO, T., *J. Biochem.,* **11,** 390; **12,** 59 (1930)

44. SEKITOO, T., *Z. physiol. Chem.,* **199,** 225 (1931)

45. SMITH, H. P., AND WHIPPLE, G. H., *J. Biol. Chem.,* **89,** 689, 705, 719, 727, 739 (1930)

46. SPERRY, W. M., *J. Biol. Chem.,* **85,** 455 (1930)

47. THANNHAUSER, S. J., AND FROMM, F., *Z. physiol. Chem.,* **187,** 173 (1930)

48. THOMAS, E., *Rev. Méd.,* **50,** 207 (1930)

49. VERZÁR, F., AND KÚTHY, A. VON, *Biochem. Z.,* **225,** 267 (1930); **230,** 451 (1931)

50. WALKER, E., *Biochem. J.,* **24,** 1489 (1930)

CHOLESTEROL

51. CANTONI, O., *Boll. soc. ital. biol. sper.,* **5,** 921 (1930)

52. EPSTEIN, E. Z., *Arch. Internal Med.,* **47,** 82 (1931)

53. GARDNER, J. A., AND GAINSBOROUGH, H., *Quart. J. Med.,* **23,** 465 (1930)

54. LEITES, S., AND GOLBITZ-KATSCHAN, Z., *Z. ges. exptl. Med.,* **72,** 690 (1930); *Klin. Wochschr.,* **9,** 1259 (1930)

55. MANCKE, R., *Deut. Arch. klin. Med.,* **170,** 385 (1931)

56. MERKULOW, G. A., *Arch. path. Anat. (Virchow's),* **280,** 829 (1931)

57. PECCO, R., *Minerva med.,* **1,** 646 (1931)

58. PFEIFFER, G., *Biochem. Z.,* **222,** 214 (1930); **232,** 255 (1931)

59. SCHÖNHEIMER, R., BEHRING, H. VON, AND HUMMEL, R., *Z. physiol. Chem.,* **192,** 93, 117 (1930)

60. SCHÖNHEIMER, R., AND HUMMEL, R., *Z. physiol. Chem.,* **192,** 114 (1930)

BILE EXCRETION

61. CAUJOLLE, F., *Bull. sci. pharmacol.,* **37,** 298 (1930)

62. CAUJOLLE, F., *Bull. soc. chim. biol.,* **12,** 299 (1930)

63. HALPERT, B., HANKE, M. T., AND CURTIS, G. M., *J. Clin. Investigation,* **9,** 359 (1930)

64. HERMANN, H., CAUJOLLE, F., AND JOURDAN, F., *Compt. rend. soc. biol.,*
    190, 78 (1930)
65. IVANOV, N. M., *J. Exptl. Med.,* **71,** 263 (1930)

CHOLAGOGUES

66. CHABROL, E., *Compt. rend. soc. biol.,* **104,** 43 (1930)
67. CHABROL, E., CHARONNAT, R., MAXIMIN, M., PORIN, J., AND BOCQUEN-
    TIN, A., *Compt. rend. soc. biol.,* **102,** 991 (1930)
68. CHABROL, E., CHARONNAT, R., MAXIMIN, M., AND WAITZ, R., *Compt.
    rend. soc. biol.,* **105,** 439 (1930)
69. CHABROL, E., CHARONNAT, R., MAXIMIN, M., AND WAITZ, R., *Compt.
    rend. soc. biol.,* **106,** 15 (1931)
70. CHABROL, E., CHARONNAT, R., MAXIMIN, M., AND WAITZ, R., *Compt.
    rend. soc. biol.,* **106,** 17 (1931)
71. GANTT, W. H., *Am. J. Med. Sci.,* **179,** 380 (1930)
72. MAXIMIN, M., AND BOCQUENTIN, A., *Compt. rend. soc. biol.,* **103,** 3 (1930)
73. PERA, G., *Arch. farmacol. sper.,* **50,** 146 (1930)
73a. SURMONT, H., AND DUMONT, Y., *Compt. rend. soc. biol.,* **104,** 565 (1930)

GLYCOGEN

74. ABELIN, E., AND SPICHTIN, W., *Biochem. Z.,* **228,** 250 (1930)
75. BRIDGE, E. M., AND BRIDGES, E. M., *J. Biol. Chem.,* **93,** 181 (1931)
76. ECKSTEIN, H. C., *Proc. Soc. Exptl. Biol. Med.,* **29,** 160 (1931)
77. FUSS, H., *Z. ges. exptl. Med.,* **73,** 506, 524, 532, 540 (1930); *Klin.
    Wochschr.,* **9,** 410 (1930)
78. GREISHEIMER, E. M., AND JOHNSON, O. H., *Am. J. Physiol.,* **94,** 11 (1930)
79. GREISHEIMER, E. M., AND JOHNSON, O. H., *J. Nutrition,* **3,** 297 (1930)
80. GREISHEIMER, E. M., AND JOHNSON, O. H., *Proc. Soc. Exptl. Biol. Med.,*
    27, 769, 770 (1930)
81. HYND, A., AND ROTTER, D. L., *Biochem. J.,* **24,** 1390 (1930)
82. KRANTZ, J. C., AND CORR, C. J., *J. Pharmacol.,* **41,** 83 (1931)
83. MEKIE, E. C., *Surg., Gynecol., Obstet.,* **53,** 329 (1931)
84. POPPER, H., AND WOZASEK, O., *Arch. path. Anat. (Virchow's),* **279,** 819
    (1931)
85. RATHERY, F., KOURILSKY, R., AND LAURENT, Y., *Compt. rend. soc. biol.,*
    103, 472 (1930)
86. RATHERY, F., KOURILSKY, R., AND LAURENT, Y., *Compt. rend. soc. biol.,*
    103, 755 (1930)
87. REWBRIDGE, A. G., AND ANDREWS, E., *Proc. Soc. Exptl. Biol. Med.,* **28,**
    126 (1930)
87a. RONCATO, A., *Boll. soc. ital. biol. sper.,* **5,** 254 (1930)
88. ROSENFELD, G., *Biochem. Z.,* **222,** 457 (1930)
89. SCHWENTKER, F. F., AND NOEL, W. W., *Bull. Johns Hopkins Hosp.,* **46,**
    259 (1930)
90. WACHSMUTH, W., *Klin. Wochschr.,* **9,** 1453 (1930)
91. WACHSMUTH, W., *Z. ges. exptl. Med.,* **73,** 659 (1930)
92. WAKEMAN, A. M., AND MORRELL, C. A., *Arch. Internal Med.,* **47,** 104;
    48, 301 (1931)

LACTIC ACID

93. ANDERSON, I. A., CLEGHORN, R. A., MACLEOD, J. J. R., AND PETERSON, J. M., *J. Physiol.*, **71**, 391 (1931)
94. ANSELMINO, K. J., AND HOFFMANN, F., *Arch. Gynäkol.*, **142**, 289 (1930)
95. BORNSTEIN, A., AND MAYER, H., *Biochem. Z.*, **225**, 318 (1930)
96. CARRUTHERS, A., *Chinese J. Physiol.*, **4**, 65 (1930)
97. DIAZ, C. J., AND CUENCA, B. S., *Ann. Méd.*, **28**, 501 (1930)
98. EGGLETON, M. G., AND EVANS, C. L., *J. Physiol.*, **70**, 269 (1930)
99. HIMWICH, H. E., CHAMBERS, W. H., KOSKOFF, Y. D., AND NAHUM, L. H., *J. Biol. Chem.*, **90**, 417 (1931)
100. KHOUVINE, Y., AUBEL, E., AND CHEVILLARD, L., *Compt. rend. soc. biol.*, **190**, 1254 (1930)
101. LOEPER, M., DEGOS, R., AND TONNET, J., *Compt. rend. soc. biol.*, **106**, 717 (1931)
102. LONG, C. N. H., AND GRANT, R., *J. Biol. Chem.*, **89**, 553 (1930)
103. MOSSOBRIO, E., AND MICHAILOFF, M., *Minerva med.*, **1**, 650 (1930)
104. ROSENTHAL, O., *Biochem. Z.*, **227**, 354 (1930) ; **233**, 62 (1931)
105. SCHNEIDER, E., AND WIDMANN, E., *Klin. Wochschr.*, **9**, 761 (1930)

EPINEPHRINE

106. CORI, C. F., AND BUCHWALD, K. W., *J. Biol. Chem.*, **92**, 367 (1931)
107. CORI, G. T., CORI, C. F., AND BUCHWALD, K. W., *J. Biol. Chem.*, **86**, 375 (1930)
108. CORKHILL, A. B., AND MARKS, H. P., *J. Physiol.*, **70**, 67 (1930)
109. EADIE, G. S., *Am. J. Physiol.*, **94**, 69 (1930)
110. FIROR, W. M., AND EADIE, G. S., *Am. J. Physiol.*, **94**, 615 (1930)
111. GEIGER, E., *Biochem. Z.*, **223**, 190 (1930)
112. LOEB, R. F., REEVES, E. B., AND GLASIER, H. P., *J. Clin. Investigation*, **10**, 19 (1931)
113. NANNINI, G., *Minerva med.*, **2**, 874 (1930)
114. SACKS, J., *Am. J. Physiol.*, **97**, 467 (1931)
115. SUCKSDORFF, W., *Finska Läkeresällskapetes Handlingar*, **72**, 99 (1930); *J. Am. Med. Assoc.*, **94**, 1810 (1930)

INSULIN

116. ALTHAUSEN, T. L., *Arch. Internal Med.*, **48**, 667 (1931)
117. ALTHAUSEN, T. L., GUNTHER, L., LAGEN, J. B., AND KERR, W. J., *Arch. Internal Med.*, **46**, 482 (1930)
118. ALTHAUSEN, T. L., AND MANCKE, R., *Deut. Arch. klin. Med.*, **170**, 294 (1931)
119. COLLAZO, J. A., AND RUBINO, P., *Klin. Wochschr.*, **9**, 217 (1930)
120. CORKHILL, B., *Biochem. J.*, **24**, 779 (1930)
121. RATHERY, F., AND KOURILSKY, R., *Ann. physiol. physicochim. biol.*, **6**, 32, 73 (1930)
122. RATHERY, F., KOURILSKY, R., AND GIBERT, S., *Compt. rend. soc. biol.*, **103**, 307, 376, 378, 474 (1930)

123. ROOT, R. W., HALL, F. G., AND GRAY, I. E., *J. Elisha Mitchell Sci. Soc.,* **46,** 15 (1930)
124. ROOT, R. W., HALL, F. G., AND GRAY, I. E., *J. Biol. Chem.,* **91,** 27 (1931)
125. SCHMIDT, A. A., AND SAATCHIAN, R. L., *Zhur. Eksptl. Biol. i Med.,* **11,** 42 (1929)

FRUCTOSE

126. BOLLMAN, J. L., AND MANN, F. C., *Am. J. Physiol.,* **96,** 683 (1931)
127. HEINICKE, E., AND PETERS, F., *Klin. Wochschr.,* **9,** 1356 (1930)
128. PETERS, F., HEINICKE, P., AND DEL'ESPINE, E., *Z. ges. exptl. Med.,* **77,** 173 (1931)

GALACTOSE

129. BAUER, R., AND WOZASEK, O., *Wien. klin. Wochschr.,* **43,** 1337 (1930)
130. BLÖCH, J., *Z. ges. exptl. Med.,* **74,** 439, 449, 454 (1930)
131. BODE, O. B., *Deut. Arch. klin. Med.,* **170,** 165 (1931)
132. BOLLMAN, J. L., POWER, M. H., AND MANN, F. C., *Proc. Staff Meetings Mayo Clinic,* **6,** 724 (1931)
133. ELMER, A. W., AND SCHEPS, M., *Lancet,* **2,** 187 (1930)
134. FIESSINGER, N., AND DIERYCK, J., *Ann. méd.,* **29,** 123 (1931)
135. PETOW, H., KOSTERLITZ, H., AND NAUMANN, H. N., *Klin. Wochschr.,* **9,** 1549 (1930)
136. ROWE, A. W., AND MCMANUS, M., *Am. J. Med. Sci.,* **181,** 777 (1931)
137. SHAY, H., SCHLOSS, E. M., AND BELL, M. A., *Arch. Internal Med.,* **47,** 391 (1931)

PROTEIN

138. ALZONA, L., *Minerva med.,* **11,** 917 (1930)
139. BOLLMAN, J. L., AND MANN, F. C., *Am. J. Physiol.,* **92,** 92 (1930)
140. CANTONI, .O., *Boll. soc. ital. biol. sper.,* **5,** 924 (1930)
141. CHRISTOMANOS, A. A., *Biochem. Z.,* **221,** 473 (1930)
142. CLEMENTI, A., *Boll. soc. ital. biol. sper.,* **5,** 1142 (1930)
143. DOCK, W., *Am. J. Physiol.,* **97,** 117 (1931)
144. GAUTIER, C., *Bull. soc. chim. biol.,* **12,** 1382 (1930)
145. GAUTIER, C., *Bull. soc. chim. biol.,* **13,** 143 (1931)
146. MARTENS, R., *Bull. soc. chim. biol.,* **12,** 1212 (1930)
147. NOTHHAAS, R., AND NEVER, H. E., *Arch. ges. Physiol.,* **224,** 527 (1930)
148. PASCHKIS, K., *Klin. Wochschr.,* **9,** 1917 (1930)
149. SALASKIN, S., *Z. physiol. Chem.,* **192,** 25 (1930)
150. SALASKIN, S., AND KRIWSKY, J., *Z. physiol. Chem.,* **196,** 121 (1931)
151. SALASKIN, S., AND SOLOWJEW, L., *Z. physiol. Chem.,* **192,** 28 (1930)
152. WAKEMAN, A. M., AND MORRELL, C. A., *Arch. Internal Med.,* **46,** 290 (1930)

FAT

153. BERG, B. N., AND ZUCKER, T. F., *Proc. Soc. Exptl. Biol. Med.,* **29,** 68 (1931)
154. BLATHERWICK, N. R., MEDLAR, E. M., BRADSHAW, P. J., POST, A. L., AND SAWYER, S. D., *Proc. Soc. Exptl. Biol. Med.,* **29,** 345 (1931)

155. Bloor, W. R., and Snider, R. H., *J. Biol. Chem.*, **89**, 399 (1930)
156. Cannavò, L., *Boll. soc. ital. biol. sper.*, **5**, 805 (1930)
157. Cannavò, L., *Biochem. Z.*, **239**, 100 (1931)
158. Cantoni, O., *Boll. soc. ital. biol. sper.*, **5**, 918 (1930)
159. Cantoni, O., *Biochim. terap. sper.*, **17**, 325 (1930)
160. Dulière, W. L., and Raper, H. S., *Biochem. J.*, **24**, 1672 (1930)
161. Hirsch, A., *Klin. Wochschr.*, **9**, 2062 (1930)
162. Jost, H., *Z. physiol. Chem.*, **197**, 90 (1931)
163. Monasterio, G., *Biochem. Z.*, **218**, 331 (1930)
164. Müller, P., *Arch. exptl. Path. Pharmakol.*, **147**, 219 (1930)
165. Orestano, G., *Boll. soc. ital. biol. sper.*, **6**, 293 (1931)
166. Page, I. H., and Pasternak, L., *Biochem. Z.*, **232**, 259 (1931)
167. Steppun, O., Timofeeva, A., and Naumova, N., *Z. ges. exptl. Med.*, **74**, 467 (1930)

COAGULATION OF FIBRINOGEN

168. Canto, A., *Compt. rend. soc. biol.*, **104**, 1103 (1930)
169. Cranston, E., and Caillet, O. R., *J. Pharmacol.*, **41**, 65 (1931)
170. De Nicola, C., *Compt. rend. soc. biol.*, **105**, 714 (1930)
171. Falkenhausen, M. von, *Z. ges. exptl. Med.*, **70**, 535 (1930)
172. Fercks, H. J., and Falkenhausen, M. V., *Arch. inter. physiol.*, **32**, 251 (1930)
173. Jones, T. B., and Smith, H. P., *Am. J. Physiol.*, **94**, 144 (1930)

DETOXICATING FUNCTION

174. Abe, Shin-ichi, *Tôhoku J. Exptl. Med.*, **17**, 174 (1931)
175. Beaver, D. C., and Robertson, H. E., *Proc. Staff Meetings Mayo Clinic*, **6**, 216 (1931)
176. Bechner, E., *Münch. med. Wochschr.*, **77**, 751 (1930)
177. Bischoff, F., and Long, M. L., *J. Nutrition*, **3**, 201 (1930)
178. Bischoff, F., and Long, M. L., *J. Pharmacol.*, **41**, 127 (1931)
179. Bourne, W., and Raginsky, B. B., *Am. J. Surg.*, **14**, 653 (1931)
180. Callaway, J. W., *Proc. Soc. Exptl. Biol. Med.*, **28**, 580 (1931)
181. Churchill, T. P., and Van Wagoner, F. H., *Proc. Soc. Exptl. Biol. Med.*, **28**, 581 (1931)
182. Cutler, J. T., *J. Pharmacol.*, **41**, 337 (1931)
183. Ellsworth, R., *Bull. Johns Hopkins Hosp.*, **46**, 296; **47**, 106 (1930)
184. Findlay, G. M., and Hindle, E., *Lancet*, **2**, 678 (1930)
185. Hepler, O. E., and Simonds, J. P., *Proc. Soc. Exptl. Biol. Med.*, **28**, 583 (1931)
186. Kauffmann, F., and Engle, R., *Z. klin. Med.*, **114**, 405 (1930)
187. Kaczander, P., *Klin. Wochschr.*, **9**, 495 (1930)
188. Lichtman, S. S., *Arch. Internal Med.*, **48**, 98 (1931)
189. Marsh, F., *Brit. Med. J.*, **1**, 146 (1930)
190. Marshall, H. T., Aydelotte, B. F., and Barbour, H. G., *Am. J. Physiol.*, **98**, 615 (1931)
191. M'Gowan, J. P., *Edinburgh Med. J.*, **37**, 281 (1930)
192. Polson, C. J., *J. Path. Bact.*, **34**, 5 (1931)

193. PRIESTLEY, J. T., MARKOWITZ, J., AND MANN, F. C., *Am. J. Physiol.*, **96**, 696 (1931)
194. ROSENTHAL, S. M., *J. Pharmacol.*, **38**, 291 (1930)
195. ROSENTHAL, S. M., AND LILLIE, R. D., *Am. J. Physiol.*, **97**, 131 (1931)
196. ROSS, J. B., *Can. Med. Assoc. J.*, **24**, 623 (1931)
197. SAUER, J., *Klin. Wochschr.*, **9**, 2351 (1930)
198. SCHOUR, M., AND ROSENGARTEN, C., *Klin. Wochschr.*, **9**, 1968 (1930)
199. SHERWOOD, K. K., AND SHERWOOD, H. H., *Arch. Internal Med.*, **48**, 82 (1931)
200. VOIT, K., AND WENDT, H., *Z. klin. Med.*, **114**, 432 (1930)
201. YOKOTA, Y., *Japan J. Obstet. Gynecol.*, **14**, 66 (1931)

ENZYMES

202. AMMON, R., AND FISCHGOLD, H., *Biochem. Z.*, **234**, 54 (1931)
203. BAMANN, E., AND LAEVERENZ, P., *Ber.*, **63**, 394 (1930)
204. BAMANN, E., AND LAEVERENZ, P., *Z. physiol. Chem.*, **193**, 201 (1930)
205. BAMANN, E., AND SCHMELLER, M., *Z. physiol. Chem.*, **188**, 251 (1930); **194**, 1, 14 (1931)
208. BIELSCHEWSKY, F., *Z. physiol. Chem.*, **190**, 15 (1930)
209. CAILLET, O. R., *Proc. Soc. Exptl. Biol. Med.*, **28**, 357 (1931)
210. EDLBACHER, S., AND BURCHARD, H., *Z. physiol. Chem.*, **194**, 69 (1931)
211. EDLBACHER, S., KRAUS, J., AND SCHEURICH, N., *Z. physiol. Chem.*, **191**, 225 (1930)
212. FABISCH, W., *Biochem. Z.*, **234**, 84 (1931)
213. FABRE, R., AND SIMONNET, H., *Compt. rend. soc. biol.*, **190**, 1233 (1930)
214. FOSSE, R., BRUNEL, A., AND DE GRAEVE, P., *Compt. rend. soc. biol.*, **103**, 67 (1930)
215. GRASSMANN, W., AND BAZU, K. P., *Z. physiol. Chem.*, **198**, 247 (1931)
216. KAZIRO, K., AND TSUJI, K., *J. Biochem.*, **11**, 333 (1930)
217. KHOUVINE, Y., AUBEL, E., AND CHEVILLARD, L., *Compt. rend. soc. biol.*, **191**, 446 (1930)
218. LASKOWSKI, J., *Med. Doświadczalna Spoleczna*, **11**, 265 (1930)
219. MISLOWITZER, E., AND KAUFFMANN, F., *Biochem. Z.*, **234**, 101 (1931)
220. MURRAY, D. R. P., AND KING, C. G., *Biochem. J.*, **24**, 190 (1930)
221. PARFENTJEV, I. A., DEVRIENT, W. C., AND SOKOLOFF, B. F., *J. Biol. Chem.*, **92**, 33 (1930)
222. PINCUSSEN, L., AND TAKUMA, T., *Biochem. Z.*, **223**, 341 (1930)
223. PRZYLECKI, ST. J. VON, AND MYSTKOWSKI, E., *Biochem. Z.*, **236**, 122 (1931)
224. RAY, G. B., AND ISAAC, L. A., *Am. J. Physiol.*, **91**, 377 (1930)
225. RONA, P., AMMON, R., AND FISCHGOLD, H., *Klin. Wochschr.*, **10**, 72 (1931)
226. RONA, P., AMMON, R., AND WERNER, M., *Biochem. Z.*, **221**, 381 (1930)
227. RONA, P., FISCHGOLD, H., AND AMMON, R., *Biochem. Z.*, **228**, 77 (1930)
228. SAKUMA, F., *J. Biochem.*, **12**, 247 (1930)
229. SALASKIN, S., AND SOLOWJEW, L., *Z. physiol. Chem.*, **200**, 259 (1931)
230. SCHMIDT, A. A., *Klin. Wochschr.*, **9**, 1021 (1930)
231. SCHMIDT, G., *Klin. Wochschr.*, **10**, 165 (1931)

232. THANNHAUSER, S. J., AND ANGERMANN, M., *Z. physiol. Chem.*, **189**, 174 (1930)

233. UMENO, M., *Biochem. Z.*, **231**, 317 (1931)

234. WESTENBRINK, H. G. K., AND ROMIJN, H. M., *Arch. néerland. physiol.*, **15**, 466, 529 (1930)

235. WIELAND, H., AND FRAGE, K., *Z. physiol. Chem.*, **186**, 195 (1930)

236. ZEILE, K., AND HELLSTRÖM, H., *Z. physiol. Chem.*, **192**, 171 (1930)

LIVER EXTRACT

237. BARLOW, O. W., *Am. J. Physiol.*, **91**, 429 (1930)

238. DE PENCIER, M. T., SOSKIN, S., AND BEST, C. H., *Am. J. Physiol.*, **94**, 548 (1930)

239. ESAU, J. N., AND STOLAND, O. O., *Am. J. Physiol.*, **92**, 35 (1930)

240. FEHER, V., *Magyar Orvosi Arch.*, **31**, 446 (1930)

241. FILO, E., *Folia Haematol.*, **44**, 368 (1931)

242. GÄNSSLEN, M., *Klin. Wochschr.*, **9**, 2099 (1930)

243. GEBHARDT, F., AND FRICKE, G., *Z. ges. exptl. Med.*, **73**, 45; **74**, 636 (1930)

244. GOLDBERGER, J., AND SEBRELL, W. H., *U.S. Pub. Health Reports*, **45**, 3064 (1930)

245. HANSSEN, O., STUB, O., AND FORBECH, V., *Acta Med. Scand.*, **76**, 26 (1931)

246. HÖGLER, F., *Klin. Wochschr.*, **9**, 2052 (1930)

247. KEEFER, C. S., HUANG, K. K., AND YANG, C. S., *J. Clin. Investigation*, **9**, 533 (1930)

248. LOMBARDI, E., *Riforma med.*, **46**, 7 (1930); *J. Am. Med. Assoc.*, **94**, 1182 (1930)

249. RABER, O., *Science*, **73**, 457 (1931)

250. SALMON, W. D., AND GUERRANT, N. B., *Science*, **73**, 243 (1931)

251. SINGER, K., *Z. ges. exptl. Med.*, **71**, 136 (1930)

252. STEPHAN, R., *Klin. Wochschr.*, **9**, 1068 (1930)

253. STERN, K. G., *Klin. Wochschr.*, **10**, 172 (1931)

254. STOLAND, O. O., AND ESAU, J. N., *Am. J. Physiol.*, **92**, 35 (1930)

255. STURGIS, C. C., AND ISAACS, R., *Ann. Internal Med.*, **5**, 131 (1931)

256. STURGIS, C. C., ISAACS, R., AND RIDDLE, M. C., *Surg., Gynecol., Obstet.*, **50**, 234 (1930)

257. VAUGHN, J. M., *Quart. J. Med.*, **23**, 213 (1930)

258. WEST, R., AND HOWE, M., *J. Biol. Chem.*, **88**, 427 (1930)

259. WHIPPLE, G. H., AND ROBSCHEIT-ROBBINS, F. S., *Am. J. Physiol.*, **92**, 388 (1930)

260. WRIGHT, G. P., AND ARTHUR, B., *J. Path. Bact.*, **33**, 1017 (1930)

261. ZERFAS, L. G., *Arch. Internal Med.*, **47**, 135 (1931)

ORGANIC CONSTITUENTS

262. GABBE, E., *Klin. Wochschr.*, **9**, 169 (1930)

263. GETTLER, A. O., AND BLUME, H., *Arch. Path. Lab. Med.*, **11**, 554 (1931)

264. HOPKINS, F. G., AND ELLIOTT, K. A. C., *Proc. Roy. Soc. Med.*, **109**, 58 (1931)

265. JACOBY, M., *Biochem. Z.*, **230**, 225 (1931)
266. KÜHNAU, J., *Biochem. Z.*, **230**, 353 (1931)
267. RANDOIN, L., AND FABRE, R., *Compt. rend. soc. biol.*, **192**, 815 (1931)
268. SCHEIFF, W., *Arch. ges. Physiol.*, **226**, 491 (1931)
269. VAUDIN, D., JAVILLIER, M., ALLAIRE, H., AND SCHIRMER, M., *Bull. soc. chim. biol.*, **12**, 894 (1930)
270. WATANABE, K., *Z. Immunitäts.*, **69**, 117 (1930)
271. WITANOWSKI, W. R., *Acta Biol. Exptl.* (*Warsaw*), **5**, 207 (1930)
272. YOSHIMURA, K., AND NISHIDA, K., *J. Agr. Chem. Japan*, **6**, 927 (1930)

INORGANIC CONSTITUENTS

273. ANDRIANOFF, N., AND ANSBACHER, S., *Deut. med. Wochschr.*, **56**, 357 (1930)
274. FUNK, E. H., AND ST. CLAIR, H., *Arch. Internal Med.*, **45**, 37 (1930)
275. HALL, E. M., AND MACKAY, E. M., *Am. J. Path.*, **7**, 327 (1931)
276. HAUROWITZ, F., *Z. physiol. Chem.*, **190**, 72 (1930)
277. HERKEL, W., *Beitr. path. Anat.*, **85**, 513 (1930)
278. LOESCHKE, A., *Z. physiol. Chem.*, **199**, 125 (1931)
279. MALLORY, F. B., AND PARKER, F., *Am. J. Path.*, **7**, 351 (1931)
280. MORRISON, D. B., AND NASH, T. P., JR., *J. Biol. Chem.*, **88**, 479 (1930)
281. SANTESSON, C. G., *Skand. Arch. Physiol.*, **61**, 79 (1931)
282. SCHÖNHEIMER, R., AND HERKEL, W., *Klin. Wochschr.*, **9**, 1449 (1930); **10**, 345 (1931)

DIVISION OF EXPERIMENTAL SURGERY AND PATHOLOGY
THE MAYO FOUNDATION
ROCHESTER, MINNESOTA

THE METABOLISM OF BRAIN AND NERVE*

By E. G. Holmes

Pharmacological Laboratory
University of Cambridge

It is the purpose of this article to discuss recent additions to our knowledge of the chemical changes which are responsible for the functioning of nervous tissue.

If an article of this kind is to have any coherence, it is essential to discuss, if only briefly, certain papers which appeared before the period under review.

Among the pioneers of the subject, certain names stand out. Winterstein and his collaborators are responsible for a long series of papers on the metabolism of central and peripheral nervous tissue. Space does not allow of any discussion of them.

Tashiro (1), (2) was the first worker to show that nerve produced CO_2 and ammonia during its metabolism, and that the amounts of these gases produced were increased by stimulation. Following him, Garrey, Parker, Adam, Fenn, Gerard, Meyerhof, and Schmitt have all investigated the gaseous metabolism of nerve, and all these workers are agreed that nerve uses oxygen and produces CO_2 during rest, and that these processes are intensified during activity. Their findings cover both medullated and non-medullated nerve. Finally, A. V. Hill and his collaborators (for most recent results, see Bronk) have shown that nerve produces a measurable amount of heat, that this heat is increased during activity, and that it is of an order which is in substantial agreement with that which would be expected from the magnitude of the oxygen consumption [see Gerard (1)]. These findings are, of course, of fundamental importance, for they show, conclusively, that the nervous impulse is a chemical affair. Evidence from other sources (for review, see Davis) has led physiologists to picture the nerve impulse as a disturbance, propagated down the length of the axon, and involving the liberation of electrically charged ions. Clearly, this disturbance is one which involves consumption of oxygen, production of CO_2 and ammonia, and the liberation of heat.

* Received December 19, 1931.

It is a metabolic change in the commonly accepted sense of the word. But it is a change of very small dimensions. Hill calculates that the heat produced on stimulation is 10^{-6} cal. per gram of nerve per impulse. It has already been stated that the dimensions of the chemical changes are of an order which agrees with the observed heat production.

Apart from the earlier work of Winterstein, attempts have been made to follow, in more detail, the chemical events occurring in nerve fibres, of both the medullated and the non-medullated type. It has been found (Holmes and Gerard) that during rest, mammalian nerve uses carbohydrate, provided oxygen is available. If the tissue is kept in nitrogen, carbohydrate disappears, and can be accounted for as lactic acid. Evidently, the familiar glycolytic mechanism is present in nerve, as in so many other tissues (see also Gerard and Meyerhof). The lactic acid, however, which is produced anaerobically, is not removed in oxygen (though, of course, an asphyxiated nerve will recover its function in oxygen). It accumulates in the isolated tissue, or, in the living animal, is, presumably, removed by the circulation. Oxygen can suppress the formation of lactic acid and cause the oxidation of its carbohydrate precursor, but it cannot secure the removal of lactic acid, once it has been formed. These findings preclude the possibility of the existence in peripheral nerve of a "carbohydrate cycle" which involves the restoration of lactic acid to a carbohydrate precursor.

In nerve, as in muscle, there is an initial and a delayed phase of heat production. In nerve, the amount of heat produced in the initial phase is about 8.9 per cent of that produced in the recovery period (Bronk). In muscles, the initial phase continues when the tissue is deprived of oxygen, but the delayed heat production disappears, only to return when oxygen is readmitted. In asphyxiated nerve, both phases persist for a time, and both gradually fail together.

Finally, Holmes, Gerard, and Solomon have shown directly that the glycogen–lactic acid mechanism is not concerned with the propagation of the nerve impulse. Sets of nerves kept in oxygen, the one set being stimulated and the other being left at rest, have, at the end of the experimental period, the same content of glycogen, "free sugar," and lactic acid. Meyerhof and Schmitt, on the other hand, have shown that the respiratory quotient of activity in nerve is 0.9.

The work hitherto discussed has dealt with medullated nerve. Hill has investigated the heat production in the non-medullated nerves of crabs; Meyerhof and Schulz (1) and Chang have determined their oxygen consumption, and Holmes (1 and 2) has investigated their carbohydrate and lactic acid content. Both Furusawa and Levin have shown that non-medullated nerves differ widely from medullated in their response to stimulation, and in the behaviour of their action currents. Hill has found that their heat production is very much greater than that of medullated nerve, and Meyerhof and Schulz (1) that they consume very much more oxygen. Heat and oxygen consumption are increased on stimulation. Holmes (1) found that, in contrast to medullated nerve, they contained large amounts of carbohydrate, both as glycogen and as "free sugar." They produced lactic acid anaerobically, and this lactic acid production was suppressed in oxygen. No data are at present available with regard to chemical changes, other than increased gaseous exchange, which takes place in non-medullated nerves as a result of stimulation. The most striking "chemical" difference between medullated and non-medullated nerve is the very great richness in carbohydrate of the latter as compared with the former. The combined glycogen, "free sugar," and lactic acid in medullated nerve amounts to, perhaps, 130 mg. per 100 grams of fresh tissue. In non-medullated crab nerve there may be as much as 2,500 mg., or about twenty times as much.

The state of affairs in central, as opposed to peripheral, nerve tissues is very different. The nerve cell is sharply marked off from the nerve fibre in its metabolic behaviour. The oxygen consumption of the brain of the living animal, both with and without anaesthesia, has been investigated by Alexander and Cserna, by Hou, by Hou and Sigiura, and by several other workers. While the problem obviously bristles with experimental difficulties, it has yet been made abundantly clear that, while the gaseous interchange of the nerve fibre, relative to its bulk, is very small, that of the nerve cell is quite large. Some of the figures would indicate, in fact, that it is very large indeed. Experiments on isolated tissue point in the same direction, and chopped brain or slices of brain cortex [Holmes (3); Dickens and Simer (2)], suspended in buffered Ringer's solution, take up oxygen at a greater rate than do specimens of most other tissues under comparable conditions. This large oxygen uptake is a characteristic of nerve cells (or possibly of synapses), for nerve fibres derived from the central nervous system show an oxygen uptake similar in magnitude to that of peripheral nerve.

This difference in oxygen consumption of the two parts of the neuron, the cell and the fibre, is reflected in the distribution of enzymes. It has been shown [Vernon (1 and 2); Holmes (3)], that nerve cells are rich in the indophenol oxidase system, and that they contain a good supply of the respiratory pigment, cytochrome. Keilin's work has established the connection between the indophenol oxidase system and cytochrome, and he believes that the function of the enzyme is to catalyse the oxidation of reduced cytochrome by molecular oxygen. Now, while nerve cells are rich in indophenol oxidase, it is almost non-existent in the peripheral nerve, and nearly, but not quite, as scanty in the white matter of the central nervous system. Holmes (3) has found that nerve cells are rich in cytochrome, that the white matter of the central nervous system has only a scanty supply, and that peripheral nerve has practically none. This last observation has recently been confirmed by Monaghan and Schmitt. Clearly, the distribution of indophenol oxidase and that of cytochrome in the nervous system run parallel. While, therefore, we are not in a position to say exactly how much of the oxygen consumption is actually due to the cytochrome-indophenol oxidase component, we may well be not far wrong in assuming that its presence accounts for a good deal of the difference between the two tissues.

In the terms of current theories of oxidation, the dehydrogenating enzymes catalyse the mobilisation of hydrogen from substrates (and hence their oxidation or partial oxidation) and the transfer of this hydrogen to cytochrome, the cytochrome thus reduced being oxidised by the indophenol oxidase system and molecular oxygen. In different tissues, different dehydrogenase mechanisms can be recognised. When the dehydrogenating mechanisms of brain cortex and peripheral nerve are compared, considerable differences become at once apparent. In the first place, the velocity of dehydrogenation is far greater in the case of the cortex than it is in the case of nerve, or of "central" white matter. In the second, the substrates attacked by the two different parts of the cell are not identical. Thus, Thunberg reported that the velocity of reduction of methylene blue by nerve was increased by glutamic, ketoglutaric, succinic, fumaric, and lactic acids. Sherif showed that neither glucose nor galactose had any effect on the reduction time. Gerard (1) had already shown that glucose tended to suppress the oxygen consumption. It has already been stated that peripheral nerve will not oxidise lactic acid (Holmes and Gerard), though white matter from the central nervous system does so to a small extent.

On the other hand, nerve cells take up extra oxygen with succinic acid [Szent-Györgyi; Quastel and Wheatley (1)] and Ashford and Holmes (2) find that the time of reduction of methylene blue by brain is reduced by lactate, glucose, succinate, glycerophosphate, and pyruvate, but is unaltered by glycerol and dihydroxyacetone, while formic and mandelic acids prolong it. Galactose effects a slight diminution in the reduction time [Holmes (3)].

Quastel and Wheatley (1) have shown that brain tissue oxidises not only succinate but also fumarate and l-malate. It does not oxidise l-aspartate. There is, however, "competitive inhibition" between succinate on the one hand, and fumarate, l-aspartate, malonate, and possibly l-malate on the other. From this they argue that the probable path of succinate oxidation is through fumarate and l-malate. In a later communication (2), they state that a number of dyes, which inhibit the oxidation of succinate by muscle, have no effect on the succin-oxidase system of brain. Quastel (1 and 2) has extended this work, and though the dyes which he and Wheatley employed are not toxic to the succin-oxidase system of brain tissue, yet certain others are extremely toxic to the fumarase system. Quastel finds that white matter as well as grey is rich in fumarase, and he describes a useful method of making a fumarase preparation. It is impossible to discuss his work here, at any length. He finds the most toxic dye-stuffs among the congo red and triphenyl methane series. Trypan blue, trypan red, and Bayer "205" are also toxic. The substrate itself (fumarate) and serum both protect the enzyme from the toxic effects of the dye. Barron finds that methylene blue increases the oxygen consumption *in vitro* (in the presence of glucose) of tissues, including brain, which possess the power of aerobic glycolysis.

Nerve cells thus differ from nerve fibres in that (a) they possess an active oxidising enzyme system which is very poorly developed in the fibre, (b) their dehydrogenating enzymes are more active, and (c) these enzymes behave rather differently, in that their choice of substrates is somewhat different.

An interesting point has been brought out in the following way: It has already been remarked that, while nerve shows no extra oxygen uptake with lactate [Gerard (1)], yet lactate will act as a hydrogen donator to methylene blue in the presence of nerve. The question naturally presented itself as to whether or not the failure of the nerve to take up oxygen with lactate was due simply to the absence of the indophenol-oxidase system. If such were the case, it should be possible to replace the system by methylene blue, if the experiments were carried out aerobically, since the dye, having been reduced by the lactate in the presence of the dehydrogenase, should be reoxidised by molecular oxygen, and thus act in the capacity of a transporter of hydrogen. As a result of some preliminary experiments, Holmes (3) concluded that no such effect could be demonstrated. Gerard (2), however, was able to show that it did occur, and there is little doubt but that his view is the correct one. Gerard used both methylene blue and 1-naphthol 2-sulphonate indophenol. He found that these dyes were capable, to some extent, of preventing the relatively slight depression in oxygen consumption which is caused by cyanide. They are also capable of increasing the oxygen consumption of the nerve to which no extra substrate has been added, as well as increasing the oxygen consumption in the presence of lactate.

It will be seen that these observations fit well with the known facts concerning the distribution of oxidising mechanisms in nerve. Evidently the absent indophenol-oxidase mechanism can be replaced by these dye-stuffs, and can increase the rate of oxygen consumption, by acting either on the substrates already present in the nerve or on lactate added from outside. In the course of these and other observations, Feng and Gerard have brought out an interesting point, namely, that the perineurium affords a barrier to the diffusion of substances from the surrounding fluid into the nerve fibres. Thus "block" of a nerve is brought about by isotonic solutions of glucose, $CaCl_2$, KCl, or NaCN much more quickly if the sheath is split before the nerve is immersed in the solution.

It is well known that nerve, deprived of oxygen, loses its activity only gradually. Gerard (1), in particular, has sponsored the view that the tissue must contain an "oxidising reserve" of some kind (1927). Subsequently (3) he has investigated in detail the response of nerve to oxygen lack.

Fenn has investigated rather fully the question of "oxygen debt." He finds that after a period in nitrogen nerve consumes more oxygen but this extra oxygen is only $\frac{1}{10}$ to $\frac{1}{4}$ the amount which would have been consumed during the asphyxial period had oxygen been available. Corresponding to the increased oxygen consumption after asphyxia there is an increased output of CO_2, but the extra CO_2 is small compared with the extra oxygen, i.e., the R.Q. of the extra oxygen is very low. In addition, the CO_2 combining power of the tissue is lower after recovery than before asphyxia. Probably this is due to accumulation of lactic acid which cannot be oxidised (Holmes and Gerard). At the same time, since a great part of the oxygen is not used to produce CO_2, it is argued that it may be employed to build up again an "oxygen reserve."

In one of the papers quoted above Gerard (2) summarises some important information about the oxygen uptake of unstimulated nerve. Frog nerve shows a seasonal variation in rate of oxygen uptake. Oxygen uptake is not affected by variations of pH between 7.0 and 9.0. At pH 5.3 it is reduced by about 50 per cent. Borate buffer does not affect it. Phosphate buffer increases it slightly, while $NaHCO_3$ has no effect. [Ashford and Holmes (2) find that there is a distinct increase in the oxygen uptake of brain tissue in CO_2 / bicarbonate buffer as opposed to that in phosphate buffer.] Ninety per cent sodium chloride, plus ten per cent magnesium, potassium, or calcium chlorides (the final solutions, of course, being isotonic) are apparently equivalent to isotonic sodium chloride. Concentrations of these metals, therefore, which would have a marked effect on the heart, have none on nerve. In isotonic calcium, potassium, or magnesium chlorides, there is a reduction in the oxygen uptake by some 50 per cent.

Gerard and Wallen investigated the inorganic, acid-stable, and acid-labile phosphate in nerve. Rest in nitrogen, or tetanisation in oxygen, leads to an increase of the inorganic, at the expense of the organic fractions. There is also evidence of an increase in total soluble phosphate. Gerard and Tupikow (1) have investigated the "free" and "bound" creatine content of nerve. They find an increase in "free" at the expense of "bound" creatine during asphyxiation of the nerve. The figures for liberation of phosphate and creatine during asphyxia fit together very well on the assumption that both substances are derived from the same source, namely, creatine phosphoric acid. In a further communication (2), these authors have shown that on exposure of the nerve to CO_2, H_2S, HCN, or sodium iodoacetate, there is in each case an increase in "free" creatine at the expense of the "bound" fraction.

Gerard (4) has also found (using the Warburg manometric technique) that methylene blue increases the anaerobic glycolysis of nerve. Sodium iodoacetate depresses glycolysis, in both the presence and the absence of the dye. As the author points out, it was to be expected rather that methylene blue would have depressed glycolysis, since the dye is reduced by nerve, and would therefore, presumably, remove lactic acid. Chang and Gerard have found that the oxygen consumption of nerve is depressed by CO in the dark and to some (but to a much lesser) extent in the light. Cresyl blue, which increases the oxygen consumption of nerve in air, is capable, to some degree, of reversing the CO effect, both in the dark and in the light. The cyanide effect is even more markedly reversed by cresyl blue.

Ronzoni finds that conduction in nerves which have been treated with monoiodoacetate and stimulated in nitrogen fails earlier than in nerves which, while stimulated in nitrogen, have not been treated with this substance.

Schmitt (2) has also investigated the effect of CO, both on the respiration and on the action potential of frog nerve. Like Gerard, he finds that CO depresses the oxygen consumption of nerve in the dark, and that this effect is partially reversed by illumination. Warburg's constant "K" has, in these experiments, a value of 8.6 in the dark and 21.2 in the light. A parallel effect is observed on the magnitude of the action potential. He finds that the action potentials disappear completely in about the same time whether the nerve is exposed to pure CO or to pure N_2. In mixtures of oxygen and CO the action potentials gradually fail [the after potential disappearing first (Schmitt and Gasser)], if the experiment is conducted in the dark. Illumination brings about a recovery to, or even above, the original value. Failure again occurs when the light is cut off. These results are interpreted as indicating, first that the nerve impulse is a process which involves oxidations, an inference which might perhaps have safely been drawn from the work, already discussed, of Hill, of Gerard, and of Schmitt himself [Meyerhof and Schmitt; Schmitt (1)]. The further deduction is made that the mechanism involved is concerned with Warburg's respiratory enzyme. The author points out that it is not necessary to suppose that a complete oxidation of materials is involved. Possibly, there is merely a partial oxidation to substances which undergo further, but not necessarily oxidative, change, the energy derived from which is used in impulse propagation. According to Schmitt's own earlier observations, however, any such partial oxidation must have an R.Q. of 0.9. In a further paper

(Schmitt and Schmitt) the authors state that the resting oxygen consumption of frog nerve can be suppressed by cyanide, and the action potential abolished. The former effect is reversed by the presence of methylene blue (see Gerard [4]), the latter is not. Schmitt and Schmitt conclude that this indicates that the chemical mechanism of resting energy production differs from that of impulse propagation, a finding which fits in with the observation that glycogen and "free" carbohydrate disappear at rest, but not to an increased extent during activity (Holmes, Gerard, and Solomon).

Necheles and Gerard have found that exposure of nerve to CO_2 has a marked effect in increasing action potential, which they interpret in terms of a "slowing of critical chemical reactions in nerve under the influence of carbon dioxide." In a subsequent paper [Gerard (5)] it is shown that CO_2 delays the appearance of, and prolongs, the "after potential."

Winterstein (1, 2) has put forward the view that the extra oxygen consumption of stimulated nerve is, in reality, an artefact in the sense that it depends on events occurring at the point of stimulation, and as a result of that process, and is unrelated to the processes of conduction.

Gerard (6) has replied to this criticism, and Meyerhof and Schulz have published a further paper (2) dealing with the point. This has evoked a further polemical publication from Winterstein (3). Should Winterstein's criticisms prove well-founded, it is clear that much of the recent work on nerve metabolism must fall to the ground. In the reviewer's opinion, the paper of Meyerhof and Schulz successfully meets his objections.

Efinoff (1, 2, 3) has compared the velocity of movements of H and OH ions through gelatine, under the influence of an applied potential difference, with their velocity in nerve under similar conditions. He finds the two velocities comparable. The strength of the gelatine solution used to make the gelatine gel naturally exerts a considerable influence on the velocity.

Roeder claims to have shown (a) that electrolytes, phosphorus and nitrogen, are unevenly distributed down the length of a nerve, and (b) that this distribution is (except in the case of nitrogen) altered by stimulation.

In attempting to appraise the present position, so far as the metabolism of peripheral nerve is concerned, one cannot help feeling that one of the most striking points is that, although we know something

of the chemical events underlying the resting metabolism of nerve—
they are oxidative in character and the materials oxidised are in part,
but not wholly, carbohydrate in nature—we are still in the dark as to
the chemical changes underlying activity. They, too, are oxidative.
They should be measurable in amount, if we may judge from the heat
evolution, and since the respiratory quotient of the whole nerve rises
from 0.77 to 0.87, and the respiratory quotient of the extra oxygen
is 0.9 (Meyerhof and Schmitt), they too should involve the burning
of carbohydrate. But it has been shown (Holmes, Gerard, and Solomon) that the glycogen-sugar-lactic acid mechanism plays no part in
the metabolism of activity. No information, however, is yet available
as to whether the galactose fraction of cerebrosides plays any part in
the process. Perhaps the most significant fact, so far, is the old finding that extra ammonia is produced during the activity of nerve. In
the light of recent work on muscle, it would suggest the possibility
of the presence of an adenylic acid mechanism.

A point which is far from being finally settled is the relationship,
if any, of the oxygen consumption of resting nerve to its functional
condition. It has been repeatedly shown that nerves subjected to
severe and deliberate maltreatment—drying, boiling, or immersion in
alcohol, acids, alkalis, etc.—cease to take up oxygen. But nerves that
have been pretty severely handled in the course of removal from the
body take up oxygen just as do those which have been very carefully
treated, though the former would probably fail to conduct an impulse.
This oxygen consumption, too, will continue for many hours, though
in the absence of glucose or galactose in the surrounding fluid it
shows a gradual failure (Sherif and Holmes). Sherif has found that
the power of resting nerves to take up oxygen and to reduce methylene blue is affected by many drugs, including many of those usually
classed as local anaesthetics; but there is no correlation between the
power of different drugs to inhibit oxidations and their potency as
local anaesthetics.

A good deal of work has been directed to the elucidation of the
chemical mechanisms underlying the functions of peripheral nerve.
Less attention has been paid to those upon which those of the brain
depend, either at rest, or during activity. In an earlier part of this
article, mention has been made of some of the work concerned with
the oxidative processes in brain tissue, and it is remarkable that, for
the most part, these stand in sharp contrast, quantitatively, and to a
lesser degree qualitatively, to those which take place in peripheral

nerve, and in the white matter of the central nervous system. Yet, in the two instances, we have to deal only with different parts of the same cell, the cell body, and its process, the axon.

Our information about the oxidative processes of the brain is, for obvious technical reasons, far less complete than about those of nerve. The large oxygen consumption of grey matter makes it difficult to ensure that isolated portions of brain are properly supplied with oxygen under experimental conditions. There is at present no method by which it can be shown that isolated brain cells are in a state of activity. On the other hand, operative procedures, by which the metabolism of the organ *in situ* might be determined, are hampered by the fact that they necessarily entail anaesthesia, which at once frustrates the purpose of the experiment. Finally, it is difficult to be sure whether any chemical event (e.g., the oxidative removal of lactic acid) is a function of the cell or whether it takes place at the synapse. Brief mention has already been made of the work which showed that the oxygen consumption of the brain was of a large order. Further discussion will be found in a short review [Holmes (1)]. Chronologically, however, it is outside the scope of this article.

There is abundant evidence that brain tissue produces lactic acid freely from glucose (anaerobically), and that glucose increases the oxygen uptake of grey matter aerobically [Warburg, Posener, and Negelein; Holmes and Holmes (1); Loebel].

Jány and Sellei find that glycolysis proceeds rapidly under aerobic, as well as under anaerobic conditions. They have calculated the heat production due (*a*) to aerobic respiration, (*b*) to aerobic glycolysis, and (*c*) to anaerobic glycolysis, and (*d*) the total aerobic heat production. They find that all these values decrease with time. The most rapid decrease is in the ratios

$$\frac{\text{Heat of aerobic glycolysis}}{\text{Total heat}} \quad \text{and} \quad \frac{\text{Heat of anaerobic glycolysis}}{\text{Heat of aerobic respiration}}$$

These decreases, however, do not proceed so rapidly as to afford an obvious explanation of the known sensitivity of the tissue to asphyxia. But it must be remembered that we know almost nothing of the relationship of these metabolic processes to nerve-cell function.

Loebel, and Dickens and Simer (1, 2) have shown that the respiratory quotient of excised brain tissue is in the neighbourhood of unity

Ashford and Holmes (2) find it (if measured over a fairly long interval) to be a little below unity, unless lactate is added, when it rises to unity. Himwich and Nahum (1) find the R.Q. of dog brain *in situ* to be unity, whether the animal is anaesthetised or not, and whether it is normal, depancreatised, phlorhizinised, or both depancreatised and phlorhizinised. Further, they (2) find that the brain removes lactic acid and sugar from the blood passing through it.

Holmes and Holmes (1), comparing the lactic acid content of brain tissue, cooled, immediately after excision, in freezing mixture, with that of brain incubated anaerobically, found very little rise after incubation. They observed, however, that the brain lactic acid varied with the blood sugar. They therefore concluded that the brain depended on the blood for lactic acid precursor, and had no store of available carbohydrate of its own.

McGinty and Gesell and Jungmann (2) and Kinnersley and Peters (1), all using a liquid-air technique, obtained lower initial values and a definite rise on incubation. They were unwilling, therefore, to accept the view of Holmes and Holmes. It is indeed clear that Holmes and Holmes' "initial" values represented maximal, or nearly maximal ones. None of these workers, however, had repeated the experiments of Holmes and Holmes, which consisted in comparing brain lactic acid values with blood sugar content, the latter being altered by the injection of glucose or of insulin. This is now again being done (Holmes and Sherif) with the use of a liquid-air technique for "initial" values. It is found that initial values are quite low, and fairly uniform, no matter what the blood sugar. There is, however, a very nearly linear relationship between blood sugar content and brain lactic acid, between values of about 40 and 200 mg. of sugar per 100 cc. of blood—i.e., roughly, within physiological limits. For very high blood sugars, the curve flattens out markedly, and this flattening can be shown to be due to the fact that, beyond a certain point, the total carbohydrate in the brain fails to run parallel to the blood sugar value. There seems to be little doubt that the brain is, in reality, dependent for carbohydrate on its blood supply, as was originally claimed.

The work of Ashford and Holmes (1) shows (a) that, while brain tissue does form lactic acid from glycogen, through the mediation of hexose phosphate, this mechanism is responsible for only an insignificant part of the total lactic acid formed; (b) that the large amounts of lactic acid which are formed from glucose do not involve the intermediate formation of hexose phosphate.

Bumm and Fehrenbach have published experiments which throw much light on the general problems of carbohydrate metabolism. In the course of their work they have confirmed these findings of Ashford and Holmes by showing that lactic-acid production in brain is not increased by the addition of co-zymase or of hexokinase, both of which are concerned in the production of lactic acid from glycogen and hexose phosphate by red muscle. It is, however, increased by "coferment T" obtained from tumour tissue. They also show that neither arsenate nor phosphate increases lactic acid production in brain, though they do increase its production from glycogen by muscle. These findings are further confirmed by Béla Tanko. Sym, Nilsson, and v. Euler claim (on the basis of fermentation experiments, using different organ extracts) that there is a fairly large amount of cozymase in grey matter, a little in white, and still less in spinal cord.

Considerable mystery surrounds the fate of the lactic acid that is removed (*in vitro*) when brain tissue is shaken in oxygen. Holmes and Ashford have found that more lactic acid disappears than can be accounted for by the oxygen used, allowance being made for oxygen consumption on account of other substrates. Brain, in fact, shows a well-marked "Meyerhof quotient." But in spite of this, there is no synthesis of carbohydrate, either as reducing sugar, glycogen, or hexose phosphate. A large fraction of the lactic acid vanishes, and, up to the present, cannot be traced, though the results of estimations of total carbon make it unlikely that it has been synthesised into a compound (e.g., a lipoid) insoluble in the precipitating reagents used. Determinations of the respiratory quotient of the tissue alone, of the tissue with the lactate added to it, and determinations of the extra CO_2 produced and oxygen used, on account of the added lactate, show that the tissue alone has an R.Q. of about 0.92, and that the volume of extra CO_2 equals that of the extra oxygen. This indicates that part, at least, of the added lactate undergoes complete combustion.

It has been mentioned that glucose enables brain tissue, *in vitro*, to consume an increased amount of oxygen. Holmes (3) has shown that this oxidation of glucose involves a preliminary conversion of the substance to lactic acid (since fluoride inhibits the extra oxygen uptake with glucose, but not that with lactic acid). This finding has been confirmed by Krebs, who used monoiodoacetate, instead of fluoride, to inhibit glycolysis. Krebs found that this substance also inhibited the oxygen uptake with pyruvate, but not with tartrate, citrate, β-hydroxybutyrate, or glycine. Holmes (3) has also shown that, while lactate is an important substrate in brain, it is by no means the only one. Quastel and Wheatley (1) and Ashford and Holmes (2) have found a very marked increase with succinic acid.

Winterstein and Hirschberg showed that the frog's spinal cord produced ammonia in small amounts. The production was not increased by stimulation. Loebel observed the aerobic production of ammonia by slices of grey matter, and showed that this ammonia production was partially decreased by the presence of glucose and of lactate. Ashford and Holmes (2) have repeated Loebel's observations with regard to the suppression of ammonia production by lactate. They find, further, that lactate suppresses the liberation of some other soluble nitrogen fraction, since there is a "sparing" of total non-protein nitrogen which exceeds the ammonia "sparing."

Schwartz and Dibold, removing small portions of cortex rapidly and using a liquid-air technique, find an ammonia content of 0.2 to 0.3 mg. of ammonia nitrogen per 100 g. of tissue. Grinding the tissue in physiological saline before estimation doubles the value, and there is also an increase if the brain is damaged. Riebeling found (apparently without the use of liquid air) an initial ammonia value in rabbits' brain of 0.1 to 1.0 mg. per cent. ("Gehirnbrei" was used. Presumably this means chopped grey and white matter together. Schwartz and Dibold used cortex only.) On incubation at 40° for two hours with two per cent bicarbonate solution, this value increased to 8 to 10 mg. per cent. The increase was partly inhibited by $M/150$ NaF. (The increase here is very great, and, even so, it seems likely that some of the ammonia would have been lost unless special precautions were taken which are not mentioned in the paper. Ammonia would escape from a two per cent bicarbonate solution at 40°.)

In view of the fact that Pohle has described the presence of adenylic acid in brain and that Holmes and Holmes (1) noted the presence of a pentose, it is tempting to ascribe this ammonia production to the breakdown of adenylic acid. The work of Rösche certainly strengthens this presumption. In pursuance of earlier work with Te Kamp he has found that there is a marked formation of ammonia in the frog's retina on exposure to light (the phenomenon can be demonstrated either in the intact animal or in the isolated retina). Visible light and X-rays of medium wave-length cause this ammonia formation, while ultra-violet light does not. Retina forms ammonia from muscle and yeast adenine phosphoric acid, and from adenosine, but not from adenine. The retina contains a structure (the layer of rods and cones plus pigment layer) which may be considered as a peripheral sense organ. In addition it contains a neurone which is analogous to the peripheral nerve plus the posterior root ganglion cell, together with the synapse connecting the neurone to the sense organ, and a synapse analogous to that in the posterior horn of the spinal cord. The ammonia formation may be a function, therefore, of the peripheral sense organ, the nerve cells, the fibres, or the synapses. It is hard to see how these can be differentiated, and it is equally plain that results, obtained with retina, cannot be assumed necessarily to throw light on those occurring in the brain tissue itself. Nevertheless, the observations are most suggestive and interesting.

Edlbacher and Kutscher find that brain tissue will not. split off phosphate from nucleic acid, though retina can do so. Both brain tissue and retina will split off phosphate from hexose diphosphate.

Several of the earlier workers, who studied the oxygen consumption of the brain (e.g., Alexander and Cserna) have claimed that the brain shows increased oxygen consumption when thrown into activity. It seems certain that the oxygen consumption of peripheral nerve is increased by activity, and there is no reason to suppose that the tracts of white fibres in the central nervous system should behave in a different manner. Ledebur has, however, advanced a claim that there is no increased output of CO_2 by the active spinal cord (frog's), even after strychnine poisoning, provided such activity is brought about by stimulating the sciatics, and not by the direct application of stimuli to the cord itself. Direct application of stimuli gives rise to increased CO_2 output, even when the cord has lost all sign of reflex activity, though even this increase is abolished by KCN. The author, of course, claims that the method of direct stimulation is unphysiological, and that the increase in CO_2 output which accompanies it has nothing to do with the true activity of the tissue. The author makes acknowledgements to Winterstein, and it is clear that his findings fall into line with the contentions of Winterstein with regard to the oxygen consumption of peripheral nerve. Winterstein, on the other hand (1), claims that there is an increase in sugar breakdown on stimulating the spinal cord whether the stimulus is direct or reflex. This increase in carbohydrate metabolism does not, according to him, involve any increase in oxidation. Jungmann (2) failed to find an increase (in fact, he observed a fall) in lactic acid production on stimulation in the absence of added glucose. If, however, glucose was added, direct stimulation gave an increase in lactic acid (3).

Very little is known, at present, about the effect of pathological conditions on the metabolism of brain. The lactic acid content of the brain is lowered in insulin hypoglycaemia, and hypoglycaemia is accompanied by nervous symptoms, whether it is caused by insulin, by hepatectomy, or by other conditions. The power of glycolysis and lactic acid oxidation is unimpaired in the brains of depancreatised animals [Holmes and Holmes (2)]. Recently, Gavrilescu and Peters (1) have shown that brain tissue of polyneuritic pigeons shows a lowered power of oxygen consumption (*in vitro*) as compared to that of normal birds. The brains of birds that have been cured with vitamin B take up oxygen in the normal way. In a subsequent communication (2) they state that the addition of yeast concentrates to the tissue *in vitro* restores the power of oxygen consumption. Kinnersley and Peters (2) had previously described a localised lactic acidosis in pigeon's brain, as a result of vitamin B deficiency.

Guha (1) failed to find any consistent difference in the oxygen uptake of the brains of beri-beri rats when compared with normal rats, either when the tissue was shaken alone, or when lactate was added. Similarly, he failed to find any significant change in the lactic dehydrogenase system of the brain. He obtained (2) in mice and rats, in which galactose formed the sole dietary carbohydrate, but which were well supplied with vitamin B, nervous symptoms similar to those of beri-beri.

May has studied the chemical changes in degenerating nerves, with special reference to water and phosphorus.

There is very little definite information about the rôle of fat in the metabolism of the nervous system. Winterstein and his collaborators claim to have demonstrated a breakdown of fat in the surviving spinal cord of the frog. The papers are outside the scope of this review. The values found by Meyerhof and Schmitt for the respiratory quotient of resting nerve are so low as to suggest that fat is the fuel used. King has investigated the activity of lecithinase, but brain tissue does not appear to be particularly rich in this enzyme. Page and Schmitt find no evidence that lecithin is attacked at all by brain extract. Page and collaborators have dealt with certain aspects of the metabolism of lipoids [Page, Pasternak, and Burt; Page and

Reside; Page and Allen; Page and Menschick (1, 2); Rudy and Page]. While these findings cannot as yet be applied directly to the problems of the central nervous system, they will doubtless find a place in our future picture of events. Much other work, for example that of Barbour and collaborators on morphinism and the interesting experiments of McCowan and Quastel on hyperglycaemia in abnormal mental states, is excluded from this article by the necessarily rigorous limitations of space.

LITERATURE CITED

ALEXANDER, F. G., AND CSERNA, S., *Biochem. Z.*, 53, 100 (1913)

ASHFORD, C. A., AND HOLMES, E. G. (1), *Biochem. J.*, 22, 748 (1929)

ASHFORD, C. A., AND HOLMES, E. G. (2), *Biochem. J.*, 25, 2028 (1931)

BARBOUR, H. G., *Science*, 73, 346 (1931)

BARBOUR, H. G., ELLERBROOK, G. E., AND HOWARD, M. W., *Proc. Soc. Exptl. Biol. Med.*, 28, 551 (1931)

BARBOUR, H. G., GREGG, D. E., AND HUNTER, I. G., *J. Pharmacol.*, 40, 433 (1930)

BARBOUR, H. G., AND MARSHALL, H. T., *J. Pharmacol.*, 43, 147 (1931)

BARBOUR, H. G., AND TAYLOR, W. F., *J. Pharmacol.*, 42, 321 (1931)

BARRON, E. S. GUZMAN, *J. Exptl. Med.*, 52, 447 (1930)

BRONK, D. W., *J. Physiol.*, 71, 136 (1930)

BUMM, E., AND FEHRENBACH, K., *Z. physiol. Chem.*, 195, 101 (1931)

CHANG, T. H., *Proc. Soc. Exptl. Biol. Med.*, 28, 954 (1931)

CHANG, T. H., AND GERARD, R. W., *Am. J. Physiol.*, 97, 511 (1931)

DAVIS, H., *Physiol. Rev.*, 6, 547 (1926)

DICKENS, F., AND SIMER, S. (1), *Biochem. J.*, 24, 905 (1930)

DICKENS, F., AND SIMER, S. (2), *Biochem. J.*, 25, 985 (1931)

EDLBACHER, S., AND KUTSCHER, W., *Z. physiol. Chem.*, 199, 200 (1931)

EFINOFF, W. W. (1), *Biochem. Z.*, 219, 349 (1930)

EFINOFF, W. W. (2), *Biochem. Z.*, 219, 354 (1930)

EFINOFF, W. W. (3), *Biochem. Z.*, 219, 361 (1930)

FENG, T. P., AND GERARD, R. W., *Proc. Soc. Exptl. Biol. Med.*, 27, 1073 (1930)

FENN, W. O., *Am. J. Physiol.*, 92, 349 (1930)

FURUSAWA, K., *J. Physiol.,* **67**, 325 (1929)

GERARD, R. W. (1), *Am. J. Physiol.,* **82**, 381 (1927)

GERARD, R. W. (2), *Proc. Soc. Exptl. Biol. Med.,* **27**, 1052 (1930)

GERARD, R. W. (3), *Am. J. Physiol.,* **92**, 498 (1930)

GERARD, R. W. (4), *Am. J. Physiol.,* **97**, 523 (1931)

GERARD, R. W. (5), *Am. J. Physiol.,* **93**, 337 (1930)

GERARD, R. W. (6), *Science,* **72**, 195 (1930)

GERARD, R. W., AND MEYERHOF, O., *Biochem. Z.,* **191**, 126 (1927)

GERARD, R. W., AND TUPIKOW, N. (1), *Proc. Soc. Exptl. Biol. Med.,* **27**, 360 (1930)

GERARD, R. W., AND TUPIKOW, N. (2), *Am. J. Physiol.,* **97**, 523 (1931)

GERARD, R. W., AND WALLEN, J., *Am. J. Physiol.,* **89**, 108 (1929)

GRAVILESCU, N., AND PETERS, R. A. (1), *Biochem. J.,* **25**, 1397 (1931)

GRAVILESCU, N., AND PETERS, R. A. (2), *J. Physiol.,* **72**, 32 (1931)

GUHA, B. C. (1), *Biochem. J.,* **25**, 1367 (1931)

GUHA, B. C. (2), *Biochem. J.,* **25**, 1385 (1931)

HILL, A. V., *Proc. Roy. Soc. (London), B,* **105**, 153 (1929)

HIMWICH, H. E., AND NAHUM, L. H. (1), *Proc. Soc. Exptl. Biol. Med.,* **26**, 496 (1929)

HIMWICH, H. E., AND NAHUM, L. H. (2), *Am. J. Physiol.,* **90**, 389 (1929)

HOLMES, E. G. (1), *Biochem. J.,* **23**, 1182 (1929)

HOLMES, E. G. (2), *Brit. Med. J.* **(1929)(2)**, 861 (1929)

HOLMES, E. G. (3), *Biochem. J.,* **24**, 914 (1930)

HOLMES, E. G., AND ASHFORD, C. A., *Biochem. J.,* **24**, 1119 (1930)

HOLMES, E. G., AND GERARD, R. W., *Biochem. J.,* **23**, 738 (1929)

HOLMES, E. G., GERARD, R. W., AND SOLOMON, E. I., *Am. J. Physiol.,* **93**, 342 (1930)

HOLMES, B. E., AND HOLMES, E. G. (1), *Biochem. J.,* **19**, 492, 836 (1925)

HOLMES, B. E., AND HOLMES, E. G. (2), *Biochem. J.,* **21**, 412 (1927)

HOLMES, E. G., AND HOLMES, B. E. (3), *Minerva medica* Ann. **8**, No. 23 (1928)

HOLMES, E. G., AND SHERIF, M. A. F., (1931). To be published

HOU, C. L., *J. Oriental Med.,* **5**, No. 2 (1926)

HOU, C. L., AND SIGIURA, K., *J. Oriental Med.,* **5**, No. 3 (1926)

JÁNY, J., AND SELLEI, C., *Biochem. Z.,* **236**, 348 (1931)

JUNGMANN, H. (1), *Biochem. Z.,* **201**, 259 (1929)

JUNGMANN, H. (2), *Biochem. Z.,* **212**, 347 (1929)

JUNGMANN, H. (3), *Biochem. Z.,* **206**, 457 (1929)

KING, E. J., *Biochem. J.,* **25**, 799 (1931)

KEILIN, D., *Proc. Roy. Soc. (London), B,* **104**, 206 (1929)

KINNERSLEY, H. W., AND PETERS, R. A. (1), *Biochem. J.,* **22**, 1126 (1929)

KINNERSLEY, H. W., AND PETERS, R. A. (2), *Biochem. J.,* **24**, 711 (1930)

KREBS, H. A., *Biochem. Z.,* **234**, 278 (1931)

LEDEBUR, J. VON, *Arch. ges. Physiol.,* **227**, 343 (1931)

LEVIN, A., *J. Physiol.,* **63**, 113 (1927)

LOEBEL, R. O., *Biochem. Z.*, **161**, 219 (1925)

McCOWAN, P. K., AND QUASTEL, J. H., *J. Mental Science*, **77**, 525 (1931)

McGINTY, D. A., AND GESELL, R., *Am. J. Physiol.*, **88**, 312 (1925)

MAY, R. M., *Proc. Soc. Exptl. Biol. Med.*, **28**, 49 (1931)

MEYERHOF, O., AND SCHMITT, F. O., *Biochem. Z.*, **208**, 445 (1929)

MEYERHOF, O., AND SCHULZ, W. (1), *Biochem. Z.*, **206**, 158 (1929)

MEYERHOF, O., AND SCHULZ, W. (2), *Biochem. Z.*, **228**, 1 (1930)

MONAGHAN, B. R., AND SCHMITT, F. O., *Proc. Soc. Exptl. Biol. Med.*, **28**, 705 (1931)

NECHELES, H., AND GERARD, R. W., *Am. J. Physiol.*, **93**, 318 (1930)

PAGE, I. H., AND ALLEN, E. V., *Arch. exptl. Path. Pharmakol.*, **152**, 1 (1930)

PAGE, I. H., AND MENSCHICK, W. (1), *Biochem. Z.*, **221**, 6 (1930)

PAGE, I. H., AND MENSCHICK, W. (2), *Naturwissenschaften*, **33**, 735 (1930)

PAGE, I. H., PASTERNAK, L., AND BURT, M. L., *Biochem. Z.*, **223**, 335 (1930)

PAGE, I. H., AND RESIDE, D. M., *Biochem. Z.*, **223**, 172 (1930)

PAGE, I. H., AND SCHMIDT, E., *Z. physiol. Chem.*, **199**, 1 (1931)

POHLE, K., *Z. physiol. Chem.*, **185**, 281 (1929)

QUASTEL, J. H. (1), *Biochem. J.*, **25**, 898 (1931)

QUASTEL, J. H. (2), *Biochem. J.*, **25**, 1121 (1931)

QUASTEL, J. H., AND WHEATLEY, A. H. M. (1), *Biochem. J.*, **25**, 117 (1931)

QUASTEL, J. H., AND WHEATLEY, A. H. M. (2), *Biochem. J.*, **25**, 629 (1931)

RIEBELING, C., *Klin. Wochschr.* **(1931) (1)**, 553 (1931)

ROEDER, F. *Biochem. Z.*, **218**, 404 (1930)

RONZONI, E. J., *J. Biol. Chem.*, **92**, iii (1930)

RÖSCHE, H., *Z. physiol. Chem.*, **186**, 237 (1930)

RÖSCHE, H., AND TE KAMP, W., *Z. physiol. Chem.*, **175**, 158 (1928)

RUDY, H., AND PAGE, I. H., *Z. physiol. Chem.*, **193**, 251 (1930)

SCHMITT, F. O. (1), *Biochem. Z.*, **213**, 443 (1929)

SCHMITT, F. O. (2), *J. Physiol.*, **95**, 650 (1930)

SCHMITT, F. O., AND GASSER, H. S., *Am. J. Physiol.*, **97**, 558 (1930)

SCHMITT, F. O., AND SCHMITT, O. H. A., *Am. J. Physiol.*, **97**, 302 (1930)

SCHWARTZ, H., AND DIBOLD, H., *Klin. Wochschr.* **(1931) (1)**, 553 (1931)

SHERIF, M. A. F., *J. Pharmacol.*, **38**, 11 (1930)

SHERIF, M. A. F., AND HOLMES, E. G., *Biochem. J.*, **24**, 400 (1930)

SYM, E., NILSSON, R., AND EULER, H. VON, *Z. physiol. Chem.*, **190**, 228 (1931)

SZENT-GYÖRGYI, A. VON, *Biochem. Z.*, **150**, 195 (1924)

TANKO, BELA, *Biochem. Z.*, **239**, 318 (1931)

TASHIRO, S. (1), *Am. J. Physiol.*, **32**, 107 (1913)

TASHIRO, S. (2), *Am. J. Physiol.*, **60**, 519 (1922)

THUNBERG, T., *Skand. Arch. Physiol.*, **43**, 375 (1923)

VERNON, H. M. (1), *J. Physiol.*, **42**, 402 (1911)

VERNON, H. M. (2), *J. Physiol.*, **44**, 150 (1912)

WARBURG, O., *"Über die katalytischen Wirkung der lebendigen Substanz"* (Springer, Berlin, 1928)

WARBURG, O., POSENER, K., AND NEGELEIN, E., *Biochem. Z.*, **152**, 309 (1924)
WINTERSTEIN, H. (1), *Science,* **71**, 641 (1930)
WINTERSTEIN, H. (2), *Arch. ges. Physiol.*, **224**, 749 (1930)
WINTERSTEIN, H. (3), *Biochem. Z.*, **232**, 196 (1930)
WINTERSTEIN, H., AND HIRSCHBERG, E., *Biochem. Z.*, **167**, 401 (1926)

PHARMACOLOGICAL LABORATORY
UNIVERSITY OF CAMBRIDGE
CAMBRIDGE, ENGLAND

CHEMICAL EMBRYOLOGY*

By Joseph Needham

*Fellow of Gonville and Caius College, Cambridge, England, and
University Demonstrator of Biochemistry*

Introduction

The subject of the chemistry of embryonic development is in a peculiarly suitable position for review in the first volume of the *Annual Review of Biochemistry,* for the publication of the first monograph in this field [Needham (1)] took place a few months ago. The nature of its plan involved the mention, or at least the attempt to make mention, of all relevant facts, but this had the disadvantage of taking several years in production, and therefore necessarily omitting work published some months before the date of its own publication. The present review takes up the story, then, from the summer of 1931 onwards.

The Egg as a Physico-Chemical System

The cuticle of the hen's egg has long been known as a thin homogeneous membrane outside the shell, not always present, but often containing a pigment. This has received of late its first chemical examination, by Furreg. Building upon the prior observations of Derrien and of Tapernoux, who found that hen's egg shell gives a red fluorescence in ultra-violet light, Furreg established the presence of porphyrins in the cuticle. But it appears to have little functional importance as a protector of the germ, as it is very easily destroyed (see the curious abstract of Querner). Shell porosity in the hen's egg has been examined anew by Almquist and Holst, who were able to obtain a quantitative measure of porosity by the use of methylene blue staining. The relation between loss of weight and porosity number was linear. The belief that shell porosity is greater at the air-space region, held often in the past and supported by the experiments of Swenson and Mottern with oil, was contradicted by the work of Almquist and Holst. If the infertile egg is kept, the porosity increases (because of the disappearance of the cuticle?).

Work of more general interest on egg-membranes has been carried

* Received November 10, 1931.

out by Leitch, who has calculated the velocity constants of the swelling of various marine eggs in various salt solutions. Other permeability studies on echinoderm eggs have been made by Howard (on the effect of the pH of the medium on egg viscosity) by Stewart (on the penetration of non-electrolytes and ammonium salts), and by Lucke (on the action of urethanes on permeability to water). Then Pumphrey studied the potential difference across the surface bounding the unfertilised trout egg. Here the sphere of yolk is bounded by a layer of protoplasm and then by a thin but tough elastic membrane, the chorion. A micro-pipette was inserted into the egg, and the potential neutralised by a slide-wire potentiometer and a Lindemann electrometer. The normal value (different for ordinary and for distilled water) was constant but fluctuated if the egg died. When the external medium was a dilute solution of a non-toxic salt, the E.M.F. was found to be a linear function of the logarithm of the ionic activity, with a gradient characteristic of the salt used. The sign was what would be expected if the membrane were more permeable to cations than anions. Pumphrey gives a discussion comparing the trout egg-membrane with other membranes and with models.

This work stands in close relation with that carried out by a group of Cambridge investigators on the vitelline membrane of the hen's egg, and the relation between the osmotic pressures of yolk and white. It had long been known that a difference of some two atmospheres existed between these phases, and that osmotic equilibrium was only very slowly attained in the intact infertile or fertile unincubated egg (3 months at 24°C.). In view of the water-current yolkwards [Needham (1), Sec. 6.4] this must be of great biological importance. Now in 1929, Straub and Hoogerduyn suggested that the mechanism responsible for this delayed equilibrium was a direct combustion of carbohydrate at the surface of the vitelline membrane—a suggestion of some interest in view of its non-protoplasmic keratinoid nature. These views were rapidly taken up in widely different quarters [Hill (1), Kluyver, Gray] and somewhat uncritically accepted, but Needham and Smith, in a review of the question, pointed out that deeper study was required. Smith and Shepherd then removed the basis from Straub's crucial experiment, by showing that the recovery of hypertony by a yolk, previously diluted by immersion in water, when it is replaced in egg-white, can be explained by a temporary heterogeneity of the diluted yolk more easily than by the performance of thermodynamic work at the membrane. Smith and Shepherd also showed that the equilibration curves indicated rather a hindered diffusion equilibration than the maintenance of a steady state terminated by death. Nor did the yolk show any tendency to maintain its hypertony when the white was concentrated by rapid evaporation.

Next Smith examined very carefully the carbon dioxide production and oxygen consumption of the infertile hen's egg with the result that, although carbon dioxide is regularly produced, this cannot be due to respiration, since there is no oxygen-uptake. This was in agreement with the work of Hill (2), who had shown that the slow rate of equilibration was unaffected by keeping the eggs in atmospheres of hydrogen, and with that of Needham, Stephenson, and Needham, who could observe no oxygen-uptake *in vitro* of yolk or vitelline membranes. Straub's process must, therefore, if it existed at all, be anaerobic. The membranes were found by Needham, Stephenson, and Needham, to be devoid of dehydrogenase activity, but these authors, using elaborate bacteriological precautions, were able to establish the existence of a slow breakdown of glucose in the yolk. The magnitude of the energy change resulting, however, was hardly answerable to that demanded on Straub's hypothesis. Finally, the osmotic properties of the vitelline membrane itself in isolation were studied by Needham (2) in a specially constructed dialysing apparatus. When placed between two salt solutions of different strengths, it opposed no resistance to the dilution of the stronger and the concentration of the weaker. When separated by a collodion membrane, yolk and white rapidly attained osmotic equilibrium, but when separated by the vitelline membrane *in vitro*, they equilibrated much more slowly though not as slowly as in the intact egg. It was concluded that the steady state of the intact egg arises out of some collaboration between yolk, white, and membrane, the two former possessing some physical structural feature which retards equilibration, and the latter being more efficient than a collodion membrane in hindering the passage of ions and water between yolk and white.

These conclusions were questioned by Grollman, who put forward the view that the osmotic pressure of yolk (Δ —0.6) as usually given, was illusory, being due to supercooling, and was really the same as that of the white. This view offered no real explanation for the correspondence between the osmotic pressure measurements and the measurements with the vapour-pressure method of Hill (1). Nor did it explain the concentration-increase with time on the part of white separated from yolk by a collodion membrane. Grollman's suggestion was subsequently withdrawn by Meyerhof, who showed that its principal support derived from an experiment in which the yolk had been diluted by the *"Quellungswasser"* contained in a collodion bag. Smith, Shepherd, and Needham also showed that yolk and white, mixed with salt solutions of presumed isotonicity, gave unaffected freezing-points.

An elaborate contribution to the chemistry of avian egg-white is that of Mazza, who gives full details concerning the physico-chemical properties of ovomucoid. His material must have been much purer than that of any previous worker; it gave a molecular weight of 49,270, and an isoelectric point of pH 2.8. Holst and Almquist report that the percentage of solids is the same in the thin and thick egg-white, as also the refractive index (in contradiction with the results of Romanov). A rapid equilibrium exists with respect to water between the thin and thick egg-white (in contradiction with the results of Smith and Shepherd), but does this conclusion necessarily follow from the data of Holst and Almquist? Further insight into the complex physical structure of the egg-white is afforded by the observations of Heringa and Valk on protein fibrils arranged concentrically. These they believe to be keratin (cf. the earlier work on egg-white structure by Remotti).

The passage of water from white to yolk in the infertile egg, studied by Needham and his collaborators, was approached from another angle by Sharp and Powell (1), who measured the degree of flattening in yolks resting upon a flat surface. Provided the elastic properties of the vitelline membrane remain the same, the greater the water-content of the yolk, the more ellipsoidal it should become. Sharp and Powell's curves for decrease of height/width ratio with time at different temperatures therefore approximate to those of Smith and Shepherd for osmotic pressure. The pH of white and yolk has been studied anew by Baird and Prentice, Gaggermeier, and Sharp and Powell (2), who, however, confined their attention to the changes which occur upon keeping in the infertile egg [Needham (1), Sec. 6.2].

New information about the fatty acids of the yolk has been given by Sueyoshi and Sueyoshi and Furukobo. The elaboration of a new method for preparing egg-yolk lecithin was followed by an examination of the fatty acids present in its molecule. The saturated ones were found to consist mainly of isopalmitic acid, with small amounts of stearic and palmitic acids; the unsaturated ones mostly of oleic but also some linolic and clupanodonic acid. Clupanodonic acid was formerly thought to occur only in fish oils, and its identification in the avian egg is of some embryological importance, in view of the probable incapacity of the early embryo to desaturate fatty acids [Needham (1), Secs. 1.9 and 11.1]. Thus Levene and Rolf in 1922 obtained arachidonic acid from ovolecithin, and Stephenson in 1912 obtained an unidentified fatty acid with 6 or 8 double bonds (clupanodonic has 4).

The effect of the diet of the maternal organism on the egg has been studied by Pollard and Carr and by Gerber and Carr. The former workers estimated the ammonia and melanin nitrogen in pigeon eggs after feeding on a variety of diets (rye, corn, kafir, wheat, oats, hemp, pea, and barley). The variations were considerable and regular, ranging in the case of melanin N from 0.7 to 4.0 per cent. Hatchable eggs were produced only from rye, wheat, oat, and corn diets; in these cases, the melanin N was above 3.3 per cent. The work was continued and extended by Gerber and Carr, who estimated the various fractions of nitrogen in protein hydrolysates from eggs of different diet groups. Ammonia N showed the greatest deviations, being 4.7 per cent of the total N for rye, 8.4 per cent for barley, and 10.4 per cent for soy bean. As judged by photographs (but quantitative data were apparently lacking) the growth of the embryo was accelerated by soy bean, hemp, wheat, and kafir, but delayed by corn and oats as much as 50 per cent below the normal. The great drawback of these interesting studies is the comparative crudeness of the available estimation methods for characterising proteins. Similar work was done by McFarlane, Fulmer, and Jukes, but with better biological background, for they related the chemical composition of their eggs with the standard mortality curve of the chick embryo [Needham (1), Sec. 18.2]. As between eggs of low and high hatchability no significant difference was found in total N, total amino N, or tyrosine, tryptophane, or cystine content. Moreover, neither these values nor the total ash and iron determinations showed much variation with the diet. Copper content, however, was very variable. The marked anaemic state which accompanies the high mortality of embryos in eggs from hens fed on tankage and meat meal remains therefore unexplained, and must be due to something rather more subtle than has so far been brought to light. Insect eggs are also susceptible to dietary abnormalities, for

Gause has shown that restricted food intake in the larval stage of *Drosophila* leads to a 6 per cent diminution in egg-size.

Researches solely directed to estimation of metals are those of Guerithault, who finds copper in avian egg-yolk but not in the white, and Glaser, who reports copper in echinoderm eggs. Skinner and Peterson find small quantities of manganese in the hen's egg [Needham (1), pp. 304, 305].

Knowledge concerning the chemical constitution of the eggs of invertebrates accumulates slowly. Thus Sagara has studied the amino-acid distribution in the protein (a keratin) of the eggshells of the gastropod *Hemifusus tuba*. Titschak has given some quantitative data on the egg of the bed-bug *Cimex lectularius,* and Sacharov on that of *Locusta migratoria*. The specific gravity of marine eggs has been studied by Sanzo and the surface tension by Harvey, while a curious phenomenon which occurs during the development of the egg of the mollusc *Limnaea* has been studied by Comandon and de Fonbrune (1). These eggs float freely in their egg-cases, and after fertilisation lie at the bottom, but when both polar globules have been emitted, they rise to the upper part of the egg-case and float there, only to fall slowly to the bottom again during the early cleavages. This diminution of specific gravity on the part of the egg can only be explained by the emission of substances heavier than the perivitelline liquid—the authors suggest glycogen, since glycogen has been observed histochemically in the perivitelline liquid. The question merits, however, further physico-chemical examination.

ON INCREASE IN SIZE AND COMPLEXITY

The striking dissociability of growth, differentiation, respiration, and fermentation [Needham (1), pp. 542 ff. and 1650] has again been made manifest by several observers. Working with heart fibroblasts in tissue culture Partachnikov has shown that quinine exercises a differential action on the growth and utilisation of glucose by the explanted cells. With rising concentration of quinine, the former is inhibited some time before the latter. Similarly, Mikhailovski reports that radium emanation has a similar effect on heart fibroblasts of the chick embryo *in vitro*.

More straightforward studies on embryonic growth have been made by Latimer and Aikman on the cat, demonstrating cephalocaudal differential growth-rate, maxima in percentage participation of parts, etc.

A fundamental contribution to the data on growth is that of Henderson, who has made a thorough study of the effect of breed and temperature upon the growth of the chick embryo. The influence of temperature was found to be considerable, especially in the earlier periods of development, for by the sixteenth day temperature control is developing (confirmation of Brody and Henderson). Temperature coefficients (but not characteristics) were calculated. Henderson fits straight lines (like Brody) not curves (like McDowell) to his data on semilog plots, and deduces the existence of three (perhaps four) periods of constant growth-rate, the limits of which occur at 4, 7, 16½, and 20 days. These periods are identified by Henderson with the periods of predominant combustion of carbohydrate protein and fat [Needham (1), Sec. 7 . 7], but it is a little difficult to picture why a characteristic growth-rate should be associated with the combustion of a particular type of chemical molecule. It would be more convincing to correlate growth-rate with the constitution of the embryonic body, and in fact this does also divide into similar periods (evidence given in Needham (1), Sec. 6 . 8). Henderson found little if any constant significant difference in the growth of embryos from different strains and breeds. The growth of the chick embryo has also been handled by Hoesslin, but not on the basis of new data. He discusses the fit of various formulae. In this connection Schmalhausen and W. Ludwig have recently engaged in a lively mathematical polemic on embryonic growth, but their arguments must be read in the original.

More interesting, perhaps, is the work of Bhatia, who has studied the growth of the muscle-cells in the developing trout, in an attempt to assess the relative importance at different stages of the two components of growth: cell-division, and increase in cell-size. In the larval, free-swimming, yolk-sac period, the relative growth of the muscle-cells is enormous, i.e., each cell expands in size, so that the transverse linear dimension of the fish plotted against the transverse linear dimension of muscle fibres gives a curve rising almost vertically. But as soon as the yolk is exhausted and the fish begins to take food, the rate of individual cell-growth falls rapidly, although the size of the whole body of the fish continues to increase. This discrepancy is made good by the formation of new cells, for cell-multiplication has now begun. Thus, before the exhaustion of the yolk, growth mainly depends on increase in size of the same cells with which the fish hatched, but afterwards it depends mainly on the formation of new

cells. These phenomena call to mind the statement of certain investigators that egg-yolk (of the chick) contains a "growth-inhibiting" or
rather, mitosis-inhibiting, substance. Bhatia's work furnishes a model
for new analysis of the components of embryonic growth in a quantitative way.

The first analytical study of the growth-rates of water, ash, protein, calcium, etc., in human pre-natal life is still in press, but an
abstract has appeared (Scammon). Three types of growth are to be
distinguished: (1) water, solids, protein; (2) ash; (3) fat. All show
different rates from the structural components, except 3.

Attempts to grow chick embryos successfully until the end of development *in vitro* have been common in the past, and not usually
very successful. A recent one is that of Romanov. But using what
seems to be a very adequate technique for this purpose, Kaufman
has investigated the quantitative differences in body-size of avian
embryos. The primitive streak was found to appear at the same time
after fertilisation in both fowls and pigeons, but from its very first
appearance the embryo of the former was statistically larger in all
dimensions than the latter. The ratio of body-size of fowl to pigeon
is therefore the same throughout embryonic life and the differences
seen later are not mere differences in the rate of growth of organisms
originally the same size.

Temperature and growth-rate have been studied by D. Ludwig
for the beetle *Popillia japonica,* by Davidson for the lucerne flea
Sminthurus viridis, by Toumanov and Zernov for *Dixippus morosus,*
and by Andersen for the "Graurüssler" beetle *Sitona lineata.* All
these data can be fitted by catenary curves following Janisch's treatment, but temperature coefficients are also given. Andersen also
studied the effect of humidity on hatching-time and observed a regular relation, dryness being a retarding agency. This is important in
view of our ignorance of the water-metabolism of terrestrial insect
eggs [Needham (1), p. 905].

Turning to studies on the chemical aspects of morphogenesis, we
have further contributions by Fell and by Fell and Robison. Fell
has given a review of the important work of the Strangeways Institute on osteogenesis *in vitro,* and Fell and Robison extended their
earlier work to the Meckel's rod of the lower jaw of the chick embryo (a cartilage which does not normally ossify) and to mandibular
osteogenic mesoderm (membrane-bone). Phosphatase measurements
were carried out parallel with histological description. It was found

that the palato-quadrate and femur, used as controls, developed high phosphatase activity, while the non-ossifying part of Meckel's rod remained devoid of phosphatase—and all this took place *in vitro* just as *in vivo*. Membrane-bone in the course of its formation also synthesised phosphatase. It will be remembered that in previous work these authors had shown the absence of ossification and phosphatase activity when explants were made of third-day limb-buds.

Attention must also be drawn to the valuable review of Hertwig and Hertwig on the regulation of growth and differentiation by external physico-chemical and other conditions. Quite new ground is broken by Woodger in a series of theoretical papers, in which he seeks to explore the possibilities of mathematical logic in relation to the organisation of embryonic development.

EMBRYONIC RESPIRATION

The old observation of Warburg and others, that the respiration of echinoderm eggs decreases in rate with rising concentration of hydrogen ions, has been confirmed by Ashbel (1). She also found that the intensity of respiration of fertilised eggs may be reduced by 70 per cent without the capacity for further development being affected. Similarly, fertilisability is not affected by drastic suppression of respiration in the unfertilised egg. Brinley made the curious observation that KCN micro-injected into the echinoderm egg had much less effect upon the subsequent rate of cleavage than immersion in KCN solutions. The classical decrease of metabolic rate with age has been established for yet another organism, the Pacific killifish, *Fundulus parvipinnis,* by Keys. Metabolic studies on the human embryo, in so far as it can be approached through the maternal body, are contained in the work of Plass and Yoakam.

Hitherto no information has been available concerning the part played by the extra-embryonic membranes in the respiration of the intact hen's egg, although in the absence of such information, no assessment of the true metabolic rate of the chick embryo can be had. Building on the extensive and careful data of Byerly for the growth of yolk-sac, allantois, etc., Needham (4) has studied the *in vitro* respiration of the membranes throughout development, with the aid of the manometric methods of Barcroft and Warburg. Changes in growth-rate of the membranes are reflected in changes in their respiratory intensities, and a maximum absolute oxygen-uptake of the membranes is reached on the seventeenth day. The maximum percentage participation, however, occurs during the first week. These results made possible the calculation of the embryo's true metabolic rate, the true plastic efficiency coefficient, and the true apparent energetic efficiency [Needham (1), Secs. 6.10 and 7.5]. During the first week an extraordinarily high efficiency of growth on the part of the blastoderm is seen.

METABOLISM OF CARBOHYDRATES

A useful piece of work on the effect of various factors on the blood-sugar of the chick embryo is due to Vladimirov, although its results were somewhat negative. Introduction of water into the airspace of the egg decreased the blood-sugar level by dilution, but no consistent effects of carbon dioxide or insulin could be observed. The influence of adrenalin could be established only during the last week of incubation, and then to but a feeble degree. Vladimirov concludes that the principal causes of regularities in the developing embryo lie in the developing cells themselves and not in the action of stimulating substances. Further work on the precise part played by endocrine influences here is much to be desired.

Doljanski (1) considers that his experiments show an antagonism between growth and glycogen-storage in explanted embryonic liver cells. Liver cells growing rapidly in tissue culture show no glycogen histochemically, but they can be made to do so if their growth is experimentally retarded. This leads to the generalisation that growth and active function cannot proceed in the same cell at the same time— a generalisation supported by previous work on explanted liver cells [Needham (1), p. 1028] and by Doljanski's (2) observation that explanted epithelium cells of the iris will synthesise melanin only if they are made to grow very slowly. Following on much older work on the mammalian "transitory liver" (see Needham, Sec. 8.5), Loveland, Maurer, and Snyder have studied the disappearance of the glycogen store in the rabbit placenta during the last third of pregnancy. Their chemical determinations show a decrease from 100 mg. glycogen at 22 days to less than 25 mg. at term (32 days), and they give good colour plates of their histochemical pictures.

METABOLISM OF NITROGEN

The excretion of nitrogenous end-products in embryonic life has invited several interesting researches. Boyden has investigated the growth of the mesonephros during the period of maximum protein catabolism of the chick embryo (fifth to fourteenth day). During this time the total nitrogen excretion (ammonia, urea, and uric acid, grows to 1,700 times its original value [Needham (1), Fig. 324] but, although the Wolffian body increases its volume twelve times, there is no significant increase in glomerular count. The tubule volume increases sixteen times, the renal corpuscle volume three times, the collecting tubule volume ten times, and the secretory tubule volume thirty-three times. These facts provoke reflection on the preparation of the embryonic kidney for its work, and are relevant to the recent conclusion of Needham (3) that the uric acid in the allantoic liquid is free. It would be interesting to know whether the reabsorption of base (now demonstrated by Wigglesworth for the Malpighian tubules of insects) occurs in the avian kidney and allantois as well as the reabsorption of water.

Silkworm and echinoderm eggs have been stated by Ashbel (2) to excrete ammonia during their development, but whereas this process possesses some *a priori* probability in the latter case, it does not in the former, and we may question whether the activities of bacteria and moulds should not be looked into before the acceptance of the results. The echinoderm eggs (*Strongylocentrotus lividus* and *Sphaerechinus granularis*) gave out from 0.12 to 1.50 mg. ammonia per hour per cubic mm. of centrifuged eggs, and the rate of production was very little affected by fertilisation (this agrees with the R.Q. of 1.0 so often found before and after fertilisation). The effects of CO and KCN were studied by Ashbel. The work of Chouke on urea excretion in foetal rabbits is also open to criticism, for he concludes that as urine is rare in the foetal bladder, urea excretion does not begin until after birth. What of the placental exit? Remarkable contractions of cleaving mollusc eggs, together with jets of liquid differing in refractive index from the perivitelline liquid, are recorded in the cinema film of Comandon and de Fonbrune (2)—an interesting field for research on nitrogen excretion in embryonic life is thus opened up. The contractile movements of the blastoderm in the fish *Oryzias latipes,* reported by Yamamoto, may also have a connection with the disposal of nitrogenous waste.

On the nutritional side, Pierantoni has studied the histochemistry of the nitrogenous yolk platelets in the frog egg, and Zifferblatt and Seelaus have found in the blood plasma of the chick embryo an excellent source of the growth-promoting proteose. The maximum of protease activity in the yolk corresponding with the time of maximum protein catabolism on the part of the embryo [Needham (1), p. 1309] established for the chick has been extended to the duck by Calzoni.

METABOLISM OF LIPOIDS, STEROLS, PHOSPHORUS, AND SULPHUR

A histochemical paper by Voss records the distribution of "plasmal" during the development of the axolotl egg. This body, which is believed to be a mixture of higher aliphatic aldehydes, shows a remarkable restriction to the ectodermal cells. Practically nothing has been done on sterol metabolism in embryonic life, but Schönheimer and Behring, in support of their view that dihydrocholesterol is formed by the body and not by bacterial action, found 7 per cent of the total cholesterol of the (sterile) meconium in human embryos to be dihydrocholesterol.

Phosphagen has recently been studied from an embryological standpoint for the first time. In the development of *Sepia officinalis,* the squid, it rises (expressed as percentage of the total water-soluble phosphorus) to a maximum towards the end, after which it falls off (Needham, Needham, Yudkin, and Baldwin). This is interpreted as a chemical aspect of the maximum ponderal participation of the muscular system in the total body-weight. Arginine phosphate has also been found by Needham, Needham, Baldwin, and Yudkin in the developing embryos of echinoderms, a possible indication that the phosphagens may be as necessary in ciliary as in muscular motion.

Kamiya has estimated the reduced glutathione during the development of the chick embryo; his data are in agreement with previous work [Needham (1), p. 1232], showing a maximum in percentage wet weight on the thirteenth day. Applying the nitroprusside test as a histochemical technique, Dulzetto was able to demonstrate the presence of reduced glutathione in the unfertilised echinoderm egg, and a marked increase of it at the very moment of fertilisation (confirmation of Shearer). His colour plates illustrate this strikingly.

INORGANIC METABOLISM

The first thorough examination of the distribution of ash in the chick embryo during development has been made by Mankin, who estimated chloride, potassium, sodium, and calcium. Plotted against wet weight, all except calcium remain roughly constant, but calcium increases some twenty times from the twelfth day onwards, corresponding with the intake of calcium from the shell [Needham (1), Fig. 406, confirming Plimmer and Lowndes]. Plotted against the dry weight, however, all the ions fall some ten times between the fourth and the twenty-first day [amplifying Needham (1), Fig. 402], except calcium, in which case the calcification and the increasing dryness of the embryo cancel each other out. The iron in the embryonic body has received a detailed study at the hands of Kojima. Starting at 0.066 mg. per gm. wet weight on the fourth day it rose to about 0.2 mg. per gm. on the tenth, after which Kojima estimated it in many organs separately. Wide variations were observed, but there were maxima at 15 days (liver), 16 (heart and brain), and 18 (leg muscles). These maxima are later than those of previous authors for glutathione and cytochrome. In fresh egg-yolk 0.03 mg. Fe per gm. wet weight was found, but in fresh egg-white none.

Iron has also been estimated in mammalian foetal livers by Roussel and Deflandre (1), and the same authors (2) have drawn attention to the masses of micro-crystals of calcium carbonate and phosphate in the foetal liver cells of cow and sheep. They have also (3) reported the presence of copper in these foetal liver cells, in amounts (histochemically) diminishing with age (see also Noel, Pigeaud, and Millet).

The effects of salts upon embryonic development have been studied in the case of the salt-resistant phyllopods by Matthias and by Boone and Becking. The latter authors found that the conditions which allow of embryonic development up to the extrusion of the inner membrane are much more varied than those which permit of the ecdysis of the embryo from this membrane. They made a thorough investigation of the proportions of salts necessary, together with the various possible antagonisms, and expressed the results in a three-dimensional isometric projection. On the basis of the experimental facts they were able to account for the peculiar ecological distribution of the organism.

Pigments

The presence of cytochrome in bee, silkworm, and hen eggs is reported by Ito, and Teodoro has written on the lipochrome pigments of silkworm eggs. With regard to mammals, Esskuchen deals with pigmentation in the developing cow foetus, and Kindred and Corey describe the haemoglobin content and the differential erythrocyte count in the foetal rat.

The most interesting work on this subject has been that of Slonimski. Using his benzidine method for the histochemical investigation of haemoglobin, he examined the formation of the blood in the amphibian embryo, and ascertained that haemoglobin is formed in the mother-cells of the erythrocytes long before they pass into the blood stream. By extirpating the primary areas of erythrocyte production Slonimski could obtain embryos with fully developed circulatory systems but devoid of haemoglobin and of red blood corpuscles. Presumptive blood "islands," grown *in vitro,* showed self-differentiation both morphological (as to vascular epithelium and erythrocytes) and chemical (as to haemoglobin formation). By further extirpation experiments Slonimski was able to show that the leucocytes do not originate from the same place as the erythrocytes. It is much to be wished that a concerted attack could be made upon the problem of haemoglobin formation from a chemical point of view.

HORMONES

Injection experiments with hen's eggs have not brought us many results of a definite character. No striking changes followed Ohnishi's (1) injection of adrenalin into the air-space of the hen's egg at the beginning of development, and the same author (2) could observe only a slight hypertrophy of testes and thyroids after the similar injection of thymus extract. Wehefritz and Gierhake also observed an effect on the testes of the developing chick embryo when menformon and progynon were injected into its egg early in development. Lehmann, working with amphibian embryos, states that adrenalin has a perceptible effect upon them, a maximum of susceptibility occurring at gastrulation.

Pankratz has made an interesting correlation between the development of the suprarenal gland in mammalian embryos and the first appearance of foetal movements. The following table shows a remarkable correspondence between the possible events in a causal chain:

Animal	Maximum of Migration of Sympatho-chromaffin Cells		Onset of Chromaffin Reaction	Onset of Positive Chemical Adrenalin Tests	First Appearance of Embryonic Movements	
	Days	mm.	Days	Days	Days	mm.
Chick	5.4	....	8.0	8.0	5.0	....
Mouse	14.5	....	14.5	14.5	16.0	....
Rat	15.5	....	....	....	16.0	....
Rabbit	15.5	....	....	....	15.5	....
Cat	....	17.0	....	....	....	18.0
Man	....	17.0	154.0	84.0	....	27.0

Having added his own observations on the developing suprarenal of the rat to all the data recorded in the literature, Pankratz draws attention to the known effect of adrenalin in affecting the threshold of skeletal muscle in the adult, and suggests a connection between foetal movements and the development of the suprarenal gland.

PLACENTAL PERMEABILITY AND PLACENTAL METABOLISM

On the general question of oviparity and viviparity, Amemiya and Murayama believe that they have glimpsed a transition stage in the normally oviparous teleost *Oryzias latipes,* in which developing eggs were sometimes found. Placentation in reptiles has been further studied by Weekes, and Hagan's brilliant investigation of the viviparous insect *Hesperoctenes fumarius* with its placentoid structures is now available. The chemical characterisation of an insect "placenta" would be of the greatest possible evolutionary interest.

Regarding the exchange between the bloods in mammals, a paper by Eastman and McLane informs us that the lactic acid in the human foetal circulation is well within normal limits, although it is regularly elevated at birth [Needham (1), p. 1527], owing to the maternal blood being then flooded with lactic acid. For protein and non-protein nitrogen in maternal and foetal cow blood, values are given by Santa, while Garofalo finds, in agreement with many other authors, that the foetal serum calcium is higher than that of the mother [Needham (1), Sec. 21.13]. A valuable paper by Haselhorst and Stromberger gives new experiments on gas exchange through the placenta, uncomplicated by the effects of birth, Caesarean sections having been made. The following table shows the results in volumes per cent:

Maternal Blood	O_2	CO_2
Going to the placenta (A. epigastrica)	14.19	38.92
Going from the placenta (uterine vein)	10.45	42.38
Foetal Blood		
Going from placenta to foetus (umbilical vein)	3.97	44.95
Going from foetus to placenta (umbilical artery)	0.84	47.03

Thus there are continuous gradients in both directions, gradients of a sufficient steepness to obviate the necessity of any appeal to secretory properties of the placental cells.

The interesting investigations of Brandstrup (1) on the equilibria between maternal and foetal bloods have been continued a good deal further. By the use of successive rabbit foetuses of one litter, sufficient blood samples can be obtained for the establishment of a curve after injection of substances into the maternal blood stream. In this way Brandstrup (1) finds that the passage of glucose and pentoses is explainable as a slow diffusion through a passive membrane, while the placental epithelium is impermeable to disaccharides. Secondly, he finds (2) that an increase in the amino-acid content of the maternal blood is immediately followed by a corresponding increase in that of the foetal blood until equilibrium is attained. But he prefers to attribute the well-known slight excess of amino-nitrogen commonly found in the foetal blood [cf. Needham (1), Sec. 21 . 10] to differences in the binding power of the colloids present, rather than to (a) a Donnan equilibrium mechanism, or (b) a secretory action of the placental cells. The old opinion that the mammalian placenta was impermeable to fatty acids, never very convincing, has now been made still more unlikely by the chemical experiments of Migliavacci. Some work on the hormone concentration of the two bloods (Siegert and Neumann) is also relevant here. Transmission of antibodies, etc., has been studied by Grasset, by Kaboth, and by Haselhorst. Harris has drawn attention to the importance of infarcts (obliterative endarteritis) in the human placenta, with regard to the exchange of biologically desirable or undesirable substances between maternal organism and foetus.

Very little has been done on the metabolism of the placental cells themselves. Bidone reports the presence of catalase in them, and Ganfini summarises current work on their characteristic hormones. Genell has found citric acid, and Laurentis other substances, in human amniotic liquid.

LITERATURE CITED

ALMQUIST, H. J., and HOLST, W. F., Hilgardia, 6, 61 (1931)

AMEMIYA, I., and MURAYAMA, S., Proc. Imp. Acad. (Tokyo), 7, 176 (1931); Ber. Wiss. Biol., 18, 703 (1931)

ANDERSON, K. T., Z. Morphol. Ökol. Tiere, 17, 649 (1930)

ASHBEL, R. (1), Pubbl. staz. zool. Napoli, 11, 194 (1913)

ASHBEL, R. (2), Pubbl. staz. zool. Napoli, 11, 204 (1931)

BAIRD, I. C., and PRENTICE, J. H., *Analyst,* 55, 20 (1930)
BHATIA, D., *Z. Zellforsch. mikrosk. Anat.,* 12, 430 (1931)
BIDONE, M., *Ann. Ostet.,* 52, 1136 (1930)
BOONE, E., and BECKING, L. G. M. B., *J. Gen. Physiol.,* 14, 753 (1931)
BOYDEN, E. A., *Proc. Soc. Exptl. Biol. Med.,* 28, 625 (1931)
BRANDSTRUP, E. (1), *Acta obstet. gyn. skand.,* 10, 251 (1930)
BRANDSTRUP, E. (2), *Acta obstet. gyn. skand.,* 11, 85 (1931)
BRINLEY, F. J., *Physiol. Zoöl.,* 3, 366 (1930)
BRODY, S., and HENDERSON, E. W., *Univ. Missouri Agr. Exptl. Sta. Bull. 99* (1927)
BYERLY, T. C., *J. Exptl. Biol.,* 9, 15 (1931)
CALZONI, M., *Riv. biol.,* 12, 14 (1930)
CHOUKE, K. S., *Proc. Soc. Exptl. Biol. Med.,* 28, 43 (1930)
COMANDON, J., and FONBRUNE, P. DE (1), *Compt. rend. soc. biol.,* 106, 181 (1931)
COMANDON, J., and FONBRUNE, P. DE (2), *Compt. rend. soc. biol.,* 106, 248 (1931)
DAVIDSON, J., *Australian J. Exptl. Biol. Med. Sci.,* 8, 143 (1931)
DERRIEN, E., *Compt. rend. soc. biol.,* 91, 634 (1924)
DOLJANSKI, L. (1), *Compt. rend. soc. biol.,* 105, 504 (1930)
DOLJANSKI, L. (2), *Compt. rend. soc. biol.,* 105, 343 (1930)
DULZETTO, F., *Arch. biol.,* 41, 221 (1931)
EASTMAN, N. J., and MCLANE, C. M., *Bull. Johns Hopkins Hosp.,* 48, 261 (1931)
ESSKUCHEN, E., *7. Zücht. Riehe B,* 19, 268 (1930); *Ber. ges. Physiol. exptl. Pharmakol.,* 60, 386 (1931)
FELL, H. B., *Arch. exptl. Zellforsch.,* 11, 245 (1931)
FELL, H. B., and ROBISON, R., *Biochem. J.,* 24, 1905 (1930)
FURREG, E., *Biol. Zentr.,* 51, 162 (1931)
GAGGERMEIER, G., *Arch. Geflügelkunde,* 4, 453 (1930)
GANFINI, G., *Boll. soc. ital. biol. sper.,* 5, 949 (1930)
GAROFALO, A., *Clin. Ostet.,* 33, 65 (1931); *Ber. ges. Physiol. exptl. Pharmakol.,* 61, 769 (1931)
GAUSE, G. F., *Biol. Zentr.,* 51, 209 (1931)
GENELL, S., *Biochem. Z.,* 232, 335 (1931)
GERBER, L., and CARR, R. H., *J. Nutrition,* 3, 245 (1930)
GLASER, O., *Anat. Record,* 24, 382 (1922)
GRASSET, E., *Pub. South African Inst. Med. Res.,* 4, 173 (1929)
GRAY, J., *A Textbook of Experimental Cytology,* Cambridge University Press, Cambridge, England (1931)
GROLLMAN, A., *Biochem. Z.,* 238, 408 (1931)
GUERITHAULT, M., *Bull. soc. sci. hyg. aliment.,* 15, 386 (1927)
HAGAN, H. R., *J. Morphol. Physiol.,* 51, 1 (1931)
HARRIS, H. A., *J. Anat.,* 64, 303 (1930)
HARVEY, E. N., *Biol. Bull.,* 60, 67 (1931)
HASELHORST, G., *Z. ges. Anat. Abt. II,* 15, 177 (1930)
HASELHORST, G., and STROMBERGER, K., *Z. Geb. Gyn.,* 98, 49 (1930)
HENDERSON, E. W., *Univ. Missouri Agr. Exptl. Sta. Bull. 149* (1930)

HERINGA, C. G., and VALK, S. H. VAN K., *Proc. Roy. Soc. (Amsterdam)*, **33**, 530 (1930); *Ber. ges. Physiol. exptl. Pharmakol.*, **57**, 396 (1931)

HERTWIG, G., and HERTWIG, P., *"Regulation von Wachstum, Entwicklung und Regeneration durch Umweltsfaktoren"* in *Handb. norm. pathol. Physiol. (Bethe)*, **16** (1930)

HILL, A. V. (1), *Proc. Roy. Soc. (London)*, B, **106**, 477 (1930)

HILL, A. V. (2), *Proc. Faraday Soc. (Symposium)* (1931)

HOESSLIN, H. VON, *Z. Biol.*, **90**, 615 (1930)

HOLST, W. F., and ALMQUIST, H. J., *Hilgardia*, **6**, 45, 49 (1931)

HOWARD, E., *Biol. Bull.*, **60**, 132 (1931)

ITO, S., *Trans. Jap. Path. Soc.*, **20**, 360 (1930); *Ber. wiss. Biol.*, **18**, 60 (1931)

KABOTH, T., *Arch. Gyn.*, **137**, 727, 752 (1929)

KAMIYA, T., *Nagoya J. Med. Sci.*, **5**, 1 (1930)

KAUFMAN, L., *Acta Biol. Exptl. (Warsaw)*, **5**, 33 (1930)

KEYS, A. B., *Bull. Scripps Inst. Oceanogr.*, **2**, 417. (1931)

KINDRED, J. E., and COREY, E. L., *Physiol. Zoöl.*, **4**, 294 (1931)

KLUYVER, A. J., *The Chemical Activities of Micro-Organisms*, London University Press, London (1931)

KOJIMA, K., *Nagoya J. Med. Sci.*, **5**, 49 (1930)

LATIMER, H. B., and AIKMAN, J. M., *Anat. Record*, **48**, 1 (1931)

LAURENTIS, G. DE, *Monit. Ostet. Ginecol.*, **1**, 830 (1929); *Ber. wiss. Biol.*, **17**, 105 (1930)

LEHMANN, F. E., *Rev. suisse zool.*, **37**, 313 (1930)

LEITCH, J. L., *Univ. California Pub. Zoöl.*, **36**, 127 (1931)

LEVENE, P. A., and ROLF, J., *J. Biol. Chem.*, **51**, 507 (1922)

LOVELAND, G., MAURER, E. E., and SNYDER, F. F., *Anat. Record*, **49**, 265 (1931)

LUCKE, B., *Biol. Bull.*, **60**, 72 (1931)

LUDWIG, D., *Am. J. Physiol.*, **85**, 389 (1928)

LUDWIG, W., *Biol. Zentr.*, **49**, 735 (1930)

McFARLANE, W. D., FULMER, H. L., and JUKES, T. H., *Biochem. J.*, **24**, 1611 (1930)

MANKIN, W. R., *Med. J. Australia*, July 12 (1930)

MATTHIAS, P., *Bull. soc. zool. (France)*, **55**, 421 (1931)

MAZZA, F. P., *Arch. sci. biol.*, **15**, 12 (1931); *Boll. soc. ital. biol. sper.*, **4**, 1151 (1929); *Ber. ges. Physiol. exptl. Pharmakol.*, **59**, 680 (1931)

MEYERHOF, O., *Biochem. Z.*, **242**, 480 (1931)

MIGLIAVACCI, A., *Riv. biol.*, **12**, 18 (1930)

MIKHAILOVSKI, B., *Ber. ges. Physiol. exptl. Pharmakol.*, **55**, 14 (1930)

NEEDHAM, D. M., NEEDHAM, J., BALDWIN, E., and YUDKIN, J., *Proc. Roy. Soc. (London)*, B, in the press (1932)

NEEDHAM, J. (1), *Chemical Embryology* (3 vols.) Cambridge University Press, Cambridge, England (1931)

NEEDHAM, J. (2), *J. Exptl. Biol.*, **8**, 330 (1931)

NEEDHAM, J. (3), *Nature*, **128**, 152 (1931)

NEEDHAM, J. (4), *Proc. Roy. Soc. (London)*, B, **110**, 46 (1932)

NEEDHAM, J., NEEDHAM, D. M., YUDKIN, J., and BALDWIN, E., *J. Exptl. Biol.*, (1932) in the press

NEEDHAM, J., and SMITH, M., *J. Exptl. Biol.*, **8**, 286 (1931)

NEEDHAM, J., STEPHENSON, M., and NEEDHAM, D. M., *J. Exptl. Biol.*, **8**, 319 (1931)

NOEL, R., PIGEAUD, H., and MILLET, P., *Bull. histol. appl.*, **8**, 27 (1931); *Ber. wiss. Biol.*, **18**, 712 (1931)

OHNISHI, Y. (1), *Ber. wiss. Biol.*, **17**, 352 (1931)

OHNISHI, Y. (2), *Ber. wiss. Biol.*, **17**, 715 (1931)

PANKRATZ, D. S., *Anat. Record*, **49**, 31 (1931)

PARTACHNIKOV, M., *Compt. rend. soc. biol.*, **104**, 1163 (1930)

PIERANTONI, U., *Boll. zool.*, **1**, 277 (1930); *Ber. wiss. Biol.*, **18**, 16 (1931)

PLASS, E. D., and YOAKAM, A., *Am. J. Obstet. Gyn.*, **18**, 556 (1929)

PLIMMER, R. H. A., and LOWNDES, J., *Biochem. J.*, **18**, 1163 (1924)

POLLARD, C. B., and CARR, R. H., *Am. J. Physiol.*, **67**, 589 (1924)

PUMPHREY, R. J., *Proc. Roy. Soc. (London), B*, **108**, 511 (1931)

QUERNER, F., *Ber. wiss. Biol.*, **18**, 489 (1931)

REMOTTI, E., *Ricerche di morfol.*, **9**, 1 (1929)

ROMANOV, A. L., *Anat. Record*, **48**, 185 (1931)

ROUSSEL, G., and DEFLANDRE, D. (1), *Ann. anat. pathol.*, **8**, 139 (1931)

ROUSSEL, G., and DEFLANDRE, D. (2), *Compt. rend. soc. biol.*, **106**, 529 (1931)

ROUSSEL, G., and DEFLANDRE, D. (3), *Compt. rend. soc. biol.*, **106**, 260 (1931)

SACHAROV, N. L., *Ecology*, **11**, 505 (1930)

SAGARA, J. I., *J. Biochem. (Japan)*, **12**, 473 (1930)

SANTA, G., *Ber. wiss. Biol.*, **17**, 655 (1931)

SANZO, L., *Boll. soc. ital. biol. sper.*, **5**, 1008 (1930)

SCAMMON, P. E., *Acta Paediatrica*, **11**, 354 (1930)

SCHMALHAUSEN, I., *Arch. Entwicklungsmech. Organ. (Z. wiss. Biol. Abt. D)*, **124**, 82 (1931); *Biol. Zentr.*, **50**, 292 (1930)

SCHÖNHEIMER, R., and BEHRING, H. VON, *Z. physiol. Chem.*, **192**, 110 (1930)

SHARP, P. F., and POWELL, C. K. (1), *J. Ind. Eng. Chem.*, **22**, 908 (1930)

SHARP, P. F., and POWELL, C. K. (2), *J. Ind. Eng. Chem.*, **23**, 196 (1931)

SIEGERT, F., and NEUMANN, S., *Zentr. Gyn.*, 1630 (1930)

SKINNER, J. T., and PETERSON, W. H., *J. Biol. Chem.*, **88**, 347 (1930)

SLONIMSKI, P., *Ber. wiss. Biol.*, **18**, 770 (1931)

SMITH, M., *J. Exptl. Biol.*, **8**, 312 (1931)

SMITH, M., and SHEPHERD, J., *J. Exptl. Biol.*, **8**, 293 (1931)

SMITH, M., SHEPHERD, J., and NEEDHAM, J., unpublished work

STEPHENSON, M., private communication to author

STEWART, D. R., *Biol. Bull.*, **60**, 152, 171 (1931)

STRAUB, J., and HOOGERDUYN, M. J. J., *Rec. trav. chim.*, **48**, 49 (1929)

SUEYOSHI, Y., *J. Biochem. (Japan)*, **13**, 145 (1931)

SUEYOSHI, Y., and FURUKOBO, T., *J. Biochem. (Japan)*, **13**, 155 (1931)

SWENSON, T. L., and MOTTERN, H. H., *Science*, **72**, 98 (1930)

TAPERNOUX, A., *Compt. rend. soc. biol.*, **105**, 405 (1930)

TEODORO, T., *Boll. zool.*, **2**, 33 (1931); *Ber. wiss. Biol.*, **18**, 507 (1931)

TITSCHAK, E., *Z. Morphol. Ökol. Tiere*, **17**, 471 (1930)

TOUMANOV, C., and ZERNOV, V., *Bull. soc. zool. (France)*, **55**, 510 (1931)

VLADIMIROV, G. E., *J. Physiol.*, **72**, 411 (1931)

VOSS, H., *Z. ges. Anat. Abt. I*, **94**, 712 (1931)

WEEKES, H. C., *Proc. Linn. Soc. N.S.W.*, **55**, 550 (1930)
WEHEFRITZ, E., and GIERHAKE, E., *Arch. Gynäkol.*, **142**, 602 (1930)
WIGGLESWORTH, V. B., *J. Exptl. Biol.*, **8**, 411, 428, 443 (1931)
WOODGER, J. H., *Quart. Rev. Biol.*, **5**, 1, 438 (1930) ; **6**, 178 (1931)
YAMAMOTO, T., *J. Faculty Sci. Imp. Univ. Tokyo (Zoöl.)*, **2**, 147, 153 (1931)
ZIFFERBLATT, A. H., and SEELAUS, H. K., *Anat. Record*, **48**, 367 (1931)

BIOCHEMICAL LABORATORY
UNIVERSITY OF CAMBRIDGE
CAMBRIDGE, ENGLAND

THE CHEMISTRY OF THE ANIMAL PIGMENTS*

By Hans Fischer and F. Wilhelm Neumann

*Organisch-chemisches Institut der Technischen Hochschule
München, Germany*

With the synthesis of haemin, research on the constitution of blood pigment found its first final goal attained. However, because of the sequence and type of substitutes known to exist, a further study of the possibilities and conditions for porphyrin formation is necessary; the method of formation of the "Porphin" skeleton in the organism, as well as of the prosthetic group of the blood pigment and also of the physiological porphyrins themselves, is not certain, and the dualism of the porphyrins still requires experimental explanation.

Numerous syntheses of new porphyrins were therefore undertaken in order to approach the explanation of these questions. H. Fischer and Rothhaas (1) found that mesoporphyrin IX, the arrangement of whose sidechains corresponds to that in protoporphyrin, gave, following reoxydation of its leucocompound, a tetramethyl-triethyl-porphin-monopropionic acid, which could not have been formed by simple decarboxylation or reduction of a carboxyl group; porphyrins obtained following such treatment, employing clearly defined syntheses, gave distinct melting-point depressions with the new product, so that the appearance of this porphyrin could be explained only by a total splitting of the molecule and re-synthesis from its component parts. Thus an exact basis was obtained upon which similar reactions in the organism as well could be brought within reach of these considerations. Syntheses of tetra- and octapropylporphin (2) enlarged these studies. H. Fischer, Treibs, and Zeile (3) explained the mechanism of iron introduction in the porphyrins with the isolation of crystalline "Häme," compounds in which the porphyrin contained only ferrous iron bound in a complex way, as for instance without crystal-pyridine, and which are to be considered as the first step in the entrance of iron into porphyrin.

Various circumstances in the preparation of protohaemin had led to haemins of different crystalline form, and opinion was at times expressed that these findings would have to be explained by different formulas for the protoporphyrin molecule (Richter and others).

* Received January 26, 1932.

H. Fischer, Treibs, and Zeile (4) studied the individual protoporphyrins of every origin. In all cases, crystals were obtained which could be derived from a basic form (Fig. 1), either through formation from

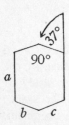

FIG. 1

face *a* or *b,* failure of appearance of face *b* or *c,* variability of the angle between *b* and *c,* or *"Korosionserscheinungen."* The type of solvent, concentration, temperature, and other conditions are responsible for external variations in appearance of chemically identical protoporphyrins. Lindenfeld (5) has likewise been occupied with this question and with the conditions under which Teichmann's and "S"-crystals form. The "S"-crystals exhibit parallel "extinction," and their differences probably depend upon variations in the "Doppelbesen." H. Fischer and Nüssler (6) synthesize the isomeric haemin III corresponding to Küster's (7) formula for natural haemin.

It is spectroscopically identical with natural haemin, and its other characteristics are not changed by virtue of the adjacent vinyl groups; the melting-point of the natural haeminester (262°) with haemin III ester (284°) exhibits, however, a definite depression, and in this indirect way new evidence for the constitution of blood pigment is obtained.

Hijmans van den Bergh in 1929 had isolated a porphyrin differing from koproporphyrin I from the urine and feces of a case of porphyrinuria, and the identity of this porphyrin with koproporphyrin III was first shown by H. Fischer and co-workers. Fischer and Hierneis (8) next carried out new syntheses of koproporphyrin, employing the pyrromethenes (Formulae 1 and 2) which in the suc-

$$HOOC \cdot H_2C \cdot H_2C \quad CH_3 \quad H_3C \quad CH_2 \cdot CH_2 \cdot COOH$$

$$H \quad CH \quad CH_3$$
$$NH \quad N$$

Formula 1

cinic acid syntheses would have to yield koproporphyrin I and III. The excretion of such a mixture could possibly be expected in cases of porphyrinuria, and their separation was therefore important. A mixture having an external appearance of uniformity but without a sharp melting-point resulted from this synthesis. By fractional crystallization it was possible to divide pure kopro III ester (M.P. 145°) and pure kopro I ester (M.P. 250°). In cases of porphyrinuria in which an ester melting-point of 250° is not quickly attained, the mixture must therefore be subjected to fractional crystallization. Studies

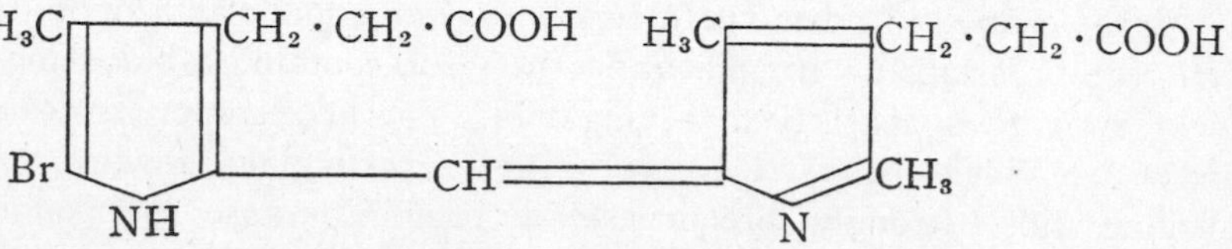

Formula 2

on the melting-points and mixed melting-points of natural and synthetic koproporphyrin III have shown that certain variations exist and depend on the frequency of recrystallization, and these perhaps explain the various melting-points reported for koproporphyrin. H. Fischer and Kürzinger (9) were further able to show that, following brief warming of opsopyrrolcarbonicacid with pyrromethene (Formula 3) in benzene-methylalcohol, koproporphyrins I and III

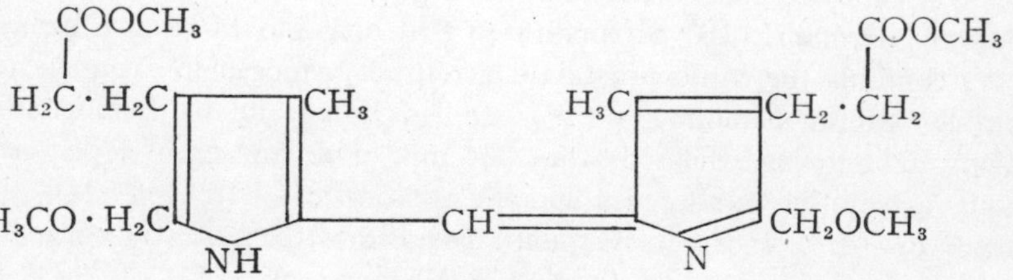

Formula 3

are formed with good yields. In connection with this and the finding mentioned above (Fischer and Rothhaas), the possibility of the biological formation of koproporphyrin I and bile pigment from blood pigment has been considered.

In the examination of a case of animal ochronosis, Hermann Fink (10) contributed to the study of experimental porphyrinuria, and later (11) from a second case isolated crystalline uroporphyrin, which, by means of a method which he describes as very sparing of material, was identified by measurement of the pH-fluorescence curve as well as by analysis.

From the physical standpoint, Harry Hellström (12) has considered the relations between constitution and spectrum of the porphyrins. The fixed variations already recognized can, under certain circumstances, be of use in the spectroscopic identification and classification of newly found porphyrins.

Gert Cosack (13) demonstrated the activation and stabilization of pancreatic diastase by haemin and other iron-containing blood pigment derivatives apart from hemoglobin. The acceleration is from six to ten times, the pH efficiency zone is, particularly toward the alkaline side, strongly broadened; a haemin-diastase compound seems possible. Michaelis and Salomon (14) showed that oxyhemoglobin on oxidation with 1 mol of $K_3Fe(CN)_6$ to methemoglobin, gives up 1 mol of oxygen. I. Brooks (15) pointed out that the oxygen in the oxidation of hemoglobin is used only for the formation of methemoglobin. Simon and Reetz (16) found in the course of their study of active iron that the hemoglobin-iron, which may be activated, has limited life in vitro. H. Fischer and Rothemund (17) have studied the behavior of haemins and pyrrol pigments using the estimation of active hydrogen according to Zerewitinoff, and determined that the frequently observed inconstancy of the values depends upon a catalytic characteristic possessed by the porphyrin molecule. Albert Kirrmann (18) demonstrated that hemoglobin from Chironomus contains the same prosthetic group as hemoglobin from vertebrates. Stefan Simonovits (19) studied horse and ox hemoglobin, using light toward the red from 644 mμ. The former in 1 per cent aqueous solution exhibited a specific rotation of $+12°$ to $+15°$, the latter of $+5°$. Horse hemoglobin reduced with $Na_2S_2O_4$ caused a rotation in 0.5 per cent solution (in 0.1 per cent NH_3) of $+23°$ to $+27°$. Hijmans van den Bergh and F. R. Revers (20) observed sulfhemoglobin in a case, in which pyridium and Bitterwasser had been taken at the same time. Warburg and Christian (21) showed that the hemochromogen-spectrum from Spirographis haemin nearly, but not entirely, coincides with that of the iron salt of phäophorbid b (phäohaemin b). Maximum absorption is at 584 mμ. Calvin B. Coulter and Florence M. Stone (22) found koproporphyrin in cultures of diphtheria bacilli, as well as another porphyrin more soluble in ether. The "haemoporphyrin" of Willstätter, previously shown by Fischer and co-workers to be a mixture on the basis of analyses, has also been identified as such by Fischer and Kirstahler (23) by synthetic methods. According to Fischer and Hendschel (24) the changes undergone by chlorophyll derivatives in the digestive tract of all caterpillars appears to be the same. There is formed a phytol- and methoxyl-free product named phyllobombycin, of the formula $C_{34}H_{36}O_6N_4$, which spectroscopically is most similar to phäophytin and whose diazomethane-ester melts at 209°.

Cytochrome

Warburg and Negelein (25) have photographically reproduced the three chief absorption bands of MacMunn's histohematin from the muscles of bees. Keilin, Dixon, and Hill (26) have described the results of their spectroscopic measurements of pure cytochrome, component c.

Bile Pigment

After more than a five-year pause, the costly study of the problems of bile pigment has been carried further by H. Fischer and Richard Hess (27). By mild reduction of bilirubin, mesobilirubin and mesobilirubinogen have been obtained (28), and by energetic reduction, bilirubinic acid, which on dehydration becomes xanthobilirubinic acid. Bilirubin has 33 carbon atoms, bilirubinic acid 17. The remaining fraction with 16 carbon atoms was still unknown. In a resorcin "melt" or by glacial-acetic-hydriodic-acid reduction, mesobilirubin gives "neoxanthobilirubinic acid," which on reduction goes over to "neobilirubinic acid," the latter containing a free methin group in the "acid" pyrrol nucleus. By condensation of "neoxanthobilirubinic acid" with formaldehyde there is formed "K-mesobilirubin," giving the same color play in the Gmelin reaction as mesobilirubin itself. Because of the mode of formation, this substance is ascribed Formula 4 and in its characteristics the substance agrees completely with mesobilirubin. The continuation of synthetic attempts by H. Fischer and Fröwis (29) led to carboxylated xanthobilirubinic acid, very similar to xanthobilirubinic acid itself.

H. Fischer and Kürzinger (9) prepared pigments by the linear coupling of 4-pyrrol nuclei, which give the Gmelin reaction so characteristic for bilirubin and mesobilirubin, and were therefore designated as "bilirubinoid." The Gmelin reaction is not dependent upon the OH-group of bilirubin; much more important is the stabilization of the system, as was shown by Fischer and Adler (30) in the course of further experiments, who, likewise, by continued attempts, carried out the synthesis of bilirubinic acid and xanthobilirubinic acid and, soon thereafter (31), that of neobilirubinic acid and mesobilirubino-gen. It is worthy of note that the basic mesobilirubin differs only in the melting-point of its ester from that of the natural, so that it is necessary to accept the existence of isomerism as a result of shifting of the double bonds; the corresponding change in natural mesobili-rubin which is perhaps possible did not occur in treatment with glacial acetic acid–hydrobromic acid. Because of the significance of

Formula 4

"bilirubinoid" pigments for the physiology and pathology of bile pig-ment, their further study was continued. "Tripyrrane" substances with 3 linear coupled pyrrol-nuclei and "tetrapyrrane," as well as their dehydration products, tri- and tetrapyrrene, were prepared. In the course of a study of the pyrroketones from the split products of blood pigment, H. Fischer and H. Orth (32) showed that the Gmelin reaction may also appear with the ketazines of pyrroketones (see For- , mula 5). Consequently the make-up necessary for the Gmelin reac-tion would seem to consist of a relatively stable system of 4-pyrrol nuclei which may be dehydrated to different oxidation steps and the urobilin appearing at the end would be considered as tetrapyrrotrien, which then breaks up by further oxidation to malein-imide deri-vatives.

Lemberg (33) obtained oocyan in crystalline form from gull's egg shells. The analytical data for the blue pigment agreed with the formula $C_{28} H_{31(33)} O_6 N_3$. A pigment very similar or perhaps identical with oocyan was isolated from the placenta of a pregnant dog

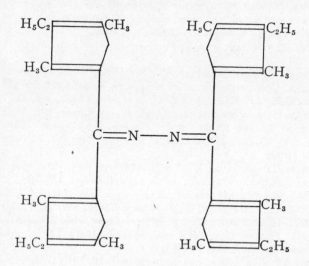

Formula 5

and from various biliverdin tests. From the reports to date, the accepted character of the product as a tripyrrane derivative seems not to be proved with certainty. Charles Dhéré (34) has reported spectrochemical studies on a bilirubin derivative with red fluorescence.

LITERATURE CITED

1. FISCHER, H., AND ROTHHAAS, A., *Ann.*, **484**, 85 (1930)
2. FISCHER, H., GOLDSCHMIDT, M., AND NÜSSLER, W., *Ann.*, **486**, 1 (1931)
3. FISCHER, H., TREIBS, A., AND ZEILE, K., *Z. physiol. Chem.*, **195**, 1 (1931)
4. FISCHER, H., TREIBS, A., AND ZEILE, K., *Z. physiol. Chem.*, **193**, 138 (1930)
5. LINDENFELD, — —., *Roczniki Chem.*, **11**, 532 (1931)
6. FISCHER, H., AND NÜSSLER, L., *Ann.*, **491**, 162 (1931)
7. KÜSTER, W., *Z. physiol. Chem.*, **163**, 267 (1927)
8. FISCHER, H., AND HIERNEIS, J., *Z. physiol. Chem.*, **196**, 155 (1931)
9. FISCHER, H., AND KÜRZINGER, A., *Z. physiol. Chem.*, **196**, 213 (1931)
10. FINK, H., *Z. physiol. Chem.*, **197**, 193 (1931)
11. FINK, H., *Z. physiol. Chem.*, **202**, 8 (1931)

ANNUAL REVIEW OF BIOCHEMISTRY

12. HELLSTRÖM, H., Z. physikal. Chem. Abt. B, 12, 353 (1931) ; 14, 9 (1931)
13. COSACK, G., Bicchem. Z., 235, 469 (1931)
14. MICHAELIS, L., AND SALOMON, K., Biochem. Z., 234, 107 (1931)
15. BROOKS, I., Proc. Roy. Soc. (London), B, 109, 35 (1931)
16. SIMON, A, AND REETZ, T., Ann., 485, 75 (1931)
17. FISCHER, H., AND ROTHEMUND, P., Ber., 64, 201 (1931)
18. KIRRMANN, A., Bull. soc. chim. biol., 12, 1146 (1930)
19. SIMONOVITS, S., Biochem. Z., 233, 449 (1931)
20. BERGH, H. VAN DEN, AND REVERS, F. R., Deut. med. Wochschr., 57, 706 (1931)
21. WARBURG, O., AND CHRISTIAN, W., Biochem. Z., 235, 240 (1931)
22. COULTER, C. V., AND STONE, F. M., J. Gen. Physiol., 14, 583 (1931)
23. FISCHER, H., AND KIRSTAHLER, A., Z. physiol. Chem., 198, 43 (1931)
24. FISCHER, H., AND HENDSCHEL, A., Z. physiol. Chem., 198, 33 (1931)
25. WARBURG, O., AND NEGELEIN, E., Biochem. Z., 233, 486 (1931)
26. KEILIN, D., DIXON, M., AND HILL, R., Proc. Roy. Soc. (London), B, 109, 29 (1931)
27. FISCHER, H., AND HESS, R., Z. physiol. Chem., 194, 193 (1931)
28. FISCHER, H., AND NIEMANN, G., Z. physiol. Chem., 137, 293 (1924)
29. FISCHER, H., AND FRÖWIS, W., Z. physiol. Chem., 195, 49 (1931)
30. FISCHER, H., AND ADLER, E., Z. physiol. Chem., 197, 237 (1931)
31. FISCHER, H., AND ADLER, E., Z. physiol. Chem., 200, 209 (1931)
32. FISCHER, H., AND ORTH, H., Ann., 489, 62 (1931)
33. LEMBERG, R., Ann., 488, 74 (1931)
34. DHÉRÉ, C., Arch. intern. pharmacodynamie, 38, 134 (1930)

ORGANISCH-CHEMISCHES INSTITUT
DER TECHNISCHEN HOCHSCHULE
MÜNCHEN, 2, N.W.

ANIMAL PIGMENTS*

By A. E. Mirsky and M. L. Anson

The Rockefeller Institute for Medical Research

Until recently the chemical physiology of animal pigments was concerned almost entirely with hemoglobin and with hemocyanin, which fulfills the same function as hemoglobin. In the last few years, however, it has become realized that substances related to hemoglobin are present generally in aërobic tissues, that they are essential to the catalysis of respiration and that they are probably responsible for the peroxidase and catalase activity of cells. The development up to 1930 of this wider study of the pigments related to hemoglobin has already been reviewed [Anson and Mirsky (3)]. At the same time, as the investigation of the biology of the heme pigments has been so greatly broadened, the classical study of the respiratory function of hemoglobin in vertebrate blood has received a great impetus from the discovery by Henriques of a new rôle played by hemoglobin in the carbon-dioxide exchange of blood.

The Properties of Hemoglobin

The system of substances in vertebrate blood which is responsible for the transportation of oxygen and carbon dioxide is relatively simple and accessible to study and so is better understood than most biological systems. Although information about this system has become steadily more precise and detailed, the discovery of an important new variable has been rare. In 1914 Christiansen, Douglas, and Haldane showed that when oxyhemoglobin becomes reduced in the tissue capillaries it liberates base which can neutralize the carbon dioxide which the tissues give off. Thus hemoglobin, besides carrying oxygen, influences greatly how much carbon dioxide blood can combine with at a given hydrogen-ion concentration. In 1928 Henriques showed further that hemoglobin influences how quickly carbon dioxide enters and leaves the blood.

Bohr long ago thought that just as oxygen combines directly with hemoglobin to form oxyhemoglobin, carbon dioxide combines directly with hemoglobin to form carbhemoglobin. This notion was given up. It became universally accepted that carbon dioxide in blood exists

* Received January 8, 1932.

only as dissolved carbon dioxide ($CO_2 \rightleftarrows H_2CO_3$) and bicarbonate. The rate of dissociation of carbon dioxide from such a system, however, is so slow that it cannot account for the rapid escape of carbon dioxide into the lungs. Henriques first pointed this out and showed that hemoglobin enormously increases the rate at which a carbon dioxide–bicarbonate solution loses carbon dioxide to a vacuum. Van Slyke and Hawkins confirmed and extended somewhat the results of Henriques, and then Dirken and Mook put the whole subject on a much better experimental basis by applying the technique used by Hartridge and Roughton in their study of the kinetics of the reaction between oxygen and hemoglobin. In the near future the details will doubtless be filled out.

To explain the hemoglobin effect Henriques went back to Bohr's idea that a large part of the carbon dioxide in blood is combined with hemoglobin. He assumed that carbhemoglobin, like oxyhemoglobin, dissociates rapidly. Some independent evidence for the existence of carbhemoglobin has been given (Henriques; Margaria). Van Slyke and Hawkins, and Stadie and O'Brien, on the other hand, believe that their results prove that in blood no significant amount of carbon dioxide is combined with hemoglobin and that, therefore, hemoglobin acts by catalyzing the dissociation of carbon dioxide from the dissolved carbon dioxide–bicarbonate system. Such a catalysis does exist, regardless of how much of the carbon dioxide in blood is combined with hemoglobin. A very small amount of hemoglobin increases greatly the rate of escape of carbon dioxide from a carbon dioxide–bicarbonate solution (Brinkman and Margaria).

It has already been said that when oxyhemoglobin is reduced in the tissue capillaries it liberates base which neutralizes carbonic acid. If the reduction of oxyhemoglobin is diminished, less base is available to neutralize carbonic acid, and the animal suffers the consequences of an increased blood acidity. Bean has brought about this chain of events by exposing animals to three atmospheres of pure oxygen. The great increase in dissolved oxygen permits the tissues to fulfill most of their oxygen needs without the normal reduction of oxyhemoglobin. There can be no doubt that a part, at least, of the mechanism of the harmful effect of high oxygen pressure has been made clear by Bean. It should be remembered, however, that Paul Bert found that organisms which do not have hemoglobin also die when exposed to high oxygen pressures.

Henderson and his collaborators have made more detailed and

precise the description of the respiratory function of human blood and have defined the variation between normal individuals. Fortunately, the now standardized methods of blood analysis, developed largely by Van Slyke, have been applied also to many bloods which are very different from human blood. (Crocodile blood, Dill and Edwards; blood of the larva, *Chironimus,* Harnisch; blood of the worm, *Urechis caupo,* Redfield and Florkin; blood of the amphibian, *Amphiuma tridactyla,* Scott; bird blood, Wastl and Leiner.) It is interesting to see how a complex chemical system changes from animal to animal to meet different respiratory problems, how even a single substance such as hemoglobin has, like the organism as a whole, the biological characteristics of adaptation and variation.

It is clear that hemoglobin changes from species to species and that these changes are sometimes, at least, of an adaptive nature. The evidence for normal and regular differences within a single species is neither so extensive nor so convincing. Haurowitz (1) has presented some suggestive but not conclusive evidence that the hemoglobin of adult man is different from that of the newborn infant. Geiger believes that there are at least two different hemoglobins in the blood of a single individual. If salt-free hemoglobin at a suitable pH is put in an electric field, some hemoglobin wanders to the anode, some to the cathode. It would be desirable to have these interesting experiments repeated with carbon monoxide hemoglobin, the most stable form of the protein, and with the salts removed by ordinary dialysis rather than by electrodialysis, which produces no better results and is much more dangerous.

The relation between the oxygen pressure and the amount of oxygen with which the hemoglobin in blood is combined is such that blood can lose a considerable amount of oxygen without the oxygen concentration in blood, and hence the rate of diffusion of oxygen out of the blood, being much diminished. This favorable relation would not exist did all the four iron atoms of the hemoglobin molecule have the same affinity for oxygen. A dilute solution of hemoglobin has an oxygen-dissociation curve of the same peculiar shape as has blood; so we are dealing with a property of the hemoglobin molecule, not with an effect due to the high concentration of hemoglobin in blood (Forbes; Forbes and Roughton).

The simplest way of regarding the reaction between the individual hemoglobin molecule and four molecules of oxygen is that one molecule of oxygen combines at a time, so that there are compounds in solution containing one, two, three, and four molecules of oxygen. Conant and McGrew believe that their experiments on the effect of oxygen pressure on the solubility of oxyhemoglobin show that this simple view is not correct, that only the compounds containing no oxygen and four molecules of oxygen exist. The argument cannot be stated briefly. Roughton does not consider the results conclusive (see the appendix to the paper by Forbes and Roughton). Conant and McGrew assume, although the assumption is not essential to their general point of view, that the solubilities of the intermediate oxy compounds if they existed would be independent of the solubility of $Hb(O_2)_4$. Actually, the slightly different hemoglobins which have been studied do not behave in this way. Donkey oxyhemoglobin probably forms a solid solution with horse oxyhemoglobin (Landsteiner and Heidelberger). Horse methemoglobin forms a solid solution with mule methemoglobin and with horse oxyhemoglobin (Anson and Mirsky, unpublished experiments).

Every year there appear many papers on the estimation of hemoglobin. The colorimetric procedures have not been improved in any important way, although there is room for decided improvement. The gasometric estimation of carbon monoxide and oxyhemoglobin, however, has been made more convenient (Sendroy, and Sendroy and Liu), and there has been further work on Wu's procedure for the estimation of minute amounts of hemoglobin with benzidine (Bing and Baker).

It is surprising that cumbersome preparations of crystalline methemoglobin are still described [Dénes; Haurowitz (2)]. All one has to do to get pure crystalline methemoglobin is to add ferricyanide to oxyhemoglobin, dialyze the solution, and then add ammonium sulphate or a phosphate buffer.

A simple method is now available for the preparation in large amounts of native globin which can combine with heme to form a methemoglobin with the same solubility as normal methemoglobin [Anson and Mirsky (3, 5); Hamsik]. Some physico-chemical measurements have been made on native globin, and oxyhemoglobins have been prepared from globin and the hemes obtained from muscle hemoglobin, helicorubin, and component c of cytochrome (Roche; Roche and Bendrihem). Just as globin is a useful reagent in the study of different hemes, so the reaction of heme with globin can also be used in following the changes in globin on denaturation and its reversal [Anson and Mirsky (2)].

Hemoglobin is easy to prepare in pure form, it behaves like a homogeneous substance, and it has the advantage of being colored. So it is not surprising that hemoglobin is continually being used in the study of the general properties of proteins. The effect of salt on protein solubility has been investigated with hemoglobin (Green; Levy). Stadie and Sunderman have measured the effect of hemoglobin on the activity of sodium ions and of sodium chloride. Following Wu, Cheng, and Li, Breinl and Haurowitz have used hemoglobin to determine the composition of the precipitate formed when a protein antigen is added to an immune serum. Boor and Hektoen have examined the species specificity of hemoglobin by the precipitin test. In order to find out whether or not there is any change of molecular weight on denaturation, the osmotic pressure of denatured hemoglobin in urea solution has been measured. Burk and Greenberg find that the molecular weight is halved on denaturation, a result possibly due to the freeing of heme; Huang and Wu, that it remains unchanged. Finally, the reversibility of protein denaturation has been studied with hemoglobin. One can prepare from hemoglobin or globin apparently denatured by heat, acid acetone, or trichloracetic acid, crystallizable methemoglobin, which has the same solubility as normal, native methemoglobin which has never been denatured [Mirsky and Anson; Anson and Mirsky (4, 5)].

THE FORMATION OF HEMOGLOBIN

It would be desirable to have an account of both the experimental anemias and the anemias encountered in the clinic, an account in which the observations recorded in these fields would be correlated. We have limited our scope, however, to the experimental anemias, with a brief reference to the isolation of the principle active in pernicious anemia. It is difficult to compare the results obtained in the study of the various experimental anemias, for what appear to be contradictions may be due merely to differences in type of anemia. The first impression gathered from a review of the literature is that surprisingly little is known about the physiological mechanism of pigment formation, since most of the investigations so far deal with nutritional balance sheets. Nearly all of these investigations on nutrition approach the problem as if hemoglobin were the only important heme compound in the body; hemoglobin formation has been studied with only slight reference to the cellular heme pigments. Finally, it is important to remember that much of the work in this field is, strictly speaking, concerned with red-cell formation rather than with pigment formation. Most of the contributions on hemoglobin formation within the past few years have come from America.

Nutritional anemia in·rats.—In 1928 it was reported by Hart, Steenbock, Waddell, and Elvehjem that anemia due to a milk diet was not cured even when the diet was supplemented by iron. Addition of a trace of copper to the diet did, however, cure the anemia. It was suggested that the beneficial effect of iron in the experiments of Mitchell and Schmidt was obtained because of the presence of copper impurities. An extension of the experiments on rats was made by Elvehjem in an investigation on the rôle of iron and copper in the growth and metabolism of yeast. He grew yeast in cultures containing little iron and copper. The yeast grew slowly, had a low respiratory quotient, low total iron content, no free inorganic iron, and a low cytochrome content. Addition of a small amount of iron increased the rate of growth, raised the respiratory quotient, and resulted in a cytochrome content equal to that normally present in commercial yeast. Addition of both iron and copper caused a further increase in growth and a marked increase in concentration of component *a* of cytochrome. These experiments on yeast indicate more clearly than do those on animals that the direct effect of copper is on the production of pigment itself rather than on the production of a red blood cell.

The experimental fact that copper in addition to iron is needed for hemoglobin production appeared to be clearly established when Krauss, and also Underhill, Orten, and Lewis stated that they could confirm the experiments of Hart and his collaborators. More recently, however, Mitchell and Miller as well as Beard, Myers, and their associates have reported that hemoglobin is formed when a milk diet is supplemented by pure iron alone. The action of copper according to these authors is to accelerate the response due to iron. The apparent contradictions in the observations of the various groups of workers have not yet been explained. The last paper to appear is by Elvehjem and Hart.

All of the authors mentioned have also investigated the effects of metals other than iron and copper on hemoglobin production. In these experiments too the absence of agreement between the various authors is striking. In their experiments on the effects of metals on nutritional anemia Myers, Beard, and their associates by studying, in addition to hemoglobin formation, the changes in numbers of erythrocytes and reticulocytes have attempted to distinguish between pigment formation, production of new cells, and maturation of cells. More recently Orten, Underhill, Mugrage, and Lewis have made a similar study.

The effect of amino acids in relieving nutritional anemia has been studied by Drabkin and Miller. They found that when milk is supplemented by a quantity of iron too small to check anemia, addition of certain amino acids will cure the anemia. Arginine and glutamic acid were found to be especially effective. Elvehjem, Steenbock, and Hart were unable to confirm the experiments on glutamic acid.

Anemia in suckling pigs.—This anemia was described by McGowan and Crichton and was supposed by them to be due to iron deficiency. Hart, Elvehjem, and Steenbock have shown that this anemia can be cured by the administration of iron alone.

Hemorrhagic anemia in dogs.—The effect of administration of iron has been studied by Whipple and Robscheit-Robbins. The amount of iron producing the greatest increase in hemoglobin formation was found to be about three times the amount lost "by wastage and withdrawal" (i.e., in bleeding). Little difference was found between the effects of ferrous and ferric salts (see, however, the experiments of Starkenstein and Weden). Other metals used with iron have little, if any, effect on hemoglobin production. Whipple and his associates (Sribhishaj, Hawkins, and Whipple; Hawkins *et al.*) have begun a series of experiments which may throw light on the mechanism of hemoglobin formation. Their new experiments, like their older ones, are on dogs made anemic by bleeding. The new feature is to produce a "renal-bile fistula," so that bile pigment output and new hemoglobin production can be measured simultaneously. When dog or sheep hemoglobin is injected into non-anemic dogs there occurs an increase in bile-pigment elimination corresponding on the average to 90 to 95 per cent of the increase expected if there were a quantitative transformation of hemoglobin to bile pigment. When hemoglobin is injected into anemic dogs the same increase in bile-pigment elimination occurs, and yet at the same time there is a quantitative return of new hemoglobin in red blood cells. "Whatever hemoglobin is accepted as the end product of the introduced hemoglobin, we face the necessity of explaining the other pigment formation." The authors suggest as a possible explanation of this interesting phenomenon that "from the injected hemoglobin is split off the pyrrol nucleus to form bilirubin and from the globin fraction, or parts of it, may come much of the new hemoglobin which appears in the circulating red cells. If this is true, it appears that the body can synthesize the pyrrol nucleus in considerable amounts in an emergency due to anemia."

It is also possible in the experiments just described that the extra bile pigment formed served as a stimulus for extra hemoglobin formation. Some recent experiments of Bencsik, Gáspár, Verzár, and Zih show that this possibility must be considered. When small quantities of bilirubin were administered orally or subcutaneously to mice, rats, and rabbits, an increase in the number of erythrocytes occurred. (Larger quantities of bilirubin resulted in a decrease of erythrocytes.) The authors think that it is not merely a matter of bilirubin setting free a reserve of erythrocytes held in the spleen or bone marrow, for by continual feeding of bilirubin the number of erythrocytes can be kept elevated for months. Bilirubin, the authors believe, serves as a regulator of the number of red blood cells.

The active principle in pernicious anemia.—As a result of their furthest fractionation of liver extract Cohn, McMeekin, and Minot suggested that the active principle was "rather a base than a peptide." The isolation of the active principle was announced by West and Howe (1) in 1930. The authors [West and Howe (2)] later withdrew their claim.

HEME COMPOUNDS AS CATALYSTS

Within the past two years there have been some investigations of great interest in this field. The new developments are in large measure due to the conceptions and methods developed during the preceding five years (from about 1925 to 1930) which have recently been reviewed by the present authors. Most of the contributions come from Europe.

The nature of catalase.—Zeile and Hellström have discovered that the enzyme catalase is a heme (that is, an iron-porphyrin) compound. Concentrated preparations of liver catalase from which hemoglobin had been completely removed were found to be rich in heme. That the heme present is the active group of catalase could be shown in the following ways: (*a*) The activity of the enzyme preparation was proportional to the heme content. This proportionality held even after the catalase activity had been considerably changed by adsorption of the enzyme on, and elution of it from, various substances. (b) The heme compound could be observed spectroscopically to form dissociable compounds with CN and H₂S, two substances that inhibit the activity of catalase. (c) In the case of inhibition by CN, the dissociation constant of the enzyme–CN complex could be calculated from the activities of enzyme preparations to which CN had been added. In the same enzyme preparations the dissociation of the heme compound–CN complex could be observed spectroscopically, and when the dissociation constant of the complex was measured it was found to agree fairly well with that of the enzyme–CN complex. The spectroscopic properties of the heme compound active as catalase were described by the authors. The pigment was not a hemochromogen but was converted into one by the addition of sodium hydrosulfite and pyridine. Hemochromogen appeared very slowly, indicating that heme may have been bound to some substance which was being displaced by pyridine. The hemochromogen so formed appeared to be the same as pyridine-hemochromogen formed from the heme of hemoglobin, indicating that the heme of catalase is probably similar to that of hemoglobin. And yet, as present in liver catalase, heme is about ten million times more active than free heme in splitting hydrogen peroxide.

Zeile has shown that the catalase of the pumpkin seed is also a heme compound, although when the same amounts of heme are present in preparations of pumpkin-seed catalase and liver catalase, the latter is considerably more active.

The nature of peroxidase.—Kuhn, Hand, and Florkin have shown that peroxidase too is probably a heme compound. The evidence given for this is similar to that given for catalase. In a recent paper by Elliott and Sutter the validity of some of the experiments on peroxidase is questioned.

The knowledge we now have of the chemical nature of the active groups in Warburg's "respiration ferment," in catalase, and in peroxidase is at present unique, for the nature of the active groups of other ferments is still unknown. It may be worth while, therefore, to consider briefly the significance of these recent discoveries. The methods employed were on the whole not those usually used by organic chemists. Peroxidase was one of the first enzymes studied by Willstätter, and he arrived at the conclusion that it was not an iron compound. It seemed to Willstätter that further progress in the elucidation of the chemical nature of this and of other ferments depended upon the elaboration of better methods of preparation, a problem to which he devoted himself. And yet the investigations on the "respiration ferment," catalase, and peroxidase have been carried out mainly in another way—by means of the inhibitor technique. This technique has its origin in physiology, where poisons have long been used as means of analysis, and from physiology it was borrowed by Warburg, who over a period of twenty years has developed it into a method of great power and precision. It is of general significance that these three enzymes having activities distinct from each other, and yet belonging to the oxidizing system of the cell, have active groups of similar chemical constitution. Apparently, enzyme specificity need not oblige us to suppose living cells to contain an almost infinite variety of entirely distinct substances.

Respiration of erythrocytes.—In 1928 it was found by Barron and Harrop that the normally low respiration of mammalian erythrocytes can be greatly increased by the addition of glucose and methylene blue. This effect of methylene blue has been investigated by Wendel and more completely by Warburg, Kubowitz, and Christian (1, 2). According to them, the action of methylene blue is to oxidize a part of the hemoglobin to methemoglobin, being itself thereby reduced to the leuco-base. The leuco-base, being autoxidizable, is oxidized by the oxygen of the air to methylene blue, which oxidizes more hemoglobin to methemoglobin. In the meantime the sugar present in the cell is being oxidized by methemoglobin, which is thereby reduced to hemoglobin. Transport of oxygen from air to sugar in this system is only slightly inhibited by carbon monoxide if the concentration of methylene blue is high, but when it is low the inhibitory action of carbon monoxide can be readily demonstrated. Carbon monoxide inhibits the oxidation of sugar by decreasing the concentration of free hemoglobin and hence decreasing the rate at which methemoglobin is formed from free hemoglobin by methylene blue.

When methemoglobin within the erythrocytes is formed by reagents other than methylene blue, a similar increase in respiration occurs. Michaelis and Salomon have considered the efficacy of various dyes in relation to their oxidation-reduction potentials. Warburg and Kubowitz found that autoxidizable heme compounds can take the place of methylene blue in oxidizing hemoglobin to methemoglobin and so increasing the respiratory rate of erythrocytes. Warburg, Kubowitz, and Christian (3) showed that phenylhydrazine causes erythrocytes to respire because it converts some of the hemoglobin present into denatured globin and heme, which is autoxidizable and which can convert hemoglobin into methemoglobin. Perhaps the most interesting case is that of phenylhydroxylamine. When this substance is added to erythrocytes, methemoglobin is formed and respiration continues even after the phenylhydroxylamine is washed away. Respiration in this case is probably not catalyzed by heme, for no detectable amount of heme is formed. In these cells methemoglobin itself acts as a true catalyst for the oxidation of sugar.

Although the respiration of erythrocytes has just been described with reference only to methylene blue (or other methemoglobin-producing substance), hemoglobin, and sugar, more than these factors are involved, for if these substances are simply mixed together in the absence of erythrocytes, no respiration occurs. Furthermore, when they are all present in erythrocytes and the latter are then cytolyzed, no respiration occurs. Respiration does proceed, however, in the presence of laked cells and methylene blue if hexosemonophosphate is substituted for glucose; and yet when hexosemonophosphate, hemoglobin, and methylene blue are mixed together in absence of erythrocytes no respiration occurs. Two "activating substances" have been prepared by rather simple chemical procedures from the fluid contained within erythrocytes, and when both of these activators are added to a mixture of hexosemonophosphate, hemoglobin, and methylene blue, a lively oxygen consumption ensues. In this system oxidation can occur without hemoglobin if the concentration of methylene blue is greatly increased; oxidation proceeds also in the absence of both methylene blue and hemoglobin if the oxygen pressure and the concentrations of both activating substances are increased. The conclusion drawn by Warburg and Christian (2) from their experiments is that respiration in the absence of iron to transport oxygen is chemically possible but that "life does not make use of this possibility."

Cytochrome and intra-cellular oxidase.—Keilin has made a penetrating study of the functions of cytochrome by taking advantage of the facts that component *c* of cytochrome can be extracted from yeast and that in an aqueous extract component *c* has the same properties that it shows in intact, living cells. Using component *c* and an oxidase prepared from heart muscle, Keilin has attempted to reconstruct a part of the respiratory system of the cell. Component *c* of cytochrome is not autoxidizable and, unlike autoxidizable heme compounds, does not catalyze the oxidation of cysteine. Oxidase rapidly oxidizes component c but does not oxidize cysteine. When oxidase and cytochrome c are brought together, a powerful catalytic system is formed which rapidly oxidizes cysteine. The activity of this system is inhibited by the same factors that inhibit the respiratory activity of the cell. Thus oxidation is inhibited by warming above 70° and by KCN, Na_2S and CO. Keilin believes that "under biological conditions cytochrome reacts on the one hand with intracellular oxidase, on the other with organic molecules or metabolites activated within the cells by dehydrogenases."

FURTHER PROPERTIES OF HEME COMPOUNDS

It is obviously important that the heme compounds which exist in nature be accurately described and that the relations of these hemes to the heme of hemoglobin be studied. Component c of cytochrome has now been obtained in concentrated, although not in pure form, its spectrum measured, and the structure of its porphyrin investigated (Keilin; Hill and Keilin; Dixon, Hill, and Keilin). By the use of suitable light filters the examination of the violet band of cytochrome has been made much more satisfactory (Warburg and Negelein). The carbon monoxide compound of Warburg's respiration ferment has bands to the red of those of the carbon monoxide hemochromogen prepared from hemoglobin but nearer to the bands of the carbon monoxide hemochromogen prepared from chlorocruorin, a pigment found in the worm *Spirographis*. Chlorocruorin is available in only small quantity, yet enough of its heme has been isolated for the study of its composition, spectrum, acid groups and reduction (Warburg, Negelein, and Haas). By the introduction of iron into pheohemin b, a chlorophyll derivative, a heme is obtained which by spectroscopic test is practically the same as the heme of chlorocruorin [Warburg and Christian (1)].

Coulter and Stone have made the interesting observation that bacterial filtrates which contain diphtheria toxin also contain a porphyrin complex whose concentration is directly proportional to the toxin concentration. They believe that this porphyrin complex contains both iron and copper, that it is probably derived from cytochrome, and that it probably contains the toxin itself.

Conant and Tongberg have measured the potentials given by solutions containing different amounts of reduced and oxidized hemes and the effect of pyridine and cyanide on these potentials. The values calculated for the oxidation-reduction potentials corresponding to a given ratio of oxidized to reduced pigment in true solution are made uncertain by the facts that the potentials measured are not steady and that the pigments are aggregated to an unknown extent. Although hemoglobin itself is oxidized only slowly by molecular oxygen (Brooks), reduced heme is extremely sensitive to minute traces of oxygen, more sensitive than any other substance studied in Conant's laboratory.

The properties of reduced or oxidized heme are very much changed, on the one hand, by combination with nitrogenous substances such as denatured globin or pyridine to form hemochromogen or parahematin and, on the other hand, by the further combination of the heme-nitrogenous compound complex with substances such as carbon monoxide or hydrogen sulphide. For instance, the catalytic effect of heme on the catalysis of the oxidation of cysteine is very much increased by the addition of pyridine and then abolished by the further addition of carbon monoxide (Krebs). Cyanide seems to be able to react with heme both like a nitrogenous compound and like carbon monoxide. It can combine with reduced heme to form a hemochromogen containing one cyanide group per heme and then combine further with this cyanide hemochromogen, just as cyanide or carbon monoxide combine with globin hemochromogen [Anson and Mirsky (3)].

LITERATURE CITED

ANSON, M. L., AND MIRSKY, A. E. (1), *J. Gen. Physiol.*, **14**, 43 (1930)

ANSON, M. L., AND MIRSKY, A. E. (2), *J. Gen. Physiol.*, **13**, 469 (1930)

ANSON, M. L., AND MIRSKY, A. E. (3), *Physiol. Rev.*, **10**, 506 (1930)

ANSON, M. L., AND MIRSKY, A. E. (4), *J. Gen. Physiol.*, **14**, 597 (1931)

ANSON, M. L., AND MIRSKY, A. E. (5), *J. Gen. Physiol.*, **14**, 605 (1931)

BARRON, E. S. G., *Medicine*, **10**, 77 (1931) (A review)

BEAN, J. W., *J. Physiol.*, **72**, 27 (1931)

BEARD, H., *J. Biol. Chem.*, **94**, 135 (1931)

BEARD, H., BAKER, R., AND MYERS, V. C., *J. Biol. Chem.*, **94**, 123 (1931)

BEARD, H., AND MYERS, V. C., *J. Biol. Chem.*, **94**, 71 (1931)

BEARD, H., RAFFERTY, C., AND MYERS, V. C., *J. Biol. Chem.*, **94**, 111 (1931)

BENCSIK, F., GÁSPÁR, A., VERZÁR, F., AND ZIH, A., *Biochem. Z.*, **225**, 278 (1930)

BING, F. C., AND BAKER, R. W., *J. Biol. Chem.*, **92**, 589 (1931)
BOOR, A. K., AND HEKTOEN, L., *J. Infectious Diseases*, **46**, 1 (1930)
BREINL, F., AND HAUROWITZ, F., *Z. physiol. Chem.*, **192**, 45 (1930)
BRINKMAN, R., AND MARGARIA, R., *J. Physiol.*, **72**, 6P (1931)
BROOKS, J., *Proc. Roy. Soc. (London)*, *B*, **109**, 35 (1931)
BURK, N. F., AND GREENBERG, D. M., *J. Biol. Chem.*, **87**, 197 (1930)
COHN, E. J., MCMEEKIN, T., AND MINOT, G. R., *J. Biol. Chem.*, **87**, xlix (1930)
CONANT, J. B., AND MCGREW, R. V., *J. Biol. Chem.*, **85**, 421 (1930)
CONANT, J. B., AND TONGBERG, C. O., *J. Biol. Chem.*, **86**, 733 (1930)
COULTER, C. B., AND STONE, F. M., *J. Gen. Physiol.*, **14**, 583 (1931)
DÉNES, A., *Biochem. Z.*, **223**, 481 (1930)
DILL, D. B., AND EDWARDS, H. T., *J. Biol. Chem.*, **90**, 515 (1931)
DIRKEN, M. N. J., AND MOOK, H. W., *Biochem. Z.*, **219**, 452 (1930)
DIRKEN, M. N. J., AND MOOK, H. W., *J. Physiol.*, **70**, 373 (1930)
DIXON, M., HILL, R., AND KEILIN, D., *Proc. Roy. Soc. (London)*, *B*, **109**, 29 (1931)
DOAN, C. A., *Medicine*, **10**, 323 (1931) (A review)
DRABKIN, D. L., AND MILLER, K. K., *J. Biol. Chem.*, **90**, 531 (1931)
ELLIOTT, K. A. C., AND SUTTER, H., *Z. physiol. Chem.*, **205**, 47 (1932)
ELVEHJEM, C. A., *J. Biol. Chem.*, **90**, 111 (1931)
ELVEHJEM, C. A., AND HART, E. B., *J. Biol. Chem.*, **95**, 363 (1932)
ELVEHJEM, C. A., STEENBOCK, H., AND HART, E. B., *J. Biol. Chem.*, **93**, 197 (1931)
FORBES, W. H., *J. Physiol.*, **71**, 261 (1931)
FORBES, W. H., AND ROUGHTON, F. J. W., *J. Physiol.*, **71**, 229 (1931)
GEIGER, A., *Proc. Roy. Soc. (London)*, *B*, **107**, 368 (1931)
GREEN, A. A., *J. Biol. Chem.*, **93**, 495, 517 (1931)
HAMSIK, A., *Z. physiol. Chem.*, **187**, 229 (1930)
HAMSIK, A., *Z. physiol. Chem.*, **190**, 199 (1930)
HARNISCH, O., *Z. vergl. Physiol. (Z. wiss. Biol. Abt. C)*, **12**, 504 (1930)
HART, E. B., ELVEHJEM, C. A., AND STEENBOCK, H., *J. Nutrition*, **2**, 277 (1930)
HART, E. B., STEENBOCK, H., WADDELL, J., AND ELVEHJEM, C. A., *J. Biol. Chem.*, **77**, 797 (1928)
HAUROWITZ, F. (1), *Z. physiol. Chem.*, **186**, 141 (1930)
HAUROWITZ, F. (2), *Z. physiol. Chem.*, **194**, 98 (1931)
HAWKINS, W. B., SRIBHISHAJ, K., ROBSCHEIT-ROBBINS, F. S., AND WHIPPLE, G. H., *Am. J. Physiol.*, **96**, 463 (1931).
HEKTOEN, L., AND BOOR, A. K., *J. Infectious Diseases*, **49**, 29 (1931)
HENDERSON, L. J., BOCK, A. V., DILL, D. B., AND EDWARDS, H. T., *J. Biol. Chem.*, **87**, 181 (1930)
HENDERSON, L. J., DILL, D. B., EDWARDS, H. T., AND MORGAN, O. P., *J. Biol. Chem.*, **90**, 697 (1931)
HENRIQUES, O. M., *Biochem. Z.*, **200**, 1, 5, 10, 18, 22 (1928)
HENRIQUES, O. M., *Ergebnisse Physiol.*, **28**, 625 (1929)
HENRIQUES, O. M., *J. Biol. Chem.*, **92**, 1 (1931)
HILL, R., AND KEILIN, D., *Proc. Roy. Soc. (London)*, *B*, **107**, 286 (1930)
HUANG, T., AND WU, H., *Chinese J. Physiol.*, **4**, 221 (1930)

KEILIN, D., *Proc. Roy. Soc. (London)*, B, **106**, 418 (1930)

KRAUSS, W. E., *J. Biol. Chem.*, **90**, 267 (1931)

KREBS, H. A., *Biochem. Z.*, **193**, 347 (1928)

KUHN, R., HAND, D. B., AND FLORKIN, M., *Z. physiol. Chem.*, **201**, 255 (1931)

LANDSTEINER, K., AND HEIDELBERGER, M., *J. Gen. Physiol.*, **6**, 131 (1923)

LEVY, M., *J. Biol. Chem.*, **89**, 173 (1930)

LINTZEL, W., *Ergebnisse Physiol.*, **31**, 844 (1931)

MARGARIA, R., *J. Physiol.*, **73**, 311 (1931)

McGOWAN AND CRICHTON, *Biochem. Z.*, **17**, 204 (1923)

McGOWAN AND CRICHTON, *Biochem. Z.*, **18**, 265 (1924)

MICHAELIS, L., AND SALOMON, K., *Biochem. Z.*, **234**, 107 (1931)

MIRSKY, A. E., AND ANSON, M. L., *J. Gen. Physiol.*, **13**, 477 (1930)

MITCHELL, H. S., AND MILLER, L., *J. Biol. Chem.*, **92**, 421 (1931)

MYERS, V. C., AND BEARD, H., *J. Biol. Chem.*, **94**, 89 (1931)

MYERS, V. C., BEARD, H., AND BARNES, B., *J. Biol. Chem.*, **94**, 117 (1931)

REDFIELD, A. C., AND FLORKIN, M., *Biol. Bull.*, **61**, 185 (1931)

ROCHE, J., *Compt. rend. trav. lab. Carlsberg*, **18**, 1 (1930)

ROCHE, J., AND BENDRIHEM, A., *Compt. rend. soc. biol.*, **107**, 639 (1931)

ROCHE, J., AND BENDRIHEM, A., *Compt. rend.*, **193**, 324 (1931)

SCOTT, W. J., *Biol. Bull.*, **61**, 211 (1931)

SENDROY, J., JR., *J. Biol. Chem.*, **91**, 307 (1931)

SENDROY, J., JR., AND LIU, S. H., *J. Biol. Chem.*, **87**, 133 (1930)

SRIBHISHAJ, K., HAWKINS, W. B., AND WHIPPLE, G. H., *Am. J. Physiol.*, **96**, 449 (1931)

STADIE, W. C., AND O'BRIEN, H., *Biochem. Z.*, **237**, 290 (1931)

STADIE, W. C., AND SUNDERMAN, F. W., *J. Biol. Chem.*, **91**, 227 (1931)

STARKENSTEIN, E., AND WEDEN, H., *Arch. exptl. Path. Pharmakol.*, **150**, 354 (1930)

UNDERHILL, F. A., ORTEN, J. M., AND LEWIS, R. C., *J. Biol. Chem.*, **91**, 13 (1931)

VAN SLYKE, D. D., AND HAWKINS, J. A., *J. Biol. Chem.*, **87**, 265 (1930)

WARBURG, O., *Bull. Johns Hopkins Hosp.*, **46**, 341 (1930) (A review)

WARBURG, O., AND CHRISTIAN, W. (1), *Biochem. Z.*, **235**, 240 (1931)

WARBURG, O., AND CHRISTIAN, W. (2), *Biochem. Z.*, **238**, 131 (1931)

WARBURG, O., AND KUBOWITZ, F., *Biochem. Z.*, **227**, 184 (1930)

WARBURG, O., KUBOWITZ, F., AND CHRISTIAN, W. (1), *Biochem. Z.*, **221**, 494 (1930)

WARBURG, O., KUBOWITZ, F., AND CHRISTIAN, W. (2), *Biochem. Z.*, **227**, 245 (1930)

WARBURG, O., KUBOWITZ, F., AND CHRISTIAN, W. (3), *Biochem. Z.*, **233**, 240 (1931)

WARBURG, O., AND NEGELEIN, E., *Biochem. Z.*, **238**, 135 (1931)

WARBURG, O., AND NEGELEIN, E., AND HAAS, E., *Biochem. Z.*, **227**, 171 (1930)

WASTL, H., AND LEINER, G., *Arch. ges. Physiol.*, **227**, 367, 421, 460 (1931)

WENDEL, W. B., *Proc. Soc. Exptl. Biol. Med.*, **27**, 624 (1930)

WENDEL, W. B., *Proc. Soc. Exptl. Biol. Med.*, **28**, 401 (1931)

WEST, R., AND HOWE, M. (1), *J. Biol. Chem.*, **88**, 427 (1930)

WEST, R., AND HOWE, M. (2), *J. Biol. Chem.*, **94**, 611 (1931)

WHIPPLE, G. H., AND ROBSCHEIT-ROBBINS, F. S., *Am. J. Physiol.,* **92,** 362 (1930)

WU, H., CHENG, L. H., AND LI, C. P., *Proc. Soc. Exptl. Biol. Med.,* **25,** 853 (1927)

ZEILE, K., *Z. physiol. Chem.,* **195,** 39 (1931)

ZEILE, K., AND HELLSTRÖM, H., *Z. physiol. Chem.,* **192,** 171 (1930)

THE HOSPITAL OF
THE ROCKEFELLER INSTITUTE FOR MEDICAL RESEARCH
NEW YORK CITY

THE ROCKEFELLER INSTITUTE FOR MEDICAL RESEARCH
PRINCETON, NEW JERSEY

PLANT PIGMENTS*

By P. Karrer and A. Helfenstein

Chemisches Institut der Universität, Zürich

I. The Carotenoids

The polyene pigments, now known and classified under the name of carotenoids, may be divided into three groups according to their chemical properties: (*a*) polyene hydrocarbons; (*b*) polyene alcohols; and (*c*) polyene carboxylic acids.

1. *Polyene hydrocarbons.*—The beautifully crystalline carotene from carrots, according to recent investigations, has proved to be a mixture of two isomers. One of these, making up the largest part of the crude carotene, is optically inactive, while the other is optically active. These observations have been made simultaneously and independently in three different laboratories [Kuhn and Lederer (1); Karrer, Helfenstein, Wehrli, Pieper, and Morf (2); Rosenheim and Starling (3); compare also Smith (3a)].

The inactive form has been designated as β carotene, the optically active as α carotene. The first has a melting-point of 182°, the latter of 172°. An approximately pure β carotene with a melting-point of 182° had already been prepared in 1929 by H. von Euler and P. Karrer (4).

The separation of a mixture of α and β carotene presents considerable difficulty. It is possible to isolate the less soluble β form in an approximately pure state by repeated fractional crystallization of the crude material. According to Kuhn and Lederer, the α carotene is best separated from the isomeric β form by fractional adsorption with fiber clay or fuller's earth. In different natural products, the β carotene seems to occur free from the α form, as for example in nettles, spinach (5), paprika, and the ovaries of cows (7). However, spectroscopic observations indicate that, in these cases also, some α carotene is present in the mother liquors. Besides occurring in carrots, mixtures of α and β carotene have been found in palm oil, rowanberry (mountain ash), and chestnut leaves (7, 8). The occurrence of pure α carotene is unknown.

Suginome and Ueno isolated from pumpkin seeds (*Cucurbita*

* Received January 28, 1932.

maxima), a pigment with the composition $C_{40}H_{56}$, which is probably identical with carotene (13). A small difference in the absorption spectrum can be explained by the assumption that the substance in question is rich in α carotene.

This α carotene possesses a high specific optical rotation, depending considerably upon the wave-length of the light employed, according to Kuhn and Lederer (7), $[\alpha]^{20}_{Cd} = +365°$; according to Karrer and Morf (6), $[\alpha]^{18}_{C} = +248°$, $[\alpha]^{18}_{643.5} = +328°$, $[\alpha]^{18}_{625.5} = +394°$, $[\alpha]^{7}_{607.5} = +458°$.

Table I compares several constants of α and β carotene.

Karrer and his associates propose the following symmetrical formula for β carotene:

I. β carotene

This formula is based upon Zechmeister's catalytic hydrogenation of carotene, which showed that eleven double bonds are present, and upon the results of the oxidation which lead to characteristic products of degradation. Treatment with potassium permanganate yields dimethyl malonic acid, dimethyl succinic acid, and α α dimethyl glutaric acid, as well as 4.5 mols of acetic acid. Oxidation with ozone yields geronic acid. Comparative quantitative experiments with β ionone on the one hand, and β carotene on the other, have shown that the amount of geronic acid produced in the ozonization of β carotene corresponds to two ionone-carbon rings. This grouping is therefore contained twice in β carotene (6). [Compare also Pummerer, Rebmann, and Reindel (11).]

The oxidation of α carotene with ozone yields neither geronic acid nor isogeronic acid. Karrer and Morf propose for this pigment either Formula II*a* or Formula II*b*; judging by the experiments hitherto performed on the cleavage of α carotene and dihydro α carotene, these formulae seem to be the most probable (12).

TABLE I

COMPARISON OF α CAROTENE AND β CAROTENE

Property	α carotene	β carotene	Literature Cited
Melting-point	174-175°, corrected	182°, uncorrected	(5, 2)
Optical rotation in benzene	$[\alpha]^{20}_{Cd} = +365°$ $[\alpha]^{18}_{643} = +328°$	Optically inactive	(5, 6)
Solubility in hexane at 0°	2.94 mg. per cc.	1.09 mg. per cc.	(7)
Points of maximum intensity of absorption bands in carbon disulphide	511 mμ, 478 mμ	521 mμ, 485.5 mμ	(5)
Absorption bands of the reaction product with SbCl$_3$ in chloroform:			
Immediately determined..........	590, 538, 493, 465 mμ	589, 437, 493 mμ	(9)
One hour later.................	−581, 539...504-483 (457), 419	−603, 563...550-526, 483, 425−	(10)

CH₃ CH₃   CH₃ CH₃
   \ /   CH₃   CH₃   CH₃   CH₃   \ /
    C   H H | H H H | H H H H | H H H | H H   C
   / \   C:C·C:C·C:C·C·C:C·C:C·C·C:C·C·C:C·C·C:C·C:C   CH₂
CH₂   CH₂
   | | H₃C·CH   CH₂
CH₂   C·CH₃ | |
   \ //   C
    C   H₂
    H

IIa. α carotene

CH₃ CH₃   CH₃ CH₃
   \ /   CH₃   CH₃   CH₃   CH₃   \ /
    C   ·H H | H H H | H H H H | H H H | H H   C
   / \   C:C·C:C·C:C·C:C·C·C:C·C:C·C·C:C·C·C:C·C·CH   CH₂
CH₂   H
   | | |
CH₂   C·CH₃   H₃C·C   CH₂
   \ //   \\ |
    C   C
    H   H

IIb. α carotene

For *lycopin,* Karrer and his collaborators have proposed Formula III, based upon the following experimental results: (*a*) catalytic hydrogenation shows thirteen double bonds; (*b*) oxidation with permanganate yields succinic acid and 4.5 mols of acetic acid; (*c*) oxidation with chromic acid yields six mols of acetic acid; and (*d*), ozonization gives acetone. By quantitative determination of the acetone formed on ozonization, it was possible to prove that both ends of the lycopin molecule are identical. In this ozonization more than one mol of acetone is formed from one mol of lycopin (14).

CH₃   CH₃
 | CH₃   CH₃   CH₃   CH₃   CH₃   CH₃ |
 | H H H | H H H | H H H | H H H H | H H H | H H H | H H H |
C:C·C·C·C:C·C:C·C·C:C·C·C·C:C·C·C·C:C·C·C:C·C:C·C·C:C·C·C:C·C·C·C:C
 | H H   H H |
CH₃   CH₃

III. Lycopin

Formula III shows the close relation to the isomeric carotene and to phytol. The hydrocarbon prepared from dihydro phytyl bromide by means of the Wurtz reaction with potassium proved on close examination to be very similar to the perhydrolycopin in its physical constants. An absolute agreement cannot be expected because of the fact that both hydrocarbons contain six asymmetric carbon atoms and represent, accordingly, mixtures of isomers.

MacGillivray has studied the stability of tomato pigment toward heat and sterilization of the fruit (14a).

2. *Polyene alcohols.*—Xanthophyll, $C_{40}H_{56}O_2$, which is always associated with carotene in parts of the green plant is, according to Karrer, a glycol of carotene. This view is substantiated by the catalytic hydrogenation of xanthophyll (Zechmeister), which showed eleven double bonds. Further support is found in the permanganate oxidation, whereby 4.5 mols of acetic acid, dimethyl malonic acid, and asymmetric dimethyl succinic acid are obtained (Karrer and collaborators). The hydroxyl function of the two oxygen atoms has been definitely proved by the determination of active hydrogen with the Zerewitinoff method, and by the synthesis of numerous esters.

The question of the unit character of leaf xanthophyll is still not definitely solved. Kuhn, Winterstein, and Lederer, who isolated xanthophyll from a great number of green plants and yellow leaves, found that these preparations, dissolved in ethyl acetate, gave optical rotations: $[\alpha]^{18}_{Cd} = +138°$ to $[\alpha]^{18}_{Cd} = +152°$. They believe the xanthophyll to be a single, uniform substance (15). Other investigators have obtained xanthophyll preparations of somewhat different specific optical rotation. As it has been found that carotene occurs frequently in two isomers, it is possible that xanthophyll, likewise, exists in isomeric forms. The melting-point of pure xanthophyll is 192°–193°.

The optical activity of leaf xanthophyll is due not only to the asymmetry of the carbon atoms to which the hydroxyl groups are attached. It is evident that still other centers of asymmetry are present. Nilsson and Karrer showed that the hydrocarbon $C_{40}H_{78}$ prepared from perhydro xanthophyll, through the corresponding dibromide, is optically active and that its optical rotation is $[\alpha]_D = +0.5°$ (16). This specific optical rotation is in agreement with that of perhydro carotene prepared by reduction of carotene, as far as both direction and order of magnitude are concerned. Therefore, it appears to be certain that leaf xanthophyll is partially or completely derived from the optically active form of carotene (α carotene).

Zeaxanthin, $C_{40}H_{56}O_2$, which is an isomer of xanthophyll, and which was found first by Karrer and Salomon in maize, appears to be very widespread in nature, frequently in esterified form. Its occurrence in the seed pods of *Evonymus europaeus* was demonstrated by Zechmeister and Tuzson (17), and in paprika by Zechmeister and Cholnoky (18).

Kuhn and Smakula (19) were able to show by spectroscopic analysis that lutein, the pigment of egg yolk, consists of approximately 30 per cent zeaxanthin and 70 per cent xanthophyll. Adsorption on calcium carbonate permits the concentration of zeaxanthin.

For capsanthin, the pigment of paprika (*Capsicum annuum*) the formula $C_{35}H_{50}O_3$ appears most probable [Karrer *et al.* (2); Zechmeister and Cholnoky (20)]. Capsanthin also belongs to the carotene series because of the fact that on oxidation with potassium permanganate dimethyl malonic acid and asymmetric dimethyl succinic acid are produced, both of which are characteristic for the ionone structure (2). Of the three oxygen atoms, two are present as hydroxyl groups because the Zerewitinoff analysis yields two volumes of methane; also numerous diesters of capsanthin may be prepared (2, 20). Zechmeister and his collaborators have shown that capsanthin in paprika is chiefly present as an ester, combined with such organic acids as oleic acid, myristic acid, palmitic acid, stearic acid, carnaubic acid, etc.

The pigment of Japanese paprika (*Capsicum frutescens* jap.) also contains capsanthin as its most important pigment (18).

Kuhn and Winterstein isolated a new carotenoid from pansies (*Viola tricolor*), with the composition $C_{40}H_{56}O_4$, which they called *violaxanthin* (21). The pigment has a melting-point of 207°–208° and a specific optical rotation of $[\alpha]^{20}_{Cd} = +35°$ in chloroform (22). A special characteristic for violaxanthin is the formation of intense blue addition compounds of a salt type. These addition compounds are similar to those of azafrin and fucoxanthin in so far as they are also stable in the presence of a certain amount of water.

Violaxanthin on oxidation with potassium permanganate gives asymmetric dimethyl succinic acid [Karrer and Morf (22)], and can therefore be considered as a derivative of carotene.

It appears to be widely distributed in the plant world. According to Zechmeister and Tuzson, it occurs in the rind of oranges and mandarins.

Taraxanthin, a new carotenoid which was discovered by Kuhn and Lederer in dandelion flowers (*Taraxacum officinale*), is an isomer of violaxanthin. In these flowers both taraxanthin and xanthophyll occur. The melting-point is 184°–185°, and the specific optical rotation, $[\alpha]^{20}_{cd} = +200°$ (23). On catalytic hydrogenation, taraxanthin takes up 10.6 mols of hydrogen, and the Zerewitinoff determination shows 3.2 atoms of active hydrogen. Taraxanthin can easily be distinguished from violaxanthin by the lack of salt formation in dilute acids.

Karrer and collaborators have repeated the preparation of fucoxanthin, which is the characteristic pigment of the brown algae, and have determined the empirical formula, $C_{40}H_{56}O_6$ (2). $[\alpha]^{18}_{c}$, in chloroform, $= +72°$ ($\pm 9°$). On catalytic hydrogenation it absorbed 10 mols of hydrogen, and in the Zerewitinoff determination a quantity of methane corresponding to 4.5 to 5 hydroxyl groups was produced. Its oxidation with potassium permanganate yielded dimethyl malonic acid, and therefore fucoxanthin seems also to be a derivative of carotene.

A polyene alcohol was also discovered by Karrer in the unsaponifiable fraction of certain fish oils (24, 25). This alcohol is responsible for the intense blue reaction which takes place when such oils are brought in contact with a solution of antimony trichloride in chloroform, and is very probably identical with vitamin A.

The compound which is formed in the liver after absorption of carotene is a carotene derivative because, like carotene, it forms geronic acid on ozonization (24, 25). That this compound is an alcohol is proved by the formation of esters. The purest preparations obtained up to the present time show analyses which correspond approximately to the formula $C_{20}H_{30}O$ (or $C_{22}H_{32}O$). Supported by these results, as well as by the results of oxidation with permanganate (2 mols acetic acid) and chromic acid (3 mols acetic acid) Karrer proposes for the polyene, the following formula:

$$CH_3 \quad CH_3$$

$$\underset{\underset{\underset{CH_2}{\diagdown\diagup}}{\overset{\displaystyle H_2C \quad \overset{\parallel}{C}\cdot CH_3}{|}}}{\overset{\overset{\displaystyle \diagdown\diagup}{C}}{\underset{\displaystyle H_2C}{\diagup\diagdown}}} \quad \overset{\displaystyle H\ H\ \ \ \overset{CH_3}{|}\ H\ H\ H\ \overset{CH_3}{|}\ H}{C\cdot C:C\cdot C:C\cdot C:C\cdot C:C\cdot CH_2OH}$$

3. *Polyene carboxylic acids.*—The aglucone of saffron pigment, α crocetin, has been investigated by Karrer and Salomon, who gave

to it the empirical formula $C_{19}H_{22}O_4$. Its hydrogenation number of 7, the analysis of its esters, and its relation to bixin, substantiated Formula IV. Oxidation with alkaline permanganate solution yielded 3 equivalents of acetic acid, in accordance with the proposed formula.

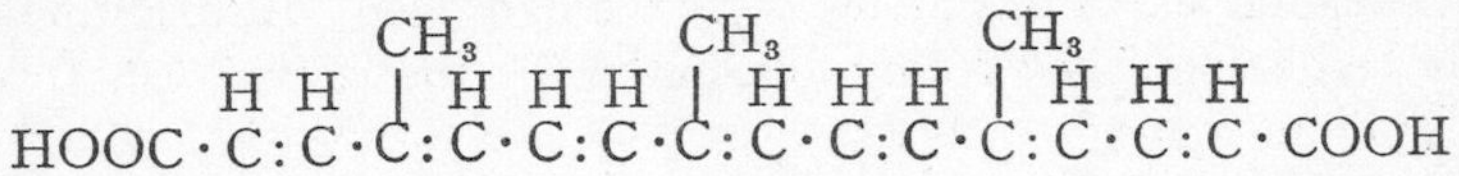

$$\begin{array}{ccccccccc} & & CH_3 & & & CH_3 & & & CH_3 \\ & H\ H & | & H\ H\ H & | & H\ H\ H & | & H\ H\ H \\ HOOC \cdot C : C \cdot C : C \cdot C : C \cdot C : C \cdot C : C \cdot C : C \cdot C : C \cdot COOH \end{array}$$

IV. α crocetin

Kuhn and l'Orsa found recently that α crocetin gives on oxidation with chromic acid 4 mols of acetic acid. New analyses and determinations of the molecular weight were in better agreement with the formula $C_{20}H_{22}O_4$. Therefore, Kuhn and l'Orsa propose the new crocetin formula, Formula V (26).

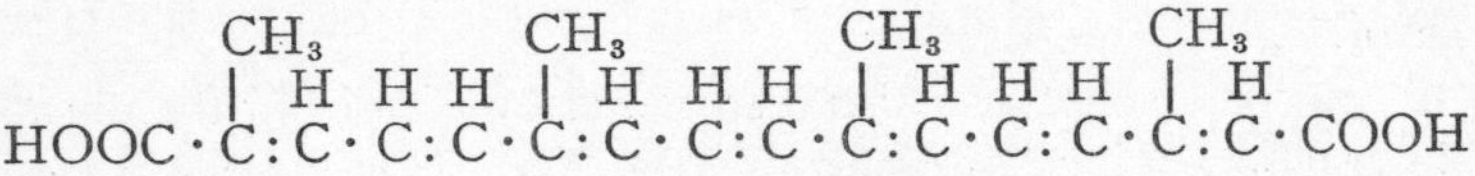

$$\begin{array}{ccccccccc} CH_3 & & & CH_3 & & & CH_3 & & & CH_3 \\ | & H\ H\ H & | & H\ H\ H & | & H\ H\ H & | & H \\ HOOC \cdot C : C \cdot C : C \cdot C : C \cdot C : C \cdot C : C \cdot C : C \cdot C : C \cdot COOH \end{array}$$

V. α crocetin

On account of the difficulties which are generally encountered in the analysis of isoprene derivatives, of which the study of bixin is a good example, it is perhaps at present not yet possible to decide definitely between the two crocetin formulae.

Azafrin, which was investigated by Liebermann from 1911 to 1915, has again been isolated from the roots of azafranilla by Kuhn, Winterstein, and Roth (27). Somewhat different analytical results were obtained. The new analysis agrees best with the formula $C_{28}H_{40}O_4$. The Zerewitinoff test indicates the presence of three active hydrogens and the treatment with dimethyl sulphate yields monomethyl azafrin. The four oxygen atoms in azafrin are therefore present as one carboxyl group, and two hydroxyl groups. The presence of a carboxyl group is confirmed by titration. Oxidation with chromic acid shows five methyl groups as acetic acid. On the basis of these results the authors therefore propose for azafrin the following tentative formula:

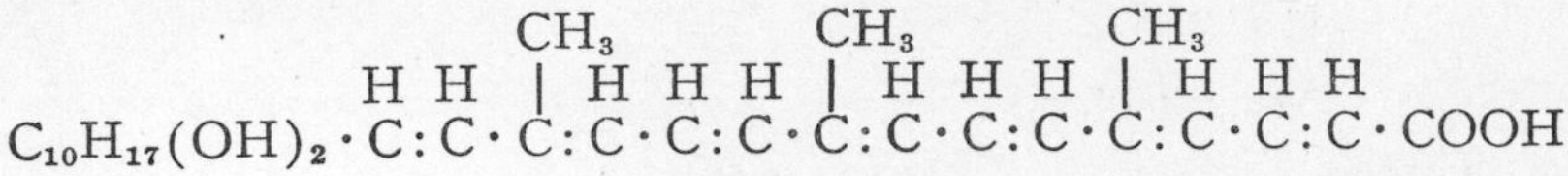

$$\begin{array}{ccccccccc} & & CH_3 & & & CH_3 & & & CH_3 \\ & H\ H & | & H\ H\ H & | & H\ H\ H & | & H\ H\ H \\ C_{10}H_{17}(OH)_2 \cdot C : C \cdot C : C \cdot C : C \cdot C : C \cdot C : C \cdot C : C \cdot C : C \cdot COOH \end{array}$$

VI. Azafrin

II. Pyrane and Quinone Pigments

1. *The anthocyanins.*—The constitution of the anthocyanidins, the basic substance of most of the red and blue berry pigments, has been substantiated by synthesis. There are, however, uncertainties about the position of the carbohydrate in the corresponding anthocyanins. Robert Robinson and collaborators have now succeeded in synthesizing a number of anthocyanins, several of which appear to be identical with natural products. The knowledge thereby acquired makes it possible to determine the position of the sugar group in other cases, and throws new light upon earlier experiments.

Robinson's method for the synthesis of 2-phenyl benzopyryllium chlorides consists of the condensation of ortho-hydroxy aldehydes with derivatives of acetophenone. The introduction of the carbohydrate in one of the components is usually accomplished with the aid of the acetobrom sugar and silver carbonate in benzene solution. In order to prevent the splitting off of the sugar in the succeeding condensation with hydrochloric acid the condensation is carried out in dry solvents free from hydroxyl, such as ethyl acetate or mixtures of ether and chloroform. Only pelargonin, the glucose residue of which adheres very strongly, could be prepared in methyl alcohol.

The anthocyanins and anthocyanidins which were prepared in 1931 are listed as follows:

VII. Chrysanthemin chloride (28)

VIII. 4'-β-glucosidyl pelargonidin chloride (29)

IX. 7-β-glucosidyl pelargonidin chloride (29)

X. Pelargonenin chloride (29)

XI. 3,7,4'-trihydroxy-5-methyl-flavylium chloride (29)

XII. 3,5,4'-trihydroxy-7-methyl-flavylium chloride (29)

XIII. 3,4'-dihydroxy-7-benzyloxy-5-methoxyflavylium chloride (29)

XIV. 5-methoxy pelargonidin chloride (29)

XV. 7-methoxy pelargonidin chloride (29)

XVI. Oenin chloride (30)

XVII. Oxycoccicyanin chloride (31, 38)

XVIII. Idaein chloride (32)

XIX. 3-β-galactosidyl peonidin chloride (32)

XX. 3-β-glucosidyl fisetinidin chloride (33)

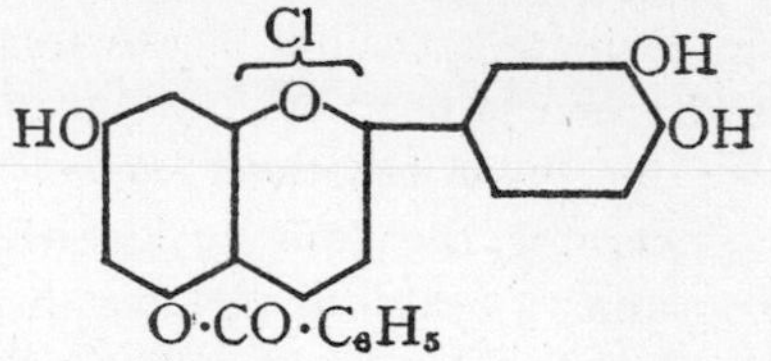

XXI. 5-benzoyloxy-luteolinidin chloride (34, 36)

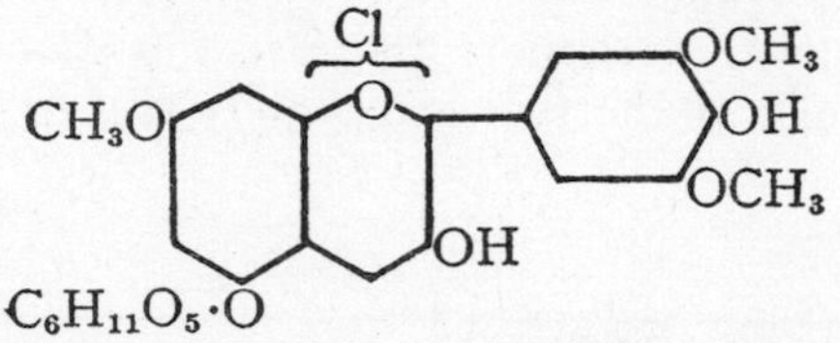

XXII. 5-β-glucosidyl hirsutidin chloride (37)

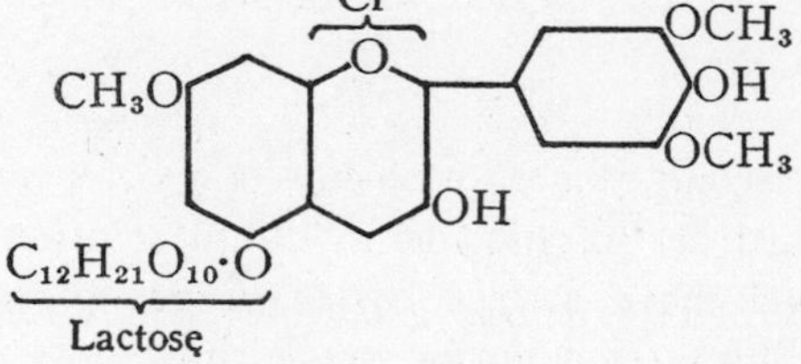

XXIII. 5-β-lactosidyl hirsutidin chloride (37)

León and Robinson prepared the already known anthocyanidins, luteolinidin (5,7,3′,4′-flavylium chloride) and fisetinidin (3,7,3′,4′-flavylium chloride), by the use of a new method with 2-benzoyl phloroglucinaldehyde. The products obtained were identical with the earlier preparations (34, 36).

The general result of the Robinson anthocyanin synthesis is that the sugar in all natural monoglucosides, synthetically prepared up to the present time, is attached in position 3 of the anthocyanidin molecule. Comparison of the color reactions makes it possible now to draw conclusions concerning the constitution of some diglucosidic anthocyanins. Mecocyanin, a cyanidin diglucoside, changes by partial hydrolysis to chrysanthemin chloride, and shows the same color reactions as this. The second sugar residue of mecocyanin, therefore, must be connected with the first one in position 3. For each of the anthocyanins, keracyanin and prunicyanin, which have similar properties as mecocyanin, the formula with the greatest probability is, likewise, that of a cyanidin-3-bioside.

Pelargonin (Formula XXIV) yields on partial hydrolysis pelargonenin. The latter is much more fluorescent in alcoholic solution, and the color reactions of the two compounds are very different. The

XXIV. Pelargonin

position of the second glucose molecule is proved by the stability of pelargonin toward ferric chloride in dilute solution. All pyryllium compounds which have a free hydroxyl group in position 3 are rapidly oxidized by ferric chloride, while those salts which have none or a substituted hydroxyl group in position 3 are stable under the same conditions (34). The same difference had been found some years before by Karrer and collaborators (35), in the oxidation with hydrogen peroxide of anthocyanins and anthocyanidins. These authors assumed that in all natural anthocyanins, the hydroxyl group in position 3 is blocked by a sugar residue. The investigations of Robinson prove the correctness of this assumption. Pelargonin can therefore be considered as pelargonidin-3,5-diglucoside (29).

The same conditions as in pelargonin also exist in the case of malvin and cyanin, the glucose residues of which must be attached to the hydroxyl groups in positions 3 and 5. This formulation brings about a satisfactory explanation for Karrer's experiments on methylation which assigned a carbohydrate group to position 3, and also for the conclusions which Robinson drew from the color reactions as to the substitution in position 5.

A serious handicap in the systematic study of the distribution of anthocyanins is the difficulty of obtaining the large amounts of blossoms and berries necessary for the isolation and identification of the pigment. G. M. and R. Robinson have now developed a method which is designed to enable the investigator to determine the nature of the pigment with very small amounts of material (39). The directions for analysis of the anthocyanins are as follows:

a) *The color of solution.*—Anthocyanidins can be easily identified by direct comparison of their solutions, for example, in 1 per cent HCl. In the case of anthocyanins the influence of accompanying substances, so-called co-pigments, interferes. The latter affect both the shade and the intensity of the color. Robinson assumes, as an explanation for this phenomenon, the formation of a complex compound the nature of which is not yet known. An example of co-pigments which is specific for its kind may be mentioned here: tannin intensifies the blue solution of oenin, an observation which was also made by Willstätter. But 2-glucosidoxyxanthone is a strong co-pigment for cyanin, weaker for chrysanthemin, and does not act at all upon mecocyanin.

b) *The color reactions with alkalies and ferric chloride.*—The number and position of the free hydroxyl groups are essential for the color changes with sodium hydroxide, sodium carbonate, and sodium acetate. The blue coloration with ferric chloride is characteristic for the cyanidin and delphinidin derivatives with neighboring free hydroxyl groups.

c) *The determination of stability against oxidation.*—The stability against oxidation provides a characteristic difference between compounds with a free hydroxyl group in position 3 and those in which this hydroxyl group is substituted. The oxidation may be carried out either with air in alkaline solution or with ferric chloride in very dilute solution. Compare also the oxidation with hydrogen peroxide according to Karrer (35).

d) *The determination of the partition coefficient between water and organic solvents.*—A characteristic for the anthocyanidins is the number of volumes of benzene necessary to force the anthocyanidin which is distributed between 1 volume of amyl alcohol and 3 volumes of 0.5 per cent HCl completely into the aqueous layer. Special mixtures which may be used for the determination of the partition coefficient are the so-called cyanidin reagent, which consists of 1 volume of cyclohexanol and 5 volumes of toluene, and the delphinidin reagent, consisting of a solution of 5 per cent picric acid in 1 volume of amyl ethyl ether and 4 volumes of anisol. Monoglucosides and diglucosides may be differentiated by the partition coefficient between a 1 per cent HCl solution and amyl alcohol. It is also possible by means of the partition coefficient to draw inferences as to the nature of the sugar as shown by comparisons of the synthetic products VII and XVII on the one hand and XVIII and XXIII on the other. Furthermore, the distribution between water and organic solvents furnishes a means of purifying anthocyanin solutions before running the color reactions, since the accompanying impurities usually possess different partition coefficients. The purification can be completed by forcing the solute in question repeatedly from one solvent to the other. The solvents have to be renewed and eventually diluted. For the extraction of diglucosides, mixtures of amyl alcohol and acetophenone in the presence of picric acid have proved to be satisfactory. For monoglucosides, cyclohexanol, which may be mixed with benzene, is suitable.

By means of the comparative experiments mentioned above, Robinson succeeded in identifying petunin as a derivative of a true anthocyanidin, the so-called petunidin, and in separating it from mixtures of malvidin and delphinidin, with which it has many properties in common (39).

As a general result of the investigation of many plants it is shown that the experimental findings can be explained by reference to the anthocyanidin known to date, viz., pelargonidin, cyanidin, paeonidin, delphinidin, petunidin, malvidin, and hirsutidin, although there is the possibility of new anthocyanidins in the material investigated. Complex anthocyanins, consisting of anthocyanidin, a carbohydrate, and, in addition, an organic acid in the form of an ester, have been found to occur in the leaves of *Coleus,* and in the flowers of *Salvia virgata nemorosa* (39). It may be mentioned at this point that Kondo has isolated a new complex anthocyanin from *Perillana ocimoides* which he calls perillanin chloride. Delphinidin and one mol each of glucose and protocatechuic acid were found to be the components (40).

Nolan and Casey were able to isolate 2 anthocyanins from elder berries (*Sambucus nigra*), one of which proved to be identical with chrysanthemin chloride. The second pigment, called "sambucicyanin," which was isolated in a small amount, seems to be a compound of molecular quantities of chrysanthemin and a cyanidin-pentose-glucoside (41).

Schmid and Huber isolated cyanidin-diglucoside from the wild poppy (*Papaver rhoeas*). The anthocyanin of the wild poppy is supposedly different from that of the cultivated form (42).

The theory that the anthocyanins in nature are formed from flavonols is supported by the experiments of Guilliermond. Guilliermond was able to prove the existence of flavonols in young blossoms before anthocyanins appeared (43). Asahina and Inubuse have described a new way of carrying out this reduction *in vitro*. They transformed rutin (quercetin-rhamno-glucoside) into cyanidin with sodium amalgam (44).

2. *Flavones and isoflavones.*—Shibata and Hatori have assigned new structural formulae to baicalein, which is now regarded as 5,7,8-trihydroxy flavone, and wogonin, which is a 5,6-dihydroxy 7-methoxy flavone (45). These formulae are based especially upon the synthesis of the wogonin dimethyl ether, which was carried out by Hattori, starting with 2,3,4-trimethoxy-6-hydroxy-acetophenone (46). The constitution of this starting material, which was formerly considered to be 2-hydroxy-3,4,6-trimethoxy-acetophenone, was proved by the preparation of the already known quercetagetin hexamethyl ether (3,5,6,7,3',4'-hexamethoxy flavone).

Schmid and Pietsch isolated from the wood of acacia, a pigment of the flavone type with the empirical formula $C_{15}H_{10}O_7$ and possessing 5 phenolic hydroxyl groups. The degradation with alkali yielded β resorcylic acid (47).

Schmid and Rumpel were able to isolate from toad flax (*Linaria vulgaris*) a pigment with the composition $C_{29}H_{34}O_{15}+H_2O$. On hydrolysis it gave one molecule of hexose, one molecule of methyl pentose, and the compound $C_{17}H_{14}O_6$. The aglucone contains 2 methoxy groups and yielded anisic acid on alkaline degradation. However, the compound does not seem to be a simple flavone because of the fact that a hydrocarbon was also liberated (48). E. Walz (49) isolated 2 dye glucosides from soy-bean meal (*Soja hispida*). One, genistin, gave on hydrolysis *d*-glucose and genistein (prunetol), i.e., 5,7,4'-trihydroxy isoflavone. The sugar residue blocks the hydroxyl group in position 7 as could be determined from the methylation product of the glucoside. Genistin, therefore, has the following formula:

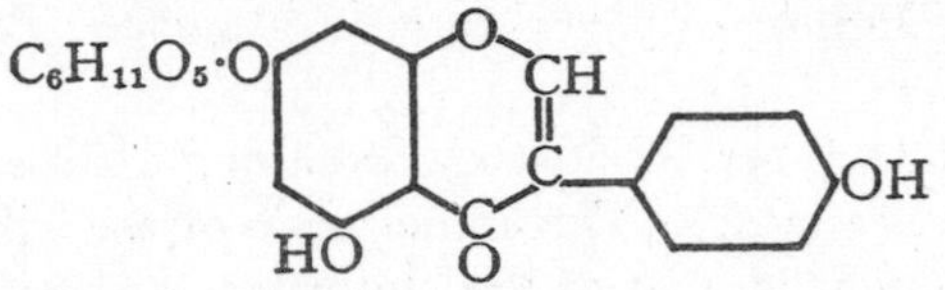

XXV. Genistin

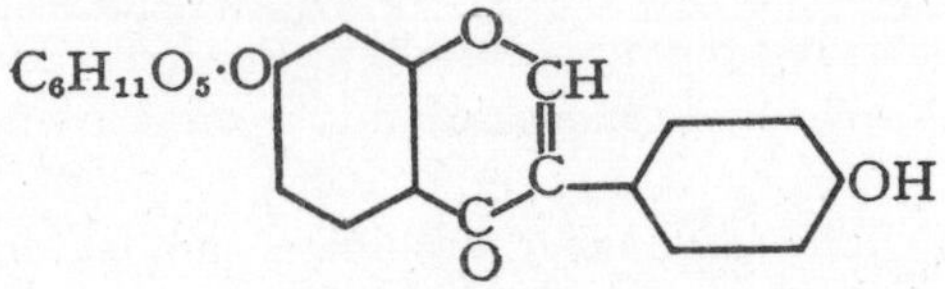

XXVI. Daidzin

The second glucoside from *Soja hispida,* called *daidzin,* decomposed on acid hydrolysis into *d*-glucose and an aglucone daidzein, $C_{15}H_{10}O_4$. The latter could be split by alkali into formic acid and 2,4-dihydroxyphenyl 4'-hydroxybenzyl ketone. This justifies for daidzin the formula of 7,4'-dihydroxy isoflavone. The dextrose group in daidzin is attached to the hydroxyl in position 7. Therefore the glucoside is constituted as indicated in the formula given above (Formula XXVI).

3. *Brasiline and quinone pigments.*—P. Pfeiffer, Breith, and Hoyer have synthesized a great number of benzylchromanones, of which compounds XXVII and XXVIII are the most closely related to brasilin, that is to say, haematoxylin. They have the same empirical composition as the natural products (50).

Shildneck and Adams have prepared polyporic acid and atromentin with a new method and in very good yield. They reduced 2,5-diphenyl quinone to the corresponding hydroquinone, the latter brominated and the dibromdiphenylhydroquinone so obtained again oxidized to the quinone. By hydrolysis of this quinone, polyporic acid was formed. Starting with dianisyl quinone, one obtains in the same manner atromentin (Formula XXIX) (51).

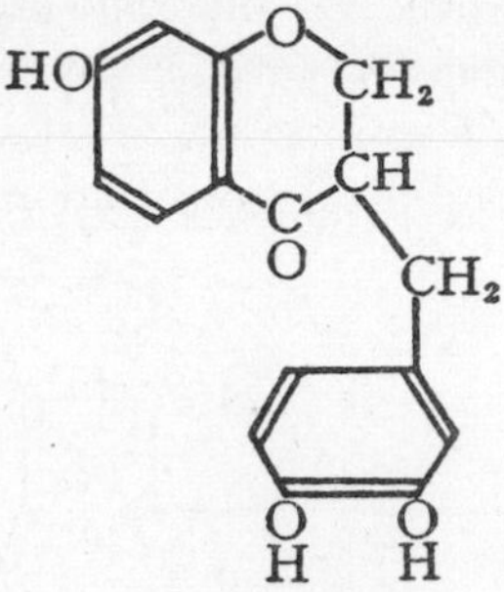

XXVII. *7,3',4'-trihydroxy-benzylchromanon*

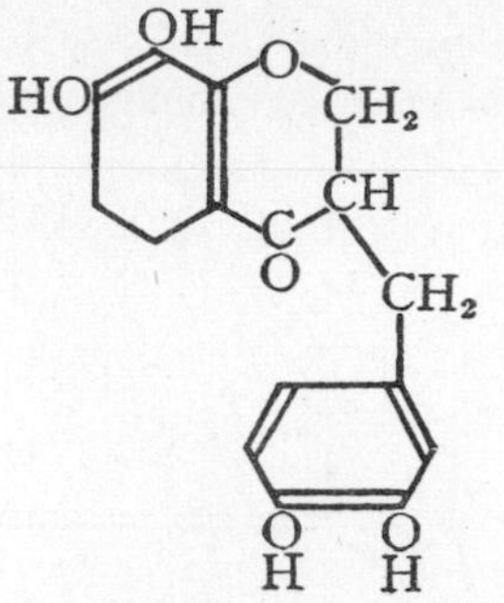

XXVIII. *7,8,3',4'-tetra-hydroxy-benzylchromanon*

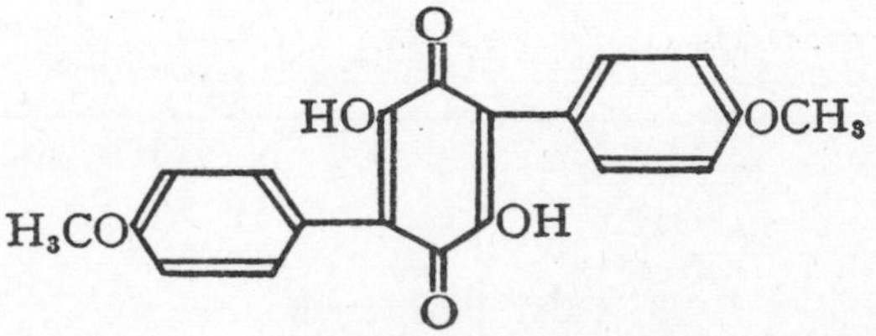

XXIX. Atromentin

III. THE CHLOROPHYLL PIGMENTS

1. *Phylloerythrin.*—The new formulae for chlorophyll-*a* and its derivatives proposed by Hans Fischer in 1931 are based upon the discovery of the constitution of phylloerythrin and desoxo-phyllerythrin. These discoveries were made in the same year and both substances were prepared from chlorophyll by simple reactions. Phylloerythrin can be prepared in good yield from primary transformation products of chlorophyll-*a* such as phaeophytin, chlorophyllid, phaeophorbid-*a* and methyl phaeophorbid-*a* by boiling for 16 hours in 20 per cent HCl solution in an air current or nitrogen atmosphere (52). For example, desoxo-phyllerythrin is made from chlorophyllid and phaeophorbid-*a* or also from phylloerythrin by heating it with hydrogen bromide in glacial acetic acid, in a bomb tube, at 180°.

The constitution of phylloerythrin (Formula XXX), having the empirical formula $C_{33}H_{34}O_3N_4$, is proved by the following experimental results. Its alcoholate degradation yielded phylloporphyrin (Formula XXXI), rhodoporphyrin (Formula XXXII), and pyrroporphyrin (Formula XXXIII) (53). The constitution of these

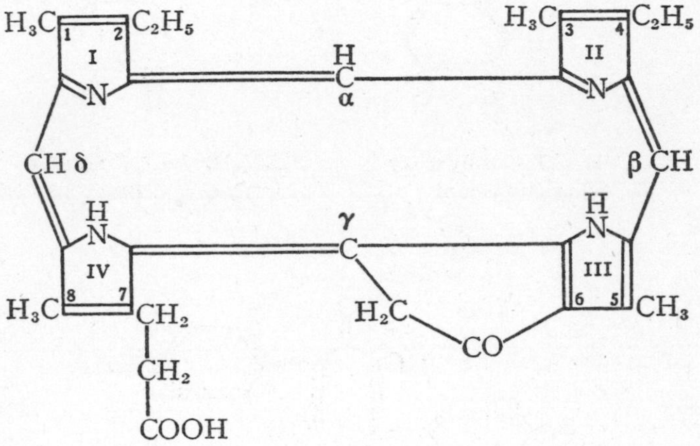

XXX. Phylloerythrin

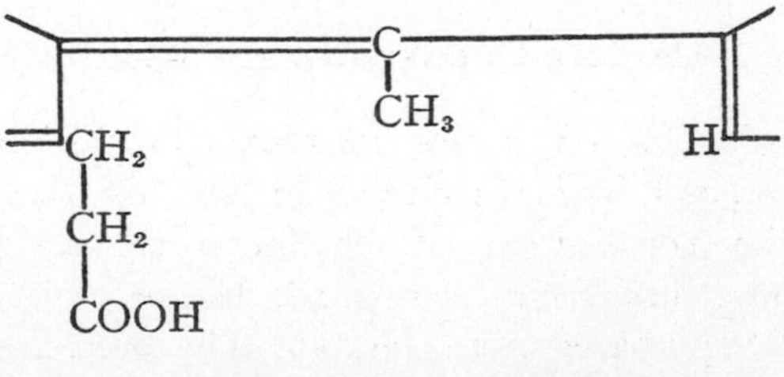

XXXI. Phylloporphyrin

substances has been established by synthesis which was accomplished by Fischer in the last few years. On degradation with methyl alcoholic potassium hydroxide solution, verdoporphyrin and a tricarboxylic acid were obtained, besides the three porphyrins mentioned above.

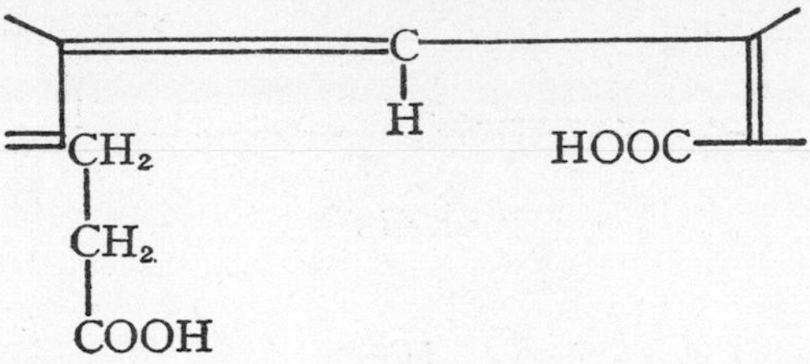

XXXII. Rhodoporphyrin

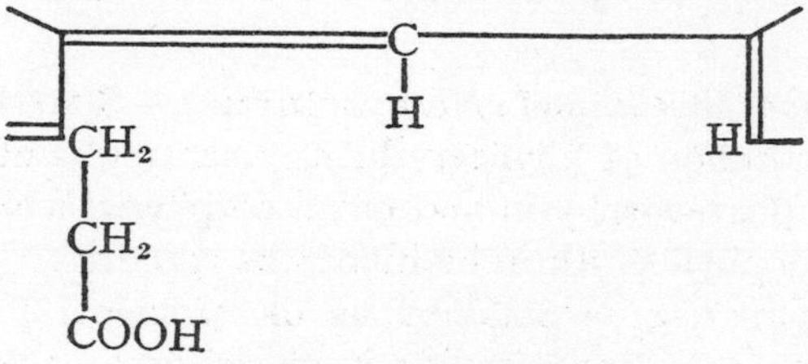

XXXIII. Pyrroporphyrin

The tricarboxylic acid was assumed to be rhodoporphyrin γ-carboxylic acid (52, 54). These results determined the position of the side chains in the porphin system. The substituents remaining for identification are attached to the carbon atoms 6 and γ. The preparation of the oxime, semicarbazone, and hydrazone shows that phylloerythrin contains one carbonyl group which by the Wolff-Kishner method can be reduced with hydrazin hydrate and sodium ethylate (53). In this way one obtains desoxo-phyllerythrin, the synthesis of which is also a proof for the formula of phylloerythrin (55). In this synthesis Fischer condensed the two methenes XXXIV and XXXV by short heating in succinic acid and obtained directly the desired desoxo-phyllerythrin, yield 0.5 per cent. The small yield is due to the fact that methene XXXIV is transformed primarily to the corresponding aetioporphyrin by the condensation of two molecules of methene (Formula XXXIV).

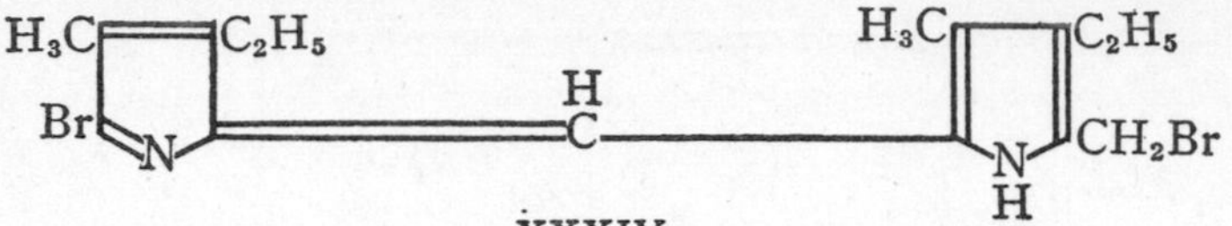

XXXIV

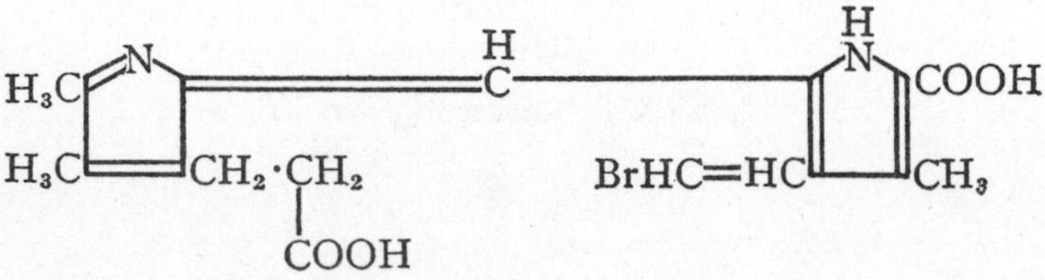

XXXV

2. *Phaeoporphyrins and chloroporphyrins.*—Starting with the established constitution of phylloerythrin, Fischer was able to propose formulae for phaeoporphyrin and chloroporphyrin which are closely connected with phylloerythrin by numerous reactions.

Phaeoporphyrin-a_5 is obtained as the principal product in the gentle reaction of hydrogen iodide in glacial acetic acid with phaeoporphyrin or chlorophyll. It is a dicarboxylic acid and contains the fifth oxygen atom in a carbonyl group, as may be demonstrated by the preparation of its oxime. The easy transformation of phaeoporphyrin-a_5 to phylloerythrin which may be brought about with hydrogen bromide or hydrochloric acid under various conditions proves its structure (Formula XXXVI). In this reaction one molecule of CO_2

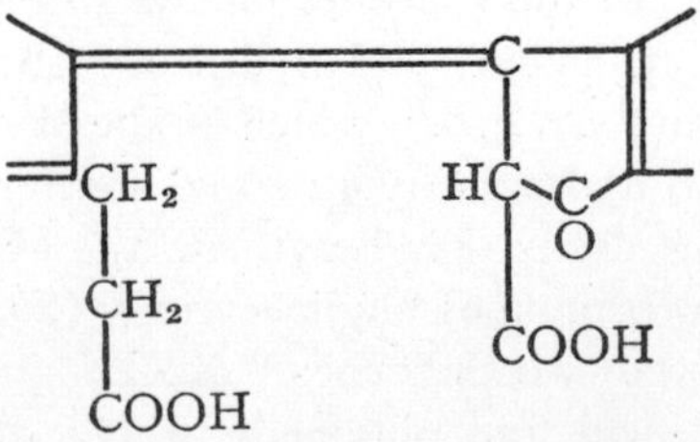

XXXVI. Phaeoporphyrin-a_5

is split off. The point of attachment of this carbonyl group is deduced from the relation of phaeoporphyrin-a_5 to chloroporphyrin-e_6, as will be mentioned later. The reduction of the double bond in the isocyclic five-membered ring, which takes place with the elimination of hydrogen bromide, is explained by the well-known reducing action of succinic acid at higher temperatures.

The assumption of the five-membered isocyclic ring condensed with the pyrrol ring III represents the newer concepts which entered the chemistry of chlorophyll-a by the analysis of phylloerythrin. Neither phylloerythrin nor any known derivative of it could be isolated in similar experiments with chlorophyll-b and its degradation product, rhodin-g (52).

Phylloerythrin, as a degradation product of chlorophyll, is of actual biological significance, because it could be prepared by Marchlewski from the bile of sheep, fed upon green stuffs (56). Fischer discovered another type of biological degradation of chlorophyll in caterpillars. He was able to isolate a new chlorophyll derivative from the excrement of the silkworm (*Bombyx mori*), which he named phyllobombycin. The compound has the composition $C_{34}H_{36}O_6N_4$, and its cleavage products were found to be phaeoporphyrin-a_5 and chloroporphyrin-e_6 (57).

In the hydrogen iodide degradation of phaeophorbid-a, both phaeoporphyrin-a_7 and phaeoporphyrin-a_5 are obtained (52). The yield of phaeoporphyrin-a_7 can be increased by passing in air during the process of preparation. Fischer suggests Formula XXXVII for

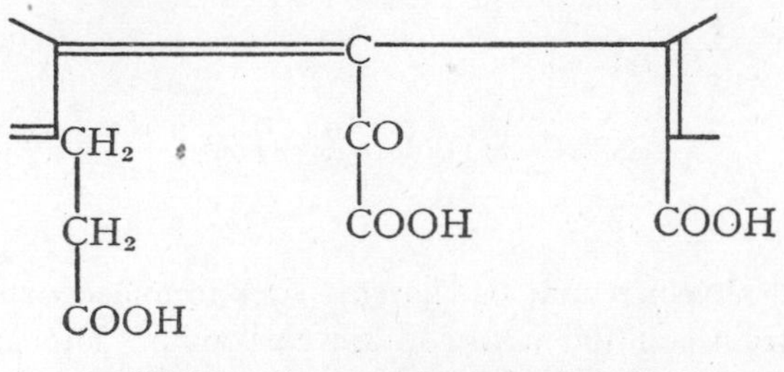

XXXVII. Phaeoporphyrin-a_7 (Fischer)
Phaeopurpurin$_7$ (Conant)

the new porphyrin, basing it upon the analysis of the tri-ester, the formation of phylloporphyrin in the reduction by the Wolff-Kishner method, and the degradation to rhodoporphyrin resulting from treatment with potassium hydroxide in methyl alcohol. Formula XXXVII was suggested by Conant for phaeopurpurin₇ which he obtained through the action of potassium hydroxide in propyl alcohol on phaeophorbid-*a* (60). Phaeopurpurin changes readily to chlorin-*f* on treatment with alkali, in the course of which oxalic acid is split off. Chlorin-*f* may be transformed into rhodoporphyrin by treatment with hydrogen iodide.

Phaeophorbid-*a* or phaeophytin on saponification for a short time with strong caustic solution gives chlorin-e_7, from which the group of chloroporphyrins is derived. On esterification with diazomethane chlorin-e_7 is simultaneously reduced to chlorin-e_6-ester. From this ester, chloroporphyrin-e_6 is obtained by the action of hydrogen iodide in glacial acetic acid, the formula of which can be derived from its relation to phaeoporphyrin-a_5 (52). The dimethyl ester of phaeoporphyrin-a_5 changes, namely, to the trimethyl ester of chloroporphyrin-e_6 by the action of a solution of HCl in methyl alcohol. The reaction is self-explanatory by assigning Formula XXXVIII to chloroporphyrin-e_6. As is to be expected, this reaction may be reversed

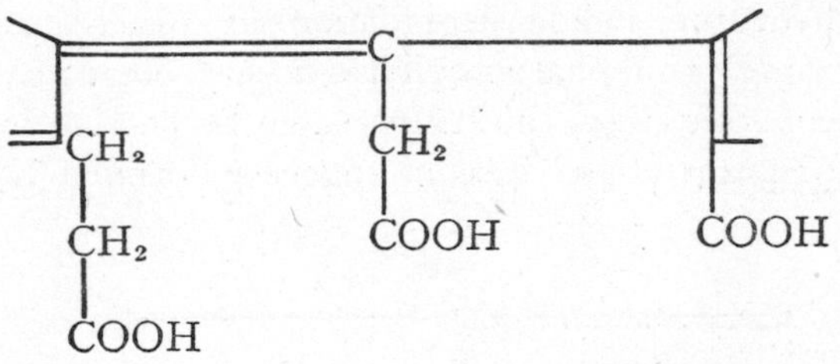

XXXVIII. Chloroporphyrin-e_6

and chloroporphyrin-e_6 may be changed back to phaeoporphyrin-a_5 by use of a pyridin solution with sodium carbonate. The same closing of the ring takes place if chlorin-*e* or chloroporphyrin-e_6 be heated with hydrogen bromide in glacial acetic acid at 50°. Phylloerythrin is thereby formed with elimination of carbon dioxide (52). The phylloerythrin so obtained was originally called pseudo phylloerythrin (53) because it possessed all the properties and reaction characteristics of phylloerythrin except that it crystallized from chloroform without chloroform of crystallization, unlike phylloerythrin. Fischer succeeded afterward in transforming pseudo phylloerythrin to phylloerythrin by purification procedures, such as treatment with fuming sulphuric acid or repeated re-crystallization from pyridin and glacial acetic acid. By the addition of 10 per cent chloroporphyrin-e to phylloerythrin, a mixture was obtained which had all the properties of pseudo phylloerythrin (54).

Chloroporphyrin-e_5 was prepared from chlorin-e_7 by the action of hydrogen iodide, with the elimination of formic acid. Fischer gave to it the formula of a γ-formyl rhodoporphyrin. This formulation is substantiated by the formation of an oxime and the production of phylloerythrin in reduction by the Wolff-Kishner method (52). The preparation of chloroporphyrin-e_5 by the oxidation of chloroporphyrin-e_6 with air in glacial acetic acid provides additional proof for the suggested structure (54).

If chloroporphyrin-e_6 is boiled with formic acid, chloroporphyrin-e_4 with elimination of carbon dioxide is obtained. Formula XXXIX is suggested by the type of formation and the products of alcoholate degradation. These were determined to be phylloporphyrin, rhodoporphyrin, and pyrroporphyrin (52).

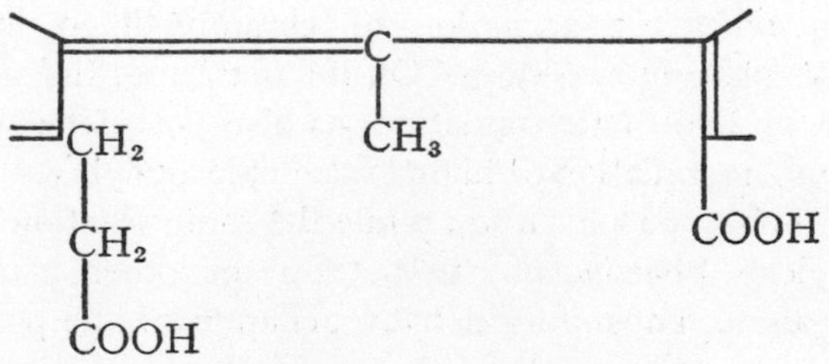

XXXIX. Chloroporphyrin-e_4

3. *The oxidation and dehydrogenation of chlorophyll.*—Chlorophyll-a and its derivatives, which may be prepared by simple saponification, are rapidly oxidized in solution by atmospheric oxygen. Conant was able to show that the same type of oxidation takes place in the so-called allomerization of chlorophyll, which results from the exposure to the air of an alcoholic solution of chlorophyll as well as in the phase test, consisting of the action of an alcoholic potassium hydroxide solution upon chlorophyll under admission of air (60). Furthermore, he obtained the same reaction with potassium-molybdic-

cyanide, $K_3Mo(CN)_8$, whereby two equivalents of the oxidizing agent were used up (61). In all these cases brief treatment with strong potassium hydroxide yielded unstable chlorins, which could be transformed into the same ester of phaeopurpurin$_7$ by means of diazo methane. Under the same conditions the ester of chlorin-e_6 is obtained from unchanged chlorophyll by application of the phase test in the absence of air. Conant therefore assumes that in all the oxidations mentioned a dehydrogenation of the glycollic-acid group attached to the carbon atom takes place, bringing about the formation of a glyoxylic acid. Fischer discovered a similar oxidation in the action of a solution of potassium hydroxide in propyl alcohol upon phaeoporphyrin-a_5 or chloroporphyrin-e_6 in the presence of air. This solution was also used by Conant in the phase test. The breaking of the ethanone bridge in phylloerythrin had been found earlier and shown to be an alkaline hydrolytic oxidation (52). By the action of propyl-alcoholic potassium hydroxide, Fischer obtained a green crystalline compound identical with that formed by the heating of rhodoporphyrin γ-carboxylic acid and which seems indeed to be the anhydride of the latter. According to this result, it may be possible that isomerism exists between chlorins and porphyrins (58).

Fischer assumes the oxidation of chlorophyll by atmospheric oxygen to take place in two steps. On the one hand, the side chain is broken down by hydrolytic oxidation, as also postulated by Conant. For this reason, degradation of allomerized chlorophyll with hydrogen iodide leads to phaeoporphyrin-a_7, while the same reaction with fresh chlorophyll yields phaeoporphyrin-a_5. On the other hand, Fischer conceives of an accompanying dehydrogenation of the porphin ring. In this dehydrogenation, hydrogen peroxide could be formed, which would then effect the oxidation of the side chain. In accordance with this view Fischer was able to dehydrogenate ethyl chlorophyllid with the aid of quinone. The use of one or two equivalents gave the same result with the formation of hydroquinone or quinhydrone, respectively. The degradation of the product of dehydrogenation with the aid of hydrogen iodide led to a new porphyrin which analysis indicated to be phaeoporphyrin-a_6. Investigation of this product shows that it occupies a mid-position between phaeoporphyrin-a_5 and phaeoporphyrin-a_7, and that it seems to correspond to chlorophyll-a in the degree of oxidation of its side chain (58).

As it is possible to dehydrogenate the porphin system of chlorophyll-a, with quinone, a new formula containing two more hydrogen atoms than previously assumed seems preferable. The results of the determination of active hydrogen by application of the Zerewitinoff method to esters of chlorophyll suggest the same conclusion (62).

The results described above led Fischer (58) to propose Formula XL for chlorophyll-*a*. The location of the double bond and the position of magnesium are arbitrarily chosen. The structure of phaeophytin follows from the splitting-off of magnesium, while phaeophorbid-*a*, frequently referred to, is obtained from phaeophytin by saponification of the phytol.[1] The given formulation results from the detection of the ethyl group in phylloerythrin ester which was obtained from ethyl chlorophyllid. The latter was formed from chlorophyll under conditions which permitted only the replacement of phytol by ethyl alcohol.

In Formula XL, the close relationship existing between chlorophyll and haemin is shown. The side chains are perfectly symmet-

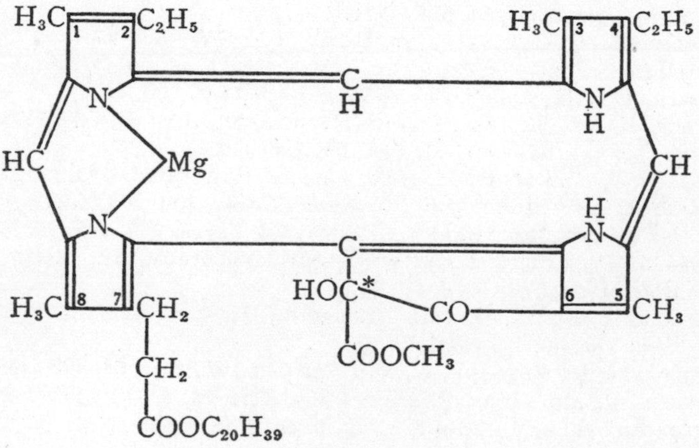

XL. Chlorophyll-*a*

rically arranged in the two compounds. The differences in the organic portion are limited to the ethyl groups of chlorophyll in

---

[1] Chlorophyll as well as its derivatives are here shown to contain an asymmetric carbon atom. However, up to the present time, no chlorophyll derivative possessed of optical activity has been observed.

positions 2 and 4, which in the case of haemin are dehydrogenated to vinyl groups and, furthermore, to the opening and reduction of the isocyclic 5-membered ring, which gives rise to a propionic acid side chain in position 6 of haemin.

Fischer was able to present new experimental evidence for these relations by the transformation of pyroporphyrin from chlorophyll into haemin-meso-porphyrin (63). The introduction of the propionic acid residue in position 6 was also accomplished (63).

LITERATURE CITED

1. KUHN, R., AND LEDERER, E., *Naturwissenschaften*, **19**, 306 (1931)
2. KARRER, P., HELFENSTEIN, A., WEHRLI, H., PIEPER, B., AND MORF, R., *Helv. Chim. Acta*, **14**, 614 (1931)
3. ROSENHEIM, O., AND STARLING, W. W., *Chemistry and Industry*, **50**, 443, (1931)
3a. SMITH, J. H. C., *J. Biol. Chem.*, **90**, 597 (1931)
4. EULER, H. VON, KARRER, P., AND RYDBOM, M., *Ber.*, **62**, 2445 (1929)
5. KUHN, R., AND LEDERER, E., *Ber.*, **64**, 1349 (1931)
6. KARRER, P., AND MORF, R., *Helv. Chim. Acta*, **14**, 1033 (1931)
7. KUHN, R., AND LEDERER, E., *Z. physiol. Chem.*, **200**, 246 (1931)
8. KUHN, R., AND BROCKMANN, H., *Z. physiol. Chem.*, **200**, 255 (1931)
9. KARRER, P., EULER, HANS VON, AND HELLSTRÖM, H., *Arkiv Kemi, Mineral. Geol. B*, **10**, 1 (1931)
10. KARRER, P., EULER, H. VON, HELLSTRÖM, H., AND RYDBOM, B., *Svensk Kem. Tid.*, **43**, 105 (1931)
11. PUMMERER, R., REBMANN, L., AND REINDEL, W., *Ber.*, **64**, 492 (1931)
12. KARRER, P., AND MORF, R., *Helv. Chim. Acta*, **14**, 833 (1931)
13. SUGINOME, H., AND UENO, K., *Bull. Chem. Soc. Japan*, **6**, 221 (C. 1931 II. 2892)
14. KARRER, P., HELFENSTEIN, A., PIEPER, B., AND WETTSTEIN, A., *Helv. Chim. Acta*, **14**, 435 (1931)
14a. MACGILLIVRAY, J. H., *Bulletin No. 350*. Purdue University, Agricultural Station, Lafayette, Ind.
15. KUHN, R., WINTERSTEIN, H., AND LEDERER, E., *Z. physiol. Chem.*, **197**, 141 (1931)
16. NILSSON, R., AND KARRER, P., *Helv. Chim. Acta*, **14**, 843 (1931)
17. ZECHMEISTER, L., AND TUZSON, P., *Z. physiol. Chem.*, **196**, 199 (1931)
18. ZECHMEISTER, L., AND CHOLNOKY, L., *Ann.*, **489**, 1 (1931)
19. KUHN, R., AND SMAKULA, A., *Z. physiol. Chem.*, **197**, 161 (1931)
20. ZECHMEISTER, L., AND CHOLNOKY, L., *Ann.*, **487**, 197 (1931)

21. KUHN, R., AND WINTERSTEIN, A., *Ber.*, **64**, 326 (1931)
22. KARRER, P., AND MORF, R., *Helv. Chim. Acta*, **14**, 1044 (1931)
23. KUHN, R., AND LEDERER, E., *Z. physiol. Chem.*, **200**, 108 (1931)
24. KARRER, P., MORF, R., AND SCHÖPP, K., *Helv. Chim. Acta*, **14**, 1036 (1931)
25. KARRER, P., MORF, R., AND SCHÖPP, K., *Helv. Chim. Acta*, **14**, 1431 (1931)
26. KUHN, R., AND L'ORSA, F., *Ber.*, **64**, 1732 (1931)
27. KUHN, R., WINTERSTEIN, A., AND ROTH, H., *Ber.*, **64**, 333 (1931)
28. MURAKAMI, S., ROBERTSON, A., AND ROBINSON, R., *J. Chem. Soc.*, 2665 (1931)
29. LEÓN, A., ROBERTSON, A., ROBINSON, R., AND SESHADRI, T. R., *J. Chem. Soc.*, 2672 (1931)
30. LEVY, L. F., POSTERNACK, T., AND ROBINSON, R., *J. Chem. Soc.*, 2701 (1931); WILLSTÄTTER, R., AND ZOLLINGER, E. H., *Ann.*, **408**, 83 (1915) and *Ann.*, **412**, 195 (1917); KARRER, P., AND WIDMER, R., *Helv. Chim. Acta*, **10**, 5 (1926)
31. LEVY, L. F., AND ROBINSON, R., *J. Chem. Soc.*, 2715 (1931)
32. GROVE, K. E., AND ROBINSON, R., *J. Chem. Soc.*, 2722 (1931)
33. FONSEKA, E. L., AND ROBINSON, R., *J. Chem. Soc.*, 2730 (1931)
34. LEÓN, A., AND ROBINSON, R., *J. Chem. Soc.*, 2732 (1931)
35. KARRER, P., WIDMER, R., HELFENSTEIN, A., HÜRLIMANN, W., NIEVERGELT, O., AND MONSARRAT-THOMS, P., *Helv. Chim. Acta*, **10**, 729 (1927)
36. ROBINSON, R., AND LEÓN, A., *Anales soc. españ. fís. quim.*, **29**, 415 (1931)
37. LEVY, L. F., AND ROBINSON, R., *J. Chem. Soc.*, 2738 (1931)
38. GROVE, K. E., AND ROBINSON, R., *Biochem. J.*, **25**, 1706 (1931)
39. ROBINSON, G. M., AND ROBINSON, R., *Biochem. J.*, **25**, 1687 (1931)
40. KONDO, K., *J. Pharm. Soc. Japan*, **51**, 25 (1931)
41. NOLAN, T. G., AND CASEY, H. M. T., *Proc. Roy. Irish Acad.*, **40**, 56 (1931)
42. SCHMID, L., AND HUBER, R., *Monatsh.*, **57**, 383 (1931)
43. GUILLIERMOND, A., *Compt. rend.*, **193**, 112 (1931)
44. ASAHINA, Y., AND INUBUSE, M., *Ber.*, **64**, 1256 (1931)
45. SHIBATA, K., AND HATTORI, S., *J. Pharm. Soc. Japan*, **51**, 15 (1931)
46. HATTORI, S., *Acta phytochim. Japan*, **5**, 99 (1930)
47. SCHMID, L., AND PIETSCH, K., *Monatsh.*, **57**, 305 (1931)
48. SCHMID, L., AND RUMPEL, W., *Monatsh.*, **57**, 421 (1931)
49. WALZ, E., *Ann.*, **489**, 118 (1931)
50. PFEIFFER, P., BREITH, E., AND HOYER, H., *J. prakt. Chem.*, **129**, 31 (1931)
51. SHILDNECK, P. R., AND ADAMS, R., *J. Am. Chem. Soc.*, **53**, 2373 (1931)
52. FISCHER, H., MOLDENHAUER, O., AND SÜS, O., *Ann.*, **486**, 107 (1931)
53. FISCHER, H., MOLDENHAUER, O., AND SÜS, O., *Ann.*, **485**, 1 (1931)
54. FISCHER, H., FILSER, L., HAGERT, W., AND MOLDENHAUER, O., *Ann.*, **490**, 1 (1931)
55. FISCHER, H., AND RIEDMAIR, J., *Ann.*, **490**, 91 (1931)
56. MARCHLEWSKI, L., *Z. physiol. Chem.*, **43**, 464 (1904); **45**, 176 (1905)
57. FISCHER, H., AND HENDSCHEL, A., *Z. physiol. Chem.*, **198**, 33 (1931)
58. FISCHER, H., SÜS, O., AND KLEBS, G., *Ann.*, **490**, 38 (1931)
59. FISCHER, H., AND SÜS, O., *Ann.*, **482**, 225 (1930)

60. CONANT, J. B., HYDE, J. F., MOYER, W. W., AND DIETZ, E. M., *J. Am. Chem. Soc.,* **53**, 359 (1931)
61. CONANT, J. B., DIETZ, E. M., BAILEY, C. F., AND KAMERLING, S. E., *J. Am. Chem. Soc.,* **53**, 2382 (1931)
62. FISCHER, H., AND ROTHEMUND, P., *Ber.,* **64**, 201 (1931)
63. FISCHER, H., AND RIEDL, H. J., *Ann.,* **482**, 214 (1931); **486**, 178 (1931)

CHEMISCHES INSTITUT DER UNIVERSITÄT
ZÜRICH, SWITZERLAND

THE TERPENES, SAPONINES, AND CLOSELY RELATED COMPOUNDS*

By L. Ruzicka

Chemisches Laboratorium, Eidgenossische Technische Hochschule, Zürich

This review[1] covers the terpenes and terpenoid compounds with the exception of certain subgroups.

In recent years this subject has been expanded in several ways. For one thing, the relationship between sapogenines and triterpenes has been revealed by formation of the same trimethylnaphthalene through dehydrogenation (Ruzicka and van Veen). It has been further shown from the structure of the carbon skeleton that the group of carotenoids belongs to the tetraterpenes;[2] also that substances such as bixin and crocetin, which are classed with the carotenoids, belong among the terpenoid compounds.

Next, we must accurately define the terms terpene and terpenoid. The designation of a compound as a terpene will be based simply upon the structure of its carbon skeleton. Terpenes are defined, therefore, as compounds the carbon structure of which may be decomposed into isoprene residues. They include, first of all, a group of compounds of unknown carbon structure, which contain their carbon atoms in multiples of five, so that, by analogy, one may infer them to be built of isoprene nuclei. We may denote as terpenoids those compounds for which this principle of construction is only partially applicable and for which the total number of carbon atoms has been found to depart from a multiple of five, as is the case for santene, irone, the sterols, bile acids, and possibly certain sapogenines.

We must reject the more restricted definition of terpenes as compounds based upon regularly conjugated isoprene chains,[3] for not only do such long-known examples of the monoterpene series as camphene, fenchone, and others, possess irregularly arranged isoprene residues, but so also do elemole in the sesquiterpenes and

---

* Received February 17, 1932.

[1] This review embraces such works as are referred to in *Chemisches Zentralblatt* for 1931.

[2] Cf. a series of articles by P. Karrer and associates.

[3] Compare, e.g., papers by Ingold; Wagner-Jauregg (1); Karrer and Helfenstein (see Literature Cited).

581

abietic and dextro-pimaric acids, as well as α-camphorene among the diterpenes (cf. further below). Also, in the year under review, the basis has been removed from too-inclusive hypotheses such as that of the construction of abietic acid from two molecules of pinene.[4] However, it has been shown that certain terpenes are constructed of two symmetrical halves with similar arrangement of the isoprene nuclei; the work of P. Karrer and associates shows this for squalene and it also appears very probable for the carotenoids.

Various sections of the field, so defined, cannot be contained in this report, for they belong, for one reason or another, to other groups of biological compounds. These include the sterols, bile acids, carotenoids, and vitamin A, though the latter may be a diterpene or at least a diterpenoid having 20 or 22 carbon atoms according to the formula of Karrer. Among the sapogenines we must further exclude the digitalis and strophanthine compounds, for these surely may not be regarded as similar to the triterpenes.

A. MONOTERPENES

During the polymerization of isoprene to caoutchouc and dipentene there is produced a second terpene whose constitution was unknown until recently. Wagner-Jauregg (2) has shown this to be monocyclic by its molecular refraction and by the course of its catalytic hydrogenation, which yields a tetrahydroterpene. With HCl, the hydrocarbon described by Aschan (1) as diprene gives carvestrene dichlorhydrate, and therefore owes its origin to a meta-

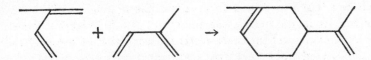

polymerization of isoprene. Steimmig had previously shown that also the preparation of synthetic caoutchouc gives rise to an irregular union of isoprene nuclei.

Winogradowa has observed the formation of small amounts of camphor and borneol when linalool is heated in a mixture of hydrocarbons containing aluminium activated by mercuric chloride and iodine. The reviewer proposes the following scheme for the elucida-

[4] Cf. the work of Dupont et al., Grün, Aschan, etc.

tion of this noteworthy rearrangement, based upon the intermediate formation of methyl nopinol and its transformation to borneol:

Linalool   Borneol

The processes of ring closure also play a part in the formation of the long-known "citrylidene malonic acid," which, according to Kuhn and Hoffer, possesses the formula of a monocyclic dilactone, whose formation from real citrylidene malonic acid can be accounted for by threefold ring closure.

Citrylidene malonic acid   Citrylidene malonic dilactone

Henry and Paget have observed the formation of β-thujaketolactone among the products of the oxidation of terpinolene with chromic acid. The constitution of this lactone was established by catalytic hydrogenation to homoterpenyl methylketone:

Terpinolene   β-thujaketolactone   Homoterpenyl methylketone

Cahn, Penfold, and Simonsen show that the material called cryptal (Formula I) and previously found in the ethereal oil of *Eucalyp-*

tus cneorifolia and *E. polybractea* is actually 4-isopropyl cyclohexene-2-one-1 (Formula II) which, until now, had not been detected in nature. On the other hand, cryptal is certainly present in the oil of *E. hemiphloia*.

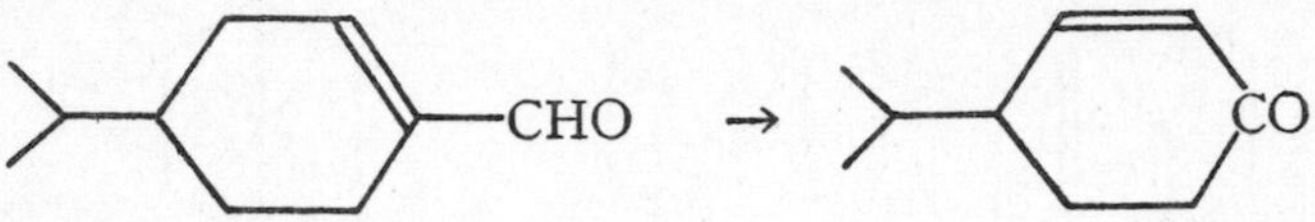

I. Cryptal   II. 4-isopropyl cyclohexene–2–one–1

The alleged new terpene chamene, isolated by Kafuku, Nozoe, and Hata from the leaf oil of *Cryptomeria obtusa*, is very probably a mixture.

According to Treibs (1), the oxidation of carvone by hydrogen peroxide in alkaline solution yields the oxyketone III, which easily changes to the dihydroxyphenol IV. However [Treibs (2)], piperi-

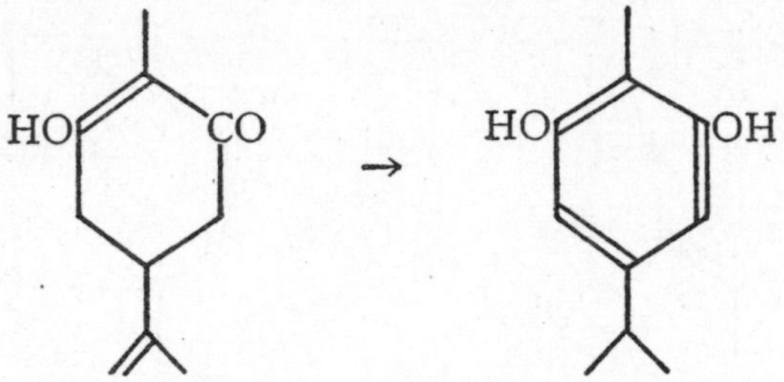

III   IV

tone (Formula V) under the same treatment splits to an oxy-acid which probably has Formula VI, since loss of water and further breakdown yield α-isopropyl glutaric acid.

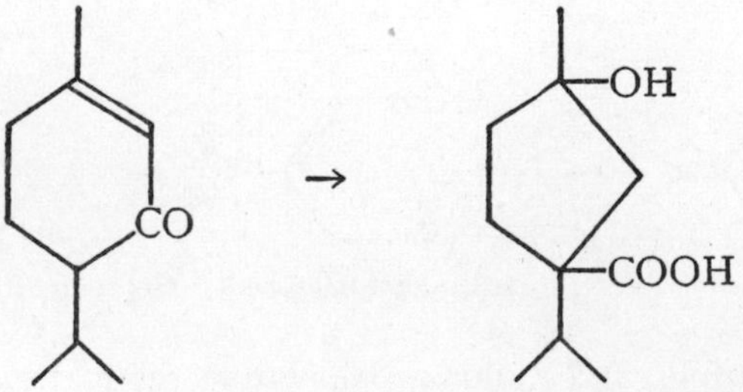

V. Piperitone   VI

By the reduction of the reaction product of piperitone and hydrazine, hitherto incompletely identified, Read and Storey (1) have obtained the previously unknown piperityl amine. By treatment of the latter with nitrous acid they then obtain piperitol, known in nature, but not previously prepared synthetically. Certain views are also expressed (2) concerning the properties of the four optically active menthylamines and a series of their derivatives.

According to Penfold and Simonsen, who base their conclusions on the preparation of 1,1-dimethyl, 2-(γ-ketobutyl)-cyclopropane, 3-carboxylic acid by oxidation, the compound discovered by Baker and Smith in the oil of *Dacrydium Franklinii* and called dacrydene, is identical with Δ^4-carene. Using the carene isolated from *Pinus longiflora,* Joffre obtains, on ozonization, formaldehyde, formic acid, and a ketone, $C_9H_{14}O$, whence is deduced the presence of the previously unobserved β-carene with a semi-cyclic methylene group.

Whilst the catalytic hydrogenation of sabinene in the presence of platinum usually yields thujane, Richter, Wolff, and Presting find that when colloidal palladium is used, two mols of hydrogen are taken up with the formation of a five-membered hydrocarbon, presumably 1,2-dimethyl, 3-isopropyl, cyclopentane, corresponding to the well-known transformation of thujone to isothujone.

Komppa and Hasselström find that the dehydration of nopinol (Formula VII) with potassium bisulphate leads to apopinene (Formula VIII), the constitution of which is known from the decomposition to norpinic acid of the acid-cleavage products obtained by means of ozone. On the contrary, according to Wallach, methyl nopinol yields no pinene.

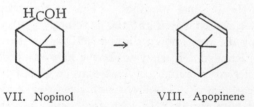

VII. Nopinol   VIII. Apopinene

It is stated by Stephan and Hammerich that camphene, α-pinene, and nopinene give solid addition products with ferrocyanic acid, $(C_{10}H_{16})_2 \cdot H_4Fe(CN)_6$, which are broken up by potassium hydroxide at 160°, to yield a mixture of terpenes $(C_{10}H_{16})$, bases

($C_{10}H_{17}NH_2$), and alcohols ($C_{10}H_{17}OH$). These arise partially from rearrangement of bicyclic ring systems, and partially from ring cleavage.

Although it has been customary to assume interaction exclusively between carbon atoms 2 and 6 during the Wagner rearrangement, it is now shown by recent work of Nametkin, Kitschkin, and Kursanoff, as well as in the independent observations of Bredt (1), and finally of Houben and Pfankuch, that this is preceded indubitably by a pinacoline rearrangement of the ordinary sort, that is, without ring rearrangement (named "camphene rearrangement of the second kind" by Houben). Of the various examples receiving investigation, only one, from the work of Bredt, will be given here. Optically active bornylene carboxylic acid (Formula IX) gives the compound of Formula X with hydrogen bromide, whence XI, the optically active trans-camphene mesocarboxylic acid, is obtained by treatment with sodium carbonate and loss of water. This gives a mixture of the acetates of racemic trans-isoborneol o-carboxylic acid (Formula XII) and racemic isoborneol p-carboxylic acid (Formula XIII) by the action of a glacial acetic–sulphuric acid mixture. The racemization may now be explained as a simple pinacoline rearrangement: XI goes over to XIV, XV, XVI, and, since a series of reversible reactions is involved, formation of the racemic XII and XIII results from the optical antipods XI and XVI.

This mechanism explains also the formation of racemic isoborneol by action of glacial acetic acid and sulphuric acid on optically active camphene. Houben and Pfankuch have investigated an analogous reaction where after a pinacoline rearrangement of the second kind no equilibrium can occur, and which has as an end product the optical antipode of the original material. (This is the transformation of l-camphor, 4-carboxylic acid into the d-isomer.)

Regarding the well-known slight reactivity of the carbonyl group in fenchone, Rupe and Kuenzy make the interesting observation that in the presence of sodium, acetylene may be added with the formation of the carbinol XVII, which is changed to the aldehyde XVIII by treatment with formic acid. An analogous property is shown by tetrahydrocarvone.

Diels and Alder describe a new application of their di-ene synthesis in the terpene series. The addition product of cyclopentadiene and crotonaldehyde (Formula XIX) is reduced by catalytic hydrogenation and thereupon changes to the enolacetate (Formula XX).

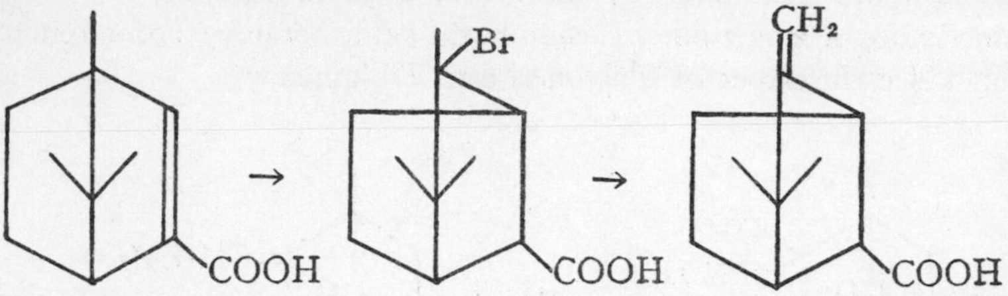

IX. Bornylene car-
boxylic acid

X

XI. Trans-camphene
mesocarboxylic acid

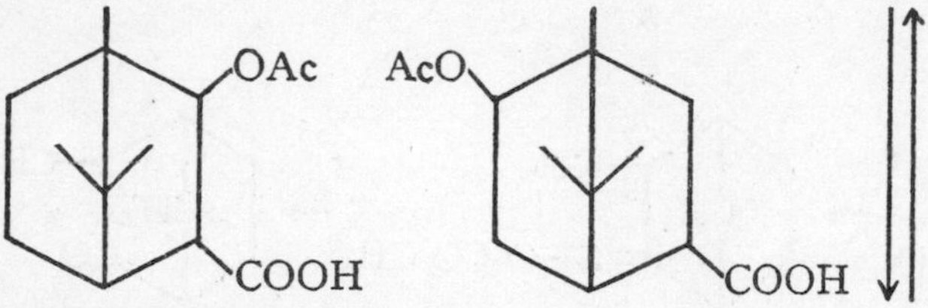

XII. Trans-isoborneol
o-carboxylic acetate

XIII. Isoborneol
p-carboxylic acetate

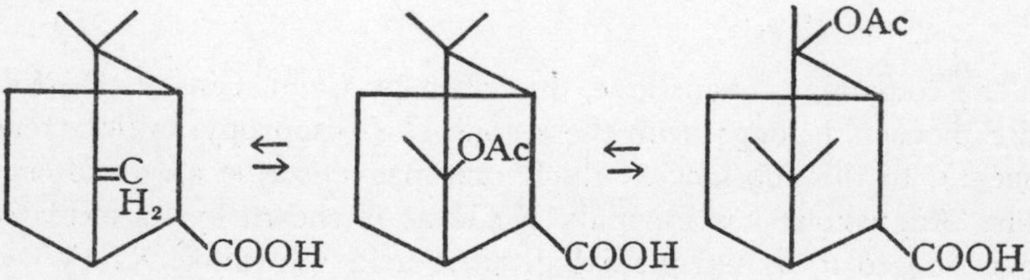

XVI

XV

XIV

By ozonization this yields 6-methyl norcamphor (Formula XXI),
which on methylation is converted to camphenilone. On the other
hand, santene is formed by treatment of XXI with methyl magnesium
iodide and loss of water.

Of further work on the camphor series, that apparently inex-
haustible source of experimental results, mention should be made of
that on epicamphor by Bredt (2), and by Nametkin and Brussowa (1); on 2-hydroxy epicamphor and 3-hydroxy camphor by
Bredt (3), as well as Bredt-Savelsberg and Bund; on π-camphor
derivatives by Hasselström (1, 2) and on 4-methyl camphor by

Nametkin and Brussowa (2), as well as Bredt-Savelsberg and Buch-kremer. For a new isomeric camphoric acid, obtained from fenchyl alcohol, see the paper of Toivonen and Tikkanen.

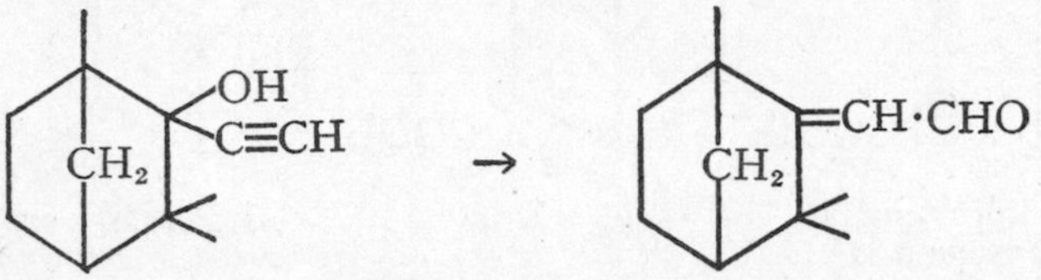

XVII   XVIII

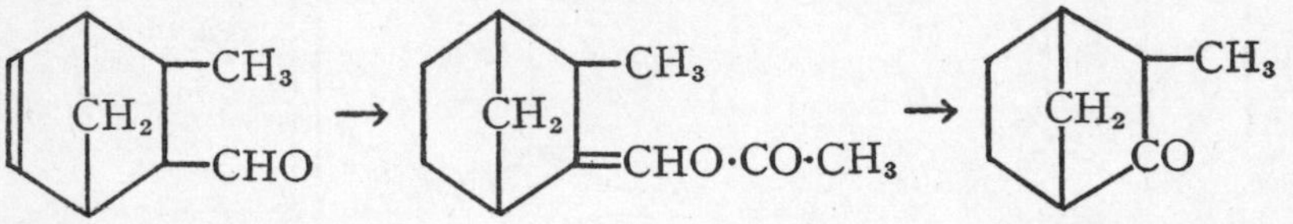

XIX   XX   XXI.
                                                 6-methyl norcamphor

The compound, angustione, described by Cahn, Gibsen, Penfold, and Simonsen, belongs, with the ketone II (4-isopropyl cyclohexene-2-one-1), to the substances which one may describe as monoterpe-noids. Angustione has Formula XXII as is shown by its oxidative conversion to α, α, γ-trimethyl glutaric acid (Formula XXIV) on treatment with potassium hypobromite, as well as the formation of compound XXIII by oxidation with potassium permanganate.

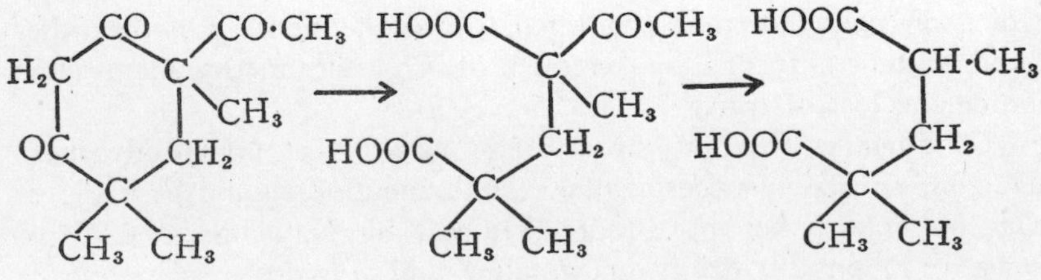

XXII. Angustione   XXIII   XXIV.
                                                 α, α, γ-trimethyl glutaric acid

B. Sesquiterpenes

Glichitch writes of a new compound, fokienol ($C_{15}H_{26}O$), supposedly a monocyclic sesquiterpene alcohol, giving by dehydrogenation cadaline, while Lehman and Lynn report the isolation of a new monocyclic sesquiterpene, picene (melting-point of the trihydrochloride 133°), from certain conifers.

The results reported by Komatsu, Fujimoto, and Tanaka concerning the constitution of sesquiterpenes and sesquiterpene alcohols of the cadinene group seem to rest on insufficient experimental evidence. Various advances have been made in the eudesmol subgroup, which now contains a series of well-crystallized compounds. Ruzicka, Wind, and Koolhaas (1) have been able to show that eudesmol and selinene, whose β-isomer possesses Formula XXVII, stand in closer relationship to each other than has been previously supposed. Both may be made to give the same dihydrochloride (Formula XXVIII) (m.p. 74°), which gives eudesmol again when treated with milk of lime. Eudesmol, like selinene, is a mixture of two isomers, α-eudesmol (Formula XXV) and β-eudesmol (Formula XXVI), since treatment with ozone yields an oxyketo acid (Formula XXIX) and an oxyketone (Formula XXX). The extra-cyclic position of the hydroxyl group in eudesmol may be determined by ozonization of the hydrocarbon XXXI, obtained from dihydro eudesmol by gentle dehydration; this ozonization gives the ketone XXXII.

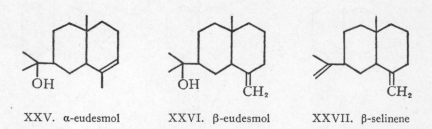

XXV. α-eudesmol   XXVI. β-eudesmol   XXVII. β-selinene

Ruzicka, Koolhaas, and Wind have shown (3), by means of the reactions pointed out above, that in various oils the substance previously called "machilol" is identical with eudesmol. They have also brought out the fact (2) that naturally occurring sesquiterpenes with hydrogenated naphthalene rings are derived from cis-decaline. The specific gravity of natural sesquiterpenes is about 0.917, whence follows the likelihood of a common decaline structure. To confirm this hypothesis, simple decaline homologues were prepared from eudesmol; reactions which could cause rearrangement of the decaline ring were avoided. The hydrocarbon (Formula XXXIII) obtained from dihydro-eudesmol by treatment with formic acid yields the ketone XXXIV on ozonization, from which by a Clemmensen reduction one may obtain 4,9-dimethyl decaline (Formula XXXV). The ketone XXXII, in analogous fashion, yields 3-ethyl 5,9-dimethyl decaline. These hydrocarbons possess $d_4^{20} = 0.890$, similar to that of cis-decaline (0.896). They are therefore cis-compounds, for the trans-form of XXXV, synthetically prepared by Ruzicka, Koolhaas, and Wind (1), has a density (d_4^{20}) of 0.863 and the trans- isomer of XXXVI, 0.870, resembling trans-decaline ($d_4^{20} = 0.867$).

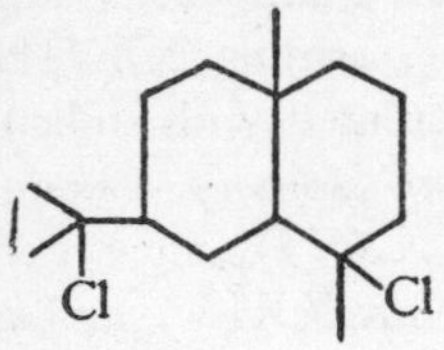

XXVIII 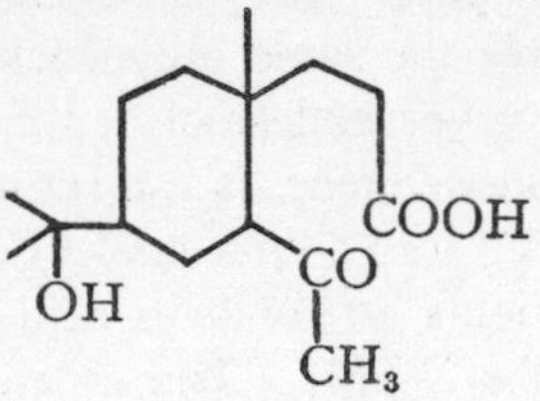 · · · · · · XXIX 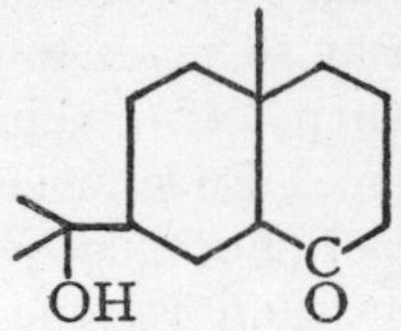 · · · · · · XXX

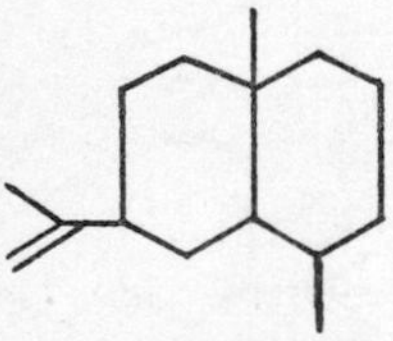

XXXI 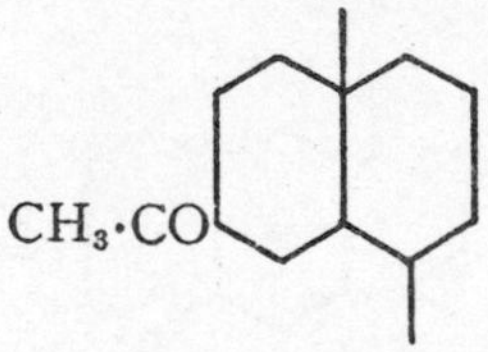 · · · · · · XXXII 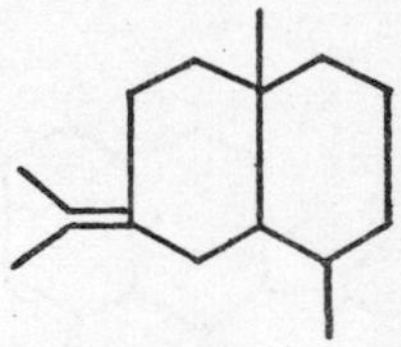 · · · · · · XXXIII

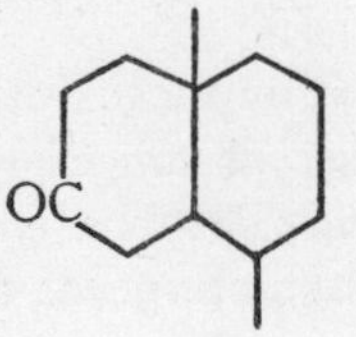

XXXIV 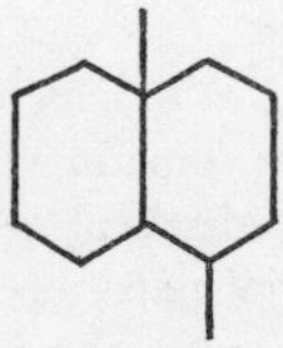 · · · · · · XXXV. 4, 9-dimethyl decaline 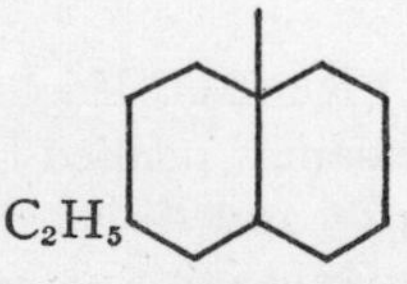 · · · · · · XXXVI

Whereas, earlier, the decomposition products containing nine or more carbon atoms from caryophyllene were found to be amorphous, Ruzicka and Wind succeeded in obtaining a crystalline dicarboxylic acid, $C_{13}H_{18}O_4$, by oxidizing caryophyllene with ozone and sodium hypobromite. Ruzicka, Bardhan, and Wind have shown that the structural formulae proposed formerly for caryophyllenic acid are erroneous. The material is a mixture of at least two crystalline acids. Finally, Ruzicka and Gibson have obtained a crystalline dicarboxylic acid, $C_{15}H_{24}O_4$ (clovenic acid), by the chromic acid oxidation of the clovene resulting from the isomerization of caryophyllene.

Ruzicka and Haagen-Smit (1) have undertaken a careful study of various azulenes, blue hydrocarbons of formula $C_{15}H_{18}$, and, on the basis of the melting-points and mixed melting-points of the picrates and styphnates, they have been able to differentiate clearly between the following four isomers: chamazulene (in chamille oil); thioguaiazulene (obtained from guaiol by dehydrogenation with sulphur); selenoguaiazulene (obtained from guaiol by dehydrogenation with selenium); and elemazulene (obtained from elemol by dehydrogenation with selenium). The "kessazulene" of Asahina and Nakanishi is found to be identical with the second. All azulenes may be hydrogenated to saturated decahydro- compounds, in consequence of which they possess two rings and five double bonds. Formula XXXVII is agreed upon for elemol; it leads to the hypothetical Formula XXXVIII for elemazulene, requiring a twofold system of

XXXVII. Elemol   XXXVIII. Elemazulene

fulvenic bonds. All azulenes absorb the same amount of oxygen on oxidation with permanganate, yielding, however, only a small amount of degradation products.

Ruzicka and Haagen-Smit (2) obtain the same crystalline reaction product, a dihydroxy oxide ($C_{15}H_{26}O_3$), during the oxidation of guaiol, $C_{15}H_{26}O$, by either ozone or potassium permanganate. Gentle treatment of this with acid or alkaline reagents gives the doubly unsaturated oxide, $C_{15}H_{22}O$.

The constitutions of the lactones contained in the currant root have been further elucidated by the extensive studies of Ruzicka and Melsen, and Ruzicka and Pieth, as well as by those of Hansen. These are alantolactone (Formula XLI), isoalantolactone (Formula XL), and dihydro isoalantolactone (Formula XXXIX), all giving the same tetrahydro lactone (probably stereoisomeric with tetrahydro deoxy santonine) on catalytic hydrogenation. On dehydrogenation with selenium, this compound gives 3-ethyl 5-methyl naphthalene (Formula XLVI), which may be identified with the synthetic product. A further elucidation of the carbon skeleton is given by the reaction of dihydro isoalantolactone with ozone, whence the ketolactone, XLII, may be isolated. A Clemmensen reduction of the latter, with loss of carbon dioxide, yields 3-ethyl 9-methyl cis-decaline (For-

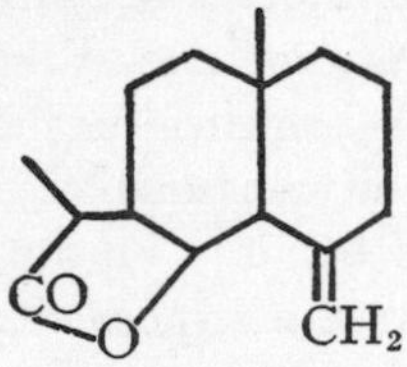

XXXIX. Dihydro isoalantolactone

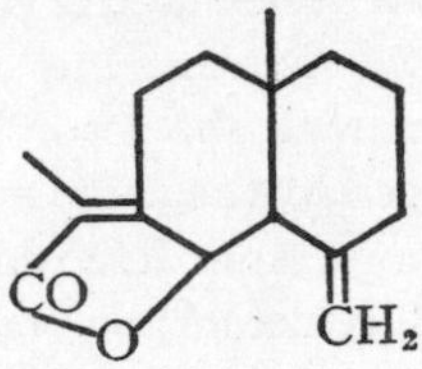

XL. Isoalantolactone

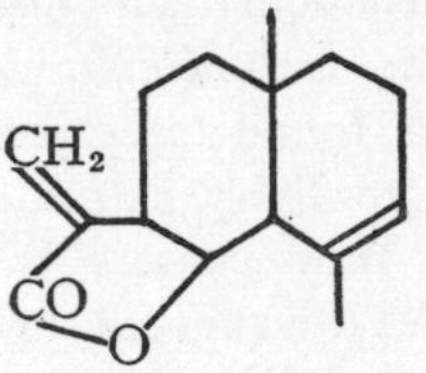

XLI. Alantolactone

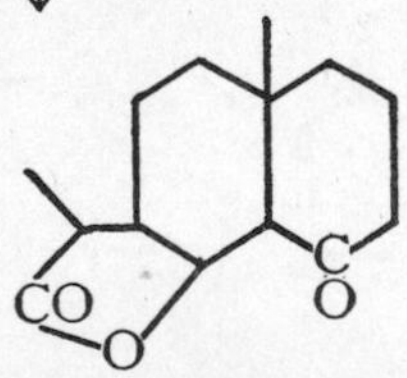

XLII

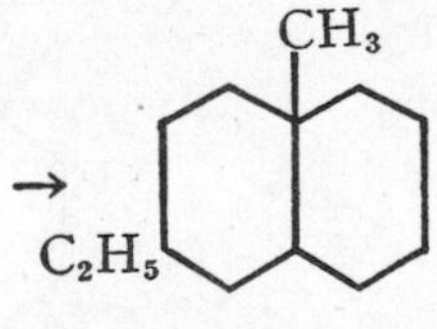

XLIII. 3-ethyl 9-methyl cis-decaline

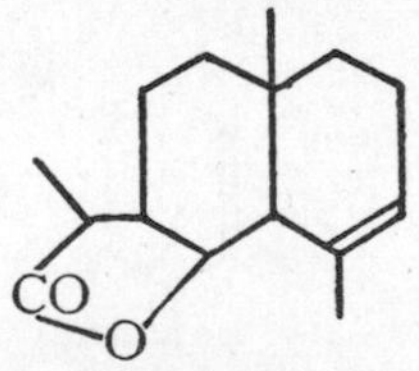

XLIV

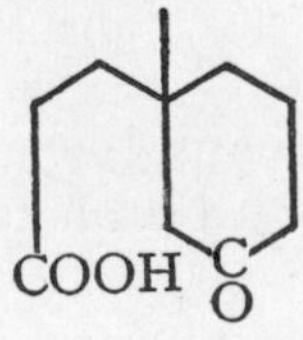

XLV

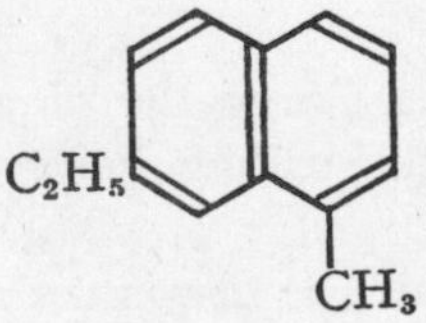

XLVI

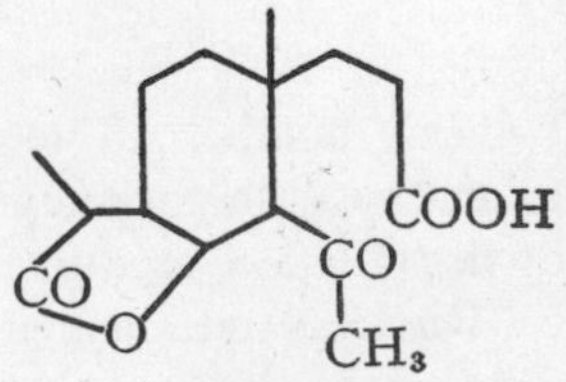

XLVII

mula XLIII). The melting-point, mixed melting-point, density, and refractive index of this compound show it to be identical with the hydrocarbon prepared by the transformation of selinene [cf. Ruzicka, Koolhaas, and Wind (2)]. This transformation leaves uncertain the position of the carbonyl group in alantolactone; previously it has been assumed to be as shown in the given formula. Apparently, these lactones should be placed, like santonine, in the eudesmol group of the sesquiterpenes. The positions of the double bonds and lactone ring of isoalantolactone have been supported by the formation, with ozone and potassium permanganate, of the keto acid $C_{10}H_{16}O_3$, which must possess Formula XLV. Further support is rendered by the detection of acetic acid during treatment with ozone and chromic acid. A certain weakness in the proof afforded by the latter requires mention, for acetic acid might have been formed from the methyl group attached to the decaline bridge. The position of the double bond in the alantolactone ring is given by the degradation of dihydro alantolactone, on treatment with ozone, to the lactone-keto acid XLVII, whilst the position of the other double bond follows from the difference of the dihydrochlorides of alanto- and isoalantolactone. The existence of a double bond in the vicinity of the carbonyl groups of XL and XLI is demonstrated by the reducibility of these to dihydro lactones on treatment with sodium amalgam.

By the selenium dehydrogenation of hexahydro santonine, obtained from santonine by catalytic hydrogenation, Ruzicka and Eichenberger have produced 3-ethyl 5-methyl naphthalene (XLVI). Clemo and Haworth obtain the same hydrocarbon by the selenium dehydrogenation of tetrahydro deoxysantonine (LI) which ensues from the Clemmensen reduction of tetrahydrosantonine. This provides indirect evidence for the attachment of a methyl group in santonine at the decaline bridge and hence support for Formula XLVIII for santonine. The latter, proposed by Clemo, Haworth, and Walton, shows that this lactone has the same carbon skeleton as eudesmol. Ruzicka and Eichenberger note that this formula yields a plausible explanation of the decomposition products which Angeli and Marino long ago found by oxidizing santonine with permanganate (cf. the Series XLIX, L, LIII). These products, by their empirical formulae, give the best support not only for the position of the methyl group at the decaline bridge, but also for the double bond. Wedekind and Tettweiler (1) consider that they have further evidence for the position of the double bond in santonine through an investigation of the chlorhydrine. In the opinion of the writer no such evidence is contained in their work. One may only say that it does not contradict Formula XLVIII. On the other hand, a later communication of theirs (2) confirms the above-mentioned discoveries of Angeli and Marino and mentions further the isolation of the compound XLIX, also obtained from the ozone decomposition of α-santonine oxide (Formula LII). This they made from santonine and perbenzoic acid. Furthermore, the dihydro- derivative of XLIX was prepared from dihydro α-santonine oxide.

XLVIII. Santonine   XLIX   L

LI. Tetrahydro deoxy-   LII. α-santonine oxide   LIII
    santonine

Corchogenine, $C_{16}H_{26}O_3$, also is a possible member of the sesquiterpenes or sesquiterpenoids. This aglucone of the glucoside corchorin, obtained from the seed of *Corchoris capsularis,* has been investigated by Sen. Corchogenine yields corchoric acid, $C_{15}H_{24}O_5$, on oxidation.

C. DITERPENES

Ruzicka, Goldberg, Huyser, and Seidel have published an article on the determination of the carbon structure of abietic acid. On the basis of previous work of Ruzicka and associates it was made plain that the carboxyl group in ring I is in secondary combination (cf.

Formulae LVI and LVII). At the same time, the position of a methyl group was not known with certainty. It must have a tertiary binding, because it splits off during dehydrogenation with sulphur or selenium. By assuming that the carbon structure must be decomposable into isoprene residues, the location of this methyl group is restricted to position 1, 11, or 12 (cf. Formula LVI). It may safely be assigned to position 12. By various degradations of abietic acid, as, for example, with potassium permanganate or ozone, there is produced a mixture of two tricarboxylic acids, $C_{11}H_{16}O_6$ (Formula LIV) and $C_{12}H_{18}O_6$ (Formula LV), readily separable. On dehydrogenation by selenium the first yields m-xylene and the second 1,2,3-trimethyl benzene, whence the position of only one carboxyl group in each remains uncertain. If one accepts for the carbon skeleton of abietic acid a grouping of isoprene residues it is seen that of the three possible positions, 2, 3, or 4, for the remaining carboxyl group, only 2 and 4 give a structure decomposable into isoprene nuclei. Therefore Formulae LVI and LVII are possible structures for abietic acid. There are assumed two possible but not definitely established positions for the double bonds therein. It is only certain that they lie in ring II or that one may be between carbon atoms 9 and 14.

Levy has obtained, by heating the dihydrochloride of abietic acid with glacial acetic acid, a monohydrochloride which on treatment with silver hydroxide goes over into dihydro hydroxy abietic acid. This compound has been described by Rao and Simonsen. Ruzicka and co-workers started with abietic acid prepared after the method of Steele by heating colophonium with glacial acetic acid, but Levy used abietic acid isomerized with hydrogen chloride. Aschan (2) produced an abietic acid which he calls "pinabietic acid" and which is not different from Levy's. He regards them as stereoisomeric. (Actually they are probably identical except for the admixture of slight impurities.) He considers that Formula LVIII, earlier proposed by himself and Virtanen, is established by various reactions of the dihydrobromide of pinabietic acid. It is necessary to observe that the above-mentioned results exclude the presence of the carboxyl group in ring II.

Rouin reports that the product of mercuric acetate and abietic acid in boiling glacial acetic acid is an acid ($C_{20}H_{28}O_4$), the constitution of which is unknown.

Dupont, Levy, and Allard have reported on the positive action of cobalt abietate on the autoxidation of abietic acid, while Dupont and Allard have published on the anti-oxidant effect of hydroquinone on the same process.

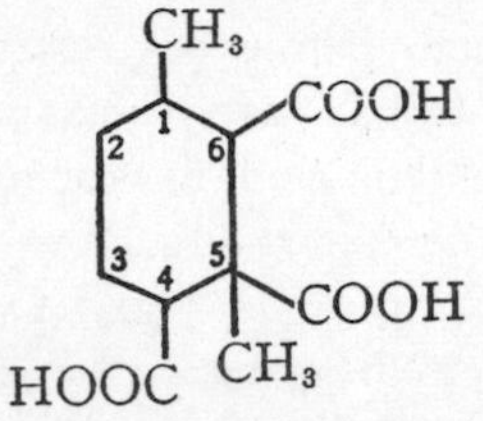

LIV

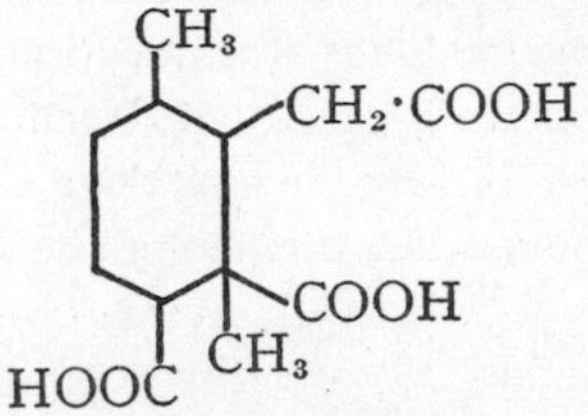

LV

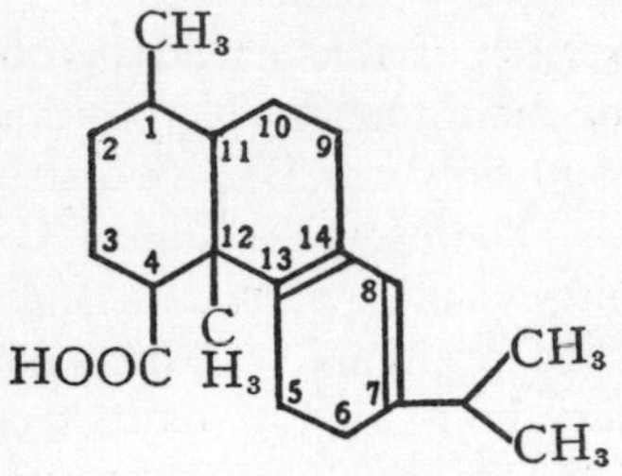

LVI. Abietic acid (Formula *a*)

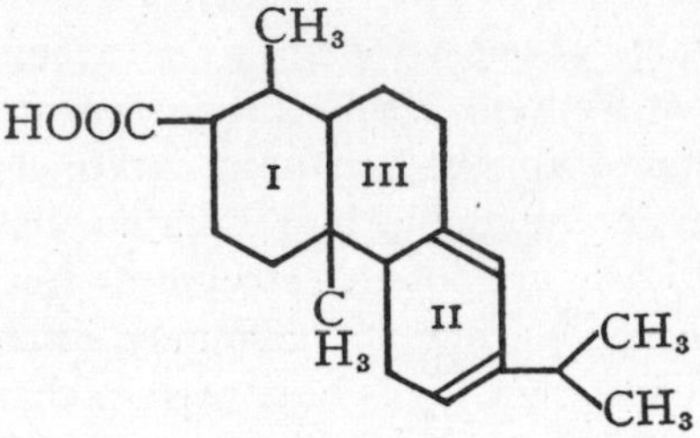

LVII. Abietic acid (Formula *b*)

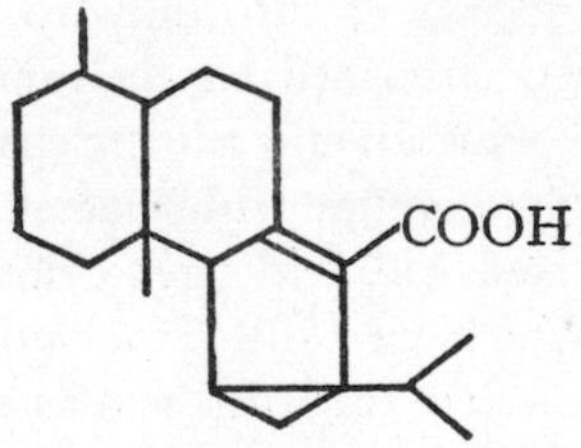

LVIII

Ruzicka and Hosking, in reporting on the constitution of agathene dicarboxylic acid from Manila- and cowry copal, assigned to it Formula LIX, partly hypothetical, which agrees with all its known properties. Treatment with formic acid results in its conversion into the tricyclic isoagathene dicarboxylic acid (Formula LX). On catalytic hydrogenation, LIX yields a tetrahydro acid, while LX yields only a dihydro acid. The molecular refraction of the esters agrees with this. Up to the present two of the selenium dehydrogenation products of the acids have been elucidated. The hydrocarbon, $C_{13}H_{14}$, prepared from LIX, is found to be identical with synthetic 1,2,5-trimethyl naphthalene[5] (Formula LXI). Pimanthrene (Formula LXII), now known to be 1,7-dimethyl phenanthrene and discovered by Ruzicka and Balas (1), who obtained it by dehydrogenating dextropimaric acid, was obtained from both LIX and LX (see below). LIX

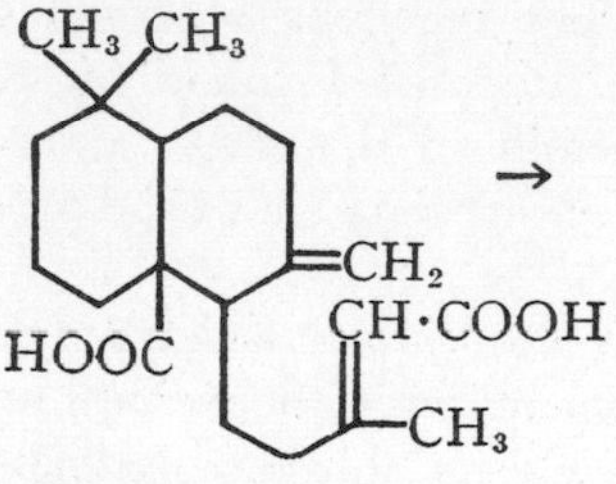

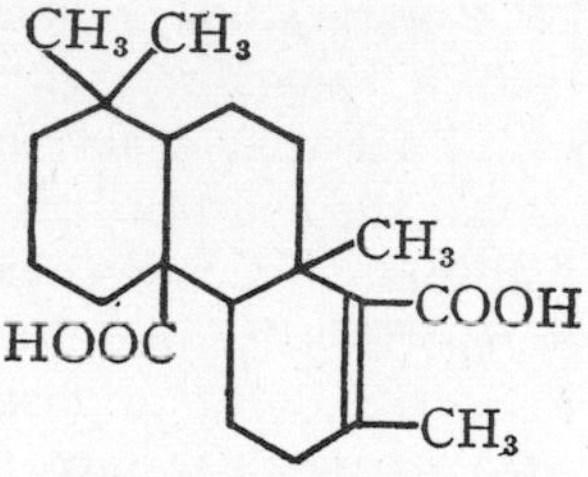

LIX. Agathene dicar-
boxylic acid

LX. Isoagathene dicar-
boxylic acid

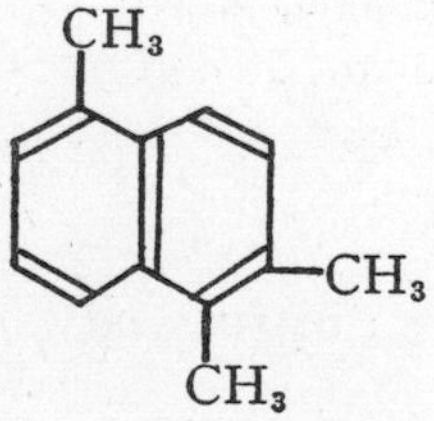

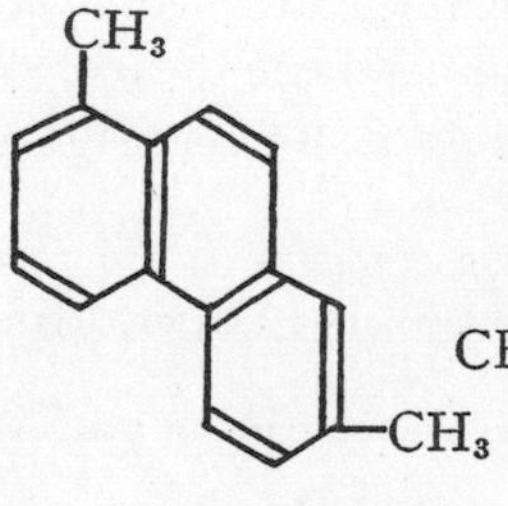

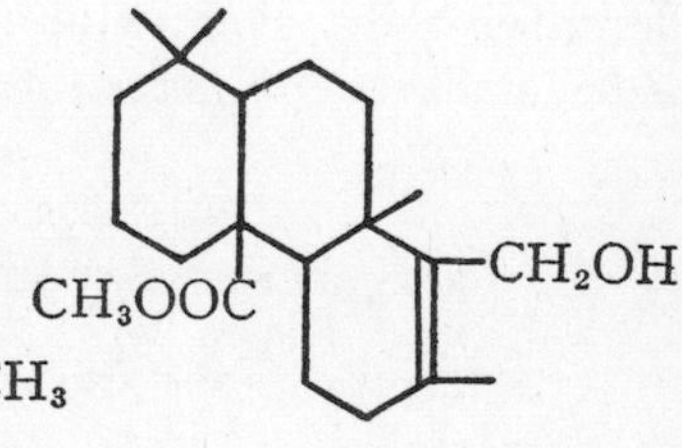

LXI

LXII. Pimanthrene

LXIII

yields formaldehyde and oxalic acid on ozonization. The hydroxy-ester, Formula LXIII, is formed by the sodium-alcohol reduction of the diester of LX. By distillation of the formate, LXIII is freed of its hydroxyl group and then by selenium dehydrogenation a new trimethyl phenanthrene, which should be 1,7,8-trimethyl phenanthrene according to the formulation above, is obtained. It is not

[5] For the mechanism of its formation from LIX, see under "squalene."

identical with an isomer previously obtained by Ruzicka and Balas (2) from the dehydrogenation of methyl dextropimarine.

The constitution assumed above for pimanthrene (Formula LXII) has been elucidated by Ruzicka, de Graaff, and Hosking. Both retene (for which the formula 1-methyl 7-isopropyl phenanthrene is definitely established) and pimanthrene give the same product (phenanthrene 1,7-dicarboxylic acid) on oxidation with potassium ferricyanide. Oxidation of their quinones with potassium permanganate (retene requires further treatment with chromic acid) yields the same diphenyl 2,3,2',4'-tetracarboxylic acid. The reactions observed by Westenberg and Wibaut agree with the proposed formula for the hydrocarbon LXI. It should also be mentioned that these authors were able to isolate the hydrocarbon by dehydrogenation of the products of dry distillation of Congo copal oil.

Janot has reported that the formula of sclareol isolated from *Salvia sclarea* is $C_{20}H_{36}O_2$, in disagreement with the values previously reported in the literature. It yields a dihydro derivative under catalytic hydrogenation, and contains two hydroxyl groups (Zerewitinoff method). With ozone, formaldehyde is formed. From the mixture of selenium dehydrogenation products of sclareol, Ruzicka and Janot have isolated 1,2,5-trimethyl naphthalene, which was described above along with agathene dicarboxylic acid. Therefore it is not unlikely that these diterpenes have the same carbon structure.

D. Triterpenes, Sapogenines, and Related Compounds

1. Hydrocarbons and Alcohols of the Triterpene Series

Squalene.—Heilbron and Wilkinson have described various degradations of the compound $C_{13}H_{14}$, obtained from tetracyclo squalene by dehydrogenation with selenium. This compound ($C_{13}H_{14}$) is identical with that from agathene dicarboxylic acid and sclareol, and the degradation products are in agreement with the formula determined by synthesis and recorded above.

Starting from the results obtained with squalene by Heilbron and co-workers and with the Karrer formula for the carotenoids, Karrer and Helfenstein obtained the hydrocarbon LXV by transformation of farnesyl chloride (Formula LXIV) with magnesium. The hexahydrochloride of LXV appears identical with that of squalene. It is thus the first complete synthesis of a naturally occurring triterpene. The constitution of tetracyclosqualene, which, according to the Heilbron method, was made by heating squalene with formic acid, may be expressed by Formula LXVI. The formation of 1,2,5-trimethyl naphthalene may be explained in the same way as with agathene dicarboxylic acid, that is, by splitting of the carbon chain at the first CH_2 group of the decaline ring.

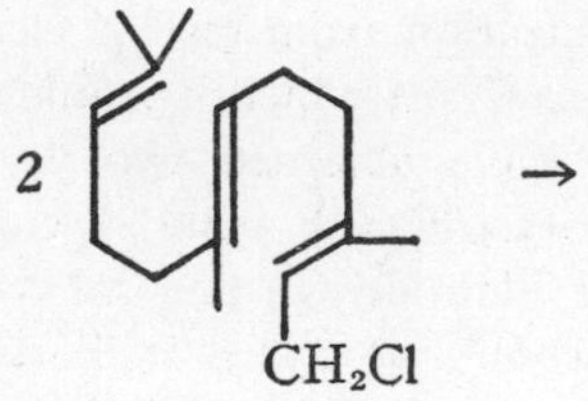

LXIV. Farnesyl chloride

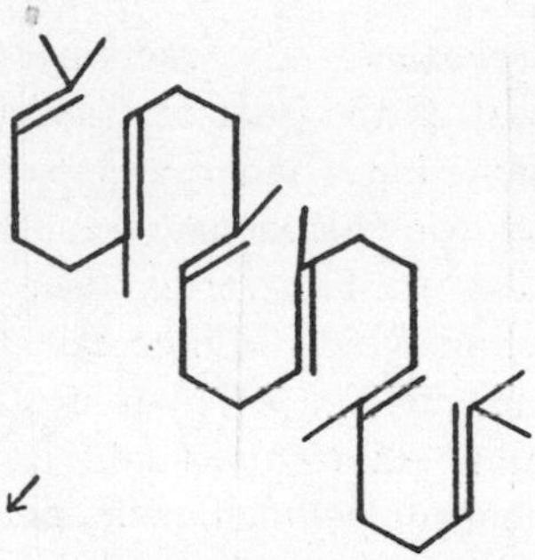

LXV. Squalene

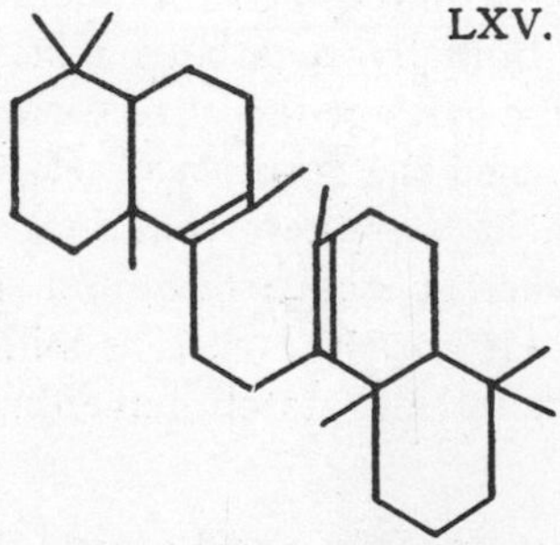

LXVI. Tetracyclosqualene

Amyrine.—Dieterle, Salomon, and Herzberg obtain a ketone, $C_{21}H_{34}O$, from the oxidation of α-amyrine, $C_{30}H_{50}O$, with chromic acid. The other products of the reaction are insufficiently characterized; likewise the decomposition products of the ozonide and the hydrocarbon obtained by selenium dehydrogenation. The investigation of the action of ozone on β-amyrine has yielded no definite result, according to Rollet.

Betuline.—The well-known apo-allobetulin, $C_{30}H_{48}O$, has been obtained by Dischendorfer and Juvan in improved yield by heating betuline with fuller's earth. Further, they are able to demonstrate the existence of a CH_2 group adjacent to the carbonyl in allobetulone, $C_{30}H_{48}O_2$, by condensation with m-nitrobenzaldehyde. (Allobetulone is obtained from allobetuline by treatment with chromic acid.) Hydroxy allobetuline, $C_{30}H_{48}O_3$, the acetate of which is prepared by oxidation of allobetulin acetate with chromic acid, gives hydroxy allobetulone, $C_{30}H_{46}O_3$, by gentle treatment with chromic acid. Further oxidation with nitric acid produces hydroxy allobetulinic acid, $C_{30}H_{46}O_6$.

Euphorbol.—By fractional crystallization from methyl alcohol of that part of the gum of *Euphorbia resinifera* which is soluble in petroleum ether, Bauer and Schröder have obtained two crystalline monohydric alcohols, α-euphorbol ($C_{26}H_{46}O$), and β-euphorbol ($C_{31}H_{52}O$). The former is probably identical, in general, with the compound which Müller called "vitorbol." α- and β-euphorbol each take up one mol of hydrogen on catalytic hydrogenation, and yield crystalline dibromides and crystalline α-naphthyl urethanes. With phosphorous pentachloride, both alcohols lose one molecule of water and form hydrocarbons, from which that deriving from α-euphorbol may be crystallized. Both hydrocarbons take up two molecules of hydrogen under catalytic hydrogenation, to form oily products. Schmid and Zacherl have assigned the formula $C_{26}H_{48}O$ to α-euphorbol and have prepared anisic acid ester therefrom.

The question of whether stigmasterol and sitosterol belong to the triterpenes (triterpenoids) or the sterols is still undecided, for these, according to Sandqvist and Bengtsson, have the formula $C_{29}H_{48}O$

2. Saponines, Sapogenines, and Related Acid Compounds

Hederagenine.—Winterstein and Meyer have isolated a bromlactone, $C_{31}H_{49}O_4Br$, from the reaction products of bromine with the sapogenine, $C_{31}H_{50}O_4$. The latter is found in ivy and Sapindus. The bromlactone was found by the method of Zerewitinoff to have two hydroxyl groups. It cannot be titrated by alkali even when hot. On boiling with alcoholic potassium hydroxide it splits to an acid different from hederagenine and so far unidentified. A neutral diformyl compound, $C_{33}H_{50}O_6$, is produced by heating hederagenine with formic acid. The method of Zerewitinoff shows that this no longer contains any active hydrogen and it remains neutral even after the hydroxyl groups have been removed by saponification with alkali. Winterstein and Wiegand find that hederagenine is regenerated when bromhederagenine is boiled with zinc dust in acetone; the lactone ring is also thereby reopened Treatment with strong acids, such as concentrated hydrochloric, isomerizes hederagenine to hederagenine lactone, which also cannot be titrated hot, and which splits only by long boiling with strong alcoholic base to an acid. The latter returns to the lactone form. Neither lactone gives a yellow color with tetranitromethane; whence one concludes that in hederagenine there is a double bond in the β,γ- or γ,δ-position with respect to the carboxyl groups, favoring lactone formation. Although neither hederagenine nor its methyl ester can be hydrogenated catalytically, Winterstein and Stein (1) have succeeded with hederabetuline, $C_{30}H_{50}O_2$, the product of decarboxylating hederagenine at 300°; hydrogenation gives a dihydro product. One atom of oxygen can be added fairly easily by the use of perbenzoic acid acting on hederabetuline diacetate; so also with betuline diacetate. However, with diacetylhederagenine this oxygenation takes place quite slowly. Hederagenine is therefore a pentacyclic compound with one inactive double bond.

Oleanolic acid.—Van der Haar demonstrated several years ago the occurrence of this compound in the free state in olive leaves and cloves, and as a saponine in sugar beets. He gave it the name "oleanolic acid." Wedekind and Schicke (2) now find it to be identical with the sapogenine of guaiac bark. With acetic anhydride, they prepared an acetyl derivative which, like oleanolic acid itself, yields a methyl ester with diazomethane. Analysis indicates the formula $C_{30}H_{48}O_3$, in contrast to the previous formulae $C_{30}H_{50}O_3$, $C_{31}H_{48}O_3$, and $C_{31}H_{50}O_3$. Winterstein and Stein confirm the identity of guaiac sapogenine with oleanolic acid and further find it to be identical with the sapogenine from the flowers of *Calendula officinalis,* but prefer the formula $C_{31}H_{50}O_3$. By the use of boiling glacial acetic and hydrochloric acids, they prepared an acetyl lactone, $C_{33}H_{52}O_4$, which, unlike oleanolic acid, gives no yellow coloration with tetranitro methane, and which by saponification with alkali yields oleanolic acid lactone, $C_{31}H_{50}O_3$. With bromine, oleanolic acid is converted into the bromlactone, $C_{31}H_{49}O_3Br$.

Winterstein and Hämmerle, in the course of several similar observations on the sapogenine from *Viscum album,* have been able to establish its identity with oleanolic acid. They further show that the bromlactone goes back to oleanolic acid when treated with zinc and glacial acetic acid, and that the oleanolic acid is a simple unsaturated pentacyclic compound.

Ursolic acid.—Sando has isolated this compound anew from apple skins, the leaves of *Uva ursi* and the leaves of *Prunus serotina,* and has established the identity of the three preparations, as van der Haar had done. On the basis of numerous analyses, he proposes the formula $C_{30}H_{48}O_3$ in place of van der Haar's $C_{31}H_{50}O_3$. By boiling it with acetic anhydride, Sando formed a diacetyl derivative which goes over to a monoacetyl derivative on boiling with alcohol. On the other hand, ursolic methyl ester is found to yield only a monoacetyl derivative and also a phthalic ester acid. Jacobs and Fleck, who also favor the formula $C_{30}H_{48}O_3$, have prepared the methyl ester of ursonic acid by the chromic acid oxidation of ursolic methyl ester in glacial acetic acid. Ursonic acid gives an oxime, while by the same oxidation in the presence of sulphuric acid there is formed a diketone, $C_{31}H_{46}O_4$, from which, however, only a mon-oxime can be obtained. The Clemmensen reduction of ursonic acid methyl ester results in ursanic acid methyl ester, $C_{31}H_{50}O_2$, which is changed by heating with one atom of sulphur to dehydro ursanic acid methyl ester, $C_{31}H_{48}O_2$. The benzoate of ursolic acid methyl ester also yields a dehydro derivative with sulphur. Thus ursolic acid behaves under partial dehydrogenation like α-amyrine, while hederagenine and β-amyrine give a derivative containing sulphur.

α-Elemolic acid.—In place of the formula $C_{27}H_{42}O_3$, earlier proposed for α-elemolic acid, Lieb and Mladenović, from the analysis of several derivatives, now suggest formula $C_{30}H_{48}O_3$. These derivatives are the dihydro acid, prepared by catalytic hydrogenation, the acetyl derivative and the bromohydrate of α-elemolic acid, and finally the substance $C_{30}H_{47}O_3Br$ obtained on removal of hydrogen bromide from the bromide of elemolic acid. The authors admit that elemolic acid is very difficult to purify. Ruzicka, Hosking, and Wick have determined the molecular refraction of the methyl and ethyl esters of α-elemolic acid and find values which suggest the presence of two double bonds. The yellow coloration of the dihydro acid with tetranitro methane is in agreement with this assumption, whereby α-elemolic acid should be regarded as a tetracyclic compound. Sapotaline (1,2,7-trimethyl naphthalene), previously prepared from various triterpenes and sapogenines, was made by dehydrogenation with selenium. The ozonization of α-elemolic acid led to no definite results, though Bauer and Dimokostoulos thereby obtain acetaldehyde. The latter authors are the first to have prepared dihydro elemolic acid and the oxime of elemonic acid. From Manila gum elemi,

Mladenović and Lieb have isolated the new γ-elemolic acid, $C_{30}H_{50}O$, from which an acetyl derivative has been prepared.

Quinovic acid.—Wieland and Utzino have reported their investigations on quinovic acid, contained in cinchona bark (Peruvian bark). They consider it to be a hydroxy dicarboxylic acid, $C_{30}H_{46}O_5$. Pyroquinovic acid, $C_{29}H_{46}O_3$, previously obtained by the careful heating of quinovic acid, yields a lactone, $C_{29}H_{44}O_4$, on ozonization, which may be acetylated, and therefore still contains a hydroxyl group. Under vigorous heating, quinovic acid loses CO_2 and water, forming anhydro pyroquinovic acid, $C_{29}H_{44}O_2$, which with ozone gives a dicarboxylic acid, $C_{26}H_{38}O_4$. Oxidation of triacetyl quinovic acid with chromic acid gives an acid of the formula $C_{32}H_{44}O_7$, which, on saponification, yields $C_{30}H_{42}O_6$, still containing carboxyl, lactone, carbonyl, and hydroxyl groups. On treatment with chromic acid this goes over to a dicarboxylic acid, $C_{30}H_{40}O_8$, probably with cleavage of the ring.

Various saponines and sapogenines.—According to Winterstein, aescine, the saponine of the horse-chestnut, like Sapindus saponine, may be split to a prosapogenine by hydrogen peroxide. Aescigenine, made therefrom by complete hydrolysis, probably has the formula $C_{35}H_{58}O_7$. This contains five hydroxyl groups and yields tiglic-acid ester on boiling with alcoholic hydrogen chloride, making it probable that tiglic acid is contained in the sapogenine either as such or in the form of a hydrate.

Aoyama (1) assigns the formula $C_{36}H_{58}O_4$ to the sapogenine of *Panax repens.* The reviewer feels that this formula and those of various transformation products are somewhat in doubt, for titration gives a lower molecular weight. One mol of hydrogen is taken up in catalytic hydrogenation. A methyl ester and an acetyl derivative may be prepared. Selenium dehydrogenation produces sapotaline and a substance with the composition of a tetramethyl naphthalene.

Aoyama (2) also isolated theasaponine, $C_{52}H_{82}O_{27}$, from the seeds of *Thea sinensis.* When subjected to hydrolysis, it yields a mol of prosapogenine $(C_{35}H_{52}O_{12})$, arabinose, galactose, and glucose. Complete hydrolysis gives glycuronic acid and theasapogenine $(C_{29}H_{44}O_6)$, which reacts with alkali when heated, to yield an oxime and a triacetyl derivative; it is therefore a trihydroxy oxolactone. Camellia-sapogenine $(C_{29}H_{44}O_5)$, also investigated by Aoyama (3), appears to have one less hydroxyl group but otherwise is of similar composition. It yields sapotaline with selenium, together with the above-mentioned compound having the structure of a tetramethyl naphthalene. These last two sapogenines seem to form a group with the githagenine, $C_{29}H_{44}O_4$, of Wedekind and Schicke (1).

· Kuwata has found two saponines in the bark of *Aralia chinensis L. var. glabrescens*. On hydrolysis both give the same endsapogenine. The hydrolysis of the less readily soluble saponine, α-taraline ($C_{50}H_{72}O_{19}$), was carefully investigated and 2 mols of glucose and one of glycuronic acid were observed to be present. Taraligenine, $C_{32}H_{46}O_4$, forms a neutral monomethyl ester and an acetyl derivative, and is characterized as a hydroxy acid with an oxide ring. The author claims to have obtained cadaline by selenium dehydrogenation, but this result, in consideration of those obtained with other sapogenines, should be subjected to further proof.

By hydrolysis of the saponine of *Equisetum arvense*, Casparis and Haas obtain, along with fructose and arabinose, a sapogenine of the approximate formula $C_{27}H_{48}O_6$.

E. CAOUTCHOUC

Staudinger and Bondy, as well as Staudinger (1), have determined the molecular weight of caoutchouc by measuring viscosities of very dilute solutions. They observe departures from Poiseuille's law which decrease with decreasing concentration. The complete absence of oxygen is essential. The molecular weight can be calculated by the formulae:

$$M = \eta_{sp}/c \cdot K_m \text{ and } M = \log \eta_r/c \cdot K_{cm}$$

Since the values of η_{sp}/c and $\log \eta_r/c$ are not constant for caoutchouc, only the order of magnitude of the molecular weight can be determined. The constants K_m and K_c are estimated for the cleavage products of low molecular weight. It follows that there must be at least 1,000 isoprene residues bound in a long-string molecule, whence the physical properties of caoutchouc also may be elucidated. The molecules are very sensitive to the influence of temperature change and chemical reagents, by which they are split into small particles of low viscosity. From these more highly polymerized compounds with three-dimensional structure and of low solubility can be regenerated by various reagents, as, e.g., oxygen in autoxidation and sulphur in the process of vulcanization. The authors find that the more readily soluble portion of caoutchouc is actually of lower molecular weight than the less readily soluble portion.

In contrast to Staudinger (1), Pummerer has taken the position that it should be possible to secure the terminal units of the caoutchouc chain, molecular weight over 300,000, in the form of decomposition products. Pummerer, Ebermayer, and Gerlach succeeded in obtaining about 90 per cent of the decomposition products, while Harries formerly got only about 57 per cent. Along with laevulinic acid and its derivatives (*ca.* 90 per cent), small amounts of formic, succinic, and acetic acids were obtained. However, since these may have arisen as further decomposition products of laevulinic acid, it is possible to derive therefrom no conclusions concerning the structure of the terminal units of caoutchouc. Neither are Pummerer and Stärk able to prove the existence of terminal conjugated double bonds by titration with iodine monochloride or dithiocyanate.

Staudinger and Senior find that, in the reduction of caoutchouc with hydrogen iodide, decomposition first takes place, followed by hydrogenation of the decomposition products (mean molecular weight 1,500). Staudinger (2), as well as Staudinger, Geiger, Huber, Schall, and Schwalbach find also that in the catalytic hydrogenation of caoutchouc, cracking occurs, followed by hydrogenation of the cleavage fragments, the process increasing as the temperature is raised. Hydro caoutchouc prepared without solvent at about 270° has a molecular weight of about 2,000 to 10,000, and gives a sol of low viscosity obeying Poiseuille's law, while the hydrogenation product prepared at lower temperatures has a molecular weight of about 30,000 and no longer gives such a sol (cf. also Staudinger and Feisst). The molecular refraction of caoutchouc gives one double bond to five carbon atoms, whereas that of hydro caoutchouc indicates a saturated structure. A certain amount of ring closure, prior to uptake of hydrogen, occurs among the cleavage fragments from the hydrogenation process. According to Staudinger and Schaal, cracking of hydro caoutchouc leads to molecules of low molecular weight, having one double bond each.

By X-ray investigation, Hopff and Susich have established the identity of the hydrocarbons of balata and gutta-percha, which differ from caoutchouc hydrocarbon. Stillwell and Clark, as well as Hauser and Susich, have observed two modifications of gutta-percha hydrocarbon, having a transition point at 68°.

Ott has ascertained that the lines of the X-ray diagram for caout-chouc become increasingly sharp as the exposures are lengthened, a result of the strong acceleration of crystallization by X-rays.

F. Physiological

Dyson has collected the data of the last ten years on the physiological activity of odorous substances and ethereal oils, and particularly on their transformations in the organism, as well as their effects on insects.

Morel, Rochaix, Dœuvre, and Guillot find that the germicidal action of aliphatic terpene alcohols, such as linalool and rhodinol, is greater than that of the phenols and is further increased by ozonization or autoxidation. Malowan shows, on the basis of investigations of Collier and Nitta, that the solubility of the ethereal oils in alcohol is closely related to their bactericidal action. For example, the alde-hyde oils are especially soluble and effective.

According to Josephson, the amide of santoninic acid no longer shows the characteristic effect of santonine on the musculature of the worm. The presence of the lactone ring in santonine seems thus to be determinative.

Saito has investigated the irritant action upon the skin of various individual constituents of the ginkgo fruit. The most effective portion is not definitely established. However, ginkgol ($C_{20}H_{32}O$), and ginkgolic acid [$C_{20}H_{30}(OH)COOH$], of which the former probably belongs to the diterpene series, as well as some of their derivatives, seem to be rather effective.

Winterstein and also Winterstein and Meyer declare that the haemolytic effect of Sapindus saponine is somewhat greater than that of aescine. According to Aoyama, theasaponine is still more active. On the other hand, the Sapindus- and theapro-sapogenines are notably less effective than the corresponding saponines themselves. Kuwata shows that α-taraline, the difficultly water-soluble saponine of *Aralia chinensis,* has a stronger haemolytic action in acid or alkaline solution than in neutral solution.

Various examples have also appeared of the action of certain saponines in other ways. For example, Langer claims that primulasaponine acts favorably in the treatment of bronchitis. The unknown saponines of the spinach leaf, which show a strong haemolytic action, also, according to Kofler, operate as strong promoters of resorption and stimulate peristalsis and the action of the digestive glands. This explains many of the effects of spinach. On the other hand, the addition of a small amount of *Gypsophylla* saponine reacted unfavorably in the feeding of pigs, according to the findings of Scharrer and Schropp.

LITERATURE CITED

ANGELI, A. VON, AND MARINO, L., *Mem. accad. Lincei,* 6, 385 (1907) ; 33, 10 (1924) ; *Ber.,* 46, 2233 (1913)

AOYAMA, S. (1), *J. Pharm. Soc. Japan,* 50, 139, 153 (1930)

AOYAMA, S. (2), *J. Pharm. Soc. Japan,* 51, 29 (1931)

AOYAMA, S. (3), *J. Pharm. Soc. Japan,* 51, 46 (1931)

ASAHINA, Y., AND NAKANISHI, G., *J. Pharm. Soc. Japan,* 46, 75 (1926)

ASCHAN, O. (1), *Ann.,* 461, 9 (1928)

ASCHAN, O. (2), *Ann.,* 483, 124 (1930)

BAUER, K. H., AND DIMOKOSTOULOS, A., *Arch. Pharm.,* 269, 218 (1931)

BAUER, K. H., AND SCHRÖDER, G., *Arch. Pharm.,* 269, 209 (1931)

BREDT, J. (1), *J. prakt. Chem.,* 131, 137 (1931)

BREDT, J. (2), *J. prakt. Chem.,* 131, 132 (1931)

BREDT, J. (3), *J. prakt. Chem.,* 131, 49 (1931)

BREDT-SAVELSBERG, M., AND BUCHKREMER, J., *Ber.,* 64, 600 (1931)

BREDT-SAVELSBERG, M., AND BUND, E., *J. prakt. Chem.,* 131, 29 (1931)

CAHN, R. S., GIBSON, C. T., PENFOLD, A. R., AND SIMONSEN, J. L., *J. Chem. Soc.,* 286 (1931)

CAHN, R. S., PENFOLD, A. R., AND SIMONSEN, J. L., *J. Chem. Soc.,* 1366 (1931)

CASPARIS, P., AND HAAS, K., *Pharm. Acta Helv.,* 6, 181 (1931)

CLEMO, R., AND HAWORTH, R. D., *J. Chem. Soc.,* 2579 (1930)

CLEMO, R., HAWORTH, R., AND WALTON, E., *J. Chem. Soc.,* 2368 (1929)

DIELS, O., AND ALDER, H., *Ann.,* 486, 202 (1931)

DIETERLE, H., SALOMON, A., AND HERZBERG, E., *Arch. Pharm.,* 269, 78 (1931)

DISCHENDORFER, O., AND JUVAN, H., *Monatsh.,* 56, 272 (1930)

DUPONT, G., AND ALLARD, J., *Bull. soc. chim.,* 47, 1216 (1930)

DUPONT, G., LÉVY, J., AND ALLARD, J., *Bull. inst. pin,* 25 (1931)

DYSON, G. M., *Perfumery Essent. Oil Record,* 21, 287 (1930)

GLICHITCH, L. S., *Compt. rend.,* 191, 1457 (1930)

HAAR, A. W. VAN DER, *Rec. trav. chim.,* 43, 546 (1924) ; *ibid.,* 46, 775 (1927)

HANSEN, F. W., *Ber.,* 64, 67, 943, 1904 (1931)

HASSELSTRÖM, T. (1), *Ann. Acad. Sci. Fennicae A,* 30, 3 (1930)

HASSELSTRÖM, T. (2), *J. Am. Chem. Soc.,* 53, 1097 (1931)

HAUSER, E. A., AND SUSICH, G. v., *Kautschuk,* 7, 120, 145 (1931)

HEILBRON, J. M., AND WILKINSON, D. G., *J. Chem. Soc.,* 2546 (1930)

HENRY, T. A., AND PAGET, H., *J. Chem. Soc.*, 25 (1931)

HOPFF, H., AND SUSICH, G. v., *Kautschuk*, **6**, 234 (1930)

HOUBEN, J., AND PFANKUCH, E., *Ann.*, **489**, 193 (1931)

INGOLD, C. K., *Proc. Leeds Phil. Lit. Soc. Sci. Sect.*, **1**, 11 (1925)

JACOBS, W. A., AND FLECK, E. E., *J. Biol. Chem.*, **92**, 487 (1931)

JANOT, M. M., *Compt. rend.*, **192**, 845 (1931)

JOFFRE, M., *Bull. inst. pin*, 79 (1931)

JOSEPHSON, K., *Svensk Farm. Tid.*, **35**, 69 (1931)

KAFUKU, K., NOZOE, T., AND HATA, CH., *Bull. Chem. Soc. Japan*, **6**, 40 (1931)

KARRER, P., AND HELFENSTEIN, A., *Helv. Chim. Acta*, **14**, 78 (1931)

KOFLER, L., *Klin. Wochsch.*, **44**, 852 (1931)

KOMATSU, S., FUJIMOTO, H., AND TANAKA, S., *Mem. Coll. Sci. Kyoto Imp. Univ. A*, **14**, 149 (1931)

KOMPPA, G., AND HASSELSTRÖM, T., *Ann. Acad. Sci. Fennicae A*, **30**, 3 (1930)

KUHN, R., AND HOFFER, M., *Ber.*, **64**, 1243 (1931)

KUWATA, S., *J. Pharm. Soc. Japan*, **51**, 7, 57 (1931)

LANGER, G., *Med. Welt*, **5**, 925 (1931)

LEHMAN, A. S., AND LYNN, E. V., *J. Am. Pharm. Assoc.*, **19**, 1304 (1930); **20**, 29 (1931)

LEVY, P., *Ber.*, **64**, 2441 (1931)

LIEB, H., AND MLADENOVIĆ, M., *Monatsh.*, **58**, 59 (1931)

MALOWAN, S. L., *Z. Hyg. Infektionskrankh.*, **112**, 93 (1931)

MLADENOVIĆ, M., AND LIEB, H., *Monatsh.*, **58**, 69 (1931)

MOREL, A., ROCHAIX, A., DŒUVRE, J., AND GUILLOT, R., *Compt. rend. soc. biol.*, **104**, 582 (1930)

NAMETKIN, S. S., AND BRUSSOWA, L. J. (1), *J. Russ. Phys. Chem. Soc.*, **62**, 333 (1930)

NAMETKIN, S. S., AND BRUSSOWA, L. J. (2), *J. Russ. Phys. Chem. Soc.*, **62**, 341 (1930)

NAMETKIN, S. S., KITSCHIN, A., AND KURSANOFF, D., *J. prakt. Chem.*, **124**, 144 (1930)

OTT, E., *J. Am. Chem. Soc.*, **52**, 4612 (1930)

PENFOLD, A. R., AND SIMONSEN, J. L., *J. Proc. Roy. Soc. New South Wales*, **63**, 95 (1930)

PUMMERER, R., *Kolloid-Z.*, **53**, 75 (1930)

PUMMERER, R., EBERMAYER, G., AND GERLACH, K., *Ber.*, **64**, 809 (1931)

PUMMERER, R., AND STÄRK, H., *Ber.*. **64**, 825 (1931)

READ, J., AND STOREY, R. A. (1), *J. Chem. Soc.*, 2770 (1930)

READ, J., AND STOREY, R. A. (2), *J. Chem. Soc.*, 2761 (1930)

RICHTER, F., WOLFF, W., AND PRESTING, W., *Ber.*, **64**, 871 (1931)

ROLLET, A., *Monatsh.*, **58**, 113 (1931)

ROUIN, G., *Bull. inst. pin*, 155 (1930)

RUPE, H., AND KUENZY, F., *Helv. Chim. Acta*, **14**, 708 (1931)

RUZICKA, L., AND BALAS, FR. (1), *Helv. Chim. Acta*, **6**, 677 (1923)

RUZICKA, L., AND BALAS, FR. (2), *Helv. Chim. Acta*, **7**, 875 (1924)

RUZICKA, L., BARDHAN, J. C., AND WIND, A. H., *Helv. Chim. Acta*, **14**, 423 (1931)

RUZICKA, L., AND EICHENBERGER, E., *Helv. Chim. Acta*, **13**, 1117 (1930)

RUZICKA, L., AND GIBSON, D. T., *Helv. Chim. Acta*, **14**, 570 (1931)
RUZICKA, L., GOLDBERG, M. W., HUYSER, H. W., AND SEIDEL, C. F., *Helv. Chim. Acta*, **14**, 545 (1931)
RUZICKA, L., GRAAFF, G. B. R. DE, AND HOSKING, J. R., *Helv. Chim. Acta*, **14**, 233 (1931)
RUZICKA, L., AND HAAGEN-SMIT, A. J. (1), *Helv. Chim. Acta*, **14**, 1104 (1931)
RUZICKA, L., AND HAAGEN-SMIT, A. J. (2), *Helv. Chim. Acta*, **14**, 1122 (1931)
RUZICKA, L., AND HOSKING, J. R., *Helv. Chim. Acta*, **13**, 402 (1930) ; **14**, 203 (1931)
RUZICKA, L., HOSKING, J. R., AND WICK, A., *Helv. Chim. Acta*, **14**, 811 (1931)
RUZICKA, L., AND JANOT, M. M., *Helv. Chim. Acta*, **14**, 645 (1931)
RUZICKA, L., KOOLHAAS, D. R., AND WIND, A. H. (1), *Helv. Chim. Acta*, **14**, 1151 (1931)
RUZICKA, L., KOOLHAAS, D. R., AND WIND, A. H. (2), *Helv. Chim. Acta*, **14**, 1171 (1931)
RUZICKA, L., KOOLHAAS, D. R., AND WIND, A. H. (3), *Helv. Chim. Acta*, **14**, 1178 (1931)
RUZICKA, L., AND MELSEN, J. A. VAN, *Helv. Chim. Acta*, **14**, 397 (1931)
RUZICKA, L., AND PIETH, P., *Helv. Chim. Acta*, **14**, 1090 (1931)
RUZICKA, L., AND VEEN, A. G. VAN, *Z. physiol. Chem.*, **184**, 69 (1929)
RUZICKA, L., AND WIND, A. H., *Helv. Chim. Acta*, **14**, 410 (1931)
RUZICKA, L., WIND, A. H., AND KOOLHAAS, D. R., *Helv. Chim. Acta*, **14**, 1132 (1931)
SAITO, J., *Tôhoku J. Exptl. Med.*, **16**, 385 (1930)
SANDO, C. E., *J. Biol. Chem.*, **90**, 477 (1931)
SANDQVIST, H., AND BENGTSSON, E., *Ber.*, **63**, 1935 (1930) ; **64**, 2167 (1931)
SCHARRER, K., AND SCHROPP, W., *Biochem. Z.*, **235**, 367 (1931)
SCHMID, L., AND ZACHERL, M. K., *Monatsh.*, **57**, 177 (1931)
SEN, N. K., *J. Indian Chem. Soc.*, **7**, 905 (1930)
STAUDINGER, H. (1), *Kolloid-Z.*, **54**, 129 (1931)
STAUDINGER, H. (2), *Helv. Chim. Acta*, **13**, 1324 (1930)·
STAUDINGER, H., AND BONDY, H. F., *Ann.*, **488**, 127, 153 (1931)
STAUDINGER, H., AND FEISST, W., *Helv. Chim. Acta*, **13**, 1361 (1930)
STAUDINGER, H., GEIGER, E., HUBER, E., SCHAAL, W., AND SCHWALBACH, A., *Helv. Chim. Acta*, **13**, 1334 (1930)
STAUDINGER, H., AND SCHAAL, W., *Helv. Chim. Acta*, **13**, 1355 (1930)
STAUDINGER, H., AND SENIOR, J. R., *Helv. Chim. Acta*, **13**, 1321 (1930)
STEIMMIG, G., *Ber.*, **47**, 350 (1914)
STEPHAN, K., AND HAMMERICH, T., *J. prakt. Chem.*, **129**, 285 (1931)
STILLWELL, CH. W., AND CLARK, G. L., *Kautschuk*, **7**, 86 (1931)
TOIVONEN, N. J., AND TIKKANEN, E., *Acta Chem. Fennica*, **2**, 169 (1929)
TREIBS, W. (1), *Ber.*, **64**, 2178 (1931)
TREIBS, W. (2), *Ber.*, **64**, 2545 (1931)
WAGNER-JAUREGG, TH. (1), *Ann.*, **488**, 181 (1931)
WAGNER-JAUREGG, TH. (2), *Ann.*, **488**, 176 (1931)
WEDEKIND, E., AND SCHICKE, W. (1), *Z. physiol. Chem.*, **190**, 1 (1930)
WEDEKIND, E., AND SCHICKE, W. (2), *Z. physiol. Chem.*, **195**, 132 (1931) ; **198**, 181 (1931)

610   ANNUAL REVIEW OF BIOCHEMISTRY

WEDEKIND, E., AND TETTWEILER, K. (1), *Ber.*, **64**, 387 (1931)
WEDEKIND, E., AND TETTWEILER, K. (2), *Ber.*, **64**, 1796 (1931)
WESTENBERG, L., AND WIBAUT, J. P., *Rec. trav. chim.*, **50**, 188 (1931)
WIELAND, H., AND UTZINO, S., *Ann.*, **488**, 242 (1931)
WINOGRADOWA, W., *Ber.*, **64**, 1991 (1931)
WINTERSTEIN, A., *Z. physiol. Chem.*, **199**, 25 (1931)
WINTERSTEIN, A., AND HÄMMERLE, W., *Z. physiol. Chem.*, **199**, 56 (1931)
WINTERSTEIN, A., AND MEYER, J., *Z. physiol. Chem.*, **199**, 37 (1931)
WINTERSTEIN, A., AND STEIN, G. (1), *Z. physiol. Chem.*, **199**, 75 (1931)
WINTERSTEIN, A., AND STEIN, G. (2), *Z. physiol. Chem.*, **199**, 64 (1931)
WINTERSTEIN, A., AND WIEGAND, W., *Z. physiol. Chem.*, **199**, 46 (1931)

CHEMISCHES LABORATORIUM
EIDGENÖSSISCHE TECHNISCHE HOCHSCHULE
ZÜRICH, SWITZERLAND

THE NITROGENOUS CONSTITUENTS OF GREEN PLANTS*

BY H. B. VICKERY

Connecticut Agricultural Experiment Station

The present review takes account of papers, published in the two-year period previous to December 1931, which deal more or less directly with the simpler nitrogenous substances found in green plants. Although the field covered is small, many of the papers, especially those that describe new methods, have considerable interest to biochemists, who are chiefly concerned with the problems of animal physiology. No attempt has been made to discuss the alkaloids, but a brief, though non-critical, review of the alkaloids discovered in the period 1920–1929, together with a full bibliography, has been published by Couch.

Some years ago Kapfhammer and Eck described the use of the ammonium salt of the so-called Reinecke's acid (tetrathiocyano-diammono chromic acid $[(SCN)_4Cr(NH_3)_2 \cdot NH_4]$) as a reagent for the isolation of proline and oxyproline from protein hydrolysates. The same reagent was later employed for the preparation of histidine, with which it forms an insoluble crystalline compound. The value of this substance as a reagent for the examination of solutions that contain basic substances is apparent, and it has already been employed by Kapfhammer and Bischoff for the isolation of acetyl choline from cattle blood (see also Bischoff, Grab, and Kapfhammer). Furthermore, these authors find it to be valuable also for the isolation and estimation of choline, and it has apparently been used for this purpose by Paal. The reagent should prove of value in the investigation of plant lecithins as well as the study of the quaternary base fraction derived from plant extracts.

The present-day tendency to search for organic substances to serve as convenient reagents for separations that are difficult or impossible by the classical methods is well illustrated by the work of Zimmermann. He has investigated the compounds formed by quinizarinsulfonic acid (1, 4-dioxyanthraquinone-2-sulfonic acid) with a large number of bases and amino acids, and has further extended the investigation to other anthraquinone derivatives. Because of the inconveniently

* Received December 24, 1931.

long chemical name of the new reagent he has suggested that it be called rufianic acid. The precipitations of the bases are carried out in faintly acid aqueous solutions, and the products are for the most part readily recrystallized from water and can be decomposed by making their solutions alkaline with barium hydroxide. The barium salt of rufianic acid is very insoluble and the free base is therefore easily accessible; these are points of great technical importance when dealing with such substances. Water-insoluble compounds are formed with histidine, arginine, lysine, guanidine, methylguanidine, creatinine, methylamine, carnosine, anserine, trigonelline, homobetaine, histamine, tetramethylammonium hydroxide, agmatine, tyrosine, phenylalanine, tryptophane, ammonia, and a number of alkaloids. The mono-amino acids, including proline and oxyproline, form compounds that precipitate from alcoholic solution, and this is also true of choline, neurine, tyramine, γ-butyrobetaine, glucosamine, di- and trimethylamine, colamine, and urea. Aspartic and glutamic acids, valine, leucine, nicotinic acid, taurine, indole, and skatole yield compounds soluble in both water and alcohol. Most of the compounds are sufficiently stable to permit recrystallization without the addition of rufianic acid.

Chattaway and Parkes have found that many of the commoner alkaloids yield well-characterized compounds when a solution of the alkaloid in concentrated hydrochloric acid is added to an excess of tetrachloroiodic acid made by saturating with chlorine a suspension of finely powdered iodine in concentrated hydrochloric acid. When the compounds are treated with a solution of potassium iodide acidified with acetic acid, iodine is quantitatively liberated, and an analytical method is founded on this reaction.

In connection with his study of acetyl choline Dudley has described a particularly ingenious method to decompose platinum salts. Finely divided silver, prepared by the reduction of silver nitrate with ferrous sulfate, is shaken for a few minutes with an aqueous solution of the chloroplatinate. After removal of the excess silver, silver chloride, and platinum, by filtration a solution of the hydrochloride of the base is secured.

An indirect method for the determination of choline has been described by Lintzel and Fomin. This is founded on the observation that choline is quantitatively decomposed with the production of trimethylamine if it is heated with strong alkali and an excess of permanganate is slowly added. The volatile bases, which distil when the method is applied to mixtures, are absorbed in acid, an excess of formaldehyde and alkali is added and the trimethylamine, which alone is volatile from such a solution, is aërated into $N/50$ sulfuric acid; back titration is carried out with $N/50$ trimethylamine. According to the authors betaine and γ-butyrobetaine are relatively stable under the conditions that decompose choline, and trimethylamine is itself not appreciably oxidized. If the method is further studied and the behavior of such substances as trigonelline and stachydrine is found to resemble that of betaine, it may serve to give valuable data on the composition of the quaternary base fraction of plant extracts.

Steiner and Löffler have carried out microchemical tests for the presence of amines and ammonia in a large number of plant species employing dinitronaphthol as a reagent. Hurd-Karrer has investigated the titration curves of extracts from wheat seedlings and has been able to prepare buffer mixtures of asparagine, malic, and other acids, the titration curves of which resemble those of the plant.

Yamafuji has studied the nitrogenous substances of tobacco leaves and has identified small amounts of adenine, histidine, and betaine. The presence of arginine in tobacco leaf is questioned by this author. The seed of the tobacco plant has been studied by Vickery, who analyzed a hot water extract of the fat-free meal. The presence of choline, betaine, adenine, guanine, and arginine was established. The observation of Scurti and Perciabosco that this seed contains allantoin was also confirmed (unpublished observation).

The synthesis of two isomeric hydroxyasparagines has been described by Chibnall and Cannan. The β-isomer $NH_2 \cdot CO \cdot CH(OH) \cdot CH(NH_2) \cdot COOH$, although it has not hitherto been found in nature, is a very probable plant constituent. It has been the experience of all who have attempted to determine the chemical nature of the amides found in plants that the yield of crystalline amide (asparagine or glutamine) falls far short of the quantity to be expected from the content of amide nitrogen; the presence of other amides and in particular of the amides of allied amino acids is therefore likely. Chibnall and Cannan have determined the properties of hydroxyasparagine and have outlined a method whereby it could probably be isolated from a plant extract.

In connection with the determination of amide nitrogen in plant extracts Vickery and Pucher have shown that the use of hydrochloric acid for hydrolysis of the amide is inadmissible if the extract, as is frequently the case, contains nitrate. Reduction of some of the nitrate to ammonia occurs under the influence of some as yet unidentified, easily oxidized substance, and the amount of ammonia produced by the hydrolysis is greatly influenced by the strength of acid used and by the time of hydrolysis; furthermore, some oxidation of ammonia also occurs. It happens that, under the conditions usually employed, and frequently designated as the Sacchse method, these two sources of error approximately compensate each other so that reasonably trustworthy results have been secured. Nevertheless it seems better to avoid both errors by substituting sulfuric acid as the hydrolyzing agent. Chibnall and Miller believe that Vickery and Pucher's easily oxidized substance is nitrogenous.

Dakin and West have synthesized the betaine of glutamic acid. Although this substance has not hitherto been found in nature, later investigation may reveal it.

Williams, Waterman, and Gurin have reinvestigated the procedure whereby Jansen and Donath isolated from rice polishings a crystalline substance of the composition $C_6H_{10}N_2O \cdot HCl$ that possessed the properties of vitamin B. Although they failed to secure crystallization of their product they obtained a highly active fraction of the antineuritic vitamin and state that their experiments betray no error in the account of the precipitation reactions of the vitamin that was given by the Dutch authors. Although much further work will be necessary before the nature of this substance is determined, the present information strongly suggests that it is an organic nitrogenous base that is fairly widely distributed in nature.

Schmalfuss and Heider have obtained evidence for the presence of tyramine and hydroxytyramine in the pods of the broom plant (*Sarothamnus scoparius Wimm.*). Both substances were secured by precipitation with methyl chlorocarbonate and were crystallized and positively identified. Hydroxytyramine had not been previously observed in nature.

The presence of a small proportion of ephedrine in the leaves of the yew (*Taxus baccata*), gathered in Scotland, has been demonstrated by Gulland and Virden. Although of no probable commercial significance, the observation is of interest since this European species is related to the Chinese species which serves as the chief natural source of the drug.

A new amino acid that is closely related to arginine has been isolated by Wada from the juice of the watermelon (*Citrullus vulgaris, Schrad.*). The juice, expressed from the ripe fruit, was concentrated and precipitated successively by basic lead acetate and by mercuric acetate and sodium carbonate. The final filtrate yielded the new amino acid as an insoluble copper salt. The free acid decomposed at 202° and had the general properties of an amino acid. On treatment with hot alkali, ammonia and carbon dioxide were eliminated and ornithine was produced. This, together with the results of analysis, suggested the structural formula $NH_2 \cdot CO \cdot NH \cdot (CH_2)_3 \cdot CH \cdot (NH_2) \cdot COOH$, which was confirmed by synthesis. Wada has suggested the name citrulline for this interesting substance. Its presence in watermelon has been confirmed by Ackermann, who has also shown that it is produced in small amounts during the putrefaction of arginine. Ackermann finds the melting-point of free citrulline to be 220–222°.

Kitagawa and Tomita have also isolated a new substance that may be allied to arginine. This was obtained from the base fraction derived from a 50 per cent alcoholic extract of jack-bean meal. Analysis of the salts suggested the formula $C_5H_{11}N_4O_3$. The new substance is precipitated, along with arginine, by flavianic acid, but can be separated from arginine because its flavianate is more soluble in water. The Sakaguchi color reaction is negative; the substance is therefore probably not a guanidino derivative. Half its nitrogen is split off as urea when the base is treated with an aqueous extract of pig liver, but only 19 per cent is liberated as ammonia after heating with 50 per cent potassium hydroxide for six hours. It is to be hoped that the somewhat confusing properties of this substance will soon be explained.

Choline has attracted considerable attention. Roman has devised a method for determining this base that consists essentially of precipitation as triiodide and titration of the iodine in the precipitate. The method of Lintzel and Fomin has already been mentioned. Klein and Zeller have investigated the different parts of various plant species for choline, employing a microchemical technique. Of the more than one hundred species examined, only three, all of them lichens, were found to contain no choline. Schroeter and Strassberger have investigated the statement of Lührs that the injury observed in certain diseases of barley was due to the toxic effect of choline. They found that both normal and diseased barley contain this base and point out that the method employed by Lührs was not specific as a test for choline.

Trigonelline has been found by Heiduschka and Brüchner in coffee from which it was extracted by very dilute sulfuric acid. The base was precipitated by bismuth triiodide and isolated as the sulfate.

Fosse, Brunel, de Graeve, Thomas, and Sarazin have isolated allantoin from the seeds of wheat, barley, maize, soy bean, and several other varieties of beans. This substance was also found in the roots of the rape. Both allantoin and allantoic acid are contained in higher concentration in young than in older beans. Allantoic acid and the enzyme allantoinase were not found in wheat, barley, or maize.

The distribution of the different forms of nitrogen in extracts of plant material has provided the theme of a number of investigations. Fagan and Watkin have worked with the oat plant at different stages of growth (compare Kiesel's investigation of rye), Pearsall has studied beet leaves, Evans has studied pasture grass, and Mulay has investigated the seasonal changes in the different forms of nitrogen in shoots of the Bartlett pear (compare Thomas' work on the apple). Maskell and Mason have continued their comprehensive study of the transport of nitrogen in the cotton plant in two papers on the interpretation of the effects of ringing with special reference to the lability of the nitrogen compounds of the bark and on the movement of nitrogen to the boll. They have controlled their results by statistical methods and have provided evidence that the conclusions are supported by significant data.

LITERATURE CITED

ACKERMANN, D., *Z. physiol. Chem.*, **203**, 66 (1931)

BISCHOFF, C., GRAB, W., AND KAPFHAMMER, J., *Z. physiol. Chem.*, **199**, 135 (1931); **200**, 153 (1931)

CHATTAWAY, F. D., AND PARKES, G. D., *J. Chem. Soc.*, 1003 (1930)

CHIBNALL, A. C., AND CANNAN, R. K., *Biochem. J.*, **24**, 945 (1930)

CHIBNALL, A. C., AND MILLER, E. J., *J. Biol. Chem.*, **90**, 189 (1931)

COUCH, J. F., *Am. J. Pharm.*, **103**, 242 (1931)

DAKIN, H. D., AND WEST, R., *J. Biol. Chem.*, **83**, 773 (1929)

DUDLEY, H. W., *Biochem. J.*, **23**, 1064 (1929)

EVANS, T. W., *Welsh J. Agr.*, **7**, 255 (1931)

FAGAN, T. W., AND WATKIN, J. E., *Welsh J. Agr.*, **7**, 229 (1931)

FOSSE, R., BRUNEL, A., GRAEVE, P. DE, THOMAS, P. E., AND SARAZIN, J., *Compt. rend.*, **191**, 1153 (1930)

GULLAND, J. M., AND VIRDEN, C. J., *J. Chem. Soc.*, 2148 (1931)

HEIDUSCHKA, A., AND BRÜCHNER, B., *J. prakt. Chem.*, **130**, 11 (1931)

HURD-KARRER, A. M., *Plant Physiol.*, **5**, 307 (1930)

JANSEN, B. C. P., AND DONATH, W. F., *Mededeel. Dienst Volksgezondheid Nederland. Indie*, pt. 1, 186 (1926)

KAPFHAMMER, J., AND BISCHOFF, C., *Z. physiol. Chem.*, **191**, 179 (1930)
KAPFHAMMER, J., AND ECK, R., *Z. physiol. Chem.*, **170**, 294 (1927)
KAPFHAMMER, J., AND SPÖRER, H., *Z. physiol. Chem.*, **173**, 245 (1928)
KIESEL, A., *Z. physiol. Chem.*, **135**, 61 (1924)
KITAGAWA, M., AND TOMITA, T., *Proc. Imp. Acad. (Japan)*, **5**, 380 (1929)
KLEIN, G., AND ZELLER, A., *Oesterr. botan. Z.*, **79**, 40 (1930)
LINTZEL, W., AND FOMIN, S., *Biochem. Z.*, **238**, 438, 452 (1931)
LÜHRS, *Berl. tierärztl. Wochschr.*, 855 (1928)
MASKELL, E. J., AND MASON, T. G., *Ann. Botany,* **44**, 233, 657 (1930)
MULAY, A. S., *Plant Physiol.*, **6**, 519 (1931)
PAAL, H., *Biochem. Z.*, **211**, 244 (1929)
PEARSALL, W. H., *J. Exptl. Biol.*, **8**, 279 (1931)
ROMAN, W., *Biochem. Z.*, **219**, 218 (1930)
SCHMALFUSS, H., AND HEIDER, A., *Biochem. Z.*, **236**, 226 (1931)
SCHROETER, G., AND STRASSBERGER, L., *Biochem. Z.*, **232**, 452 (1931)
SCURTI, F., AND PERCIABOSCO, F., *Gazz. chim. ital.,* **36**, II, 626 (1906)
STEINER, M., AND LÖFFLER, H., *Jahrb. wiss. Botan.*, **71**, 463 (1929)
THOMAS, W., *Plant Physiol.*, **2**, 55 (1927)
VICKERY, H. B., *Carnegie Inst. Wash. Year Book*, **29**, 381 (1930)
VICKERY, H. B., AND PUCHER, G. W., *J. Biol. Chem.*, **90**, 179 (1931)
WADA, M., *Proc. Imp. Acad. (Japan)*, **6**, 15 (1930); *Biochem. Z.*, **224**, 420
    (1930)
WILLIAMS, R. R., WATERMAN, R. E., AND GURIN, S., *J. Biol. Chem.*, **87**, 559
    (1930)
YAMAFUJI, K., *J. Agr. Chem. Soc. (Japan)*, **7**, 121 (1931)
ZIMMERMANN, W., *Z. physiol. Chem.*, **188**, 180 (1930); **189**, 155 (1930); **192**,
    124 (1930)

CONNECTICUT AGRICULTURAL EXPERIMENT STATION
NEW HAVEN, CONNECTICUT

MINERAL NUTRITION OF PLANTS*

By D. R. Hoagland

Laboratory of Plant Nutrition
University of California

The phrase "mineral nutrition of plants" may easily imply a range of investigational activities entirely too broad to be reviewed in a single chapter, especially in one so strictly limited as to length. It is, therefore, necessary to impose certain rather arbitrary restrictions in the selection of material to be dealt with. The subject of "permeability" *per se* of living cells occupies so prominent a place in biological literature that a separate chapter has been allotted to it. The gradual accumulation and utilization of mineral elements by plants must obviously be regarded as within the province of this chapter. It has been agreed that no attempt shall be made to review soil chemistry or field experiments with fertilizers. Those who are interested in the applied aspects of the mineral nutrition of plants are referred to the review by Crowther. Even after delimiting the scope of the present review, as above described, there remains for attention a very long list of titles. Merely to mention as many papers as possible would be of slight service. The intention is to outline, of necessity with great brevity, the conclusions of a limited number of recent researches[1] and to point out the general nature of the progress being made on some important phases of the mineral nutrition of plants, with special reference to the higher plants.

Chemical elements essential to the growth of the higher plants.— A list of ten chemical elements essential to higher green plants became embedded in the literature of plant physiology, although about twenty years ago Mazé in France presented evidence that this list was incomplete. It took many years to excite general interest in this question. Sometimes the additional elements were conceived to be merely "stimulants." Such a term meant very little, and its use was not conducive to progress. During the past few years the problem of chemical elements essential in only small quantities has begun to receive that

* Received January 4, 1932.

[1] With few exceptions the period covered is 1930–31. Generally, it has not been feasible to consider papers received after December 1, 1931.

careful thought and study which its importance justifies. Two articles appearing almost simultaneously [Sommer (69), Lipman and Mackinney (43)] announce definite evidence that copper is one of the elements essential for plant growth, at least for plants of the several types under investigation. In the case of barley, as studied by Lipman and Mackinney, vegetative growth was augmented by the presence of copper in the nutrient solution (the experiments were conducted by the methods of "water culture"), but the notable feature of plant response was expressed in seed production. No normal seed was produced by plants growing in an otherwise adequate solution from which copper was excluded as rigidly as possible. The addition of one-sixteenth to one-eighth of a part per million of copper permitted the production of normal grain. These investigators also refer to an earlier unpublished experiment with flax from which very similar conclusions were reached. Sommer, working independently, grew flax, tomato, and sunflower plants with and without addition of copper. Lack of copper caused all these plants to show very striking inhibition of growth even in the vegetative stages. In view of the evidence now available, nothing seems to be gained by classifying copper as merely a "stimulant."

Only highly controlled experiments with specially purified salts can furnish proof that an element like copper is essential to plant growth, but certain effects of copper have been observed under practical conditions. Bryan finds that copper salts (as well as manganese salts) have a remarkably beneficial influence on the growth of various plants (beans, sorghum, cowpeas, etc.) in the Everglade soils of Florida. Symptoms of nutritional disease were overcome not only by adding copper salts to the soil, but also by applications made directly to leaf surfaces. Some years ago, copper was found to be effective in a nutritional disease of plants growing in certain muck soils in Holland (Smith). In California, plant pathologists have observed that the "exanthema" disease of fruit trees may often be arrested by the use of copper salts. Haas and Klotz suggest that copper salts may correct the so-called "decline" disease of date palms. One explanation of the influence of copper under field conditions is that it inactivates some toxic substance developed in the soil, but the phenomenon is still obscure. Actual lack of copper has not been positively excluded from consideration in most of the cases. [See also McHargue and Calfee (46, 47) on effects of manganese, copper, and zinc on growth of yeast and of *Aspergillus flavus;* Mokragnatz (53) on effect of nickel on *Aspergillus niger;* Bertrand and Mokragnatz (4) on distribution of cobalt and nickel in plant tissues.]

The animal biochemist will be interested in these researches on plants, because of the work of recent years bearing on the suggested function of copper in animal metabolism. Neal, Becker, and Shealy (55) have just reported the existence of a disease of cattle living on the native vegetation growing on certain soils of Florida, which is controlled by the administration of copper salts but not of iron compounds alone.

Clark and Fly (15) question the universality of the need of manganese by plants, since, in their experiments, this element did not seem to have an essential rôle in the development of *Lemna major.* This conclusion is contested by Hopkins, who advances evidence that manganese is essential for *Lemna minor* and expresses the opinion that it is probably required for all green plants.

Earlier experiments, made in Europe and in America, have demonstrated that boron is an essential element for many, if not all, types of higher plants. The boron question continues to interest investigators of plant nutrition. Haas and Klotz (27) show that boron is an essential element for citrus, and that its deficiency may induce certain well-defined symptoms of tissue breakdown. Although a minute amount of boron is essential to citrus growth, at the same time certain species are very easily injured by a relatively small concentration of this element in the culture medium. Another plant recently shown to have a definite boron requirement is tobacco [McMurtrey (48)]. Johnston and Fisher (40) have extended previous studies on the relation of boron to the growth of the tomato plant. They state that boron is necessary not only for normal vegetative growth but also for the setting and development of fruit. A continuous supply of boron in the culture medium is required throughout the growth period.

Eaton has noted a curious effect of boron absorbed by barley on resistance to attack of powdery mildew. Spot-blotch, caused by *Helminthosporium sativum,* did not develop when boron was omitted from the culture solution. On the other hand, in summer plantings of barley, mildew caused by *Erysiphe graminis* was abundant in plants without boron and absent when boron was supplied.

Burk and Lineweaver (12) have discovered that calcium and strontium are not required for the normal growth of *Azotobacter* in fixed nitrogen, providing certain other elements, such as magnesium, barium, or beryllium, are present in sufficient concentration. However, the chemical mechanism of nitrogen fixation requires either calcium or strontium (not necessarily both) in relatively large concentrations. Normal fixation is attained when the concentration of these elements reaches 25 to 50 p.p.m., but rates of fixation are inappreciable when only 1 to 5 p.p.m. are present. Calcium and strontium apparently cannot be replaced for this purpose by any other elements, since fifty other elements were tested and gave entirely negative results. Possibly a large proportion of the calcium and strontium employed may be diverted to ordinary metabolic processes and only very small amounts of these elements may be directly concerned in fixation.

Accumulation of mineral elements by plants.—It has become evident during recent years that the absorption and accumulation of mineral elements by plant cells in the course of their normal nutrition involve processes which may easily escape proper study, in so far as most investigations on permeability are concerned. The investigator of the permeability of plant cells is often constrained to employ highly artificial environmental conditions (high concentrations of solutes, use of solutes foreign to the cell, unsuitable conditions of light or aëration, etc.) or to work over very short periods of time. We are here concerned with the gradual intake of electrolytes by the growing or actively metabolizing plant. The electrolytes may accumu- in the sap of vacuolated cells until frequently a far higher concentration is attained than in the culture solution.; or they may, in part, become bound up with organic substances synthesized by the plant. Of course the term permeability may be so defined or modified (physiological permeability, etc.) as to include all the processes now referred to, but there seems to be a distinct disadvantage to clarity of thought in making one word mean so much. As already stated, the review on permeability is presented in another chapter.

Earlier investigations on *Valonia macrophysa* cells (very large marine algal cells from which uncontaminated sap is obtainable) indicated that potassium attained a concentration in the cell sap much higher than that in sea-water, the potassium-sodium relation being reversed. Accumulation of potassium is, of course, a very general process in plant cells. Several years ago, however, Osterhout and Dorcas (60) investigated the sap of another marine alga, *Halicystis,* and concluded that no accumulation of potassium had occurred. On the contrary, sodium predominated in the sap as it does in sea-water.

The question arose whether the cells investigated were in a normal condition. Brooks (8) examined a Pacific Coast form (*Halicystis ovalis*) and found the usual predominance of potassium over sodium. Blinks and Jacques (6) have now re-investigated the question, using cells detached from their places of growth at Bermuda. The analyses of sap from cells considered to be certainly in a normal state were in general agreement with those heretofore reported. According to evidence now available, we have, therefore, an extraordinary instance of apparently closely related algal cells, all living in sea-water, behaving entirely differently in regard to the accumulation of potassium and sodium. Evidently highly generalized statements with regard to the physical chemical properties of different chemical elements in relation to their intake by plant cells must be made with caution. Another large-celled alga (*Chara ceratophylla*) was studied in Finland by Collander (17). This organism lives in brackish water. The uncontaminated cell sap has a composition between that of *Valonia macrophysa* and that of the fresh-water *Nitella clavata*. The conclusion of Collander is in general agreement with those reached from studies on the last-mentioned cells, namely, that ions can exist at much higher concentrations in the sap than in the surrounding medium. Organic combination or adsorption cannot be offered as adequate explanations.

Zscheile (79) has re-computed published data on *Valonia* and *Nitella* on a modern thermodynamic basis. While the general problem is not changed by this method of interpretation, the opinion is expressed by Zscheile that considerable modifications may need to be made in comparisons of different ionic relations, as considered by physiologists, when activities, instead of simple concentration values, are taken into account.

Evidence from studies on *Nitella* cells has led to emphasis on the metabolic activities of living cells in relation to the accumulation of mineral elements. Steward has recently carried out a series of very carefully controlled studies on the accumulation of certain elements (especially potassium and bromine) by potato tissues. It is clearly shown that the respiratory activities of the cells are indispensably involved in the process of accumulation. For example, significant accumulation of bromine ions did not occur (that is, an attainment of a concentration within the sap expressed from the tissues higher than in the outside solution) except when the tissues were suitably aërated. Under proper conditions, however, the tissues acquired a striking ability to accumulate potassium and bromine. It was not merely a question of carrying away carbon dioxide but also of supplying oxygen at a proper rate, taking care to avoid mechanical injury to tissues. Maximum accumulation of electrolytes was attained under those conditions which produced maximum aërobic respiration. Certain significant anatomical and cytological changes were observed in the surface cells under the metabolic conditions favorable to the process of accumulation. These experiments differ from earlier experiments on storage tissues in the special care taken to provide the tissues with a favorable gaseous environment. It would seem that earlier results will require re-examination in the light of the information now available. Further reference to these researches can be deferred until the details are published.

In the absence of suitable conditions of aëration, excised root systems may show but little power to accumulate electrolytes, as is illustrated by the experiments of Pirschle and Mengdehl (63), but when proper provision is made for maintaining active respiration and preventing injury, excised root systems of barley and wheat accumulate certain ions very rapidly, as has been illustrated by experiments carried on in the laboratory of the reviewer. The metabolic state of the roots, as determined by the culture conditions existing previous to excision, is also of great importance.

The animal physiologist will recall that these problems of the plant physiologist have their analogies in the animal organism. There, too, questions arise concerning the relation of the activities of living cells to the movements of solutes against concentration gradients. A. V. Hill (31) calls attention to the universality of this type of process and to the importance of the oxidation reactions generally involved. He points out that dynamic "steady states" and expenditures of energy at membrane boundaries are indispensable to understanding such a system.

The mechanisms of living cells involved in accumulation, which may be of exceeding great intricacy, have not yet been disclosed through any direct experimental approach, but among the theories advanced during the past few years should be mentioned those of Brooks (9) and of Briggs (7). Both of these theories rest on an ionic exchange basis. It will be recalled that Osterhout (60) and his associates take the view that undissociated molecules, and not ions, are chiefly concerned in the accumulation of electrolytes. This latter generalized view is not accepted by Brooks (10), who in a preliminary statement sets forth arguments against it. Presumably there is no opposition to the idea that certain undissociated molecules, especially NH_3 or NH_4OH, readily penetrate living cells. The question at issue is whether, in the gradual accumulation of such elements as potassium, sodium, etc., a satisfactory explanation can be based on other than an ionic hypothesis. Both ionic and molecular hypotheses have involved the assumption that gradients of hydrogen ion concentration between cell sap and culture solution play a part in the accumulation of potassium. The question has been raised whether such a gradient is always indispensable to the accumulation (32). Further discussion falls in the field of another reviewer.

Absorption and utilization of nitrogen by plants.—The synthesis by plants of the most complex nitrogenous bodies from very simple compounds is of remarkable interest from both the scientific and the practical points of view. Nitrogen fertilizers are the most widely applied and the most expensive of all fertilizers. Moreover, rapid advances have been made in the development of methods for the fixation of atmospheric nitrogen and in the production of forms of nitrogen not previously available. The almost exclusive emphasis often placed on nitrates as a source of nitrogen for higher plants is being questioned more frequently than before.

During the past few years, definite progress appears to have been made in understanding certain phases of the nitrogen metabolism of plants. It will be recalled that, according to the earlier view of Prianischnikov (64), asparagine (or glutamine) performs an essential storage function in plants and prevents ammonia from accumulating in toxic amount. Under proper conditions of carbohydrate supply, etc., ammonium salts are considered to be as suitable or even a more suitable source of nitrogen than nitrates. A very interesting development of our knowledge of the relation of the ammonia forms of nitrogen to plant metabolism was described by Ruhland (66) and his associates. Ruhland divided plants into two general classes—the "ammonia" or "acid" plants, and the "amid" plants. Plants of the latter type fall within the scheme of Prianischnikov, but plants of the first type have the property of storing ammonium salts without damage to themselves. The reason for this is that such plants can readily produce acids, particularly oxalic acid, and the ammonium salts of these acids are non-toxic, under the low pH conditions prevailing in the sap. In the case of "amid" plants ammonia must be converted into asparagine (or glutamine) to prevent injury [see review by

Chibnall and Pryde (14)]. According to Mevius and Engel (52) the distinction between the two types of plants is not a sharp one and the relative importance of the two processes is influenced by temperature and other environmental conditions.

Mevius and Engel carried out extensive experiments bearing on the nature of ammonia toxicity, and on the conditions governing the absorption of nitrogen when present in the form of ammonium salts. The reaction of the solution is of predominant importance, in conformity with the following illustration of a culture solution containing ammonium salts:

$$NH_4Cl \leftrightarrows NH_4^+ + Cl^-$$

$$H_2O \leftrightarrows OH^- + H^+$$
$$\uparrow\downarrow$$
$$NH_4OH \leftrightarrows NH_3 + H_2O$$

The physiological effect of ammonium salts is determined to a large extent by the degree of hydrolytic cleavage and the corresponding NH_3 tension. As the pH of the solution is increased, the rate of penetration of NH_3 (or NH_4OH) into the cell is likewise increased, and injury may result from a too rapid accumulation of ammonia. Naturally the concentration of ammonium salts is important as well as the pH value of the solution, but it was found that at values of pH 5.3 to 5.6 large concentrations of ammonium salts could be employed without injury. Temperature is important because of its influence on the hydrolytic dissociation of ammonium salts. Carbohydrate synthesis is also of great consequence, since the detoxication of ammonia through the formation of asparagine requires a supply of carbohydrate. Emphasis is placed on the toxicity of ammonia under certain conditions, rather than on the "physiological" acidity developed in a solution of ammonium salts through the preferential absorption of the basic part of the salt. When a very low pH prevails in the culture solution, the absorption of nitrogen from ammonium salts may be so retarded as to bring about nitrogen starvation.

In another communication, Mevius and Dikussar (51) describe experiments on nitrite, which is utilizable by plants under suitable conditions. The effect of pH is not the same as with ammonium salts. Acute injury arises only in acid solutions and is not influenced by carbohydrates. After absorption by the plant, nitrite is subject to reduction to NH_3, which must then be taken care of as in the case of plants originally supplied with ammonium salts. A definite distinction is made between ammonium nitrogen or nitrite nitrogen on the one hand and nitrate nitrogen on the other. The former cannot be stored as such (except for the storage of ammonium salts in the special types of plants already referred to) to any large extent, while the latter can often be accumulated in the plant in high concentration.

The general course of nitrogen metabolism is conceived by Engel according to the following scheme:

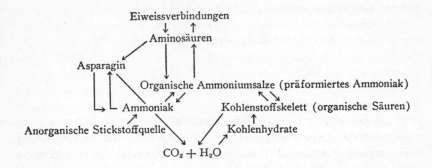

Tsung-Lê Loo (44, 45) compared the absorption of nitrogen from solutions of nitrates and of ammonium salts, using numerous culture solutions of different composition. Earlier conclusions on the influence of pH on the absorption of ammonia nitrogen were confirmed. In addition, certain of the experiments indicated that the total concentration of the nutrient solution determined whether ammonia or nitrate nitrogen was predominantly absorbed when both were present.

Naftel (54) conducted a series of studies on nitrogen absorption from a more practical point of view. Again it was found that the amount of nitrogen absorbed from ammonium salts increased as the pH of the solution increased. On the other hand, the highest absorption of nitrate occurred at pH 5.0, which is in accord with work by other investigators showing that nitrate absorption is favored by an acid reaction. Naftel observed that the growth and fruiting of cotton were at a maximum only when both ammonia and nitrate nitrogen were supplied. Ammonia nitrogen was absorbed in larger amount than nitrate nitrogen by the young seedlings, while at a later stage of growth nitrate was absorbed more readily. Similar results from experiments on oats and buckwheat are reported by the New Jersey Agricultural Experiment Station.

Beaumont (5) and his associates studied the nitrogen assimilation of tobacco plants in sterile and non-sterile water and sand cultures. Nitrates were found to be most readily assimilated, followed in order by urea, ammonia, asparagine, cystine. Most of the amino acids used were not assimilated. These investigators did not find any prevailing views entirely satisfactory in explaining the difference between nitrogen in the form of ammonium salts and of nitrates.

K. Pirschle (61) concludes that ammonium salts are equal to nitrates only in a limited pH range, 5 to 7. In the discussions of Mevius and Dikussar, in which the work of Pirschle is considered, attention is drawn to the importance of calcium, potassium, and magnesium in connection with comparisons of nitrate and ammonium salts. In the former case, the rapidly absorbable anion may accelerate the intake of cations. When nitrogen is present in the cation form, the absorption of calcium and other cations tends to be retarded and their concentrations in the culture solution become of special importance. Pirschle, in a second article, also emphasizes the importance of cation concentrations, and other factors which influence the intake of nitrogen. In his later work, with flowing culture solutions, he finds, as before, that it is only at a moderate acidity that ammonium nitrogen is of equal value to nitrate nitrogen. Maize, oats, wheat, peas, buckwheat, mustard, rice, and Tradescantia were studied. Pirschle stresses the complexity of relations between hydrogen ion concentration and other factors.

Allison (1) also has called attention to the suitability of ammonium salts as a source of nitrogen. He presents an extensive review (2) of the relation of forms of nitrogen utilized by the plant to the reaction of the soil medium.

Tiedjens and Robbins (74), in the most recently received contribution, report excellent success in using various ammonium salts as sources of nitrogen for tomato and other plants. Tomato plants assimilated (absorbed and synthesized) ammonia nitrogen most efficiently at an initial pH of 8. No toxicity was observed. This observation is not necessarily in conflict with others already cited, since the initial pH was subject to rapid decrease in the sand culture medium. Furthermore, the tomato plant was considered to have exceptional ability to metabolize rapidly absorbed ammonia nitrogen.

In an investigation of another type, already referred to, Jacques and Osterhout (35), and Cooper and Osterhout (19), as a result of their work on *Valonia macrophysa* conclude that ammonia penetrates into the plant cell in the form of undissociated molecules and that the pH of the culture medium is influential in determining the rate of penetration.

[Also compare Yamaguchi (78) on absorption of urea by maize under sterile conditions; Sakamura (67) on absorption of ammonia and nitrate by *Aspergillus oryzae;* and Urhan (76) on absorption of nitrogen by *Chlorella* and *Scenedesmus;* Ribbert (65), micro-injection experiments.]

In summarizing, we may conclude that nearly all of the recent research leads to essential agreement on several points. The reaction of the solution is a very important matter in connection with the use of ammonium salts, the rate of absorption of nitrogen increasing with increase of pH. Toxicity is more likely to occur with ammonium salts than with nitrates as a source of nitrogen if various factors, such as temperature, illumination, and pH of medium, are not properly adjusted. Most plants can easily store large amounts of nitrate without injury, but this is not in general true of nitrite or ammonium salts, except for the special case of "ammonia" plants. No doubt is expressed by any of the investigators that ammonium nitrogen may be an entirely suitable source of nitrogen, under favorable conditions, but apparently there is, in general, a greater range of safety in the use of nitrate nitrogen for the majority of agricultural plants studied. However, the consensus is that within the plant, ammonia nitrogen is formed as one of the stages of synthesis or breakdown of complex nitrogenous compounds.

Potassium.—Apart from certain definitely known órganic combinations, the functions of mineral elements in plant metabolism remain to a large degree obscure. Potassium is required by higher plants in relatively large amount, but indispensable organic combinations of potassium have not been discovered. Very frequently all, or nearly all, the potassium contained in plant tissues is easily soluble in water. There is, in fact, much reason to suppose that potassium exists in plant cells primarily in inorganic form. Researches on the functions of potassium are necessarily concerned with resultant effects of potassium deficiency on plant growth and metabolism. A number of papers describing researches of this type have lately appeared. The effects of potassium, nitrogen, and phosphate deficiencies on the respiration and assimilation rates in barley were investigated by Gregory and Richards (26). The method was to grow plants under definitely known nutritional conditions and then to remove leaves at various intervals of time and determine assimilation and respiration rates with the aid of a katharometer, as described earlier by Waller. The effects of potassium deficiency were, in several important respects, unlike those caused by deficiency of nitrogen or of phosphate. Under conditions of potassium deficiency, respiration rates were found to be supernormal and assimilation rates subnormal.

Sand culture experiments with tomato plants by Nightingale, Schermerhorn, and Robbins (58) revealed that striking modifications in the chemical constitution of the plant resulted from potassium deficiency. It was assumed that potassium was directly or indirectly essential for carbohydrate synthesis, yet in certain cases potassium deficiencies were associated with large accumulations of available carbohydrates in the plant tissues. In order to understand this it is essential to take into account also the nitrogen metabolism and the rôle of potassium therein. It is thought by the investigators cited above that accumulation of carbohydrates may be one result of a retardation of nitrate assimilation following a shortage of potassium. It was not a question of failure to translocate sugars or to digest starch, for these processes were found to proceed readily even in plants extremely low in potassium. In brief, potassium was considered to be probably essential to the following processes: carbon dioxide assimilation, reduction of nitrate, cell-division, synthesis of proteins of meristematic tissues. Potassium was easily translocated to regions of active cell-division, when necessary.

Jannsen and Bartholomew, also investigating the effects of potassium deficiencies on the growth of tomato plants, found that total and soluble nitrogen were much higher in low-potassium plants than in high-potassium plants. The mobility of potassium was demonstrated by microchemical studies. Most of the potassium in potassium-starved plants could be transferred to and localized in the meristematic tissues. It was concluded that potassium was essential to cell division. Bartholomew and Jannsen later studied the absorption of potassium by plants from culture solutions. Their results agree with those of several other investigators in indicating that very low concentrations of potassium maintained in a nutrient solution may suffice for the needs of the plant. Potassium taken up at early stages of plant growth may later be translocated and reutilized. This process is thought to be of great importance when plants are growing in soils incapable of supplying large amounts of potassium to crops over a long period.

Hartt made a series of studies on the potassium nutrition of sugar cane, and among other results she found that potassium-deficient plants had greater percentages of total sugars than did plants supplied with an adequate amount of potassium.

Davis grew young wheat plants under controlled conditions of nutrient medium (water cultures), light, and temperature. In this way experiments could be exactly duplicated. A deficiency of potassium was always associated with largely increased percentages of soluble sugar in all parts of the plant. It was evident that synthesis and translocation of sugars took place readily in these young plants, even when growth (dry weight yield) was definitely limited by lack of potassium.

James has discussed the physiological rôle of potassium on the basis of evidence obtained at the Rothamsted Experimental Station, using potato plants. The rate of formation of starch per unit of leaf area was increased by potash fertilization, especially when the sulphate form was employed. It was also thought probable, although not definitely proved, that translocation was accelerated by the same treatment. Theoretical consideration of possible mechanisms involved led to emphasis on the influence of potassium on the activity of diastatic enzymes. A general effect of potassium was the delaying of senescence. Tubbs re-investigated the old question of the relation between potassium and the mechanical strength of cereal straw. Barley plants were grown in sand cultures, with and without adequate supplies of potassium, phosphate, and nitrogen. The straw was subjected to specially devised crushing tests and was also examined microscopically. The conclusion was reached that potassium does have some rather direct relation to mechanical strength. In contrast to nitrogen and phosphate, potassium appeared to influence both the quality and the amount of tissues lending mechanical strength to the plant. The lignification of parenchyma tissue in the potassium-deficient plants was less than normal.

In reflecting on the discussions of the rôle of potassium in plant growth, one is left in a more or less puzzled state of mind. Potassium is said to be essential to a great variety of processes, but there seems to exist little or no evidence that can be interpreted as directly indicating the nature of the mechanism by which potassium functions. Certain types of data lead to the view that potassium has a specific rôle in carbon assimilation, translocation of sugars, and starch formation. Yet young plants may suffer an inhibition of growth as a result

MINERAL NUTRITION OF PLANTS

of potassium deficiency and at the same time accumulate and translocate large amounts of sugar or starch. The difficulty is to allocate the functions of potassium to specific steps in the whole chain of metabolic processes. The actual measurements of the investigator are concerned only with resultant effects of an exceedingly complex series of processes, disturbance of any one of which may change the end condition of the plant, with respect to content of carbohydrates or potentialities of carbohydrate metabolism. Thus if deficiency of potassium at certain stages of growth can limit protein formation and cell-division to a greater extent than photosynthesis or condensation of sugars, sugars or starch may accumulate in plant tissues in larger concentration than usual. This, of course, does not prove that a certain unknown quantity of potassium is not essential to photosynthesis or to condensation and translocation of sugars. On the other hand, if deficiency of potassium at some stage of plant growth results in a lowered carbohydrate content in the tissues, or in a decrease in rate of carbon assimilation, these observations in themselves may prove only that some part of the machinery has broken down, the normal operation of the whole system being essential to the continued synthesis of carbohydrates. Recent literature gives the impression that increasing attention is being devoted to nitrogen metabolism and to general processes of cell-division as influenced directly or indirectly by potassium.

Phosphorus.—Certain functions of phosphorus in plant growth are easily ascribable to the formation of essential organic compounds containing phosphorus. Apparently phosphate may also influence plant metabolism in less obvious ways. Kraybill, in a preliminary paper, discusses some of the effects produced by limiting the supply of phosphate for the tomato plant. In comparison with plants grown in full nutrient solution, the low-phosphorus plants were found to be high in reducing sugars, sucrose, total nitrogen, ammonia nitrogen, ether-soluble nitrogen, nitrate nitrogen, total amino nitrogen, and amid nitrogen, and lower in starch. Phosphorus seemed to be essential to the utilization of nitrogen in the form of proteins. There were certain striking differences between nitrogen-deficient and phosphate-deficient plants in general appearance and in chemical composition, although in certain other respects there was a similarity between the two types of plants.

A number of suggestive conclusions were reached by Eckerson, also working with tomato plants. Phosphate deficiency was associated with (*a*) rapid decrease in reducase activity (an abundance of nitrate was present but was not usable by the plant); (*b*) a breakdown of complex phosphatides after soluble phosphorus compounds had disappeared. As the inorganic phosphate was used up, the juice of the plants lost almost all power to reduce nitrates. Starch increased at first, but later decreased. Sucrose and reducing sugars continued to increase, as in the experiments of Kraybill (42). Anatomical changes in the plant were also observed. These included increased cell-wall thickening and decrease of rate of cell-division. Cockefair (16) suggests that carbohydrate-phosphate esters serve the same purpose in higher green plants as in muscular contraction and yeast fermentation. The evidence presented is very limited.

The influence of phosphate concentration in culture solutions on phosphate absorption by plants was investigated by Tidmore. In an attempt to maintain desired low concentrations of PO_4 fairly constant during the growth of the plant, larger culture vessels were used than any heretofore employed, each vessel being of 1,000-liter capacity. Maximum growth of corn, sorghum, and tomatoes was obtained at 0.5 p.p.m. PO_4 concentration. Growth of corn and sorghum was good even at 0.2 p.p.m. concentration. These are very low concentrations, but the soil chemist is interested in the fact that good growth of crops may be obtained in some soils even when the soil solution (displacement method) contains only a few hundredths of a part per million of phosphate, much less than an adequate concentration in an artificial culture solution. Explanations of the apparent anomaly have been advanced, but do not fall within the scope of the present review. Much work is being carried on in Germany by Von Wrangell and her associates on the absorption of phosphate and potassium from dilute artificial culture solutions and from soil media.

With reference to the functions of phosphate in plant growth as disclosed by the investigations reviewed, apparently some of the effects of phosphate deficiency are similar to those of potassium deficiency. In both cases, there may be found, at some stages of plant growth, accumulation of excess sugars and soluble nitrogen compounds. Nitrate reduction may be more or less retarded as a consequence of either deficiency. Cell-division may not proceed normally and, at certain stages of plant growth, the formation of new tissues may be restricted to a greater degree than photosynthesis and translocation of sugars.

Other elements and miscellaneous.—For a long time the importance of silica in plant growth has been discussed, especially in connection with the phosphate nutrition of the plant. A question of soil and plant interrelations is involved which it is not feasible to consider here, but attention may be called to a physiological study by Mengdehl (50) dealing with the influence of colloidal silica on the absorption of various nutrient elements from culture solutions. Silica was rapidly absorbed by wheat, barley, maize, peas, etc. In fact, more silica than phosphate was taken up in some cases. The absorption of other elements was influenced by the presence of silica, but it was decided that none of the theories concerning the rôle of silica satisfactorily explained the experimental data.

Nightingale (57) and his associates depict the nature of the changes occurring in the tomato plant as calcium becomes seriously deficient. Calcium-deficient plants were practically unable to absorb or assimilate nitrates, although they could absorb calcium immediately. A few hours after absorption of calcium, there was absorption and assimilation of nitrates. Calcium-deficient plants accumulated carbohydrates in large quantities. Nearly all the calcium was insoluble in water and was re-utilized very slowly.

Chibnall and Channon (13), in continuing previous researches, have given further attention to the calcium phosphatides of leaf cytoplasm. The question is raised whether these phosphatides may not play a vital rôle in plant metabolism, as lecithin does in the animal. Apparently, an iron phosphatid compound is also present in the ether-soluble fraction of the leaf cytoplasm. The conclusion of Kostytschew and Berg (41) that all calcium in the plant is present in inorganic form is not confirmed.

Sorokin and Sommer (70), and Day (22), have published researches bearing on the function of calcium in plant growth as evidenced by anatomical observations on pea roots. The first-named investigators concluded that calcium was a constituent of the protoplast essential for normal mitotic division in the meristematic region. Day did not find evidence for this function of calcium, but the results of both investigations agree in failing to show separation of cell walls as a result of calcium deficiency, as might have been expected according to certain views often held with regard to calcium pectate.

The transport of nitrogen, phosphorus, potassium, and calcium through the plant involves problems of plant anatomy not appropriate for discussion in this chapter, but it is desirable to call attention to the extensive investigations of Mason and Maskell (49). They suggest .that the re-export toward the roots of certain elements, via the phloem, may have a bearing on the rate of absorption of such elements by root cells [compare James (37) on potassium]. The relation, or lack of relation, between transpiration and accumulation of mineral elements, is also thought to be involved.

Among recent general reviews pertaining to the mineral nutrition of plants is one by Thomas (72) on the "feeding power" of plants, with the citation of over 200 papers. A *"Handbuch der Pflanzenernährung und Düngerlehre"* appeared in 1931 with sections on the mineral nutrition of plants by Baresch and by Von Wrangell.

LITERATURE CITED

1. ALLISON, F. E., *J. Amer. Soc. Agron.,* **23**, 878 (1931)
2. ALLISON, F. E., *Quart. Rev. Biol.,* **6**, 313 (1931)
3. BARTHOLOMEW, R. P., AND JANNSEN, G., *Arkansas Agr. Exp. Sta. Bull.,* **265** (1931)
4. BERTRAND, G., AND MOKRAGNATZ, M., *Bull. soc. chim.,* **47**, 326 (1930)
5. BEAUMONT, A. B., LARSINOS, G. J., PIEKENBROCK, P., AND NELSON, P. R., *J. Agr. Res.,* **43**, 559 (1931)
6. BLINKS, L. R., AND JACQUES, A. G., *J. Gen. Physiol.,* **13**, 733 (1930)
7. BRIGGS, G. E., *Proc. Roy. Soc. (London), B,* **107**, 248 (1930)
8. BROOKS, S. C., *Protoplasma,* **8**, 389 (1929)
9. BROOKS, S. C., *Proc. Soc. Exptl. Biol. Med.,* **27**, 409 (1930)
10. BROOKS, S. C., *Science,* **73**, 589 (1931)
11. BRYAN, O. C., *J. Amer. Soc. Agron.,* **21**, 923 (1929)
12. BURK, D., AND LINEWEAVER, H., *Arch. Microbiol.,* **2**, 155 (1931)
13. CHIBNALL, A. C., AND CHANNON, H. J., *Biochem. J.,* **23**, 176 (1929)
14. CHIBNALL, A. C., AND PRYDE, J., *Ann. Rep. Chem. Soc. (London),* **27**, 229 (1930)
15. CLARK, N. A., AND FLY, C. L., *Plant Physiol.,* **2**, 241 (1930)
16. COCKEFAIR, E. A., *Am. J. Bot.,* **18**, 582 (1931)
17. COLLANDER, RUNAR, *Acta Botanica Fennica,* **6**, 3 (1930)
18. COOPER, W. C., JR., DORCAS, M. J., AND OSTERHOUT, W. J. V., *J. Gen. Physiol.,* **12**, 427 (1929)
19. COOPER, W. C., JR., AND OSTERHOUT, W. J. V., *J. Gen. Physiol.,* **14**, 117 (1930)
20. CROWTHER, E. M., *Rep. Prog. App. Chem.,* **14**, 511 (1930)
21. DAVIS, A. R., *Abst. Amer. Soc. Plant Physiol.,* Pasadena (1931)
22. DAY, D., *Plant Physiol.,* **4**, 493 (1929)
23. EATON, F. M., *Phytopathol.,* **20**, 967 (1930)
24. ECKERSON, S. H., *Cont. Boyce-Thompson Inst.,* **3**, 197 (1931)
25. ENGEL, H., *Planta,* **7**, 133 (1929)
26. GREGORY, F. G., AND RICHARDS, F. J., *Ann. Bot.,* **43**, 119 (1929)

27. HAAS, A. R. C., AND KLOTZ, L. J., *Hilgardia,* **5,** 175 (1931)
28. HAAS, A. R. C., AND KLOTZ, L. J., *Hilgardia,* **5,** 511 (1931)
29. *"Handbuch der Pflanzenernährung,und Düngerlehre,"* **1,** .. (Julius Springer, Berlin, 1931)
30. HARTT, C. E., *Bot. Gaz.,* **88,** 229 (1929)
31. HILL, A. V., *Trans. Faraday Soc.,* **26,** 667 (1930)
32. HOAGLAND, D. R., *Contributions to Marine Biology,* Stanford University Press, Stanford Unversity, California, p. 131 (1930)
33. HOAGLAND, D. R., *Plant Physiol.,* **6,** 373 (1931)
34. HOPKINS, E. F., *Science,* **74,** 551 (1931)
35. JACQUES, A. G., AND OSTERHOUT, W. J. V., *J. Gen. Physiol.,* **14,** 301 (1930)
36. JAMES, W. O., *Ann. Bot.,* **44,** 173 (1930)
37. JAMES, W. O., *Ann. Bot.,* **45,** 425 (1931)
38. JANNSEN, G., AND BARTHOLOMEW, R. P., *J. Agr. Res.,* **38,** 447 (1929)
39. JANNSEN, G., AND BARTHOLOMEW, R. P., *J. Agr. Res.,* **40,** 243 (1930)
40. JOHNSTON, E. S., AND FISHER, P. L., *Plant Physiol.,* **3,** 387 (1930)
41. KOSTYTSCHEW, S., AND BERG, V., *Planta,* **8,** 55 (1929)
42. KRAYBILL, H. R., *J. Ind. and Eng. Chem.,* **22,** 275 (1930)
43. LIPMAN, C. B., AND MACKINNEY, G., *Plant Physiol.,* **6,** 593 (1931)
44. LOO, TSUNG-LE, *Bull. Dept. Biol. (College Sci., Sun Yatsen Univ.),* **10,** 1 (1931)
45. LOO, TSUNG-LE, *J. Faculty Agr. (Hokkaido Imp. Univ.),* **30,** 1 (1931)
46. MCHARGUE, J. S., AND CALFEE, R. K., *Bot. Gaz.,* **91,** 183 (1931)
47. MCHARGUE, J. S., AND CALFEE, R. K., *Plant Physiol.,* **6,** 559 (1931)
48. MCMURTREY, J. E., JR., *J. Agr. Res.,* **38,** 371 (1929)
49. MASON, T. G., AND MASKELL, E. J., *Ann. Bot.,* **45,** 125 (1931). (Also series of articles on nitrogen in same journal.)
50. MENGDEHL, H., *Jahrb. wiss. Bot.,* **75,** 252 (1931)
51. MEVIUS, W., AND DIKUSSAR, I., *Jahrb. wiss. Bot.,* **73,** 633 (1930)
52. MEVIUS, W., AND ENGEL, H., *Planta,* **9,** 1 (1929)
53. MOKRAGNATZ, M., *Bull. soc. chim. biol.,* **13,** 61 (1931)
54. NAFTEL, J. A., *J. Amer. Soc. Agron.,* **23,** 141 (1931)
55. NEAL, W. M., BECKER, R. B., AND SHEALY, A. L., *Science,* **74,** 418 (1931)
56. *New Jersey Agr. Exp. Sta., 50th Annual Report,* p. 44 (1929)
57. NIGHTINGALE, G. T., ADDOMS, R. M., ROBBINS, W. R., AND SCHERMERHORN, L. G., *Plant Physiol.,* **6,** 605 (1931)
58. NIGHTINGALE, G. T., SCHERMERHORN, L. G., AND ROBBINS, W. W., *New Jersey Agr. Exp. Sta. Bull.,* **499** (1930)
59. OSTERHOUT, W. J. V., *J. Gen. Physiol.,* **14,** 285 (1930)
60. OSTERHOUT, W. J. V., AND DORCAS, M. J., *J. Gen. Physiol.,* **7,** 633 (1925)
61. PIRSCHLE, K., *Planta,* **9,** 84 (1929)
62. PIRSCHLE, K., *Z. Pflanzenernährung, Düngung, Bodenkunde,* **A 22,** 51 (1931)
63. PIRSCHLE, K., AND MENGDEHL, H., *Jahrb. wiss. Bot.,* **74,** 297 (1931)
64. PRIANISCHNIKOV, D. N., *Deut. Ges. Studium Osteuropas,* Ost-Europa-Verlag, Berlin (1929)
65. RIBBERT, A., *Planta,* **12,** 603 (1931)
66. RUHLAND, W., AND WETZEL, K., *Planta,* **1,** 558 (1926)

67. SAKAMURA, T., *Planta, 2,* 765 (1930)
68. SMITH, W. S. (quoted by Sommer)
69. SOMMER, A. L., *Plant Physiol.,* 6, 339 (1931)
70. SOROKIN, H., AND SOMMER, A. L., *Am. J. Bot.,* 16, 23 (1929)
71. STEWARD, F. C., *Brit. Assoc. Adv. Sci. (London), Sec. K* (1931). (Further report in press, *Protoplasma*)
72. THOMAS, W., *Plant Physiol.,* 5, 443 (1930)
73. TIDMORE, J. W., *Soil Sci.,* 30, 13 (1930)
74. TIEDJENS, V. A., AND ROBBINS, W. R., *New Jersey Agr. Exp. Sta. Bull.,* 526 (1931)
75. TUBBS, R., *Ann. Bot.,* 44, 147 (1930)
76. URHAN, O., *Jahrb. wiss. Bot.,* 75, 1 (1931)
77. VON WRANGELL, *Handb. Pflanzenernähr. u. Düngerlehre,* 1, 635 (1931)
78. YAMAGUCHI, S., *J. Faculty Sci. (Hokkaido Imp. Univ.),* 1, 37 (1930)
79. ZSCHEILE, F. P., *Protoplasma,* 11, 481 (1930)

UNIVERSITY OF CALIFORNIA
BERKELEY, CALIFORNIA

THE CHEMISTRY OF THE BACTERIA*

By M. Stephenson

Biochemical Laboratory, University of Cambridge
Cambridge, England

Owing to the large number of papers published it has not been possible to deal with all aspects of the subject in the current *Review*. It is hoped to deal in the next issue with the sections unavoidably omitted in this.

Fermentation

The acetic bacteria are at present providing material for controversy, and are therefore in little danger of neglect. In order to make the present position clear it is necessary to allude to the earliest contribution to the discussion (Neuberg and Windisch), in which it was shown that three strains of acetic bacteria (*Bact. ascendens, Bact. pasteurianum,* and *Bact. xylinum*) are capable of dismuting acetaldehyde anaerobically to equimolecular proportions of ethyl alcohol and acetic acid. It was hence inferred that the aerobic oxidation of ethyl alcohol to acetic acid, as it occurs in the vinegar industry, is in reality two processes, an aerobic oxidation of ethyl alcohol to acetaldehyde, followed by a dismutation of the latter to equimolecular proportions of acetic acid and ethyl alcohol, the latter again becoming oxidised to acetaldehyde, and so on till the process is complete. This view was challenged (Wieland and Bertho) on the ground that, though a dismutation of acetaldehyde by these organisms can and does actually occur, this process is not operative to any important extent in the aerobic production of vinegar (by *Bact. orleanense*); it was shown that, though an anaerobic dismutation of acetaldehyde occurs under the influence of this organism, the direct aerobic oxidation of acetaldehyde to acetic acid occurs at about forty times the rate, hence aerobically dismutation can play only an insignificant part as compared with direct oxidation. The matter does not rest here, however; according to Simon (1930) the relative rates of dismutation and oxidation depend somewhat on reaction. The earlier work, on which the dismutation theory was based, was carried out in the presence of excess of calcium carbonate (pH 8.1) whilst the later

* Received January 12, 1932.

work was done at a pH of 5.5. At the more acid reaction dismutation was at a minimum (1.2 to 3 per cent of theory), whilst at the alkaline reaction alcohol was produced from acetaldehyde in amounts equal to 8 to 10 per cent of theory. Hence it was concluded that, though at neutrality dismutation may play a significant part in acetic acid production in the more acid conditions pertaining in the industry, this is probably negligible, and direct oxidation is the significant course of reaction. In a more recent contribution from the opposing school (Bertho and Basu) the authors were unable to confirm the important effect attributed to change in pH and find no significant increase in the dismutation of acetaldehyde at neutral over acid values of pH.

Independent observations from a third school of workers offer a somewhat different interpretation of the observations under discussion (Tamiya and Tanaka; Tanaka). These observers point out *inter alia* that the dismutation of acetaldehyde is in reality a special case of dehydrogenation where acetaldehyde is the hydrogen acceptor for the aldehyde hydrate, and is strictly parallel to other dehydrogenations where other hydrogen acceptors, such as methylene blue or quinone, are employed. All these three dehydrogenations (occurring under the influence of the acetic bacteria) differ from oxidations where oxygen is the hydrogen acceptor in not being affected by low concentrations of cyanide or by carbon monoxide or toluene. Aerobic oxidations of both ethyl alcohol and acetaldehyde by the acetic bacteria are powerfully inhibited by carbon monoxide in the dark, the effect being reversed on exposure to light and also by toluene treatment. (The cyanide effect is masked owing to its interaction with acetaldehyde.) These facts suggest that a second mechanism is present in the aerobic oxidations which is absent in the other dehydrogenase systems, including the mutase. The behaviour with carbon monoxide and toluene is precisely analogous to that of the cytochrome and indophenol oxidase (*Atmungsferment*) system, and points to the conclusion (on other grounds highly probable) that this or something similar is operative in *Bact. pasteurianum* and distinguishes the oxidising mechanism from the mutase system. Tanaka confirms Simon's observation that acetone treatment completely inhibits the aerobic oxidation of acetaldehyde but does not affect the mutase to a comparable extent. According to Tanaka this does not imply a difference between a dehydrogenase and a mutase, but rather points to a susceptibility towards acetone on the part of the cytochrome-oxidase part of the system.

As a valuable by-product of the acetic controversy an interesting observation of Simon must be noted. He showed that both *Bact. pasteurianum* and *acetobacter suboxydans,* when acting in heavy suspensions on glucose anaerobically, effect a fermentation resembling an alcoholic fermentation in that ethyl alcohol and carbon dioxide are produced in roughly equimolecular proportions (Table I).

TABLE I

FERMENTATION OF GLUCOSE BY *Bact. pasterianum* AND *Acetobacter suboxydans*

Organism	Percentage of Sugar Fermented	Percentage of Sugar Added Carbon Dioxide	Alcohol
Acetobacter suboxydans	Not stated	18.4	19.17
Acetobacter suboxydans	24.5	15.5	23.7
Bact. pasteurianum	Not stated	15.1	19.7
Bact. pasteurianum	14	14.7	11.77

The data at present to hand are insufficient to tell us whether the fermentation resembles a yeast alcoholic fermentation in the course of the hexose breakdown as well as in the nature and proportion of the end products. Simon has shown that the following enzymes are present in dried preparations of his organisms: carboxylase, keto-aldehyde mutase (glyoxalase), glycolase (methyl glyoxal was produced in about 5 per cent yield from magnesium hexose diphosphate by the Neuberg-Kobel method), and aldehyde mutase. It thus appears that the strains of acetic bacteria studied possess an outfit of enzymes capable of producing a dismutation of hexose on the same lines as that occurring with yeast. Glyoxalase, on the other hand, may result in some part of the sugar molecule stabilizing itself as lactic acid. This last, together with traces of formic acid, has actually been reported from the action of *Bact. xylinum* on sugar (Haehn and Engel, 1929). In the presence of formic dehydrogenase and in the absence of the enzyme producing *molecular* hydrogen from formic acid (Stickland) the hexose molecule might be dismuted thus:

$$C_6H_{12}O_6 \rightarrow 2\,C_3H_6O_3 \rightarrow H \cdot COOH + CH_3CHO \rightarrow C_2H_5OH + CO_2$$

instead of by the course usually postulated for yeast fermentation, viz.:

$$C_6H_{12}O_6 \xrightarrow{\quad\quad} 2\,C_3H_6O_3 \xrightarrow{(+\,2O\,-\,2H_2O)} 2\,CH_3 \cdot CO \cdot COOH \xrightarrow{(+\,2H_2)}$$

$$\xrightarrow{\quad\quad} 2\,C_2H_5OH + 2CO_2$$

As pointed out by Kostytschew, Gwaladse, and Eliasberg, we are probably wrong in attributing the rôle of intermediary metabolites of fermentation to isolatable substances such as methyl glyoxal or pyruvic or formic acids—substances having double bonds. These appear only when the molecule is stabilised and inactive; the real intermediaries are probably substances with free valencies instead of double bonds. Nevertheless the stabilised products are an indication of the path along which the fermentation has traveled, and a fermentation in which formic and lactic acids occur along with alcohol and carbon dioxide has presumably arrived by a different route from one in which these products are invariably absent.

A very valuable and important contribution to the chemistry of the acetic bacteria, and one which fills a gap, must now come under consideration (Hermann and Neuschul). The gap in question has yawned since the classical work of Bertrand on the sorbose bacillus (1904). This organism, it will be remembered, belongs to the acetic bacteria and, in common with them, oxidises aldehydic sugars to acids, but is distinguished by its power of oxidising two secondary alcoholic groups (when, and only when, these are in the adjacent position) to the corresponding ketone: thus for example *l-arabitol, d-sorbitol,* and *l-mannitol* are oxidised to arabinulose, sorbose, and fructose, respectively, whilst xylitol and dulcitol are not attacked. In the present work fourteen well-differentiated strains of acetic bacteria were studied. All are characterised by the power to oxidise ethyl and propyl alcohol to acetic and propionic acids; all, with one exception *(Bact. ascendens)*, oxidise glucose to gluconic acid; all, with three exceptions, oxidise arabinose and galactose to arabonic and galactonic acids. In other respects the group falls quite sharply into two divisions, the ketogenic and the aketogenic. Members of the former, like the sorbose bacillus, are able to oxidise secondary alcohols, with adjacent OH groups, to ketones, bringing about the following oxidations: glycerol to dihydroxyacetone, erythritol to erythrulose, mannitol to levulose, sorbitol to sorbose, gluconic acid to 5-ketogluconic acid. The production of a substance reducing Fehling's solution on a glycerol medium, i.e., formation of dihydroxyacetone, is a convenient test for distinguishing the members of this class. In the aketogenic division, the power of oxidising secondary alcoholic groups is absent. The strains studied are classified as follows:

Ketogenic: *Bact. gluconicum, xylinum, xylinoides, orleanense, aceti*
(Hansen).

Aketogenic: *Bact. aceti* (Henneberg), *pasteurianum, acetorum, rancens, ascendens, vini acetati Kützingianum, ascendens* (Henneberg).

Important information on the course of hexose breakdown by *Bact. coli* is supplied by data on the fermentation of dihydroxyacetone and glyceraldehyde (Virtanen and Peltola; Virtanen, Karström, and Turpeinen). Using heavy suspensions of bacteria, dihydroxyacetone is decomposed mainly according to the equations:

$$2\,C_3H_6O_3 + H_2O = C_3H_8O_3 + (C_3H_6O_4{}^{*})$$
$$C_3H_6O_4 \quad = CH_3COOH + H \cdot COOH$$
$$H \cdot COOH = CO_2 + H_2.$$

It will be noticed that the first stage is a Cannizzaro reaction in which one molecule of dihydroxyacetone is reduced to glycerol and the other oxidised to acetic and formic acids. Glyceric acid in similar conditions is decomposed to equimolecular parts of acetic and formic acids.

The relative rates of these reactions are puzzling; on the one hand, the rate of fermentation of glyceric acid is less than that of dihydroxyacetone, which is evidence against the glyceric aldehyde acting as an intermediary. On the other hand, relative rates of fermentation seem to be somewhat fluctuating; those of the fermentation of dihydroxyacetone and of glucose were found to depend on the history of the organism. When the bacteria used for the fermentation were grown on broth or sugar broth, the rate of glucose fermentation was 1.6 times that of the dihydroxyacetone. If 0.22 per cent of the latter compound were introduced into the broth on which the organisms were grown, the subsequent rates of fermentation of glucose and dihydroxyacetone were reversed and the latter was then fermented at twice the rate of the former. Besides the fermentation products already mentioned dihydroxyacetone yielded (contrary to earlier observations) varying amounts of succinic acid up to 5 per cent, which, considering that half the substrate was playing the part of hydrogen acceptor, is equivalent to 10 per cent in the case of a glucose fermentation; small amounts of ethyl alcohol (1 to 3 per cent) were also formed from both trioses but no lactic acid.

* Constitution uncertain.

No scheme of fermentation of hexose by *Bact. coli* seems quite to fit the new data. Possibly glucose breaks down into two triose molecules, one of which is an active form of the common enolic form of both glyceric aldehyde and dihydroxyacetone, and this gives acetic and formic acids with glycerol or some other reduction product. The other triose may be the active form of methyl glyoxal, which is known to break down quantitatively to lactic acid under the influence of glyoxalase present in *Bact. coli* and many other bacteria. The origin of succinic acid still awaits a satisfactory explanation; the idea put forward by several workers and supported by a certain amount of evidence, that it arises from a hexose by a split into a 4- and a 2-carbon compound, is somewhat weakened by its appearance in the fermentation of a 3-carbon compound, though the theory that two molecules of the latter may undergo a preliminary combination may still be resorted to.

The rate of fermentation of both glucose and dihydroxyacetone was shown to be much increased (82 and 67 per cent, respectively) by phosphate (0.5 to 1 per cent P_2O_5). The mechanism of this catalysis awaits further work.

The rôle of phosphate in lactic fermentations by *Bact. casei* has now been further elucidated (Virtanen and Tikka). It appears that, whereas live cultures of the organism change glucose to lactic acid quantitatively (glucose → hexose monophosphoric ester ["Robison" ester] → lactic acid [100 per cent]), with dried preparations of the organism 50 per cent only of lactic acid is obtained, the remaining 50 per cent being found as phosphoric esters. These may be separated by means of the barium salts into two approximately equal fractions. The one easily soluble barium salt precipitated by acetone contains one phosphorus atom and two carboxyl groups to every twelve carbon atoms and corresponds with the formula

$$C_{12}H_{19}O_{16}PBa_2 \; ([\alpha]_D = -8°)$$

The second barium salt is sparingly soluble in water; the analyses point to the relation $C_6/P/Ba = 1/1/1$. This ester does not reduce Fehling's solution and gives no reducing substance on boiling with acid.

If the action of the dried bacteria is interrupted about half-way to completion, a hexose monophosphoric ester identical with the "Robison" ester can be isolated; as the fermentation is completed this ester disappears with the formation of lactic acid and the two new esters. The following scheme for the fermentation by living and dried bacteria, respectively, is put forth.

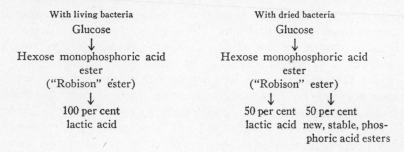

A highly important contribution to fermentation chemistry is made in the study of a new type of fermenting organism *Termobacterium mobile* (Kluyver and Hoppenbrouwers), a rare organism found chiefly in the agava juice of Mexico.

Hitherto all fermenting bacteria have fallen into one of the four classes, viz., lactic fermenters, butyric and butyl alcohol fermenters, propionic acid fermenters, and the *colon-aerogenes* group (mixed fermenters). We have now an example of a new class which ferments sugars in anaerobic conditions almost quantitatively to ethyl alcohol and carbon dioxide; this occurs equally on a beer wort or on a mineral medium (Table II).

TABLE II

PRODUCTS OF THE FERMENTATION OF GLUCOSE BY *Termobacterium mobile*
(IN PERCENTAGE OF GLUCOSE FERMENTED)

Medium	Carbon Dioxide	Ethyl Alcohol	Lactic Acid	Total
Beer wort	45.5	45.7	7.2	98.4
Mineral medium	45.6	41.1	5.8	92.5

Of the eleven sugars tested only glucose, fructose, and sucrose were fermented. It is remarkable that the closely related mannose was unattacked, a fact which, coupled with the ease with which the other two monoses are fermented, offers a method for the quantitative estimation of these three sugars in the presence of each other. It is also noteworthy that in aerobic conditions the yield of ethyl alcohol was much decreased, the exact significance of which fact is not yet clear.

HYDROGENASE

The existence of an enzyme activating molecular hydrogen has been inherently probable since the discovery of bacteria living by the oxidation of hydrogen gas. Recently it was shown (Tausz and Donath) that a culture of *Bact. aliphaticum liquefaciens* reduces methylene blue when a stream of hydrogen is led through the apparatus. The existence of a well-defined enzyme occurring in several members of the *coli-typhosus* group has now been demonstrated and its kinetics studied; in accordance with current nomenclature this enzyme is called *hydrogenase* [Stephenson and Stickland (1)]. By means of hydrogenase, bacterial cultures in which it is present reduce nitrate, fumarate, methylene blue, and oxygen by means of gaseous hydrogen.

A case of special interest is the action of hydrogenase in a sulphate-reducing organism of the usual type; this association of enzymes results in the reduction of sulphate quantitatively to sulphide by gaseous hydrogen [Stephenson and Stickland (2)]; sulphite and thiosulphate are also reduced by this organism.

The existence of hydrogenase now alters our conception of the behaviour of hydrogen in fermentation equilibria; whereas formerly it was regarded as an inactive stable end product, the possibility of its playing a part as a reducing agent must now be reckoned with.

An interesting instance is reported where the end products of a fermentation are influenced by the gaseous environment (Eliasberg). Butyric fermentations carried out under a pressure of hydrogen were found to give an excess of reduction products as compared with normal anaerobic conditions. Thus:

TABLE III

INFLUENCE OF GASEOUS ENVIRONMENT ON BUTYRIC FERMENTATIONS

	Butyric Acid *gm.*	Butyl Alcohol *mg.*	Butyl Alcohol per 1,000 parts of Butyric Acid
H_2 pressure			
0 atm.	1.62	12	0.7
100 atm.	0.65	380	58
0 atm.	1.53	15	1.0
80 atm.	0.75	400	53
N_2 pressure			
0 atm.	1.05	15	1
85 atm.	0.73	120	16
0 atm.	2.51	20	0.8
90 atm.	0.78	115	15

The author attributes the phenomenon to the influence of high gas pressure on the organism and notes a similar though less pronounced effect of high nitrogen pressures. It seems, however, also possible that the actual utilisation of hydrogen may be due to the presence of hydrogenase.

Methane Fermentation

An important contribution to the subject of methane fermentation (Fischer, Lieske, and Winzer) is the demonstration that in mud cultures carbon monoxide may be quantitatively reduced by hydrogen thus:

$$CO + 3H_2 = CH_4 + H_2O$$

The reaction is accelerated by mud, which may be replaced by dilute agar (0.01 per cent) or by freshly precipitated iron or aluminium hydroxide. The authors make no claim that their culture is pure and consider that it is similar to, or identical with, that used by Sohngen in his well-known work on the production of methane from fatty acids.

Another study of methane production from fatty acids by mixed cultures from sewage sludge (Neave and Buswell) follows closely the earlier work of Sohngen. The authors find that acetic, propionic, n-butyric, and n-valeric acid are quantitatively decomposed to methane and carbon dioxide according to the following general equation:

$$C_nH_{2n}O_2 + \frac{n-2}{2} H_2O = \frac{n+2}{4} CO_2 + \frac{3n-2}{4} CH_4$$

e.g.,

$$4 C_3H_6O_2 + 2 H_2O = 5 CO_2 + 7 CH_4.$$

Thus in the fatty acids above acetic the utilisation of water is involved in the decomposition of the fatty acid and is presumably accompanied by an intramolecular rearrangement before the decarboxylation occurs.

Factors Influencing Enzyme Production

It seems that the fact must now be faced that bacterial species are not constant in regard to their enzymic content but vary sharply according to their nutritional environment.

Working on the sugar-splitting enzymes Karström has established the fact that certain of these are present in demonstrable amount only if the organism has been grown in the presence of its specific substrate. For example, a xylose fermenting strain of *Bact. aerogenes* was grown on whey, and the organisms were centrifuged and washed and suspended in 0.8 per cent xylose in the presence of chalk. No sign of fermentation had occurred in fifteen hours. A source of nitrogen was then added to the tube (yeast water or ammonium sulphate), whereupon fermentation occurred two hours later. If, on the other hand, the organism was grown in xylose broth, and treated as before, fermentation set in immediately. It thus appears that certain sugar-splitting enzymes are not a permanent part of the cell outfit, but appear only when the cell is grown in the presence of the specific substrates; for these the term "adaptive" is suggested by the author. Some enzymes, on the other hand, are developed irrespective of the media upon which the organism is grown; these are termed "constitutive." Table IV below shows that for the pentose fermenter *Betacoccus arabinosaceus,* lactase, galactase, arabinase are adaptive, whilst glucase and sucrase·are constitutive; the position of maltase is doubtful. Tables V and VI show that, for *Bact. coli,* glucase and sucrase are constitutive, xylase and arabinase are adaptive, whilst maltase and lactase are again doubtful.

TABLE IV*

FERMENTATION BY *Betacoccus arabinosaceus*

Grown in	Sugars Subsequently Fermented							
	Glucose	Fructose	Mannose	Galactose	Arabinose	Sucrose	Maltose	Lactose
Glucose (2 per cent)...........	+	+	+	0	0	0	0	0
Sucrose (2 per cent)...........	+	+	—	0	0	+	0	0
Maltose (2 per cent)...........	+	+	—	0	0	+	+	0
Lactose (1 per cent)...........	+	+	—	+	0	+	0	+
Galactose (0.8 per cent).......	+	+	—	+	0	+	0	0
Arabinose (0.8 per cent)......	+	+	+	—	+	—	—	—
Carbohydrate, free medium.....	+	+	+	—	—	+	+	0

* 0 = not fermented; — = absence of data.

The variation in enzyme content has a quantitative as well as a qualitative aspect. Thus if the sucrase activity of *Bact. coli* (in which this enzyme is "constitutive") is measured, it is found to vary widely according to the medium on which the organism was grown (see Table VII).

TABLE V*

FERMENTATION BY *Bact. coli*

Grown in	Sugars Subsequently Fermented				
	Glucose	Sucrose	Raffinose	Maltose	Lactose
Sucrose (3 per cent)............	+	+	0	0	0
Maltose (1 per cent)............	+	+	—	+	0
Lactose (1 per cent)...........	—	0	—	+	+

* 0 = not fermented; — = absence of data.

TABLE VI*

FERMENTATION BY *Bact. coli*

Grown in	Sugars Subsequently Fermented			
	Xylose	Arabinose	Rhamnose	Glucose
Arabinose (0.5 per cent).......	0	+	0	+
Xylose (0.5 per cent)..........	+	0	0	+

* 0 = not fermented; — = absence of data.

TABLE VII

PRODUCTION OF SUCRASE BY *Bact. coli*

Grown in	Sucrase Content of Bacteria (IF)*
Sucrose	376
Maltose	28.6
Glucose	12.4
Lactose	39
Sugar-free medium	27.2

$$* IF = \text{inverting power} = \frac{K \times \text{g. sucrose}}{\text{g. enzyme prep.}}$$

NITROGEN FIXATION

This subject has recently benefited by a notable advance in technique. If a growing culture of *azotobacter* is estimated (*a*) in dry weight, (*b*) by counting, (*c*) in mg. of nitrogen, the growth-time curves are superimposable on each other and on the respiration curve; hence oxygen uptake (in the absence of fixed nitrogen) may be used as a measure of nitrogen fixation. This enables the latter to be studied more accurately than heretofore, and permits experiments of short duration (4 to 6 hours) for which earlier methods of measurement were too crude [Meyerhof and Burk; Burk (1, 2)]. It was thus shown that in the case of *azotobacter* oxygen uptake (respiration) and oxygen pressure are in an unusual relation; thus rate of respiration is maximal at 0.15 atm. and diminishes on each side of this value, being one-third of the maximum at 0.005 and also at 1.0 atm., the decrease between 0.2 and 1 atm. being linear. Moreover, the changes in respiration rate (whether due to increased or decreased pressure of oxygen) are immediate and reversible. This is in striking contrast to most cells and tissues hitherto studied, the respiration of yeast, for example, being independent of oxygen pressure between 0.03 and 0.97 atm. *Azotobacter* also seems to be distinguished by a high respiration rate, amounting to 2,000 cmm. of oxygen per mg. (dry weight) per hour, whereas an average for yeast and other forms of bacteria is about 1/25 of this value. It has not so far been shown that these unusual reactions to oxygen are connected with the power to fix nitrogen, since they occur both when the organism is fixing nitrogen and also when it is growing on fixed nitrogen; on the other hand, it is not inconceivable that these respiratory peculiarities may be causally connected with nitrogen fixation even though they occur also when this power is in abeyance. The chemical aspect of the respiration–oxygen pressure relation has been discussed by the author in the light of two possible theories, one of chain kinetics and one of contact catalysis [Burk (2)].

The rate of nitrogen fixation is influenced by oxygen pressure, being maximal at 0.04 atm. of oxygen, falling off to 1/3 to 1/6 of its optimal rate at 0.008 and 0.21 atm. The effect of nitrogen pressure on fixation is more regular [Burk (1)]; working at 0.2 atm. of oxygen, nitrogen fixation is inappreciable below 0.05 atm. and reaches a maximum at 0.5 to 1.0 atm. Between 0.05 and 5 atm. the rate of fixation is proportional to the pressure, whilst in conditions which favour growth (e.g., the presence of humic acid) the linear relation can be shown to hold from zero pressures of nitrogen upwards.

The new technique has disclosed a higher efficiency ratio for nitrogen fixation than has been previously obtained. From theoretical considerations it has been deduced that the maximum value for the ratio $\frac{\text{Mols. N}_2 \text{ fixed}}{\text{Mols. O}_2 \text{ used}}$ on a glucose medium is 0.915. Earlier workers obtained a value of 0.005 to 0.01. It is now shown that the efficiency ratio rises as the oxygen pressure decreases, and also with increasing rate of growth; by these means values as high as 12 per cent have been obtained. In other words, *azotobacter* normally uses oxygen greatly in excess of its metabolic needs, and its efficiency is therefore raised by decreasing its oxygen consumption and increasing its growth rate.

Another point of great interest which has been disclosed by these studies is the fact that calcium and strontium are specific and necessary catalysts for nitrogen fixation, though not for growth on fixed nitrogen. In the presence of 1 to 5 p.p.m. of calcium, nitrogen fixation is inappreciable, whilst 25 to 50 p.p.m. give normal growth rates (Burk and Lineweaver).

An interesting biological study (Iwasaki) relating to this subject (and obtained by the respirometer technique) shows that, on a medium free from fixed nitrogen, cell-multiplication may occur without nitrogen fixation and conversely nitrogen fixation without cell-division. The first of these conditions occurs when an old culture (3 to 6 days) is diluted with three times its volume of new medium; respiration now rises 2 to 3 fold that of the parent culture, and cell-multiplication occurs without nitrogen fixation, the size of the cells decreasing from $2.0\ \mu$ to $0.2\ \mu$ in diameter ("multiplication phase"). After about ten hours, when the population has attained that of the parent culture, the respiration resumes its steady rate and cell-division ceases; simultaneously nitrogen fixation sets in and the cells grow and attain their original size of about $2\ \mu$ diameter ("storage phase"). If instead of diluting the original culture three times it be diluted twenty times, a "multiplication phase" sets in as before; this is followed by a simultaneous "multiplication" and "fixation" phase in which the cells increase in both number and size; when the cell population has attained its original numerical value multiplication ceases and a "storage phase" sets in till all the cells have reached their maximal size. The influences governing the cessation of cell-division are not very clear, and may possibly be due to exhaustion of some nutrient material; one is also reminded of the early observation of Adrian Brown in which he showed that, even in good nutritional conditions, yeast ceases to multiply when the cell population passes a certain fixed value. Whatever may be the underlying causes, the dissociation of nitrogen fixation from cell-multiplication and the possibility of obtaining a storage of nitrogen accompanied by increase in cell size without increase in numbers is a highly interesting phenomenon not before demonstrated.

The action of humin on increasing growth rate both on free and fixed nitrogen has again been demonstrated [Burk (1)]. It has now been shown that humin owes its action to its iron content and can be quantitatively replaced by iron salts (Burk, Lineweaver, Horner, and Allison).

The inability of nodule bacteria to fix nitrogen in the absence of the host plant has been confirmed [Burk (1)].

Denitrification

A quantitative study on denitrification (Lloyd and Cranston), in which the rate of evolution of nitrogen and of bacterial multiplication were both measured, disclosed the fact that in nitrite broth cultures a lag of thirteen hours occurs between inoculation and appearance of gas; this lag is partly bacterial and partly chemical. Thus if nitrite is present in the flask at the time of inoculation gas begins to appear in thirteen hours; but if to a similar tube nitrite is introduced at nineteen hours (i.e., when bacterial lag is over and gas production in the first culture is in full swing) gas is not immediately evolved but a "chemical" lag of about four hours intervenes. Furthermore nitrate produces the same "chemical" lag as twice the equivalent amount of nitrite, from which the authors deduce that nitrogen is produced both from nitrate and nitrite by intermediate reduction of both to hyponitrite, and that not until this reaction is complete is the hyponitrite itself reduced with evolution of nitrogen. Thus:

$$2 \, KNO_3 - 2 \, O_2 = K_2 \, N_2 \, O_2$$
$$2 \, KNO_2 - O_2 = K_2 \, N_2 \, O_2.$$

Nitrification

Four bacterial species have now been isolated oxidising ammonia to nitrite. These differ fundamentally from *nitrosomonas* in being able to develop on the usual nutrient media and in the presence of sucrose. The investigation of these organisms from the biochemical standpoint offers an interesting field for research (Cutler and Mukerji).

Metabolism

The metabolism of the *pneumococcus* changes considerably in passing from the smooth (capsulated) to the rough (non-capsulated) form, but the changes are not constant for the three types studied (Finkle). Thus the "respiration" in the presence of glucose (i.e., cmm. of oxygen taken up per mg. dry weight of bacteria) changes in passing from S to R mutant as follows: type I increases 110 per cent, type II decreases 16 per cent, and type III decreases 45 per cent. The anaerobic glycolysis shows an increase of 25 per cent in all three types. The aerobic glycolysis is completely lost in type I; is absent in both forms in type II; and is absent in the S but appears in the R in type III. Thus the R form of type I is more active both in oxidation and in glycolysis than the S, and both forms of type II are more energetic oxidisers than type I, but in this case the S is superior to the R, whilst in glycolysis the R is superior to the S.

Evidence as to the course of bacterial decomposition of succinic and aspartic acid has been adduced by a study of relative rates of decomposition of these and possible intermediaries (fumaric and *l*-malic acids) (Quastel and Wheatley). In general the evidence favours the view that succinic acid breaks down to fumaric and *l*-malic. Aspartic acid appears to be degraded via fumaric and *l*-malic in the case of facultative anaerobes, i.e., those previously shown to possess aspartase, but in the case of strict aerobes a different and undetermined route is indicated. A series of papers (Kendal, Friedemann and Ishikawa) show a striking dissimilarity in the ease with which certain compounds are attacked by different organisms. Suspensions of "resting" bacteria were used over short-time periods both aerobically and anaerobically. The results are summarised below (Table VIII):

TABLE VIII
ACTIVATION BY "RESTING" BACTERIA

		Glucose	Lactic Acid	Pyruvic Acid	Alanine
B. coli	aer.	+ +	+ +	+ +	(+)
	anaer.	+	+	+ +	0
Staph. aureus	aer.	+ +	—	+ +	+
	anaer.	+ +	—	+ +	0
Bact. pyogenes foetidus	aer.	+ +	+ +	—	—
	anaer.	+	+	—	—
Vibrio 11 61	aer.	0	+ +	0	0
	anaer.	0	0	0	0
B. procyaneus	aer.	+	(+)	+ +	+ +
	anaer.	0	0	+	+
B. alcaligenes	aer.	0	+ +	(+)	+ +
	anaer.	0	0	0	0

It is noteworthy that the two organisms which fail to attack glucose also fail to attack pyruvic acid, a substance commonly held to be extremely reactive with bacteria. Alanine is attacked by only two out of the six strains.

Of interest as a contribution to intermediary metabolism is a study on pyruvic acid (Cook). This confirms the view that *Bact. coli* does not decarboxylate pyruvic acid but decomposes it mainly to acetic acid, carbon dioxide, and hydrogen. It was also shown by the use of bisulphite as a fixative and subsequent estimation that (with the same organism) pyruvate occurs aerobically from glucose, but whether as an oxidation product of lactate or from some earlier decomposition is uncertain.

PYOCYANINE

When pyocyanine is added to washed suspensions of *B. pyocyaneus* in concentrations of 1/5000 M the endogenous respiration is much increased (Friedheim); moreover, the carbon dioxide output is increased disproportionately, the R.Q. being raised from 0.1–0.17 to 0.77–0.9. The oxidation of added metabolites (glucose, pyruvic acid, and asparagine) is unaffected by the addition of the pigment. The fact that both the normal respiration and the increased respiration due to pyocyanine are inhibited by cyanide and by carbon monoxide shows that the system is linked with the *Atmungsferment*.

The dye not only catalyses the respiration of its own cell (*B. pyocyaneus*) but also that of other bacterial species and red blood cells.

OXIDATION-REDUCTION POTENTIAL

Evidence gathers that the reduction potential of a medium as measured by the electrode influences growth. In connection with *Cl. tetani* a very good case has been made out for the statement that a definite negative reduction potential must be reached before the spores of this organism can germinate [Fildes; Knight (1, 2); Knight and Fildes]. In this series of experiments the negative drift which sterile bacterial media commonly undergo in anaerobic conditions was poised by passing through a stream of very dilute oxygen in nitrogen, by which technique the Eh was held constant. Into the electrode vessel containing the medium tetanus spores were introduced, and samples were withdrawn at intervals and examined for germination; a relation between time required for spores to germinate and the oxidation-reduction potential level at the electrode was thus found. The shortest germination time was four hours; this occurred when the medium was poised at an Eh of − 0.05 volts (or negative to that). As more positive media were employed the lag increased so that at Eh, + 0.10 volts, it was eight to ten hours. At levels more positive than Eh, $+ 0.11$ volts (pH 7.0 to 7.65), germination did not occur, though spores maintained their viability.

Indirect evidence has also been obtained that a too positive reduction potential may inhibit the germination of tetanus spores *in vivo* [Fildes (2); Campbell and Fildes]. Another study on somewhat similar lines (Plotz and Geloso) is concerned with the limits of rH within which a number of organisms are capable of multiplication. *Cl. tetani* were sown into a meat broth medium (pH 7.1) the Eh of which was initially $+ 0.10$ volts; this fell rapidly to Eh, $- 0.13$ volts, more slowly to Eh, $- 0.195$, and finally became constant at Eh, $- 0.265$ volts (rH $= 5.5$). By introducing a series of reducing agents the medium was poised at certain values of rH; on introducing *Cl. tetani* into such media the same rH was always reached irrespective of whether the initial value was positive or negative to this. Thus, using the reducing agents cysteine, sodium hydrosulphite, titanium citrate, and glucose plus platinum black, the medium was initially poised at Eh, $- 0.180$, $- 4.90$, $- 0.440$, and $- 0.08$ volts, respectively. After the development of the organism the Eh of all the media became constant at Eh, $- 0.265$ (rH $= 5.5$). Rather unexpectedly the final rH value of 5.5 (± 0.6) was reached irrespective of the organism employed (*B. coli, Botulinus Bifermentans, Tissier, Putrificus B. sporogenes, Histolyticus, V. septique alpha*), and also of whether the initial potential was positive or negative to this value. An rH of $- 2.0$ proved inhibitory to the growth of *tetanus* and also (as might be expected) an rH of $+ 27$ poised by ferro-ferricyanide. These results are not strictly comparable to those mentioned on p. 652, as no distinction is made between spores and vegetative forms.

Other studies on this subject by Hewitt may be referred to (see Literature Cited).

LITERATURE CITED

BERTHO, A., AND BASU, K. P., *Ann.*, **485**, 26 (1931)

BERTRAND, G., *Ann. chim. phys.*, **8**, (3) 181 (1904)

BROWN, A. J., *J. Chem. Soc.*, **61**, 369 (1892)

BURK, D. (1), *J. Phys. Chem.*, **34**, 1174 (1930)

BURK, D. (2), *J. Phys. Chem.*, **34**, 1195 (1930)

BURK, D., AND LINEWEAVER, H., *Arch. Microbiol.*, **2**, 155 (1931)

BURK, D., LINEWEAVER, H., HORNER, C. K., AND ALLISON, F. E., *Science*, **74**, 522 (1931)

CAMPBELL, J. A., AND FILDES, P., *Brit. J. Exptl. Path.*, **12**, 77 (1931)

COOK, R. P., *Biochem. J.*, **24**, 1538 (1930)

CUTLER, D. W., AND MUKERJI, B. K., *Proc. Roy. Soc. (London), B*, **108**, 384 (1931)

ELIASBERG, P., *Biochem. Z.*, **220**, 259 (1930)

FILDES, P. (1), *Brit. J. Exptl. Path.*, **10**, 151 (1929)

FILDES, P. (2), *Brit. J. Exptl. Path.*, **10**, 197 (1929)

FINKLE, P., *J. Exptl. Med.*, **53**, 661 (1931)

FISCHER, F., LIESKE, R., AND WINZER, K., *Biochem. Z.*, **236**, 247 (1931)

FRIEDHEIM, E. A. H., *J. Exptl. Med.*, **54**, 207 (1931)

HAEHN, H., AND ENGEL, M., *Zentr. Bakt. Parasitenk. II Abt.*, **79**, 129 (1929)

HERMANN, S., AND NEUSCHAL, P., *Biochem. Z.*, **233**, 129 (1931)

HEWITT, L. F., *Biochem. J.*, **24**, 669, 676, 983, 1551 (1930); **25**, 169, 858, 1447, 1452 (1931)

IWASAKI, K., *Biochem. Z.*, **226**, 32 (1930)

KARSTRÖM, H., *Über die Enzymbildung in Bakterien*, University of Helsingfors (1930)

KENDALL, A. I., FRIEDEMANN, T. E., AND ISHIKAWA, M., *J. Infectious Diseases*, **47**, 194, 206, 212, 219, 223, 229 (1931)

KLUYVER, A. J., AND HOPPENBROUWERS, W. J., *Arch. Microbiol.*, **2**, 245 (1931)

KNIGHT, B. C. J. G. (1), *Biochem. J.*, **24**, 1066 (1930)

KNIGHT, B. C. J. G. (2), *Biochem. J.*, **24**, 1075 (1930)

KNIGHT, B. C. J. G., AND FILDES, P., *Biochem. J.*, **24**, 1496 (1930)

KOSTYTSCHEW, S., GWALADSE, W., AND ELIASBERG, P., *Z. physiol. Chem.*, **188**, 127 (1930)

LLOYD, B., AND CRANSTON, J. A., *Biochem. J.*, **24**, 529 (1930)

MEYERHOF, O., AND BURK, D., *Z. physik. Chem.*, **139**, 117 (1928)

NEAVE, S. L., AND BUSWELL, A. M., *J. Am. Chem. Soc.*, **52**, 3308 (1930)

NEUBERG, C., AND WINDISCH, F., *Biochem. Z.*, **166**, 454 (1925)

PLOTZ, H., AND GELOSO, J., *Ann. inst. Pasteur*, **45**, 613 (1930)

QUASTEL, J. H., AND WHEATLEY, A. H. M., *Biochem. J.*, **25**, 117 (1931)

SELIM, M., *Zentr. Bakt. Parasitenk. II Abt.*, **83**, 311 (1931)

SIMON, E., *Biochem. Z.*, **224**, 253 (1930)

STICKLAND, L. H., *Biochem. J.*, **23**, 1187 (1929)

STEPHENSON, M., AND STICKLAND, L. H. (1), *Biochem. J.*, **25**, 205 (1931)

STEPHENSON, M., AND STICKLAND, L. H. (2), *Biochem. J.*, **25**, 215 (1931)

TAMIYA, H., AND TANAKA, K., *Acta Phytochim. (Japan)*, **5**, 167 (1930)

TANAKA, K., *Acta Phytochim. (Japan)*, **5**, 239 (1931)

TAUSZ, J., AND DONATH, P., *Z. physiol. Chem.*, **190**, 141 (1930)

VIRTANEN, A. I., KARSTRÖM, H., AND TURPEINEN, O., *Z. physiol. Chem.*, **187**, 7 (1930)

VIRTANEN, A. I., AND PELTOLA, E., *Z. physiol. Chem.*, **187**, 45 (1930)

VIRTANEN, A. I., AND TIKKA, J., *Biochem. Z.*, **228**, 407 (1930)

WIELAND, H., AND BERTHO, A., *Ann.*, **476**, 95 (1928)

UNIVERSITY OF CAMBRIDGE
CAMBRIDGE, ENGLAND

IMMUNOCHEMISTRY*

By Michael Heidelberger

Department of Medicine, College of Physicians and Surgeons, Columbia University, and Presbyterian Hospital, New York

In the following review an attempt has been made to cover the literature from January 1930 as far as possible into 1931. Immuno-chemistry is construed in the literal sense, and no paper is included which does not bear in some way on the chemical basis of immunology. The subject-matter has appeared to group itself naturally under three main headings: I. Antigens and Haptens: (*a*) Proteins, (*b*) Toxins, (*c*) Carbohydrates, (*d*) Lipoids, (*e*) Miscellaneous topics; II. Antibodies; III. Antigen-Antibody Reactions.

I. Antigens and Haptens

a) Proteins.—Immunochemical researches on the proteins have dealt largely with the influence of the protein type or the character of substituents on the specificity. To begin with the animal proteins, Kyes and Porter (1) have purified fowl fibrinogen and found it to be a species-specific antigen distinct from fowl globulin or albumin. The proteins of the crystalline lens were again investigated by Hoffmann (2) and while their organ specificity was confirmed, the independent antigenicity of α- and β-crystallin could not be established. Wormall (3) has studied the halogenated and nitro proteins and confirmed older findings that iodination results in a loss of species specificity and the appearance of a new specificity. Crossing with bromo proteins was observed, however, and since the iodo- and bromo-protein precipitin reactions could be inhibited with 3,5, diiodo-, dibromo-, and dichloro-tyrosine, it is believed that the observed change in specificity is at least partly due to the introduction of the two halogen atoms into the tyrosine groupings of the protein. Nitro proteins showed cross reactions with diazo proteins (from the protein and nitrous acid) and very little crossing with the halogenated compounds, introduction of a single group *ortho*- to the phenolic hydroxyl of the tyrosine grouping being perhaps responsible for the differences. In all cases the antisera reacted somewhat more strongly to the homologous antigen than to heterologous, similarly treated protein.

* Received January 14, 1932.

Landsteiner and van der Scheer (4) have studied the phenylazo-heteroalbumoses and protoalbumoses and found that antisera prepared from these degradation products of horse serum give cross reactions with both products, but not with similar products prepared from other proteins. Azo-protein derivatives have also been studied by Avery and Goebel and will be discussed under Section C.

As regards vegetable proteins, in two instances protein fractions have been found responsible for the allergic activity of pollens. Moore, Cromwell, and Moore (5) report evidence of albumin, proteose, and globulin antigens in timothy and giant ragweed pollens, while Stull, Cooke, and Chobot (6) believe an albumin to be the sole active constituent of the latter pollen. This work, however, is suggestive rather than convincing, and in view of the fact that Black (7) reports a nitrogen-containing, protein-free polysaccharide as a highly active constituent of the same pollen, the subject is in a confused state.

Several papers have appeared on the bacterial proteins, the first being that of Fischer and Hochberg on the nature of the "H" (coarse-flocking) and "O" (fine-flocking) agglutinogens (8). It was found, in agreement with earlier workers, that the agglutinogens could be completely extracted by water from both *Proteus X 19* and typhoid organisms, the "H" agglutinogen showing precipitation optima at pH 4.0 and 3.8 in the two cases, and the "O" agglutinogen at pH 3.4 and 3.2. The former products were precipitable by 20 to 30 per cent saturation with ammonium sulfate, the latter by 50 to 60 per cent saturation. The fractions gave all the protein reactions, a positive Molisch test, were heat coagulable, contained no sulfur and showed little difference in carbon, hydrogen, nitrogen, and phosphorus. Although the phosphorus content was 2.6 to 2.9 per cent, a qualitative test for nucleic acid was negative and the remarkable conclusion was drawn that the two agglutinogens represent identical globulins in different states of dispersion.

A more detailed study has been made of the acetic acid precipitable proteins of a strain of scarlatinal *Streptococcus hemolyticus* by Heidelberger and Kendall (9). The dried, ground organisms were first acidified with buffer at pH 4 to free the isoelectric proteins, and were then extracted with buffer at pH 6.5 and successive solutions of increasing alkalinity. A number of fractions were obtained, of which those extracted at alkaline reaction corresponded roughly to the "nucleoprotein" as ordinarily obtained. The initial fraction at pH 6.5, however, was an extremely labile nucleo-protein (or perhaps nuclein) of high phosphorus content, which split off nucleic acid even in $N/200$ alkali and was changed into products resembling the other fractions. In its original form the new fraction showed a specificity distinct from that of the succeeding ones. Moreover, in the precipitin reaction with rabbit antisera its reactivity was less than that of the fractions obtained by alkaline extraction, while in the sera of a number of human beings suffering from streptococcus infections the picture appeared to be reversed. The chemical properties of the new fraction supported the view that the combination of protein and nucleic acid in nucleoproteins is of the ester type rather than salt-like.

The composite protein synthesized by the colon bacillus has been analyzed by Eckstein and Soule (10) and found to be very high in arginine, histidine, and lysine nitrogen.

Seibert has continued her study of tuberculin (11) and found the new unheated ultrafiltered tuberculin to be especially potent in producing and detecting precipitins in guinea pigs. These appeared to be largely type-specific for the human, bovine, avian, and timothy varieties. The separation of the various protein fractions was complicated by the presence of an acidic polysaccharide which could be removed only by precipitation of the protein at pH 4.8 with a consequent loss of toxicity. From the results of ultrafiltration through guncotton membranes of varying porosity it was concluded that degradation products of the original tuberculin protein at least as far down as "proteose" (not precipitable by trichloroacetic acid, not dialyzable) can produce the antigenic and skin effects, while with further degradation, toxicity for the normal guinea pig is produced, and finally all biological activity is lost when the particle size becomes less than 1,000 to 2,400. Maschmann and Küster (11a) also conclude that the substance in tuberculin which kills tuberculous guinea pigs is of low molecular weight, since, contrary to Seibert, they found it to be slowly dialyzable. Dialyzed, acid-precipitated "Sauton" tuberculin gives up its active material to kaolin at an acid reaction. The toxic substance may be extracted in good yield by very weak ammonia and a 60-fold purification and separation from accompanying polysaccharides is said thus to be effected. The product behaves like a polypeptide.

b) Toxins.—While much work has been done during the period on toxins from the preparative standpoint and on the study of the reactions of toxins, the true nature of these substances is still uncertain. Maver (12) has succeeded in obtaining low-grade diphtheria toxin using a modified Braun-Hofmeier "synthetic" medium and has found it to be closely associated with the synthesized proteins. It is to be hoped that work will be continued along these lines until potent preparations can be obtained and studied.

Many excellent methods for the preliminary, far-reaching purification of toxins have been published, but since they have not as yet been pushed to the point of yielding detailed knowledge as to the nature of toxins the references are all grouped under 13a, b, c. In this connection it should be mentioned that Ando, Kurauchi, and Nishimura (13b) have called attention to confusing skin reactions with crude scarlatinal toxin due to the presence of bacterial nucleoprotein, and have shown that this can be removed by a preliminary precipitation with acetic acid.

Locke and Main (14) analyzed their purified diphtheria toxin for metals and found iron and an unusually large amount of copper present. They believe the neurotoxins "to be dispersions of bacterial protoplasm containing deeply embedded fragments of a positively charged . . . . respiratory substance having copper as the predominant catalyst" and resembling "the respiratory enzymes of the oxidase type and the proteases of the pH 8 erepsin type. . . . . The hemotoxins appear to contain fragments of negatively charged respiratory substance having ferrous iron as the predominant catalyst" and resembling "the respiratory enzymes of the dehydrogenase type and the protease of the pH 4 papain type. . . . ." The evidence presented is suggestive and gains in weight through the finding of Coulter and Stone (15) that diphtheria toxin contains a complex copper-iron porphyrin compound, the amount of which parallels the toxicity. Whether or not the copper is actually a part of the toxin molecule has not yet been proved, and while Locke and Main found that colorless fractions were non-toxic, although retaining their flocculating power, it must be borne in mind that colorless diphtheria anatoxin fractions are so easy to obtain[1] as to make it difficult to believe that the metal or its complex can be "deeply embedded." Coulter and Stone also point out that the metal-porphyrin compound, though perhaps formed in the same reaction as the toxin, is probably not actually a part of it, since the color is not carried down by toxin-antitoxin flocculation.

---

[1] Unpublished experiments of the reviewer.

The mechanism of the conversion of diphtheria toxin into toxoid or anatoxin has been the subject of a number of memoirs. Krestownikowa and Rjachina, Kissin and Bronstein, and Hewitt (16) have reached divergent conclusions which are analyzed with great care by Hewitt, who calls attention to the number of alternatives. Bunney (17) was unable to convert acid-purified toxin into anatoxin [see, however, Krestownikowa and Rjachina (16)] without previous addition of broth, peptone, or, best, 1 per cent glutamic acid. He has thus furnished evidence that it is combined, not free, formaldehyde which is concerned in the reaction.

The stability of toxins in the presence of numerous substances has also been studied. Schmidt (18), among others, has found dialyzed or purified toxin to be less stable than the crude material. The latter is more sensitive to salts of aromatic acids than to other salts, is more easily destroyed by amyl alcohol than by other alcohols, and is destroyed by ether. Aldehydes were found to be generally destructive, the effect varying greatly with the structure. In the aliphatic acid series the destructive effect of the salts reached a maximum with C_{10}, a 0.01 N solution destroying the toxin in one week. Oleate and ricinoleate in 0.1 N concentration showed a similar effect.

Vincent and Velluz (19) have found sodium 3,5, diiodo-salicylate to be 280 times as active in neutralizing tetanus toxin as is sodium salicylate, 0.5 mg. added to 1 cc. of a toxin containing 500 M.L.D. being sufficient to convert it into an anatoxin capable of producing immunity. This was the most effective substance of the hydroxybenzoic acid series.

c) *Carbohydrates.*—Much work has been done during the period on specific polysaccharides. Fundamental to an understanding of their significance is the coupling of the nitrogen-free pneumococcus Type III specific carbohydrate (S III) with protein by Goebel and Avery (20) and the immunological study of the resulting product [Avery and Goebel (21)]. A *p*-aminobenzyl ether of S III was synthesized, diazotized, and coupled with horse-serum globulin. Rabbits immunized with the resulting reconstituted Type III pneumococcus were highly immune to rabbit-virulent strains of the microörganism and yielded antisera which protected mice specifically, which precipitated S III, its *p*-aminobenzyl ether, and the complete azo antigen, and which agglutinated Type III pneumococci specifically. Thus type-specific protection, agglutination, and precipitation are conclusively shown to be functions of the antibodies directed against the type-specific polysaccharide.

The final proof of the connection between virulence and the capsular specific polysaccharide of Type III pneumococcus has also been furnished in a far-reaching investigation from the same laboratory. Dubos and Avery (22) have isolated, from a microbe occurring in peat soil, an enzyme capable of rapidly splitting S III and destroying its specificity both *in vitro* and *in vivo*. Avery and Dubos (23) have shown that Type III pneumococci grown in the presence of the enzyme lose their virulence and are converted into the easily phagocytable decapsulated form. In this way enzyme preparations not only protect mice specifically but even act rapidly enough to effect cures long after septicemia has set in.

Concluding the discussion of the work on S III, mention must be made of Babers and Goebel's estimate of the molecular weight of this substance as 118,000 (24). However, it is shown in work now in press from the reviewer's laboratory that the method used is inapplicable in the form used.

A species-specific pneumococcus polysaccharide has been discovered by Tillett and Francis and studied and partly characterized by Tillett, Goebel, and Avery (25). This "C-substance" (so called from its analogy to the species-specific polysaccharide of the hemolytic streptococcus) is elaborated by the R-forms as well as the S-forms of pneumococci and is thus unrelated to virulence. Antibodies to it occur in many of the otherwise type-specific sera. Like the Type I pneumococcus specific carbohydrate, it contains nitrogen and is destroyed by nitrous acid, but is only weakly dextrorotatory. Heidelberger and Kendall also encountered the substance in their study of Type IV pneumococcus polysaccharides (see below) and in the mother-liquors of S I and S III preparations. With the aid of larger quantities they were able to fix its rotation at about $+40°$, its nitrogen content at 6.1 per cent, and to demonstrate a small but definite amino nitrogen content of 0.9 per cent. It differs from S I in containing acetyl nitrogen (3.7 per cent) and in not being insoluble at its isoelectric point, and differs from the pneumococcus type-specific carbohydrates in containing phosphorus (4.0 per cent).

The crude polysaccharide obtained by Heidelberger and Kendall (26) from the new Type IV (27) of Group IV pneumococcus was separated into three fractions: (*a*) the "C-substance" described above, (*b*) a type-specific polysaccharide with $[\alpha]_D$ about $+30°$, and

5.5 per cent of nitrogen, all of which was in the acetylated form, and (c) a serologically inactive carbohydrate, somewhat similar to the Type IV specific substance, but resembling chitin more closely in its hydrolyzability by snail juice. The Type IV specific polysaccharide thus differs markedly from those of Types I, II, and III pneumococcus, and from the species-specific polysaccharide.

Specific polysaccharides have again been isolated from tuberculin by Dorset and Henley (28), Johnson and Renfrew (28a) and by Masucci, et al. (29), and from the lipoids of tubercle bacilli by Chargaff and Anderson (30).[2] While Dorset and Henley reported the presence of "arabinose" and mannose, the other workers identified the first sugar as d-arabinose, thus establishing another rare natural occurrence of this sugar. In addition to mannose, Chargaff and Anderson also found galactose and inosite in their product.

Morgan (31) has obtained a specific polysaccharide from the Shiga dysentery bacillus with $[\alpha]_{Hg\ green}$ about 70° and containing 2.5 per cent of nitrogen. Amino nitrogen was not present, nor were pentose reactions observed. K. Meyer (32) has found the heterogenetic antigen in Shiga bacilli to be inseparable from the specific polysaccharide, a conclusion borne out in general by Eisler's experiments (33).

Specific polysaccharides of yeasts have aided in the serological differentiation of strains (Tomcsik, 34) and have also been of like service in the case of the Monilia group [Kesten, Cook, Mott, and Jobling (35)].

The question of the antigenicity of specific polysaccharides has occupied a number of workers. Schiemann and his associates (36) have again reported the active protection of mice with minute amounts of Type I pneumococcus polysaccharide (S I), larger quantities being ineffective. From the details it is evident that their product was not of the highest purity attainable. Enders (37) has obtained evidence of a non-protein, type-specific antigen in unfiltered Pneumococcus I autolysates, precipitating antisera prepared from such autolysates or antisera absorbed with highly purified S I, and shocking guinea pigs sensitized with such sera. Wadsworth and Brown (38) have confirmed the observations of the preceding workers and believe a type-specific polysaccharide distinct from S I or containing

---

[2] The specificity of the polysaccharide fractions associated with the lipoids has been shown (unpublished results).

S I as a radical to be responsible. It is to be hoped that more chemical work will be done in order to elucidate the matter. Products of this nature may account for the protective antibody "neutralizing substance" postulated by Felton (39). Ross (40) has likewise found that rats acquire a limited degree of protection when fed S I. Zozaya (41), in a preliminary publication, reports that bacterial polysaccharides become antigenic when adsorbed on collodion particles, extremely small amounts stimulating antibody production.

Sordelli and Mayer (42) have pointed out that a 1/400,000 solution of agar (gelose) is enough to yield precipitates with anti-typhoid and anti-anthrax sera, so that many of the cross-precipitin reactions observed in the typhoid and paratyphoid group may be ascribed to the medium and not to bacterial polysaccharides. This is possibly an explanation of some, at least, of the numerous polysaccharide cross-reactions observed by Zozaya (43).

Since the first aldobionic acid was discovered as a component of a specific polysaccharide (44), and other similar sugar acids have been found to occur in several specific carbohydrates as well as in many plant gums, it is of interest that in Haworth's laboratory (45) one of the two alternative structures proposed by Heidelberger and Kendall (46) has been confirmed for the aldobionic acid obtained from gum arabic. Linkage of the glucuronic acid to the galactose portion at position 3 is thus excluded and the substance is shown to be β(?)-glucurono-6-α-galactose, the glucuronic acid being in the pyranose form.

d) Lipoids.—The fundamental work on the lipoids of the tubercle bacillus group now being carried on by Anderson and his collaborators is described in another chapter. The immunological significance of the products isolated has barely been touched upon, but there is evidence that the phosphatide fraction may give rise to antibodies [Doan and Moore (47)] and that it is also responsible for tubercle formation [Sabin, Doan, and Forkner (48)], the active constituent being, possibly, phthioic acid (49).

Wadsworth and Brown (50) have found the ether extract of Type I pneumococci to give complement fixation with antisera to the various types. Sera obtained by injecting the extract into rabbits contained no agglutinins, precipitins, or complement-fixing antibodies, but gave some degree of type-specific passive protection in mice. Further purification should show whether or not a lipoid antigen is actually present.

Moran's work (51) on organ-specific extracts has been quoted (52) as evidence for the ability of lipoids to stimulate antibody production. However, Moran extracted the moist pulped organs with 5 volumes of 95 per cent alcohol and used the extracts without further purification. While some evidence for organ specificity is presented, the participation of proteins in the reactions is not excluded.

e) Miscellaneous substances.—Landsteiner and van der Scheer (53) have studied the effect of a large number of simple organic substances in inhibiting the precipitin reaction. Their experiments confirm their earlier conclusion that the specificity of the inhibition is influenced in the case of the aromatic acids by the position of the substituent. With specific groups of simple constitution in the antigen, distantly related compounds often inhibited, but when the specific group was of sufficient complexity, such as in azo proteins derived from an aminotartranilic acid, more rigorously specific inhibitions were obtained, and it is thus "possible to distinguish such compounds by serological tests as readily as proteins can be differentiated with the aid of precipitating sera." It was also found (54) that substances of this type, when diazotized and coupled with resorcin, are capable of causing anaphylactic shock in a small proportion of guinea pigs sensitized with the azo protein.

The remarkable results of Jermoljewa and Bujanowskaja (55) are mentioned here in the hope that they will be checked elsewhere. Rabbits repeatedly injected with trimethylamine and the C_5, C_6, C_7, and C_{17} primary aliphatic amines responded with the formation of precipitins and antibodies protecting against otherwise lethal doses of the amine. The sera showed marked specificity, although crossing somewhat with neighbors in the homologous series. If simple aliphatic amines can function as antigens, many current views will necessarily have to be modified.

II. Antibodies

Most workers in this field now hold the view that antibodies are modified serum globulins, and much has been accomplished toward a clearer idea of the mechanism of their formation. Manwaring's views (56) as to the "homologization" of parenterally introduced protein are very persuasive, but in the opinion of the reviewer are subject to alternative interpretations which the experiments offered do not exclude. That the antigen itself does not enter into antibody globulin is indicated by several results. Somewhat along the lines of Doerr's statement (57) that arsenic in an atoxyl-azo antigen leads to an arsenic-free antibody, although the arsonic acid radical determines .the specificity, Heidelberger and Kendall (58) found that R-salt-azobenzidineazo-egg albumin gives rise to colorless antibodies, although the colored part of the antigen is the portion determining the specificity. Moreover, as much as 8 mg.[3] of circulating antibody may be produced per milligram of antigen injected, and since this is only a portion of the total antibody produced, the amount seems inconsistent with the idea that specific antigen fragments are present, though the evidence is not conclusive. Reasoning along the same lines, Hooker and Boyd (59) followed recent calculations of Topley (60) which bring out clearly the disproportion between antigen and antibody, and conclude that one molecule of antigen, if incorporated into agglutinin, "is brought into operative correspondence with 600 bacteria," the surface relationship being as 1/25,000,000.

Breinl and Haurowitz (61) report experiments showing the close relation of antibody to serum globulin. They believe that the antigen disturbs the normal mechanism of globulin synthesis, probably in the amino acid-peptide stage, modifying the method of union or the spatial relations of the globulin components so that a new globulin, an antibody, is formed, which reacts specifically with the antigen by virtue of the distortion caused by the presence of the antigen at the moment of its synthesis, for if the antigen can only affect amino acids having affinity for it, these should retain that affinity after their synthesis into globulin. This conception accords with the absence of antibodies in the blood of the newborn before the appearance of globulin, the necessity of an incubation period, the fact that this period is not proportional to the amount of antigen injected, and the failure thus far to demonstrate antibody formation *in vitro*. Changes in serum proteins on immunization have also been discussed by Walton (62), and Schmidt and Tuljschinskaja (63) have shown that the process does not necessarily lead to an increase of total globulin in rabbits and dogs, bleeding alone often resulting in an increase of globulin at the next bleeding.

Avery and Goebel (21) found that their reconstituted pneumococcus gave rise to antibodies reacting with horse-serum globulin as well as with the pneumococcus. This is considered due to the pos-

---

[3] This figure has since been raised to 12 to 50 mg. (unpublished results).

sible presence of unchanged globulin in the antigen, and also to the possibility that the compound antigen may give rise to both types of antibodies. The reviewer considers both explanations reasonable, since in coupling proteins with diazo compounds a whole series of products may be formed, with unchanged protein at one end and a maximally coupled protein of completely altered specificity at the other. In order to obtain a product entirely free from the original specificity, intermediate fractions must be discarded which, from their properties, can scarcely contain the original unaltered antigen, but evidently still contain free, specifically reactive groupings of the antigen.[4]

That the converse may be true, as well, or that a single antibody may react with more than one antigen, is indicated by von Gara (64) who demonstrates clearly the observation often made that in animals treated with polyvalent antigens, absorption with one antigen reduces the antibody titer for the others.

The purification of antibodies has been the subject of a number of papers, but since the methods, while often effecting far-reaching purification, have not as yet led to an understanding of the differences of antibody from normal serum globulin, they are grouped under a single reference (65a, b, c). The stability of antitoxin has also been studied by Schmidt (65b).

Vaccine-virus-neutralizing antibodies have been shown by Findlay (66) to occur in the globulin fraction, in confirmation of earlier work. The globulins also contained the flocculating antibody and possessed the power to increase phagocytosis of the virus. The substance responsible for passive skin transfer in allergic conditions occurs in the pseudoglobulin fraction [Smyth and Bain (67)].

The existence of antienzymes now seems well established. Harvey and Deitrick (68) injected crude luciferase from a luminous ostracod crustacean into rabbits, observing that antibodies to the accompanying luciferin were not formed. Antiluciferase was measured by the inhibition of the luminescence of the system luciferin-luciferase. Sumner and Kirk (69) immunized rabbits with crystalline urease and obtained sera capable of neutralizing 30 to 40 urease units per cubic centimeter, as measured by the inhibition of urea-phosphate hydrolysis by the enzyme. The sera also protected animals against lethal doses of urease and even saved them when near death. Since

---

[4] Unpublished results.

the relative antibody titer is easily measured, the urease-anti-urease system may become useful in quantitative studies of immune reactions.

Zozaya, Boyer, and Clark (70) have developed the precipitin titer of earlier workers into a rapid routine test for the estimation of antibodies during the course of immunization and have proposed it as an alternative to the costly and tedious mouse-protection test in Type I antipneumococcus sera. Heidelberger, Sia, and Kendall (71) have shown a parallel between mouse protection and the maximum amount of specifically precipitable protein in Type I pneumococcus antisera, using the homologous specific polysaccharide as precipitant and determining the amount of protein precipitated by the micro-Kjeldahl method. This method also is proposed as a substitute for the mouse-protection test. It is the first to afford an absolute (though not necessarily highly accurate) and not relative determination of antibody provided antibody be considered a protein, and has been shown applicable to other antigen-antibody systems (58).

Felton (72) has confirmed the value of the preceding methods as substitutes for the mouse-protection test in Type I pneumococcus antisera, finding a high correlation between mouse protection, neutralization titer, precipitin titer, agglutination titer, and the amount of specific precipitate in these sera, thus affording, in addition, further evidence for the unitarian theory of antibodies.

The chemical alteration of the species specificity of antibodies by coupling them with diazo compounds without alteration of the antibacterial specificity has been undertaken by Bronfenbrenner (73) with the idea of avoiding anaphylactic effects. Reiner (73a) has attempted to obtain a chemotherapeutic effect by a similar alteration. Sufficient details are not yet available to permit evaluation of the results.

III. Antigen-Antibody Reactions

Mudd and his collaborators have continued their study (74) of the rôle of surface phenomena in opsonin and bacteriotropin action and have concluded that the effects are due to a combination on the antigen surface with the modified globulin antibody. A somewhat similar view regarding agglutination has been put forward by Eagle (75) and extended to specific precipitation. It is based also on cataphoresis measurements, the assumption that adsorption phenomena are involved, and the interplay of hydrophilic and hydrophobic groups. Once antigen has combined with antibody the remaining phenomena of agglutination and precipitation shown by the thus denatured antibody are considered to be solely due to the denatured antibody and the cations of the medium. While an orderly and logical picture is presented from the colloid chemical standpoint, and one which may ultimately be of considerable service, recent work has shown that this is not the only point of view tenable (76). Eagle's views are also difficult to reconcile with the fact that a specific precipitate may contain less than 1 per cent of hapten (76), so that to speak of an appreciable degree of denaturation, or the masking of a significant number of so-called hydrophilic groups under such circumstances appears far-fetched.

Continuing their earlier quantitative studies on the precipitin reaction (76), Heidelberger and Kendall (77) have given a preliminary account of an antigen-antibody system. In order to differentiate antigen nitrogen from antibody nitrogen, a deep red azo protein, R-salt-azobenzidineazo-egg albumin was prepared and separated from all by-products retaining the original specificity before animals were injected and antibodies produced. Checks on the results were obtained by analysis of the supernatant (by difference) and the precipitate for both components of the system. In this way, the initial ratio of antigen to antibody when the latter was in large excess was shown to be about 1/15; at the "equilibrium point," at which the amount of antigen was increased so that a small amount began to appear in the supernatant, the ratio was about 1/7.5, and in the inhibition zone, when the precipitate had almost redissolved in the excess of antigen, the ratio was about 1/3. In this case, also, it appeared possible to express the findings in a series of mass-law equations, although not quite so simply as in the case of the Type III pneumococcus specific polysaccharide-antibody system previously studied. Exception has been taken to this method of treatment by Breinl and Haurowitz (61), who studied the hemoglobin-antibody system. The ratios between antigen and antibody found by these workers varied in much the same fashion as those given above, but they were unable to obtain evidence of an inhibition zone or to account quantitatively for their results. The specific precipitate was found to contain 2 to 9 molecules of globulin per molecule of hemoglobin. Breinl and Haurowitz point out that the precipitin reaction is one between antigen and a soluble salt compound of insoluble antibody, and should therefore not be treated as a precipitation reaction between two soluble substances, precipitation possibly occurring as a result of the displacement of salt by the antigen from the surface of the soluble salt-antibody compound. While this is a reasonable view and the effect of salt must be considered in a complete explanation of precipitin equilibria it does not invalidate a simpler treatment under conditions of constant salt concentration, and indeed, Breinl and Haurowitz' data may be accounted for quantitatively on a mass-law basis.[5]

Quantitative aspects of the precipitin reaction have also been studied by Marrack and Smith (78), who followed previous workers in adopting iodoprotein or azoprotein as antigens in their later work. While Marrack and Smith also take exception to the applicability of mass-law equilibria, they agree with the other workers in that the precipitate is a series of chemical compounds of antigen with antibody. Their articles contain a mass of useful and interesting information on the effect of washing the precipitate, the influence of electrolytes, the negligible influence of pH between 6.6 and 8.0, the independence of the composition of the precipitate of non-specific protein, the influence of the strength of the serum on the composition of the precipiate, etc. They conclude that the relation between antibody and antigen in various sera is about what would be expected if the strength of the serum depended on the amount of antibody globulin and the number of combining groups per molecule of antibody. Nonspecific adsorption is ruled out by the fact that precipitates containing an excess of antigen can combine with more antibody under conditions in which very little non-specific protein is taken up.

That the bacterial precipitin reaction and the Ramon flocculation phenomenon in diphtheria toxin-antitoxin mixtures are entirely distinct and independent has once more been demonstrated by Hazen (79). Marrack and Smith (80) studied the composition of the floccules prior to their other work quoted above. The floccules consisted of denatured pseudoglobulin, and their amount was independent of a variety of conditions, particularly of the amount of non-specific protein. Precipitation of an antitoxin with anti-horse pseudoglobulin rabbit serum removed up to 88 per cent of the antitoxin, the precipitate being capable of fixing toxin, indicating that a molecular grouping was involved different from that combining with the antibody. No pH changes could be observed during the reaction, nor was any measurable heat evolution found, contrary to Bayne-Jones.

[5] Unpublished results.

Quantitative studies on the formation of staphylococcus anatoxin and the reactions of the staphylococcus toxin-antitoxin system have led Burnet (81) to the conclusion that toxin and anatoxin react similarly with antitoxin, that the reaction is initially stoichiometric, but that the insoluble compound formed provides a surface upon which any of the components of the system may be adsorbed according to an equation which is given and explained in detail. The existence of the Bordet-Danysz phenomenon is considered as an argument in favor of adsorption, but it may be used equally well as an argument in favor of the existence of a series of definite compounds.

The rate of formation, stability, and dissociation of toxin-antitoxin floccules have been studied anew under many conditions, notably by Ramon and by Madsen and Schmidt (82). Ramon and his co-workers have found that most of the anatoxin can be recovered by heating the floccules in water at 95 to 100° for 10 minutes. This destroys the antitoxin, but methods of separation were not worked out. In elaboration of an earlier observation, confirmed by Ramon, that a neutral toxin-antitoxin mixture becomes toxic if anatoxin is added, Schmidt has developed a theory of the detoxification of toxin by antitoxin, based on the assumption, also held by Ramon, that ana-toxin or toxoid possesses a greater affinity for antitoxin than does the original toxin itself. Heidelberger and Kendall (83) have pointed out, however, that this assumption is unnecessary if the mass law applies, since anatoxin or toxoid might disturb the equilibrium of a neutral mixture even if its affinity for antitoxin were only one-hundredth as great. Neither Ramon nor Schmidt (84) accepts this criticism, however, although the latter has since modified his views to some extent.

As regards hemolysis, Abramson (85) concludes that sensitiza-tion does not change the isoelectric point of red cells, nor is the ob-served diminution in mobility a specific effect, hemolysis in the presence of complement evidently being capable of occurring when only a very small part of the cell surface is changed. A quantitative basis for the technique of the complement-fixation reaction has been sought by Wadsworth, Maltaner, and Maltaner (86).

That phagocytosis and microörganisms may be influenced by changing the ionic atmosphere in which the reaction takes place is indicated by the work of Broom and Brown (87), who observed an inhibition by the ferrocyanide ion.

Recent work by Fuchs (88) has tended to confirm his original finding of the identity of the midpiece, or main component, of complement with prothrombin. He also points out that in hemolytic systems a second reaction takes place independently, involving the inactivation of complement through its conversion into thrombin in the presence of the serum calcium by the cytozyme phosphatides liberated by the hemolyzed cells.

Following Krueger's development of methods for the determination of phage (P) and bacteria (B), in the presence of each other (89), Krueger and Northrop (90) have studied the kinetics of the reaction in the case of *Staphylococcus aureus*. They find lytic destruction of B to begin only after log $P/B = 2.1$; that during B growth all but 10 to 30 per cent of P becomes attached to B and the relative amount attached remains constant, suggesting the behavior of a simple chemical compound, rather than that of an organized parasite; that during the logarithmic B-growth phase, P formation is also logarithmic, but proceeds at a faster rate; that during B-lysis much P is destroyed; and that P and B formation have different temperature coefficients. Many other observations are made and a mathematical formula for the process is given, according to which the calculated times of lysis for various concentrations of P and B agree excellently with those observed. Krueger (91) has also studied the union of P with living and dead B and found that in the former case P is distributed reversibly in a manner typical of numerous materials soluble in both phases of a two-phase system, while distribution is of the adsorptive type with dead susceptible B. By means of diffusion experiments Hetler and Bronfenbrenner (92) have concluded that P is attached to particles varying in radius from 0.6 mμ to 11.4 mμ.

The Wassermann reaction and related flocculation reactions have been thoroughly studied by Eagle (93). The results are interpreted in a fashion similar to that developed by the same worker for specific agglutination and precipitation (75). It is held that in the flocculation reactions the colloidal "antigen" combines with specifically altered serum globulin (reagin). The latter is denatured by the combination and flocked by the electrolyte present. The Wassermann reaction is entirely analogous, in that complement fixation is accomplished by the process outlined above, whether or not macroscopic flocculation takes place. The sensitizing action of cholesterol upon the antigen is considered due to its effect in coarsening the particles of the antigen dispersion.

LITERATURE CITED

1. KYES, P., AND PORTER, R. I., *J. Immunol.*, **20**, 85 (1931)
2. HOFFMANN, H., *Z. Immunitäts*, **71**, 171 (1931)
3. WORMALL, A., *J. Exptl. Med.*, **51**, 295 (1930)
4. LANDSTEINER, K., AND VAN DER SCHEER, J., *Proc. Soc. Exptl. Biol. Med.*, **27**, 812 (1930) ; **28**, 983 (1931) ; *Z. Hyg. Infektionskrankh.*, **113**, 1 (1931)
5. MOORE, M. B., CROMWELL, H. W., AND MOORE, E. E., *J. Allergy*, **2**, 85 (1931)
6. STULL, A., COOKE, R. A., AND CHOBOT, R., *J. Biol. Chem.*, **92**, 569 (1931)
7. BLACK, J. H., *J. Allergy*, **2**, 161 (1931)
8. FISCHER, M. N., AND HOCHBERG, R. B., *Z. Immunitäts*, **68**, 43 (1930)
9. HEIDELBERGER, M., AND KENDALL, F. E., *J. Exptl. Med.*, **54**, 515 (1931)
10. ECKSTEIN, H. C., AND SOULE, M. H., *J. Biol. Chem.*, **91**, 395 (1931)
11. SEIBERT, F. B., *Am. Rev. Tuberc.*, **21**, 370 (1930) ; SEIBERT, F. B., AND MUNDAY, B., *Am. Rev. Tuberc.*, **23**, 23 (1931)
11a. MASCHMANN, E., AND KÜSTER, E.,. *Z. physiol. Chem.*, **193**, 215 (1930)
12. MAVER, M. E., *J. Infectious Diseases*, **49**, 1 (1931)
13a. *Diphtheria toxin:* BUNNEY, W. E., CIANCIARULO, J., AND KIAMIL, M., *J. Immunol.*, **20**, 417, 433 (1931); LINDERSTRÖM-LANG, K., AND SCHMIDT, S., *Compt. rend. soc. biol.*, **103**, 620 (1930) ; MASCHMANN, E., KÜSTER, E., AND FISCHER, W., *Ber.*, **64**, 2174 (1931) ; OHYAMA, S., *J. Biochem. (Japan)*, **13**, 255 (1931) ; SCHMIDT, S., AND COLLABORATORS, *Compt. rend. soc. biol.*, **103**, 1296, 1305, 1307 (1930) ; **105**, 323, 326, 332, 334 (1931) ; *Z. Immunitäts*, **71**, 101 (1931)
13b. *Streptococcus toxin:* SHINN, L. E., *J. Infectious Diseases*, **46**, 76 (1930) ; ANDO, K., KURAUCHI, K., AND NISHIMURA, H., *J. Immunol.*, **18**, 223, 257 (1930) ; WADSWORTH, A., AND QUIGLEY, J. J., *J. Immunol.*, **20**, 459 (1931)
13c. *Tetanus toxin:* FELIX, K., AND ENGEL, C., *Z. Immunitäts*, **70**, 41 (1931) ; MASCHMANN, E., *Z. physiol. Chem.*, **201**, 219 (1931) ; VELLUZ, L., *Compt. rend. soc. biol.*, **106**, 887 ; **107**, 674 (1931)
14. LOCKE, A., AND MAIN, E. R., *J. Infectious Diseases*, **43**, 43 (1928) ; **46**, 393 (1930) ; **48**, 419 (1931)
15. COULTER, C. B., AND STONE, F. M., *Proc. Soc. Exptl. Biol. Med.*, **27**, 715 (1930) ; *J. Gen. Physiol.*, **14**, 583 (1931)
16. KRESTOWNIKOWA, W. A:, AND RJACHINA, E. M., *Z. Immunitäts*, **65**, 444 (1930) ; KISSIN, D., AND BRONSTEIN, L., *Z. Immunitäts*, **66**, 210 (1930) ; HEWITT, L. F., *Biochem. J.*, **24**, 983 (1930)
17. BUNNEY, W. E., *J. Immunol.*, **20**, 47 (1931)
18. SCHMIDT, S., *Compt. rend. soc. biol.*, **103**, 95, 104 (1930) ; **108**, 146, 149, 151, 154 (1931)
19. VINCENT, H., AND VELLUZ, L., *Compt. rend.*, **192**, 648 (1931) ; *Compt. rend. soc. biol.*, **107**, 583 (1931)
20. GOEBEL, W. F., AND AVERY, O. T., *J. Exptl. Med.*, **54**, 431 (1931)
21. AVERY, O. T., AND GOEBEL, W. F., *J. Exptl. Med.*, **54**, 437 (1931)
22. DUBOS, R., AND AVERY, O. T., *J. Exptl. Med.*, **54**, 51 (1931)

23. AVERY, O. T., AND DUBOS, R., *J. Exptl. Med.,* **54,** 73 (1931)
24. BABERS, F. H., AND GOEBEL, W. F., *J. Biol. Chem.,* **89,** 387 (1930)
25. TILLETT, W. S., AND FRANCIS, T., *J. Exptl. Med.,* **52,** 561 (1930); TILLETT, W. S., GOEBEL, W. F., AND AVERY, O. T., *J. Exptl. Med.,* **52,** 892 (1930)
26. HEIDELBERGER, M., AND KENDALL, F. E., *J. Exptl. Med.,* **53,** 625 (1931)
27. COOPER, G., EDWARDS, M., AND ROSENSTEIN, C., *J. Exptl. Med.,* **49,** 461 (1929)
28. DORSET, M., AND HENLEY, R. R., *J. Am. Vet. Med. Assoc.,* **76,** 696 (1930)
28a. JOHNSON, T. B., AND RENFREW, A. G., *Am. Rev. Tuberculosis,* **22,** 655 (1930)
29. MASUCCI, P., MCALPINE, K. L., AND GLENN, J. T., *Am. Rev. Tuberculosis,* **22,** 669, 678, 682 (1930)
30. CHARGAFF, E., AND ANDERSON, R. J., *Z. physiol. Chem.,* **191,** 172 (1930)
31. MORGAN, W. T. J., *Brit. J. Exptl. Path.,* **12,** 62 (1931)
32. MEYER, K., *Z. Immunitäts,* **68,** 98 (1930); **69,** 499 (1931)
33. EISLER, M., *Z. Immunitäts,* **70,** 48 (1931)
34. TOMCSIK, J., *Z. Immunitäts,* **66,** 8 (1930)
35. KESTEN, H. D., COOK, D. H., MOTT, E., AND JOBLING, J. W., *J. Exptl. Med.,* **52,** 813 (1930); KESTEN AND MOTT, *J. Exptl. Med.,* **53,** 803, 815 (1931)
36. SCHIEMANN, O., LOEWENTHAL, H., AND.HACKENTHAL, H., *Z. Hyg. Infektionskrankh.,* **112,** 315 (1931)
37. ENDERS, J. D., *J. Exptl. Med.,* **52,** 235 (1930)
38. WADSWORTH, A., AND BROWN, R., *J. Immunol.,* **21,** 245 (1931)
39. FELTON, L. D., *J. Immunol.,* **19,** 511 (1930)
40. ROSS, V., *J. Exptl. Med.,* **54,** 899 (1931)
41. ZOZAYA, J., *Science,* **74,** 270 (1931)
42. SORDELLI, A., AND MAYER, E., *Compt. rend. soc. biol.,* **107,** 736 (1931)
43. ZOZAYA, J., *J. Exptl. Med.,* **56,** 725 (1931)
44. HEIDELBERGER, M., AND GOEBEL, W. F., *J. Biol. Chem.,* **70,** 613 (1926); **74,** 613 (1927)
45. CHALLINOR, S. W., HAWORTH, W. N., AND HIRST, E. L., *J. Chem. Soc.,* **1931,** 258
46. HEIDELBERGER, M., AND KENDALL, F. E., *J. Biol. Chem.,* **84,** 639 (1929)
47. DOAN, C. A., AND MOORE, D. M., *Am. Rev. Tuberc.,* **23,** 409 (1931)
48. SABIN, F. R., DOAN, C. A., AND FORKNER, C. E., *J. Exptl. Med.,* **52,** Suppl. 3 (1930)
49. ANDERSON, R. J., *J. Biol. Chem.,* **83,** 169 (1929)
50. WADSWORTH, A., AND BROWN, R., *J. Immunol.,* **21,** 255 (1931)
51. MORAN, F., *Z. Immunitäts,* **67,** 115 (1930)
52. EDITORIAL, *J. Am. Med. Assoc.,* **97,** 1628 (1931)
53. LANDSTEINER, K., AND VAN DER SCHEER, J., *J. Exptl. Med.,* **54,** 295 (1931)
54. LANDSTEINER, K., AND VAN DER SCHEER, J., *Proc. Soc. Exptl. Biol. Med.,* **27,** 811 (1930)
55. JERMOLJEWA, Z., AND BUJANOWSKAJA, I., *Z. Immunitäts,* **68,** 342 (1930)
56. MANWARING, W. H., *J. Immunol.,* **19,** 155 (1930); SOX, H. C., AZEVEDO, J. L., AND MANWARING, W. H., *J. Immunol.,* **21,** 409 (1931)

57. DOERR, R., *Arch. Dermatol. Syphilis*, **151**, 11 (1926)
58. HEIDELBERGER, M., AND KENDALL, F. E., *Science*, **72**, 253 (1930)
59. HOOKER, S. B., AND BOYD, W. C., *J. Immunol.*, **21**, 113 (1931)
60. TOPLEY, W. W. C., *J. Path. Bact.*, **33**, 339 (1930)
61. BREINL, F., AND HAUROWITZ, F., *Z. physiol. Chem.*, **192**, 45 (1930)
62. WALTON, S. T., *J. Exptl. Med.*, **54**, 859 (1931)
63. SCHMIDT, A. A., AND TULJSCHINSKAJA, K., *Z. Immunitäts*, **70**, 8 (1931)
64. GARA, P. VON, *Z. Immunitäts*, **71**, 1 (1931)
65a. *Antibacterial antibodies:* FALK, K. G., McGUIRE, G., VALENTINE, E., AND WHITNEY, E., *J. Immunol.*, **21**, 199, 221 (1931) ; FELTON, L. D., *J. Immunol.*, **21**, 357 (1931)
65b. *Antitoxins:* BARR, M., AND GLENNY, A. T., *J. Path. Bact.*, **34**, 539 (1931) ; LINDERSTRÖM-LANG, K., AND SCHMIDT, S., *Compt. rend. soc. biol.*, **103**, 618 (1930) ; and *Compt. rend. trav. lab. Carlsberg*, **18**, No. 3 (1930) ; REUTER, F., *Biochem. Z.*, **231**, 175 (1931) ; SCHMIDT, S., *Z. Immunitäts*, **66**, 292, 506 (1930) ; WERNICKE, R., AND MODERN, F., *Compt. rend. soc. biol.*, **103**, 1277 (1930)
65c. *Hemolysins:* EULER, H. VON, AND BRUNIUS, E., *Z. Immunitäts*, **68**, 124 (1930)
66. FINDLAY, G. M., *Brit. J. Exptl. Path.*, **12**, 13 (1931)
67. SMYTH, F. S., AND BAIN, K., *J. Allergy*, **2**, 177 (1931)
68. HARVEY, E. N., AND DEITRICK, J. E., *J. Immunol.*, **18**, 65 (1930)
69. SUMNER, J. B., AND KIRK, J. S., *Science*, **74**, 102 (1931) ; *J. Biol. Chem.*, **94**, 21 (1931)
70. ZOZAYA, J., BOYER, J., AND CLARK, J., *J. Exptl. Med.*, **52**, 471 (1930)
71. HEIDELBERGER, M., SIA, R. H. P., AND KENDALL, F. E., *J. Exptl. Med.*, **52**, 477 (1930)
72. FELTON, L. D., *J. Immunol.*, **21**, 341 (1931)
73. BRONFENBRENNER, J., *Proc. Soc. Exptl. Biol. Med.*, **27**, 734 (1930) ; BRONFENBRENNER, J., HETLER, D. M., AND EAGLE, I. O., *Science*, **73**, 455 (1931)
73a. REINER, L., *Science*, **72**, 483 (1930)
74. MUDD, S., LUCKÉ, B., McCUTCHEON, M., AND STRUMIA, M., *J. Exptl. Med.*, **52**, 299, 313 (1930) ; *J. Gen. Physiol.*, **13**, 669 (1930)
75. EAGLE, H., *J. Immunol.*, **18**, 393 (1930)
76. HEIDELBERGER, M., AND KENDALL, F. E., *J. Exptl. Med.*, **50**, 809 (1929)
77. HEIDELBERGER, M., AND KENDALL, F. E., *Science*, **72**, 252 (1930)
78. MARRACK, J., AND SMITH, F. C., *Brit. J. Exptl. Path.*, **12**, 30, 182 (1931)
79. HAZEN, E. L., *J. Immunol.*, **19**, 393 (1930)
80. MARRACK, J., AND SMITH, F. C., *Proc. Roy. Soc. (London)*, B, **160**, 1 (1930) ; SMITH AND MARRACK, *Brit. J. Exptl. Path.*, **11**, 494 (1930)
81. BURNET, F. M., *J. Path. Bact.*, **34**, 471 (1931)
82. RAMON, G., *Compt. rend. soc. biol.*, **104**, 31, 131, 141 (1930) ; RAMON, G., LEGROUX, R., AND SCHOEN, M., *ibid.*, **106**, 525, 779 (1931) ; MADSEN, T., AND SCHMIDT, S., *Z. Immunitäts*, **65**, 357 (1930) ; SCHMIDT, S., *Compt. rend. soc. biol.*, **102**, 1095 (1929) ; *ibid.*, **103**, 104, 106, 272 (with MÖRCH, J. R.), 1293 (1930) ; *Z. Immunitäts*, **67**, 197 (1930) ; *Compt. rend. soc. biol.*, **106**, 583, 586 (1931) ; MODERN, F., AND WERNICKE, R., *ibid.*, **105**,

119 (1930); KJAER, T., *ibid.*, **107**, 333 (1931); BERTHELSEN, K. C., *J. Immunol.*, **21**, 21, 43 (1931)

83. HEIDELBERGER, M., AND KENDALL, F. E., *Compt. rend. soc. biol.*, **104**, 37 (1930); *Science*, **71**, 511 (1930)

84. SCHMIDT, S., *Compt. rend. soc. biol.*, **105**, 94 (1930); RAMON, G., *Compt. rend. soc. biol.*, **104**, 938 (1930); **105**, 173 (1930)

85. ABRAMSON, H. A., *J. Gen. Physiol.*, **14**, 163 (1931)

86. WADSWORTH, A., MALTANER, E., AND MALTANER, F., *J. Immunol.*, **21**, 313 (1931)

87. BROOM, J. C., AND BROWN, H. C., *Brit. J. Exptl. Path.*, **11**, 305 (1930)

88. FUCHS, H. J., *Z. Immunitäts*, **67**, 272 (1930); **69**, 330 (1931)

89. KRUEGER, A. P., *J. Gen. Physiol.*, **13**, 553, 557 (1930)

90. KRUEGER, A. P., AND NORTHROP, J. H., *J. Gen. Physiol.*, **14**, 223 (1931)

91. KRUEGER, A. P., *J. Gen. Physiol.*, **14**, 493 (1931)

92. HETLER, D. M., AND BRONFENBRENNER, J., *J. Gen. Physiol.*, **14**, 547 (1931)

93. EAGLE, H., *J. Exptl. Med.*, **52**, 717, 739, 747 (1930)

DEPARTMENT OF MEDICINE
COLLEGE OF PHYSICIANS AND SURGEONS
COLUMBIA UNIVERSITY, NEW YORK

THE BIOCHEMISTRY OF THE FUNGI*

By N. N. Iwanoff

Department of Plant Physiology
University of Leningrad

In 1930 Tamiya and Morita published a paper under the title "Bibliographie von *Aspergillus* 1729 bis 1928." At the present time (after Tamiya) the papers connected with the investigation of this fungus have been counted, and a steady increase in their number has been observed. In 1927, 129 works were published; in 1928 the number was 135. In subsequent years a further increase was to be expected. The number, for 1930 and 1931 only, exceeds 300. Though not all of these are of a biochemical character, there is no denying the fact that *Aspergillus,* as well as other mould fungi, are favourable objects of study in our physiological and biochemical laboratories and have served to solve a series of problems connected with the conversion and the accumulation of substances in the plant cell, as well as the problem of the formation and action of enzymes.

It is evident that if we were to discuss all works on the chemistry and biochemistry of fungi published during the last two years, a considerable part of the pages we have at our disposal would be filled merely by the list of these works. Therefore we shall discuss only certain aspects of the biochemistry of fungi, at the same time leaving aside everything pertaining to yeast. In view of the fundamental significance and wide expanse of the biochemical problems connected with yeast, which are now being successfully studied by such eminent biochemists as Neuberg, Euler, Harden, and others, it deserves to be treated separately.

Mention should be made of the comprehensive work (367 pages) *Studies in the Biochemistry of Micro-organisms* carried out in the laboratories of H. Raistrick, Robert Robinson, and others, in England, in collaboration with Charles Thom, of the United States Department of Agriculture. This exceptional co-operative work on the biochemistry of lower fungi, having led to most valuable results, cannot be treated adequately in our survey, in view of the quantity of data supplied by it. In our opinion the investigation of Raistrick

* Received, March 1, 1932.

and his colleagues is one of the first models science should strive to imitate if it wishes to achieve its purposes in a short time. Complex problems should be solved conjointly by a series of laboratories, attacking them from different sides, after a preliminary division of the work. It is according to this method of complex and systematized scientific work that science is based in the Soviet Union (U.S.S.R.).

Formation and accumulation of reserve substances in fungi.— Among the various substances observed in fungi particular attention has been drawn to the accumulation of mannitol. Even in 1890, Bourquelot had pointed out the presence of mannitol and of trehalose in *Aspergillus niger,* as well as the variation in proportion undergone by these two substances at different stages of growth. A thorough investigation was carried out in this field by the colleagues of Raistrick (p. 153) who, working with the white species of *Aspergillus,* as well as with *A. elegans* and *A. nidulans,* succeeded in noting that up to 50 per cent of the glucose may be converted into mannitol. An important rôle in the accumulation of mannitol is played by the access of air; with increase of aëration the amount of mannitol increases until a certain limit is reached; with still further increase, the amount of mannitol diminishes.

In continuing this work Coyne and Raistrick discovered that mannitol is formed from glucose, mannose, galactose, xylose, and arabinose, in an amount varying from 15 to 35 per cent. From fructose no mannitol is formed, though the fungus consumes up to 40 per cent of the sugar. Here we observe a picture which is the reverse of that seen in bacterial fermentation, where, according to the data of the Wisconsin biochemists, Stiles, Peterson, and Fred, "the bacteria used convert only fructose into mannitol." The cause of this disagreement, and of the failure of mannitol formation from fructose, we have not been able to determine. It is possible that here a reserve polysaccharide is first formed, which afterward is converted into mannitol.

Obaton, working with *Sterigmatocystis nigra,* has observed that the addition of glucose to the nutritive liquid leads to a high yield of trehalose in the mycelium, and to little mannitol; with invert sugar and levulose the inverse proportion is obtained—little trehalose and a high yield of mannitol.

One of the greatest experts in the chemistry of the higher fungi, J. Zellner, has published an essay in collaboration with Zikmunda in which the products secreted by the fungus *Polyporus sulfurens L.* are studied; especially interesting among them is a mixture of ergosterol and fungisterol which frequently occurs in fungi and may be extracted according to the method of Windaus (1907); of the other substances the presence of resinic acids, as well as of fumaric and oxalic acid (the latter in the form of the potassium salt), should be mentioned. The study of the sterols of fungi is especially important in connection with provitamin D. Takata has extracted from 1 kg. of dry mycelium of *Aspergillus oryzae* 2.1 gr. of crystalline sterol, which after irradiation by ultra-violet light exerted a healing influence on rachitis. The sterol proved akin to the fungisterol of Tanret and contained a certain amount of ergosterol. Prickett and his collaborators have pointed out the conditions favourable to the greatest accumulation of cholesterol—a neutral and slightly alkaline medium, good aëration, a combination of salts inducing an increase in weight of the fungus, and a nutritive medium of sugar beet molasses.

Chrzaszcz and Tinkow (1, 2, 3) mention the formation in mould fungi of starch, or, more precisely, of starch-like substances called by former authors "mould starch." The Polish authors even divide many of the species of *Penicillium,* investigated by them, into three groups: (*a*) true starch formers; (*b*) species accumulating acids, chiefly citric acid, and (*c*) species forming neither starch nor acids.

The accumulation of nutritive reserve substances depends on the form assumed by the fungus. To Lüers and his collaborators is due an interesting investigation on the transformation of the substances in *Mucor Guillermondi.* In a highly nutritive medium, with insufficient aëration and the presence of sugars, the mycelium of this fungus may be converted into typical yeast. The yeast form of the fungus differs from the mycelium by an increased content of glycogen and protein, and a more energetic metabolism, as well as by the number, but not the quality of enzymes.

In the writer's laboratory a work, not yet published, has been carried out by Gudlet. Its object was to study the extraction of protein from the fruit body of *Boletus edulis.* By infusing the powder of the mushroom with the gastric juice of a dog, up to 85 per cent of the total nitrogen present in the mushroom went into solution; from the latter were extracted the peptones soluble in 85 per cent alcohol. These contained up to 16 per cent of nitrogen, half of which belonged to the diamino-acid fraction.

Mention should be made of the monograph by Kiesel on the chemistry of protoplasm, based upon the study of the lower mucilaginous fungi, the *Myxomycetes*. In this work the chemistry of Reinke's plastin is discussed in detail, as well as a series of problems connected with the proteins of fungi. In view of the vastness of the material dealt with in the work, the readers interested in this problem must be referred to the original.

The ash elements of fungi also have received considerable study. Rippel and Behr have shown that magnesium may be extracted almost entirely (97 per cent) from the mycelium of *Aspergillus niger* by weak hydrochloric or by acetic acid; organic solvents, however, do not bring it into solution. With the growth of the fungus, the accumulation of magnesium is not parallel to that of the other ash elements. Trischler indicates how one may employ this fungus for ascertaining whether or not a given soil is rich in potassium, as *Aspergillus niger* reacts with more constancy on the content of potassium than on phosphoric acid. Very interesting analyses of the mineral substances in fungi have been carried out by the spectroscopic method by Ramage. Much potassium was found and little calcium; in addition, lithium and iron were contained in the fungi, and the presence ever of silver (0.001–0.01 per cent) and of copper (0.002–0.02 per cent) could be recorded.

The pigments of fungi.—The works treating of the pigments of the fungi are of a purely qualitative character. Blochwitz points out that the pigments of mould fungi readily change their colour with a change of reaction; the same pigments make it possible for us to judge of the reaction of the medium in the tissues of the fungus. When the pigment of *Penicilliopsis,* as well as its solubility in different solvents, was investigated, it showed a change of colour. Data on the nature of the pigments of *Penicillium glaucum* may be also found in Manceau.

A new pigment formed by the fungus *Citromyces* from glucose has been chemically investigated. This substance was crystallised from 50 per cent alcohol in the form of lemon-yellow needles and has been called by Hetherington and Raistrick (see Raistrick, page 209) *citromycetin.* The formation of the pigment requires free access of air. The citromycetin possesses the formula $C_{14}H_{10}O_7 \cdot 2H_2O$, which may be represented graphically as shown on the opposite page. Citromycetin is a strong dyestuff recalling by its hue the dye luteolin. The reactions of the compound correspond to some extent with the dyes of the xanthone or flavone group; it forms a green fluorescent solution with sulphuric acid.

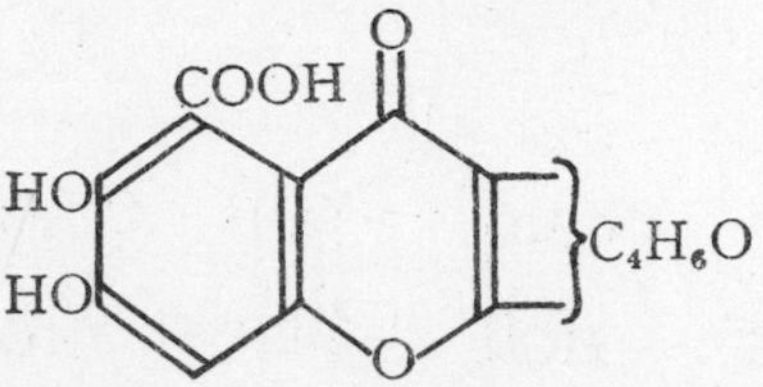

Citromycetin

The same authors (p. 269) have obtained from *Penicillium citrinum* a lemon-yellow pigment, *citrinin,* having the empirical formula, $C_{13}H_{14}O_5$.

The products of the breakdown of citrinin have been investigated. Coyne, Raistrick, and Robinson (see Raistrick, p. 297) have studied its structure and propose the following formula:

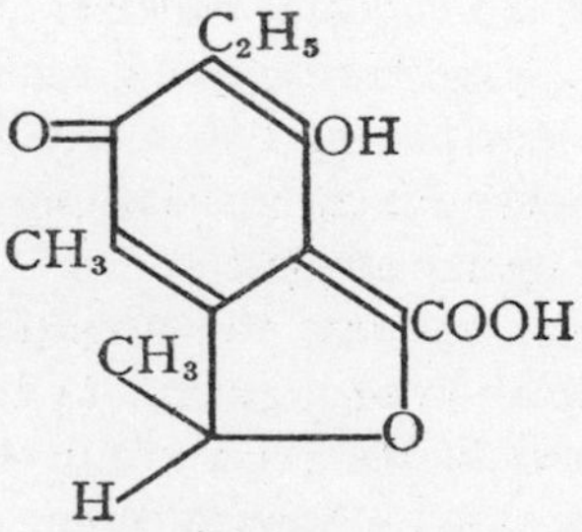

Citrinin

Upon the addition of ferric chloride solution citrinin deposits a buff-coloured precipitate; upon the addition of $KMnO_4$ it becomes instantly discoloured.

Birkinshaw and Raistrick (see Raistrick, p. 245) have obtained from three races of *Penicillium spinulosum* a new pigmented substance, methoxy-dihydroxy-toluquinone, produced by the fungi from glucose. This substance crystallises in purple-black crystals similar in appearance to potassium permanganate. On careful oxidation it proved to be a derivate of quinone. Its structure may be expressed by one of the following three formulae:

a   b   c

This is the first recorded instance of the production of a quinone derivative from glucose by fungi.

Raistrick and Rintoul (see Raistrick, p. 255) have extracted and studied a mucilaginous substance, luteic acid, produced by the fungus *Penicillium luteum*. This substance, the salts of which give rise to very viscous solutions, is a colloidal material of high molecular weight built up of unusual polysaccharide units, each of which is a product arising from the condensation of two molecules of glucose with one molecule of malonic acid; one carboxyl group of the latter is left free and two molecules of water are lost.

Some authors point out that the presence of particular ions is necessary for the formation of pigments in fungi. Metz has investigated colour formation in the representatives of *Ascomycetes*. In *Penicillium luteum* the usual yellowish colour of the lower side of the mycelium was turned blue-red through the presence of iron. *Fusarium* requires the presence of zinc, iron, and copper for the normal development of its colour.

The pigments of higher fungi have been studied by Kögl and his collaborators. From the red pilei of the fly agaric (*Amanita muscaria* L.) Kögl and Erxleben (1) extracted a crystalline glucoside called by them *muscarufin*. The authors obtained from 500 kg. of fresh agarics only 850 mg. of glucoside, the empirical formula of which is $C_{25}H_{16}O_9$. Muscarufin has been chemically studied by the authors in a detailed way, and variants of the structural formula have been given.

Zopf (1889) extracted from fungi belonging to the·species, *Thelephora,* a peculiar pigment, *thelophoric acid,* the alcohol solution of which showed a deep red colour. According to Zellner (1915, 1917), thelophoric acid is contained also in *Hydnum ferrugineum.* Kögl, Erxleben, and Jänecke have extracted, by means of hot pyridine, a substance whose large crystals resembled in colour $KMnO_4$. The empirical formula of thelephoric acid is $C_{20}H_{12}O_9$. The general data lead us to the following structural formula for thelephoric acid:

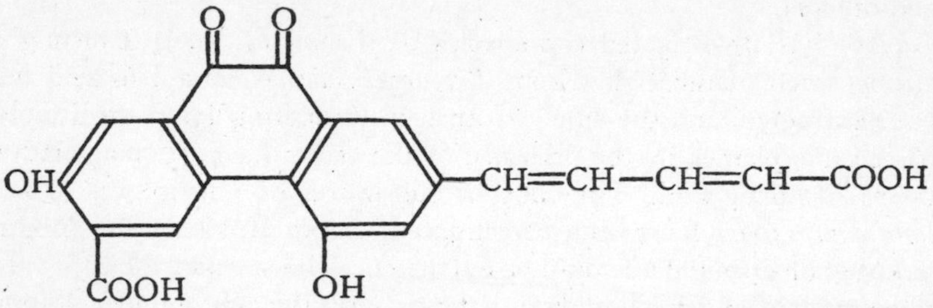

Up to the present time there has been no evidence of the presence in the plant cell of pigments of the phenanthrene series, though in alkaloids (morphine), derivatives of the series are met with. To such derivatives of the phenanthrene series belongs the pigment xylindein extracted by Kögl and Erxleben (2) from decaying wood.

Poisonous and odorous substances of fungi.—The majority of works on the poisonous substances contained in fungi are of a tentative character, works in which the presence of poison in a given fungus has been ascertained by tests on animals. There even exist data (Pilàt) in which the investigator, in testing the species *Hebeloma,* observed all the symptoms of poisoning on his own person.

In view of the foregoing, the investigation of Kögl, Duisberg, and Erxleben, who studied the chemical composition of muscarine and the strength of its physiological action by a quantitative method, is of surpassing interest. As the unit of action of muscarine the authors accepted M.W.E. (Muscarin-Wirkungs-Einheit), the amount which in Ringer's solution reduced the activity (Hubhöhe) of an isolated frog heart by 25 ± 5 per cent. The muscarine base contains 184 million M.W.E. in 1 gr.

When distilled with Ag_2O, muscarine yields trimethylamine, $(CH_3)_3N$, and the acid, $(C_4H_9O_2) \cdot COOH$, which is α, β-dihydroxy *n*-valeric acid; muscarine has an aldehydic group in view of which the authors give as the most probable formula:

$$CH_3 \cdot CH_2 \cdot CHOH \cdot CH \cdot CHO$$
$$HO \cdot N \equiv (CH_3)_3$$

There exist data on the odorous principles of fungi, in particular on one which suggests the odor of phenol (Kallenback; Passecker; and others).

Aye has investigated the species of *Trametes,* fungi emitting a strong smell of aniseed. From *Trametes suaveolens* anisic acid has been extracted, and the smell of aniseed emanating from the fungus has been explained by the presence of the esters (in particular methyl ester) of anisic acid. The odorous substances of mushrooms (*Psalliota campestris*) have been investigated. From 10 kg. of the fungus 0.125 g. of essential oil could be extracted. The substance has proved to be an acid of semi-liquid consistency with the acid number 48 and the ester number 95. *Boletus edulis* also contains an odorous substance; from 1 kg. of dried mushrooms, 0.35 gr. of this substance could be extracted. But in this case, as well as in the other fungi investigated, the author has obtained no derivates of anisic acid.

Organic acids of fungi.—The formation of organic acids should be considered in detail for two reasons: (*a*) just now a series of exceptionally interesting facts regarding the genesis of these acids has been established; (*b*) a series of industries for the technical manufacture of citric and gluconic acid with the aid of mould fungi has been organized.

Let us examine together the formation of citric and of oxalic acid. As early as 1893 Wehmer established that the fungus *Citromyces* accumulates citric acid from sugar. Later on it was shown that the faculty of forming citric acid is widespread among the lower fungi. At the present time the process is extensively studied for its industrial application in the manufacture of citric acid from sugar. Butkewitsch (1922–1924) showed that when the fungus is cultivated in a neutral solution a mixture of oxalic and nitric acid is obtained; when cultivated in an alkaline medium (in the presence of $CaCO_3$) only oxalic acid is formed, while cultivation in an intensely acid medium leads to the formation of only citric acid. The early works of Butkewitsch (1922) and Molliard (1922) have moreover established a connection between the accumulation of citric acid and the special nitrogenous nutrition of the fungus. With ample nitrogenous food there is usually accumulated comparatively less acid than with an insufficient supply of nitrogen. However, the data of Bernhauer (1926) have shown that in some cases citric acid is accumulated even with an abundant nitrogenous supply.

Butkewitsch has demonstrated that citric acid is formed directly from sugar, not from proteins, as supposed by other authors. Kostytschew and Tschesnokow have shown that as long as the fungus absorbs nitrogen from the solution it accumulates no citric acid. As soon as the absorption of nitrogen ceases, citric acid begins to accumulate, if the growth of the fungus is not checked by the ageing of the mycelium. While the acid is being formed, no absorption of nitrogen takes place. Kostytschew has expressed the view that the formation of citric acid is connected with the absorption of nitrogen, consequently with the structure of the proteins of the fungus. It may be supposed that citric acid represents the modified and oxidized skeleton of the "abortive" links of the protein molecule.

The method of Kostytschew is as follows: The fungus *Aspergillus niger* is grown under optimum conditions of mineral and nitrogenous nutrition; after 24 to 48 hours it has formed a continuous film, being in the stage of vigorous growth and synthesis of proteins. At this time the nutrient solution is poured off and replaced by a pure concentrated sugar solution containing neither mineral elements nor nitrogen. After three days the process of citric acid formation is usually at an end; in normal cultures the yield of acid reaches 40 to 50 per cent of the total sugar present in the solution.

In cultivating *Aspergillus niger* on 10 per cent raffinose as a source of carbon, Amelung has shown that citric acid is formed from the fructose obtained through the splitting of raffinose into fructose and melibiose; the latter is not consumed by the fungus as melibiase is not contained therein.

A series of hypotheses as to the mechanism of citric acid formation by fungi from sugar has been advanced. Bernhauer and Siebenäuger, according to a recent paper, are inclined to think that it forms from sugar through acetic acid. In support of this view there are the works of Butkewitsch and Fedoroff, as well as of Chrzaszcz and Tinkow (1, 2). The latter have shown that *Penicillium X* possesses the faculty of forming, along with succinic, fumaric (as has been shown by Russian authors), malic, and oxalic acids, also citric acid, from sodium acetate and potassium acetate. The process of the formation of citric acid from acetic acid may be in accordance with the following schema:

$$
\begin{array}{cccc}
\text{COOH} & \text{COOH} & \text{COOH} & \text{COOH} \\
| & | & | & | \\
\text{CH}_3 \quad (-\text{H}_2) & \text{CH}_2 \quad (-\text{H}_2) & \text{CH} \quad (+\text{H}_2\text{O}) & \text{CH}_2 \\
\xrightarrow{\qquad} & \xrightarrow{\qquad} & \xrightarrow{\qquad} & \\
\text{CH}_3 & \text{CH}_2 & \text{CH} & \text{CHOH} \\
| & | & \| & | \\
\text{COOH} & \text{COOH} & \text{COOH} & \text{COOH}
\end{array}
$$

$$
\begin{array}{c}
\text{CH}_2 \cdot \text{COOH} \\
| \\
\text{CHOH} \cdot \text{COOH}
\end{array}
+
\begin{array}{c}
\text{CH}_3 \\
| \\
\text{COOH}
\end{array}
\xrightarrow{(-\text{H}_2)}
\begin{array}{c}
\text{CH}_2 \cdot \text{COOH} \\
| \\
\text{COH} \cdot \text{COOH} \\
| \\
\text{CH}_2 \cdot \text{COOH}
\end{array}
$$

This important discovery of Russian and Polish investigators points to the possibility of a wide generalization based upon a relationship between the course of acid formation in fungi and the process of alcoholic fermentation, on the lines laid down by Neuberg in 1911: sugar → pyruvic acid → acetaldehyde → ethyl alcohol; the last becomes oxidized to acetic acid. Bernhauer and Siebenäuger, having adopted the same scheme, have shown that two races of *Aspergillus niger* are endowed with the faculty of converting ethyl alcohol into citric acid; they likewise have been able to demonstrate that it is possible, by means of special races of *Aspergillus niger*, to obtain from acetic acid up to 16 per cent of citric acid, calculated from the weight of the acetic acid used up in the experiment.

As for oxalic acid, the recent work of Butkewitsch and Fedoroff (2) shows that this acid also may be readily obtained, by means of *Mucor stolonifer*, from acetates. This is confirmed by a new work of Bernhauer and Siebenäuger. These authors have drawn up a plan for the conversion of acetic acid into oxalic acid, either (*a*) through glycollic and glyoxylic acids:[1]

$$
\begin{array}{c}
\text{CH}_3 \\
| \\
\text{COOH}
\end{array}
\rightarrow
\begin{array}{c}
\text{CH}_2\text{OH} \\
| \\
\text{COOH}
\end{array}
\rightarrow
\begin{array}{c}
\overset{\text{O}}{\underset{\backslash \text{H}}{\text{C}\!\!\nearrow}} \\
| \\
\text{COOH}
\end{array}
\rightarrow
\begin{array}{c}
\text{COOH} \\
| \\
\text{COOH}
\end{array}
$$

[1] Cf. Walker, Subramanian, and Challenger.

or (b) from acetic acid through succinic, fumaric, malic, and óxal-acetic acids:

$$
\begin{array}{ccccccc}
\text{COOH} & & \text{COOH} & & \text{COOH} & & \text{COOH} \\
| & & | & & | & & | \\
\text{CH}_3 & \xrightarrow{(-H_2)} & \text{CH}_2 & \xrightarrow{(-H_2)} & \text{CH} & \xrightarrow{(+H_2O)} & \text{CHOH} \\
| & & | & & \| & & | \\
\text{CH}_3 & & \text{CH}_2 & & \text{CH} & & \text{CH}_2 \\
| & & | & & | & & | \\
\text{COOH} & & \text{COOH} & & \text{COOH} & & \text{COOH}
\end{array}
$$

$$
\begin{array}{ccc}
& \text{COOH} & \text{COOH} \\
& | & | \\
\xrightarrow{(-H_2)} & \text{C}=\text{O} & \text{COOH} \\
& | & \overline{} \\
& \text{CH}_2 & \text{CH}_3 \\
& | & | \\
& \text{COOH} & \text{COOH}
\end{array}
$$

Chrzaszcz and Tinkow (1, 3) hold that the amount of oxalic acid formed from sugar depends on the amount of amino-acids and on their structure, as well as on their participation, along with ammonia, in the building up of the protein molecule; as for citric acid, it is not connected with the formation of proteins, as was supposed by Kostytschew.

The formation of gluconic acid was studied by Molliard in 1922, Butkewitsch in 1924, and Bernhauer in 1924. It has proved that a whole series of mould fungi of the genera *Aspergillus*, *Penicillium*, and *Citromyces* are typical formers of gluconic acid. Bernhauer, in his former work, held the view that the accumulation of gluconic acid depends in a considerable degree on the race of the fungus. According to the data of Kostytschew, gluconic acid is formed only in case the nitrogen content in the mycelium of the fungus is below a certain norm, so that it is possible to regulate the process of acid formation in such a way as to check the production of oxalic and gluconic acid.

Schober, in his careful work, has ascertained that the assimilation of atmospheric nitrogen leads to a loss of energy resulting from the oxidation of glucose to gluconic acid. If glucose is replaced by fructose no nitrogen is fixed and no gluconic acid is formed.

Recently the formation of d-mannonic acid from d-mannose by means of the races of *Penicillium* has been demonstrated by Angeletti and Cerruti.

Walker, Subramanian, and Challenger have demonstrated the formation of saccharic acid by *Aspergillus niger,* and its conversion into citric acid.

According to the patent of Herrick and May (see Bernhauer) the formation of gluconic acid takes place in an acid medium, in the absence of neutralizing agents, but there may be found data in the literature on patents that gluconic acid is obtained in the form of a "salt of calcium" in the presence of $CaCO_3$.

Wehmer in 1918 was the first to show that succinic and fumaric acids are formed by *Aspergillus fumaricus;* it has been proved that a series of other fungi of the genera *Mucor* and *Rhizopus* (after F. Ehrlich, 1911) form fumaric acid. Butkewitsch and Fedoroff (1) have shown that *Rhizopus nigricans* is able to form 30 to 40 per cent of fumaric acid, calculated from the sugar consumed; if we consider that part of the sugar is used up in forming mycelium and alcohol, the yield of fumaric acid, calculated from sugar, reaches up to 50 per cent. As regards the chemism of the formation of these acids, attention should be directed to the data of Takahashi and Asai (1925), and in particular to that of Butkewitsch and Fedoroff, as to the formation of succinic and fumaric acid from acetates by the genus *Rhizopus.* An especially sensational discovery of the two latter authors is that succinic acid may be formed from ethyl alcohol. Based upon these data, the following schema for the conversion of sugar with alcoholic fermentation may be drawn up:

$$C_6H_{12}O_6 \rightarrow 2CO_2 + 2 \begin{array}{c} CH_2OH \\ | \\ CH_3 \end{array} \longrightarrow 2 \begin{array}{c} COOH \\ | \\ CH_3 \end{array}$$

$$\xrightarrow{(-H_2)} \begin{array}{c} CH_2 \cdot COOH \\ | \\ CH_2 \cdot COOH \end{array} \xrightarrow{(-H_2)} \begin{array}{c} CH \cdot COOH \\ || \\ CH \cdot COOH \end{array}$$

Succinic acid   Fumaric acid

The conversion of succinic acid into fumaric acid probably takes place under the influence of the enzyme succino-dehydrogenase, while fumaric acid may be converted into malic acid after the addition of water to the double bond.

On the basis of his discovery, Butkewitsch thinks that if his schema for the formation of succinic acid is confirmed in experiments with alcoholic fermentation, we shall have to return to the views of Pasteur, who held that succinic acid forms from sugar in fermentation; more exactly, we shall have to admit two sources of succinic acid—from sugar, according to Pasteur, and from glutamic acid, according to F. Ehrlich.

Not all fungi show the faculty of accumulating fumaric acid. Thies in cultivating *Aspergillus fumigatus* under different conditions has found this acid only in inconsiderable quantities; Thies supposes that as time goes on the fungus greatly changes the course of its chemical processes.

Kojic acid (5-hydroxy 2-hydroxymethyl pyrone) was isolated by Saito (1907) in *Aspergillus oryzae*. Jabuta (1924) has given it its name and has definitely established its structure.

Kojic acid

Corbellini and Gregorini have studied the formation of this acid on different carbon sources, with the aid of different races of the fungus *Aspergillus flavus,* and have come to the conclusion that the pyrone nucleus is synthesised from substances containing three carbon atoms which, in turn, have resulted from the breakdown of large molecules —pentoses or hexoses. These authors suppose that the synthesis of the acid takes place under the influence of the enzyme carboligase discovered by C. Neuberg in yeast.

Mauer has recently synthesised kojic acid, starting from aceto-brom-glucose, and has confirmed the structure established by Jabuta in 1924.

May, Moyer, Wells, and Herrick have studied in detail the formation of kojic acid by *Aspergillus flavus* under different conditions of nitrogenous nutrition, temperature, concentration of sugar, and depth of the cultural liquid. The authors succeeded in showing that this organism, when grown in a 20 per cent solution of dextrose, is able to convert, in the course of twelve days after sowing, over 45 per cent of the dextrose present (55 per cent of that consumed) into kojic acid. As for the mode of formation of this acid, the authors are inclined to think that the sugar and the other carbon compounds first split into simple substances, out of which kojic acid is then synthesised. What these simple substances are like, and whether or not acetaldehyde is among them, are questions to be answered by further investigations. An analogous phenomenon—the formation of succinic and fumaric acid from ethyl alcohol and acetic acid by means of *Mucor stolonifera*—has been observed by Butkewitsch and Fedoroff (1).

The schema of transformation of glucose into kojic acid may be represented as follows:

$$
\begin{array}{ccc}
\begin{array}{l}
\text{CHOH--} \\
\text{H} \cdot \text{C} \cdot \text{OH} \\
\text{HO} \cdot \text{C} \cdot \text{H} \quad \text{O} \rightarrow \\
\text{H} \cdot \text{C} \cdot \text{OH} \\
\text{HC} \\
\text{CH}_2\text{OH}
\end{array}
&
\begin{array}{l}
\text{CHOH--} \\
\text{H} \cdot \text{C} \cdot \text{OH} \\
\text{C=O} \quad \text{O} \rightarrow \\
\text{H} \cdot \text{C} \cdot \text{OH} \\
\text{H} \cdot \text{C} \\
\text{CH}_2\text{OH}
\end{array}
&
\begin{array}{l}
\text{CH--} \\
\text{C} \cdot \text{OH} \\
\text{C=O} \quad \text{O} \\
\text{CH} \\
\text{C} \\
\text{CH}_2\text{OH}
\end{array}
\end{array}
$$

Kojic acid

Wykman obtained with *Aspergillus flavum* a great quantity of kojic acid, but with *Penicillium glaucum,* under the same conditions, a crystalline substance was obtained, the molecular weight of which was over twice that of kojic acid.

Raistrick in his important work (pp. 140 and 148) describes a method of determining kojic acid, based on the molecule of kojic acid absorbing ten atoms of iodine. A qualitative determination of the products of the reaction between kojic acid and iodine in alkaline solution indicates the presence of iodoform, iodide, formic acid, oxalic acid, and glycollic acid. The author studies the transformation of kojic acid according to its various stages, mentioning among the intermediate products pyruvic alcohol (CH_3COCH_2OH) and glyoxal. Ultimately the reaction may be expressed in the following equations:

$$C_6H_6O_4 + 5I_2 + 11NaOH \rightarrow CHI_3 + 7NaI + H \cdot COONa$$
$$+ \begin{array}{l} COONa \\ COONa \end{array} + \begin{array}{l} CH_2OH \\ COONa \end{array} + 6H_2O$$

Recently, 6-hydroxy 2-methyl benzoic acid has been mentioned by Anslow and Raistrick as a product of the metabolism of glucose by the fungus.

As regards the conditions of organic acid formation, Behr positively states that, in the autolysis of *Aspergillus niger,* no organic acids are formed from the deamination of the amino-acids.

As may be seen from the works mentioned above, the theories of organic acid formation have entered the stage of vast generalization. The obtaining of succinic, fumaric, and citric acids from acetic acid and alcohol shows definitely that we may accept a uniform schema of sugar metabolism for yeast, as well as for mould fungi, in which, after the breakdown of the sugar has been carried to acetaldehyde, in some cases (yeast) ethyl alcohol is formed, in other cases (through acetic acid or through ethyl alcohol) compound organic acids, such as succinic, fumaric, citric, and other acids, appear. The comprehension of the origin of these acids, as well as of their frequent simultaneous presence, a fact pointing to their common origin, is considerably facilitated. Two courses adopted in research have proved productive: the first, alteration of the cultural conditions (pH, concentration of sugar, amount of nitrogen), with the formation, by the same fungus species, of certain acids and the suppression of others; the second, the study of the various fungi, as well as of their races, with considerable differences in the nature of the acids being formed. The comparison of all data obtained from the two lines of investigation will afford a clear picture of the genesis of organic acids in fungi.

The enzymes of fungi.—Up to now the higher fungi have been little studied from the point of view of enzyme content. Among them, however, there occur parasites living on wood which indubitably must possess an active enzymatic apparatus. This fact has drawn the attention of Czapek, Zellner, and others. Lutz investigated the soluble enzymes secreted by the species of *Hymenomycetes.* He determined the decomposition of hemicelluloses—arabans, mannans, and galactans—which occur as gums in many plants (*Ceratonia siliqua, Gleditschia triacanthos*). Lutz (1) cultivated the fungi *Stereum hirsulum, Polyporus pinicola,* etc., on solutions of nutritive salts, giving them different gums as carbon sources; it could be observed that a liquefaction and dissolution of the fungi took place, and by means of reagents the presence of mannose and galactose could be revealed, i.e., the enzymatic breakdown of hemicellulose could be established.

In studying the conversion of hemicellulose in the soil, Waksman and Diehm observed that the number of fungi able to decompose hemicellulose is much greater than that of fungi decomposing pure cellulose; this is a property of many fungi belonging to the higher as well as to the lower groups. The authors have tested a series of pure cultures of fungi belonging to the genera *Actinomyces, Rhizopus, Penicillium, Aspergillus,* etc., which in a sandy medium decomposed mannan, xylan, and galactan, whereby galactan proved more resistant to decomposition by fungi than mannan and xylan. Hemicelluloses serve both for the building up of fungi and as sources of energy. In this process much carbon dioxide is eliminated, and very little organic acid formation takes place.

Lutz (2) has studied the decay of wood caused by the enzymes secreted by the fungi *Cariolus versicolor, Polyporus pinicola,* and others. The wood decays gradually, first the lignin, which passes from the stage of insoluble gums to soluble ones, then the cellulose and the median plate of the cell walls. Among the products of conversion (acetone and glucuronic acid) the formation of sugars has been observed also.

N. N. Iwanoff, Dodonowa, and Tschastuchin have investigated the enzymes of higher fungi. The triturated mass of the fruit body of the mushroom proved incapable of inducing the splitting of sucrose in a 0.5 per cent solution. In other experiments, a 1 per cent solution of sucrose penetrated through the stalk into the pileus of the mushroom and accumulated there without hydrolysis. Hence the authors draw the conclusion that such a widespread enzyme as sucrase (invertase) is not contained in mushrooms. Mushrooms grown in pure cultures do not secrete into the surrounding medium either sucrase, inulase, or urease; under these conditions there have been studied in fungi, maltase, glycogenase, amylase, a proteolytic enzyme, and catalase. Weidenhagen has pointed out that he has succeeded in finding sucrase in the water-extract of mushrooms. However, in our (unpublished) experiments no sucrase could be detected in mushrooms, so that Weidenhagen's data have received no confirmation. On the whole, it has been proved that the enzymes secreted by mushrooms are weaker than those secreted by mould fungi, a fact pointed out in the last work of Tschastuchin. The feeble enzyme equipment of higher fungi must be associated with their limited distribution in nature.

Lutz, continuing his experiments with soluble enzymes secreted by fungi, has studied the oxidation-reduction systems present. He has succeeded in showing that fungi are rich in oxidising as well as in reducing enzymes and that quinone is regenerated into hydroquinone, which later on must act as *"antioxygène."* In media reducing quinone to hydroquinone a considerable acceleration of the reduction processes is observed. In another work Lutz (3) has studied the reducing action of several substances belonging to the essential oils, availing himself of the enzymes secreted by *Hymenomycetes.* Still resorting to the enzymes of fungi, Lutz (4) has shown further that, in comparison to a series of phenols tested by the author, tannin possesses a much higher *"pouvoir antioxygène."* Hence he has drawn the conclusion that this *pouvoir antioxygène* of tannin is its principal biological property.

The oxidation-reduction systems of a series of fungi have been studied by Labrousse and Philippon, who used as indicators methylene blue, cresol blue, and guaiacol. *Armillaria mella, Fusarium* and other fungi oxidize guaiacol, because near the developed mycelium a red-brown colour is observed; in the presence of methylene blue and cresol blue no change of colour takes place.

Of the enzymes connected with the transformation of nitrogen, Schmalfuss and Mothes have studied asparaginase (hydrolase) in *Aspergillus niger,* proceeding according to the equation : Asparagin $+$ water $\rightleftarrows$ ammonium aspartate. The enzyme acts not only in the living cell, but may be extracted from the mycelium of the fungus by water or glycerol; it is sensitive to drying and to treatment with alcohol, ether, and acetone. N. N. Iwanoff and Awetissowa have shown that, under certain conditions, *Aspergillus niger* may well assimilate guanidine as a nitrogen substratum, owing to the occurrence of a special enzyme, guanidinase. By means of the dried mycelium of the fungus containing guanidinase, and containing no urease, guanidine may be quantitatively split into urea and ammonia :

$$NH_2 \cdot C \overset{NH_2}{\underset{N}{\Big\backslash}} \quad or \quad NH = C \overset{NH_2}{\underset{NH}{\Big\backslash}} + H_2O \longrightarrow NH = C \overset{NH_3}{\underset{O}{\Big\backslash}} + NH_3$$

Recently Brunel has pointed out the presence of allantoinase in many fungi, an enzyme splitting allantoin into urea and glyoxylic acid.

Lately Kertesz has suggested a simple formula which makes it possible to determine the total amount (E_1) of the enzyme sucrase in the mycelium of a mould culture. With adequate salt nutrition E_1 increases with increase in the amount of sucrose in the nutritive solution; if the necessary inorganic elements (K, P, Mg) are lacking, E_1 remains about constant even though the sucrose supply be increased. In the author's opinion, this method makes it possible to study the distribution of the enzyme between mycelium and medium. Simultaneously the work of Doby and Feher was published, from which it may be seen that there exists a parallel action of the ions on the development of the mycelium of *Penicillium,* as well as on the formation of sucrase in it. In the absence of K, Mg, and P, the mycelial dry weight and the amount of the enzyme are diminished; increase in the concentration of sucrose leads to a still greater decrease in sucrase. By way of contrast the same concentration of sugar leads to an increase in the yield of sucrase if Ca is absent and P is slightly deficient, thus producing the same result as would be observed in a normal nutrient medium.

There exists a series of communications on the increased activity of esterase and protease of fungi, in connection with nutrition (Naylor); in other works the optimum of the activity of lipase is sought for (Juracec); the influence of acetates and of phosphates on the activity of amylase in *Aspergillus oryzae* is investigated (Caldwell and Tyler); and a series of other works pertain to the enzymes in lower fungi.

The transformation of nitrogen in fungi.—There exists an old and vast literature on the assimilation of nitrogen from the air by mould fungi, in which positive results frequently alternate with negative ones. Schober conducted nutrition experiments with *Aspergillus niger* and has demonstrated that this fungus fixes nitrogen from the atmosphere. It draws the energy for the assimilation of nitrogen from the combustion of carbon compounds, chiefly glucose. The acids formed and the addition of bound nitrogen check the fixation of nitrogen. There are also the interesting data of Badanes that *Aspergillus niger* is found in the caries of teeth where it assimilates the nitrogen from the air, converts the bound nitrogen into nitrites and nitrates, and forms citric acid from sucrose.

As regards other transformations of nitrogen, the work of Sakamura on the assimilation by *Aspergillus oryzae* of ammonia and nitrate from NH_4NO_3 should be mentioned. It has proved that the assimilation of one ion before the other depends on the racial distinctions of the fungus, on the conditions of earlier culture, and even on the method of sowing. Among the external factors the pH of the medium plays a rôle; the source of carbon nutrition is also important. For these reasons the culture may at one time be ammoniophilous, at another, nitratophilous.

Somewhat different relations were obtained by Rippel in working with *Aspergillus niger*. The latter is an ammoniophilous fungus; nitrate is absorbed by it after the ammonium has been used up, whereby no preference is given to organic nitrogen over inorganic nitrogen. Other fungi show a different behaviour in relationship to the pH; for instance *Mucor silvaticus* does not at all consume KNO_3. These observations are supported by the experiments of Labrousse, in which $Ca(NO_3)_2$, $Ca(NO_2)_2$, NH_4NO_3, and $(NH_4)_2SO_4$ served as nitrogen sources. In applying the appropriate indicators, various changes in the reaction of the medium were observed, depending upon the nature of the nitrogen compound employed. It was proved that the fungi *Cladosporium cucumerinum* and *Verticillium dahlicae* almost instantly change the reaction of their medium to an alkaline one if the nitrogen source is $Ca(NO_3)_2$ or $Ca(NO_2)_2$. If, on the other hand, NH_4NO_3 or $(NH_4)_2SO_4$ is used, the acidity rapidly increases. Fungi incapable of developing on $Ca(NO_2)_2$ do not change their original reaction. According to the experiments of the author, two types of fungi exist; in some of them, in consequence of selective absorption, a rapid change in the reaction of the medium takes place rather passively; in others a slow change in the reaction of the medium sets in, associated with the development of the fungus and its metabolism.

Behr has ascertained that in an acid nutritive solution (pH $=1$) with $(NH_4)_2SO_4$, after the carbohydrates have been used up, autolysis sets in, with the splitting of protein and the formation of a yellow pigment; neutral autolysis (pH $=6.5$) in the presence of $NaNO_3$ leads to the cleavage of protein and chitin, and the formation of ammonia, a violet pigment, and some humin-like material.

The factors stimulating the growth of fungi.—Quite long ago Javillier (1912) tested a great number of chemical elements for their influence on the development of *Aspergillus*, in order to find among them substitutes for the action of zinc, which considerably accelerates the growth of this fungus. Butkewitsch and Orloff (1921) found that the salts of cobalt and mercury can stimulate the development of the mycelium in a way analogous to zinc sulphate. Mokragnatz tested nickel sulphate and cobalt sulphate for the purpose of finding an optimum concentration for increasing the yield of *Aspergillus niger*. The greatest effect was obtained with nickel sulphate in a concentration of 1 : 15,000. With cobalt no positive results were obtained; its suppressing influence became noticeable in a concentration of 1 : 250,000, while with 1 : 2,500 the growth of the fungus was entirely checked. The following results were obtained:

Culture	Dry Weight of Fungus (*Gr.*)
Control culture	0.691
With Ni 1 : 15,000.............	1.270
With Zn 1 : 100,000...........	3.186

McHargue and Calfee have observed that in *Aspergillus flavus* and *Rhizopus nigricans* the rate of growth increases with an optimum concentration of copper (.05 per cent), manganese (.025 per cent), and zinc (.01 per cent). A combination of these metals accelerated growth more successfully than each of them separately, whereby with the last combination the dry weight of the mycelium increased nine-fold in comparison to the control. The amount of fat in the fungi increased under the influence of manganese. It is interesting to note that Metz has observed in *Penicillium luteum* that the lack of copper induces a considerable decrease of spore formation, up to complete sterility of the mycelium. In *Aspergillus* the lack of copper determines the yellow colour of the spores. In a still more detailed way the action of zinc has been studied by Roberg, who has demonstrated that a very small quantity of zinc is necessary as a nutritive substance; in increased concentration zinc stimulates vegetative growth; a greater amount of zinc induces a toxic action. The less iron present in the medium, the more harmful is the influence of zinc.

An increased yield of *Aspergillus niger,* of from 20 to 50 per cent, was observed by Mengdehl under the influence of colloidal, soluble, and precipitated silicic acid. In this case silicic acid was consumed more intensively than phosphoric acid; the presence of silicic acid promoted the accumulation of nitrogen and potassium.

Takata studied the influence of "Bios" on the growth of *Aspergillus oryzae* and *Saccharomyces Sake* and found that in the latter organism growth is accelerated almost proportionally to the content of "Bios." In *Aspergillus oryzae* the weight increases only up to a certain concentration of "Bios," while with a still higher content the toxic action of "Bios" becomes manifest.

To the "Bios" of yeast are devoted the exact studies of R. J. Williams and his pupils, who have divided the "Bios" of Wildiers into two fractions by the use of fractional electrolysis. To the same category belongs a substance extracted by Okunuki from pink yeast, which, along with showing a toxic influence, stimulates the growth of mould fungi.

Conclusion.—The ways in which the investigations of the biochemistry of fungi are carried on are various and promise fair results to the investigator. The value of higher fungi as a food has given rise to a vast literature, though the majority of the old data ought to be revised and tested by new methods. In particular, attention should be given to the proteins of fungi, which up to now remain almost unknown; especially few are the data regarding their relationship to the other constituents of fungi. Wide prospects open before us in connection with the study of separate fungi for their vitamin content, in particular, provitamin D (ergosterol). The lower fungi are made wide use of in industry for the manufacture of organic acids (citric, gluconic). Probably it will also be possible to prepare mannitol by the use of fungi which convert 50 per cent of glucose into this compound. But it cannot yet be said that we have entirely mastered these processes; their study will have to continue. The mysterious pigments and toxic substances of fungi must remain the objects of further study, as being of importance in the chemistry of the plant cell, generally. The fermentative apparatus of the fungi deserves particular attention, since it is possible to retard the action of some enzymes and to stimulate that of others, which enables the investigator to control the course of the processes taking place in the cells. The biochemical study of fungi is illustrative of the utilization of theoretical laboratory investigation for the purposes of industry.

LITERATURE CITED

AMELUNG, H., Z. physiol. Chem., **187,** 171 (1930)

ANGELETTI, A., AND CERRUTI, C. F., Ann. Chim. Applicata, **20,** 424 (1930)

ANSLOW, W. K., AND RAISTRICK, H., Biochem. J., **25,** 39 (1931)

AYE, D., Arch. Pharm., **269,** 246 (1931)

BADANES, B. B., Dental Cosmos, **73,** 780 (1931)

BEHR, G., Arch. Mikrobiol., **1,** 418 (1930)

BERNHAUER, K., Oesterr. Chem. Z., **34,** 159, 167 (1931)

BERNHAUER, K., AND SIEBENÄUGER, H., *Biochem. Z.*, **240**, 232 (1931)
BLOCHWITZ, A., *Ber. deut. botan. Ges.*, **49**, 131, 319 (1931)
BRETIN, P., MANCEAU, P., AND COCHET, —, *Compt. rend. soc. biol.*, **106**, 195 (1931)
BRUNEL, A., *Compt. rend.*, **192**, 442 (1931)
BUTKEWITSCH, W. S., AND FEDOROFF, M. W. (1), *Biochem. Z.*, **206**, 440 (1929) ; **207**, 302 (1929)
BUTKEWITSCH, W. S., AND FEDOROFF, M. W. (2), *Biochem. Z.*, **219**, 87, 103 (1930)
CALDWELL, M. L., AND TYLER, M. G., *J. Am. Chem. Soc.*, **53** (1931)
CHRZASZCZ, T., AND TINKOW, D. (1), *Biochem. Z.*, **218**, 73 (1930)
CHRZASZCZ, T., AND TINKOW, D. (2), *Biochem. Z.*, **222**, 243 (1930)
CHRZASZCZ, T., AND TINKOW, D. (3), *Biochem. Z.*, **229**, 343 (1930)
CORBELLINI, A., AND GREGORINI, —, *Gazz. chim. ital.*, **60**, 244 (1930)
COYNE, E..P., AND RAISTRICK, H., *Biochem. J.*, **25**, 1513 (1931)
DOBY, G., AND FEHER, E., *Z. physiol. Chem.*, **196**, 89 (1931)
HERRICK, H. T., AND MAY, O. E., *Patent* 1,726.067 (1929) after Bernhauer
IWANOFF, N. N., DODONOWA, E. W., AND TSCHASTUCHIN, W. J., *Ferment-forschung*, **11**, 433 (1929)
IWANOFF, N. N., AND AWETISSOWA, A. N., *Biochem. Z.*, **231**, 67 (1931)
JURACEC, A., *Bull. soc. sci. acad. roumaine*, **13**, 103, 169 (1930)
KALLENBACH, F., *Z. Pilzkunde*, **9**, 108 (1930)
KERTESZ, Z. I., *J. Biol. Chem.*, **90**, 15 (1931)
KIESEL, A., *Chemie des Protoplasmas*, Berlin (1930)
KÖGL, F., AND ERXLEBEN, H. (1), *Ann.*, **479**, 11 (1930)
KÖGL, F., AND ERXLEBEN, H. (2), *Ann.*, **484**, 65 (1930)
KÖGL, F., ERXLEBEN, H., AND JÄNECKE, L., *Ann.*, **482**, 105 (1930)
KÖGL, F., DUISBERG, H., AND ERXLEBEN, H., *Ann.*, **489**, 156 (1931)
KOSTYTSCHEW, S., AND TSCHESNOKOW, W., *Planta* (*Z. wiss. Biol.* Abt. E), **4**, 181 (1927)
KOSTYTSCHEW, S., *"Schriften des Zent. biochem. Forschungs-instituts der Nahrungs- und Genussmittel-industrie"* (Russian) in press
LABROUSSE, F., *Compt. rend.*, **192**, 981 (1931)
LABROUSSE, F., AND PHILIPPON, S., *Compt. rend.*, **190**, No. 6 (1930)
LÜERS, H., KÜHLES, R., AND FINK, H., *Biochem. Z.*, **217**, 253 (1930)
LUTZ, L. (1), *Compt. rend.*, **190**, 14 (1930)
LUTZ, L. (2), *Compt. rend.*, **190**, 1755 (1930) ; *Bull. soc. chim. biol.*, **13**, 436 (1931)
LUTZ, L. (3), *Compt. rend.*, **191**, 880 (1931)
LUTZ, L. (4), *Compt. rend.*, **193**, 608 (1931)
McHARGUE, I. S., AND CALFEE, R. K., *Bot. Gaz.*, **91**, 183 (1931)
MANCEAU, P., *Compt. rend. soc. biol.*, **107**, 634 (1931)
MAUER, K., *Ber.*, **63**, 25 (1930)
MAY, O. E., MOYER, A. J., WELLS, P. A., AND HERRICK, H. T., *J. Am. Chem. Soc.*, **53**, 774 (1931)
MENGDEHL, H., *Jahrb. wiss. Botanik*, **75**, 252 (1931)
METZ, O., *Arch. Mikrobiol.*, **1**, 197 (1930)
MOKRAGNATZ, S., *Bull. soc. chim. biol.*, **13**, 61 (1931)

NAYLOR, N., AND OTHERS, *Iowa State College J. Sci.,* **4,** 465 (1930)
OBATON, M., *Compt. rend. soc. biol.,* **105,** 673 (1931)
OKUNUKI, K., *Japan J. Bot.,* **5**, 401 (1931)
PASSECKER, F., *Z. Pilzkunde,* **9,** 60, 175 (1930)
PILÀT, —., *Z. Pilzkunde,* **9,** 191 (1930)
PRICKETT, P., MASSENGALE, O., COX, M., JR., AND BILLS, C., *Proc. Soc. Exptl. Biol. Med.,* **27,** 701 (1930)
RAISTRICK, H., AND OTHERS, *Trans. Roy. Soc. (London) B,* **220,** 1 (1931)
RAMAGE, H., *Nature,* **126,** 279 (1930)
RIPPEL, A., AND BEHR, G., *Arch. Mikrobiol.,* **1,** 271 (1930)
RIPPEL, K., *Arch. Mikrobiol.,* **2,** 72 (1931)
ROBERG, M., *Zentr. Bakt. Parasitenk.,* II Abt., **84,** 196 (1931)
SAKAMURA, T., *Planta (Z. wiss. Biol.* Abt. E), **11,** 765 (1930)
SCHMALFUSS, K., AND MOTHES, K., *Biochem. Z.,* **221,** 134 (1930)
SCHOBER, R., *Jahrb. wiss. Bot.,* **72,** 1 (1930)
STILES, H. R., PETERSON, W. H., AND FRED, E. B., *J. Biol. Chem.,* **64,** 643 (1925)
TAKATA, R., *J. Soc. Chem. Ind. Japan* (Suppl.), **32,** 268 B, 269 B, 307 B (1931)
TAMIYA, H., AND MORITA, S., *Bot. Mag. Tokyo,* **43,** 506 (1929) ; **44,** 524 (1930)
TAMIYA, H., *Bot. Mag. Tokyo,* **45,** 530 (1931)
THIES, W., *Zentr. Bakt. Parasitenk.,* II Abt., **82,** 321 (1930)
TINKOW, D., *Zentr. Bakt. Parasitenk.,* II Abt., **83,** 385 (1931)
TRISCHLER, J., *Wiss. Arch. Landw.,* Abt. A, *Pflanzenbau,* **7,** 39 (1931)
TSCHASTUCHIN, W. J., *Materials of Phytopathology and Mycology* (Russian), (1931)
WAKSMAN, S. A., AND DIEHM, R. A., *Soil Sci.,* **32,** 97 (1931)
WALKER, T. K., SUBRAMANIAN, V., AND CHALLENGER, F., *J. Chem. Soc.,* 3044 (1927)
WEIDENHAGEN, R., *Z. Ver. deut. Zuckerind.,* **80,** 374 (1930)
WILLIAMS, R. J., AND TRUESDAIL, J. H., *J. Am. Chem. Soc.,* **53,** 4171 (1931)
WILLIAMS, R. J., AND BRADWAY, E., *J. Am. Chem. Soc.,* **53,** 783 (1931)
WYKMAN, N., *Ann.,* **485,** 61 (1931)
ZELLNER, J., AND ZIKMUNDA, E., *Monatsh.,* **56,** 204 (1930)

INSTITUTE OF PLANT INDUSTRY,
UL. HERZEN, 44
LENINGRAD, U.S.S.R.

INDEX OF NAMES

Juhasz-Schäffer, A., 399
Juhn, M., 416
Jukes, T. H., 188, 511
Julian, R. R. St., 344, 366, 386
Jungmann, H., 498, 502
Juracec, A., 692
Juvan, H., 599

K

Kaboth, T., 522
Kaczander, P., 476
Kafuku, K., 584
Kahlenberg, C. J., 342, 383, 398
Kajdi, L., 35
Kallenbach, F., 682
Kallinikova, M. N., 38
Kamerling, S. E., 576
Kamiya, T., 518
Kandel, E., 334
Kapeller-Adler, R., 302, 435
Kapfhammer, J., 611
Kapsinow, R., 41
Karell, A., 345
Karnshan, M., 392
Karrer, P., 104, 105, 225, 371, 372, 373, 374, 375, 400, 551, 552, 553, 554, 555, 556, 557, 561, 564, 565, 581, 582, 598
Karström, H., 80, 239, 641; 646
Kase, K., 301
Katz, L. N., 313
Katzman, P. A., 416, 421
Kauffmann, F., 78, 303, 475
Kaufman, L., 514
Kaufmann, C., 269, 288
Kawakami, K., 375
Kay, H. D., 188, 197, 199, 202, 203, 204, 257, 290, 385, 389
Kaye, G., 461
Kayser, C., 42
Kaziro, K., 128
Keenan, J. A., 384
Keeton, R. W., 333
Keil, H. L., 320, 321
Keil, W., 302, 435

Keilin, D., 60, 61, 490, 531, 545, 546
Keines, C. J., 434
Keller, W., 302
Kellner, L., 396
Kelly, G. L., 416
Kelly, H. E., 74
Kemmerer, A. R., 326
Kendall, A. I., 651
Kendall, E. C., 173
Kendall, F. E., 656, 660, 662, 664, 666, 667, 669
Kennedy, C., 333, 345
Kennedy, D., 353
Kerly, M., 259, 435, 444
Kern, R., 388
Kerppola, W., 375
Kerr, W. J., 470
Kertesz, Z. I., 691
Kešáns, A., 206
Kesten, H. D., 661
Key, K. M., 379, 380
Keys, A. B., 515
Khouvine, Y., 261, 467
Kiamil, M., 658
Kiech, V. C., 301, 306, 309, 312, 313
Kiesel, A., 678
Kik, M. C., 323, 345, 347, 354, 366, 386
Kiliani, H., 215
Kimura, Y., 128
Kindred, J. E., 519
King, A. T., 172
King, E. J., 145, 180, 194, 195, 196, 288, 384, 388, 502
King, F. E., 237
King, H., 145, 155
Kinnersley, H. W., 337, 338, 343, 352, 498, 502
Kinoshita, K., 26, 241
Kirk, J. S., 665
Kirk, P. L., 156, 158, 171
Kirrmann, A., 530
Kirsch, W., 391
Kirstahler, A., 530
Kisch, B., 301, 314
Kisch, E., 390
Kiss, A., 34
Kissin, D., 659
Kitagawa, M., 153, 615

Kitasato, T., 375
Kitschin, A., 586
Kiyokawa, M., 304
Kjaer, T., 669
Klabunde, H. K., 155
Klarmann, E., 166
Klaussner-Croheim, I., 383
Klebermass, L., 83, 200, 231
Klebs, G., 576, 577
Klein, D., 385
Klein, G., 615
Klein, H., 392
Klein, L., 240
Klein, R. I., 382, 384
Klein, W., 225
Kleiner, I. S., 78
Kleinmann, H., 74
Kleitzien, S. W. F., 386, 391
Klement, R., 190, 191, 192
Klenk, E., 90, 91, 92, 135, 136, 137, 141, 142, 143, 280, 281
Klenk, L., 75
Kline, O. L., 384, 391
Kline, R., 422
Kloster, J., 382
Klotz, L. J., 619, 620
Kluyver, A. J., 508, 643
Knight, B. C. J. G., 103, 652
Knoop, F., 64
Knowlton, G. C., 392
Knudson, A., 291, 395
Kobel, M., 81, 82, 241, 258
Kober, S., 413, 417
Koch, F., 147, 284
Koch, F. C., 416
Koch, K., 207
Kocholaty, W., 77
Kodama, S., 160
Kögl, F., 680, 681
Köhler, F., 75, 76
Köser, I., 131, 394
Koessler, K. K., 304
Kofanov, J., 46
Kofler, L., 607
Kohn, R., 301, 303
Kojima, K., 519
Komatsu, S., 589

Mazza, F. P., 510
Medlar, E. M., 473
Meeker, Dorothy, 35
Meesemaecker, R., 395
Meier, R., 202, 314
Meigs, E. B., 144, 293
Meiser, W., 235
Mekie, E. C., 467
Meldrum, N. V., 161
Mellanby, E., 258, 347,
    366, 367, 368, 372, 393
Mellanby, M., 366, 384,
    392, 393
Mellish, C. H., 415
Melsen, J. A. van, 592
Mendel, L. B., 277, 278,
    293, 332, 339, 381, 399
Mendenhall, D. R., 323
Mengdehl, H., 623, 633,
    694
Menschick, W., 130, 385,
    390, 502, 503
Menten, M. L., 69, 238
Mering, J. von, 312
Merklen, P., 140
Merkulow, G. A., 464
Merz, W., 92, 136, 141,
    230
Mestscherskaja, K., 14
Metz, E., 444, 680, 694
Mevius, W., 625, 627
Meyer, A. H., 205
Meyer, B. S., 39
Meyer, C. E., 155
Meyer, C. R., 381
Meyer, G. M., 218, 224
Meyer, J., 600, 606
Meyer, K., 63, 199, 420,
    441, 661
Meyer, K. H., 446
Meyer, R. K., 415, 418
Meyer, W., 390
Meyerhof, O., 43, 56, 63,
    187, 188, 199, 247, 248,
    249, 256, 257, 260, 261,
    262, 314, 431, 432, 435,
    438, 441, 443, 444, 445,
    447, 449, 487, 488, 489,
    494, 495, 496, 502, 510,
    648
Meyer-Weddell, L., 271
Mezzadroli, G., 232
Michaelis, L., 57, 65, 69,
    74, 238, 530, 544

Michailoff, M., 468
Michaux, A., 37
Micheel, F., 214
Micheel, H., 214
Michelazzi, L., 388
Migliavacci, A., 522
Mikeska, L. A., 222
Mikhailovski, B., 512
Milbradt, W., 147
Miller, E. G., 365
Miller, E. J., 614
Miller, E. R., 152
Miller, G. E., 388
Miller, H. K., 322
Miller, K. K., 541
Miller, L., 320, 321, 324,
    328, 540
Miller, R. C., 325
Miller, W. L., 356
Millet, P., 519
Milroy, J. A., 270
Milroy, T. H., 187, 247,
    248, 431, 445, 448
Minibeck, H., 464
Minot, G. R., 542
Minsaas, J., 214, 234
Mirskaia, L., 417
Mirsky, A. E., 161, 535,
    538, 539, 547
Mirvish, L., 384
Mislowitzer, E., 78, 303
Mitchell, H. H., 176, 333
Mitchell, H. S., 320, 321,
    324, 328, 540
Mitchell, P. H., 157
Miyamoto, S., 156, 159,
    163, 164
Mjassnilow, A. L., 460
Mladenović, M., 602,
    603
Modern, F., 665, 669
Mörch, J. R., 669
Mörner, C. T., 152
Moïse, T. S., 331
Mokragnatz, M., 619,
    620
Mokragnatz, S., 693
Moldenhauer, O., 569,
    570, 571, 572, 574, 575,
    576
Molitor, H., 34
Moll, T., 387, 389, 397
Molnar, E., 175
Monaghan, B. R., 490

Monasterio, G., 142, 153,
    473
Mond, R., 435
Monsarrat-Thoms, P.,
    564, 565
Montgomery, A. F., 388
Montignie, E., 132, 133
Mook, H. W., 434, 536
Moore, C. R., 415, 418,
    420
Moore, D. D., 300
Moore, D. M., 662
Moore, E. E., 656
Moore, M. B., 656
Moore, R. B., 389, 396
Moore, T., 345, 371, 372,
    373
Moran, F., 663
Moran, T., 26
Morel, A., 606
Morelle, J., 384, 388
Morf, R., 551, 552, 553,
    556, 557
Morgan, A. F., 381, 389
Morgan, B. G. E., 379,
    380, 381
Morgan, J. E., 334
Morgan, O. P., 536
Morgan, W. T. J., 188,
    189, 194, 195, 196, 661
Morgulis, S., 183, 191,
    192, 205
Mori, T., 201
Morin, G., 386
Morita, S., 675
Moritz, A. R., 384
Morrell, C. A., 467, 471
Morrison, A. L., 124
Morrison, D. B., 476
Morse, J. K., 193
Morse, T. S., 344
Mortens, R., 471
Morton, R. A., 372, 373,
    375, 376, 377, 378, 379
Moschcowitz, E., 333
Mossobrio, E., 468
Mothes, K., 691
Mott, E., 661
Mottern, H. H., 507
Mouriquand, G., 370,
    385, 395
Mourot, G., 300
Moya, A., 290
Moyer, A. J., 240, 687

Thompson, A., 219, 376, 377
Thompson, W., 201
Thomson, D. L., 418, 419, 421
Thorn, G. W., 423
Thudicum, J. L. W., 152
Thunberg, T., 55, 58, 440, 490
Tidmore, J. W., 632
Tiedcke, C., 101
Tiedjens, V. A., 627
Tikka, J., 189, 642
Tikkanen, E., 588
Tilden, E. B., 365
Tillett, W. S., 660
Timofeeva, A., 473
Timpe, O., 302
Tinkow, D., 677, 683, 685
Tipson, R. S., 218, 223, 232
Tobey, E. R., 329
Titschak, E., 512
Todd, A. R., 120
Toennies, G., 172
Toennissen, E., 258, 262, 265, 449, 456
Toepffer, H., 235
Toivonen, N. J., 588
Tomcsik, J., 661
Tomita, T., 615
Tomiyama, T., 153
Tompsett, S. L., 180
Tongberg, C. O., 546
Tonnet, J., 468
Topley, W. W. C., 370, 664
Torquati, T., 152
Toumanov, C., 514
Tourtellotte, D., 305
Toverud, G., 391, 392
Toverud, K. U., 391, 392
Towne, B. W., 155
Townsend, W. C., 333
Trancu-Rainer, M., 422
Trautmann, S., 309
Trautwein, K., 62
Treibs, A., 527, 528
Treibs, W., 584
Trimble, H. C., 253
Trischler, J., 678
Trost, J. F., 373

Truesdail, J. H., 356, 695
Tsai, C., 254, 437
Tsai, L. S., 345
Tschastuchin, W. J., 690
Tschesche, R., 339
Tschesnokow, W., 683
Tschinkel, H., 227, 241
Tsujimoto, J., 305
Tsujimoto, M., 103, 104
Tubbs, R., 630
Tuljschinskaja, K., 664
Tum Suden, C., 423
Tupikow, N., 493
Turner, K., 91, 144
Turner, R. G., 366, 370
Turpeinen, O., 6, 641
Tu Tungi, D. F., 383
Tuzson, P., 556
Tyler, M. G., 692

U

Ueno, K., 551, 552
Ueno, S., 104
Umschweif, B., 432, 442
Underhill, F. A., 321, 540, 541
Underhill, F. P., 41
Uraki, Z., 128
Urban, F., 175
Urhan, O., 628
Utevski, A., 261
Utzino, S., 603

V

Vack, C., 383
Vahlquist, B., 206, 273
Valentin, F., 213, 235
Valentine, E., 665
Valissant, Mme., 292
Valk, S. H. van K., 510
Van Donk, E., 399
Van Slyke, D. D., 9, 10, 153, 187, 203, 536, 537
Van Wagoner, F. H., 476
Vara-Lopez, R., 388, 390
Vareton, E., 232
Vars, H. M., 153
Vasarhelyi, B., 204
Veen, A. G. van, 339, 581

Veibel, S., 189
Veline, M., 292
Velluz, L., 658, 659
Venus-Danilova, E., 228
Vernier, C., 102
Vernon, H. M., 490
Verzár, F., 271, 399, 460, 463, 542
Vickery, H. B., 151, 155, 159, 381, 399, 613, 614
Villard, P., 206
Vincent, H., 659
Virden, C. J., 614
Virgilio, B., 241
Virtanen, A. I., 80, 189, 641, 642
Visco, S., 49
Vladesco, R., 302
Vladimirov, G. E., 516
Vocke, F., 112
Voegtlin, C., 182, 346
Völker, H., 310
Vogel, J. C., 206
Vogt, M., 258, 447
Vogt-Møller, P., 399
Voit, K., 474
Volk, H., 119
Von Wrangell, —, 632, 634
Voss, H. E., 416, 518
Voss, O., 73
Votoček, E., 213, 214

W

Wachsmuth, W., 467
Wada, C., 345
Wada, M., 152, 614, 615
Waddell, J., 328, 399, 540
Wade, N. J., 415
Wadsworth, A., 139, 140, 658, 661, 662, 669
Waele, A. de, 132
Wagner, E., 381
Wagner-Jauregg, T., 581, 582
Wahl, R., 147
Wahlin, B., 391
Waitz, R., 466
Wakeman, A. M., 300, 467, 471
Waksman, S. A., 690

Date Due
